(7–10) $v_{ce(\text{max avg})} = 0.138 \cdot V_{CE(Q)}$

(7–11) $P_{D(\text{max})} \cong (V_{CE(Q)})^2/10\,R_L$

(7–12) $P_{L(\text{max})} = (v_{L(\text{max})})^2/R_L = (0.707\,V_{Ce(Q)})^2/R_L$

(7–13) $P_{DC(\text{max})} = i_{c(\text{max avg})} \cdot V_{CC}$

Power Ratings and Thermodynamics

(7–25) $P_{D(\text{max at operating temp})} = P_{D(\text{max at }25°\,C)} - [(T_C - 25°\,C) \cdot D]$

(7–26) $P_D = (T_C - T_A)/R_\theta$

(7–27) $T_C = (P_D \cdot R_\theta) + T_A$

JFET Parameters

(8–1) $I_D = I_{DSS} \cdot [1 - (V_{GS}/V_{GS(\text{off})})]^2$
(for JFETs and D-type MOSFETs)

(8–2) $g_m = \Delta I_D/\Delta V_{GS}$

(8–3) $g_{m-VGS} = g_{m0} \cdot [1 - (V_{GS}/V_{GS(\text{off})})]$
(for JFETs and D-type MOSFETs)

(8–4) $r_{ds} = \Delta V_{DS}/\Delta I_D = 1/g_{os}$

JFET Self-Bias Analysis

(8–5) $I_{D(Q)} = |V_{GS(Q)}|/R_S = V_{RS(Q)}/R_S$

(8–6) $V_{RD(Q)} = I_{D(Q)} \cdot R_D$

(8–7) $V_{DS(Q)} = V_{DD} - V_{RD(Q)} - V_{RS(Q)}$

JFET Self-Bias Design

(8–8) $R_S = V_{RS(Q)}/I_{D(Q)}$
(where $V_{RS(Q)} = |V_{GS(Q)}|$)

(8–9) $R_D \cong (V_{DD}/I_{DSS}) - R_S$

Common-Source Amplifier

(8–13) $A_V = v_{\text{out}}/v_{\text{in}} = g_m \cdot (R_D \| R_L)$
(ideal, with source at AC ground)

(8–15) $C_B \geq 1.59\,g_m/f_{\text{low}}$

Common-Drain Amplifier

(8–17) $A_V = R_S/((1/g_m) + R_S)$ (no load)

Common-Gate Amplifier

(8–23) $A_V = g_m(R_d \| R_L)$ (with load)

Zer... MO...

(8–?)

E-Type MOSFET

(8–25) $I_D = K(V_{GS} - V_{GS(\text{th})})^2$

Miller Capacitance

(9–8) $C_{\text{in(Miller)}} = C_f(A_V + 1)$
(for inverting amplifiers)

(9–9) $C_{\text{out(Miller)}} = C_f(A_V + 1)/A_V$
(for inverting amplifiers)

For All Amplifiers

(9–12) $f_T = A_V BW$

(9–13) $BW = f_T/A_V$

(9–14) Slope (dB/decade) $= 20\log(V_{Ufco}/V_{10Ufco})$

(9–15) Slope (dB/decade) $= 20\log(V_{Lfco}/V_{0.1Lfco})$

Differential Amplifiers

(10–1) $A_V = R_C/2r_e'$ (single output)

(10–2) $A_V = R_C/r_e'$ (differential output)

(10–3) $A_{V(\text{com})} \cong R_C/2R_E$
(common-mode gain)

(10–4) $\text{CMRR} = A_{V(\text{diff})}/A_{V(\text{com})}$

Op-Amp Electrical Characteristics

(10–10) $\text{CMRR} = A_{OL}/A_{V(\text{com})}$

(10–11) $v_{\text{out}} = A_{OL}v_{\text{diff}}$

(10–12) $v_{\text{diff}} = v_{\text{in}} - v_f$

Noninverting Amplifiers

(10–13) $B = R_I/(R_I + R_F)$

(10–14) $v_f = v_{\text{out}} \cdot R_I/(R_I + R_F) = Bv_{\text{out}}$

(10–15) $v_{\text{diff}} = v_{\text{in}} - Bv_{\text{out}}$

(10–16) $A_V = v_{\text{out}}/v_{\text{in}} = A_{OL}/(1 + A_{OL}B)$

(10–17) $A_V \cong 1/B = (R_I + R_F)/R_I$

(10–18) Loop gain $= A_{OL}B$

(10–19) $Z_{\text{in}} = r_{\text{in}}(1 + BA_{OL})$

(10–20) $Z_{\text{out}} = r_{\text{out}}/(1 + BA_{OL})$

(10–21) $g_m = i_{\text{out}}/v_{\text{in}} = 1/R_F$

Exploring Electronic Devices

Exploring Electronic Devices

Mark E. Hazen

SAUNDERS COLLEGE PUBLISHING
Harcourt Brace Jovanovich College Publishers
Fort Worth   Philadelphia   San Diego
New York   Orlando   Austin   San Antonio
Toronto   Montreal   London   Sydney   Tokyo

Text Typeface: Times Roman
Compositor: Bi-Comp, Incorporated
Acquisitions Editor: Barbara Gingery
Developmental Editor: Lloyd Black
Managing Editor: Carol Field
Senior Project Manager: Sally Kusch
Copy Editor: Andrew Potter
Manager of Art and Design: Carol Bleistine
Art Director: Christine Schueler
Art and Design Coordinator: Doris Bruey
Text Designer: Gene Harris
Cover Designer: Lawrence R. Didona
Text Artwork: GRAFACON
Photo Researcher: Teri Stratford
Layout Artist: York Production Services
Director of EDP: Tim Frelick
Production Manager: Charlene Squibb
Marketing Manager: Denise Watrobsky

Cover: Silicon wafer filled with integrated circuit chips. (FPG International/Dick Luria Photo, Inc.)

Printed in the United States of America

Exploring Electronic Devices

0-03-028533-X

Library of Congress Catalog Card Number: 90-053486

234567 061 98765432

To my wife Sharon, my son Jon, and my daughter Valerie for all their patience, support, and understanding and for the sacrifices they have made.

Preface

Exploring Electronic Devices was written for the introductory two-term course covering discrete and integrated semiconductor devices. Created for the electronics technician and technology curriculum, this text offers a thorough presentation of device and circuit theory, device and circuit analysis, circuit design, and device and circuit troubleshooting. Developed from an extensive survey of educational institutions and industry, the book reflects the needs and wishes of instructors across the country in a way not fully realized until now.

SUBJECT DEVELOPMENT AND APPROACH

In general, the text progresses from the simple to the complex with a continual emphasis on the role circuits play in electronic systems. Though not overly emphasized, the systems concept is clearly presented and related to analysis, design, and troubleshooting. The use of the popular block approach to system design, analysis, and troubleshooting allows students to gain a real-world sense of electronic systems.

Integrated with this building-block approach are motivational elements designed to maintain student interest while aiding learning. Throughout the text the student will discover "Need-To-Know" scenarios and practical applications, be guided with the use of sectional Self-Checks and worked examples, and instructed through the use of lucid narrative and numerous clear illustrations. This emphasis on the applied nature of electronics is evident in that most circuits presented in the figures and examples are thoroughly labeled with standard values and can be built by the student for the purposes of experimentation and theory verification. In fact, most of the circuits have been built and tested by the author. This consistent link to situations encountered in the workaday world reinforce the text-to-lab-bench-to-work-environment path that technical students usually follow.

Instructors will find this text of great benefit not only because of its pedagogical value to the student but because of its modular approach in handling major topics. Chapters are divided into sections, each with its own Self-Check, and the end-of-chapter questions and problems are grouped by section. Thus, instructors do not need to rearrange their preferred order of subject presentation to fit the text.

Instructors will find that this text covers more devices and circuits than most of the competing texts presently available. As a result, the student is offered a much broader understanding of the world of electronic devices and is far better prepared for more advanced courses.

CHAPTER ORGANIZATION

Each chapter is organized with the following pedagogical and instructional elements:

- two-color text format
- chapter outline
- list of objectives
- motivational "Need To Know" scenario
- introduction
- numbered sections and accompanying Self-Checks
- worked examples and illustrations
- Design Notes
- boldfaced special terms
- three-part summary including formulas, concepts, and procedures
- "Need To Know" solution
- questions grouped by section
- problems grouped by section
- additional problems representative of the entire chapter
- answers to Self-Checks
- Suggested Projects

INNOVATIVE FEATURES

MODULAR CHAPTER ORGANIZATION

Each chapter is divided into several sections, and each section concludes with a Self-Check. At the end of each chapter, answers to Self-Checks are identified by section. Also, questions and problems are arranged by section. This modular flexibility enables the text to conform to any instructional program—the program, or the instructor, does not have to conform to the text.

NEED TO KNOW

Each chapter begins with a motivational section that establishes the student's need to know. The "Need To Know" presents students with an interesting real world problem that they can solve after learning the material covered in the chapter. A "Need To Know" solution is always provided at the end of each chapter.

DESIGN NOTES

Design Notes are special features that spotlight theory, analysis, and design through the use of BASIC programs. Procedures are outlined in the BASIC program steps.

REPRODUCIBLE CIRCUITS
Virtually all of the circuits that appear in the figures and examples are labeled with standard component values so the student can build and test the circuit described. In a very real sense, this text can serve as a lab manual as well.

END-OF-BOOK MATERIAL

The following helps are provided at the end of this book:

APPENDICES
These include manufacturers' data sheets, a glossary of device parameters, and derivations of selected formulas.

GLOSSARY
The extensive glossary offers students definitions to all important technical terms used in the text.

ANSWERS TO ODD-NUMBERED PROBLEMS
Answers to all odd-numbered problems are provided so students can have immediate feedback as to their understanding of problem solving.

ANCILLARY PACKAGE

The following are available to adopters of *Exploring Electronic Devices:*

INSTRUCTOR'S MANUAL WITH TRANSPARENCY MASTERS
Written by the text author and free to all adopters, this instructor's manual provides fully worked-out solutions to all end-of-chapter problems and a generous set of transparency masters to aid class lectures.

LABORATORY MANUAL
Written by the text author, this laboratory manual includes a sufficient number of experiments to satisfy a two-semester course.

INSTRUCTOR'S LABORATORY MANUAL
This supplement, free upon adoption of the student laboratory manual, contains suggested laboratory results.

DESIGN NOTE SOFTWARE
All circuit analysis and design programs featured in the Design Note sections of the text are available on IBM® PC diskette. This software is free to all adopters.

**ACKNOWLEDG-
MENTS**

I wish to thank my wife Sharon, my son Jonathan, and my daughter Valerie, for their patience, sacrifice, and understanding during the development of this book. The author is not the only one who must make sizeable sacrifices when a project of this magnitude is undertaken.

Second, I wish to express my appreciation to the hardworking professional team at Saunders College Publishing: Barbara Gingery (Senior Acquisitions Editor), Laura Shur (Assistant Editor), Lloyd W. Black (Senior Developmental Editor), and Sally Kusch (Senior Project Manager).

Finally, I want to thank the reviewers of and contributors to my work for their dedication and mutual concern toward the development of a text of high quality. The following professionals have enhanced the quality of this project with their insights, suggestions, and information.

Richard Anderson, Northwestern Electronics Institute
Thomas J. Bingham, Jr., Florrisant Valley Community College
K. J. Braun, Houston Community College
Richard C. Bridgeman, Bolingbrook, Illinois
Donald Embree, Seminole Community College
Patrick Francois, Rancho Santiago College
Duane H. Henninger, Lincoln Technical Institute
Bradley Jenkins, St. Petersburg Junior College
Theodore W. Johnson, Berkshire Community College
Amin Karim, Illinois Technical College
Oleh Kuritza, College of DuPage
Clay Laster, San Antonio College
William Mack, Harrisburg Community College
Eugene Maples, Oklahoma City Community College
Roger Mussell, William Rainey Harper College
Jack Nudelman, Orange Coast College
L. Oliver, Columbus State Community College
J. C. Rawlins, Eastfield College
Robert N. Reaves, Durham Technical Community College
William O. Reed, DeVry Institute of Technology, Kansas City
Bernard Rudin, Community College of Philadelphia
Paul Svatik, Owens Technical College
Gary Vaughn, Piedmont Technical College

A special thank you is reserved for Bradley Jenkins of St. Petersburg Junior College who was tireless in his pursuit of errors as the accuracy reviewer of the problem sets and examples. I would also like to thank the industry professionals whose services and support greatly enhanced the quality and accuracy of this book: Linda Craig (Marketing Manager) of EXAR Integrated Circuit Systems; Seth Ellis (Product Manager, Circuitmate DMMs) of Beckman Industrial; S. Hirota (President) and Joan Roy (Marketing Administrator) of Leader Instruments Corporation; Greg Elmore (Marketing Manager) of B & K Precision–Maxtec International Corporation; L. Jefferson Gorin (Manager, Media Relations) of Motorola, Inc.; Dawn Schulman (Program Administrator), Gary Banta (Analog Product Marketing Director), Dian Shepherd (Marketing Manager), and Ann Wilkinson (Marketing Manager) of National Semiconductor Corporation; Todd A. Hadbavny (Educational Marketing Manager) and Norb Luersen (Marketing Manager) of Tektronix, Inc.; George Badger (Product Manager) of Eimac, Varian Associates, Inc.

A SPECIAL NOTE TO THE STUDENT

The exploration you are about to begin is far more exciting than you can imagine. Through these pages, I will have the pleasure of introducing you to the wonderful world of electronics. You will gain new knowledge and make exciting discoveries. Your exploration here is not of words, diagrams, and pages but of electronic devices, circuits, and systems that make up the high-tech world in which we live. Your natural sense of creativity and curiosity will feed on every concept, theory, and application. And that is where the strength of this text lies, in the real application of a great variety of electronic devices in practical, modern circuits and systems. By the time you finish this book, you will be armed with a solid understanding of real electronics, the kind you can get a grip on and use.

To help you in your exploration, I have included the following special features:

1. As with my other books, I begin each chapter with a **"Need To Know"** scenario. These brief sorties are designed to help you prepare mentally for the material covered in the chapter. Their main purpose is to establish in your mind a need to know certain concepts and practices.
2. Every chapter is divided into sections with a short **Self-Check** involving questions and problems at the end of each section. All answers to these Self-Checks are provided at the end of the chapter. The Self-Check is intended to help you see if you are understanding the material.
3. At the end of each chapter, **questions and problems** are divided according to section to help you focus on a smaller area at one time. Answers to all odd-numbered problems are given at the end of the book.
4. Virtually all circuits in examples and figures are labeled with standard component values so you can build and test any circuit. Not only will this reinforce theory but it will give you a large selection of building-block type circuits that you can use in your own system designs.
5. In some chapters, I have included what I call **Design Notes.** These are special emphasis features that include diagrams, circuits, formulas, and BASIC computer programs that you can use to analyze or design circuits. The programs will run on any IBM® PC. A few of the programs use high-resolution monochrome graphics.
6. I have included **data sheets** of many popular devices and integrated circuits in several chapters and in an **appendix** at the end of the book. Be sure to look at these and refer to them as you progress in your exploration.
7. Don't overlook the **Suggested Projects** section at the end of each chapter. If you like to experiment building circuits, you may find some of these projects challenging and stimulating.

Oh, by the way, I highly recommend that you keep this text in your personal technical library. You will find it to be very helpful as you take higher-level courses and as a reference as you begin your career.

You may be wondering who I am. I often wondered who the authors of some of my textbooks were. So, let me tell you just a little bit about myself. Looking back, I have had a very exciting career in electronics that started in the United States Air Force. I taught electronics almost 20 years ago at Keesler Air Force Base in Biloxi, Mississippi. Since then, I have been all over the world, not to mention the United States. Among my adventures, I installed a control room in a recording studio in Monte Carlo, a 400,000-W AM broadcast transmitter in Sri Lanka, a 100,000-W shortwave transmitter on Guam, and wired a professional recording studio complex in Hong Kong. I taught electronics at DeVry Institute of Technology in Phoenix, Arizona, for over five years and have been writing full time for the past few years. I am now back teaching at the Florida Advanced Technology Center of Brevard Community College in Palm Bay, Florida. Maybe I'll meet you one day. We have much in common you and I—we are both learning. That's what makes me so excited about electronics—there is always something new to challenge and stimulate the imagination. You're not alone in your exploration. Enjoy!

Mark Edward Hazen
November 1990

Contents Overview

Contents

Six-foot model of uranium-235 atom, first atom split by man. (The Bettmann Archive.)

1 Introduction to Electronics

OBJECTIVES

After studying this chapter, you will be able to

■ identify a few of the early pioneers in electronics.
■ explain the difference between conductors, insulators, and semiconductors in terms of atomic structure.
■ describe the crystalline structure of semiconductors.
■ explain *n*- and *p*-type semiconductor materials in terms of doping.
■ explain electrical current in semiconductor materials.
■ describe the formation of the *pn* junction and discuss the depletion region and barrier potential.
■ explain forward and reverse bias of the *pn* junction in terms of majority and minority charge carriers.
■ explain the difference between conduction-band current and valence-band current.

NEED TO KNOW

Suppose you are a technician working in a repair center that handles a great variety of equipment. One day you are handed a cellular telephone unit that is in need of repair. You have never seen this particular make and model before. As part of your standard procedure, you locate the complete repair documentation provided by the manufacturer for this particular unit. A review of the operator's manual enables you to begin your diagnosis of the problem by checking and verifying the reported symptoms. Once the symptoms have been clearly identified, you are ready to proceed. But what do you do next? Consider the following list of possible actions you now may take:

1. Remove the casing and begin testing each component with the appropriate test equipment.

2. Study the system block diagram and try to match symptoms with a particular functional block.
3. Study the complete schematic diagram of the unit to see how it works.
4. Stealthily set the unit on someone else's repair bench.

Which of the above do you think is the best choice (other than option 4)? You might be right or perhaps you will change your mind as you study this chapter. We'll discuss these options at the end of the chapter.

INTRODUCTION   You should be introduced to at least three significant areas before you dive headlong into a study of electronic devices and circuits. No matter what the subject, background is always important to set the stage for learning. In this case, a brief examination of the history of electronics, a study of basic semiconductor theory, and an overview of electronic systems will do nicely. The goal here is for you to gain an appreciation for the relatively new era of electronics, a basic understanding of the physics behind modern electronics, and an overall perspective on electronic systems. This should set the stage adequately for you to begin an exciting exploration into the world of electronic devices. The theory and electronic system information will be built upon and added to when appropriate throughout the remaining chapters. Enjoy!

1–1 HISTORICAL BACKGROUND

THE DAWN OF A NEW ERA

Most of us today are busily utilizing all of the high-tech gadgetry we can get our hands on. It seems that every day a new electronic consumer product, manufacturing technique, medical diagnostic instrument, or military weapon is introduced. Everywhere we look, microcircuits and microcomputers are playing a significant role in the betterment and well-being of mankind. We are so caught up in the marvels of today and tomorrow that it seems as though some of the technology has always been with us. Certainly, we are not overly impressed, as we once were, with each new technological announcement. By now, many of us have worn out early personal home computers and have upgraded once, twice, or even three times to keep pace with advancements. The technology is advancing so rapidly that the word obsolete is defined in terms of months and weeks instead of years. This, too, makes it seem as though the electronics era has been with us a very long time.

Yet this era of electronics technology is relatively new; its primitive beginnings are as recent as the span of a human lifetime. Some people living today were born at the time of the birth of this new era of electronics. The electronic era of active devices such as amplifiers was itself born out of the electricity era of the 1800s. Late-19th-century and turn-of-the-century scientists such as Sir William Crookes, Thomas Edison, John Fleming, and Lee de Forest opened the door to this new era. It began with these men, whose crude electronic devices led to the vacuum-tube amplifier.

Figure 1–1 Sir William Crookes (1832–1919). (Culver Pictures, Inc.)

Figure 1–2 Thomas Alva Edison (1847–1931). (Culver Pictures, Inc.)

Sometime around 1878, a British scientist named Sir William Crookes (Figure 1–1) discovered that electric current consisted of particles. His experiments utilized evacuated glass tubes that had two electrodes: a cathode and an anode. He discovered that rays of particles, emitted from the cathode, caused the opposite end of the tube to glow. When he placed a metal mask in the path of the rays, a shadow was cast on the end of the tube. He also discovered that magnetic flux influenced the beam of particles. The **Crookes tube** was the early forerunner of the cathode ray tube and picture tube.

Thomas Edison (Figure 1–2) discovered that, in an evacuated glass bulb, electrons would flow from a heated filament to a metal plate when a positive potential was applied to the metal plate. This became known as the *Edison effect*. Edison patented this device but made little or no use of it.

In 1904, the British scientist John Fleming (Figure 1–3) designed and constructed a vacuum-tube **diode** (having two electrodes) that would pass current in only one direction, negative cathode to positive anode (+plate). As in Edison's bulb, electrons flowed from a heated cathode to a collector plate that was at a positive potential. Acting like a water-pipe check valve that allows flow in only one direction, the vacuum diode became known as the **Fleming valve.**

The era of electronics really began to move forward when, in 1907, the American inventor Lee de Forest (Figure 1–4) patented the first amplifying

Figure 1–3 John Ambrose Fleming (1849–1945). (UPI/Bettmann Newsphotos.)

Figure 1–4 Lee DeForest (1873–1961). (Culver Pictures, Inc.)

device. The electronic device is a Fleming valve with a third electrode inserted between the cathode and anode. The middle electrode turns the diode into a **triode.** This middle electrode, called a control grid, can be used to control the current between the cathode and plate. The overall effect is that of amplification. A small signal on the control grid causes great variations in voltage on the plate of the device. In this way, a small signal is transformed into a much larger signal (amplified). The new vacuum triode was named the **audion.**

From 1907 to 1930, the Fleming valve and audion were improved upon and modified by many scientists of the world. Radio receiver circuits were greatly improved by the addition of amplifiers and oscillators. Crookes's early discoveries were built upon in the development of the iconoscope television camera and the kinescope picture tube by American scientist Vladimir Zworykin.

From the early 1930s to the close of World War II, vacuum-tube concepts were expanded even further in the areas of microwave, radar, and computers. The first radar systems were made by the British with the magnetron tube invented by Henry Boot and John Randall in 1939. The Varian brothers, Russell and Sigurd, were American scientists who invented the klystron microwave power tube in 1939. In 1946, the first vacuum-tube computer was built by engineers at the University of Pennsylvania. Named ENIAC, for *E*lectronic *N*umerical *I*ntegrator *A*nd *C*alculator, it contained some 18,000 vacuum tubes, weighed 30 tons, and used over 130,000 watts of power.

THE SOLID-STATE REVOLUTION

The size, weight, and power demands of vacuum-tube equipment was enough incentive to drive scientists forward to discover solid-state amplification. *Solid-state* means "formed of a single solid block" and involves physics of solid semiconductor materials such as silicon (Si), germanium (Ge), and galium arsenide (GaAs). The solid-state revolution officially began at Bell Labs in 1947 when three American scientists, John Bardeen, Walter Brattain, and William Shockley (Figure 1–5), developed the first transistor. In 1956, they were awarded the Nobel Prize in physics for their contribution. By the late 1950s, people everywhere were enjoying the new freedom of portable transistor radios. The transistor immediately revolutionized consumer electronics, industrial electronics, and computers.

THE FRONTIER OF VERY-LARGE-SCALE INTEGRATION

In 1958, Jack Kilby of Texas Instruments opened a whole new frontier of technology by designing the first monolithic chip that contained more than one transistor. These chips became known as **integrated circuits,** because many transistors were formed on one small piece of semiconductor material (called a **substrate**). The transistors are interconnected to perform a specific function such as amplification, phase comparison, oscillation, frequency mixing, signal conditioning, or digital logic.

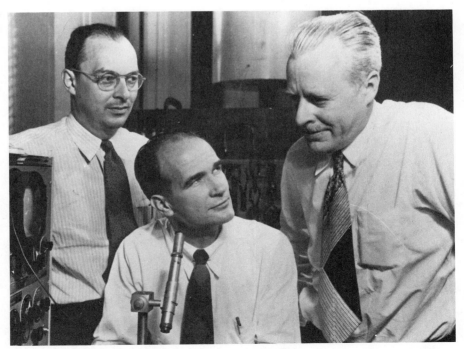

Figure 1–5 John Bardeen, William Shockley, and Walter Brattain: 1956 Nobel Prize winners and inventors of the transistor. (UPI/Bettmann Newsphotos.)

By the early 1970s, large-scale integration (LSI) had been achieved. The technology had advanced to permit thousands of transistors on one chip (substrate). Desktop calculators and portable scientific calculators were introduced at premium prices. In 1971, the Intel Corporation marketed the first microcomputer on a chip, the Intel 4004 microprocessor. The 4004 was a four-bit microprocessor that could perform 100,000 operations per second. Marvelous as this computer chip was, it became obsolete in less than two years, with the introduction of Intel's 8008 and the popular 8080, both eight-bit microprocessors of greater capability than the 4004.

Very-large-scale integration (VLSI) technology was in use all over the world by the late 1970s. Hundreds of thousands of transistors were being placed on tiny silicon substrates. Programmable scientific calculators were available at a fraction of the cost of the relatively simple calculators of a few years before. Random access memory (RAM) chips became a major factor in the reduction of computer size and power consumption. By the mid 1980s, RAM chips contained more than a million transistors. Today, thanks to the research and development departments of companies such as IBM of the United States and Matsushita of Japan, more than 64 million bits of information can be stored in a single RAM chip.

Thus, the frontiers of electronics continue to expand as electronic devices and systems become smaller. New discoveries in electronics, which open new frontiers in all areas of human endeavor, seem to arise daily. Whether in medicine, ocean exploration, space exploration, manufacturing and robotics, or communications, we take our technology with us, or rather, the technology leads us there. Just think, in less than a century, we have come from dim electric light bulbs to deep space exploration, from the slide rule to computer systems that monitor and control the world. What will be said of the next 100 years?

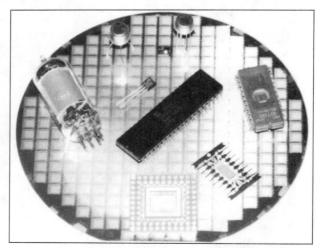

Figure 1–6   Seventy years of progress: the vacuum tube (1907), the transistor (1947), small-scale integration (SSI, late 1950s), large-scale integration (LSI, late 1960s), very-large-scale integration (VLSI, late 1970s).

**Self-Check
1–1**

1. The first vacuum-tube diode was also named what?
2. Who developed the first vacuum triode?
3. How did vacuum tubes impact electronics in the very early 1900s?
4. What historical event ushered in the solid-state revolution?
5. What is very-large-scale integration?

1–2 ATOMIC THEORY

ATOMIC STRUCTURE

Elements and Atoms

A fundamental understanding of the atom is necessary to understand the semiconductor theory behind the many devices in the electronics world. Let's begin with the basics of atomic structure. The simplest and most basic substances in the universe, of which all things are made, are called **elements.** The smallest part of an element that still retains the characteristics of that element is the **atom.** We begin our investigation of the atom with the simplest of all atoms, the hydrogen atom. As you can see from Figure 1–7, the hydrogen atom is made of a central area called the **nucleus** and a small particle, called an **electron,** which can be pictured as orbiting the nucleus.

Atomic Particles

In the hydrogen (H) atom, the nucleus consists of a single particle called a **proton,** a rather heavy little particle that has a mass 1836 times greater than an electron. However, hydrogen is the simplest of all the elements known and is actually missing a nuclear particle common to all other elements. That particle is the **neutron,** which has a mass slightly greater than the proton. So, in the atoms of the remainder of the known natural elements, the nucleus is composed of protons *and* neutrons. The helium atom (also shown in Figure 1–7), which consists of two neutrons, two protons, and two electrons, illustrates this fact.

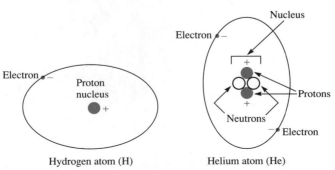

Figure 1–7 Hydrogen and helium atoms.

The Periodic Table

All elements are composed of atoms, which contain different numbers of protons, neutrons, and electrons. In fact, elements are listed by the number of protons in the nucleus of their atoms in a special table known as the **Periodic Table.** The number of protons in the nucleus of an atom is known as the atomic number. Hydrogen has one proton in its nucleus. So its atomic number is 1. Helium (He) is next in the Periodic Table because it has an atomic number of 2 (two protons in the nucleus).

Planetary Structure

Atomic structure is most often described as being planetary in nature, a model first proposed by Niels Bohr in 1913. That is, the electrons orbit the nucleus as planets orbit a star in a solar system. The structure of an atom is three-dimensional, as shown in Figure 1–8, and is composed of energy levels or regions in which certain electrons might be found, but textbook models are usually two-dimensional, to illustrate easily the various distinct energy levels and the number of electrons contained in each level. Each electron in any energy level has a path or paths that it may follow around the nucleus.

Physicists tell us that electrons and protons are charged particles. Years ago the proton was assigned a positive charge and the electron a negative charge. Each charge is equal in magnitude but opposite in sign or polarity. These opposite charges on the proton and electron create a force of attraction that counters the centrifugal, or outward, force of the electrons to keep them in orbit. Furthermore, the number of protons in the nucleus is balanced by an equal number of electrons in orbit. Therefore, the overall charge on the atom is neutral, just as the neutrons in the nucleus are neutral.

Shells

It has long been known that electrons orbit the nucleus at different distances and energy levels. Electrons orbiting at greater distances from the nucleus

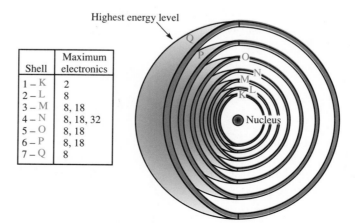

Shell	Maximum electronics
1 – K	2
2 – L	8
3 – M	8, 18
4 – N	8, 18, 32
5 – O	8, 18
6 – P	8, 18
7 – Q	8

Figure 1–8 Atomic shells. These spherical energy levels are not solid matter. The atom is not solid. The shells merely demonstrate the areas in which electrons exist. (Diagram courtesy of William Reed, DeVRY, Kansas City.)

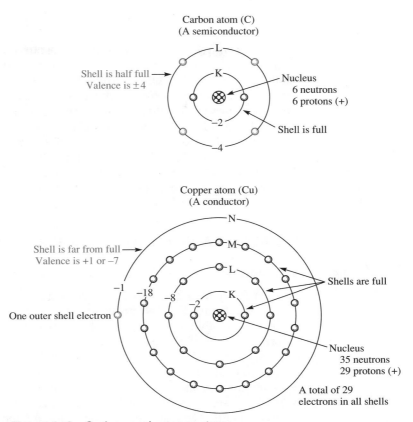

Figure 1-9 Carbon and copper atoms.

are said to exist at higher energy levels. These orbits, or energy levels, are called **shells.** As many as seven shells may surround the nucleus of an atom. As shown in Figure 1–8, they are labeled alphabetically, starting with K as the first or innermost shell.

Figure 1–9 shows the carbon (C) and copper (Cu) atoms. The carbon atom has two shells, K and L. Notice that the K shell, closest to the nucleus, has only 2 electrons, and the outer shell has 4 electrons. Why are there not 4 electrons in the inner shell and 2 in the outer shell, or perhaps some other combination? Scientists have discovered that there is a maximum number of electrons permitted in each shell. The first shell is full when 2 electrons are present and the second shell is full when 8 electrons are present. As you can see, the outer shell of the carbon atom is not full, nor does it have to be.

The *outermost shell* of an atom of any element never contains more than 8 electrons. If the *outer* shell of an atom is full, it will have 8 electrons (except for helium which has 2) and the element is said to be very stable. Inert gases such as helium, neon, argon, and so on, are full in the outer shell and are very stable elements. *Stable* means they will not react chemically and combine with other elements. (Note: Depending on the element, lower-level shells of an atom may have more than 8 electrons, but the outer shell never has more than 8 electrons.)

Valence

The **valence** of an atom is a positive or negative number that indicates the number of electrons contained in the outer shell (also called the valence shell). If an element, such as carbon, has 4 electrons in the valence shell, we say the valence is +4. We might also say that carbon has a valence of −4. The −4 indicates that the valence shell is 4 electrons short of being full (remember 8 is full). As shown in Figure 1–9, copper has one electron in its outer shell. Therefore, it has a valence of +1. We may also say that copper has a valence of −7, because its valence shell is 7 electrons short of being full. The valence indicates how stable an element is or how readily an element might enter into a chemical reaction. As you can see, copper is more chemically reactive than carbon and carbon more so than an inert gas.

CONDUCTORS, INSULATORS, AND SEMICONDUCTORS

Conductors

In order for an element to conduct electricity, there must be an ample supply of free electrons. **Free electrons** are electrons that normally exist in the valence shell of an atom but are able to break free under the influence of an external source of energy. Metals such as silver (Ag), copper (Cu), gold (Au), aluminum (Al), and iron (Fe) are considered good conductors because they have many free electrons (silver being the best conductor, then copper, gold, aluminum, and iron). Valence electrons in these elements are loosely held to the atom and are easily dislodged by heat, voltage potentials, and magnetic fields. Even at room temperature, a conductor has trillions of free electrons moving from the valence shell of one atom to another in a random manner. Generally, conductors have three or fewer valence electrons and are willing to give them up in a chemical reaction or as free electrons for electrical current.

Insulators

Compounds (combined elements) such as air, glass, ceramic, plastics, resins, wax, and rubber that are normally chemically stable are called **insulators.** In these substances, there are no free electrons. All valence electrons are bonded tightly in small atomic structures called **molecules.** Molecules are formed when valence electrons are shared between atoms of an element or between two or more different elements. This is known as **covalent bonding.** Good insulators hold these valence electrons securely in each molecule. As a result, insulators conduct very little or no electrical current at all. We are all aware of at least some of the many applications for insulators in electronics—such as wire insulation, packaging transistors and integrated circuits and other components, and for safety in isolating dangerous high voltages.

Semiconductors

Semiconductors usually have four valence electrons in each atom and are not as willing to give them up as free electrons. Figure 1–10 illustrates the silicon and germanium atoms. These semiconductors are called **tetravalent** because

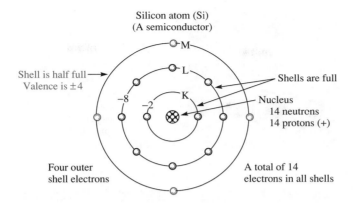

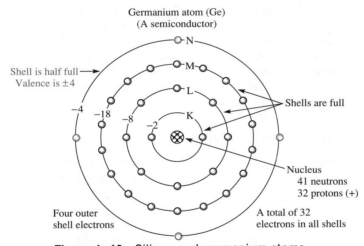

Figure 1–10 Silicon and germanium atoms.

there are four electrons in the valence shell. Semiconductors are poor conductors. Nevertheless, they serve valuable purposes in electronics. Carbon is the most common semiconductor; it is widely used in carbon-composition and carbon-film resistors. Germanium (Ge) and silicon (Si) are semiconductor elements used in devices such as diodes, transistors, and integrated circuits.

Review this important section and test your knowledge with Self-Check 1–2.

Self-Check 1–2

1. What particles make up the nucleus of an atom?
2. In reference to atoms, what is a shell?
3. How is the valence of an atom specified?
4. Compare conductors, insulators, and semiconductors in terms of valence electrons.
5. What is covalent bonding?

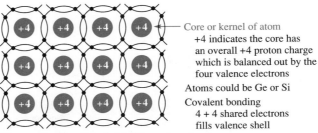

Figure 1–11   Crystal lattice structure.

1–3 THE NATURE OF SEMICONDUCTORS

SILICON VS GERMANIUM

In the early years of transistors, germanium was used. Today, germanium is rarely used, because silicon is a much better semiconductor material for the fabrication of diodes, transistors, and integrated circuits. Germanium gives up too many free electrons under the influence of heat, even at room temperature. With increasing temperature, germanium acts more like a conductor than a semiconductor. This is not at all desirable in semiconductor devices. You will soon discover why silicon is preferred.

THE CRYSTAL LATTICE

Figure 1–11, a simplified atomic structure diagram, illustrates the molecular crystalline structure of intrinsic semiconductor material such as germanium or silicon (**intrinsic** means pure). Notice that each atom of the crystalline structure shows only the valence shell in which covalent bonding takes place. The dark center of each atom is referred to as the **core** or **kernel.** The core contains the nucleus and all shells and electrons below the valence shell. Each core is labeled with a +4. This indicates that the nucleus included in the core has 4 protons available to balance the negative charge of the four valence electrons. As you can see, each outer shell of each atom is filled by sharing electrons—4 valence electrons plus 4 shared electrons (covalent bonding). This diagram shows the semiconductor at a very low temperature, absolute zero (−273°C). At this extremely low temperature, all electrons remain in the valence shells, which means the semiconductor has no free electrons.

THE ENERGY DIAGRAM

Another way to visualize atomic or crystalline structure is the energy diagram. Figure 1–12 is an energy diagram for one atom of silicon. The energy diagram shows each shell of the atom and its contents. Notice the three shaded shells that contain electrons. These shells are energy levels, or bands, in which the electrons exist. Between the shells are **forbidden bands,** in which the electrons cannot exist. The top band is known as the **conduction band.** Under the influence of an external source of energy such as heat, light,

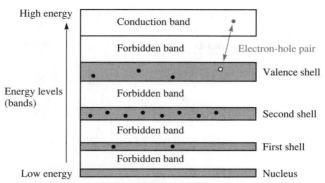

Figure 1–12   Energy diagram for silicon (Si).

or voltage, a valence electron may gain enough energy to break free from the atom. When it becomes free, it enters the conduction band. A **hole** (a place of vacancy) is then left in the valence shell of the atom. The electron in the conduction band and the hole in the valence shell form an **electron-hole pair.** When an electron falls back into a hole, recombination occurs. The length of time the electron remains in the conduction band is known as its **lifetime** (which is usually very short). The overall activity is called **electron-hole-pair generation,** and occurs constantly at room temperature.

CURRENT THROUGH SEMICONDUCTORS

When a difference of potential (voltage) is applied across a semiconductor material, electrical current can flow in one of two ways. The first involves electrons in the conduction band. The external electrical pressure and energy causes the conduction-band electrons to travel between the atoms of the semiconductor material. This, of course, is known as **conduction-band current,** or **electron flow.** The electrons are referred to as **charge carriers** because they are the means of charge flow, or current.

The second type of semiconductor current is called **valence-band current,** often called **drift current** and **hole flow.** This current takes place at the energy level of the valence shells. The holes, left by the absence of electrons, appear to move from the positive end of the semiconductor material to the negative end. This apparent hole motion is due to the shifting of neighboring valence electrons into the hole. As the valence electrons drift toward the positive potential from hole to hole, the holes appear to drift toward the negative potential. Since the holes make this type of current possible, they are also charge carriers.

n AND *p* SEMICONDUCTOR MATERIALS

Doping

Semiconductor materials are not very useful in their *intrinsic* (pure) state. Diodes, transistors, and integrated circuits are made using a combination of two types of semiconductor material, *n*-type and *p*-type. Each of these types is made from a semiconductor material such as silicon. Intrinsic silicon is made into an *n*- or *p*-type by a technique known as doping. In **doping,** atoms of another element are added to the silicon structure to modify its structure and electrical characteristics. These other elements are known as **impurities.** When impurities are added, the silicon becomes **extrinsic,** meaning impure.

n-Type Semiconductor Material

Because *n*-type semiconductor material has an abundance of free electrons conduction-band current flows easily. This type of material is formed by doping the semiconductor with **pentavalent** atoms of elements such as antimony, arsenic, and phosphorus. The atoms of these elements have five electrons in the valence shell. Figure 1–13 illustrates what happens when this type of doping occurs. As you can see, one electron is made free when a covalent bond is formed between a pentavalent impurity atom and tetravalent semiconductor atoms. Thus, one free electron is donated by each impurity atom. That is why each impurity is referred to as a **donor atom.** The total number of free electrons depends on how heavily the material is doped.

The overall energy diagram shows the conduction band filled with an abundance of free electrons. Note that there are very few holes. Holes that do occur, due to thermal agitation, have very short lifetimes. Thus, conduction-band current can be very heavy and valence-band current extremely light. That is why the free electrons are called **majority carriers** and the holes are called **minority carriers.** When a difference of potential is placed across

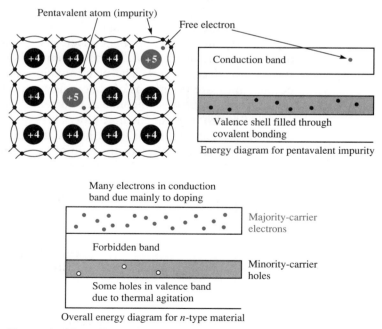

Figure 1–13   n-Type semiconductor material.

an *n*-type semiconductor material, the majority of the current occurs with the electrons in the conduction band.

p-Type Semiconductor Material

The *p*-type semiconductor material has an abundance of holes, making valence-band current easy. This type of material is formed by doping the semiconductor with **trivalent** atoms of elements such as boron, gallium, and indium. The atoms of these elements have three electrons in the valence shell. Figure 1–14 illustrates what happens when this type of doping occurs. As you can see, one hole is produced when a covalent bond is formed between a trivalent impurity atom and tetravalent semiconductor atoms. Thus, one hole is produced for every impurity atom. Because it can potentially receive or accept a free electron, each impurity atom is called a **receptor** or **acceptor**. The total number of holes and receptor atoms depends on how heavily the material is doped.

The overall energy diagram shows the valence band filled with an abundance of holes. Note that there are very few free electrons. Free electrons that do occur due to thermal agitation have very short lifetimes. Thus, valence-band current can be very heavy and conduction-band current extremely light. That is why the holes are called the majority carriers and the free electrons are called the minority carriers. When a difference of potential is placed across a *p*-type semiconductor material, the majority of the current occurs with the holes in the valence band.

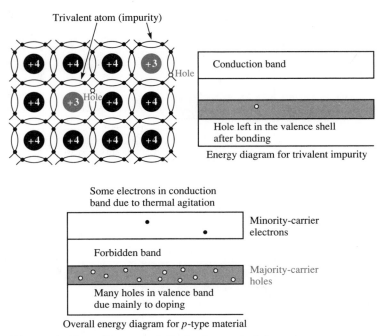

Figure 1–14   p-Type semiconductor material.

THE *pn* JUNCTION

Junction Formation

Semiconductor devices, such as diodes, transistors, and so on, are formed by layering *p* and *n* material. The result is the formation of a *pn* junction that has some very interesting and useful characteristics, the most noted of which is that, ideally, current can only flow in one direction across a *pn* junction.

Consider Figure 1–15. When the *n* and *p* materials are layered together, as shown in 1–15a, free electrons of the *n* material diffuse over into the adjoining holes of the *p* material. This leaves atoms on the *n* side with a net positive charge, because the cores of those atoms have an extra proton that is no longer balanced in charge by the free electron. On the *p* side, the free electron has fallen into a hole. This makes the trivalent receptor atom negatively charged because there are not enough protons in its nucleus to cancel the charge of this new electron. Thus, positive ions are formed on the *n* side and negative ions are formed on the *p* side through a process called **diffusion.** The diffusion and formation of ions continues until a difference of potential exists on each side of the junction. This acts as a barrier to further diffusion.

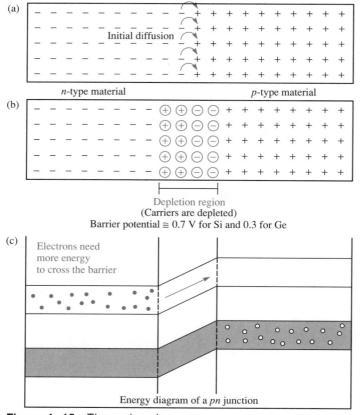

Figure 1–15   The *pn* junction.

In other words, the buildup of negative ions on the *p* side of the junction repels free electrons on the *n* side from diffusing over (Figure 1–15b). Thus, an equilibrium is established.

The Depletion Region and Barrier Potential

The ionized region on both sides of the junction is known as the **depletion region,** sometimes called the **depletion layer,** because, due to diffusion and recombination, all free electrons and holes have been depleted from this area. The difference of potential that exists across the depletion region due to the positive and negative ions is called the **barrier potential** because it is a potential that forms a barrier to further diffusion. Further diffusion and recombination can only take place if an external voltage is applied in the proper polarity to overcome the barrier potential. The energy diagram, Figure 1–15c, shows the free electrons on the *n* side separated from the holes on the *p* side. The electrons cannot cross the barrier unless they gain energy.

Forward-Biased *pn* Junction

Figure 1–16 illustrates what happens when the *pn* junction is forward biased. An external voltage equal to or greater than the barrier potential (about 0.7 V for Si and 0.3 V for Ge) is connected negative side to the *n* material and positive side to the *p* material. This provides the energy needed for the free electrons to cross the barrier. The applied voltage causes the depletion re-

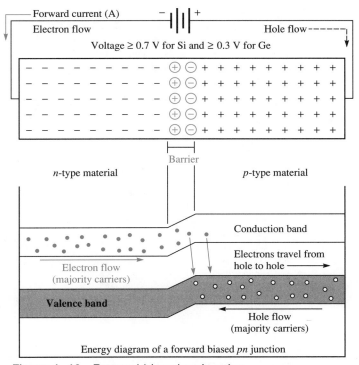

Figure 1–16 Forward-biased *pn* junction.

gion to become narrow by reversing the ionization process. Notice, as is shown in the energy diagram, that the majority-carrier electrons drop into the valence-band holes as soon as they cross the junction. This encourages majority-carrier hole flow on the *p* side. Thus, a continuous and rather heavy current is produced via the conduction band on the *n* side and the valence band on the *p* side.

Reverse-Biased *pn* Junction

Figure 1–17 illustrates the reverse-biased *pn* junction. Notice that the depletion region is now very wide. The reverse bias has encouraged further ionization, which increases the barrier potential. The depletion region grows, and so the barrier potential grows until it matches the externally applied voltage. This barrier expansion occurs very quickly, almost instantaneously. From the energy diagram of Figure 1–17, you can see that there is no chance for majority-carrier current as described earlier. Ideally, there should be no current at all. However, due mainly to thermally agitated electron-hole pairs, a very small minority current exists. This minority current is called **leakage current** or **reverse current.** Leakage current nearly doubles for every 10-C° increase in temperature. Fortunately, leakage current for silicon semiconductor materials is very small—measured in the nanoamps (nA) compared to microamps for germanium.

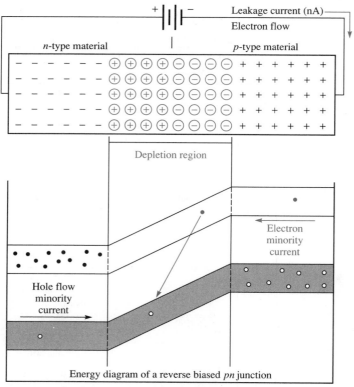

Figure 1–17   Reverse-bias and leakage current.

Reverse Bias Breakdown

If the reverse bias voltage is increased steadily, the depletion region will continue to increase. In the process, the stress on the atomic structure of the entire chip increases. Finally, it reaches a breaking point and the *pn* junction can be permanently damaged, depending on its design and the nature of the breakdown. **Zener breakdown** takes place when the reverse voltage is high enough to tear large numbers of electrons from the atoms in the depletion region. This drastically increases the minority current. **Avalanche breakdown** takes place as valence electrons leave their shells and collide with other valence electrons, knocking them from their valence shells. The process quickly turns into a chain reaction that creates an avalanche of free electrons. In severe cases, permanent damage to the semiconductor material can occur.

Review this important section and test your knowledge with Self-Check 1–3.

Self-Check 1–3

1. Which are found in the conduction band, (a) holes or (b) electrons?
2. How is *n*-type semiconductor material created?
3. Describe the depletion region that exists between *n*- and *p*-type material.
4. Does forward bias utilize (a) majority carriers or (b) minority carriers? Explain.
5. What are the two types of reverse bias breakdown?

1–4 ELECTRONIC SYSTEMS

The atomic and semiconductor theory discussed thus far will be utilized in chapters to come. In this section, we complete your broad introduction to electronics with an important discussion of electronic systems. This will establish the systems concept early in your thinking as you begin your exploration of electronic devices, circuits, and systems.

SYSTEM ORGANIZATION

Repairing a large piece of electronic equipment for the first time can be a little scary. On the outside you see a panel filled with switches, knobs, and various meters. When the cover is removed from whatever this piece of equipment is, you see a dozen or so cable bundles, a big transformer, and several large circuit boards. Yes, it does seem overwhelming. What should you do first? A schematic diagram of the monster will help, but where do you begin? The secret to troubleshooting a large electronic system such as this is to match trouble symptoms with a specific functional block or blocks in the system.

Any electronic system is organized into functional blocks. Each **functional block** is a circuit that performs a specific task, service, or function for the overall system. The functional block may be an integrated circuit with external support components such as resistors and capacitors, or it may be many integrated circuits and transistors working together to form the block. A functional block may also have other functional blocks within itself.

Logically, then, it would be nice if we had a block diagram of the system, so we could see all of the functional blocks in relation to each other. This way, we could break the larger system down into subsystems (functional blocks) to match trouble symptoms with block function. Once the block is isolated, the actual component or device within the block can be found and replaced.

As you can see, understanding system organization is important for troubleshooting. It is also important in design work. Design engineers do not start the design of an electronic system by drawing a massive schematic. The overall system concept is first achieved by assembling functional blocks on paper. Each functional block is assigned specifications to which it must conform in performing its function in the overall system. Once all blocks have been specified and clearly defined, a schematic of the actual components can be rendered for each. A prototype is then assembled and tested.

You, too, will learn to do this. As you explore electronics, you will collect diagrams of interesting circuits, of which there are many in this book, along the way. These circuits are functional blocks that you will learn to combine with others to form systems. New systems are designed every day simply by combining familiar functional blocks in new ways.

Let's take a look at some of the more common analog functional blocks; then we will see how they can be used in systems.

COMMON BLOCKS AND SYMBOLS

Amplifier Blocks

Shown in Figure 1–18, the amplifier block is perhaps the most common of all functional blocks. The purpose of this block is to increase the voltage amplitude and/or power level of a signal. This is called **amplification.** The signal may be a specific frequency, your voice, music, or a large band of frequencies. The amplifier block is specified in terms of gain (amount of amplification), frequency range, input and output levels, internal noise level, and distortion (any modification to the signal's waveform by the amplifier). Note that many different block symbols are used for the amplifier. A square or rectangular box can be used for the amplifier (or any other functional block)

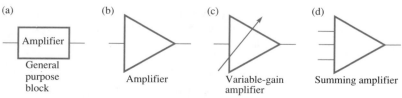

Figure 1–18 Amplifier blocks.

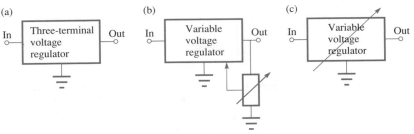

Figure 1–19 Voltage regulator blocks.

as long as it is labeled or identified in some way. The triangle is also commonly used. A slanted arrow indicates that the gain of the block can be varied. The summing amplifier is a linear mixer that is commonly used in audio mixers in recording studios. All input signals are amplified by the same amount and placed on the same output wire. There are many other types of amplifiers you will discover later.

Voltage Regulator Blocks

Another common functional block is the voltage regulator. Shown in Figure 1–19, the voltage regulator supplies a pure DC at a constant level to the overall electronic system. A change in load at the regulator's output terminal or line voltage will not cause a change in output voltage because the regulator monitors its own output and instantly counteracts any would-be change in voltage. Figures 1–19b and 1–19c are variable voltage regulators. These regulators allow you to set the output voltage to the desired amount. The regulator then makes sure the output voltage stays at that amount. As you continue in this textbook, you will eventually see and understand exactly how this is done.

Oscillator/Generator Blocks

Many systems require a functional block that creates a specific frequency, waveform, and amplitude. Such a block is called an **oscillator** or **generator.** The oscillator can be designed to produce a sine wave, square wave, or ramp voltage at any desired frequency and voltage level. Notice, from Figure 1–20, the block symbol can be square or circular with the waveform indicated. The slanted arrow indicates the frequency is variable over some range.

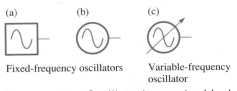

Fixed-frequency oscillators   Variable-frequency oscillator

Figure 1–20 Oscillator/generator blocks.

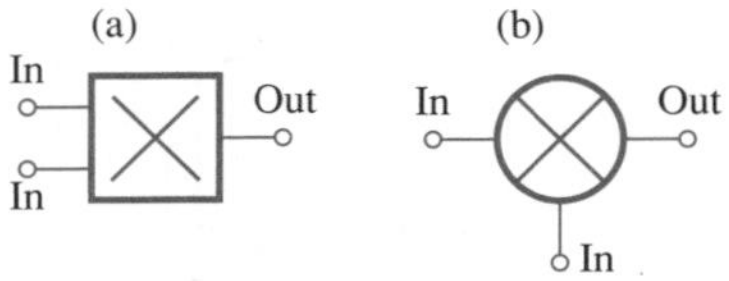

(a)   (b)

In
         Out   In   Out
In
                            In

Figure 1–21   Nonlinear mixer blocks.

Nonlinear Mixer Blocks

Figure 1–21 illustrates common symbols for nonlinear mixer blocks. These blocks are very important in electronic communication equipment. In this block, two signals are mixed together in such a way as to produce two new frequencies, or sets of frequencies. One set is the sum of the two input signals, the other is the difference between the two input signals. For example, if 200 kHz is applied to one input terminal and 50 kHz is applied to the second input terminal, four individual frequencies will appear at the output terminal: 200 kHz, 50 kHz, 250 kHz (the sum of 200 kHz and 50 kHz), and 150 kHz (the difference between 200 kHz and 50 kHz). Using a parallel resonant circuit, the mixer may be tuned to permit only one of the signals (such as 150 kHz) to exit the mixer. We will explore this more later.

Filter Blocks

Often a system requires a block or blocks that are able to filter out unwanted signals. The filter block, as shown in Figure 1–22, is usually a square or rectangular box. Either it is literally labeled as highpass, lowpass, bandpass, or bandstop, or there is a small diagram inside or next to the box that illustrates the frequency response of the filter.

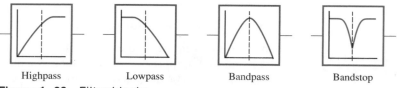

Highpass   Lowpass   Bandpass   Bandstop

Figure 1–22   Filter blocks.

Phase Comparators

Once again, as shown in Figure 1–23, a square or circular block may be used. The purpose of the phase comparator is to produce a DC level at the output terminal that is proportionate to the difference in phase of the two input signals. One of the input signals is often a very stable reference frequency, to which the other input signal is compared in frequency and phase. Any difference in phase between the two signals is translated into a DC error voltage. This DC voltage may then be used to correct the frequency of the second signal. You'll see this at work much later when you study frequency synthesis.

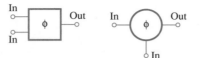

Figure 1–23   Phase comparators.

Timer Blocks

Many systems require a timer, or timers, to control the sequence of events that occur in the system. The timer circuit provides a needed delay in the operation of a block, or blocks, in the system. Notice, the timer blocks of Figure 1–24 contain a square wave pulse. The ON time of the pulse represents the time delay or duration of a time-controlled event.

Fixed timer   Fixed timer   Variable timer

Figure 1–24   Timer blocks.

Many other functional blocks could be covered here if space would allow. However, we have covered some of the most common and useful ones. Think of them as building blocks as you consider some of the common electronic systems to follow.

COMMON ELECTRONIC SYSTEMS

As we explore some common electronic systems, it is important for you to realize that you are not expected to understand these systems in detail at this time. They are merely presented so you can become familiar with the *system concept*. That is, *all electronic systems, no matter how complex, are made up of interconnected functional blocks that are an aid in design and troubleshooting*. As you continue to explore electronics in the remaining chapters of this book, you will gain an understanding of how these functional blocks actually work and how they are actually made. An overview of these common systems now will help establish your need to know for future study.

The Regulated AC to DC Converter

The system shown in Figure 1–25 is a regulated DC power supply. The first block is a step-down transformer that transforms the AC to 12.6 VAC. The next block is a rectifier that converts the 12.6 VAC to positive pulsating DC. The pulsating DC is then filtered to remove the pulsations. The lowpass filter blocks the 120-Hz pulsations and passes a fairly pure DC to the regulator. You may recall from previous study that the lowpass filter is also an integrator that averages or smoothes out the pulses. In this case, the filter is a

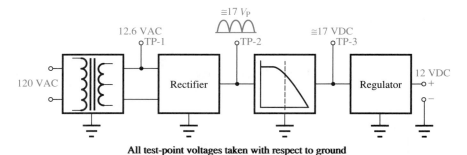

All test-point voltages taken with respect to ground

Figure 1–25 Regulated AC to DC converter (regulated DC power supply).

capacitive input type of filter that charges up to the peak DC voltage. Once the DC has been filtered, it is passed on to the regulator, which maintains the output voltage at 12 VDC over a wide range of load- and line-voltage variations. You will learn much about all of this later in the pages of this book. However, the point we need to make here is, with the system laid out in blocks like this, you can quickly and easily isolate a trouble to a specific block using the testpoints. The system block diagram is a valuable troubleshooting tool.

Three-Stage Audio Amplifier

Figure 1–26 illustrates a three-stage audio amplifier. The low-noise amplifier is a specially designed amplifier that generates very little internal noise itself. This allows very-low-level signals from microphones to be amplified without the annoying background hiss so common in early public address systems. The block diagram indicates that the volume is adjusted by varying the gain of the second amplifier (you will see how this is actually done later). The final power amplifier provides the power needed to drive a speaker system. Notice that a 12-V regulator is placed in the positive supply line (bus) for the low-noise amplifier. This is because the power amplifier can cause rapid variations in voltage on the +24 VDC line, variations that would be sent back to the low-noise amplifier and possibly cause distortion of the signal.

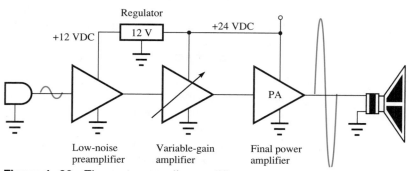

Figure 1–26 Three-stage audio amplifier.

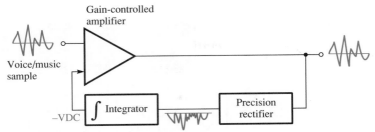

Figure 1–27   Automatic gain control (AGC).

The 12-V regulator prevents this from occurring. Though not marked, logical testpoints would be at the output of each amplifier stage. Using the oscilloscope and a test signal, say 1 kHz at 10 mV$_{P-P}$, you would expect to see an undistorted sine wave of greater amplitude at each stage output. In this way, any trouble is quickly isolated to the specific block.

Automatic Gain Control (AGC)

Another common system is automatic gain control (AGC), also referred to as automatic level control (ALC). The system shown here is a very simple audio AGC system (sometimes called an audio compressor). The system is supposed to maintain the audio at the output at a nearly constant level over a wide range of input levels. In order for this to work properly, the output must be monitored and a control voltage must be produced that can adjust the gain of the amplifier as needed to maintain a fairly constant output level. The amplifier has a DC control voltage input. If the output signal is a little high, the DC control voltage will be more negative, which causes the amplifier to reduce its gain (amplify less). If the output signal is too low, the DC control voltage will be less negative, which causes the amplifier's gain to increase (amplify more). Thus, the output signal level is kept within a small range of change. The precision rectifier converts the audio signal to a negative pulsating DC and the integrator converts the negative pulsating DC to a pure −VDC to control the amplifier. Once again, checking the output of each block with the oscilloscope can isolate a problem stage.

One final note: There is no indication of power supply connections to the blocks of the AGC system, no +VDC, and no ground indicated. Very often these connections are omitted in the block diagram and it is assumed that power is available for all blocks that need it.

AM Radio Receiver

The block diagram is an excellent way to learn the fundamentals of radio receivers. Figure 1–28 shows a typical AM radio block diagram. Often, block diagrams include oscilloscope displays of signals that should appear at certain points in a system. Also, notice how generously labeled this system is. A block diagram like this is of tremendous value when it comes to understanding and troubleshooting a complex system.

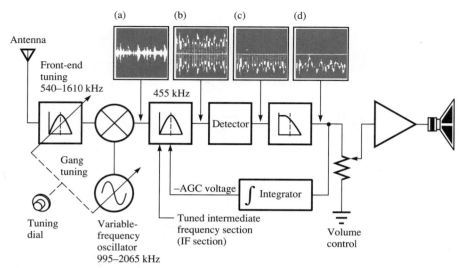

Figure 1–28 AM radio receiver block diagram.

You have already been introduced to the functional blocks that make up the AM receiver system. It is possible that you could work your way through the system on your own to understand its basic operation. However, let me be of assistance with the following brief description.

The antenna on the left receives all AM stations at the same time. The front-end tuning is a bandpass filter that can be varied over the entire AM band from 540 kHz to 1610 kHz. Because of the selectivity (bandwidth) of the variable front-end tuning, only two or three stations can reach the input to the mixer (the one desired station being stronger than the other one or two adjacent stations). The variable oscillator is adjusted to provide a frequency to mix with the desired station frequency. In a standard AM receiver, the mixer is *tuned* to 455 kHz. The *difference* between the desired station frequency and the oscillator frequency must be 455 kHz. For example, say the dial is set to a station at 800 kHz. The gang tuning sets the front-end tuning bandpass filter right on 800 kHz, and at the same time sets the variable oscillator for 1255 kHz. The 800-kHz station mixes with the 1255-kHz oscillator signal to produce a 455-kHz signal at the mixer output (1255 − 800 = 455). All of the music and voice of the station signal is now at a frequency of 455 kHz. The oscilloscope display at (a) shows this weak signal at the mixer output. The signal enters the IF section, also tuned to 455 kHz, where it is filtered, to remove adjacent channel interference from neighboring stations, and amplified. The greatly amplified signal, shown on oscilloscope display (b), is then applied to the detector (c), which allows only the negative half of the 455-kHz signal to pass. Shown on display (d), the lowpass filter block removes any 455-kHz signal from the audio information. The lowpass filter has a cutoff frequency of about 10 kHz or less. The pure audio is passed through the volume control to the amplifier and speaker.

Notice the −AGC voltage applied to the IF section. The gain of the amplifiers in the IF is controlled by this AGC voltage. A strong station produces a strong audio, which the integrator converts to a large −AGC voltage, which reduces the gain of the IF section. A weak station produces a very low $-$AGC voltage, which allows the gain of the IF amplifiers to be much higher. This relieves you from having to drastically adjust the volume control every time you change stations.

You may not yet really understand how the AM receiver works. That is OK. You will be introduced to it again in greater detail in other courses and textbooks. The point we must make here is once again that of the *overall system concept*. Complex systems are composed of less complex functional building blocks. Knowing the purpose for each block can make troubleshooting and understanding the system much easier.

Throughout this book, you will learn about the devices that are used to create these functional blocks; you will also discover the theory of operation of these devices in each block. I hope this introduction to electronic systems has given you an overall understanding of system theory that will have lasting value as you explore the world of electronics. In the chapters to follow, we will often refer back to some of these systems as the inner secrets of each functional block are unlocked.

Self-Check 1–4

1. Which is easier, (a) to troubleshoot a system at the component level using a schematic or (b) to troubleshoot a system at the functional block level using a system block diagram? Explain why.
2. A functional block that is circular and has one cycle of a sine wave drawn in its center represents what?
3. A slanted arrow drawn through a block indicates what?
4. Explain what a nonlinear mixer block does.
5. What are two ways filter blocks can be identified?
6. System block diagrams are never used in design work, only troubleshooting. True or false?

SUMMARY

CONCEPTS

■ The vacuum-tube diode was named the Fleming valve after its inventor John Fleming.
■ The first vacuum-tube triode amplifier was invented by Lee de Forest in 1907.
■ Vacuum tubes greatly expanded the capabilities of radio receivers and transmitters in the early 1900s.
■ The solid-state revolution began in 1947 with the invention of the first transistor by John Bardeen, Walter Brattain, and William Shockley.
■ Electrons orbit the nucleus of an atom at various energy bands called *shells*.
■ Outer-shell valence electrons conduct electricity.
■ Current is conducted in the conduction band as electron flow or in the valence band as drift current or hole flow.
■ The *n*-type of semiconductor material is doped with pentavalent impurities to create an excess of free electrons once covalent bonding has taken

place in the crystalline structure. Conduction-band electrons are majority charge carriers and valence-band holes are minority carriers.

■ The *p*-type of semiconductor material is doped with trivalent impurities to create an excess of holes once covalent bonding has taken place in the crystalline structure. Conduction-band electrons are minority charge carriers and valence-band holes are majority carriers.

■ When a valence electron is forced to leave the valence shell of an atom in a crystalline structure, an electron-hole pair is created. The time it takes for recombination to occur is the electron's *lifetime*.

■ The depletion region of a *pn* junction is a layer in which all majority carriers have been depleted through diffusion and recombination. The depletion region is formed by oppositely charged ions that create a barrier voltage that opposes further diffusion. This barrier potential is approximately 0.7 V for silicon and 0.3 V for germanium *pn* junctions.

■ An ideal *pn* junction conducts current in only one direction under forward bias conditions.

■ Real *pn* junctions permit a very weak leakage current under reverse bias conditions.

■ Electronic systems are made up of interconnected functional blocks that are an aid in design and troubleshooting.

NEED-TO-KNOW SOLUTION

1. Testing every component is very time-consuming and will benefit you very little, especially if you are not already familiar with the equipment. Accomplishing a repair in this manner would almost be accidental.

2. Examining the entire system from the block diagram, with the symptoms in mind, is the best second step in the repair process (the first step being a clear identification of symptoms). The block diagram tells you how the overall system works and divides the system into logical functional blocks. Often, the trouble symptom can be quickly related to the function of a particular block, or blocks.

3. Studying the overall schematic is the next best thing to do. However, as you study it, you will look for subcircuits or blocks that perform various functions in the system. In effect, you create a system block diagram in your mind as you try to match the symptom to a section of the system.

4. Stealthily transferring the troubled equipment to someone else's bench is not advisable. This could have negative effects on your job security and physical health.

QUESTIONS

1–1 HISTORICAL BACKGROUND

1. What was Sir William Crookes's contribution to electronics?
2. Who invented the vacuum triode amplifier?
3. What was Thomas Edison's contribution to the new era of electronics?
4. What was the name given to the first vacuum-tube diode and why?
5. Describe the first vacuum-tube computer.

6. What does *solid-state* mean?
7. Who invented the first transistor amplifier? When? Where?
8. What is an integrated circuit?
9. What is the difference between large-scale integration (LSI) and very-large-scale integration (VLSI)?
10. Who invented the first microprocessor chip? When?

1–2 ATOMIC THEORY

11. What are the three main particles of an atom? Which is negative? Which is positive? Which is neutral?
12. Which of the three main atomic particles has the greatest mass? Which has the least mass?
13. The energy levels, or bands, that surround the nucleus of an atom are called what?
14. What is another name for the outer shell of an atom?
15. The outermost shell of an atom is considered to be full with how many electrons?
16. How many valence electrons do atoms of each of these elements have: (a) copper, (b) carbon, (c) silicon, (d) germanium?
17. What does *tetravalent* mean? List three tetravalent elements.

1–3 THE NATURE OF SEMICONDUCTORS

18. What is intrinsic silicon?
19. What makes up the core, or kernel, of an atom?
20. Describe the crystal lattice structure in terms of covalent bonding.
21. At room temperature, intrinsic silicon has no free electrons. True or false?
22. What does an energy diagram show?
23. What is a hole and an electron-hole pair?
24. What is it called when an electron falls into a hole?
25. What are the charge carriers for conduction band current?
26. What is drift current?
27. Describe how *n*-type silicon is made.
28. Is *p*-type silicon made with trivalent impurities or pentavalent impurities? Explain.
29. In *p*-type material, what are the majority carriers? Why?
30. What is the relationship between holes and free electrons in *n*-type material?
31. Describe the formation of the depletion region in a *pn* junction.
32. What is the barrier voltage for a silicon *pn* junction? for a germanium *pn* junction?
33. Describe a forward-biased *pn* junction in terms of majority-carrier current and depletion-region width.
34. Is there any current at all when the *pn* junction is reverse biased? Explain.
35. What is the difference between zener breakdown and avalanche breakdown?

1–4 ELECTRONIC SYSTEMS

36. What is a system block diagram?
37. Explain the value of a system block diagram to a repair technician.
38. Do design engineers use block diagrams? Explain.
39. What is a functional block?
40. List five different common functional blocks and briefly describe the purpose for each.
41. What symbol can you use to indicate that a block is variable?
42. List the functional blocks of an AC to DC converter and describe the purpose for each block.
43. List the three basic functional blocks of an audio AGC system and describe the purpose for each block.
44. Explain how the block diagram of Figure 1–28 can be a valuable aid to troubleshooting an AM receiver.
45. If you come up with an idea for an electronic system, should you begin the design by drawing the schematic of the entire system or should you begin with a system block diagram? Explain.

ANSWERS TO SELF-CHECKS

SELF-CHECK 1–1

1. Fleming valve.
2. Lee de Forest.
3. Transmitters and radio receivers were greatly improved.
4. The solid-state revolution was ushered in by John Bardeen, Walter Brattain, and William Shockley as they invented the first transistor at Bell Labs in 1947.
5. The construction of hundreds of thousands of transistors on a single chip.

SELF-CHECK 1–2

1. Neutrons, protons.
2. A shell is an energy level, surrounding the nucleus of an atom, in which electrons may exist.
3. The valence number is specified as the number of electrons in the outer shell.
4. Conductors have less than 4 electrons in the outer shell. Insulators have more than 4 electrons in the outer shell. Semiconductors have 4 electrons in the outer shell.
5. Covalent bonding takes place when valence electrons are shared between atoms of an element or of two or more different elements.

SELF-CHECK 1–3

1. Free electrons are found in the conduction band.
2. A pure semiconductor material is doped with pentavalent impurities to form an extrinsic *n*-type semiconductor material.

3. The depletion region is a region shared by the p and n material around the junction. It is an area depleted of free electrons on the n side and depleted of holes on the p side, due to diffusion and recombination.
4. (a) Majority carriers. Forward bias promotes conduction-band electron flow on the n side and valence-band hole flow on the p side of a pn junction.
5. Zener breakdown and avalanche breakdown.

SELF-CHECK 1–4

1. (b) Using the block diagram. The block diagram breaks the system down into functional blocks, each having a specific purpose. Trouble symptoms can be matched with block function.
2. An oscillator or generator.
3. A variable block.
4. A nonlinear mixer creates two new frequencies from two original frequencies. The output of the mixer includes the two original frequencies, the sum of the two original frequencies, and the difference between the two original frequencies. If the mixer is tuned, its output is either the sum frequency or the difference frequency.
5. With a written label or a frequency plot diagram.
6. False.

SUGGESTED PROJECTS

1. In preparation for the next chapter on diodes, obtain a step-down transformer (120 V/25.2 CT @ 450 mA), four 1N4002 silicon rectifier diodes, and a 50-V, 1000-μF electrolytic capacitor.

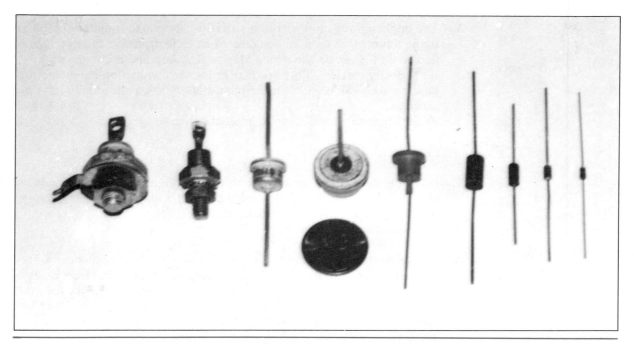

Semiconductor diodes, ranging from low-current diodes on the top to high-current diodes on the bottom. Diodes are manufactured in a wide range of voltage and current ratings. Diodes are also manufactured differently to obtain desired characteristics for specialized applications.

Semiconductor Diodes

OBJECTIVES

After studying this chapter, you will be able to

- explain the semiconductor theory of a *pn* junction, covering the topics of forward and reverse bias.
- understand common diode ratings as presented on manufacturer's data sheets.
- test a diode using an ohmmeter.
- explain the difference between half-wave and full-wave rectifiers and be able to analyze and design them.
- analyze capacitor-input and inductor-input power supply filters.
- troubleshoot a full-wave rectifier power supply.

NEED TO KNOW

Suppose you have a car stereo (AM/FM/Cassette) that you want to use in the house. The specifications in the owner's manual for the stereo indicate that the unit is designed for 12 to 17 V and will draw a maximum of 3 A. Can you design an AC to DC converter to run the stereo unit in the house? Believe it or not, you will be able to do this by the time you finish this chapter. You may want to actually build this just as an educational exercise. In later chapters, you will learn about voltage regulation and you will be able to improve your design. As always, a solution to this Need to Know is provided at the end of this chapter. You may want to see if you can design this supply before you look at the solution.

INTRODUCTION

In this chapter, you will be introduced to semiconductor diodes, their characteristics, and one of their most common applications, rectification. What is rectification? It is the process of converting an AC signal to a pulsating DC signal. Here you will learn how to use diodes to convert AC voltage and current to a pulsating negative or positive DC voltage and current. In so doing, you will learn how to analyze, build, and troubleshoot AC to DC power supply circuits. The AC to DC converter is a basic building block found in virtually all AC-powered electronic equipment. I am sure you will enjoy this chapter.

2–1 DIODE CHARACTERISTICS

SYMBOLIC AND PHYSICAL CHARACTERISTICS

Diode Symbol

The diode is the *pn* junction discussed in Chapter 1. As shown in Figure 2–1, the diode is simply a "sandwich" of *n*-type and *p*-type semiconductor material with a diffused depletion region forming the junction. The diode permits very large amounts of current in one direction due to majority carriers and a very small amount of current in the opposite direction due to minority carriers, depending on the polarity of voltage applied across the diode. As you can see from Figure 2–1, the schematic symbol for a diode is basically an arrow. The arrow indicates the direction of majority-carrier hole flow (conventional flow). The cathode of the diode is the negative side, made of *n* material, and is always at the point of the arrow. The flat side of the arrow is always the anode, made of the *p* material. Conventional current is always in the direction of the arrow, from anode to cathode.

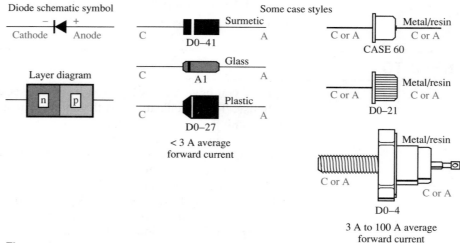

Figure 2–1 Diodes.

Case Styles

Diodes are manufactured in a great variety of sizes and case styles to accommodate wide ranges of voltage and current ratings. Though not conclusive, the case style is often a good indication of the diode type (germanium or silicon) and current-handling capability. Notice, in Figure 2–1, smaller diodes are end-marked, either with a painted ring or a conical shape, to indicate the cathode. Larger, metal/resin diodes are manufactured for heat-sink mounting and may have a cathode or anode casing. The diode type number is used to consult a data book to determine the cathode and anode terminal, or the diode can be tested to make that determination.

FORWARD BIAS CHARACTERISTICS

Forward Voltage and Current

Figure 2–2 illustrates a test circuit used to graph the relationship between the forward voltage (V_F) and forward current (I_F) of a forward-biased diode. Notice that the positive terminal of the variable voltage source is connected to the anode of the diode via the series current-limiting resistor. As the source voltage is increased from 0 V, the voltage across the diode begins to increase. Before the diode voltage becomes equal to the barrier potential (V_B), the rise in forward current is very gradual and nonlinear. The opposition of the barrier potential is the major factor that limits current until the barrier potential is matched and exceeded. The decrease in the size of the depletion region as forward voltage is increased from 0 V to 0.7 V permits greater and greater majority-carrier current, which causes the graph to be nonlinear or curved. Once the barrier potential is overcome, with V_F exceeding approximately 0.6 to 0.7 V for silicon and 0.2 to 0.3 V for germanium, the diode conducts a large amount of forward current, which increases linearly with further increases in forward voltage.

Forward Bias Behavior

The forward-biased diode can be thought of in one of three different ways, depending on the application and the need for accuracy. As shown in Figure 2–3a, the forward-biased diode can ideally be thought of as a closed switch. In this case, the diode is idealized as having no internal resistance and no voltage drop. Current instantly jumps to a maximum value when the ideal

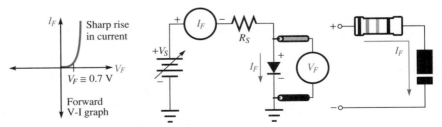

Figure 2–2 Forward-biased diode.

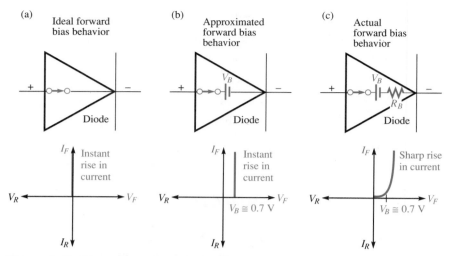

Figure 2–3   Diode forward bias behavior.

diode is forward biased (switch closed). This view of a forward-biased diode is fine for many applications, where relatively high voltage is involved. For example, if 100 VDC is applied to a diode in series with a resistor, the diode will drop approximately 0.7 V and the resistor will receive 99.3 V. The difference is insignificant, so the diode can be considered ideal and we can say the resistor gets the full 100 V.

In Figure 2–3b, the 0.7-V barrier potential is taken into consideration. Since the 0.7-V barrier potential must be overcome before any significant current is passed to a load device, we can approximate the diode as a switch that closes only when the 0.7-V threshold is reached (0.3 V for germanium). This approximation is necessary for low-voltage applications. Say you connect a 3-V source to a diode in series with a resistor. The diode drops approximately 0.7 V and the resistor gets the remaining 2.3 V. You cannot idealize and say the resistor gets the full 3 V. The difference between 2.3 V and 3 V is too great.

The actual, real behavior of the forward-biased diode is shown in Figure 2–3c. The graph, also called a *characteristic curve,* shows the gradual non-linear rise in forward current as the barrier potential is being overcome, then a sharp linear rise in current once V_B is exceeded. This graph shows that the forward current does not jump instantly to a maximum value when the 0.7-V threshold is exceeded. The linear slope is the result of the internal bulk resistance of the n and p semiconductor material. The **bulk resistance** (R_B) is the opposition the semiconductor material offers to majority carrier current. This resistance is usually very low, less than 1 Ω. Nevertheless, it is significant enough to cause the forward voltage drop of the diode to increase somewhat above the approximately 0.7-V barrier potential. The bulk resistance may cause the diode voltage drop (V_F) to increase to a volt or more at maximum forward current. Thus, the forward voltage drop of a silicon diode may be anywhere between approximately 0.6 and 1 V or so, depending on the amount of forward current.

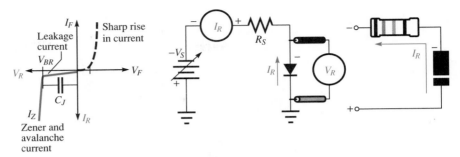

Figure 2-4   Reverse-biased diode.

REVERSE BIAS CHARACTERISTICS

Reverse Voltage and Current

Figure 2-4 shows the polarity of the source voltage reversed to place a negative potential on the anode of the diode (V_R). The result is a very weak reverse current (I_R), ranging from picoamps to microamps. This current, referred to as *leakage current,* is made up of minority-carrier current. As the reverse voltage is increased from 0 V, the leakage current increases very little, because the available current carriers are generated mainly due to heat (thermally). However, if the reverse voltage continues to increase, a breakdown point is reached where current increases radically. The breakdown voltage (V_{BR}) is a reverse voltage that is strong enough to tear large numbers of valence electrons loose from the depletion region, causing a sudden zener current and a chain-reaction current called avalanche current, both lumped together and labeled I_Z. This often causes permanent damage in the form of an internal short. However, some diodes (zener diodes) are made to operate in this breakdown region. More on this in the next chapter.

Junction Capacitance

Notice the capacitor symbol along the leakage current region of the characteristic curve in Figure 2-4. A diode that is reverse biased between 0 V and V_{BR} is also a capacitor. The depletion region inside the diode acts as the dielectric for the outer p and n materials, which act as plates. As the reverse voltage is increased above 0 V, the depletion region gets wider, thus *separating* the plates by a greater distance. As you know, increasing the distance between plates reduces the capacitance. Thus, due to this junction capacitance (C_J), the reverse-biased diode acts like an electrically controlled variable capacitor. As we will investigate in the next chapter, some diodes are designed specifically for this purpose.

Reverse Bias Behavior

Figure 2-5 illustrates ideal and actual reverse-biased diode behavior. Ideally we may think of the reverse-biased diode as an open switch. With the switch

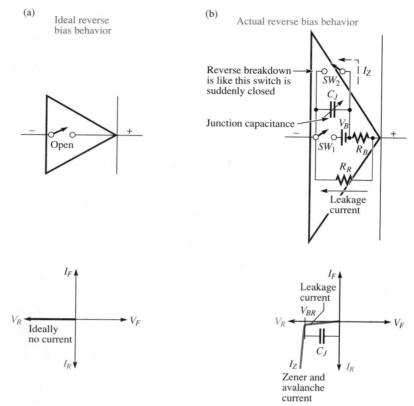

Figure 2–5 Diode reverse bias behavior.

open, there is absolutely no current and all of the reverse voltage appears across the diode. For many applications, this ideal diode model is adequate. However, for some applications the characteristic leakage current and/or junction capacitance is significant. In high-impedance DC circuits, the leakage current may be enough to cause unwanted voltages to appear across other components. In high-frequency AC circuits, the junction capacitance may be enough to pass the high-frequency AC on to a circuit. In many pieces of electronic communications equipment, different circuits are switched in and out by forward and reverse biasing switching diodes. These diodes are chosen for their very low leakage current and low junction capacitance.

Figure 2–5b shows a diode model that includes all of the diode reverse bias characteristics. Notice that the forward bias switch (SW_1) is open and the leakage path for current is through a very large resistance (R_R). Junction capacitance exists only in the leakage-current region of reverse bias with SW_1 and SW_2 both open. When the breakdown voltage is exceeded, it is as though SW_2 were closed, and a very large reverse current results (I_Z). The reverse resistance (R_R) may range between 10 kΩ and 10 GΩ, the leakage current (I_R) may range between 10 pA and 10 mA, and the junction capacitance may be between a few and a few hundred picofarad, all depending on the type of diode.

IMPORTANT ELECTRICAL RATINGS

Maximum Reverse Voltage (V_{RM}, PIV)

The maximum reverse voltage is an important rating since many diodes are permanently damaged when this rating is exceeded. The maximum reverse voltage (V_{RM}) is a voltage beyond which breakdown may occur. This rating is also referred to as the peak inverse voltage (PIV) rating, the working peak reverse voltage ($V_{RM(wkg)}$) rating, and the peak repetitive reverse voltage ($V_{RM(rep)}$) rating (which means the peak of an applied AC voltage must not exceed this rating).

RMS Reverse Voltage (V_r)

The RMS reverse voltage (V_r) rating is simply the RMS value of the V_{RM} or PIV value. For example, if $V_{RM} = 50\ V_P$, $V_r = 35$ V ($0.707 \cdot 50\ V_P$).

Average Forward Current (I_F, I_O)

This is a main diode rating. As a component rating, it is the maximum average current that can safely be sustained by the diode. In practice, the actual average current through the diode will depend on the circuit configuration and load.

Maximum Forward Surge Current ($I_{FM(surge)}$)

The maximum forward surge current ($I_{FM(surge)}$), also known as the nonrepetitive peak surge current, is the maximum forward current the diode can survive from a single pulse.

Operating and Storage Temperature Range (T_J, T_{stg})

The operating and storage junction temperature range (T_J, T_{stg}) rating specifies the safe temperature range for the diode in degrees centigrade (°C). A typical temperature range for a silicon rectifier diode is −65 to +175°C.

Maximum Reverse Current (I_R, I_{RM})

The maximum reverse current rating tells you the maximum amount of reverse current, or leakage current, you can expect from a certain diode when it is operated within its maximum reverse voltage rating. The reverse current rating is temperature dependent—the higher the temperature, the higher the leakage current.

RECTIFIER DIODES AND CHARACTERISTICS

Among the diode ratings discussed, the most significant ratings for diodes used for rectification in AC to DC converters are: average forward current (I_O), peak inverse voltage (PIV), or maximum reverse voltage (V_{RM}), and the maximum forward surge current for one nonrepeating DC pulse (I_{FSM}). Figure 2–6 shows a variety of common rectifier diodes in their case styles and significant ratings.

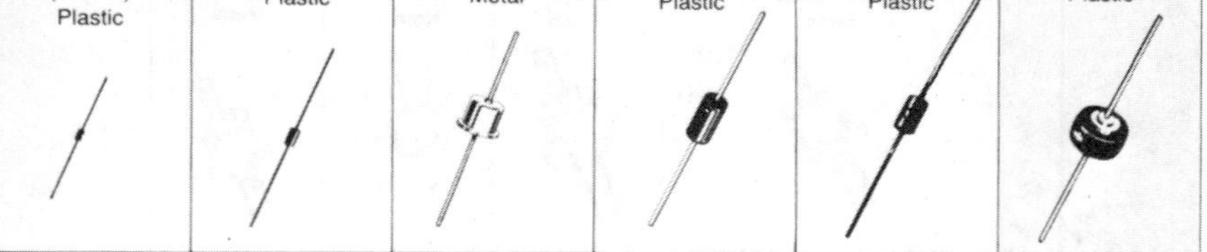

	I_O, AVERAGE RECTIFIED FORWARD CURRENT (Amperes)					
	1.0	1.5	3.0			6.0
	59-03 (DO-41) Plastic	59-04 Plastic	60-01 Metal	267-03 Plastic	267-02 Plastic	194-04 Plastic
V_{RRM} (Volts)						
50	†1N4001	**1N5391	1N4719	**MR500	1N5400	MR750
100	†1N4002	**1N5392	1N4720	**MR501	1N5401	MR751
200	†1N4003	1N5393 *MR5059	1N4721	**MR502	1N5402	MR752
400	†1N4004	1N5395 *MR5060	1N4722	**MR504	1N5404	MR754
600	†1N4005	1N5397 *MR5061	1N4723	**MR506	1N5406	MR756
800	†1N4006	1N5398	1N4724	MR508		MR758
1000	†1N4007	1N5399	1N4725	MR510		MR760
I_{FSM} (Amps)	30	50	300	100	200	400
T_A @ Rated I_O (°C)	75	$T_L = 70$	75	95	$T_L = 105$	60
T_C @ Rated I_O (°C)						
T_J (Max) (°C)	175	175	175	175	175	175

† Package Size: 0.120″ Max Diameter by 0.260″ Max Length.
* 1N5059 series equivalent Avalanche Rectifiers.
** Avalanche versions available, consult factory.

Figure 2–6 Common low-power rectifier diodes. (Copyright by Motorola, Inc. Used by permission.)

The average forward current (I_O) is simply the average DC current that the diode must handle (pass) during a complete rectified AC cycle. The amount of average current is determined by the demand, or load, and the rectifier design.

The maximum reverse voltage (V_{RM}), or peak inverse voltage (PIV), is the maximum voltage that can be applied to the diode in the reverse bias polarity before reverse voltage breakdown occurs. In power supply design, care must be taken to insure that this peak AC rating is much greater than the actual peak inverse voltage of the circuit.

The maximum forward surge current (I_{FSM}) is the maximum, or peak current, the diode can withstand during one nonrepeating forward current pulse surge. If more than one surge pulse flows through the diode in a repeating fashion, this value is reduced. For example, a 1N4001 can withstand a single 30-A_P surge pulse (one cycle), seven 15-A_P surge pulses (7 cycles), twenty 10-A_P surge pulses (20 cycles), or an unlimited number of 3-A_P pulses. This information is obtained from graphs provided in manufacturer's data books. You will see the significance of this when we discuss power supply filtering.

Time for a review and a self-check.

Self-Check 2–1

1. Describe how you can visually determine the cathode end of a small glass diode.
2. In which direction does conventional current flow through a diode, (a) from anode to cathode or (b) from cathode to anode?
3. Explain what causes the sloped linear rise in forward current once the barrier potential of a diode has been exceeded.
4. An actual reverse-biased diode has what two characteristics that may be a disadvantage in circuit operation?
5. Two major diode ratings are PIV and I_O. Explain these ratings.

2–2 DIODE TESTING

DIODE TROUBLES

When a diode fails because of exceeded ratings, it first shorts internally. If a circuit-protection device such as a fuse is present, or there is a current-limiting resistor, the diode will be discovered in this shorted condition. However, if there is no circuit-protection device or current-limiting resistor, the diode will eventually burn open or destroy other components. Diodes that have burned open are usually easily recognized by discoloration, a cracked casing, and/or odor. A shorted diode may look very normal. Thus, the diode must be tested to determine its actual condition.

When you test a diode, what characteristics should you look for? Naturally, the diode should conduct heavily in one direction and virtually not at all in the other. The suspected diode can be removed from its circuit and tested in many ways. One method is shown in Figure 2–7.

TESTING WITH THE OHMMETER

As shown in Figure 2–7, the ohmmeter can be used to check a diode. The diode should test open in the reverse direction and have some resistance reading in the forward direction. The readings will vary widely between diodes and for different types of ohmmeters. The main thing to look for is a large difference in readings from forward to reverse bias polarity. Note that a shorted diode will have a measurable but very low resistance when tested in either direction.

OTHER DIODE TESTS

Many multimeters, such as the Circuitmate DM27 shown in Figure 2–8, have a diode test function. In most cases, this makes use of the internal battery to place enough voltage across the diode to completely forward bias it. The forward voltage is measured and displayed by the meter. A reading between 0.6 V and 0.75 V in the forward bias direction and out-of-range in the reverse bias direction indicates the diode is good.

A simple continuity tester may also be used to test many diodes. The tester may consist of two 1.5-V cells in series (3 V) and a flashlight bulb. The

Good diode

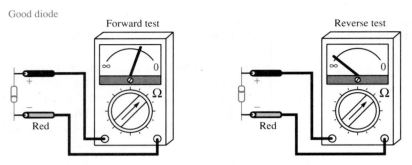

Note: The red lead on most analog multimeters is the negative polarity when using the ohmmeter function.

Shorted diode

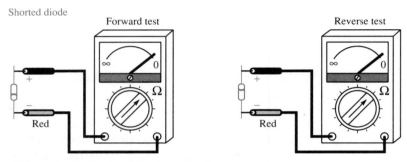

Figure 2–7   Testing diodes with the ohmmeter.

diode is used to complete the circuit. If the diode is good, the bulb will light only with the diode in one direction, the forward bias direction. If the diode is shorted, the bulb will light with the diode in either direction. If the diode is open, the bulb will not light with the diode in either direction.

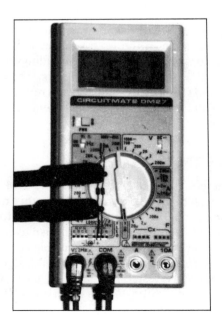

Figure 2–8   Using the diode test function of a multimeter to test diodes. (Equipment courtesy of Beckman Industrial Corporation.)

Self-Check 2-2

1. If a diode checks as an infinite resistance regardless of the way an ohmmeter's leads are connected to the diode, what is wrong with the diode?
2. Using the diode test function of a multimeter, a diode measures out of range in one direction and 0.68 in the other direction. Is this diode good? What is the meaning of the 0.68-V reading?
3. What is the condition of a diode that has a very low ohmmeter reading in both directions?

2-3 HALF-WAVE RECTIFIERS

INTRODUCTION TO THE HALF-WAVE RECTIFIER

The block diagram of a complete AC to DC converter, or DC power supply, is shown in Figure 2-9. Our discussion here focuses only on the first two blocks of the supply—the AC transformation block and the rectification block. In later discussions, we will continue to explore the remaining blocks of the supply. The symbols and waveforms shown with the blocks indicate that the AC to DC converter employs half-wave rectification.

A half-wave rectifier is a circuit that uses a device that is able to block one alternation of an AC cycle and pass the other. Naturally, the diode is able to do this because it passes current when forward biased and blocks current

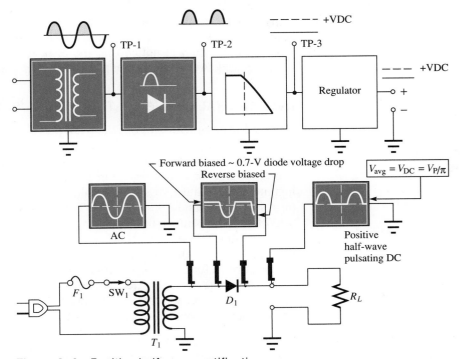

Figure 2-9 Positive half-wave rectification.

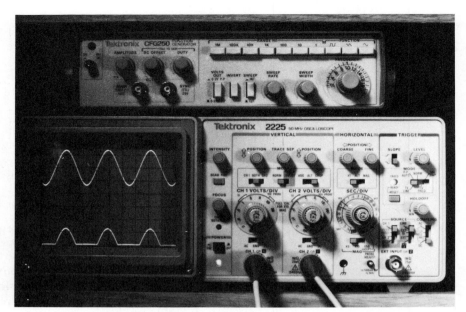

Figure 2–10   An oscilloscope comparison of an AC voltage and its half-wave rectified voltage. (Equipment courtesy of Tektronix, Inc.)

when reverse biased. As you can see in Figure 2–9, only the positive alternation is able to pass through the diode to the load resistor. When the diode is forward biased, the positive alternation is all passed on to the load, except an approximately 0.7-V diode drop. Thus, the peak load voltage is equal to the transformer's peak secondary voltage less 0.7 V. Figure 2–10 shows an actual half-wave rectified AC voltage in relation to the AC voltage. If you look closely, you will notice that the peak rectified voltage is slightly less than the peak AC voltage, due to the forward voltage drop of the diode.

AVERAGE HALF-WAVE VOLTAGE AND CURRENT

The load resistor averages out the peak pulses over an entire cycle. In other words, the actual power dissipated by the resistor in the form of heat is determined by the average current and voltage over one complete cycle. The average value of one alternation is the average of an infinite number of instantaneous values, or samples, taken from 0° to 180°, or from 180° to 360° ($v = V_P \cdot \sin\underline{/\theta}$, and $i = I_P \cdot \sin\underline{/\theta}$). For each AC alternation, the average is 0.637 times the peak value. However, since there is only one alternation per AC cycle in a half-wave rectified waveform, the average DC value is half the average value for the alternation itself. Thus, the average DC value of voltage or current for half-wave rectified waveforms is (0.637/2) times the peak value. Also, the average value can be thought of as the area contained under the peak being spread out over the time for one complete cycle. Through the use of calculus, this is shown mathematically to be (peak value)/π.

$$V_{DC} = V_{avg} = V_{P(load)}/\pi = 0.318 \cdot V_{P(load)} \qquad \text{(for half-wave)} \qquad (2\text{–}1)$$

Consider Examples 2–1 and 2–2.

EXAMPLE 2–1 ▌

A 24-V AC signal is half-wave rectified. What is the peak load voltage, the average load voltage, and the average current if the load resistance is 150 Ω?

- The peak AC voltage is 24 V · 1.414 = 33.9 V_P.
- The actual peak load voltage is $V_{P(load)}$ = 33.9 V_P − 0.7 V = 33.2 V_P, because there is an approximate 0.7-V diode voltage drop.
- The average load voltage is V_{DC} = 0.318 · 33.2 V_P = 10.6 V.
- The average current is 10.6 V/150 Ω = 70.7 mA.

EXAMPLE 2–2 ▌

A 6.3-V AC signal is half-wave rectified and applied to a 33-Ω load resistance. Determine the peak load voltage, the average load voltage, and the average current?

- The peak AC voltage is 6.3 V · 1.414 = 8.91 V_P.
- The actual peak load voltage is 8.91 V_P − 0.7 V = 8.21 V_P.
- The average load voltage is V_{DC} = 0.318 · 8.21 V_P = 2.61 V.
- The average current is 2.61 V/33 Ω = 79.1 mA.

PEAK INVERSE VOLTAGE (PIV)

The actual amount of peak inverse voltage across the diode is equal to the peak AC voltage applied to the rectifier (diode). When the diode is reverse biased, during the negative alternation, it acts like an open. Since the diode is in series with the source and load, all of the voltage of the negative alternation will appear across the reverse-biased diode. Thus, the peak inverse voltage is equal to the peak value of the negative alternation. When designing a rectifier circuit such as this, remember that the maximum reverse voltage *rating* of the diode must be greater than the actual peak inverse voltage. A reverse voltage rating of at least twice the actual peak inverse voltage provides an adequate margin of safety. Study Example 2–3.

EXAMPLE 2–3 ▌

Consider the following for a 12.6-V transformer secondary, half-wave rectified, supplying a 100-Ω load resistor.

- The peak secondary voltage is 1.414 · 12.6 V = 17.8 V_P.
- The maximum reverse voltage rating of the diode must be greater than 17.8 V.
- $V_{P(load)}$ = $V_{P(secondary)}$ − 0.7 V = 17.8 V_P − 0.7 V = 17.1 V_P.
- V_{DC} = 0.318 · $V_{P(load)}$ = 0.318 · 17.1 V_P = 5.44 V.
- The average current is 5.44 V/100 Ω = 54.4 mA.
- From a design standpoint, a diode such as the 1N4001 would be a good choice in this case.

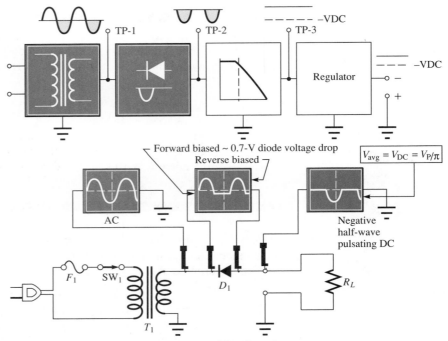

Figure 2–11   Negative half-wave rectification.

Figure 2–11 shows how a negative DC voltage can be obtained. Note that the diode is simply reversed. This permits the negative alternation to pass to the load while the positive alternation is blocked. Once again, the diode drops approximately 0.7 V during forward bias and the average DC load voltage is $0.318 \cdot V_{P(load)}$.

Time for a self-check. You can use this self-check as a guided review of this section.

Self-Check 2–3

1. The 12.6-V secondary of a transformer is connected to a half-wave rectifier and a 20-Ω load device. Calculate the average DC output voltage and average current. From Figure 2–6, which rectifier diode would be adequate for this application?

2. The 24-V secondary of a transformer is connected to a half-wave rectifier and a 50-Ω load device. Calculate the average DC output voltage and average current. From Figure 2–6, which rectifier diode would be adequate for this application?

2–4 FULL-WAVE RECTIFIERS

HALF-WAVE + HALF-WAVE = FULL-WAVE

Notice the AC to DC converter circuit of Figure 2–12; it contains two diodes and is using a transformer that has a center-tapped secondary. Each half of the secondary works with a diode to form a half-wave rectifier circuit. The

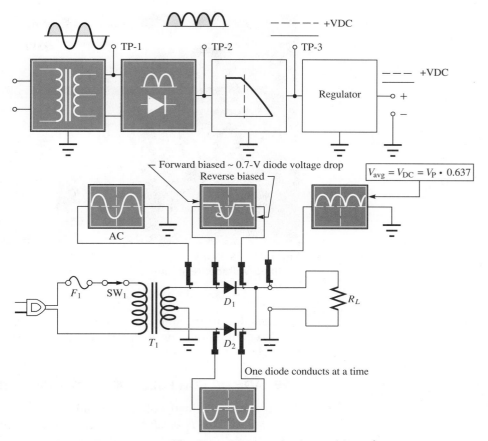

Figure 2–12 Full-wave rectification with a center-tapped transformer.

two half-wave rectifiers connected to the same load result in full-wave rectification. The waveform shown at the output, across the load resistor, is a full-wave rectified pulsating DC. The two diodes take turns conducting and supplying current to the load. When one diode is on (forward biased) the other diode is off (reverse biased). Thus, each diode contributes only half of the total average load current. Full-wave rectification provides twice the average voltage and current that half-wave rectification does, assuming the same peak value and load resistance. Also, the frequency of the full-wave pulsating DC is twice the frequency of the AC voltage.

The center tap on the secondary winding effectively cuts the secondary in half. The peak voltage passed by each diode to the load is only half of the total peak secondary voltage. However, the peak inverse voltage that appears across each diode is nearly the full peak secondary voltage. When D_1 is conducting, D_2 is reverse biased and appears open. Thus, the entire secondary voltage appears across D_2 by way of D_1. So, for design purposes, the diodes must be chosen according to the entire peak secondary voltage.

Figure 2–13 shows a full-wave rectified voltage (lower trace), comparing it to the original AC voltage (upper trace). Once again, if you look closely, you will see the slight difference in peak pulsating DC voltage and peak AC

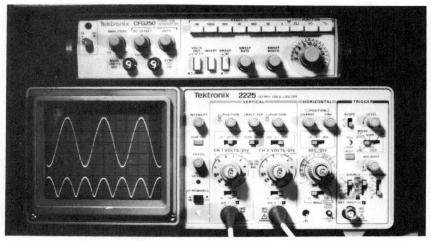

Figure 2–13 An oscilloscope comparison of an AC voltage and its full-wave rectified voltage. (Equipment courtesy of Tektronix, Inc.)

voltage, due to the diode drop for each alternation. Also, notice that the pulse repetition rate, or pulse frequency, is 120 Hz, whereas the AC voltage is 60 Hz.

AVERAGE DC FOR FULL-WAVE RECTIFICATION

The average DC load voltage for full-wave rectification is twice the half-wave value. This is because there are two DC pulses per AC cycle.

$$V_{DC} = V_{avg} = 2V_{P(load)}/\pi = 0.637 \cdot V_{P(load)} \qquad \text{(for full wave)} \qquad (2-2)$$

EXAMPLE 2–4

Consider the following for a full-wave rectifier used with a 12.6-V center-tapped secondary and a 100-Ω load.

- Each half of the secondary is 6.3 V_{RMS}.
- The peak voltage for each half is 1.414 · 6.3 V = 8.91 V_P.
- The peak load voltage is 8.91 V_P − 0.7 V (diode drop) = 8.21 V_P.
- The average load voltage is 0.637 · 8.21 V_P = 5.23 V.
- The average load current is 5.23 V/100 Ω = 52.3 mA.
- The average current conducted by each diode is half this value, because each diode conducts only half of the time.

$$I_{D1} = I_{D2} = 52.3 \text{ mA}/2 = 26.2 \text{ mA}$$

- The actual peak inverse voltage across one diode while the other diode is conducting is 1.414 · 12.6 V = 17.8 V_P (actually 17.1 V_P because there is a 0.7-V drop across the conducting diode). For design purposes, the reverse voltage rating of the diode should be about twice this value. A 1N4001 is fine for this application.

EXAMPLE 2–5 ■■■■■■■■■■■■■■■■■■■■■■■

A center-tapped secondary transformer winding has a full secondary voltage of 25.2 V. A full-wave rectifier is used, supplying pulsating DC to a 30-Ω load.

- Each half of the secondary is 12.6 V_{RMS}.
- The peak voltage for each half is 1.414 · 12.6 V = 17.8 V_P.
- The peak load voltage is 17.8 V_P − 0.7 V = 17.1 V_P.
- The average load voltage is 0.637 · 17.1 V_P = 10.9 V.
- The average load current is 10.9 V/30 Ω = 363 mA.
- $I_{D1} = I_{D2}$ = 363 mA/2 = 181.5 mA.
- The actual peak inverse voltage across one diode while the other diode is conducting is 1.414 · 25.2 V = 35.6 V_P (actually 34.9 V_P since there is a 0.7-V drop across the conducting diode). 1N4001 or 1N4002 diodes are fine for this application.

THE BRIDGE RECTIFIER

The bridge rectifier, shown in Figure 2–14, is the most popular full-wave rectifier. When using a bridge, there is no need for a center tap and the full secondary can be used. Four diodes must be used, but this does not usually increase the cost, because all four can be purchased in one small package at a cost comparable to that of one or two individual diodes. The diode-bridge package has four leads and is labeled much like the block diagram shown in Figure 2–14a, two small sine wave symbols for the AC terminals and a positive and negative terminal. If a negative DC supply is needed, the positive lead/terminal is connected to ground and the negative terminal is connected to the filter/regulator/load.

Compare Figure 2–14b and 2–14c. See how the diodes conduct in pairs? In Figure 2–14b, diodes 1 and 2 conduct and automatically switch the negative secondary lead to ground and the positive lead to the load resistor. In Figure 2–14c, diodes 3 and 4 conduct, again switching the negative secondary lead to ground and the positive lead to the load resistor. The diodes instantly and automatically direct the negative potential to ground and the positive potential to the load.

Since there are always two diodes conducting, we must subtract 1.4 V from the peak secondary voltage to determine the peak load voltage. For high-voltage supplies this is not necessary, but for low-voltage supplies it is often significant. Consider Examples 2–6 and 2–7.

EXAMPLE 2–6 ■■■■■■■■■■■■■■■■■■■■■■■

For a bridge rectifier between a 12.6-V transformer secondary and a 100-Ω load resistance, determine the following: average DC load voltage and current, and the actual peak inverse voltage and average current for each diode.

(a)
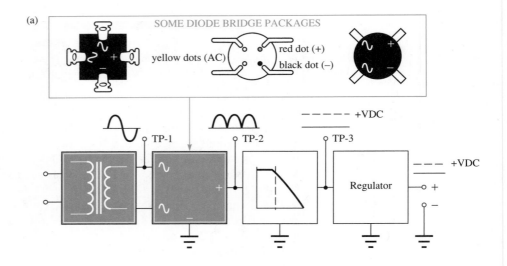

(b)
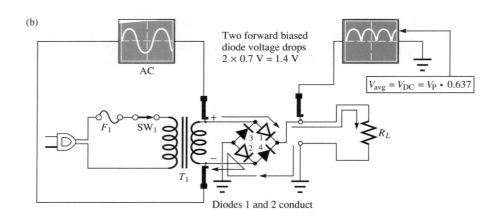

(c)
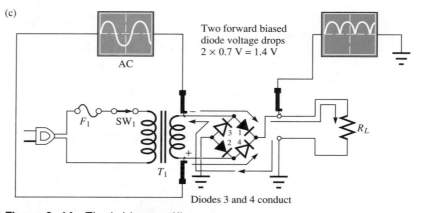

Figure 2–14 The bridge rectifier.

- The peak secondary voltage is $1.414 \cdot 12.6$ V $= 17.8$ V_P.
- The peak load voltage is 17.8 $V_P - 1.4$ V $= 16.4$ V_P.
- The average DC load voltage is $0.637 \cdot 16.4$ $V_P = 10.4$ V.
- The average DC load current is 10.4 V/100 $\Omega = 104$ mA. Each diode pair conducts for only a half-cycle.
- The average current for each diode is 104 mA/$2 = 52$ mA.
- The peak inverse voltage across each diode is approximately the entire peak secondary voltage because when diodes 1 and 2 conduct, the entire secondary voltage is across diodes 3 and 4, and while diodes 3 and 4 conduct, the entire secondary voltage is across diodes 1 and 2.

EXAMPLE 2–7

For a bridge rectifier between a 100-V transformer secondary and a 2.2-$k\Omega$ load resistance, determine the average DC load voltage and current, and the actual peak inverse voltage and average current for each diode.

- The peak secondary voltage is $1.414 \cdot 100$ V $= 141.4$ V_P.
- The peak load voltage is 141.4 $V_P - 1.4$ V $= 140$ V_P.
- The average DC load voltage is $0.637 \cdot 140$ $V_P = 89.2$ V.
- The average DC load current is 89.2 V/2.2 $k\Omega = 40.5$ mA.
- The average current for each diode is 40.5 mA/$2 = 20.25$ mA.
- PIV $= 140$ V. Use 1N4004 diodes with a 400-V rating.

DUAL-POLARITY AC TO DC CONVERTER

A bridge rectifier and a center-tapped transformer can be combined to form a dual-polarity DC supply (often called a *bipolar* supply). Figure 2–15 shows how this is done. Notice that diodes 1 and 4 take turns supplying a positive potential to load 1 and diodes 2 and 3 take turns supplying a negative potential to load 2. Thus, the circuit is actually two full-wave, center-tapped rectifiers in one. The peak load voltage, for either load, is half of the peak secondary voltage minus a diode drop.

Notice that the ground current is indicated with a dashed, double-ended arrow. This indicates that the direction of ground current could be in either direction, or not exist at all. If the current flowing through R_{L1} is equal to the current flowing through R_{L2}, there is no ground current. Why? First of all, I_{RL1} is flowing through R_{L1}, through the ground, back to the center tap, while I_{RL2} is attempting to flow from the center tap through ground, through R_{L2}. As a result, there is a cancelling effect in the ground. If the two currents are equal, there is total cancellation. Does this mean the loads do not receive power? No. The current flowing through R_{L1} continues through R_{L2} and finds its way back to the transformer winding via diode 2, as shown in Figure 2–12. However, if the load resistances are not equal, the load currents will not be equal and there will not be total cancellation of ground current. The

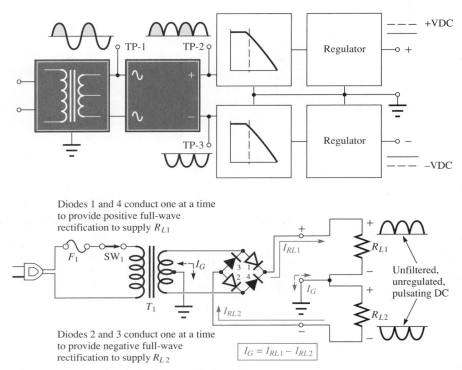

Figure 2–15   Dual-polarity AC to DC converter.

ground current will be the difference between I_{RL1} and I_{RL2}. If one of the load resistors is suddenly removed, the ground current will immediately equal the remaining load current. The direction of ground current will depend on which load remains.

Here is an interesting problem for you. Suppose R_{L1} is greater than R_{L2} and the center-tap ground connection becomes open. What happens to the voltage across R_{L1} and R_{L2}? That's right, the load voltages become unbalanced. The voltage across R_{L1} is suddenly greater than the voltage across R_{L2}, because the two loads simply form a voltage divider and split the total rectified secondary voltage according to the voltage divider rule. The four diodes act as a normal bridge rectifier, supplying a positive and negative potential to a load. A solid, reliable ground connection is necessary to tie the two loads back to the center tap and ensure that the peak voltage across either load is never more than half the peak secondary voltage (minus one 0.7-V diode drop, of course).

Time for a self-check.

Self-Check 2–4

1. Which type of rectifier has a total of approximately 1.4 V of diode voltage drops?
2. Calculate the approximate peak inverse voltage across a diode in a bridge rectifier circuit that is connected to a 30-V secondary.

3. If a full-wave rectifier supplies 2 A of current to a load device, how much average current does each rectifier diode handle?

4. If the AC line frequency is 50 Hz, what is the pulse frequency at the output of a half-wave rectifier? of a full-wave rectifier?

2–5 FILTERING PULSATING DC

FILTERING

As you can see in Figure 2–16, we now progress to the next block in the diagram of the AC to DC converter. After the AC is rectified, it must be filtered to smooth out the radical pulsations. In actuality, the filtering process is an integration process in which the pulsating DC is smoothed or averaged out. Ideally, we would want to obtain a DC output that is as smooth as that which comes from a battery. However, a perfectly smooth output is difficult to obtain. We can, however, come close. For most applications, close is close enough. We will discuss this more later. At the moment, consider two common filtering schemes used in AC to DC converters.

CAPACITOR-INPUT FILTERS

Figure 2–17 illustrates the simple capacitor filter. It is simple in design and relatively inexpensive. It is also more than adequate in performance, especially when followed by a regulator. The theory of operation is simple. When a pulse is present, the capacitor quickly charges to the peak value through the secondary winding resistance and the diode bulk resistance. While no pulse is present, or while the pulse drops off, the capacitor discharges through the load and series resistor, if there is one. If the capacitor is large enough, it will be discharged very little until the next pulse peak arrives to recharge it. In practice, the 5RC charge time is much shorter than the 5RC discharge time because the capacitor charges through the low resistance of the transformer winding and forward-conducting diodes. With each pulse cycle, the capacitor's voltage varies up and down an amount that depends on the size of the capacitor and the size of the load. This variation in DC voltage, known as *DC ripple,* will be discussed in detail shortly.

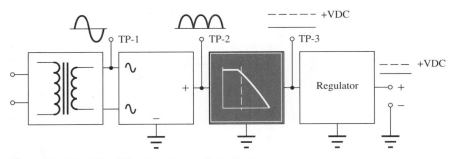

Figure 2–16   The filter block—an integrator.

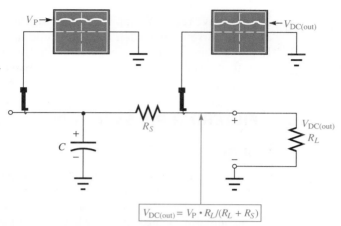

Figure 2–17   The capacitor-input filter.

Notice the series resistor (R_S) in Figure 2–17. This series resistor acts as a voltage divider with the load. If the peak pulsating DC from the rectifier (V_P) is too high for the load device, the series resistor can be selected to drop some of the voltage according to the voltage divider rule. As shown in the figure, the filter capacitor charges to the peak value of the pulsating DC.

INDUCTOR-INPUT FILTERS

Figure 2–18 shows an inductor-input filter. This filter is a better performer than the simple capacitor filter but is more costly, heavier, and requires more space. Because contemporary integrated-circuit voltage regulators are very inexpensive, the large inductor input filter is rarely needed or used. What the simple capacitor filter cannot filter, the voltage regulator simply removes (more on this in a later chapter).

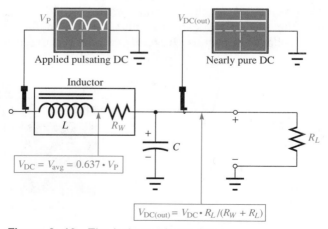

Figure 2–18   The inductor-input filter.

The theory of operation for the inductor input filter is also relatively straightforward. The inductor integrates, or smoothes out, the DC current that charges the capacitor. In so doing, the inductor provides the capacitor with a prefiltered charge current. The average DC current permits the capacitor to charge to the average full-wave DC level, which is $0.637 \cdot V_P$. There is also a small voltage drop across the resistance of the windings of the inductor (R_W). This is usually insignificant. The DC voltage at the load is usually very pure with very little ripple.

DC RIPPLE

Any filter's performance is ultimately judged by the amount of DC ripple that is riding on the DC voltage. Figure 2–19 shows an oscilloscope display being used to observe DC ripple riding on the DC voltage. Notice the ripple can be measured in peak-to-peak ($V_{r(P-P)}$). Also, the DC voltage (V_{DC}) extends from the zero reference line to the middle, or average, of the DC ripple. Thus, the actual DC voltage is

$$V_{DC} = V_P - (V_{r(P-P)}/2) \qquad (2-3)$$

A power supply filter is designed for a certain percent ripple. The percent ripple is determined from the ripple factor (r) which is the ratio of the RMS ripple voltage (V_r) and the DC voltage (V_{DC}).

$$\% \text{ ripple} = 100\% \cdot r \qquad (2-4)$$

$$r = \text{ripple factor} = V_r/V_{DC} \qquad (2-5)$$

where V_r is the RMS ripple voltage.

The ripple voltage waveform is not a sine wave. It is much more like a sawtooth waveform, with a rapid rise and gradual drop. In this case, the RMS value of ripple voltage is found as follows:

$$V_r = V_{r(P)}/\sqrt{3} = V_{r(P-P)}/(2 \cdot \sqrt{3}) = 0.289 \cdot V_{r(P-P)} \qquad (2-6)$$

Consider Examples 2–8 and 2–9.

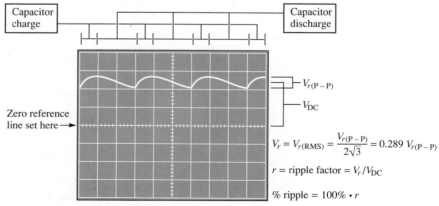

Figure 2–19   DC ripple voltage.

EXAMPLE 2–8

Let's assume the volts/division control is set for 5 V/div to obtain the display shown in Figure 2–19.

- $V_{DC} \cong 12$ V.
- $V_{R(P-P)} \cong 2$ V_{P-P}.
- $V_r = 0.289 \cdot 2$ $V_{P-P} = 0.578$ V.
- $r = V_r/V_{DC} = 0.578$ V/12 V $= 0.048$ (no units).

This is equal to 4.8% ripple (4.8% $= 100\% \cdot 0.048$).

EXAMPLE 2–9

A filtered DC voltage has a peak value of 6.97 V and contains 340 mV$_{P-P}$ ripple. Determine the RMS ripple voltage and the ripple factor.

- $V_{DC} = 6.97$ $V_P - (340$ mV$_{P-P}/2) = 6.8$ V.
- $V_r = 0.289 \cdot 340$ mV$_{P-P} = 98.3$ mV.
- $r = V_r/V_{DC} = 0.0983$ V/6.8 V $= 0.0145$ (no units).

This is equal to 1.45% ripple (1.45% $= 100\% \cdot 0.0145$).

RECTIFICATION AND RIPPLE

Figure 2–20 illustrates the effects of half-wave and full-wave rectification on ripple. Notice that for a given load and capacitance, the full-wave rectifier has less ripple (half the ripple that results when half-wave rectification is

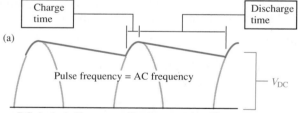

(a)

DC ripple: half-wave rectification, capacitor filter

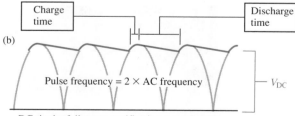

(b)

DC ripple: full-wave rectification, capacitor filter

Figure 2–20 Rectification and DC ripple. Full-wave rectification creates less DC ripple and a higher average DC than half-wave rectification given the same load and capacitor filter.

used). From this, you can see the obvious advantage of using full-wave rectification. Also, the DC voltage (V_{DC}) is higher when ripple is less.

Take time to answer the questions of Self-Check 2–5 before continuing.

Self-Check 2–5

1. Which type of power supply filter costs more?
   (a) capacitor input   (b) inductor input
2. Which type of filter is used the most?
   (a) capacitor input   (b) inductor input
3. A filtered output contains an average DC level of +11.5 V and 0.75 V_{P-P} ripple. Calculate the RMS ripple voltage and the percent ripple.

2–6 DESIGNING A FILTERED BRIDGE-RECTIFIER DC SUPPLY

DESIGN STEPS

The design of any electronic circuit or system must begin with practical guidelines or specifications. To design a DC power supply (AC to DC converter), we must start with certain given information. Obviously, we must have an application in mind for the DC supply. The DC supply will be constructed to power some electrical device or piece of equipment that requires a specific voltage and current. That is where you must start. Let's follow the steps that are needed to design a DC supply as shown in Design Note 2–1.

STEP 1   Determine the required load voltage and load current.
STEP 2   Decide on the percent ripple that is acceptable for the application.

If a voltage regulator is to be added to the circuit, you can tolerate ripple as high as 10% or so. The regulator will rapidly compensate for the ripple variations and provide a nearly smooth DC output to the load. If you are not planning to use a regulator, you will most likely want to keep the ripple down to the neighborhood of 1%. If the ripple is too great, it may show up as a loud hum in the speaker of audio or communications equipment.

STEP 3   Select a transformer whose peak secondary voltage is a standard value greater than the needed DC load voltage (assuming a capacitor-input filter is used). The secondary current rating should be greater than the maximum load current.

Transformer windings are rated according to RMS voltage and current. For example, a 12.6-V secondary is 12.6 V_{RMS}. This is fine for a DC supply less than approximately 17 V, assuming a capacitor-input filter is used and depending on the size of the filter capacitor and load (the heavier the load, the lower the DC voltage). Standard transformer voltages can be obtained from a parts supply catalog or manufacturer's data books.

STEP 4   Determine the ratings for the individual diodes or the diode-bridge package.

DESIGN NOTE 2–1 BRIDGE RECTIFIER DC SUPPLY

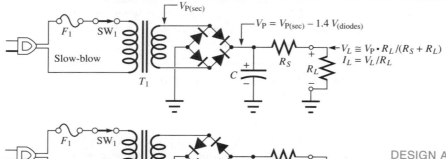

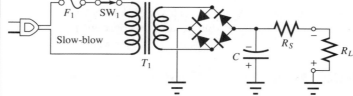

DESIGN APPROACH

Load voltage (V_L) and load (I_L) must be known. The transformer secondary voltage (RMS) is a standard value greater than V_L.

DESIGN FORMULAS

COMPONENT RATINGS
DIODE

$$\text{PIV} = V_R \geq 2\, V_{P(sec)}$$
$$I_F = I_O \geq I_L$$

TRANSFORMER

$$V_{secondary} = \text{Standard value}$$
$$I_{secondary} > I_L$$

CAPACITOR

$$\text{WVDC} > V_P$$
$$C = 0.289/[f \cdot (R_S + R_L) \cdot r]$$
$$f = 2 \cdot \text{AC freq.}$$

SURGE RESISTOR

$$R_S = (V_P - V_L)/I_L$$
$$P_{RS} \geq 2 \cdot I_L^2 \cdot R_S$$

FUSE (Slow-blow)

$$F_1 = 1.5 \cdot I_L \cdot V_{sec}/V_{pri}$$

BASIC PROGRAM

```
1 REM *** DN2-1 ***
10 CLS
20 PRINT"DESIGN PROGRAM FOR BRIDGE
RECTIFIER, CAPACITOR FILTER, AC/DC
CONVERTERS"
30 PRINT""
40 INPUT"ENTER THE DESIRED DC LOAD
VOLTAGE - ";VL
50 INPUT"ENTER THE LOAD CURRENT -
";IL
60 INPUT"ENTER THE AC LINE VOLTAGE
(PRIMARY VOLTAGE) - ";VPRI
70 INPUT"ENTER THE AC LINE FREQUENCY
- ";F
80 PRINT"** REFER TO A PARTS CATALOG
FOR STANDARD TRANSFORMER SECONDARY
VOLTAGES **"
90 INPUT"ENTER A STANDARD SECONDARY
VOLTAGE THAT IS GREATER THAN VL -
";VSEC
100 INPUT"ENTER THE DESIRED DC RIPPLE
FACTOR (DECIMAL) - ";R
110 PRINT""
120 PRINT"DIODE PIV IS EQUAL TO OR
GREATER THAN ";2 * VSEC * 1.414;"
VOLTS."
130 PRINT"DIODE AVERAGE CURRENT
RATING IS GREATER THAN ";IL;" AMPS."
140 PRINT"TRANSFORMER SECONDARY
CURRENT RATING IS GREATER THAN ";IL;"
AMPS."
150 PRINT"THE FILTER CAPACITOR
VOLTAGE RATING IS GREATER THAN ";VSEC
* 1.414;" WVDC."
155 F = 2*F:RL = VL/IL:VP = (1.414 *
VSEC)-1.4:RS = (VP-VL)/IL
160 PRINT"THE CAPACITANCE IS EQUAL TO
OR GREATER THAN
";(.289/(F*(RS+RL)*R))/.000001;"
MICROFARADS."
165 VP = (VSEC * 1.414) - 1.4
170 PRINT"THE SERIES RESISTANCE IS
";RS;" OHMS."
180 PRINT"THE SERIES RESISTOR POWER
RATING IS EQUAL TO OR GREATER THAN
";2 * (IL^2 * RS);" WATTS."
190 PRINT"THE FUSE CURRENT RATING IS
A STANDARD VALUE CLOSE TO ";1.5 * IL
* VSEC/VPRI;" AMPS."
200 PRINT"USE A SLOW-BLOW FUSE."
210 PRINT""
220 END
```

The maximum reverse voltage rating, or PIV rating, of the diodes should be equal to or greater than twice the peak secondary voltage. This gives the diodes more than adequate "headroom" in case of a line-voltage surge. The forward current rating should be no less than the actual load current. Since the diodes conduct half the time, their average current will actually be half of the load current, providing a sufficient design margin.

STEP 5   Determine the resistance and power rating of the series resistor if one is used.

Ohm's Law is used to calculate the series resistance. The actual voltage across the resistor is the difference between the peak voltage minus two diode drops ($V_P - 1.4$ V) and the load voltage (V_L). The current through the series resistor is the same as the load current (I_L). Thus,

$$R_S = (V_P - 1.4 \text{ V} - V_L)/I_L \qquad (2\text{–}7)$$

The power dissipated by the series resistor is simply I^2R. However, for a fair design margin the power rating of the resistor should be at least twice the actual dissipation.

STEP 6   Determine the size and voltage rating of the filter capacitor.

The capacitor receives the full peak secondary voltage minus the total 1.4-V diode drops. The capacitor's WVDC rating must be greater than the peak secondary voltage. The capacitance is determined using the decided ripple factor (r) and the following formula. (See the appendices for the derivation of the formula.)

$$C = 0.289/[f \cdot (R_S + R_L) \cdot r] \qquad (2\text{–}8)$$

where f is the pulsating DC frequency after rectification, R_S is the series dropping resistance (if one is used), R_L is the load resistance, and r is the ripple factor.

STEP 7   Determine the size fuse required for the primary side of the transformer (line side).

A fuse is essential in the design of a safe power supply. The fuse prevents costly wholesale destruction of the power supply in the event of a short. It may also prevent a fire. Notice, from the design note, that the fuse should have a standard current rating that is about 1.5 times the calculated primary current ($I_{pri} = I_L \cdot V_{sec}/V_{pri}$). Make sure the voltage rating of the fuse is adequate for the line voltage. Also, use a switch that is rated for the job. Finally, a three-pronged plug with ground is the best choice because the chassis can be safely grounded. Consider Examples 2–10 and 2–11.

EXAMPLE 2–10

Say you need an 18-V DC supply that can provide 1 A of current with a maximum of 2% ripple. The ripple factor is 0.02 and the load resistance is 18 V/1 A = 18 Ω.

Design Steps

1. $V_L = 18$ V, $I_L = 1$ A.
2. % ripple $= 2\%$, $r = 0.02$.
3. Select a standard transformer, such as one with a 25.2-V secondary and a secondary current rating greater than 1 A. Use a bridge rectifier to take advantage of the full secondary voltage.
4. Diode PIV rating $= 2 \cdot V_{P(sec)} = 2 \cdot 1.414 \cdot 25.2$ V $= 71$ V.
   Use a 100-V diode, such as a 1N4002, for good design margin. A 1-A current rating is adequate because each diode conducts half the time. Average current for each diode is 0.5 A maximum.
5. $R_S = (V_P - 1.4$ V $- V_L)/I_L = (35.6$ V $- 1.4$ V $- 18$ V$)/1$ A $= 16.2$ Ω.
   Power rating $\geq 2 \cdot I_L^2 \cdot R_S = 2 \cdot 1 \cdot 16.2 = 32.4$ W.
   A standard 50-W, 16-Ω, wirewound resistor is adequate.
6. The WVDC rating of the electrolytic should be greater than 36 V. A 50-V capacitor is fine.
   $C = 0.289/[f \cdot (R_S + R_L) \cdot r] = 0.289/(120$ Hz $\cdot 34$ Ω $\cdot 0.02) = 3{,}542$ μF.
   A 5,000-μF capacitor is a good choice for a standard value.
7. The fuse in the primary circuit $\cong 1.5 \cdot I_L \cdot V_{sec}/V_{pri} = 1.5 \cdot 1$ A $\cdot 25.2$ V$/15$ V $= 0.33$ A.
   A standard 3/8-A, 250-V, slow-blow fuse is adequate.

EXAMPLE 2–11

Suppose you need a 4-A DC supply with an output voltage of 9 V and a maximum of 5% ripple ($r = 0.05$). The load resistance is 2.25 Ω.

Design Steps

1. $V_L = 9$ V, $I_L = 4$ A maximum.
2. % ripple $= 5\%$, $r = 0.05$ maximum.
3. Select a standard transformer, such as one with a 12.6-V secondary and a secondary current rating greater than 4 A. Use a bridge rectifier.
4. Diode PIV rating $= 2 \cdot V_{P(sec)} = 2 \cdot 1.414 \cdot 12.6$ V $= 35.6$ V.
   Use a 50-V diode such as the MR750, which has an average forward current rating of 6 A. A 6-A current rating is more than adequate because each diode conducts half the time. Average current for each diode is 2 A maximum.
5. $R_S = (V_P - 1.4$ V $- V_L)/I_L = (17.8$ V $- 1.4$ V $- 9$ V$)/4$ A $= 1.85$ Ω.
   Power rating $\geq 2 \cdot I_L^2 \cdot R_S = 2 \cdot 16 \cdot 1.85$ Ω $= 59.2$ W.
   Resistor power rating should be at least 50 W.
6. WVDC > 17.8 V $- 1.4$ V $= 16.4$ V.
   A 20-V capacitor is fine.
   $C = 0.289/[f \cdot (R_S + R_L) \cdot r] = 0.289/(120$ Hz $\cdot 4.1$ Ω $\cdot 0.05) = 11{,}748$ μF.
   The capacitor must be greater than 11,748 μF.

7. The fuse in the primary circuit $\cong 1.5 \cdot I_L \cdot V_{sec}/V_{pri} = 1.5 \cdot 4\,A \cdot 12.6$ V/115 V $= 0.657\,A$
A standard $\frac{1}{2}$-A or $\frac{3}{4}$-A, 250-V, slow-blow fuse is adequate.

Test your understanding with Self-Check 2–6.

Self-Check 2–6

1. Design an AC to DC converter for a 28-V, 2-A load. The rectifier shall be a bridge and the filter shall be capacitor input. The ripple factor shall be 0.05 (5% ripple) or less. Assume a 60-Hz line frequency. (Hint: A transformer with a 25.2-V secondary may be used because the peak voltage is 35.6 V.)

2–7 TROUBLESHOOTING AC TO DC CONVERTERS

Troubleshooting the converter can be done with the power off using an ohmmeter to check isolated diodes and capacitor(s). The oscilloscope can also be used to investigate the supply as it operates. Keep safety in mind as you do so. Know where the lethal voltage is and avoid it. Use one hand to make measurements whenever possible to avoid the body bridge (a body path via arms and torso).

Figure 2–21 charts the conditions, testpoint measurements, and causes for common power supply troubles. Notice that in nearly every case, the noticeable symptom is an increase in DC ripple voltage. If the load device is an audio amplifier, or a system containing one, there is a good chance this ripple would be heard as an objectionable hum in the speaker.

Note that when a diode shorts, the secondary of the transformer is shorted with every half-cycle. This repeated short condition will blow the fuse, if there is one and it is properly rated. If not, the diode will literally burn open or the transformer's secondary will burn open. In either case, a telltale odor will be obvious in the air. When electrolytic capacitors short, they leak, sweat, and often explode. Shorted diodes and capacitors are common troubles. That's why a fuse is essential.

One trouble condition not shown in Figure 2–21 is that of a leaky capacitor (electrically leaky). A leaky capacitor will discharge itself internally as though the load had increased. This causes an increase in ripple. (Note: The term *load* implies current demand of the load device.)

As you can see from the chart, a shorted diode, an open diode, and now a leaky capacitor, cause the ripple to increase. If there is no odor or obviously burned diode, the capacitor is probably the cause of the increased ripple.

Time for a self-check.

Self-Check 2–7

1. Describe the effects of a shorted filter capacitor on the operation of a power supply. (Discuss output voltage, secondary current, primary current, and so on)
2. Describe the effects of a shorted diode on the operation of a power supply. (Discuss output voltage, secondary current, primary current, ripple, and so on)

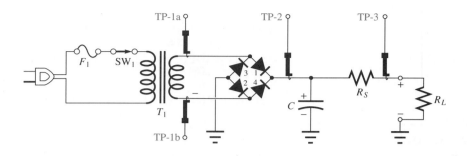

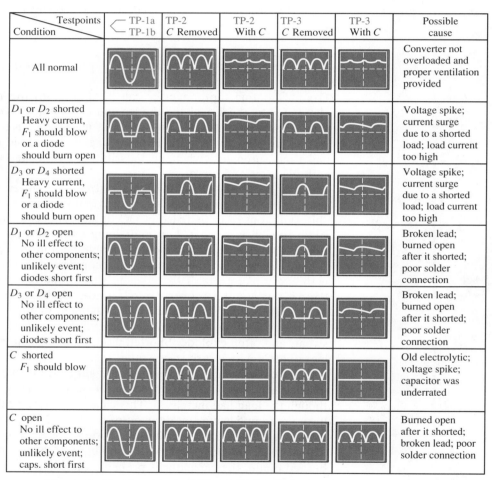

Figure 2–21   Troubleshooting the AC to DC converter.

SUMMARY

FORMULAS

(2–1) $V_{DC} = V_{avg} = V_{P(load)}/\pi = 0.318 \cdot V_{P(load)}$ (for half-wave)

(2–2) $V_{DC} = V_{avg} = 2V_{P(load)}/\pi = 0.637 \cdot V_{P(load)}$ (for full-wave)

(2–3) $V_{DC} = V_{P(load)} - (V_{r(P\text{-}P)}/2)$

(2–4) % ripple $= 100\% \cdot r$

(2–5) $r =$ ripple factor $= V_r/V_{DC}$

(2–6) $V_r = V_{r(P)}/\sqrt{3} = V_{r(P\text{-}P)}/(2 \cdot \sqrt{3}) = 0.289 \cdot V_{r(P\text{-}P)}$

(2–7) $R_S = (V_P - 1.4\text{ V} - V_L)/I_L$

(2–8) $C = 0.289/[f \cdot (R_S + R_L) \cdot r]$

CONCEPTS

- Forward current in a diode consists of conduction-band electron flow in the n material and valence-band hole flow in the p material.
- Reverse current in a diode consists of minority-carrier free electrons in the p material and minority-carrier holes in the n material. This reverse current is tied to temperature.
- The average forward current and maximum reverse voltage ratings of a diode must not be exceeded or the diode will short.
- RECTIFIER SUMMARY

	Half-Wave	Full-Wave	Bridge	Dual-Polarity
Ripple frequency	$f_{(AC\ in)}$	$2f_{(AC\ in)}$	$2f_{(AC\ in)}$	$2f_{(AC\ in)}$
Number of diodes	1	2	4	4
DC diode current	I_{load}	$0.5\ I_{load}$	$0.5\ I_{load}$	$0.5\ I_{load}$
PIV$_{(w/cap\ filter)}$	$\sim 2\ V_{P(sec)}$	$\sim V_{P(sec)}$	$\sim V_{P(sec)}$	$\sim V_{P(sec)}$
V$_{DC(out)(w/cap\ filter)}$	$V_{P(sec)} - 0.7$	$0.5\ V_{P(sec)} - 0.7$	$V_{P(sec)} - 1.4$	$0.5\ V_{P(sec)} - 0.7$

- Capacitor-input filters provide a filtered DC voltage approximately equal to the peak voltage that is applied to the filter.
- Inductor-input filters provide a filtered DC voltage approximately equal to the average value of applied pulsating DC.
- Ripple is due to incomplete filtering. The ripple frequency is equal to the frequency of the applied pulsating DC.

PROCEDURES

Bridge Rectifier/Capacitor Filter DC Power Supply Design

1. Determine the required load voltage and current.
2. Decide on the percent ripple (ripple factor r).
3. Select a transformer whose *peak** secondary voltage is a standard value greater than the needed DC load voltage and whose secondary current rating is greater than the maximum load. *Assume a capacitor-input filter is used.
4. Determine the ratings for the individual diodes or the diode-bridge package.
5. Determine the resistance and power rating of the series resistor.
6. Determine the capacitance and voltage rating of the filter capacitor.
7. Determine the size of fuse required for the primary side of the transformer.

NEED-TO-KNOW SOLUTION

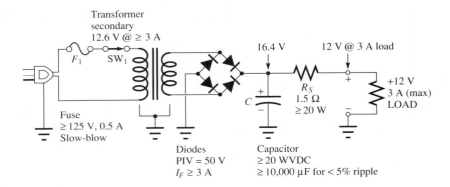

QUESTIONS

2-1 DIODE CHARACTERISTICS

1. Very briefly describe the construction of a solid-state diode.
2. Which end of the diode is the cathode?
3. Name two semiconductor materials of which diodes are commonly made.
4. Describe current flow through a forward-biased diode in terms of majority carriers.
5. Describe current flow through a reverse-biased diode in terms of minority carriers.
6. What is bulk resistance?
7. Describe junction capacitance.
8. Name and define two very important, or main, diode ratings.

2-2 DIODE TESTING

9. When a diode fails, it opens first then shorts. True or false?
10. Describe a method of testing a diode.
11. Describe ohmmeter readings when a shorted diode is tested.
12. If a multimeter with a diode test function is used to test a diode and a reading of 0.64 is obtained in one direction only, what does that indicate?

2-3 HALF-WAVE RECTIFIERS

13. What is the total diode forward voltage drop for a half-wave rectifier?
14. How many diodes does a half-wave rectifier require?
15. What determines the polarity of the output voltage from a half-wave rectifier?
16. Why is the average DC voltage from a half-wave rectifier so low?

2-4 FULL-WAVE RECTIFIERS

17. Which type of rectifier, (a) half-wave, or (b) full-wave, supplies the highest average DC current and voltage? Why?

18. What is the total diode forward voltage drop for a full-wave (center-tapped) rectifier?
19. What is the total diode forward voltage drop for a bridge rectifier?
20. Which of the rectifiers is the most popular? Why?
21. Describe what results if the center-tap-to-ground connection in a dual-polarity DC supply circuit becomes open (assume the two loads to be different).

2–5 FILTERING PULSATING DC

22. What is the advantage of using a capacitor-input filter instead of an inductor-input filter? Which is the most commonly used?
23. Describe DC ripple.
24. Which produces less ripple, (a) a half-wave rectifier, or (b) a full-wave rectifier? Why?
25. The output voltage from a full-wave rectifier that is followed by an inductor-input filter is equal to:
(a) V_P (b) $0.637 \cdot V_P$ (c) $0.318 \cdot V_P$

2–6 DESIGNING A FILTERED BRIDGE-RECTIFIER DC SUPPLY

26. What information must you first know to design a DC supply?
27. If a voltage regulator is to be used, the filter capacitor can be a lower value than otherwise. True or false? Why?
28. Describe a safe PIV rating for the diodes used in a bridge rectifier.
29. Describe a safe average forward current rating for the diodes of a bridge rectifier.
30. Describe a safe power rating for a series dropping resistor in a DC supply.
31. What factors determine the size of the filter capacitor in a capacitor-input filter?

2–7 TROUBLESHOOTING AC TO DC CONVERTERS

32. List the possible causes for a noticeable increase in ripple at the output of a DC supply. Which of these components is the most likely cause? How can you check to know for sure?
33. Describe the results of a shorted filter capacitor in a DC supply.
34. Describe the results of an open diode in a full-wave-rectified DC supply.

PROBLEMS

2–3 HALF-WAVE RECTIFIERS

1. A half-wave rectifier produces a pulsating DC that is $+24\ V_P$. Calculate the average DC voltage (V_{DC}).
2. Calculate the average voltage for a half-wave rectified load voltage of $-38\ V_P$.
3. What is the peak load voltage from a half-wave rectifier if the average load voltage is 8 V?

4. Calculate the peak load voltage produced by a half-wave rectifier if the average load voltage is -14.8 V.
5. What is the average current supplied to a 33-Ω resistor from a half-wave rectifier that produces 15-V_P pulsating DC?
6. Calculate the average current supplied to a 330-Ω resistor from a half-wave rectifier that produces 250-V_P pulsating DC.
7. What is the average forward diode current for a half-wave rectifier that supplies a 22-V_P pulsating DC to a 47-Ω load resistor?
8. Determine the average forward diode current for a half-wave rectifier that supplies a 6-V_P pulsating DC to a 150-Ω load resistor.

2-4 FULL-WAVE RECTIFIERS

9. What is the actual peak reverse voltage across each diode in a full-wave rectifier circuit (center-tapped secondary) if the full secondary voltage is 25.2 V?
10. Calculate the actual peak reverse voltage across each diode in a full-wave rectifier circuit (center-tapped secondary) if the full secondary voltage is 80 V.
11. Calculate the average forward diode current for the diodes of a full-wave rectifier circuit (center-tapped secondary) if the full secondary voltage is 12.6 V and the load resistor is 27 Ω.
12. Calculate the average forward diode current for the diodes of a full-wave rectifier circuit (center-tapped secondary) if the full secondary voltage is 36 V and the load resistor is 9 Ω.
13. Suggest appropriate ratings for the diodes of a bridge rectifier that is connected between a 25.2-V secondary and a 10-Ω load resistor.
14. Suggest appropriate ratings for the diodes of a bridge rectifier that is connected between a 240-V secondary and an 800-Ω load resistor.
15. A 100-V center-tapped secondary and a bridge-diode array are used to make a dual-polarity supply. The positive terminal load is 220 Ω and the negative terminal load is 330 Ω.
    a. Calculate the average current supplied to each load resistor.
    b. Calculate the average ground current.
16. A 24-V center-tapped secondary and a bridge-diode array are used to make a dual-polarity supply. The positive terminal load is 48 Ω and the negative terminal load is 81 Ω.
    a. Calculate the average current supplied to each load resistor.
    b. Calculate the average ground current.

2-5 FILTERING PULSATING DC

17. Calculate the peak DC load voltage that results from a full-wave 17-V_P pulsating DC applied to a capacitor input filter.
18. Calculate the peak DC load voltage that results from a full-wave 40-V_P pulsating DC applied to a capacitor input filter.
19. Calculate the average DC voltage (V_{DC}) across a load if the peak-to-peak ripple voltage is measured to be 1.4 V_{P-P} and the peak load voltage is 11 V_P. Also, calculate the ripple factor.
20. Calculate the average DC voltage (V_{DC}) across a load if the peak-to-

peak ripple voltage is measured to be 0.8 V_{P-P} and the peak load voltage is 24.5 V_P. Also, calculate the ripple factor.

21. Calculate the percent ripple if the average filtered DC load voltage is 31.2 V and the ripple is 2.55 V_{P-P}.

22. Calculate the percent ripple if the average filtered DC load voltage is 8.66 V and the ripple is 45 mV_{P-P}.

2–6 DESIGNING A FILTERED BRIDGE-RECTIFIER DC SUPPLY

23. Design a bridge-rectifier AC to DC converter. The load voltage shall be 6 V and the load resistance is 15 Ω. The ripple factor shall be 0.05. Use a transformer with a 6.3-V secondary.
    a. Determine the minimum current rating for the transformer secondary.
    b. Determine the PIV rating and current rating for the bridge diodes.
    c. Calculate the value and power rating for the series resistor.
    d. Calculate the minimum capacitor value and voltage rating.
    e. Determine the fuse rating for the primary of the transformer. Assume a 115-V primary.

24. Design a bridge-rectifier AC to DC converter. The load voltage shall be 60 V and the load resistance is 20 Ω. The ripple factor shall be 0.01. Use a transformer with a 60-V secondary.
    a. Determine the minimum current rating for the transformer secondary.
    b. Determine the PIV rating and current rating for the bridge diodes.
    c. Calculate the value and power rating for the series resistor.
    d. Calculate the minimum capacitor value and voltage rating.
    e. Determine the fuse rating for the primary of the transformer. Assume a 230-V primary.

25. Design a bridge-rectifier AC to DC converter. The load voltage shall be 9 V and the load resistance is 40 Ω. The ripple factor shall be 0.10. Use a transformer with a 12.6-V secondary.
    a. Determine the minimum current rating for the transformer secondary.
    b. Determine the PIV rating and current rating for the bridge diodes.
    c. Calculate the value and power rating for the series resistor.
    d. Calculate the minimum capacitor value and voltage rating.
    e. Determine the fuse rating for the primary of the transformer. Assume a 230-V primary.

26. Design a bridge-rectifier AC to DC converter. The load voltage shall be 250 V and the load resistance is 5 kΩ. The ripple factor shall be 0.05. Use a transformer with a 200-V secondary.
    a. Determine the minimum current rating for the transformer secondary.
    b. Determine the PIV rating and current rating for the bridge diodes.
    c. Calculate the value and power rating for the series resistor.
    d. Calculate the minimum capacitor value and voltage rating.
    e. Determine the fuse rating for the primary of the transformer. Assume a 115-V primary.

ADDITIONAL PROBLEMS

27. A DC supply consists of a transformer with a 12.6-V secondary, a single diode, and a 30-Ω load resistance. Calculate:
a. the peak load voltage.
b. the average DC load voltage.
c. the average load (current).
d. the average diode current.
e. the peak reverse voltage across the diode.

28. A DC supply consists of a transformer with a 12.6-V center-tapped secondary, two diodes, and a 16-Ω load resistance. Calculate:
a. the peak load voltage.
b. the average DC load voltage.
c. the average load (current).
d. the average diode current.
e. the peak reverse voltage across the diodes.

29. A DC supply consists of a transformer with a 48-V center-tapped secondary, two diodes, and a 20-Ω load resistance. Calculate:
a. the peak load voltage.
b. the average DC load voltage.
c. the average load (current).
d. the average diode current.
e. the peak reverse voltage across the diodes.

30. A DC supply consists of a transformer with a 36-V center-tapped secondary, two diodes, a 2,000-μF capacitor, a 25-Ω series resistor, and a 100-Ω load resistance. Calculate:
a. the peak load voltage.
b. the ripple factor. (*Hint:* Rearrange Formula 2–8.)
c. the approximate RMS ripple voltage at the filter capacitor. (*Hint:* Rearrange Formula 2–5 and use the peak capacitor voltage as an approximation for V_{DC}.)
d. the peak-to-peak ripple voltage at the capacitor. (*Hint:* Rearrange Formula 2–6.)
e. the average DC voltage across the capacitor.
f. the average DC load voltage.

31. A DC supply consists of a transformer with a 12.6-V center-tapped secondary, two diodes, a 5,000-μF capacitor, a 25-Ω series resistor, and a 50-Ω load resistance. Calculate:
a. the peak load voltage.
b. the ripple factor.
c. the approximate RMS ripple voltage at the filter capacitor.
d. the peak-to-peak ripple voltage at the capacitor.
e. the average DC voltage across the capacitor.
f. the average DC load voltage.
g. the average current in each half of the secondary.

32. A DC supply consists of a transformer with a 6.3-V secondary, a bridge rectifier, a 1,000-μF capacitor, no series resistor, and a 100-Ω load resistance. Calculate:

a. the peak load voltage.

b. the ripple factor. (*Hint:* Rearrange Formula 2–8.)

c. the approximate RMS ripple voltage at the filter capacitor. (*Hint:* Rearrange Formula 2–5 and use the peak capacitor voltage as an approximation for V_{DC}.)

d. the peak-to-peak ripple voltage. (*Hint:* Rearrange Formula 2–6.)

e. the average DC voltage across the load.

f. the average load (current).

g. the average diode current in the bridge rectifier.

33. A DC supply consists of a transformer with a 24-V secondary, a bridge rectifier, a 10,000-μF capacitor, a 56-Ω series resistor, and a 100-Ω load resistance. Calculate:

a. the peak capacitor voltage.

b. the ripple factor. (*Hint:* Rearrange Formula 2–8.)

c. the approximate RMS ripple voltage at the filter capacitor. (*Hint:* Rearrange Formula 2–5 and use the peak capacitor voltage as an approximation for V_{DC}.)

d. the peak-to-peak ripple voltage at the capacitor. (*Hint:* Rearrange Formula 2–6.)

e. the average DC voltage across the capacitor.

f. the average load voltage.

g. the average diode current in the bridge rectifier.

34. Design a 15-V, 1-A DC supply with a maximum of 2% ripple voltage. Use a transformer with an 18-V secondary (no center tap).

a. Determine the minimum current rating for the transformer secondary.

b. Determine the PIV rating and current rating for the diodes.

c. Calculate the value and power rating for the series resistor.

d. Calculate the minimum capacitor value and voltage rating.

e. Determine the fuse rating for the primary of the transformer. Assume a 115-V primary.

35. Design a 24-V, 3-A DC supply with a maximum of 10% ripple voltage. Use a transformer with a 25.2-V secondary (no center tap).

a. Determine the minimum current rating for the transformer secondary.

b. Determine the PIV rating and current rating for the diodes.

c. Calculate the value and power rating for the series resistor.

d. Calculate the minimum capacitor value and voltage rating.

e. Determine the fuse rating for the primary of the transformer. Assume a 115-V primary.

36. Design a dual-polarity DC supply that provides ± 12 V at 1 A with less than 1% ripple. Use a transformer with a 25.2-V center-tapped secondary.

a. How many diodes do you need?

b. Suggest reasonable PIV and average current ratings for the diodes.

c. Calculate the minimum value for each filter capacitor.

d. Calculate the value and reasonable power rating for each series resistor.

ANSWERS TO SELF-CHECKS

SELF-CHECK 2–1

1. The cathode end has a color band (ring), usually white or black.
2. a
3. The current is limited mainly by the bulk resistance of the semiconductor material.
4. leakage current and breakdown voltage
5. The PIV rating is the peak inverse voltage rating. It is the maximum reverse voltage the diode is designed to handle before voltage breakdown occurs. The I_O rating is the maximum average forward current that the diode can safely handle.

SELF-CHECK 2–2

1. The diode is open.
2. The diode is good. The 0.68-V reading is the forward voltage drop.
3. The diode is shorted.

SELF-CHECK 2–3

1. 5.44 V, 272 mA, 1N4001
2. 10.6 V, 211 mA, 1N4001

SELF-CHECK 2–4

1. bridge
2. $\cong 42 \, V_P$
3. 1 A
4. 50 Hz for half wave and 100 Hz for full wave

SELF-CHECK 2–5

1. b, inductor input
2. a, capacitor input
3. 217 mV RMS ripple, 1.9% ripple

SELF-CHECK 2–6

1. $V_L = 28$ V, $I_L = 2$ A, 5% ripple, $V_{sec} = 25.2$ V $= 35.6 \, V_P$, diode voltage rating ≥ 50 V, diode average current rating ≥ 1 A, $R_S = 3.1 \, \Omega$ (use 3 Ω), power rating for the series resistor is ≥ 20 W, $C \geq 3,000 \, \mu$F, 50 WVDC, fuse should be $\frac{1}{2}$A to $\frac{3}{4}$A slow-blow.

SELF-CHECK 2–7

1. If the filter capacitor shorts, the output voltage will be 0 V and the secondary and primary currents of the transformer will be very high. A diode or diodes will short and the diode(s), the secondary, or the pri-

mary will burn open. All damage beyond the shorted capacitor can be avoided if a fuse of the proper size is used in the primary.
2. A shorted diode will cause increased ripple and heavy transformer current until a fuse blows or a diode opens to relieve the secondary.

SUGGESTED PROJECTS

1. Add some of the main concepts, formulas, and procedures from this chapter to your personal Electronics Notebook.
2. Use the parts you gathered at the end of Chapter 1 in "Suggested Projects," and design and build a DC supply that will provide 12 V to a maximum load of 100 mA. Make sure all high-voltage connections are secured and well insulated before power is applied. Also, you should use a slow-blow $\frac{1}{4}$A fuse in the primary circuit. When finished, analyze your circuit using the oscilloscope. Calculate RMS ripple, ripple factor, and percent regulation. Think about which type of rectifier is best for this design and these voltage levels.

A simple test circuit composed of a small battery and a series resistor is used to test a 6-V zener diode. The multimeter indicates the zener is good. The zener voltage will vary somewhat depending on the amount of zener current, which is determined by the series resistor.

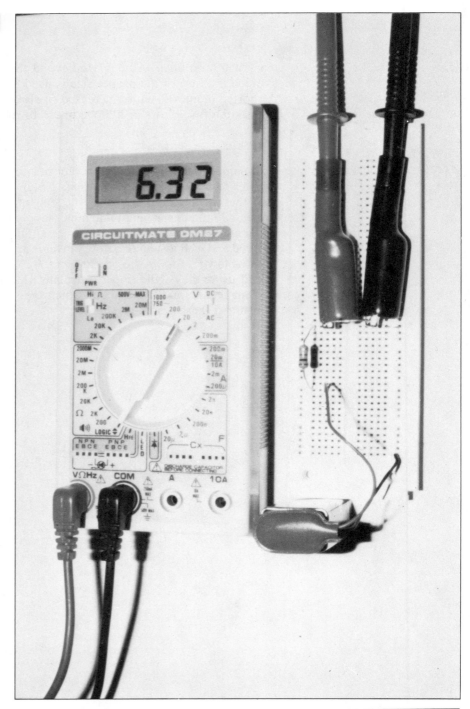

3 Diode Applications

OBJECTIVES

After studying this chapter, you will be able to

- analyze and design zener-diode voltage regulators.
- identify various voltage multiplier circuits.
- identify and analyze voltage limiters and clampers.
- identify the schematic symbols and state uses for special diodes such as the LED, photodiode, varactor, tunnel diode, Schottky diode, PIN diode, and step-recovery diode.

NEED TO KNOW

Suppose you have a portable AM/FM radio that you want to operate from the cigarette lighter in your car. The radio requires 6 V at a maximum of 100 mA. Can you design a regulator that will convert the 12- to 14-V car voltage down to 6 V for the radio?

Believe if or not, you will be able to do this by the time you finish this chapter. You may want to actually build the regulator as an educational exercise. In later chapters, you will learn more about voltage regulation and you will be able to improve your design.

A solution to this Need to Know is provided at the end of this chapter. You may want to see if you can design this supply before you look at the solution.

INTRODUCTION

In this chapter, you will explore a variety of common diode types with applications. In so doing, you will see how the diode plays an important role in a wide variety of electronic systems and circuits. Your exploration begins with diode voltage regulators (zener diodes), which you will learn to analyze, troubleshoot, and design. You will then learn how to use rectifier diodes to multiply voltage in the process of rectification. Using diodes as voltage limiters and clampers will also be explored. Finally, you will be introduced to a variety of special diodes and circuit applications. Enjoy!

3–1 DIODE VOLTAGE REGULATORS

VOLTAGE REGULATION

Voltage regulation is the act of controlling the amplitude of voltage applied to a load device even if the load varies or the line voltage (source voltage) varies. In other words, if a regulator is designed for 12-VDC output, the output voltage will stay at or close to 12 V over a wide range of load (wide range of current to the load device), and a wide range of change in line voltage.

In the previous chapter, we discussed unregulated power supplies. For these circuits, the voltage across the load resistor (R_L) depends completely on the ratio of $R_L/(R_L + R_S)$—the voltage divider rule, where R_S is any resistance in series with the DC voltage and the load resistance. If the load resistance decreases, the loading increases (current increases) and the voltage drop on the series resistor increases, leaving less voltage for the load itself. Thus, if it is desired to have a constant load voltage, the load resistance must not change. A voltage regulator circuit instantly and automatically compensates for any changes in the load so the output voltage can remain constant. Voltage regulators also compensate for changes in line or source voltage. The simplest of all voltage regulators is the zener-diode voltage regulator shown in Figure 3–1.

ZENER-DIODE VOLTAGE REGULATOR THEORY

Zener Regulation

The zener-diode regulator, shown in Figure 3–1, is a **shunt regulator.** That is, the diode is placed in parallel with the load. The theory of operation for this circuit is quite simple. The zener diode is capable of *changing its internal resistance* instantly, to compensate for any change in the load resistance. If the load resistance increases, the zener diode's resistance decreases, and vice versa. Therefore, the total parallel resistance of the zener diode and the load device is held constant. Since the parallel resistance does not change, the output voltage will not change.

Here is another way to look at it. The output voltage is held constant as long as the voltage across the series resistor is constant (assuming the DC input voltage is constant). The voltage across R_S will not change unless the total current changes. The zener diode's job is to make sure the total current remains constant. If the load increases, the zener current decreases, and vice versa. Thus, I_T remains the same. If the total current is held constant, the load voltage cannot change because $V_{DC(out)} = V_{DC(in)} - V_{RS}$.

If the DC input voltage changes, the current through and voltage across the series resistor will change but the zener voltage will not. For example, if

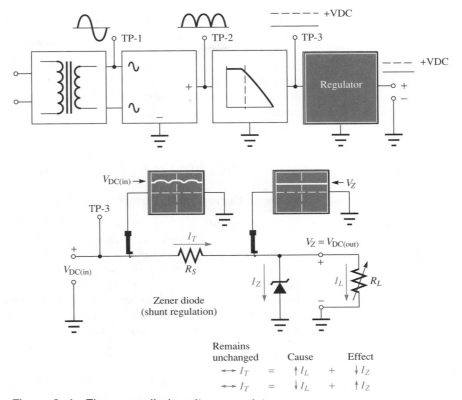

Figure 3–1 The zener-diode voltage regulator.

the DC input voltage increases, I_T increases, V_{RS} increases, I_Z increases, V_Z remains the same, $V_L = V_{DC(out)}$ remains the same, and I_L remains the same. Thus, the zener holds the load voltage and current constant.

Zener Characteristics

As you can see from Figure 3–2, the zener is operated in reverse bias. The zener voltage is the voltage across the reverse-biased *pn* junction in the reverse voltage breakdown region. The zener is designed to operate in this

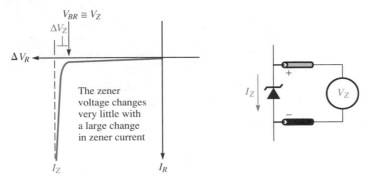

Figure 3–2 Zener characteristics.

breakdown region and will do so without harm as long as the power rating of the diode is not exceeded. Figure 3–2 shows the interesting relationship between V_Z and I_Z. Notice that there is a slight change in the zener voltage over an extreme change in zener current. This indicates that the zener is not a perfect voltage regulator—that, in fact, the voltage across the zener diode changes slightly with changes in zener current. Thus, as previously discussed, if the load changes, the zener current will change and the zener voltage will change only slightly.

ZENER-DIODE VOLTAGE REGULATOR ANALYSIS

Voltage, Current, and Power

Let's begin with a given set of parameters and analyze a zener regulator circuit. In our analysis, we will want to find the total current, the zener current, the zener power dissipation, the series resistor power dissipation, and the power dissipated by the load. The formulas used in the analysis process are very basic: Ohm's Law and the power formulas. There are four parameters that we must already know (or be able to measure): the DC input voltage, the zener voltage, the series resistance, and the load resistance (or load current). Consider Examples 3–1 and 3–2.

EXAMPLE 3–1

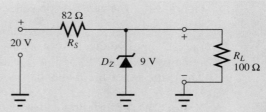

Figure 3–3

Given $V_{DC(in)} = 20$ V, $V_Z = 9$ V, $R_S = 82$ Ω, and $R_L = 100$ Ω, find I_T, I_L, I_Z, P_Z, P_{RS}, and P_L.

1. $I_T = V_{RS}/R_S = (20\ \text{V} - 9\ \text{V})/82\ \Omega = 134\ \text{mA}$
2. $I_L = V_Z/R_L = 9\ \text{V}/100\ \Omega = 90\ \text{mA}$
3. $I_Z = I_T - I_L = 134\ \text{mA} - 90\ \text{mA} = 44\ \text{mA}$
4. $P_Z = I_Z \cdot V_Z = 44\ \text{mA} \cdot 9\ \text{V} = 0.396\ \text{W}$
5. $P_{RS} = I_T \cdot V_{RS} = 134\ \text{mA} \cdot 11\ \text{V} = 1.47\ \text{W}$
6. $P_L = I_L \cdot V_Z = 90\ \text{mA} \cdot 9\ \text{V} = 0.81\ \text{W}$

Note that no special formulas were needed to analyze the zener regulators of Examples 3–1 and 3–2. Ohm's Law and the power formulas are all that is needed.

Silicon to Circuit:
IC Fabrication

from *ICs made simple* by National Semiconductor

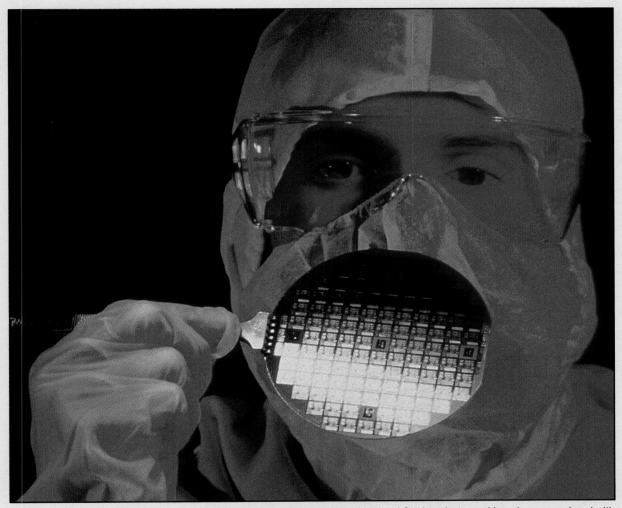

(All photographs are the copyright of National Semiconductor and have been reproduced with written permission.)

The design phase

In most cases it takes approximately one year to create an integrated circuit. It all begins with an idea and a need. That is what determines the specific functions that must be performed in microsystem fashion in the IC. Also, the application determines electrical characteristics and the process technology used to fabricate the chip.

Circuit design begins with the use of a computer-aided design (CAD) system containing standard electronic symbols to represent each of the circuit elements such as transistors, resistors, and capacitors. The CAD system is able to evaluate circuit operation, simulate performance, verify circuit parameters, and conduct worst-case analysis to detect potential temperature, voltage, speed, or timing problems.

Large-scale drawings

The next major step is to create large-scale drawings of the circuitry. These *composite drawings* are 400 times actual size. Here, electronic symbols are converted to actual shapes of the circuit elements and reproduced in separate color-coded layers. These *layer drawings* are then digitized and stored in a data base for the next step.

Mask-making

Depending on the level of complexity, an IC will require 5 to 18 different glass masks, or *workplates,* to create the layers of the circuit patterns that must be transferred to the surface of a silicon wafer. Each mask contains row upon row of thousands of exact replicas of one circuit layer in actual size.

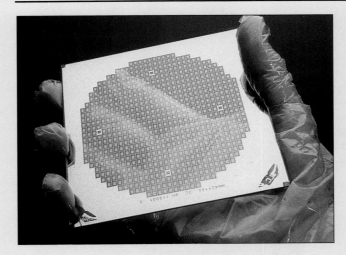

Mask-making begins with an electron-beam exposure system called MEBES®. MEBES translates the digitized data base information into physical form by shooting an intense beam of electrons at a chemically coated glass plate. The result is an exact actual-size rendering of the circuit layer repeated over and over covering the entire mask. Working with incredible precision, MEBES can produce a line one-sixtieth the thickness of a human hair. (MEBES is a registered trademark of Perkin-Elmer.)

For more dense IC layers that require even greater precision, another type of mask called a *reticle* is used. It contains a layer pattern that is five or ten times larger than actual size. During wafer fabrication, the pattern is reduced and reproduced directly on the wafer.

Wafer preparation

Silicon is the second most abundant substance on earth since it is extracted from rocks and common beach sand. Through an exhaustive purification process, the silicon becomes the purest industrial substance produced by man. The impurity count is less than one in a billion—the equivalent of one tennis ball in a string of golf balls stretching from the earth to the moon.

After purification, the molten silicon is *doped* to give it the desired electrical characteristics. Then the molten mix is grown as a crystal, forming a cylindrical ingot.

A diamond saw is used to slice the silicon ingot into thin circular wafers. They are then polished to a perfect mirror finish. The wafers are now ready for IC fabrication to begin.

On-wafer fabrication

IC fabrication involves a multi-step process using various photochemical etching and metallurgical techniques. For sake of clarity and space limitation, we will follow the fabrication process of a single bipolar transistor that is one small element of an IC. A complex IC such as National's 32-bit microprocessor, contains 60,000 transistors, and a single 5-inch wafer contains more than 20,000,000 transistors.

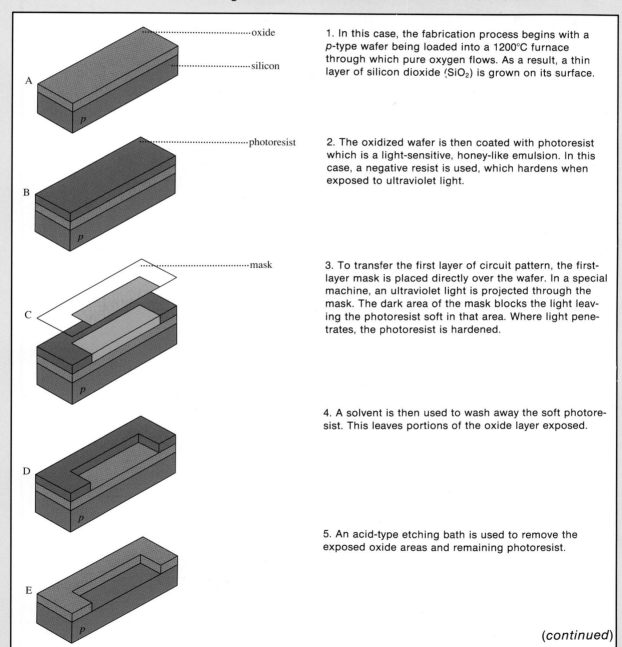

A — oxide / silicon

1. In this case, the fabrication process begins with a p-type wafer being loaded into a 1200°C furnace through which pure oxygen flows. As a result, a thin layer of silicon dioxide (SiO_2) is grown on its surface.

B — photoresist

2. The oxidized wafer is then coated with photoresist which is a light-sensitive, honey-like emulsion. In this case, a negative resist is used, which hardens when exposed to ultraviolet light.

C — mask

3. To transfer the first layer of circuit pattern, the first-layer mask is placed directly over the wafer. In a special machine, an ultraviolet light is projected through the mask. The dark area of the mask blocks the light leaving the photoresist soft in that area. Where light penetrates, the photoresist is hardened.

D

4. A solvent is then used to wash away the soft photoresist. This leaves portions of the oxide layer exposed.

E

5. An acid-type etching bath is used to remove the exposed oxide areas and remaining photoresist.

(continued)

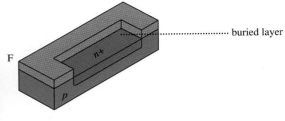

buried layer

F

6. The wafer is then placed in a diffusion furnace which will be filled with gaseous compounds, in this case *n*-type dopants, for a process known as *impurity doping*. In the hot furnace, the dopant atoms penetrate (diffuse into) the areas of exposed silicon forming a pattern (layer) of *n*-type material.

7. An etching bath removes the remaining oxide layer and a new layer of *n*-type silicon is deposited onto the wafer. The first layer of the IC, in this case, transistor, is now complete.

The process of oxidizing, photoresisting, masking, etching, and doping is repeated many times over, in some cases up to 18 times, until all layers have been created. Naturally, precise alignment of each mask is of extreme importance. If alignment is off by one micrometer ($1 \cdot 10^{-6}$ m), the entire wafer is worthless.

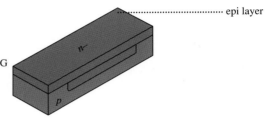

epi layer

G

8. A final oxide layer covers the IC and is etched away to expose contact areas underneath.

oxide

H

9. A thin layer of metal, usually aluminum, is deposited over the entire wafer surface and is masked and etched to form interconnections between elements of the IC and each individual device.

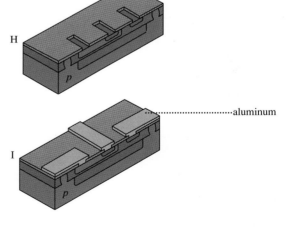

aluminum

I

10. The final layer is vapox which is vapor-deposited oxide. This is a glass-like material that protects the IC from contamination and damage. It too is masked and etched to expose bonding pads, to which wires will be connected later.

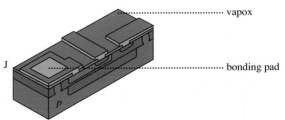

vapox

bonding pad

J

Assembly and packaging

Once on-wafer fabrication is complete, each IC is tested by a special machine that has fine needles that come in contact with the bonding pads. The machine deposits a drop of ink on each IC that tests bad.

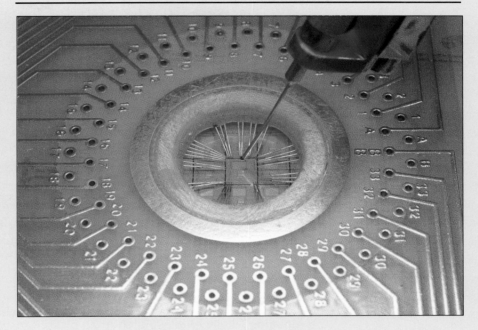

After testing, a diamond saw is used to cut the ICs apart as individual chips ready for assembly.

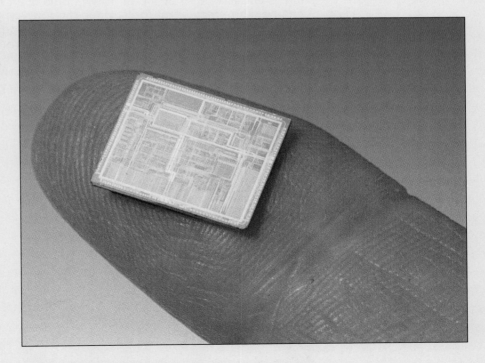

Assembly begins by mounting the chip in a ceramic or metal package, or in metal lead frames that will be encapsulated in plastic. Ultrathin wires are connected between each bonding pad on the chip and a particular lead on the package. The package is hermetically sealed, meaning totally encapsulated in an airtight material such as plastic. The shape of the package may cater to a single row of pins (SIP: single in-line package) or a dual row of pins (DIP: dual in-line package). The package may be of the surface-mount type that has short bent pins called "j" pins that are soldered to the surface of the PC board. For extremely complex chips such as microprocessors and gate arrays, special packages called chip carriers have been developed. The 120-pin chip carrier is quite common now. Shown below is National Semiconductor's 120-pin microCMOS gate array.

Once the IC is packaged, it is again run through a series of computer-controlled tests. Samples are also pulled for reliability testing. Any flaws are tracked back through the manufacturing process.

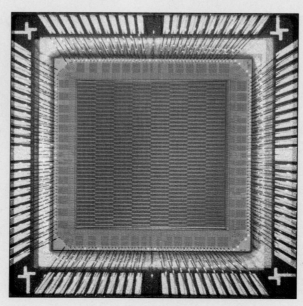

EXAMPLE 3–2

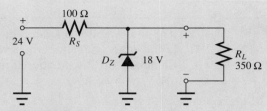

Figure 3–4

Given $V_{DC(in)} = 24$ V, $V_Z = 18$ V, $R_S = 100$ Ω, and $R_L = 350$ Ω, find I_T, I_L, I_Z, P_Z, P_{RS}, and P_L.

1. $I_T = V_{RS}/R_S = (24$ V $- 18$ V$)/100$ Ω $= 60$ mA
2. $I_L = V_Z/R_L = 18$ V$/350$ Ω $= 51.4$ mA
3. $I_Z = I_T - I_L = 60$ mA $- 51.4$ mA $= 8.6$ mA
4. $P_Z = I_Z \cdot V_Z = 8.6$ mA $\cdot 18$ V $= 155$ mW
5. $P_{RS} = I_T \cdot V_{RS} = 60$ mA $\cdot 6$ V $= 360$ mW
6. $P_L = I_L \cdot V_Z = 51.4$ mA $\cdot 18$ V $= 925$ mW

PERCENT REGULATION

Referring back to Example 3–1, suppose the load resistor is removed and the zener voltage jumps up to 9.2 V. This is a likely occurrence since the zener will now have all of the total current flowing through it (134 mA). (Notice from Figure 3–2 that the zener voltage increases slightly with large increases in zener current—from 44 mA to 134 mA is a large increase.)

The jump from 9 V to 9.2 V is not very much when you consider that the output voltage would have jumped to 20 V if the zener diode was not there. The change in voltage can be converted to percent and used as a figure of merit to judge the performance of a regulator. The full-load voltage (V_{FL}) and the no-load voltage (V_{NL}) at the output of the regulator must be known.

$$\% \text{ regulation} = 100\% \cdot (V_{NL} - V_{FL})/V_{FL} \qquad (3\text{–}1)$$

In the case just discussed, the percent regulation is found to be 2.2% (% reg. = $100\% \cdot (9.2$ V $- 9$ V$)/9$ V $= 100\% \cdot 0.022 = 2.2\%$). Notice that without the zener diode the percent regulation is 122% (% reg. = $100\% \cdot (20$ V $- 9$ V$)/9$ V $= 100\% \cdot 1.22 = 122\%$)—the higher the percent, the poorer the regulation. Study Example 3–3.

EXAMPLE 3–3

When the load is removed from a 12-V zener regulator, the zener voltage jumps to 12.13 V. Calculate the percent regulation.

$$\% \text{ regulation} = 100\% \cdot (V_{NL} - V_{FL})/V_{FL}$$

$$\% \text{ regulation} = 100\% \cdot (12.13 \text{ V} - 12 \text{ V})/12 \text{ V} = 1.08\%$$

Test your knowledge and skills on Self-Check 3–1.

Self-Check
3–1

1. Are zener diodes operated in (a) forward bias, or (b) reverse bias?
2. Is the zener diode a perfect voltage regulator? Explain.
3. Calculate the % regulation if the zener voltage is 6.2 V with full load and 6.4 V with no load.

3–2 ZENER-DIODE REGULATOR DESIGN

ZENER-DIODE VOLTAGE REGULATOR DESIGN

Design Objectives

When designing a zener-diode voltage regulator, you must make sure the zener diode and the series resistor have a sufficiently high power rating. Thus, the goal of your design calculations is to determine the minimum power rating for the zener diode and the series resistor. In so doing you will also calculate the value of series resistance.

Design Steps

To begin a design, you must know the DC input voltage (source voltage), the desired output voltage (zener voltage), and the range of load (minimum and maximum current to the load device). Design Note 3–1 illustrates the design process in the BASIC program. We list the steps here.

1. Select a standard voltage zener diode that is close to the desired output voltage (see Figure 3–5).
2. Select a standard zener-diode power rating as determined by the following formula (see Figure 3–5).

$$P_Z = \text{Standard Value} > 1.1 \cdot I_{L(\max)} \cdot V_Z \tag{3–2}$$

Why use the maximum load current to determine the zener power rating? Recall that the zener diode conducts any part of the total current not conducted by the load device. If the load device suddenly becomes open or is disconnected, the load current shifts over to the zener diode. Under these conditions, the zener dissipates the most power and is in greatest danger of burning open. Why the 1.1 factor in Formula 3–2? The .1 of the 1.1 represents an additional 10% current for the zener diode. In other words, when the load device is connected and is drawing maximum current, the zener is conducting 10% of the load. The total current conducted by the series resistor is always the maximum load current plus the additional 10% for the zener. Thus, $I_T = 1.1 \, I_{L(\max)}$ all the time and $I_Z = 1.1 \, I_{L(\max)}$ when the load is disconnected. The 10% current value for the zener gives the zener some current to regulate the load should it vary slightly above the $I_{L(\max)}$ design value. For example, if the maximum load is assumed to be 200 mA and it suddenly increases to 210 mA, the zener will give up 10 mA to maintain the total current at 220 mA (the zener is still conducting 10 mA).

Nominal Zener Voltage (*Note 1)	500 mW Cathode = Polarity Mark		1 Watt Cathode = Polarity Mark		1 Watt Cathode to Case (*Note 7)	1.5 Watt Cathode = Polarity Mark (*Note 8)	5 Watt Cathode = Polarity Mark (*Note 8)
	(*Notes 4,11) Glass Case 362-01	(*Notes 9,11)	(*Note 6) Glass Case 59-04 (DO-41)	(*Notes 6,12) Glass Case 362B-01	Metal Case 52-03 (DO-13)	Sumetic 30 Case 59-03 (DO-41)	Sumetic 40 Case 17-02
1.8							
2.0							
2.2							
2.4	MLL4370	MLL5221A					
2.5		MLL5222A					
2.7	MLL4371	MLL5223A					
2.8		MLL5224A					
3.0	MLL4372	MLL4225A					
3.3	MLL746	MLL5226A	1N4728	MLL4728	1N3821	1N5913A	1N5333A
3.6	MLL747	MLL5227A	1N4729	MLL4729	1N3822	1N5914A	1N5334A
3.9	MLL748	MLL5228A	1N4730	MLL4730	1N3823	1N5915A	1N5335A
4.3	MLL749	MLL5229A	1N4731	MLL4731	1N3824	1N5916A	1N5336A
4.7	MLL750	MLL5230A	1N4732	MLL4732	1N3825	1N5917A	1N5337A
5.1	MLL751	MLL5231A	1N4733	MLL4733	1N3826	1N5918A	1N5338A
5.6	MLL752	MLL5232A	1N4734	MLL4734	1N3827	1N5919A	1N5339A
6.0		MLL5233A					
6.2	MLL753	MLL5234A	1N4735	MLL4735	1N3828	1N5920A	1N5341A
6.8	MLL754 MLL957A	MLL5235A	1N4736	MLL4736	1N3829 1N3016A	1N5921A	1N5342A
7.5	MLL755 MLL958A	MLL5236A	1N4737	MLL4737	1N3830 1N3017A	1N5922A	1N5343A
8.2	MLL756 MLL959A	MLL5237A	1N4738	MLL4738	1N3018A	1N5923A	1N5344A
8.7		MLL5238A					1N5345A
9.1	MLL757 MLL960A	MLL5239A	1N4739	MLL4739	1N3019A	1N5924A	1N5346A
10	MLL758 MLL961A	MLL5240A	1N4740	MLL4740	1N3020A	1N5925A	1N5347A
11	MLL962A	MLL5241A	1N4741	MLL4741	1N3021A	1N5926A	1N5348A
12	MLL759 MLL963A	MLL5242A	1N4742	MLL4742	1N3022A	1N5927A	1N5349A
13	MLL964A	MLL5243A	1N4743	MLL4743	1N3023A	1N5928A	1N5350A
14		MLL5244A					1N5351A
15	MLL965A	MLL5245A	1N4744	MLL4744	1N3024A	1N5929A	1N5352A
16	MLL966A	MLL5246A	1N4745	MLL4745	1N3025A	1N5930A	1N5353A
17		MLL5247A					1N5354A
18	MLL967A	MLL5248A	1N4746	MLL4746	1N3026A	1N5931A	1N5355A
19		MLL5249A					1N5356A
20	MLL968A	MLL5250A	1N4747	MLL4747	1N3027A	1N5932A	1N5357A
22	MLL969A	MLL5251A	1N4748	MLL4748	1N3028A	1N5933A	1N5358A
24	MLL970A	MLL5252A	1N4749	MLL4749	1N3029A	1N5934A	1N5359A
25		MLL5253A					1N5360A
27	MLL971A	MLL5254A	1N4750	MLL4750	1N3030A	1N5935A	1N5361A
28		MLL5255A					1N5362A
30	MLL972A	MLL5256A	1N4751	MLL4751	1N3031A	1N5936A	1N5363A
33	MLL973A	MLL5257A	1N4752	MLL4752	1N3032A	1N5937A	1N5364A
36	MLL974A	MLL5258A	1N4753	MLL4753	1N3033A	1N5938A	1N5365A
39	MLL975A	MLL5259A	1N4754	MLL4754	1N3034A	1N5939A	1N5366A
43	MLL976A	MLL5260A	1N4755	MLL4755	1N3035A	1N5940A	1N5367A
47	MLL977A	MLL5261A	1N4756	MLL4756	1N3036A	1N5941A	1N5368A
51	MLL978A	MLL5262A	1N4757	MLL4751	1N3037A	1N5942A	1N5369A
56	MLL979A	MLL5263A	1N4758	MLL4758	1N3038A	1N5943A	1N5370A
60		MLL5264A					1N5371A
62	MLL980A	MLL5265A	1N4759	MLL4759	1N3039A	1N5944A	1N5372A
68	MLL981A	MLL5266A	1N4760	MLL4760	1N3040A	1N5945A	1N5373A
75	MLL982A	MLL5267A	1N4761	MLL4761	1N3041A	1N5946A	1N5374A
82	MLL983A	MLL5268A	1N4762	MLL4762	1N3042A	1N5947A	1N5375A
87		MLL5269A					1N5376A
91	MLL984A	MLL5270A	1N4763	MLL4753	1N3043A	1N5958A	1N5377A
100	MLL985A		1N4764	MLL4764	1N3044A	1N5949A	1N5378A
110	MLL986A				1N3045A	1N5950A	1N5379A
120					1N3046A	1N5951A	1N5380A
130					1N3047A	1N5952A	1N5831A
150					1N3048A	1N5953A	1N5383A
160					1N3049A	1N5954A	1N5384A
170							1N5385A
175							
180					1N3050A	1N5955A	1N5386A
200					1N3051A	1N5956A	1N5388A

Figure 3–5 Common zener diodes. (Copyright Motorola, Inc. Used by permission.)

3. Select a standard value series resistance close to the value calculated as follows:

$$R_S = (V_{DC(in)} - V_Z)/(1.1\ I_{L(max)}) \qquad \text{(Ohm's Law)} \qquad (3\text{–}3)$$

Once again, $1.1\ I_L$ is used because this is the value of total current that is flowing through the series resistor ($I_T = 1.1\ I_L$).

4. Select a standard resistor power rating that is greater than the actual dissipated power. (Actually, the power rating should be at least twice the calculated dissipation.)

$$P_{RS} = \text{Standard Value} > (1.1\ I_{L(max)})^2 \cdot R_S \qquad (3\text{–}4)$$

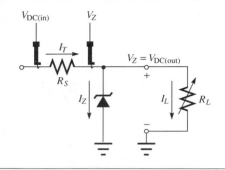

DESIGN APPROACH

DC input voltage, desired load voltage, and range of load (current) must be known.

DESIGN FORMULAS	BASIC PROGRAM

DESIGN FORMULAS

COMPONENT RATINGS

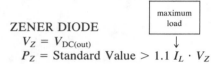

ZENER DIODE

$V_Z = V_{DC(out)}$

P_Z = Standard Value $> 1.1\, I_L \cdot V_Z$

SERIES RESISTOR

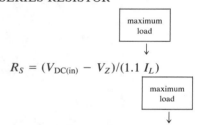

$$R_S = (V_{DC(in)} - V_Z)/(1.1\, I_L)$$

maximum load

P_R = Standard Value $> (1.1\, I_L)^2 \cdot R$

BASIC PROGRAM

```
10 CLS
20 PRINT"ZENER DIODE VOLTAGE
REGULATOR DESIGN PROGRAM"
30 PRINT"":PRINT""
40 PRINT"THE DC SOURCE VOLTAGE,
THE DESIRED LOAD VOLTAGE AND THE
MAXIMUM"
50 PRINT"LOAD CURRENT MUST BE
KNOWN."
60 PRINT""
70 INPUT"ENTER THE DC SOURCE
VOLTAGE - ";VS
80 INPUT"ENTER THE DC LOAD
VOLTAGE - ";VL
90 INPUT"ENTER THE MAXIMUM LOAD
CURRENT - ";IL
100 PRINT""
110 VZ = VL
120 PZ = 1.1 * IL * VZ
130 RS = (VS - VZ)/(1.1 * IL)
140 PR = (1.1 * IL)^2 * RS
150 PRINT"USE A ZENER DIODE
WHOSE ZENER VOLTAGE IS CLOSE
TO ";VZ;" VOLTS."
160 PRINT"THE POWER RATING OF
THE ZENER MUST BE GREATER
THAN ";PZ;" WATTS."
170 PRINT"THE SERIES RESISTOR
MUST BE A STANDARD VALUE
CLOSE TO ";RS;" OHMS."
180 PRINT"THE RESISTOR POWER
RATING MUST BE GREATER THAN
";PR;" WATTS."
190 PRINT""
200 INPUT"ANOTHER PROBLEM?
(Y/N)";A$
210 IF A$="Y" THEN GOTO 60
220 END
```

Consider design Examples 3–4 and 3–5:

EXAMPLE 3–4 ▮▬▬▬▬▬▬▬▬▬▬▬

Design a zener regulator to supply approximately 9 V to a load. The source voltage is 17 V and the range of load current is from 0 A to 200 mA.

1. $V_Z = 9.1$ V
2. $P_Z > 1.1 \cdot I_{L(\text{max})} \cdot V_Z = 1.1 \cdot 200$ mA $\cdot 9.1$ V $= 2$ W
    The 1N5346A (5 W) is the best choice.
    Note: If you can guarantee that the load will never be disconnected while the DC input voltage is applied, the zener can have a much lower power rating (even a 500-mW zener would be fine). The actual power dissipation of the zener while the load is drawing 200 mA is 182 mW (9.1 V $\cdot$ 20 mA $= 182$ mW). Recall that the zener current is 10% of the maximum load ($I_Z = 200$ mA $\cdot 0.1 = 20$ mA).
3. $R_S = V_{RS}/I_T = (V_{\text{DC(in)}} - V_Z)/(1.1\, I_{L(\text{max})}) = (17$ V $- 9.1$ V$)/220$ mA $= 36\ \Omega$
    Use a 36-Ω resistor.
4. $P_{RS} > (1.1\, I_{L(\text{max})})^2 \cdot R_S = (220$ mA$)^2 \cdot 36\ \Omega = 1.74$ W
    Use at least a 3-W resistor (5-W is better).

EXAMPLE 3–5 ▮▬▬▬▬▬▬▬▬▬▬▬

A 6-V regulator is needed to power an AM/FM/Cassette unit. The source voltage is 12 V, as from the cigarette lighter outlet in a car. When the radio is played, the unit draws 70 mA. When the cassette is played, the unit draws 400 mA due to the drive motor. The regulator must be designed for the worst case, which is the 400-mA load. (Note: Provide plenty of ventilation for your diode and resistor so the heat can escape.)

1. $V_Z = 6.0$ V
2. $P_Z > 1.1 \cdot I_{L(\text{max})} \cdot V_Z = 1.1 \cdot 400$ mA $\cdot 6.0$ V $= 2.64$ W
    The 1N5346A (5 W) is the best choice.
3. $R_S = V_{RS}/I_T = (V_{\text{DC(in)}} - V_Z)/(1.1\, I_{L(\text{max})})$
    $= (12 - 6.0)/440$ mA $= 13.6\ \Omega$
    Use a 13-Ω resistor. This increases the total current slightly to 462 mA (6 V/13 Ω = 462 mA).
4. $P_{RS} > (1.1\, I_{L(\text{max})})^2 \cdot R_S = (462$ mA$)^2 \cdot 13\ \Omega = 2.77$ W
    Use at least a 5-W resistor.

Zener Power Dissipation

In Example 3–5, it is important to realize that the zener is dissipating the *least* amount of power when the cassette is playing and the *greatest* amount of power when the entire unit is turned off or disconnected. During operation, the zener dissipates the most power when the radio is playing because the zener conducts 392 mA while the radio conducts 70 mA (using the 13-Ω series resistor, the total current remains at 462 mA). The series resistor dissipates the same amount of power all the time since the total current does not change (assuming the source voltage remains at 12 V).

The Input Voltage

Our designs in Examples 3–4 and 3–5 assume that the input voltage (source voltage) does not change with changes in load. This is normally a safe assumption because the load that the source sees is always constant, equal to the total current (the source supplies the total current). However, *if* the input voltage (source voltage) does vary, the zener will still maintain the output at the zener voltage unless the input voltage drops too low. In other words, the source voltage must be high enough to provide a load voltage that is greater than the zener voltage with the zener removed ($V_{DC(in)} \cdot R_L/(R_S + R_L)$ must be greater than V_Z).

Test your knowledge and skills on Self-Check 3–2.

Self-Check 3–2

1. Design a zener-diode voltage regulator for a 9-V transistor radio. The source is a nominal 12 V and the radio demands a maximum of 80 mA.

3–3 DIODE VOLTAGE MULTIPLIERS

HALF-WAVE MULTIPLIERS

Diode voltage multipliers offer an economical means of obtaining high DC voltages from a lower-voltage AC source. In cases where a high-voltage, low-current DC source is needed, the voltage multiplier is ideal. Transformers are very costly, and the higher the voltage, the more costly they become. As you will see, voltage multiplier circuits employ relatively inexpensive diodes and capacitors. Multipliers also provide the advantages of less weight and space. One disadvantage is that they are intended as low-current sources only.

The Half-Wave Voltage Doubler

Figure 3–6 illustrates the very simple half-wave voltage doubler. Perhaps you will recognize D_1 as half-wave rectifier and C_1 as its filter. C_1 charges to the peak value of the secondary voltage when terminal A is negative. When alternation 2 begins and terminal A becomes positive, it is as though the secondary is a battery series aiding the already charged capacitor C_1. Thus, the peak secondary voltage plus the capacitor C_1 voltage is used to charge capacitor C_2 through D_2. C_2 charges to a DC level that is approximately twice the peak secondary voltage. If the peak secondary voltage is 1,000 V, the load voltage is 2,000 V. However, this all depends on the load being very light (high resistance, low current). If C_2 is discharged too quickly by the load, the ripple will be severe and the average DC voltage will be less than ideal (less than $2V_P$).

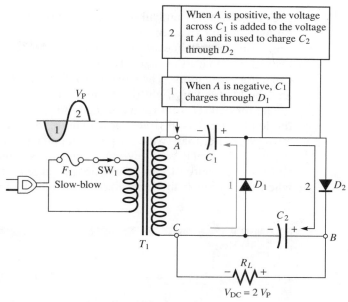

Figure 3–6 Half-wave voltage doubler.

Voltage Tripling and Quadrupling

Figure 3–7 shows how additional diode-capacitor sections can be added to increase the multiplication factor of the circuit. Notice that each added L section is an inverted version of the prior section. The number of sections determines the multiplication factor. The circuit of Figure 3–7 is a quadrupler, but may also be used as a voltage doubler or tripler. Note: Between terminals 1 and 3, $V_{DC} = V_P$; between terminals 2 and 4, $V_{DC} = 2V_P = V_P + V_{C1}$; between terminals 1 and 5, $V_{DC} = 3V_P = V_P + V_{C2}$; between terminals 2 and 6, $V_{DC} = 4V_P = V_P + V_{C1} + V_{C3}$.

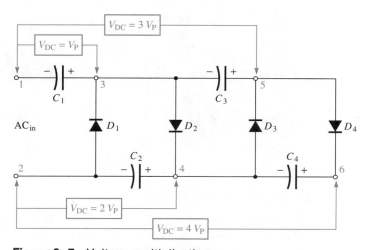

Figure 3–7 Voltage multiplication.

C_1 charges to V_P and all other capacitors charge to $2V_P$. Thus, the WVDC rating of each capacitor must be higher than twice the peak secondary voltage. The capacitance of the capacitors depends on the actual load—the heavier the load, the larger the capacitor must be. However, larger-value capacitors cost more. The capacitors often fall in the range of 10 μF to 50 μF and the load is very light (in the milliamps).

The forward current rating of the diodes can be low (usually 1 A) because the load current is also very low. The reverse voltage rating of the diodes must be greater than twice the peak secondary voltage. Though not shown in Figure 3–7, a relatively low-value resistor is often placed in series with C_1 and the AC source to prevent a heavy surge of current through C_1 and D_1 when the circuit is first energized. Consider Example 3–6.

EXAMPLE 3–6 ▮

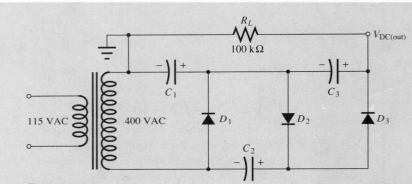

Figure 3–8

Determine the DC output voltage from the voltage multiplier shown in Figure 3–8. Also, determine the minimum PIV and current rating for the diodes and the minimum WVDC rating for the capacitors.

The circuit is a half-wave voltage tripler.

$V_{DC(out)} \cong 3V_P = 3 \cdot (400 \text{ V} \cdot 1.414) = 1,697 \text{ V}$

$I_L = 1,697 \text{ V}/100 \text{ k}\Omega \cong 17 \text{ mA}$

PIV diode rating $> 2V_P = 2 \cdot (400 \text{ V} \cdot 1.414) = 1,131 \text{ V}$

Use 2,000-V, 1-A diodes.

Capacitor WVDC $> 2V_P = 2 \cdot (400 \text{ V} \cdot 1.414) = 1,131 \text{ V}$

Capacitor WVDC should be $\geq 1,500$ V

FULL-WAVE MULTIPLIER

Figure 3–9 illustrates a full-wave voltage doubler. It is two half-wave rectifier/filters in one. One of the rectifiers is negative (D_1 and C_1) and the other is positive (D_2 and C_2). Each capacitor is charged independently of the other

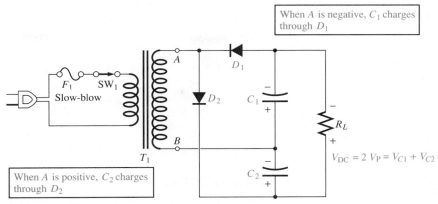

Figure 3–9 Full-wave voltage doubler.

during every half-cycle. Since the capacitors are electrically series-aiding, the load voltage is the sum of the two capacitor voltages. Each capacitor charges to the peak secondary voltage, so the output voltage (load voltage) is $2V_P$.

The voltage rating of each capacitor must be greater than the peak secondary voltage and the reverse voltage rating of the diodes must be greater than twice the peak secondary voltage (the reverse diode voltage = the peak secondary voltage + the capacitor voltage).

This is also called a *floating supply* because neither terminal A nor terminal B can be grounded. Either end of the load can be grounded, but the secondary must be insulated from ground (floating). This is not the case with half-wave doublers, because terminal C of Figure 3–6 can be connected to common ground. Consider Example 3–7.

EXAMPLE 3–7

A full-wave voltage doubler like that of Figure 3–9 has a 250-V secondary. Calculate the DC load voltage and suggest voltage ratings for the diodes and capacitors.

$V_L = V_{DC(out)} = 2V_P = 2 \cdot (250 \text{ V} \cdot 1.414) = 707 \text{ V}$

PIV diode rating $> 2V_P = 2 \cdot (250 \text{ V} \cdot 1.414) = 707 \text{ V}$

Use 1,000-V diodes.

Capacitor WVDC $> V_P = 250 \text{ V} \cdot 1.414 = 354 \text{ V}$

Use 500-V capacitors.

Take time now for a self-check.

**Self-Check
3–3**

1. Why are diode voltage multipliers used instead of high-voltage trans-formers?
2. What is a disadvantage of using diode voltage multipliers?
3. How many diode-capacitor sections would a 7× voltage multiplier have?
4. What is a practical difference between the full-wave doubler and the half-wave doubler?

3–4 LIMITERS AND CLAMPERS

VOLTAGE LIMITERS

Limiters (Clippers)

Voltage limiters are circuits designed to limit the amplitude of voltage that is passed on to a load. The limiter guarantees that the voltage applied to a load device will not exceed a certain preset, or predetermined, level. Limiters are also called *clippers* because they have a voltage threshold above which it appears the applied waveform has been clipped off. Limiters are very useful for any application that requires over-voltage protection. Many transistor devices and circuits are protected from dangerous voltage spikes by diode limiter (clipper) circuits. In many cases, the diode limiter is manufactured on the same tiny silicon chip as the transistor, so the transistor is always pro-tected from static charges. Let's take a few minutes to see how these limiter circuits function.

Negative Limiters

Figure 3–10 shows three variations of the negative limiter. These are de-scribed as negative limiters because the *positive* peak voltage is never modi-fied (affected). The circuit of Figure 3–10a is a simple, unbiased limiter. The diode in this circuit conducts only during the negative alternation of the applied AC. Ideally, the diode acts as a short during the negative alternation and as an open during the positive alternation. In practice, the diode does not act as a pure short, because approximately 0.7 V appears across the forward-biased silicon diode. Notice that, during the positive alternation when the diode acts as an open, the peak output voltage is determined by the voltage divider rule ($5\,V_P \cdot R_L/(R_L + R_S) = 4.55\,V_P$). As you can see, nearly all of the negative alternation has been clipped because the output voltage during the negative alternation is the diode's forward voltage drop.

The circuit of Figure 3–10b is a reverse-biased diode limiter. Notice that the diode will conduct during the negative alternation, but only when the negative-going alternation is able to overcome the reverse bias from V_{BB}. The diode acts as an open and the AC signal passes to the load resistor unaltered until the negative alternation reaches −3.7 V. Once this limit-ing threshold is reached, the negative alternation is held at approximately −3.7 V.

Clipping, or limiting, only takes place while the diode is forward biased.

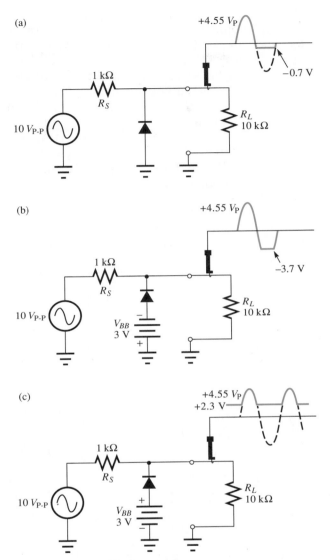

Figure 3–10 Negative limiters (clippers).

The forward-biased diode in the limiter circuit of Figure 3–10c is normally conducting. Even with no AC signal applied, the load resistor sees a constant +2.3 V (3 V − 0.7-V diode drop). Thus, with AC applied, positive voltages exceeding 2.3 V during the positive alternation will cancel V_{BB} and reverse bias (turn off) the diode. Once the diode is reverse biased, it is effectively removed from the circuit and the positive load voltage rises with the positive peak. As soon as the positive peak falls to approximately +2.3 V, the diode once again becomes forward biased and supplies the load with a steady +2.3 V.

Positive Limiters

Positive limiters follow the same basic theory as do negative limiters. The main concern here is to be able to determine if the limiter is negative or positive. You must decide during which alternation the diode conducts. If the diode, in parallel with the load, conducts during the positive alternation of the applied AC, the circuit is a positive limiter. Figure 3–11 illustrates three positive limiter cases previously discussed for negative limiters. Figure 3–11a is an unbiased positive limiter. The diode conducts and limits the voltage to +0.7 V during the positive alternation and acts as an open during the negative alternation.

The diode in the circuit of Figure 3–11b is reverse biased and will not conduct until the +3 V_{BB} and the 0.7 V diode junction voltage is overcome. Thus, the diode is off (open) for most of the AC cycle and only conducts during the portion of the positive alternation that exceeds +3.7 V.

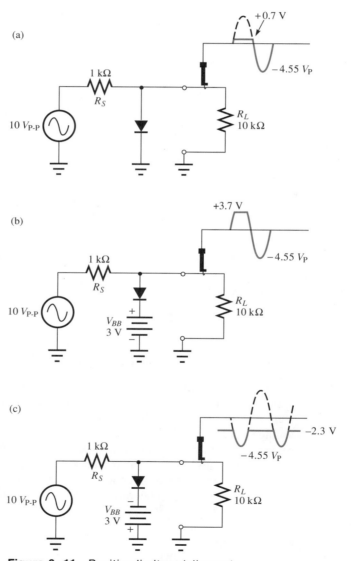

Figure 3–11   Positive limiters (clippers).

In Figure 3–11c, the diode is forward biased and supplies the load resistor with a constant −2.3 V (3 V − 0.7 V diode drop). The diode will only stop conducting when the negative alternation is strong enough to reverse bias the diode. Thus, any portion of the negative alternation between −2.3 V and −4.55 V will cause the diode to act as an open.

Combined Limiters

Very often, positive and negative limiters are combined in order to limit both alternations of the applied AC. Notice, in Figure 3–12a and 3–12b, that the limiting is symmetrical. That is, both alternations are limited to the same voltage, though opposite in sign.

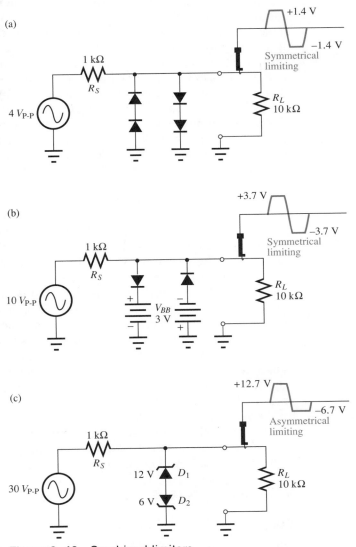

Figure 3–12 Combined limiters.

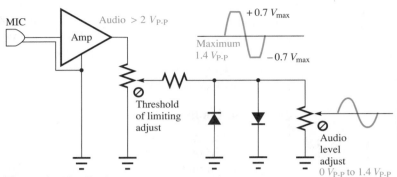

Figure 3–13   Typical audio limiter.

Figure 3–12c demonstrates an asymmetrical limiter that employs two end-to-same-end zener diodes. Note that it is the zener voltage of each diode that makes the limiter asymmetrical (not symmetrical). The two zeners take turns being forward and reverse biased with each alternation. During the positive alternation, D_1 is reverse biased, providing a 13-V drop, and D_2 is forward biased, providing the nominal 0.7-V drop. Thus, during the positive alternation, the total of the diode drops is +12.7 V and the positive alternation is limited to that value. During the negative alternation, D_2 is reverse biased, providing a −6-V drop and D_1 is forward biased, providing the nominal −0.7-V drop. Thus, during the negative alternation, the total of the diode drops is −6.7 V and the negative alternation is limited to that value. Naturally, the zeners may be the same value if a symmetrically limited waveform is desired.

Figure 3–13 illustrates a typical, or common, audio limiter circuit. Such a circuit can be found in FM communications equipment and CB transceivers. The purpose for the circuit is to limit the audio (your voice) amplitude to a presettable maximum level in order to prevent the transmitter from being overdriven. The very weak voltage from the microphone ($\cong$50 mV or so) is amplified to a peak-to-peak voltage greater than the diode threshold voltage (greater than 0.7 V per peak). The threshold potentiometer at the output of the amplifier is used to adjust the level of audio across the diodes just at a point where limiting begins (so the diodes conduct briefly at the voltage peaks). This is done while the operator speaks into the microphone as he or she normally would in operation. As shown in Figure 3–14, an oscilloscope is used to view the diode voltage waveform as the threshold potentiometer is adjusted. The upper trace on the CRT is the unclipped audio and the lower trace is the clipped or limited audio.

The audio-level-adjust potentiometer is adjusted last and is used to set the audio at a level that produces the maximum or desired modulation of the transmitter. Once both potentiometers are properly adjusted, a strong voice at the microphone will not overdrive the transmitter.

VOLTAGE CLAMPERS

Clampers

Diode clampers may look like limiters but they perform a much different task. A clamper acts as a waveform shifter, shifting the waveform up or

Figure 3–14 Using the oscilloscope to adjust the amount of audio limiting. Lower trace is limited audio. (Equipment courtesy of Tektronix, Inc.)

down, positive or negative. The waveform itself is not modified. It is merely displaced.

Positive Clampers

Figure 3–15 illustrates a simple positive clamper. Notice the series capacitor instead of a series resistor. When the AC is first applied, the capacitor quickly charges through the diode during the first negative alternation. The capacitor discharges through the load resistor during each positive alternation, but only slightly. Any slight decrease in capacitor charge is restored with each negative alternation. The charged capacitor acts as a battery in series with the AC source. The load sees the DC voltage from the charged capacitor and the AC voltage from the source. The AC is superimposed on the DC according to the superposition theorem.

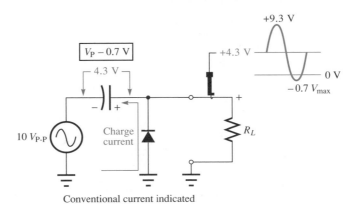

Conventional current indicated

Figure 3–15 A positive diode clamper.

As you can see, not all of the AC waveform is shifted above the 0-V line. This is because the negative peak voltage, minus the diode's forward voltage drop, is used to charge the capacitor. If the diode were ideal, there would be no 0.7-V drop, the capacitor would charge to peak value, and the negative peak of the AC waveform would rest exactly on the 0-V reference line.

Negative Clampers

Figure 3–16 shows a negative clamper. Notice that the capacitor is reversed and the diode is inverted. In this case, the capacitor charges and the diode conducts during the positive alternation. Once charged, the capacitor acts as a battery, supplying the load with −4.3 VDC. The AC is superimposed on the DC, shifting the entire waveform in the negative direction. Once again, the AC waveform is not totally shifted below the 0-V line because the 0.7-V diode drop prevents the capacitor from charging to the full negative peak voltage.

Whether the clamper provides negative or positive clamping action, the RC time constant must be very long. For satisfactory results, $R_L \cdot C$ should be greater than ten times the time (T) for one alternation ($CR_L > 10 \cdot (T/2) = 5T$, where $T = 1/f$ and f is the frequency of the applied AC). You will recognize this clamping action later when you explore class C amplifiers. For now, take time to review by answering the questions of Self-Check 3–4.

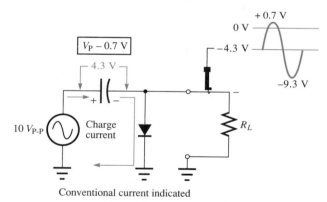

Conventional current indicated

Figure 3–16   A negative diode clamper.

Self-Check 3–4

1. Draw the output voltage waveform and label voltage levels produced by the circuit of Figure 3–17.

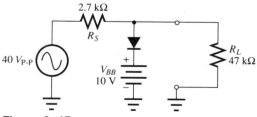

Figure 3–17

2. Is this a symmetrical or an asymmetrical limiter? Draw the output voltage waveform and label voltage levels produced by the circuit of Figure 3–18.

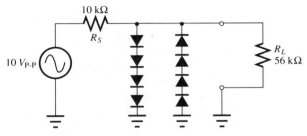

Figure 3–18

3. Draw the output voltage waveform and label voltage levels produced by the circuit of Figure 3–19.

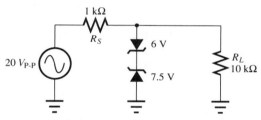

Figure 3–19

4. Is this a clipper or a clamper? Draw the output voltage waveform and label voltage levels produced by the circuit of Figure 3–20.

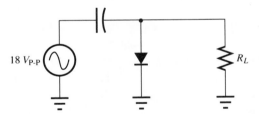

Figure 3–20

3–5 SPECIAL DIODES AND CIRCUITS

LIGHT-EMITTING DIODE (LED)

The **light-emitting diode (LED)** is very familiar to everyone in electronics today. It has replaced the small lamps (light bulbs) used as status indicators and the old gas-discharge alphanumeric displays used as digital meter displays. Their reliability, adaptability, and relatively low power consumption has made them very desirable.

Figure 3–21 illustrates the schematic symbols and a pictorial of a common LED. Notice, from the circuit, that the LED operates in the forward bias

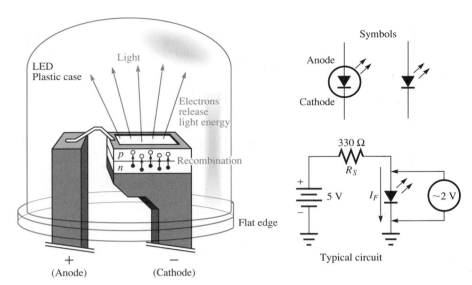

Figure 3–21   The light-emitting diode (LED).

mode. A series resistor is used to limit the current to a safe value below the maximum forward current rating (usually 5 to 50 mA, 10 mA typical). The forward voltage drop across the LED will be between 1.5 and 2.5 V depending on the amount of forward current and the type of LED. Examples 3–8 and 3–9 illustrate series-resistor calculations.

$$R_S = V_{RS}/I_{\text{LED}} = (V_S - V_{\text{LED}})/I_{\text{LED}} \tag{3–5}$$

where I_{LED} is the desired LED current, V_{LED} is the resulting forward voltage drop, V_S is the DC source voltage, and R_S is the series current-limiting resistor.

EXAMPLE 3–8

An LED has a forward voltage drop of 1.8 V with a forward current of 13 mA. Calculate the series resistor needed to limit current to 13 mA from a 12-V source.

$$R_S = V_{RS}/I_{\text{LED}} = (V_S - V_{\text{LED}})/I_{\text{LED}} = (12\text{ V} - 1.8\text{ V})/13\text{ mA} = 785\ \Omega$$

Use a standard 750-Ω or 820-Ω resistor.

EXAMPLE 3–9

An LED has a forward voltage drop of 2.1 V with a forward current of 21 mA. Calculate the series resistor needed to limit current to 21 mA from a 9-V source.

$$R_S = V_{RS}/I_{\text{LED}} = (V_S - V_{\text{LED}})/I_{\text{LED}} = (9\text{ V} - 2.1\text{ V})/21\text{ mA} = 329\ \Omega$$

Use a standard 330-Ω resistor.

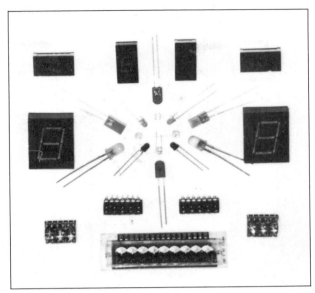

Figure 3–22 LEDs are used as indicator lights and alphanumeric displays.

Light-emitting diodes are made of special semiconductor materials that have the interesting ability to convert energy lost by electrons into light energy. Electrons move from the n material conduction band across the junction to the p material and fall into the lower-energy valence-band holes. The energy lost during this recombination is mostly converted to light instead of heat, as in conventional diodes. The color, or frequency, of light that is emitted depends on the semiconductor material and doping. Gallium arsenide (GaAs) light-emitting diodes produce infrared light. Gallium arsenide phosphide (GaAsP) light-emitting diodes produce yellow and red light. Gallium phosphide (GaP) light-emitting diodes produce red or green light. Other materials are being developed to produce other colors. Figure 3–22 shows some of the many ways LEDs are packaged and utilized.

Figure 3–23 shows a valuable application for LEDs—the seven-segment numeric display. Notice that the DIP package contains seven bar-shaped LEDs and a small dot LED as the decimal point. These displays are manufactured as common anode or common cathode as illustrated. Current-limiting resistors must be used externally to insure a safe forward current. In practice, digital electronic switches are used to energize the group of LEDs needed to form each digit from 0 to 9. Integrated circuit display drivers have been developed for this purpose. These circuits convert 4-bit binary numbers to the proper display segment selection.

PHOTODIODE

The **photodiode,** shown in Figure 3–24, is the opposite of an LED. It is biased in the reverse direction and the amount of reverse current is determined by the intensity of light that falls on the exposed chip. A lens or simply a clear plastic case permits light to hit the surface of the chip and impart energy to the electrons. The greater the light, the greater the number of free

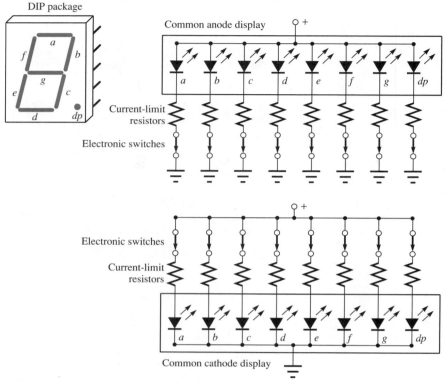

Figure 3–23   The seven-segment LED display.

electrons and the greater the reverse current. The dark current for a photo-diode is usually in the range of 10 to 50 μA. Under the influence of light, the reverse current can increase to about 500 μA. Effectively, the resistance of the photodiode decreases as light intensity increases.

Photodiodes are most sensitive to light in a specific portion of the light spectrum. Design engineers try to match the photodiode with a light source that emits energy in its range of greatest sensitivity. Manufacturer's data sheets make this very clear with graphs showing the diode's sensitivity over the light spectrum.

One use for the photodiode is in event-counter circuits in which an object interrupts a beam of light and the photodiode produces an electrical pulse

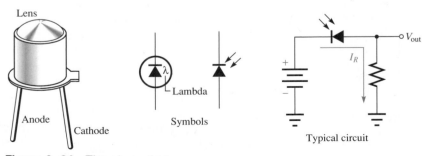

Figure 3–24   The photodiode.

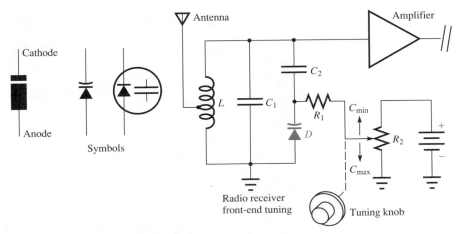

Figure 3–25 The varactor diode.

that is either counted by an electronic circuit or used to alert the electronic circuit. Another common application is in the area of fiber optics. The photodiode is used as a receiver on the receiving end of a fiber-optic cable. The light in the fiber is rapidly turned on and off, which causes the reverse current of the photodiode to vary correspondingly. The transmitted information can be analog (the light source varies in brightness) or digital (the light source is turned on and off).

VARACTOR DIODE

The **varactor (vari**able re**actor) diode,** shown in Figure 3–25, is another diode that is intended to operate in the reverse bias mode. When reverse biased, it acts mainly as a capacitor. Recall from our discussion of diode theory that the junction capacitance changes inversely with the barrier width. The usual change in capacitance is between $3:1$ and $4:1$. For example, a varactor may have 50 pF of capacitance with no bias and 15 pF with maximum reverse bias. Some varactors are specially doped to provide a much larger range (up to $10:1$). Also, varactors are designed for different ranges of voltage to suit different applications.

Notice the receiver circuit of Figure 3–25. Here, the varactor is used to tune the front end of a receiver to the desired station frequency. Most of the capacitance needed by the tank circuit is provided by C_1. The total capacitance is the parallel combination of C_1 and D, the varactor. C_2 is a relatively large-value capacitor (0.01 to 0.1 μF) used to block the DC varactor bias voltage from getting to the amplifier or being shorted to ground through the inductor. Thus, the resonant frequency of the tuned circuit is determined using the standard resonant frequency formula as follows:

$$f_r = 0.159/\sqrt{L \cdot (C_1 + C_V)} \tag{3–6}$$

where C_V is the capacitance of the varactor at any bias voltage. The varactor diode must be selected from manufacturer's data sheets to provide the desired range of capacitance, for the established range of reverse bias voltage. Consider Example 3–10.

EXAMPLE 3–10

For a circuit as shown in Figure 3–25, $L = 2.4\ \mu\text{H}$, $C_1 = 100$ pF, $C_2 = 0.01\ \mu\text{F}$, and the varactor has a capacitance range of 10 pF to 55 pF. What is the range of tuning for the circuit?

$$f_r = 0.159/\sqrt{L \cdot (C_1 + C_V)}$$

For the lowest resonant frequency,

$$f_r = 0.159/\sqrt{2.4\ \mu\text{H} \cdot (100\ \text{pF} + 55\ \text{pF})} = 8.24\ \text{MHz}$$

For the highest resonant frequency,

$$f_r = 0.159/\sqrt{2.4\ \mu\text{H} \cdot (100\ \text{pF} + 10\ \text{pF})} = 9.79\ \text{MHz}$$

Thus, the circuit is voltage tunable over a range of 8.24 to 9.79 MHz.

TUNNEL DIODE

Figure 3–26 shows the schematic symbols commonly used for the tunnel diode and its characteristic I–V curve. Tunnel diodes are constructed of very heavily doped germanium or gallium arsenide. As a result, they conduct immediately with the slightest forward bias voltage. At very low voltages, below V_P (peak voltage), the tunnel diode acts like a conductor. Once V_P is reached, the tunnel diode begins to act as a negative resistance device. As the bias voltage increases from V_P to V_V (valley voltage), the resistance of the diode increases and its forward current decreases. Above the valley-voltage point, the tunnel diode acts as a normal diode. The peak voltage (V_P) is usually near 30 mV and the valley voltage (V_V) is in the neighborhood of 300 mV.

In operation, the tunnel diode is forward biased somewhere in the negative resistance region. In this way, the tunnel diode is able to increase current to a circuit when voltage drops off. It acts much like a pump when used with a tuned circuit (tank circuit). The ringing of the tank can actually be sustained by the tunnel diode, keeping the tank supplied with current at the right time. Thus, a tunnel diode, a DC source, and a tank circuit can form a simple oscillator circuit, converting DC to a desired AC frequency.

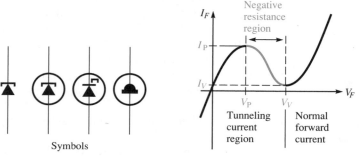

Figure 3–26   The tunnel diode.

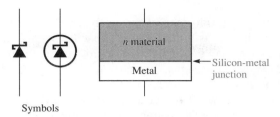

Symbols

Figure 3–27   The Schottky diode.

SCHOTTKY DIODE

The **Schottky diode,** illustrated in Figure 3–27, is also known as the **hot-carrier diode** and is used for high-speed switching in computer circuits and very-high-frequency rectification in radio circuits. This diode is very interesting because the junction is formed between lightly doped silicon (usually *n*-type) and metal (gold, silver, platinum). Since there is no *p* material in which valence-band conduction would normally take place with forward bias, all of the conduction takes place in the conduction band of the *n* material and the metal. However, the conduction-band electrons of the *n* material are at a slightly lower energy level than are the free electrons of the metal. Therefore, a forward bias potential is needed to impart energy to the *n*-material electrons. The forward bias results in a large forward current.

This design prevents the junction from storing a relatively large capacitive charge when forward bias is removed. Thus, the diode is able to switch ON and OFF at much higher frequencies. At high frequencies, a normal diode appears not to be OFF when reverse biased, because of the stored charge. For example, at 30 MHz (30,000,000 Hz), the time for one alternation is 16.7 ns ($16.7 \cdot 10^{-9}$ s). If it takes 10 ns to discharge the junction of a normal diode (referred to as *recovery time*), the diode will appear to be ON for most of the reverse bias alternation. This is not the case with the Schottky diode, which is capable of handling frequencies in the hundreds of megahertz.

PIN DIODE

The **PIN diode,** shown in Figure 3–28, is a three-layer "sandwich" of heavily doped *p* material, intrinsic material, and heavily doped *n* material. When forward biased, it acts as a variable resistance, with the resistance of the

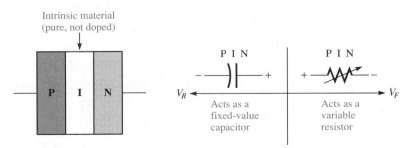

Figure 3–28   The PIN diode.

intrinsic material decreasing as forward current increases. When reverse biased, it acts as a fixed value capacitor (nearly fixed).

This special diode is used to modulate (change in amplitude) a high-frequency radio signal by varying the forward bias with a low-frequency audio signal. PIN diodes are also used as electronic attenuator devices, because a forward DC current can be used to control the resistance of the diode. A remote DC voltage or current can be used to change the resistance of the diode in a circuit that is sensitive to stray capacitance and inductance. An AC signal (usually high-frequency) that is dropped across the diode can be reduced in amplitude by an increase in DC current to the diode.

STEP-RECOVERY DIODE

The **step-recovery diode** is used in very-high-frequency and switching applications much as is the Schottky diode. However, unlike the Schottky diode, the step-recovery diode is formed of p and n material. The doping of the materials is unusual because it is increasingly dense farther away from the junction. Close to the junction, the doping is very light. This reduces the stored-charge effect found in common diodes and permits very rapid ON–OFF and OFF–ON switching.

Time for a self-check.

Self-Check 3–5

1. Of the diodes discussed in this section, list those that are normally operated reverse bias.
2. Which type of diode would you select to use as a receiver in a fiber-optic system?
3. Briefly describe the operation and use of a varactor diode.
4. Describe the negative resistance characteristic of a tunnel diode.
5. Which diode type would you select to use as an electronic attenuator? Why?
6. What are the advantages of the Schottky diode?
7. Compare the step-recovery diode to the Schottky diode.

SUMMARY

FORMULAS

(3–1) $\%$ regulation $= 100\% \cdot (V_{\mathrm{NL}} - V_{\mathrm{FL}})/V_{\mathrm{FL}}$

(3–2) $P_Z =$ Standard Value $> 1.1 \cdot I_{L(\max)} \cdot V_Z$

(3–3) $R_S = (V_{\mathrm{DC(in)}} - V_Z)/(1.1\, I_{L(\max)})$

(3–4) $P_{RS} =$ Standard Value $> (1.1\, I_{L(\max)})^2 \cdot R_S$

(3–5) $R_S = V_{RS}/I_{\mathrm{LED}} = (V_S - V_{\mathrm{LED}})/I_{\mathrm{LED}}$ (for LED current limiting)

(3–6) $f_r = 0.159/\sqrt{L \cdot (C_1 + C_V)}$ (for varactor tuning)

CONCEPTS

■ The zener diode can be used as a shunt voltage regulator.
■ The zener regulator is usually used for low-power applications.
■ The worst-case operating conditions for the zener regulator occur when

the load is disconnected and power is still applied to the regulator, in which case zener current and dissipation is maximum.
- Diode voltage multipliers provide high voltages at a lower cost than high-voltage transformers but are suitable only for low current loads.
- Diode limiters are used for over-voltage protection and prevent AC peaks from exceeding set values.
- Diode clamper circuits shift an applied AC signal almost completely above or below the 0-V where the AC rides on a DC reference.

DIODE SUMMARY

Type	Operating Mode	Some Applications
Rectifier diode	forward/reverse	power supplies, limiters, clampers
Zener diode	reverse bias	voltage regulation, limiting
LED	forward bias/ON	status indicator, alphanumeric displays
Photodiode	reverse bias	event counters, fiber-optic receiver
Varactor diode	reverse bias	radio and TV tuned circuits/oscillators
Tunnel diode	forward bias	oscillators
Schottky diode	forward/reverse	high-speed switching, high-frequency rectification in radio circuits
PIN diode	forward	DC controlled attenuator, modulator
Step-recovery diode	forward/reverse	high-speed switching

PROCEDURES

Zener-Diode Voltage Regulator Design

1. Select a standard voltage zener diode that is close to the desired output voltage. (See Figure 3–2.)
2. Select a standard zener-diode power rating. (See Figure 3–2.)
3. Select a standard value series resistance close to the value calculated using the design formula (Ohm's Law).
4. Select a standard resistor power rating that is greater than the actual dissipated power. Twice the dissipated power is a good rule of thumb.

NEED-TO-KNOW SOLUTION

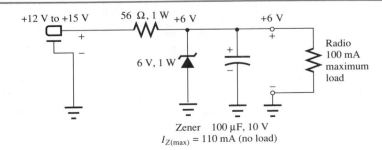

Zener   100 μF, 10 V
$I_{Z(max)} = 110$ mA (no load)

With full load (100 mA) the zener current will be approximately 10 mA and the total current through R_S will always be approximately 110 mA. The series resistor and the zener diode are both rated at 1 W. Worst-case conditions exist when the load is disconnected while power is still applied to the regulator. The 100-μF capacitor is a filter capacitor used to help remove alternator whine, which is DC ripple that rides on (is superimposed on) the DC. The zener diode does a fairly good job of removing this whine even without the filter capacitor.

QUESTIONS

3–1 DIODE VOLTAGE REGULATORS

1. If the DC supply is well filtered, why is a voltage regulator necessary?
2. What type of voltage regulator is the zener regulator? Why?
3. Does the zener normally operate in (a) forward bias, or (b) reverse bias?
4. Describe the relationship between load current, zener current, and total current. Under what circumstances does the zener conduct the most current?
5. How is the percent regulation determined?

3–2 ZENER-DIODE REGULATOR DESIGN

6. Explain how to determine the power *rating* of the zener for a particular application.
7. Explain how to determine the power *rating* of the series resistor for a particular application.
8. Should the zener regulator be designed for (a) full-load, or (b) no-load operating conditions? Why?

3–3 DIODE VOLTAGE MULTIPLIERS

9. What advantage do voltage multipliers offer?
10. What disadvantage comes with the use of voltage multipliers?
11. What can you do to increase the multiplication factor of a voltage multiplier circuit?
12. Which type of voltage doubler is called a floating supply? Why?

3–4 LIMITERS AND CLAMPERS

13. What is the purpose for a limiter circuit?
14. What is another name for limiter circuits?
15. What is a diode clamper circuit?
16. Describe, or draw and label, a limiter needed to clip positive peaks at 6 V and negative peaks at −12 V.
17. For good clamper action, the *RC* time constant should be (a) very short, (b) very long. Explain.

3–5 SPECIAL DIODES AND CIRCUITS

18. Describe the theory of operation of an LED.
19. What determines the color of light emitted by an LED?
20. List some applications for LEDs.
21. Describe the theory of operation for a photodiode.
22. List applications for the photodiode.
23. Describe the theory of operation for varactor diodes.
24. List some applications for varactors.
25. Describe some of the peculiar characteristics of the tunnel diode.
26. Describe a use for the tunnel diode.
27. Is the tunnel diode operated in (a) forward bias, or (b) reverse bias?
28. What makes the Schottky diode so different from other diodes in construction and operation?
29. List some uses for the hot-carrier diode.
30. Describe how the PIN diode acts when (a) forward biased, and (b) reverse biased.
31. What is unusual about the doping of the step-recovery diode? What is the effect, or purpose, of this doping technique?

PROBLEMS

3–1 DIODE VOLTAGE REGULATORS

1. Analyze a zener diode regulator circuit from the following information: $V_{DC(in)} = 42$ V, $V_Z = 30$ V, $R_S = 1$ kΩ, $R_L = 10$ kΩ. Find I_T, I_L, I_Z, P_Z, P_{RS}, P_L.
2. Analyze a zener-diode regulator circuit from the following information: $V_{DC(in)} = 18$ V, $V_Z = 9$ V, $R_S = 470$ Ω, $R_L = 680$ Ω. Find I_T, I_L, I_Z, P_Z, P_{RS}, P_L.
3. Analyze a zener-diode regulator circuit from the following information: $V_{DC(in)} = 12$ V, $V_Z = 6.1$ V, $R_S = 25$ Ω, $R_L = 35$ Ω. Find I_T, I_L, I_Z, P_Z, P_{RS}, P_L.
4. Analyze a zener-diode regulator circuit from the following information: $V_{DC(in)} = 36$ V, $V_Z = 12$ V, $R_S = 330$ Ω, $R_L = 200$ Ω. Find I_T, I_L, I_Z, P_Z, P_{RS}, P_L.
5. For Problem 3, calculate the zener current and the zener power dissipation with the load resistor removed.
6. For Problem 4, calculate the zener current and the zener power dissipation with the load resistor removed.

3–2 ZENER-DIODE REGULATOR DESIGN

7. Design a zener-diode voltage regulator from the following information: $V_{DC(in)} = 16$ V, $V_{DC(out)} = 5.1$ V, $R_L = 47$ Ω. Find R_S, $P_{RS(rating)}$, $P_{Z(rating)}$.
8. Design a zener-diode voltage regulator from the following information: $V_{DC(in)} = 170$ V, $V_{DC(out)} = 110$ V, $R_L = 1$ kΩ. Find R_S, $P_{RS(rating)}$, $P_{Z(rating)}$.
9. Design a zener-diode voltage regulator from the following information: $V_{DC(in)} = 18$ V, $V_{DC(out)} = 14$ V, $R_L = 90$ Ω. Find R_S, $P_{RS(rating)}$, $P_{Z(rating)}$.

10. Design a zener-diode voltage regulator from the following given information: $V_{DC(in)} = 24$ V, $V_{DC(out)} = 20$ V, $R_L = 650\ \Omega$. Find R_S, $P_{RS(rating)}$, $P_{Z(rating)}$.

3–3 DIODE VOLTAGE MULTIPLIERS

11. With 230 VAC applied to terminals 1 and 2 of the half-wave voltage multiplier in Figure 3–29, determine the DC output voltage between terminals:
    (a) 1 and 3   (b) 3 and 5   (c) 2 and 4   (d) 2 and 6

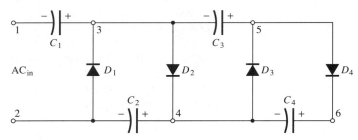

Figure 3–29

12. What should the voltage rating of the capacitors and diodes be for the multiplier circuit of Figure 3–29 with 230 VAC applied to terminals 1 and 2?
13. With 300 VAC applied to terminals 1 and 2 of the half-wave voltage multiplier in Figure 3–29, determine the DC output voltage between terminals:
    (a) 1 and 3   (b) 3 and 5   (c) 2 and 4   (d) 2 and 6
14. What should the voltage rating of the capacitors and diodes be for the multiplier circuit of Figure 3–29 with 300 VAC applied to terminals 1 and 2?
15. If the secondary voltage of the full-wave doubler in Figure 3–30 is 400 VAC, what is the DC load voltage? What is the actual peak inverse voltage across each diode?

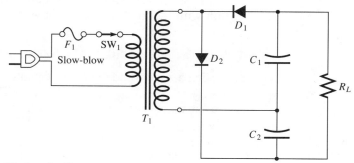

Figure 3–30

16. If the secondary voltage of the full-wave doubler in Figure 3–30 is 670 V_{P-P}, what is the DC load voltage? What is the actual peak inverse voltage across each diode?

3–4 LIMITERS AND CLAMPERS

17. Identify the circuit of Figure 3–31 and draw and label the output voltage waveform.

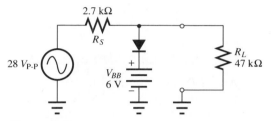

Figure 3–31

18. Identify the circuit of Figure 3–32 and draw and label the output voltage waveform.

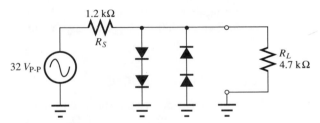

Figure 3–32

19. Identify the circuit of Figure 3–33 and draw and label the output voltage waveform.

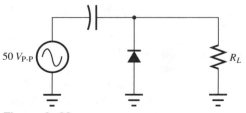

Figure 3–33

20. Identify the circuit of Figure 3–34 and draw and label the output voltage waveform.

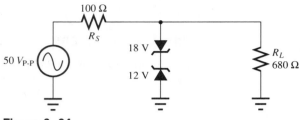

Figure 3–34

3–5 SPECIAL DIODES AND CIRCUITS

21. An LED is to be used to indicate when a 48-V circuit is energized. Calculate the series resistance needed to limit the LED forward current to 10 mA. (LED forward voltage = 2 V)
22. An LED is to be used to indicate when a 12-V circuit is energized. Calculate the series resistance needed to limit the LED forward current to 5 mA. (LED forward voltage = 1.7 V)
23. A varactor diode has a capacitance range of 10 to 80 pF. What is the tunable frequency range when it is placed in parallel with a 9-μH inductor and a 300-pF fixed-value capacitor?
24. A varactor diode has a capacitance range of 15 to 90 pF. What is the tunable frequency range when it is placed in parallel with a 6-μH inductor and a 400-pF fixed-value capacitor?

ADDITIONAL PROBLEMS

25. A zener-diode regulator circuit has the following parameters: $V_{DC(in)} = 48$ V, $V_Z = 36$ V, $R_S = 430\ \Omega$, $R_L = 1.5$ kΩ. Find $I_T, I_L, I_Z, P_Z, P_{RS}, P_L$.
26. Calculate I_Z for Problem 25 if R_L is changed to 3 kΩ.
27. Calculate the maximum power that might be dissipated by the zener diode of Problem 25.
28. Design a zener-diode voltage regulator from the following specifications: $V_{DC(in)} = 13.6$ V, $V_{DC(out)} = 9$ V, $R_L = 88\ \Omega$. Find R_S, $R_{RS(rating)}$, $P_{Z(rating)}$.
29. Design a zener-diode voltage regulator from the following specifications: $V_{DC(in)} = 24$ V, $V_{DC(out)} = 19$ V, $R_L = 23\ \Omega$. Find R_S, $P_{RS(rating)}$, $P_{Z(rating)}$.
30. Design a zener regulator using a 1-W, 12-V zener diode. The DC input voltage shall be 18 V. Calculate R_S so the zener dissipates its maximum rated power under worst-case conditions ($P_{Z(max)} = 1$ W).
31. Design a zener regulator using a 500-mW, 6.2-V zener diode. The DC input voltage shall be 9 V. Calculate R_S so the zener dissipates its

maximum rated power under worst-case conditions ($P_{Z(max)} = 500$ mW).

32. The data sheet for an LED indicates that the forward voltage drop is approximately 1.8 V at 10 mA. Calculate the value of series resistance needed to limit the LED current to 10 mA from a 24-V DC source.

33. Each segment of a seven-segment LED display is rated at 1.7 V and 15 mA. Calculate the value of the current-limiting resistor needed for each segment when a 5-V DC source is used.

34. A varactor diode has a capacitance range of 5 to 35 pF. What is the tunable frequency range when the diode is placed in parallel with a 1.5-μH inductor and a 150-pF fixed-value capacitor?

ANSWERS TO SELF-CHECKS

SELF-CHECK 3–1

1. (b)
2. No. The zener voltage varies slightly with large changes in zener current.
3. 3.23% regulation

SELF-CHECK 3–2

1. The series resistor shall be 33 Ω, 0.5 W and the zener shall be 9 V, 1 W. The 1N4739 or 1N5924A would be adequate.

SELF-CHECK 3–3

1. Lower cost, lower weight, smaller
2. They are intended for low-current loads.
3. 7
4. The half-wave doubler can be grounded at the transformer secondary and the full-wave doubler cannot. The secondary of a full-wave doubler is floating.

SELF-CHECK 3–4

1.

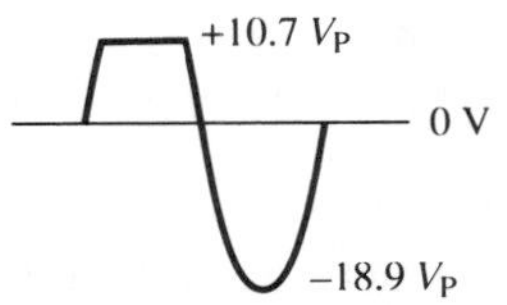

Figure 3–35

2. Symmetrical limiter

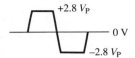

Figure 3–36

3.

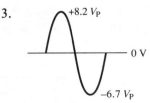

Figure 3–37

4. Clamper

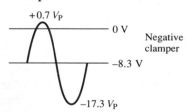

Figure 3–38

SELF-CHECK 3–5

1. Zener, photodiode, varactor
2. Photodiode
3. The barrier width and junction capacitance of a varactor diode varies inversely with the amount of reverse bias voltage.
4. The tunnel diode has a small range of forward voltage in which increases in voltage cause an increase in resistance and a decrease in forward current. This is the negative resistance region.
5. PIN diode. When forward biased, the PIN diode acts as a variable resistance as its forward bias voltage is varied.
6. The Schottky diode has very little storage charge after being forward biased. Thus, it is able to turn on and off very rapidly handling very high frequency signals.
7. The step-recovery diode and Schottky diode are used for similar applications but their construction and theory of operation are very different. The step-recovery diode has p and n materials both doped in a graded manner and the Schottky diode has a metal to semiconductor junction.

SUGGESTED PROJECTS

1. Add some of the main concepts, formulas, and procedures from this chapter to your Electronics Notebook.

2. Use the parts you gathered at the end of Chapter 1, "Suggested Projects," and design and build a DC supply that will provide a regulated 12 and 9.1 V to a maximum 100-mA load. Make sure all high-voltage connections are secured and well insulated before power is applied. Also, you should use a slow-blow $\frac{1}{4}$-A fuse in the primary circuit. Remember, with no load and with the power on, the zeners and series resistors will be hot. When you are finished, analyze your circuit using the oscilloscope. Calculate RMS ripple, ripple factor, and percent regulation.

   Hint: Think about which type of rectifier is best for this design and these voltage levels. A little forethought here will save you from buying high-wattage series resistors. Ask your teacher to approve your design.

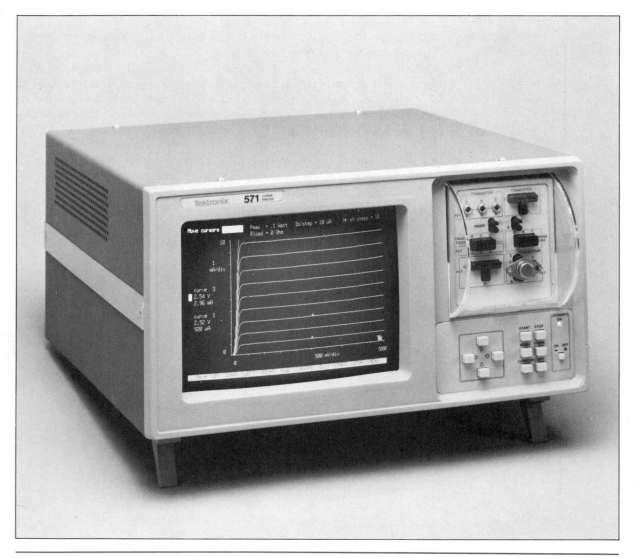

The Tektronix 571 Curve Tracer is a new computerized component tester. It is used to display the characteristic curves for diodes, transistors, and thyristors. In this case, a family of collector curves for an NPN transistor is displayed. Component characteristics are digitized and stored in computer memory to be used for the display screen or a hardcopy printout. (Photograph courtesy of Tektronix.)

Introduction to Amplifiers and Bipolar Transistors

CHAPTER OUTLINE

4–1 AMPLIFIER SYSTEMS
4–2 TRANSISTOR CONSTRUCTION AND THEORY
4–3 IMPORTANT TRANSISTOR PARAMETERS
4–4 TRANSISTOR OPERATING CHARACTERISTICS

OBJECTIVES

After studying this chapter, you will be able to

- explain the purpose for an amplifier and define its performance in terms of decibels.
- explain the differences between NPN and PNP transistors.
- explain the relationship between base current, emitter current, and collector current.
- explain some of the important transistor parameters and ratings.
- describe and explain transistor collector-current curves.
- construct a DC load line for any given transistor circuit.

NEED TO KNOW

Suppose you want to design a semiautomatic watering system for your garden. (Come on now, just pretend.) You have an integrated circuit (IC) timer that runs off of +12 VDC. When a button is pressed, the timer IC makes one of its pins go high for one hour. That means its output pin (terminal) goes from 0 V to +12 V and stays at +12 V for one hour. You also have an electric control valve for the watering system that requires 12 V and 1 A of current to energize. You discover you cannot simply connect the control valve to the output pin of the timer because the timer can handle only 100 mA (maximum). The problem you must solve is how to interface the electric control valve to the timer so you can water your garden for one hour at the push of a button.

As always, a solution to this Need to Know is provided at the close of this chapter. Try not to look now. As you study this chapter, see if you can figure out how to use a transistor to interface the timer and control valve. Enjoy!

INTRODUCTION

In this chapter you will learn much about amplifiers and transistors. Let me caution you not to expect too much from this one chapter. The subject of transistors is very broad and cannot possibly be covered in one chapter. However, as in most things, you must learn to walk before you can run. This chapter will teach you to ''walk.'' You will learn the basics of amplifier theory, transistor theory, transistor construction, and transistor DC operating characteristics. The overall purpose for this chapter is to familiarize you with the concept of amplification and to begin the topic of transistor amplifiers with an exploration of transistor theory and DC characteristics. Once you understand the DC aspects of transistor circuits, you will be ready for AC applications and analysis in later chapters. Therefore, the material covered in this chapter is extremely important for your future success and understanding.

4–1 AMPLIFIER SYSTEMS

AMPLIFIER BLOCK DIAGRAMS

In this chapter, you begin to learn about transistor amplifiers. You will learn much about amplifier biasing schemes and configurations. Before we charge ahead, let us take a little time here to establish an overall understanding of amplification. Knowing ahead of time where you are going may make the study of transistors more interesting and understandable.

Transistor amplifiers are able to amplify voltage, current, and power. A low-level signal is applied to the input of the amplifier; the amplifier is then able to reproduce that input signal with much greater amplitude at the output. A transistor amplifier may be one stage or many stages working together. Figure 4–1 illustrates a simple multistage amplifier system. Note that the entire system may be represented by one triangular block (rectangular blocks may also be used) or by many blocks, each representing one stage. Very often, the entire amplifier serves as a single block in a larger electronic system. Each stage contributes some amplification to the overall amplifier because no single stage is able to provide the total amount of amplification needed. The gain (amount of amplification) for each stage and the entire system is often expressed in decibels. In this case, the decibels indicate the amount of voltage amplification provided by each stage. Decibels are a very important unit of measurement for voltage and power levels, for they are used all over the world in nearly all areas of electronics. We will discuss decibels now in relation to the subject of amplifiers, so we may use these units freely later on.

VOLTAGE DECIBELS (dB)

Decibels are based on the Bel, named in honor of Alexander Graham Bell (1847–1922). The Bel represents a $10\times$ multiple of acoustical power, which

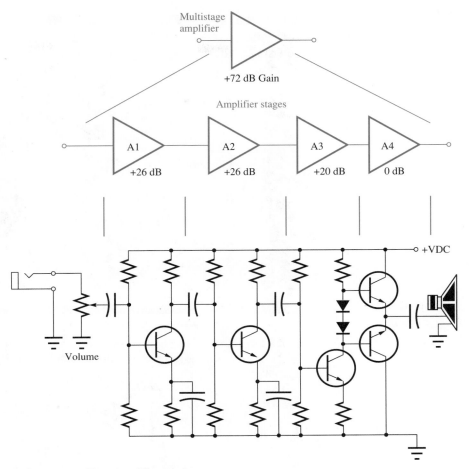

Figure 4–1 The amplifier system.

is perceived by the human ear as a doubling of loudness. The decibel is one-tenth of a Bel. Thus it takes 10 decibels to equal 1 Bel. The decibel (dB) is the unit that is commonly used.

Decibels can be used to express the relationship between voltage levels or between power levels. When decibels are used to compare voltage levels, such as an amplifier's output compared to its input, the ratio of V_{out}/V_{in} is placed in this formula:

$$\#\text{dB} = 20 \cdot \log_{10}(V_{out}/V_{in}) \tag{4–1}$$

The voltages may be expressed as RMS, peak, or peak-to-peak, as long as the same units are used for both voltages being compared. Use the formula to verify that a doubling of voltage is a 6-dB gain and 10 times the voltage is a 20-dB gain. Also, take time to carefully study Examples 4–1, 4–2 and 4–3.

EXAMPLE 4–1 ▮▮▮▮▮▮▮▮▮▮▮▮▮▮▮▮▮▮▮▮▮▮▮▮▮▮▮▮▮▮▮▮▮

Express the V_{out}/V_{in} voltage gain of the Figure 4–2 amplifier block in units of decibels.

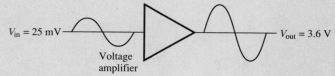

Figure 4–2

#dB = 20 · log (3.6 V/25 mV)

= 20 log (144)   (voltage ratio = 144 : 1)

= 20 · 2.16

= +43.2 dB gain

EXAMPLE 4–2 ▮▮▮▮▮▮▮▮▮▮▮▮▮▮▮▮▮▮▮▮▮▮▮▮▮▮▮▮▮▮▮▮▮

Determine V_{out} in Figure 4–3. Also, express the amplifier gain in decibels, the voltage-divider gain in decibels, and the overall gain in decibels.

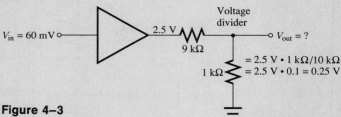

Figure 4–3

Amplifier Gain

= 20 · log (2.5 V/60 mV)
= 20 log (41.67)
= 20 · 1.62
= +32.4 dB gain

Voltage-Divider Gain

= 20 · log (0.25 V/2.5 V)
= 20 log (0.1)
= 20 · −1
= −20 dB gain

Total gain = +32.4 dB + (−20 dB) = +12.4 dB

Notice that the total decibel gain is the sum of the individual decibel gain of consecutive stages or blocks. The voltage-divider gain is easily identified as a loss by the negative sign preceding the decibel figure (−20 dB).

The output voltage can be determined using the voltage-divider rule as shown in Figure 4–3 or from decibel information. The gain of the voltage divider is −20 dB. This dB figure can be used to work backward in the decibel formula to determine the V_{out}/V_{in} ratio, which is the voltage-divider ratio.

$\#dB = 20 \log_{10}(V_{out}/V_{in})$

$\#dB/20 = \log_{10}(V_{out}/V_{in})$

$invlog_{10}(\#dB/20) = V_{out}/V_{in}$

$V_{in} \cdot [invlog_{10}(\#dB/20)] = V_{out}$

Now let's apply values.

$V_{out} = 2.5 \text{ V} \cdot [invlog_{10}(-20/20)] = 2.5 \text{ V} \cdot [invlog_{10}(-1)]$

$= 2.5 \text{ V} \cdot 0.1 = 0.25 \text{ V}$

The overall decibel gain of Figure 4–3 can be used to determine the output voltage from the 60-mV input voltage.

$V_{out} = 60 \text{ mV} \cdot [invlog_{10}(+12.4/20)]$

$= 60 \text{ mV} \cdot [invlog_{10}(0.62)]$

$= 60 \text{ mV} \cdot 4.17 = 0.25 \text{ V}$

EXAMPLE 4–3

An amplifier system has an input attenuator with an attenuation ratio of 1/3, an amplifier stage with a voltage gain of 12/1, a second amplifier stage with a voltage gain of 23/1, and an output attenuator with an attenuation ratio of 5/6. Convert each ratio to decibels and express the overall system gain in dB.

$\#dB = 20 \cdot \log_{10}(V_{out}/V_{in})$

Input attenuator: $\#dB = 20 \log_{10}(1/3) = -9.54 \text{ dB gain}$

Amplifier #1: $\#dB = 20 \log_{10}(12) = +21.6 \text{ dB gain}$

Amplifier #2: $\#dB = 20 \log_{10}(23) = +27.2 \text{ dB gain}$

Output attenuator: $\#dB = 20 \log_{10}(5/6) = \underline{-1.58 \text{ dB gain}}$

Total gain:
$\#dB = 20 \log_{10}[(1/3) \cdot 12 \cdot 23 \cdot (5/6)] \qquad = +37.7 \text{ dB gain}$

POWER DECIBELS (dB)

As stated earlier, decibels are also used to compare power levels. Linear amplifiers, used to increase the output power of a transmitter, are rated in dB of gain. An amplifier that has a power gain of 10 dB is able to amplify an input power level 10 times. An amplifier with a power gain of 20 dB amplifies the input power 100 times, 30 dB is 1,000 times, 40 dB is 10,000 times, and so on. The following formula is used to calculate the power gain in decibels when the P_{out}/P_{in} ratio is known:

$\#dB = 10 \cdot \log_{10}(P_{out}/P_{in})$ (4–2)

Study Examples 4–4, 4–5, and 4–6 carefully. Notice that an increase in power yields +dB and a loss of power (attenuation) yields −dB.

EXAMPLE 4–4

Express the P_{out}/P_{in} power gain of Figure 4–4 in decibels.

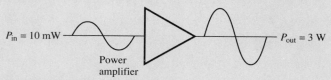

$P_{in} = 10$ mW   Power amplifier $P_{out} = 3$ W

Figure 4–4

$\#dB = 10 \cdot \log_{10}(P_{out}/P_{in})$

$\#dB = 10 \cdot \log_{10}(3 \text{ W}/10 \text{ mW}) = 10 \log_{10}(300)$

$= 10 \cdot 2.48 = +24.8$ dB gain

EXAMPLE 4–5

Express the gain of each stage and the overall gain of Figure 4–5 in decibels.

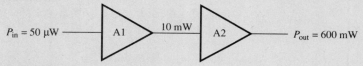

$P_{in} = 50$ μW   A1   10 mW   A2 $P_{out} = 600$ mW

Figure 4–5

$\#dB = 10 \cdot \log_{10}(P_{out}/P_{in})$

Gain of A_1

$= 10 \cdot \log(10 \text{ mW}/50 \text{ μW})$
$= 10 \log (200)$
$= 10 \cdot 2.3$
$= +23$ dB gain

Gain of A_2

$= 10 \cdot \log(600 \text{ mW}/10 \text{ mW})$
$= 10 \log (60)$
$= 10 \cdot 1.78$
$= +17.8$ dB gain

Total gain $= A_1 + A_2 = +23$ dB $+ 17.8$ dB $= +40.8$ dB

Note that, as with voltage decibels, the power dB formula can be rearranged to determine output power from input power using overall dB gain.

$\#dB = 10 \cdot \log_{10}(P_{out}/P_{in})$

$P_{out} = P_{in} \cdot [\text{invlog}_{10}(\#dB/10)]$

$= 50 \text{ μW} \cdot [\text{invlog}_{10}(+40.8/10)]$

$= 50 \text{ μW} \cdot [\text{invlog}_{10}(4.08)]$

$= 50 \text{ μW} \cdot 12023 = 601$ mW

EXAMPLE 4–6 ▮▬▬▬▬▬▬▬▬▬▬▬▬▬▬▬▬▬▬▬▬▬▬▬▬▬▬▬

Express the gain of the Figure 4–6 power attenuator in decibels.

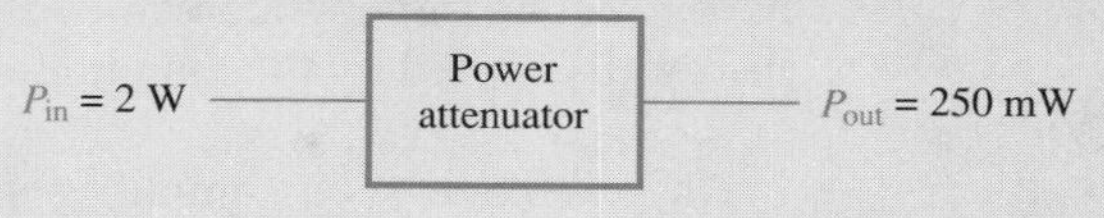

$P_{in} = 2$ W ———————| Power attenuator |——————— $P_{out} = 250$ mW

Figure 4–6

$\#dB = 10 \cdot \log_{10}(P_{out}/P_{in})$

$\#dB = 10 \cdot \log(250 \text{ mW}/2 \text{ W})$

$\quad = 10 \log(0.125) \qquad$ (power ratio is less than 1)

$\quad = 10 \cdot -0.903$

$\quad = -9.03$ dB gain = a loss of 9.03 dB

COMPARING VOLTAGE AND POWER DECIBELS

Consider the following comparison of voltage and power decibels in which the voltage and power ratios are the same. You should note that the number of voltage decibels is always twice the number of power decibels for the same ratio.

- voltage ratio of 2/1 = +6 dB = $20 \cdot \log_{10}(2) = 20 \cdot 0.3$
- power ratio of 2/1 = +3 dB = $10 \cdot \log_{10}(2) = 10 \cdot 0.3$

- voltage ratio of 1/2 = −6 dB = $20 \cdot \log_{10}(0.5) = 20 \cdot -0.3$
- power ratio of 1/2 = −3 dB = $10 \cdot \log_{10}(0.5) = 10 \cdot -0.3$

- voltage ratio of 10/1 = +20 dB = $20 \cdot \log_{10}(10) = 20 \cdot 1$
- power ratio of 10/1 = +10 dB = $10 \cdot \log_{10}(10) = 10 \cdot 1$

- voltage ratio of 1/10 = −20 dB = $20 \cdot \log_{10}(0.1) = 20 \cdot -1$
- power ratio of 1/10 = −10 dB = $10 \cdot \log_{10}(0.1) = 10 \cdot -1$

When the voltage and power decibels are equal in number, the voltage and power ratios are not. Voltage and power decibels are equal (have the same value) in the same circuit in regard to the same load impedance. Look at Example 4–7.

EXAMPLE 4–7 ▮▬▬▬▬▬▬▬▬▬▬▬▬▬▬▬▬▬▬▬▬▬▬▬▬▬▬▬

If the voltage across a 10-Ω resistor is increased from 1 V to 10 V, the voltage increases 10 times while the power dissipation increases 100 times ($P = V^2/R$). Therefore, the decibel increase in voltage and power is +20 dB:

voltage dB = $20 \log_{10}(10) = 20 \cdot 1 = +20$ dB

power dB = $10 \log_{10}(100) = 10 \cdot 2 = +20$ dB

Though the voltage and power ratios are not the same, the number of decibels are—as long as you are calculating voltage and power gain for a specific load impedance. In other words, an increase or decrease in voltage across a load impedance will cause the same decibel increase or decrease in power dissipated by the load impedance, as is demonstrated in Example 4–7.

As you have seen, amplifier systems are made of amplifier blocks that work together to create the desired overall amplification ratio or gain in decibels. System gain in decibels is the sum of all decibel block gains in the system. The entire amplifier may be represented as a single block in a larger system. Starting with the next section, you will see how transistor amplifiers are manufactured and begin to see how they function. Time now for a brief self-check.

Self-Check 4–1

1. An amplifier can be a complete system or a single stage. True or false?
2. Why is more than one stage needed in an amplifier system?
3. What does amplifier gain mean?
4. The gain of an amplifier can be expressed in what world-wide unit?
5. An amplifier has an input voltage of 40 mV and an output voltage of 6 V. What is its gain in dB?

4–2 TRANSISTOR CONSTRUCTION AND THEORY

INTRODUCTION TO TRANSISTORS

The active devices in many amplifier systems and blocks are transistors. Transistors are called *active devices* because they can amplify current—a capability that resistors and diodes lack. In this section, you will explore the two main types of transistors, NPN and PNP. You will learn how these transistors are constructed and how they are able to amplify current. There is much that you need to know about these devices before we consider them in practical amplifier circuits. A look at the inner construction of the transistor will help you understand their operation. Figure 4–7 illustrates the schematic symbols and layer diagram for NPN transistors and Figure 4–8 illustrates the PNP transistor. Notice that each type of transistor is, in a sense, a sandwich of the two types of doped semiconductor materials. For this reason, these transistors are said to be *bipolar* and are referred to as **bipolar junction transistors** or **BJTs.** Let us first take a close look at the NPN BJT of Figure 4–7.

THE NPN TRANSISTOR

NPN Symbols and Construction

The first thing you should recognize about the NPN transistor symbol is the arrow on the emitter lead. For NPN transistors, this arrow always points away from the base material (the center of the transistor). Notice, from the

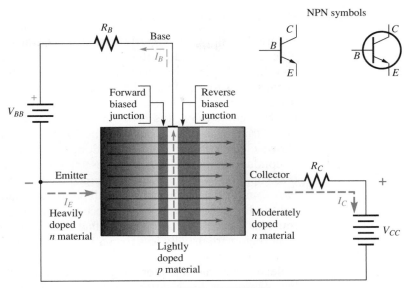

ELECTRON FLOW SHOWN

Figure 4–7   The NPN transistor.

layer diagram, that the NPN transistor is a sandwich of two layers of *n* material with a *p* layer in the middle.

The emitter (*E*) layer is a heavily doped layer of *n* material. The base (*B*) is a lightly doped middle layer of *p* material. The collector (*C*) is the largest layer of moderately doped *n* material. Like diodes, most transistors today are made of silicon as opposed to germanium, which was used in the past.

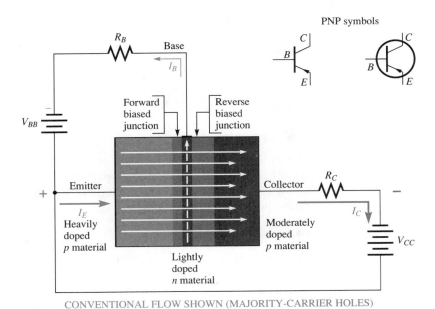

CONVENTIONAL FLOW SHOWN (MAJORITY-CARRIER HOLES)

Figure 4–8   The PNP transistor.

NPN Transistor Theory

Figure 4–7 shows a properly biased NPN transistor (layer diagram). Two junctions are formed by the sandwiched layers—the base–emitter junction and the collector–base junction. The base–emitter junction is very narrow, because it is forward biased by V_{BB}, and the collector–base junction is very wide, because it is reverse biased by the difference between V_C, the collector voltage, and V_B, the base voltage, V_C being more positive than V_B. In NPN transistors, electrons are the majority carriers. Thus, the diagram shows electron flow. The heavily doped emitter provides a generous supply of conduction-band electrons. These electrons gain energy from the forward bias supplied by V_{BB}. As these energized electrons cross the forward-biased base–emitter junction, only a small percentage fall into the few holes of the lightly doped base region. This recombination creates a majority drift current that arrives at the base terminal. The electrons that recombine in the base region are usually less than 5% of the emitted electrons. The rest (over 95%) continue across the reverse-biased collector–base junction and are collected by the collector. The electrons are able to cross this junction because of the large difference of potential (provided by V_{CC}) that exists across the transistor from collector to emitter. As the electrons cross the reverse-biased junction, they fall into the conduction band of the n-type collector region and release energy in the form of heat. Therefore, the collector region is usually bonded to a metal surface that doubles as a terminal and heat sink.

The amount of V_{BB} and the size of R_B determine the amount of base current (I_B). The amount of base current is an indication of the degree to which the base–emitter junction is forward biased—the more base current, the greater the forward bias. It is the amount of base current (forward bias) that determines the amount of emitter (I_E) and collector (I_C) current—more base current means more collector current. Thus, any change in base current is reflected as a much larger change in collector current, which directly affects the voltage drop across the collector resistor. I_B is the cause; I_C and V_{RC} are the effects.

THE PNP TRANSISTOR

PNP Symbols

The PNP BJT is the complement of the NPN transistor. Figure 4–8 shows the schematic symbols and the properly biased layer diagram. Note the small arrow in the emitter lead of the transistor symbols. For PNP transistors, the arrow points toward the base region.

PNP Transistor Theory

Like the NPN transistor, the PNP transistor is made of three semiconductor layers forming two junctions. However, for PNP transistors, the emitter is heavily doped p material, the collector is moderately doped p material, and the base is lightly doped n material. Notice that this requires the emitter to be positive, the base to be negative, and the collector to be very negative in

Figure 4–9 Current in NPN and PNP transistors.

order for the base–emitter junction to be forward biased and the collector–base junction to be reverse biased. Conventional current is shown in Figure 4–8 because the majority carriers in the emitter and collector are holes.

Electron Flow and Conventional Flow

Figure 4–9 shows the proper biasing polarities for NPN and PNP transistors. The direction of current through each transistor type depends on the type of current you wish to use—electron flow or conventional flow (hole flow). Just remember that conventional flow is always in the direction of the arrow on the emitter lead. The arrow represents forward bias conventional current for the base–emitter junction. Recall that this is true for diodes as well. Electron flow is always against the arrow. The type of current that is used is really not that important. What is important is the polarity of voltage drops that result from the current. The polarity of the voltage drops across junctions and resistors will always be the same whether the current used is electron or conventional.

For most circuits in this book, we will use conventional flow to avoid confusion. However, the main purpose for current arrows in the transistor circuits will be to emphasize proper conduction paths and relative amounts of current.

TRANSISTOR ARCHITECTURE AND PACKAGING

Architecture

Figure 4–10 illustrates a very common method of bipolar junction transistor (BJT) fabrication. This architecture is called *planar* because all *pn* junctions terminate in the same geometric plane, at the surface where ohmic contacts

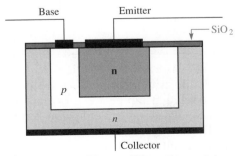

Figure 4–10 Planar-diffused transistor architecture.

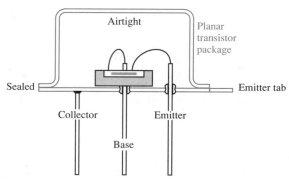

Figure 4–11 Transistor packaging.

(lead connections) are made. The transistors are often referred to as **planar transistors** having a planar geometry or planar architecture. The process of fabrication involves masking and acid-etching the collector n material to form a pocket. The base region p material is then deposited in the pocket. Masking and acid-etching a second time produces the smaller pocket for the emitter n material. Once the emitter region is deposited, metallic contacts are bonded to the planar surface for the emitter and base. Then a silicon dioxide (SiO_2) coating is applied as an insulator/sealer to prevent surface leakage current between layers across the planar surface.

Packaging

Figure 4–11 gives you an idea of how the transistor chip is packaged. For power transistors, the collector region is bonded to a metal casing to serve the dual purpose of heat sink and contact. Very fine wires are used to connect the base and emitter regions to the wire leads, which are insulated and protrude from the package. The entire package is encapsulated in plastic or ceramic and is airtight to prevent contamination and corrosion (hermetically sealed).

Transistor packages vary greatly depending on the purpose and power of the transistor. Figure 4–12 shows a variety of common packages and makes generalizations about them. The manufacturer's data sheet for a particular transistor should always be consulted to determine the actual lead identification for that transistor. Lead assignments often vary for different transistors using the same package.

Self-Check 4–2

1. Describe the biasing of the junctions for a properly biased transistor.
2. Describe the polarity of biasing on the leads of an NPN transistor.
3. What is the relationship between I_B and V_{RC}?
4. What is the polarity of the collector, emitter, and base of a properly biased PNP transistor?
5. How can you tell if the schematic symbol for a transistor is NPN or PNP?

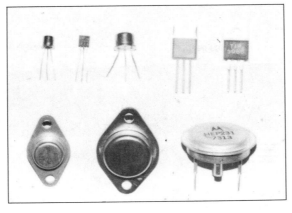

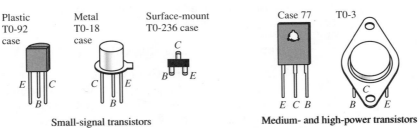

Plastic T0-92 case   Metal T0-18 case   Surface-mount T0-236 case   Case 77   T0-3

Small-signal transistors   **Medium- and high-power transistors**

Figure 4–12 Some transistor case styles.

6. How does conventional current relate to the schematic symbols for transistors?

7. For power transistors, which semiconductor layer is bonded to the metal case? Why?

4–3 IMPORTANT TRANSISTOR PARAMETERS

TRANSISTOR CURRENTS AND VOLTAGES

Base, Collector, and Emitter Currents

Figure 4–13 shows the three significant currents that exist in a properly biased transistor circuit. Notice that the polarity of V_{BB} provides the required forward bias for the base–emitter junction. The actual voltage across the base–emitter junction is in the range of 0.65 to 0.75 V since the base–emitter junction is a forward-biased diode. This forward bias permits a relatively large emitter current, a small part of which becomes base current. Most of the emitter current continues to the collector region and can be measured as collector current. The emitter current is the greatest, the collector current is almost as great, and the base current is very small. Therefore, according to Kirchhoff's current law,

$$I_B + I_C = I_E \qquad (4\text{--}3)$$

$$I_E - I_C = I_B \qquad (4\text{--}4)$$

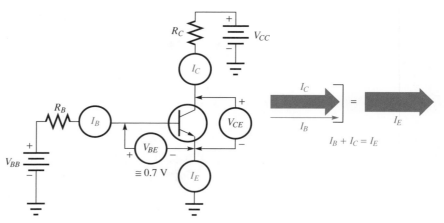

Figure 4–13 Transistor currents and voltages.

Transistor Leakage Currents

If the base of the transistor is left unbiased, or open, an ideal transistor will conduct no current between collector and emitter. However, transistors are not ideal and they do conduct a leakage current, known as I_{CEO} (see Figure 4–14). The subscript CEO indicates that the collector and emitter are properly connected but the base is left open. This leakage current, normally very small, is due to minority current carriers in the semiconductor layers. This minority current is directly related to temperature. As temperature increases, the leakage current increases (roughly doubles for every 10-C° increase in temperature). Leakage current is sometimes called *cutoff current* and is usually in the low nanoamps at 25°C.

Another leakage current that is temperature related is I_{CBO}. As shown in Figure 4–14, I_{CBO} is specified as the reverse leakage current between the collector and base with the emitter disconnected. This current is also normally very small, ranging in the low nanoamps (depending on transistor type and power rating). Like I_{CEO}, I_{CBO} exists in a fully connected and functioning transistor circuit. Both leakage currents increase with temperature and can cause significant changes in bias and transistor operation. We will investigate this more later.

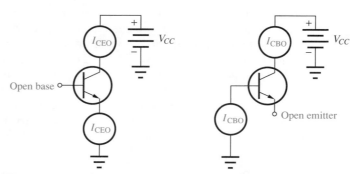

Figure 4–14 Collector–emitter and collector–base leakage current.

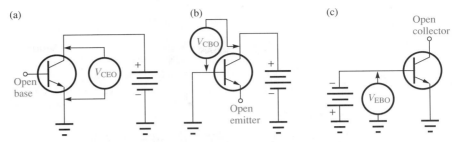

Figure 4–15 Transistor maximum voltage ratings.

TRANSISTOR RATINGS

Maximum Voltage Ratings

Among the most significant transistor ratings are the maximum voltage ratings. These are reverse voltage ratings that indicate the maximum reverse voltages the transistor should be subjected to during operation, as illustrated by the test circuits of Figure 4–15. These voltages *must not* be exceeded. Figure 4–15a illustrates the collector–emitter voltage with the base open (V_{CEO}). With the base open, the worst-case condition is when all of the supply voltage is across the transistor, because the transistor acts nearly like an open. The supply voltage must not exceed the V_{CEO} rating, or voltage breakdown and permanent damage may occur. In Figure 4–15b, the collector–base junction is reverse biased. Again, the supply voltage must not exceed the V_{CBO} rating. Finally, Figure 4–15c shows the base–emitter junction in reverse bias. The point of this rating is to make sure that your circuit design will never place a reverse voltage greater than the V_{EBO} rating across the base–emitter junction. Under normal circuit conditions, this rating cannot be exceeded because the base–emitter junction is operated in forward bias. Table 4–1 shows some of the important ratings for the 2N3904 NPN small-signal transistor and its complement, the 2N3906 PNP transistor.

TABLE 4–1   MAXIMUM RATINGS FOR 2N3904 AND 2N3906

Rating	Symbol	Value
Collector–emitter voltage	V_{CEO}	40 V
Collector–base voltage	V_{CBO}	
2N3904		60 V
2N3906		40 V
Emitter–base voltage	V_{EBO}	
2N3904		6 V
2N3906		5 V
Collector current—continuous	I_C	200 mA
Total device dissipation at $T_A = 25°C$	P_D	625 mW
Derating factor above 25°C		5 mW/°C
Operating and storage junction temperature range	T_J, T_{stg}	−55 to +150°C

Maximum Current Rating

Transistors are rated for a maximum DC current. Note that 2N3904 and 2N3906 transistors are rated for a maximum continuous current of 200 mA. This does not necessarily mean that you can design an amplifier circuit with the 2N3904 conducting a normal 200 mA of current. Much more must be considered, such as the power rating of the transistor.

Maximum Power Dissipation Rating

Notice, from Table 4–1, that the 2N3904/6 has a maximum power dissipation rating of 625 mW at an ambient (surrounding) temperature of 25°C. As shown in Figure 4–16, this means the operating current times the collector–emitter voltage must never exceed 625 mW with an ambient temperature of 25°C.

$$P_D = I_C \cdot V_{CE} \tag{4-5}$$

According to the derating data given for the 2N3904, the power rating must be reduced by 5 mW for every 1°C above 25°C. The 5 mW/1°C is the **derating factor.** Consider Examples 4–8 and 4–9.

EXAMPLE 4–8

The 2N3904 is rated for 625 mW of dissipation at an ambient temperature of 25°C. What is its power rating at 60°C?

60°C is 35° higher. The rating must be reduced by 5 mW for every 1°C above 25°C. Therefore, the rating must be reduced by 5 mW · 35 = 175 mW. The rating at 60°C = 625 mW − 175 mW = 450 mW. Therefore, $I_C \cdot V_{CE}$ cannot exceed 450 mW if the surrounding temperature is 60°C.

EXAMPLE 4–9

In a transistor circuit, a 2N3904 transistor has a collector current of 70 mA and a collector–emitter voltage of 7.14 V. The temperature surrounding the transistor is 70°C. Is the transistor in danger?

$$P_D = I_C \cdot V_{CE} = 70 \text{ mA} \cdot 7.14 \text{ V} = 500 \text{ mW}$$

Derating factor = 5 mW/1°C

70°C − 25°C = 45°C

Rating = 625 mW − (45°C · 5 mW/1°C)

$\qquad$ = 625 mW − 225 mW = 400 mW

The actual dissipation of the transistor is 500 mW, which is 100 mW more than the 70°C derated value of 400 mW. The transistor is definitely in danger of burning up.

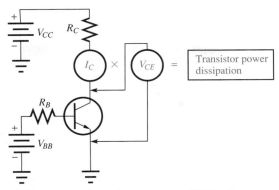

Figure 4–16 Transistor power dissipation.

TRANSISTOR CURRENT RELATIONSHIPS

Forward Current Transfer Ratio (β_{DC}, h_{FE})

The current gain, or forward current transfer ratio, of a transistor is a very important parameter. It is the ratio of the collector current to the base current. If the current gain of the transistor is known, you can determine the amount of base current required for the transistor to produce a desired amount of collector current. Data sheets include this important parameter in the listing of electrical characteristics for the transistor of interest. The symbol for the transistor current gain is the Greek letter beta (β_{DC}) with a DC subscript or the hybrid symbol h_{FE}. Usually, the h_{FE} symbol is used in data sheets.

$$\beta_{DC} = h_{FE} = I_C/I_B \tag{4–6}$$

The β_{DC} of a transistor is not a fixed quantity. Its actual value depends on the transistor design, the amount of collector current, and the temperature. Consider test circuit (a) of Figure 4–17. A potentiometer is used to vary the voltage applied to R_B and in so doing vary the base current. As the potentiometer is increased from 0 V, the base current begins to increase. The result is an increase in collector current as measured by the collector ammeter. The associated graph is a plot of the collector current that results from the base current. The slope of the graph at any point is the β_{DC} of the transistor for that particular base current and collector current. The upper curved portion of the graph represents less slope and a lower β_{DC}. Below about 8 μA of base current, the graph is also slightly curved, indicating a lower β_{DC}. In this low-base-current area of the curve, the transistor is heading for cutoff (very low collector current). In the upper portion of the graph, say above 50 μA of base current, the transistor is heading into saturation. Full saturation is in the area above 12 mA of collector current. Here the transistor is unable to provide any further significant increase in collector current even with large increases in base current.

Diagram (b) of Figure 4–17 shows the same test setup but the collector and base resistors have been reduced ten times. The collector current can now theoretically be as high as about 120 mA, because V_{CC} is 12.4 V and R_C is 100

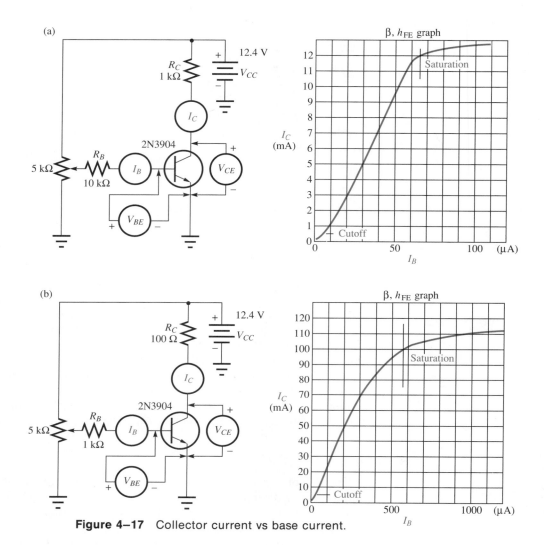

Figure 4–17   Collector current vs base current.

Ω ($I_{C(\text{max})} \cong 12.4$ V/100 $\Omega = 124$ mA). Note that the maximum current of about 120 mA does not exceed the maximum current rating for this transistor (200 mA). Once again the potentiometer is carefully adjusted and values of base and collector current are recorded and plotted. This time, the graph reveals that β_{DC} is maximum between 10 and 70 mA of collector current.

Table 4–2 contains all of the data collected from the test circuits of Figure 4–17. Consider the data carefully. See how the voltage across the transistor (V_{CE}) decreases as I_B and I_C increase. Also note how β_{DC} varies with collector current. Of further interest is the relatively limited range of base—emitter voltages for each circuit (0.64 to 0.74 V and 0.69 to 0.9 V). This is why it is customary to use a value of 0.7 V_{BE} in transistor circuit analysis.

Actual transistor β_{DC} can be measured using a multimeter that has an h_{FE} test function. Figure 4–18 shows the Circuitmate DM27 being used to measure the β_{DC} of a 2N2222 NPN transistor. Knowing the actual β_{DC} at room temperature increases the accuracy of design and circuit analysis.

Figure 4–18 Using a multimeter's h_{FE} Test Function to determine the actual β_{DC} for a transistor. (Equipment courtesy of Beckman Industrial Corp.)

β_{DC} and Temperature

As an operating transistor warms, its β_{DC} increases. This can be very troublesome in a transistor circuit that uses a form of biasing that is beta-dependent. As we continue and discuss different biasing schemes, this will become apparent. Figure 4–19 graphically illustrates the influence of collector current and temperature on β_{DC}. The graphs are normalized against some value of h_{FE} (β_{DC}) that exists at $+25°C$ and 8 mA of collector current. For exam-

TABLE 4–2   TEST DATA

I_B (μA)	I_C (mA)	β_{DC}	V_{BE} (V)	V_{CE} (V)	I_B (μA)	I_C (mA)	β_{DC}	V_{BE} (V)	V_{CE} (V)
8.06	1	124	0.64	11.37	45	10	222	0.69	11.37
13.6	2	147	0.66	10.4	82	20	244	0.7	10.3
18.4	3	163	0.67	9.44	124	30	242	0.71	9.4
22.9	4	175	0.675	8.4	166	40	241	0.715	8.46
28.2	5	177	0.68	7.44	208	50	240	0.72	7.45
31.8	6	189	0.683	6.55	251	60	240	0.725	6.5
36.1	7	194	0.688	5.57	297	70	236	0.73	5.5
41.1	8	195	0.695	4.55	373	80	214	0.745	4.6
46	9	196	0.7	3.55	444	90	203	0.76	3.6
51.4	10	195	0.705	2.58	572	100	175	0.78	2.65
56.5	11	195	0.71	1.66	960	110	115	0.81	1.77
62.6	12	192	0.712	0.67	1970	120	61	0.84	0.83
107.8	12.7	118	0.74	0.2	6350	127	20	0.9	0.2

$R_B = 10$ kΩ, $R_C = 1$ kΩ (left section) | $R_B = 1$ kΩ, $R_C = 100$ Ω (right section)

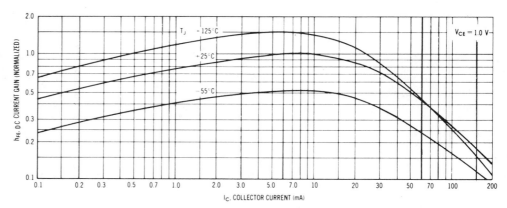

Figure 4–19 β_{DC} related to collector current and junction temperature. (Copyright Motorola, Inc. Used by permission.)

ple, if h_{FE} is 200 at +25°C and 8 mA of collector current, then h_{FE} will be just below 300 at +125°C and 8 mA of collector current and slightly greater than 100 at −55°C and 8 mA of collector current.

The Alpha (α) Relationship

Another current relationship, known as alpha (α) or h_{FB}, is the relationship between collector current and emitter current. This is a decimal number that approaches 1. It is a kind of efficiency factor that indicates the efficiency of electron transfer from the emitter to the collector.

$$\alpha = h_{FB} = I_C/I_E \tag{4–7}$$

Let's use some of the 2N3904 data recorded in Table 4–2 to calculate alpha. At 40 mA of collector current, the base current is 166 μA. That means the emitter current must be 40.166 mA ($I_E = I_B + I_C$). The alpha factor is then found to be: $\alpha = h_{FB} = 40/40.166 = 0.99587$, indicating an efficiency of 99.587% (100% · 0.99587).

The Alpha–Beta Relationship

The alpha factor calculated above implies that the base current is 0.413% of the emitter current. If the collector current is 99.587% of the emitter current, the remaining 0.413% must be the base current (100% − 99.587% = 0.413%). Since $\beta_{DC} = I_C/I_B$, β_{DC} must equal 99.587%/0.413% = 241. This checks with the original data. This process reveals a formula used to extract β_{DC} from the alpha factor: 99.587%/0.413% = 0.99587/0.00413 = $\alpha/(1 - \alpha)$. Therefore,

$$\beta_{DC} = h_{FE} = \alpha/(1 - \alpha) \tag{4–8}$$

From this formula, we can use simple algebra to rearrange the variables to solve for alpha when beta is known.

$$\alpha = \beta_{DC}/(1 + \beta_{DC}) \tag{4–9}$$

Let's test this formula for $\beta_{DC} = 241$.

$\alpha = \beta_{DC}/(1 + \beta_{DC}) = 241/(1 + 241) = 241/242 = 0.99587$

It checks.

Understanding alpha and beta relationships is very important, so take time to study Examples 4–10 and 4–11 carefully.

EXAMPLE 4–10

A certain transistor has 22 mA of collector current when the base current is 147 μA. Calculate I_E, h_{FE}, and h_{FB}.

$$I_E = I_B + I_C = 147\ \mu\text{A} + 22\ \text{mA} = 22.147\ \text{mA}$$

$$\beta_{DC} = h_{FE} = 22\ \text{mA}/147\ \mu\text{A} = 149.7$$

$$\alpha = h_{FB} = I_C/I_E = 22\ \text{mA}/22.147\ \text{mA} = 0.99336$$

$$\alpha = \beta_{DC}/(1 + \beta_{DC}) = 149.7/150.7 = 0.99336 \qquad (99.336\%\ \text{efficient})$$

$$\beta_{DC} = h_{FE} = \alpha/(1 - \alpha) = 0.99336/(1 - 0.99336) = 149.6$$

EXAMPLE 4–11

A certain transistor has 150 mA of emitter current when the base current is 1.6 mA. Calculate I_C, h_{FE}, and h_{FB}.

$$I_C = I_E - I_B = 150\ \text{mA} - 1.6\ \text{mA} = 148.4\ \text{mA}$$

$$\beta_{DC} = h_{FE} = 148.4\ \text{mA}/1.6\ \text{mA} = 92.75$$

$$\alpha = h_{FB} = I_C/I_E = 148.4\ \text{mA}/150\ \text{mA} = 0.98933$$

$$\alpha = \beta_{DC}/(1 + \beta_{DC}) = 92.75/93.75 = 0.98933 \qquad (98.933\%\ \text{efficient})$$

$$\beta_{DC} = h_{FE} = \alpha/(1 - \alpha) = 0.98933/(1 - 0.98933) = 92.72$$

Time for a self-check.

Self-Check 4–3

1. Which of the three main transistor currents is the greatest?
2. What is I_{CBO} and how does temperature affect it?
3. Explain the maximum V_{CEO} rating and tell why it must not be exceeded.
4. A transistor's maximum power dissipation is 400 mW at 25°C and its derating factor is 10 mW/°C. What is its maximum power rating at +50°C?
5. Explain how the DC beta of a transistor can be determined experimentally.
6. If $I_C = 8.5$ mA and $I_B = 40\ \mu$A, calculate β_{DC} and α.
7. Explain the effects of temperature and collector current on β_{DC}.
8. $\beta_{DC} = 316$. Find α.

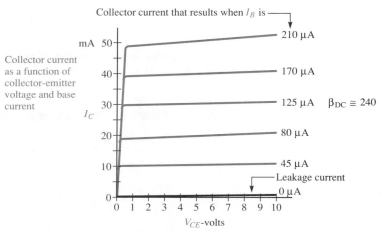

Figure 4–20   Family of collector-current curves.

4–4 TRANSISTOR OPERATING CHARACTERISTICS

THE COLLECTOR-CURRENT CURVES

Figure 4–20 shows a family of collector-current curves for the 2N3904 transistor we tested in the previous section. These curves are obtained through experimentation—setting the base current to a fixed value and holding it there while the voltage across the transistor (V_{CE}) is increased from zero volts. A new collector-current curve (graph) is drawn for each base-current setting.

Collector curves can be produced automatically on the face of an oscilloscope by using a transistor-curve-tracer adapter. The curve tracer can be used to examine the characteristics of many solid-state devices, making it a valuable laboratory instrument.

Figure 4–21 shows the Tektronix 571 curve tracer. This curve tracer is actually a computer that can be used to test many different types of solid-

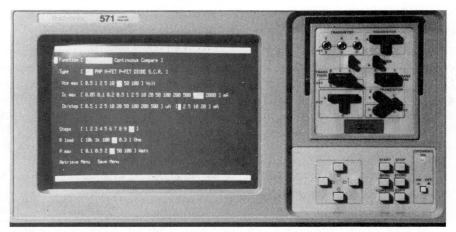

Figure 4–21 The Tektronix 571 Curve Tracer. (Equipment courtesy of Tektronix, Inc.)

state devices. The setup screen shown enables you to set test parameters such as device type, maximum V_{CE}, maximum I_C, I_B steps, the number of steps, the load resistance, and the maximum power dissipation while under test. Parameters are assigned values by moving the reverse-video cursors on the screen to the desired values using the four cursor-movement buttons on the lower front panel. The device under test (DUT) is plugged into the appropriate front-panel socket and the start button is pressed to obtain a set of characteristic curves. During the transistor test operation, the transistor's base current is set to different levels in specific steps. At each step, the collector–emitter voltage is varied over the specified range and the resulting collector current is measured and converted to digital information, which is stored in the computer's memory. The digitized information in memory is used for the curve display and can be sent out to a dot-matrix printer via a rear jack.

In Figure 4–22, the 571 curve tracer is used to test a 2N3904 transistor. Figure 4–22a shows the setup screen. (Note: The device type is set for NPN,

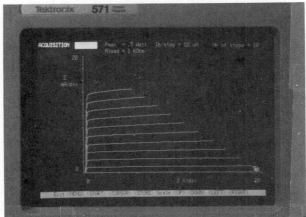

Figure 4–22 Using the 571 to test a 2N3904 Transistor: (a) the setup screen; (b) the test display screen. (Equipment courtesy of Tektronix, Inc.)

$V_{CE(\text{max})} = 20$ V, $I_{C(\text{max})} = 20$ mA, $I_{B(\text{step})} = 10$ μA, 10 steps, $R_L = 1$ kΩ, and $P_{D(\text{max})} = 0.5$ W. The four directional buttons on the front panel (shown in Figure 4–21) were used to make these selections.) In a matter of seconds, Figure 4–22b is generated when the start button is pressed. Sets of collector curves for the same transistor type or different transistors can quickly be compared.

As you examine Figures 4–20 and 4–22, it is important for you to realize that each curve is a graph of collector current, not base current. Each curve is the result of a change in collector—emitter voltage at a fixed value of base current. For example, in Figure 4–20, if the base current is held constant at 125 μA, the collector current will be close to 30 mA as the collector—emitter voltage is increased from about 0.4 V to 10 V. Notice also that the beta (h_{FE}) is about 240 for this particular family of collector curves. However, β_{DC} does vary depending on base current ($\beta_{DC} = 30$ mA/125 μA $= 240$, 10 mA/45 μA $= 222$, 50 mA/210 μA $= 238$).

COLLECTOR-CURVE CHARACTERISTICS

Let's take a close look at just one collector-current curve. Figure 4–23 shows a collector curve extended to the voltage **breakdown region.** When the maximum collector–emitter voltage rating of the transistor is exceeded, the transistor is in danger of voltage breakdown of the reverse-biased collector–base junction. When this occurs, permanent damage is done to the transistor.

At the other end of the curve is the **saturation region.** It is in this region that the collector–base junction becomes forward biased and normal transistor action ceases. Recall that the base voltage for an NPN transistor is about +0.7 V (emitter to ground). When the collector voltage falls below +0.7 V, the collector–base junction becomes forward biased to some degree. For example, if the base–emitter voltage is +0.7 V and the collector–emitter voltage is +0.3 V, the collector–base junction has a difference of potential of 0.4 V. This is a forward bias potential that causes some undesirable forward current across the collector–base junction. Thus, the transistor is saturated with undesired forward collector–base current. Also, the emitter current is

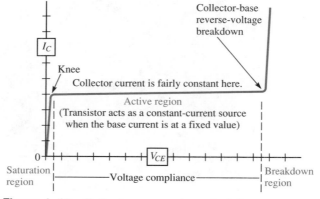

Figure 4–23   Collector-curve characteristics.

now attracted to the base instead of to the collector because the base is at a higher potential ($V_B = 0.7$ V, $V_C = 0.3$ V). All of this results in less and less collector current as V_{CE} decreases further.

The **active region** is the working region for the transistor. It covers a range of collector–emitter voltage extending from the top of the saturation knee to the beginning of the breakdown knee. This region is also known as the **range of voltage compliance** or just **range of compliance.** Within this region, the transistor acts as an imperfect constant-current source. With the base current at some fixed value, the collector current remains somewhat constant over the range of compliance. This constant-current characteristic is an important one for you to remember. We will discuss it by way of application later.

THE DC LOAD LINE

Defining the DC Load Line

Within a circuit, the transistor is constrained to operate over a specific voltage range, as determined by V_{CC}, and a specific range of collector current, as determined by V_{CC} and any collector or emitter resistance. V_{CC} must be less than the maximum voltage rating of the transistor and the maximum collector current must be less than the maximum current rating. In no case should the product of V_{CE} and I_C be greater than the maximum power dissipation rating of the transistor, taking into consideration ambient temperature and derating.

The operating range of the transistor in a specific circuit can be examined by developing a load line. In this case, it is called a **DC load line,** since we have not yet considered the AC characteristics of the transistor. Figure 4–24 illustrates a DC load line for the test circuit shown. The load line is drawn on the collector-curves chart to show the relationship between I_C, V_{CE}, and I_B for this circuit. We will use load lines extensively in transistor-amplifier analysis, so it is important for you to understand them now.

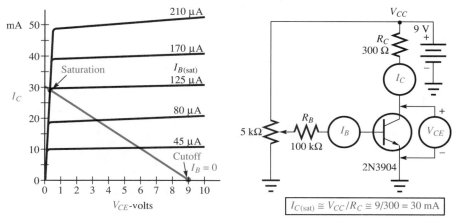

Figure 4–24   The DC load line.

Notice that the load line extends between two extreme points, saturation and cutoff. These two points depend on the base current. When the base current is zero, the transistor is turned off (cut off) and there is no significant collector current. Thus, the transistor acts like an open and all of the source voltage is dropped across the transistor ($V_{CE} = V_{CC} = 9$ V). When the base current is greater than about 125 μA, the collector current reaches a maximum value as V_{CE} drops below 0.7 V and the transistor becomes saturated. Thus, the transistor is driven to the maximum and appears as a near short from collector to emitter. The maximum possible collector current, known as saturation current, is then determined using R_C and V_{CC} ($I_{C(\text{sat})} = V_{CC}/R_C = 9$ V/300 $\Omega = 30$ mA).

DC Load Line

Cutoff: $I_{C(\text{cutoff})} = 0$ A, $V_{CE(\text{cutoff})} = V_{CC}$,

Saturation: $I_{C(\text{sat})} = V_{CC}/R_C$, $V_{CE(\text{sat})} \cong 0$ V.

The Q Point

Figure 4–25 illustrates the use of the load line to determine a desired quiescent operating point **(Q point).** In some cases, it is desirable to bias the transistor for a Q point in the center of the load line. This is known as **midpoint bias.** Notice that when the base current is set at approximately 60 μA, the collector current is approximately 15 mA and the collector–emitter voltage is nearly in the middle of the active voltage range. Naturally, these values are for the 2N3904 transistor in the circuit of Figure 4–24.

The Q point is an idling operating point for the transistor. Notice that the load line reveals what happens to V_{CE} and I_C if the base current is increased or decreased above and below the Q point (60 μA). Reducing base current results in an increase in collector–emitter voltage and a decrease in collector current. Increasing base current results in a decrease in collector–emitter voltage and an increase in collector current. That is what happens when an AC signal is applied to the base of the transistor. The AC alternations add, too, and subtract from the base current, which causes great variations in collector current and voltage. More on this later.

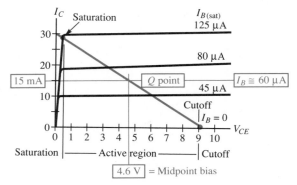

Figure 4–25   The quiescent (Q) operating point.

Establishing the Q Point

The quiescent collector current and Q point are set by the quiescent base current, which is determined by the base-bias circuit. In Figure 4–24, the base-bias circuit is composed of the 5-kΩ potentiometer and the base-bias resistor R_B. Very simply, the voltage across R_B determines I_{RB}, which is the same as I_B. Ohm's Law tells us that I_B must equal V_{RB}/R_B. For midpoint bias where $I_C = 15$ mA and $I_B \cong 60$ μA, V_{RB} must be approximately 60 μA · 100 kΩ = 6 V. Moving the wiper arm of the potentiometer changes V_{RB}, which changes I_B and the Q point. If the wiper is moved down, V_{RB} decreases, I_B decreases, I_C decreases, V_{RB} decreases, and V_{CE} increases. In the next chapter, you will have the opportunity to explore many biasing techniques. We will save the mathematical analysis until then.

MAXIMUM POWER DISSIPATION AND THE LOAD LINE

As you know, power is the product of current and voltage. Therefore, a transistor's power dissipation is the product of I_C and V_{CE}. Notice, in Figure 4–25, that the power dissipation of the transistor at cutoff is 0 W, because 0 A · 9 V = 0 W. Also, at saturation the transistor's power dissipation is very low because V_{CE} is very low (28 mA · 0.5 V = 14 mW). But when is the transistor's power dissipation the highest? The power dissipation is the greatest at midpoint bias (15 mA · 4.6 V = 69 mW). Try other pairs of I_C and V_{CE} above and below midpoint bias to see for yourself if there is a greater power dissipation anywhere else along the load line. The maximum possible power dissipation of the transistor can be approximated by taking the product of 0.5 $I_{C(sat)}$ and 0.5 V_{CC}. This value must be less than the power dissipation rating of the transistor. Notice the power dissipation (69 mW) of the 2N3904 in Figure 4–24 is far below the maximum rating (625 mW). Study Example 4–12.

$$P_{D(max)} \cong 0.5\ I_{C(sat)} \cdot 0.5\ V_{CC} = 0.25\ I_{C(sat)}V_{CC} \qquad (4\text{–}10)$$

EXAMPLE 4–12

Determine the maximum possible power dissipation for the transistor in Figure 4–26.

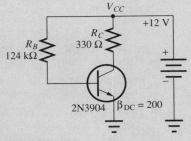

Figure 4–26

$$I_{C(\text{sat})} = V_{CC}/R_C = 12 \text{ V}/330 \text{ }\Omega = 36.4 \text{ mA}$$

$$P_{D(\text{max})} \cong 0.5 \ I_{C(\text{sat})} \cdot 0.5 \ V_{CC} = 0.5 \cdot 36.4 \text{ mA} \cdot 0.5 \cdot 12 \text{ V}$$

$$= 18.2 \text{ mA} \cdot 6 \text{ V} = 109 \text{ mW}$$

109 mW is well below the 625-mW rating for the 2N3904.

Take a few minutes now to test your understanding of this section.

Self-Check
4–4

1. What is meant by the range of voltage compliance for a transistor?
2. What does it mean to say the transistor acts like a constant-current source in the active region of the collector-current curve?
3. Explain how the DC load line for a transistor in a circuit is developed.
4. Explain midpoint bias.
5. If a transistor is biased at midpoint, will increasing the base current cause the collector–emitter voltage to increase?
6. At what point on the load line will the transistor dissipate the most power?

SUMMARY

FORMULAS

(4–1) $^{\#}\text{dB} = 20 \cdot \log_{10}(V_{\text{out}}/V_{\text{in}})$

(4–2) $^{\#}\text{dB} = 10 \cdot \log_{10}(P_{\text{out}}/P_{\text{in}})$

(4–3) $I_B + I_C = I_E$

(4–4) $I_E - I_C = I_B$

(4–5) $P_D = I_C \cdot V_{CE}$

(4–6) $\beta_{\text{DC}} = h_{\text{FE}} = I_C/I_B$

(4–7) $\alpha = h_{\text{FB}} = I_C/I_E$

(4–8) $\beta_{\text{DC}} = h_{\text{FE}} = \alpha/(1 - \alpha)$

(4–9) $\alpha = \beta_{\text{DC}}/(1 + \beta_{\text{DC}})$

(4–10) $P_{D(\text{max})} \cong 0.5 \ I_{C(\text{sat})} \cdot 0.5 \ V_{CC} = 0.25 \ I_{C(\text{sat})}V_{CC}$

CONCEPTS

- Amplifiers multiply voltage, current, and power. The amplification can be represented as a ratio (output/input) or in decibels.
- NPN and PNP transistors are opposites in terms of construction and voltage polarities, yet they follow the same basic theory and can complement one another in the same circuit.
- Base current is very small, collector current is relatively large, and emitter current is the sum of the two.
- Maximum voltage, current, and power transistor ratings must not be exceeded in amplifier design.

- Transistor collector-current curves are useful in amplifier analysis and design because they show the relationship between base current, collector current, and collector–emitter voltage.
- The DC load line is drawn between cutoff and saturation on the collector-curves chart.
- The transistor dissipates the most power at midpoint bias.

PROCEDURES

Establishing the DC Load Line

1. Mark the cutoff point at $V_{CE(cutoff)} = V_{CC}$, where $I_C = 0$.
2. Mark the saturation point at $I_{C(sat)} = V_{CC}/R_C$, where $V_{CE} = 0$.
3. Draw the load line from $I_{C(sat)}$ to $V_{CE(cutoff)}$.

NEED-TO-KNOW SOLUTION

The solution to this Need to Know applies the theory discussed in this chapter and gives you a peek at what is to come in the next chapter, where you will explore transistor biasing techniques and perform mathematical analysis and design.

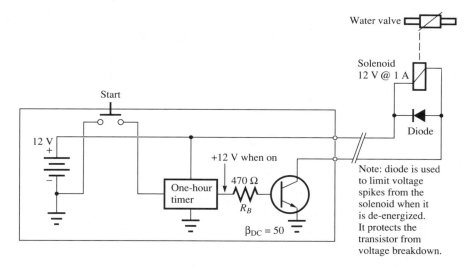

The transistor should have a current rating of 2 A or more to provide a safe margin for continuous collector current. The transistor will be conducting 1 A of current when biased ON. This 1 A of current is limited by the resistance of the solenoid's windings, not by the transistor. The transistor must be fully saturated. If the transistor's beta is 50, the base current must be greater than 20 mA to fully saturate the transistor (1 A/50 = 20 mA). Thus, the base resistor should be less than 565 Ω but not less than 113 Ω, because the maximum current the timer can supply is 100 mA. V_{DC} is given as +12 V. The base-emitter forward voltage V_{BE} is a nominal 0.7 V.

$$I_{B(sat)} = I_{C(sat)}/\beta_{DC} = 1 \text{ A}/50 = 20 \text{ mA}$$

$$R_B = (V_{DC} - V_{BE})/I_B = (V_{DC} - 0.7 \text{ V})/I_B$$

$$R_{B(max)} = (12 \text{ V} - 0.7 \text{ V})/20 \text{ mA} = 565 \text{ }\Omega$$

$$R_{B(min)} = (12 \text{ V} - 0.7 \text{ V})/100 \text{ mA} = 113 \text{ }\Omega$$

A 470-Ω resistor for R_B is a good choice because it will ensure that the transistor is fully saturated to drive the solenoid.

$$I_B = (V_{DC} - V_{BE})/R_B = (12 \text{ V} - 0.7 \text{ V})/470 \text{ }\Omega = 24 \text{ mA}$$

24 mA is more than enough to ensure that the transistor delivers 1 A to the solenoid, because 24 mA · 50 > 1 A.

QUESTIONS

4–1 AMPLIFIER SYSTEMS

1. What are two geometric symbols commonly used to represent an amplifier?
2. What does amplifier gain mean?
3. The gain of an amplifier is the ratio of what two quantities?
4. The amplification ratio of an amplifier can be expressed in what logarithmic units?
5. Is a gain of −6 dB an actual gain or a loss?

4–2 TRANSISTOR CONSTRUCTION AND THEORY

6. Describe the semiconductor layers of an NPN transistor.
7. For a PNP transistor, describe the proper polarity of voltages on its terminals.
8. For normal operation, describe which transistor junction is forward biased and which is reverse biased.
9. Describe the relationship between the emitter, base, and collector currents.
10. Describe the effect changes in base current have on the collector–resistor voltage.
11. Briefly describe the direction of electron flow in NPN transistors.
12. Do the arrows on schematic symbols for diodes and transistors go along with (a) conventional flow, or (b) electron flow?
13. What is a planar transistor?
14. What does it mean when a device is hermetically sealed?

4–3 IMPORTANT TRANSISTOR PARAMETERS

15. Name two transistor leakage currents that are related to temperature.
16. What negative effect might leakage currents have on transistor amplifiers?
17. If a transistor has a V_{CEO} rating of 80, what does that mean?
18. What does the total device dissipation rating of a transistor have to do with its collector current and collector–emitter voltage?

19. If a transistor is rated at 25°C and is operated at 10°C, should the transistor be derated?
20. Transistor DC current gain is the ratio of what?
21. The beta of a transistor is determined by what three factors?
22. Describe how beta is related to temperature.
23. From Table 4–2, what is the approximate beta for the 2N3904 with 6 mA of collector current?
24. From Table 4–2, what is the relationship between V_{BE} and V_{CE}?
25. What does the alpha of a transistor tell you?

4–4 TRANSISTOR OPERATING CHARACTERISTICS

26. A family of collector-current curves demonstrates what relationship(s).
27. Is beta constant for all values of collector current on a collector-current curve chart?
28. Describe transistor collector current and collector–emitter voltage when a transistor is saturated.
29. Describe transistor collector current and collector–emitter voltage when a transistor is cut off.
30. What is meant by a transistor's range of voltage compliance?
31. How is the DC load line developed (drawn, determined, created)?
32. What is meant by midpoint bias?
33. At what point on the load line will the transistor dissipate the most power?
34. What factors establish the Q point?

PROBLEMS

4–1 AMPLIFIER SYSTEMS

1. The signal voltage at the input of an amplifier is 20 mV and the voltage at the output of the amplifier is 450 mV. What is the gain of the amplifier expressed in decibels?
2. An amplifier has a voltage gain of 20 dB. The input voltage is 500 mV. What is the amplitude of the output voltage?
3. Determine the output voltage and overall decibel gain for Figure 4–27.

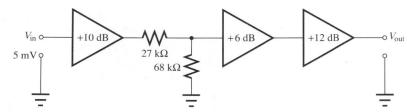

Figure 4–27

4. 100 mW is applied to a power amplifier. The resulting output power is 6 W. What is the gain of the amplifier, expressed in decibels?
5. An amplifier has a power gain of 20 dB. The input power is 50 mW. What is the amount of the output power?

6. Determine the output power and overall decibel power gain for Figure 4–28.

Figure 4–28

4–3 IMPORTANT TRANSISTOR PARAMETERS

7. If a transistor's emitter current is 26 mA and its collector current is 25.8 mA, how much is the base current?
8. If a transistor's emitter current is 130 mA and its collector current is 129.1 mA, how much is the base current?
9. If a transistor's collector current is 82 mA and its base current is 435 μA, how much is the emitter current?
10. If a transistor's base current is 55 μA and its emitter current is 6.33 mA, how much is the collector current?
11. The voltage across a transistor is 10 V and the collector current is 750 mA. How much power is the transistor dissipating?
12. For an operating transistor, $V_{CE} = 5.8$ V and $I_C = 48$ mA. How much power is the transistor dissipating?
13. If the base current of a transistor is 80 μA and the emitter current is 5 mA, what is the transistor's beta (h_{FE})?
14. If the base current of a transistor is 0.2 mA and the emitter current is 17 mA, what is the transistor's beta (h_{FE})?
15. If a transistor has an alpha (α) of 0.9962, what is its beta?
16. If a transistor has an alpha (α) of 0.8972, what is its beta?
17. If a transistor has a β_{DC} of 130, what is its alpha (α)?
18. If a transistor has a β_{DC} of 65, what is its alpha (α)?

4–4 TRANSISTOR OPERATING CHARACTERISTICS

19. Make a simple I_C/V_{CE} chart and draw the load line for a transistor circuit that has a 3.4-kΩ collector resistor and a V_{CC} of 20 V.
20. Make a simple I_C/V_{CE} chart and draw the load line for a transistor circuit that has a 150-Ω collector resistor and a V_{CC} of 14 V.
21. Calculate the maximum power that the transistor in Problem 19 could possibly dissipate.
22. Calculate the maximum power that the transistor in Problem 20 could possibly dissipate.

ADDITIONAL PROBLEMS

23. Use the overall dB gain of Figure 4–29 to determine the input voltage.
24. Determine the voltage between stages 2 and 3 in Figure 4–29.

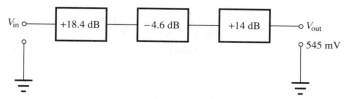

Figure 4–29

25. Determine the decibel power gain for each stage of Figure 4–30.

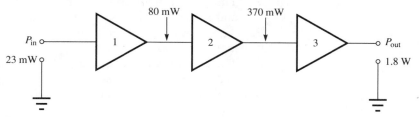

Figure 4–30

26. Determine the output power for Figure 4–30 if stage 2 becomes defective and has an effective gain of −21 dB.
27. If a transistor has an alpha (h_{FB}) of 0.98925, what is its beta (h_{FE})?
28. If a transistor has an alpha of 0.89954 and its collector current is 1.5 A, how much is the base current?
29. If a transistor has an alpha of 0.85562 and the base current is 11 mA, how much is the collector current?
30. Determine the quiescent collector current and collector–emitter voltage if Figure 4–31 is midpoint biased.

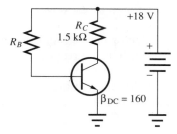

Figure 4–31

31. What is the maximum power the transistor in Figure 4–31 can possibly dissipate?
32. Determine the value of R_B in Figure 4–31 needed to establish midpoint bias.

**ANSWERS TO
SELF-CHECKS**

SELF-CHECK 4–1

1. True
2. One stage is not able to provide all of the needed gain.

3. The ratio of the output to the input
4. Decibels (dB)
5. 43.5 dB

SELF-CHECK 4–2

1. The base–emitter junction must be forward biased and the base–collector junction must be reverse biased.
2. The emitter is negative, the base is positive with respect to the emitter, and the collector is positive with respect to the emitter and the base.
3. As the base current increases, the voltage across the collector resistor increases and vice versa.
4. The emitter is positive, the base is negative with respect to the emitter, and the collector is negative with respect to the emitter and the base.
5. If the emitter arrow is pointing away from the base, the transistor is an NPN.
6. Conventional flow is *with the arrow* in semiconductor device schematic symbols.
7. Collector. This is the layer that dissipates most of the heat.

SELF-CHECK 4–3

1. Emitter current
2. I_{CBO} is reverse leakage current between the collector and the base; it increases with temperature.
3. V_{CEO} is the maximum voltage that can safely appear across the transistor from collector to emitter. Voltages above this maximum rating may cause the transistor to break down.
4. 150 mW
5. Measure the collector current and the base current. β_{DC} is the ratio of collector current to base current.
6. $\beta_{DC} = 212.5$ and $\alpha = 0.9953$
7. Beta increases with temperature and may go up or down with collector current depending on the value of collector current.
8. 0.9968

SELF-CHECK 4–4

1. The active region between the saturation knee and the breakdown knee on the collector-current curve
2. If the base current is held constant, the collector current will remain fairly constant over a wide range of collector–emitter voltage.
3. The load line is drawn between the saturation point ($I_{C(sat)}$ and $V_{CE} \cong 0$ V) and the cutoff point ($I_{C(min)}$ and $V_{CE} = V_{CC}$).
4. The transistor is biased so $I_{C(Q)} \cong 0.5\ I_{C(sat)}$ and $V_{CE} \cong 0.5\ V_{CC}$.
5. No. It decreases.
6. Midpoint bias

**SUGGESTED
PROJECTS**

1. Add some of the main concepts, formulas, and procedures from this chapter to your Electronics Notebook.
2. Set up a test circuit like that of Figure 4–17a and graph the relationship between I_B and I_C. Use a low-power NPN transistor such as the 2N3904 or the 2N2222.
3. Using Figure 4–17a as a model, reverse the V_{CC} polarity and replace the NPN transistor with a PNP transistor such as the 2N3906. Graph the relationship between I_B and I_C.
4. Construct the circuit of Figure 4–24 and plot the DC load line—V_{CE} and I_C over a wide range of I_B (from 0 A to approximately 500 μA).

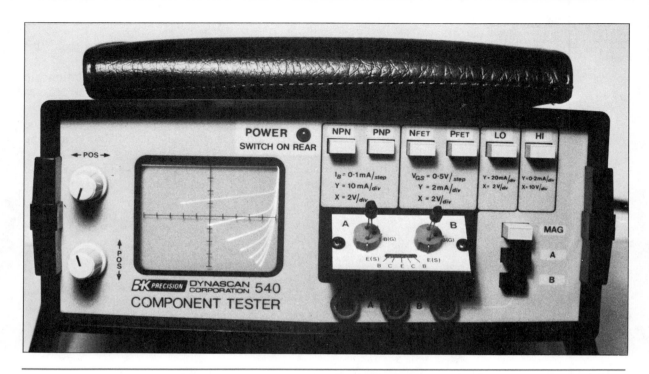

A family of collector curves for the 2N3906 PNP transistor is displayed on this BK Precision 540 Component Tester. A and B pushbuttons are provided to do immediate comparisons between two devices–in this case, two 2N3906s. As shown, the upper right corner of the display is the zero point. Each vertical division is 10 mA and each horizontal division is −2 V. The transistor's base current is stepped in 0.1-mA increments for each of the collector-current curves. (Photograph courtesy of BK Precision.)

5 Transistor Biasing Techniques

OBJECTIVES

After studying this chapter, you will be able to

■ analyze base-bias, collector-feedback-bias, voltage-divider-bias, and emitter-bias transistor circuits.
■ design base-bias, collector-feedback-bias, voltage-divider-bias, and emitter-bias transistor circuits.
■ describe factors that affect bias temperature stability.
■ test transistors and troubleshoot transistor circuits.

NEED TO KNOW

In the last chapter, you learned about many operating characteristics of transistors and about the DC load line for transistor amplifiers. You also learned a little bit about something called *midpoint bias*. Much more will be said about that in this chapter and the next. Biasing a transistor for midpoint bias, or any other location on the load line, is a skill that you will develop over time through study and experimentation. You will discover the importance of using good bias techniques in your amplifier designs to overcome the effects of temperature on the transistor. Transistor characteristics are variable with temperature and can cause an amplifier to self-destruct if proper design steps are not taken. So, what are these design steps? What must I know to insure long life for my transistor amplifiers in the presence of wide temperature variations? These are good questions, the answers to which you surely have a need to know.

As always, a solution to this Need to Know is provided at the close of this chapter. As you study this chapter, see if you can find the answers to the questions posed above. Enjoy your exploration!

INTRODUCTION The overall purpose for this chapter is to familiarize you with the transistor in DC circuits with no AC signal applied. You will learn different techniques for biasing transistors and their relative effectiveness in countering transistor characteristic changes due to temperature variations. We will also discuss transistor troubleshooting. Upon completing this chapter, you will be ready for AC applications and analysis in the next chapter. Therefore, the material covered in this chapter is extremely important for your future success and understanding.

5–1 BASE BIAS

TRANSISTOR BIASING

Proper biasing of the transistor means everything. A transistor amplifier cannot function properly if it is not biased properly. But what does it mean to bias a transistor? The word **bias** means to offset or to establish preset conditions. A transistor must be set up in a circuit that is designed to provide the offset voltage(s) for the desired preset conditions. In this way, base and collector currents are established as **idling currents,** most often called **quiescent currents** (static currents). These quiescent currents then establish **quiescent voltages** across the transistor and associated resistors. Here, you begin your exploration of biasing schemes with the simplest of biasing techniques, called **base bias.**

BASE-BIAS ANALYSIS

Figure 5–1 illustrates what is known as a base-biased transistor amplifier. This is a very simple biasing scheme. As you can see, establishing quiescent currents and voltages requires only two resistors. The theory of operation is very straightforward. The collector current is determined by the amount of base current and the beta (β_{DC}, h_{FE}) of the transistor. The size of the base

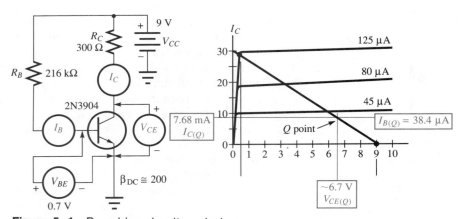

Figure 5–1 Base-bias circuit analysis.

resistor establishes the amount of base current needed to establish the desired amount of collector current.

When analyzing a base-biased circuit, you always start with the base circuit. The goal is to determine the quiescent collector current and collector—emitter voltage. Thus, for analysis, start on the base side and work toward the collector side.

First, calculate the base current. Ohm's Law is used here.

$$I_{B(Q)} = (V_{CC} - 0.7 \text{ V})/R_B \tag{5-1}$$

Note that the base–emitter voltage, estimated to be about 0.7 V for silicon transistors, must be subtracted from the source voltage to obtain the actual voltage across the base resistor. In Figure 5–1, the base current is found to be 38.4 μA ($I_{B(Q)} = (9 \text{ V} - 0.7 \text{ V})/216 \text{ k}\Omega = 38.4 \text{ μA}$).

Next, in order to calculate the collector current, the beta of the transistor must be known. Recall that the collector current is the product of the base current and beta. The transistor in the circuit of Figure 5–1 has a beta of approximately 200. Remember, beta depends on transistor design, operating temperature, and amount of collector current. If the beta is in fact 200, the collector current will be 7.68 mA ($200 \cdot 38.4 \text{ μA} = 7.68 \text{ mA}$).

Once the collector current is known, the collector–emitter voltage can be determined. In this case, the voltage across the transistor ($V_{CE(Q)}$) is the difference between the source voltage (V_{CC}) and the collector-resistor voltage (V_{RC}).

$$V_{CE(Q)} = V_{CC} - V_{RC} = V_{CC} - (I_{C(Q)} \cdot R_C) \tag{5-2}$$

For the circuit of Figure 5–1,

$$V_{CE(Q)} = 9 \text{ V} - (7.68 \text{ mA} \cdot 300 \text{ } \Omega) = 6.7 \text{ V}$$

Finally, a load line can be drawn to visualize the quiescent operating conditions. Recall that the load line is drawn on a graph (family of collector curves) that shows the relationship between base current, collector current, and collector–emitter voltage. The line itself is drawn between saturation ($V_{CE} = 0$, $I_{C(sat)} = V_{CC}/R_C$) and cutoff ($I_C = 0$, $V_{CE(cutoff)} = V_{CC}$). The quiescent collector current and collector–emitter voltage are crossplotted to designate the Q point on the load line. Later you will see the significance of knowing the position of the Q point. For now, consider the analysis shown in Example 5–1.

EXAMPLE 5–1 ▰▰▰▰▰▰▰▰▰▰▰▰▰▰▰▰▰▰▰▰▰▰▰▰▰

Analyze the circuit of Figure 5–2 to determine quiescent values of base current, collector current, and collector–emitter voltage. Draw the DC load line and plot the Q point.

DC Load Line

$I_{C(sat)} = V_{CC}/R_C = 10 \text{ V}/430 \text{ } \Omega = 23.3 \text{ mA}$, where $V_{CE(sat)} = 0 \text{ V}$.

$V_{CE(cutoff)} = V_{CC} = 10 \text{ V}$, where $I_C = 0 \text{ A}$.

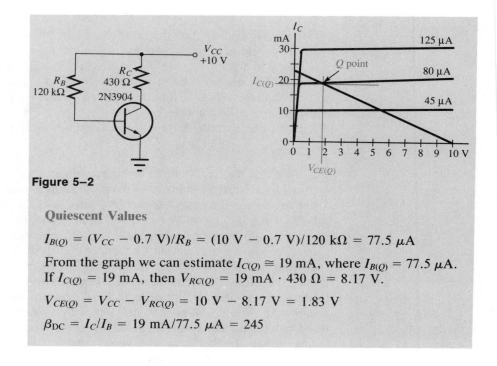

Figure 5–2

Quiescent Values

$I_{B(Q)} = (V_{CC} - 0.7 \text{ V})/R_B = (10 \text{ V} - 0.7 \text{ V})/120 \text{ k}\Omega = 77.5 \text{ }\mu\text{A}$

From the graph we can estimate $I_{C(Q)} \cong 19 \text{ mA}$, where $I_{B(Q)} = 77.5 \text{ }\mu\text{A}$. If $I_{C(Q)} = 19 \text{ mA}$, then $V_{RC(Q)} = 19 \text{ mA} \cdot 430 \text{ }\Omega = 8.17 \text{ V}$.

$V_{CE(Q)} = V_{CC} - V_{RC(Q)} = 10 \text{ V} - 8.17 \text{ V} = 1.83 \text{ V}$

$\beta_{DC} = I_C/I_B = 19 \text{ mA}/77.5 \text{ }\mu\text{A} = 245$

BASE-BIAS DESIGN

In a moment, I will suggest to you that the base-bias technique is not worth using for two very good reasons. So why spend time learning how to design it? The design procedure will help you understand transistor operation and other bias techniques a little better. Fortunately, the design procedure is very simple.

First, determine a safe operating current and voltage from the data sheet for the transistor you are using. For low-power designs, the quiescent current and collector–emitter voltage is often far below the transistor's maximum ratings. Figure 5–3 is a case in point. As you can see, this particular

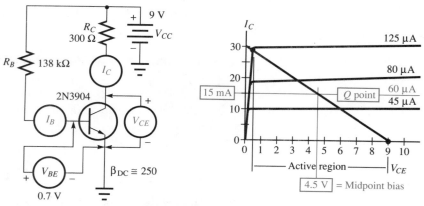

Figure 5–3 Base-bias circuit design.

design uses the 2N3904 transistor, whose maximum collector current rating is 200 mA.

Next, calculate the resistance of the collector resistor. This is the resistance needed to limit the collector current to a maximum value in saturation. In Figure 5–3, the collector resistance is 300 Ω, since it has been decided that that maximum saturation current shall be limited to 30 mA (R_C = 9 V/30 mA = 300 Ω).

$$R_C = V_{CC}/I_{C(sat)} \tag{5–3}$$

Finally, draw the load line as shown in Figure 5–3 and choose the desired operating point (Q point). We will discuss this in greater detail later. For now, assume that the center of the load line is the best choice for the initial operating point for the transistor. As you can see, this allows the collector current and the collector–emitter voltage to increase or decrease an equal amount. The desired Q point is then established by selecting the correct value of base resistance (R_B). The base resistance determines the base current, which determines the collector current.

$$R_B = (V_{CC} - 0.7 \text{ V})/I_{B(Q)} \tag{5–4}$$

where $I_{B(Q)} = I_{C(Q)}/\beta_{DC}$

For the circuit of Figure 5–3,

$I_{B(Q)} = 15 \text{ mA}/250 = 60 \text{ }\mu\text{A}$ and $R_B = 8.3 \text{ V}/60 \text{ }\mu\text{A} = 138 \text{ k}\Omega$.

Take a close look at the slightly different design approaches featured in Examples 5–2, 5–3, and 5–4.

EXAMPLE 5–2 ▮▮▮▮▮▮▮▮▮▮▮▮▮▮▮▮▮▮▮▮▮▮▮▮▮▮▮▮▮▮▮▮▮▮▮▮

Design a base-biased transistor amplifier for midpoint bias. The saturation current shall be 10 mA. V_{CC} = 13.6 V. Assume the transistor has a β_{DC} of 145 when I_C is near 5 mA. Determine the proper value for R_C and R_B.

$R_C = V_{CC}/I_{C(sat)} = 13.6 \text{ V}/10 \text{ mA} = 1360 \text{ }\Omega$

$I_{C(Q)} = I_{C(sat)}/2 = 10 \text{ mA}/2 = 5 \text{ mA}$

$I_{B(Q)} = I_{C(Q)}/\beta_{DC} = 5 \text{ mA}/145 = 34.5 \text{ }\mu\text{A}$

$R_B = (V_{CC} - 0.7 \text{ V})/I_{B(Q)} = (13.6 \text{ V} - 0.7 \text{ V})/34.5 \text{ }\mu\text{A} = 374 \text{ k}\Omega$

EXAMPLE 5–3 ▮▮▮▮▮▮▮▮▮▮▮▮▮▮▮▮▮▮▮▮▮▮▮▮▮▮▮▮▮▮▮▮▮▮▮▮

Design a base-biased transistor amplifier and bias it so that $V_{CE(Q)}$ = 8 V. The saturation current shall be 20 mA. V_{CC} = 12 V. Assume the transistor has a β_{DC} of 170 when I_C is near 7 mA. Determine the proper value for R_C and R_B.

$$R_C = V_{CC}/I_{C(\text{sat})} = 12 \text{ V}/20 \text{ mA} = 600 \text{ }\Omega$$

$$V_{RC} = V_{CC} - V_{CE(Q)} = 12 \text{ V} - 8 \text{ V} = 4 \text{ V}$$

$$I_{C(Q)} = V_{RC}/R_C = 4 \text{ V}/600 \text{ }\Omega = 6.67 \text{ mA}$$

$$I_{B(Q)} = I_{C(Q)}/\beta_{\text{DC}} = 6.67 \text{ mA}/170 = 39.2 \text{ }\mu\text{A}$$

$$R_B = (V_{CC} - 0.7 \text{ V})/I_{B(Q)} = (12 \text{ V} - 0.7 \text{ V})/39.2 \text{ }\mu\text{A} = 288 \text{ k}\Omega$$

EXAMPLE 5–4

Design a base-biased transistor amplifier and bias it so that $V_{CE(Q)} = 6$ V and $I_{C(Q)} = 8$ mA. $V_{CC} = 9$ V. Assume the transistor has a β_{DC} of 180 when I_C is near 8 mA. Determine the proper values for R_C and R_B.

$$R_C = (V_{CC} - V_{CE(Q)})/I_{C(Q)} = 3 \text{ V}/8 \text{ mA} = 375 \text{ }\Omega$$

$$I_{B(Q)} = I_{C(Q)}/\beta_{\text{DC}} = 8 \text{ mA}/180 = 44.4 \text{ }\mu\text{A}$$

$$R_B = (V_{CC} - 0.7 \text{ V})/I_{B(Q)} = (9 \text{ V} - 0.7 \text{ V})/44.4 \text{ }\mu\text{A} = 187 \text{ k}\Omega$$

BASE-BIAS TEMPERATURE STABILITY

At this point you realize that in a base-bias design the quiescent voltage and currents are strongly dependent on the transistor's β_{DC}. Recall how beta changes with temperature. As the transistor operates, it warms from internal power dissipation and ambient (surrounding) temperature change. Naturally, the transistor's beta increases with temperature, which causes the quiescent collector current to increase for a given base current. In many cases, the increasing collector current causes a further increase in beta, which causes a further increase in collector current. A snowball effect takes place. This is why the base-bias design is very poor, and for many applications unusable. Not only is the design unstable, the circuit cannot be reproduced reliably using other transistors of the same type. Transistors of the same type have a range of beta. The actual beta of the transistor may be anywhere within a 3:1 or 4:1 range. For the 2N3904 transistor, the beta could be anywhere between 100 and 300. As you can see, manufacturers stay away from the base-bias design for good reasons—poor stability and poor reproducibility.

Test your understanding with Self-Check 5–1.

Self-Check 5–1

1. In a base-bias amplifier, what determines the amount of quiescent collector current?
2. What factors must be known to calculate collector current in a base-bias amplifier?
3. A base-bias transistor amplifier depends greatly on what factor?

4. A base-bias transistor amplifier has a 15-V DC supply, a quiescent collector current of 5 mA, and a transistor β_{DC} of 160. Calculate the value of R_B. Assume $V_{BE} = 0.7$ V.

5. Explain how the quiescent collector current is affected by temperature variations.

5–2 COLLECTOR-FEEDBACK BIAS

COLLECTOR-FEEDBACK-BIAS ANALYSIS

The amplifier design shown in Figure 5–4 employs collector feedback. In this case, the bias voltage is obtained from the collector voltage. Changes in collector voltage are fed back to the base circuit through the base resistor, offering some improvement in bias-point stability. Like base bias, this design requires only two resistors.

The analysis of a collector-feedback stage begins by knowing the value of the collector–emitter voltage. The collector current is calculated using Ohm's Law to determine the collector-resistor current.

$$I_{C(Q)} = (V_{CC} - V_{CE(Q)})/R_C \qquad (5\text{–}5)$$

For the circuit of Figure 5–4, $V_{CE(Q)}$ is known to be 6 V. Therefore, the quiescent collector current is $(9\ \text{V} - 6\ \text{V})/300\ \Omega = 10$ mA.

The base current is calculated in either of two ways. Since the base current still depends on β_{DC}, $I_{B(Q)} = I_{C(Q)}/\beta_{DC}$. Also, the base current can be calculated using Ohm's Law to determine I_{RB}, which is $I_{B(Q)}$.

$$I_{B(Q)} = (V_{CE} - 0.7\ \text{V})/R_B \qquad (5\text{–}6)$$

Notice in Figure 5–4 that the base current is found to be 45 μA using either method (if $\beta_{DC} = 222$, then $I_{B(Q)} = 10$ mA/222 = 45 μA). The load line can be drawn and the quiescent collector current and collector–emitter voltage can be crossplotted to identify the Q point. Note that the Q point for Figure 5–4 is not at midpoint. This is not necessarily a problem, as you will understand later. For now, consider Example 5–5.

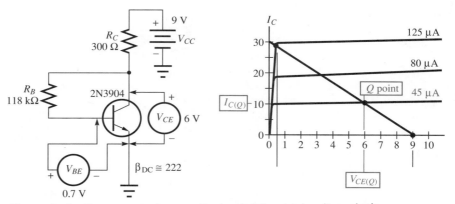

Figure 5–4 Common-emitter, collector-feedback circuit analysis.

EXAMPLE 5-5

Determine $I_{C(Q)}$ and $I_{B(Q)}$ for the collector-feedback amplifier of Figure 5–5.

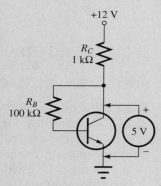

Figure 5–5

$$I_{C(Q)} = (V_{CC} - V_{CE(Q)})/R_C = (12\ \text{V} - 5\ \text{V})/1\ \text{k}\Omega = 7\ \text{mA}$$

$$I_{B(Q)} = (V_{CE} - 0.7\ \text{V})/R_B = (5\ \text{V} - 0.7\ \text{V})/100\ \text{k}\Omega = 43\ \mu\text{A}$$

$$\beta_{DC} = h_{FE} = I_C/I_B = 7\ \text{mA}/43\ \mu\text{A} = 163$$

COLLECTOR-FEEDBACK-BIAS DESIGN

Designing the collector-feedback circuit is like designing base-bias circuits. Start with the load line drawn between the maximum current point (saturation) and the maximum collector–emitter voltage point (cutoff). As before, the maximum current, or saturation current, is determined by V_{CC} and R_C. If it is decided that the saturation current shall be 30 mA, as in Figure 5–6, the collector resistor must be 300 Ω. For now, we will again use midpoint bias, where the quiescent collector current is half of the saturation current. In Figure 5–6, the quiescent current is selected to be 15 mA, resulting in a quiescent collector-emitter voltage of 4.5 V:

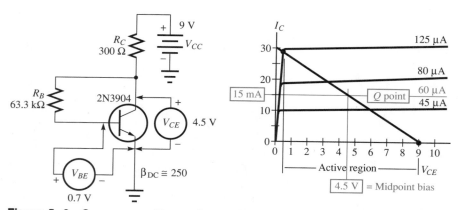

Figure 5–6 Common-emitter, collector-feedback transistor circuit design.

$$V_{CE(Q)} = V_{CC} - V_{RC} = V_{CC} - (I_{C(Q)} \cdot R_C)$$
$$= 9\text{ V} - (15\text{ mA} \cdot 300\ \Omega) = 9\text{ V} - 4.5\text{ V} = 4.5\text{ V}$$

The base resistor can now be calculated:

$$R_B = (V_{CE} - 0.7\text{ V})/I_{B(Q)} \tag{5–7}$$

where $I_{B(Q)} = I_{C(Q)}/\beta_{DC}$

Also, we can substitute $I_{C(Q)}/\beta_{DC}$ for $I_{B(Q)}$ in Formula 5–7 to yield $R_B = (V_{CE} - 0.7\text{ V})/(I_{C(Q)}/\beta_{DC})$, which is equal to

$$R_B = \beta_{DC} \cdot (V_{CE} - 0.7\text{ V})/I_{C(Q)} \tag{5–8}$$

As you can see, the value of resistance needed for R_B in Figure 5–6 is 63.3 kΩ. ($R_B = 250 \cdot (4.5\text{ V} - 0.7\text{ V})/15\text{ mA} = 63.3\text{ kΩ}$.) Now, take time to study Examples 5–6 and 5–7.

EXAMPLE 5–6 ▮▮▮▮▮▮

Design a collector-feedback amplifier with midpoint bias. $I_{C(\text{sat})}$ shall be 45 mA and $V_{CC} = 18$ V. The transistor has a β_{DC} of 200 when I_C is near 20 mA. Calculate the power dissipation of the transistor.

$$R_C = V_{CC}/I_{C(\text{sat})} = 18\text{ V}/45\text{ mA} = 400\ \Omega$$

$$V_{CE} = V_{CC}/2 = 18\text{ V}/2 = 9\text{ V}$$

$$V_{RC} = V_{CC} - V_{CE} = 18\text{ V} - 9\text{ V} = 9\text{ V}$$

$$I_{C(Q)} = V_{RC}/R_C = 9\text{ V}/400\ \Omega = 22.5\text{ mA}$$

$$I_{B(Q)} = I_{C(Q)}/\beta_{DC} = 22.5\text{ mA}/200 = 113\ \mu\text{A}$$

$$R_B = (V_{CE} - 0.7\text{ V})/I_{B(Q)} = 8.3\text{ V}/113\ \mu\text{A} = 73.5\text{ kΩ}$$

$$P_{D(Q)} = I_{C(Q)} \cdot V_{CE(Q)} = 22.5\text{ mA} \cdot 9\text{ V} = 203\text{ mW}$$

EXAMPLE 5–7 ▮▮▮▮▮▮

Design a collector-feedback amplifier so that $I_{C(Q)} = 18$ mA and $V_{CE(Q)} = 12$ V. The transistor has a β_{DC} of 190 when I_C is near 18 mA. $V_{CC} = 18$ V. Calculate the power dissipation of the transistor.

$$V_{RC} = V_{CC} - V_{CE} = 18\text{ V} - 12\text{ V} = 6\text{ V}$$

$$R_C = V_{RC}/I_{C(Q)} = 6\text{ V}/18\text{ mA} = 333\ \Omega$$

$$I_{B(Q)} = I_{C(Q)}/\beta_{DC} = 18\text{ mA}/190 = 94.7\ \mu\text{A}$$

$$R_B = (V_{CE} - 0.7\text{ V})/I_{B(Q)} = 11.3\text{ V}/94.7\ \mu\text{A} = 119\text{ kΩ}$$

$$P_{D(Q)} = I_{C(Q)} \cdot V_{CE(Q)} = 18\text{ mA} \cdot 12\text{ V} = 216\text{ mW}$$

COLLECTOR-FEEDBACK-BIAS TEMPERATURE STABILITY

The idea behind using collector feedback is to obtain better temperature stability than that which is obtained from base bias. In theory, if the collector current begins to increase as a result of increasing temperature and beta, the collector–emitter voltage will decrease. This is because the increased current causes V_{RC} to increase, leaving less voltage for the transistor ($V_{CE} = V_{CC} - V_{RC}$). The decrease in V_{CE} causes the voltage across R_B to decrease, which causes I_B to decrease. The decrease in base current is supposed to reduce the collector current, returning it to the normal quiescent value. This feedback loop is supposed to keep the collector current at the quiescent value.

Does it work? Somewhat, but not as well as you might think. Let's derive a new formula that shows the effect of beta on collector current. We'll use Kirchhoff's Voltage Law and form a loop equation for the base loop. This will include V_{RC}, V_{RB}, V_{BE}, and V_{CC}.

$$V_{RC} \quad + \quad V_{RB} \quad + V_{BE} - V_{CC} = 0$$

$$(I_C \cdot R_C) + (I_B \cdot R_B) + V_{BE} - V_{CC} = 0$$

Since $I_B = I_C/\beta_{DC}$, we can make the following substitution:

$$(I_C \cdot R_C) + (I_C \cdot R_B/\beta_{DC}) + V_{BE} - V_{CC} = 0$$

Solving for I_C:

$$I_C \cdot [R_C + (R_B/\beta_{DC})] + V_{BE} - V_{CC} = 0$$

$$I_C \cdot [R_C + (R_B/\beta_{DC})] = V_{CC} - V_{BE}$$

$$I_C = \frac{V_{CC} - V_{BE}}{R_C + (R_B/\beta_{DC})} \tag{5–9}$$

From Formula 5–9 we see beta's influence on the collector current. In Figure 5–6, if beta is 250, the collector current is about 15 mA. If beta increases to 300, the collector current increases to approximately 16.2 mA:

$$I_C = \frac{V_{CC} - V_{BE}}{R_C + (R_B/\beta_{DC})} = \frac{9\text{ V} - 0.7\text{ V}}{300\ \Omega + (63.3\text{ k}\Omega/300)} = \frac{8.3\text{ V}}{511\ \Omega} = 16.2\text{ mA}$$

This increase in current causes the collector–emitter voltage to decrease to 4.14 V (9 V − V_{RC} = 9 V − 4.86 V). This change in Q point may or may not be significant. The point is, the Q point is not rock solid in this design, though it is an improvement over base bias.

Test your understanding with self-check 5–2.

Self-Check 5–2

1. Analyze the circuit of Figure 5–7 to find $I_{C(Q)}$ and $I_{B(Q)}$. Assume midpoint bias is used.
2. If the collector resistor of Figure 5–7 is changed to 3.3 kΩ, what must the value of R_B be to maintain midpoint bias?
3. Explain why collector-feedback bias is an improvement over base bias in terms of temperature stability.

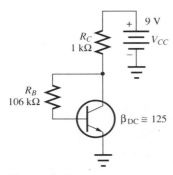

Figure 5–7

5–3 VOLTAGE-DIVIDER BIAS

VOLTAGE-DIVIDER-BIAS ANALYSIS

Voltage-divider bias is the most common means of transistor biasing. As shown in Figure 5–8, it requires four resistors instead of just two. This increases the cost per amplifier stage, which is a concern in manufacturing, but the benefits of stability and reproducibility far outweigh the cost.

The basic idea behind voltage-divider bias is that a voltage divider provides a fixed bias voltage to the base of the transistor. This fixed base voltage $(V_B = V_{R2})$ then determines the voltage across the emitter resistor $(V_E = V_{RE} = V_B - 0.7$ V) See Figure 5–7. This emitter voltage then determines the emitter and collector current.

Voltage-divider bias includes an emitter resistor that did not appear in the designs previously discussed. The emitter resistor serves several important functions. It provides some voltage feedback to the base–emitter junction. If the collector current (emitter current) does attempt to increase, due to temperature effects, the emitter-resistor voltage must also increase ($\uparrow V_{RE} = \uparrow I_E \cdot R_E$). Since the voltage divider provides a fixed base voltage, the increase in emitter voltage reduces V_{BE}, causing I_B to decrease and I_C to remain near the designed Q point ($\leftrightarrow V_B = \downarrow V_{BE} + \uparrow V_{RE}$). Also, the emitter resistor helps determine the gain, or amplification factor, for the transistor

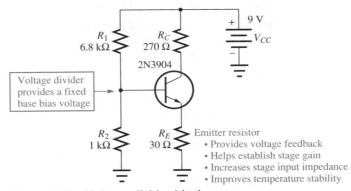

Figure 5–8 Voltage-divider biasing.

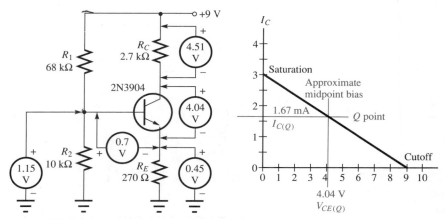

Figure 5–9 Voltage-divider bias circuit analysis.

stage and increases the input impedance at the base. We will discuss stage gain and input impedance later.

There are six basic steps to voltage-divider bias circuit analysis. This procedure is important since it helps you thoroughly understand the circuit's theory of operation, which in turn enables you to successfully troubleshoot the amplifier. In troubleshooting, you compare predicted (calculated) values with measured values. Let us examine these six analysis steps and apply them to Figure 5–9.

Voltage-Divider Bias Analysis Steps

1. Establish the load line using $R_C + R_E$ to determine the saturation collector current.

$$I_{C(sat)} \cong V_{CC}/(R_C + R_E) = 9 \text{ V}/(2700 \ \Omega + 270 \ \Omega) \cong 3 \text{ mA}$$

$$V_{CE(cutoff)} = V_{CC} = 9 \text{ V}$$

2. Start at the voltage divider and calculate the base voltage.

$$V_B \cong V_{R2} = V_{CC} \cdot R_2/(R_1 + R_2) \tag{5-10}$$

$$V_B \cong 9 \text{ V} \cdot 10 \text{ k}\Omega/(68 \text{ k}\Omega + 10 \text{ k}\Omega) = 1.15 \text{ V}$$

Formula 5–10 is an approximation because the base has some loading effect on V_{R2}. In other words, we ignore I_B here.

3. Next, calculate the emitter voltage ($V_E = V_{RE}$). According to Kirchoff's Voltage Law,

$$V_E = V_{RE} = V_B - V_{BE} \cong V_B - 0.7 \text{ V} \tag{5-11}$$

where $V_B = V_{R2}$

$$V_E \cong 1.15 \text{ V} - 0.7 \text{ V} = 0.45 \text{ V}$$

4. Now, calculate the collector current using Ohm's Law.

$$I_C \cong I_E = V_{RE}/R_E \tag{5-12}$$

$$I_C \cong 0.45 \text{ V}/270 \ \Omega = 1.67 \text{ mA}$$

5. Calculate V_{RC} using Ohm's Law, where $V_{RC} = I_C \cdot R_C$.

$$V_{RC} = 1.67 \text{ mA} \cdot 2.7 \text{ k}\Omega = 4.51 \text{ V}$$

6. Determine the collector–emitter voltage according to Kirchhoff's Voltage Law.

$$V_{CE(Q)} = V_{CC} - V_{RC} - V_{RE} \tag{5–13}$$

$$V_{CE(Q)} = 9 \text{ V} - 4.51 \text{ V} - 0.45 \text{ V} = 4.04 \text{ V}$$

Finally, if desired, crossplot the quiescent collector current and collector–emitter voltage on the load line to identify the Q point. Carefully study Example 5–8.

EXAMPLE 5–8 ▮

Analyze the voltage-divider-biased amplifier of Figure 5–10.

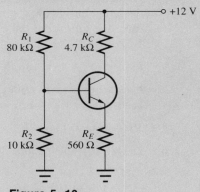

Figure 5–10

$$V_B \cong V_{CC} \cdot V_{R2}/(V_{R1} + V_{R2}) = 12 \text{ V} \cdot 10 \text{ k}\Omega/(80 \text{ k}\Omega + 10 \text{ k}\Omega)$$

$$= 12 \text{ V} \cdot 10 \text{ k}\Omega/90 \text{ k}\Omega = 12 \text{ V} \cdot 0.111 = 1.33 \text{ V}$$

$$V_E = V_{RE} \cong V_B - 0.7 \text{ V} = 1.33 \text{ V} - 0.7 \text{ V} = 0.63 \text{ V}$$

$$I_{C(Q)} \cong I_{E(Q)} = V_{RE}/R_E = 0.63 \text{ V}/560 \ \Omega = 1.13 \text{ mA}$$

$$V_{RC} = I_{C(Q)} \cdot R_C = 1.13 \text{ mA} \cdot 4.7 \text{ k}\Omega = 5.31 \text{ V}$$

$$V_{CE(Q)} = V_{CC} - V_{RC} - V_{RE} = 12 \text{ V} - 5.31 \text{ V} - 0.63 \text{ V} = 6.06 \text{ V}$$

$$P_{D(Q)} = I_{C(Q)} \cdot V_{CE(Q)} = 1.13 \text{ mA} \cdot 6.06 \text{ V} = 6.85 \text{ mW}$$

VOLTAGE-DIVIDER BIAS DESIGN

The design of a voltage-divider-biased transistor amplifier, unlike analysis, begins on the collector and emitter side of the circuit instead of on the base side. You must determine the values of R_C and R_E needed to limit current to the desired saturation value. Then, quiescent collector current, base current, and voltage-divider current can be determined. Consider the following design steps.

Voltage-Divider Bias Design Steps

1. Decide on a safe value of saturation current well below the maximum current rating of the transistor. Notice in Figure 5–9 that the saturation current was chosen to be about 3 mA.

2. The sum of R_C and R_E is determined using Ohm's Law.

$$R_C + R_E = V_{CC}/I_{C(\text{sat})} \qquad (5\text{--}14)$$

3. Now decide on the relative sizes of R_E and R_C. The collector resistor may be anywhere between 1 and 30 times the emitter resistor. It is helpful here to know that the voltage amplification factor of the amplifier depends largely on the ratio of R_C/R_E. If $R_C = 2{,}700\ \Omega$ and $R_E = 270\ \Omega$, the amplifier will amplify an input signal approximately ten times (2,700/270 = 10). This is the case in Figure 5–9. Note that the sum of R_E and R_C must be close to the resistance calculated using Formula 5–14.

4. Next, determine the desired quiescent collector–emitter voltage and collector current. Assume we want midpoint bias for Figure 5–9 as our design example ($V_{CE(Q)} = 4.5$ V). This leaves 4.5 V for $R_E + R_C$. Therefore, the quiescent collector current must be 1.52 mA (4.5 V/2,970 Ω = 1.52 mA).

$$I_{C(Q)} = (V_{CC} - V_{CE})/(R_E + R_C) \qquad (5\text{--}15)$$

5. Use the quiescent collector current to calculate the emitter voltage. For Figure 5–9, $V_E = 1.52$ mA $\cdot$ 270 Ω = 0.41 V.

$$V_E = V_{RE} = I_{C(Q)} \cdot R_E \qquad (5\text{--}16)$$

6. Determine the required base-bias voltage. $V_B = 0.7$ V $+$ 0.41 V = 1.11 V.

$$V_B = V_{R2} = V_{BE} + V_E \cong 0.7 \text{ V} + V_E \qquad (5\text{--}17)$$

7. Select a standard-value resistor for R_2 that will permit a voltage-divider current of at least 10 times the base current, where $I_B = I_C/\beta_{DC}$ and $I_{R2} \geq 10I_B$. This prevents the base from loading down the voltage divider significantly. For design work, use the minimum value of DC beta given on the data sheet. Assume the minimum beta to be 200 for Figure 5–9. The base current is 7.6 μA ($I_B = 1.52$ mA/200 = 7.6 μA).

$$R_2 \leq V_B/10I_B \qquad (5\text{--}18)$$

Applying Formula 5–18 to Figure 5–9, we find that R_2 must be less than or equal to 14,605 Ω (1.11 V/76 μA = 14,605 Ω). The 10-kΩ resistor selected for R_2 is a good choice.

8. Finally, calculate the resistance of R_1. Ohm's Law is used here.

$$R_1 = V_{R1}/(I_{R2} + I_B) \qquad (5\text{--}19)$$

where $V_{R1} = V_{CC} - V_{R2}$ and $I_{R2} = V_B/R_2$.

If R_2 is 10 kΩ, the correct resistance for R_1 in Figure 5–9 is

$$R_1 = V_{R1}/(I_{R2} + I_B) = (9 \text{ V} - 1.11\text{V})/(111\ \mu\text{A} + 7.6\ \mu\text{A}) = 66.5 \text{ k}\Omega$$

A variable resistor, a combination of resistors, or a close-precision resistor may be used to obtain the 66.5 kΩ. Also a standard value such as 68 kΩ may be used with some shifting in the bias and Q point. Consider Example 5–9 and take time to carefully study Design Note 5–1.

DESIGN NOTE 5–1 VOLTAGE DIVIDER AMPLIFIER DESIGN

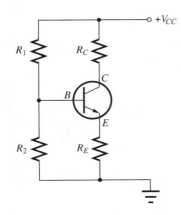

DESIGN APPROACH

R_C/R_E = desired voltage gain ≤ 30

$I_{R2} = 10I_B$

V_{CC}, R_C, and V_{CE} must be specified for this design approach. Always make sure the transistor you choose has maximum ratings well above the saturation collector current and the transistor power dissipation.

BASIC PROGRAM

```
10  CLS
15  CLEAR
20  PRINT"VOLTAGE-DIVIDER BIAS AMPLIFIER DESIGN"
30  PRINT""
40  INPUT"ENTER THE SOURCE VOLTAGE - VCC = ";VCC
50  INPUT"ENTER THE COLLECTOR RESISTOR - RC = ";RC
60  INPUT"ENTER THE DESIRED COLLECTOR-EMITTER VOLTAGE - VCE = ";VCE
70  INPUT"ENTER THE DESIRED VOLTAGE GAIN (1 TO 30) - G = ";G
80  INPUT"ENTER THE APPROXIMATE DC BETA FOR THE TRANSISTOR - B = ";B
90  PRINT""
100 RE = RC/G
110 IE = (VCC - VCE)/(RC + RE)
120 IB = IE/B
130 VRE = IE * RE
140 VB = VRE + .7
150 IR2 = 10 * IB
160 R2 = VB/IR2
170 R1 = (VCC - VB)/(10 * IB + IB)
200 REM  ** OUTPUT SECTION **
210 PRINT"THE VALUE OF THE EMITTER RESISTOR IS ";RE;" OHMS."
220 PRINT"THE VALUE OF R2 IS ";R2;" OHMS."
230 PRINT"THE VALUE OF R1 IS ";R1;" OHMS."
235 PRINT"SELECT STANDARD RESISTOR VALUES FOR RE, R1, AND R2."
240 PRINT""
250 INPUT"WOULD YOU LIKE TO DESIGN ANOTHER CIRCUIT?  (Y/N) ";A$
260 IF A$="Y" THEN GO TO 10
270 END
```

EXAMPLE 5–9

Design a voltage-divider-biased amplifier. The collector saturation current shall be 12 mA, V_{CC} shall be -12 V, and $V_{CE(Q)} \cong 6$ V. Let $R_C/R_E \cong$ 15. The minimum h_{FE} from the data sheet is 100.

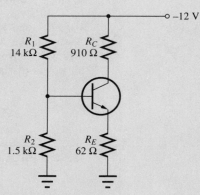

Figure 5–11

$$R_C + R_E = 12 \text{ V}/12 \text{ mA} = 1 \text{ k}\Omega$$

$$R_C = 1 \text{ k}\Omega - R_E$$

$R_C/R_E = 15$, so

$$(1 \text{ k}\Omega - R_E)/R_E = 15$$

$$(1 \text{ k}\Omega/R_E) - 1 = 15$$

$$1 \text{ k}\Omega/R_E = 16$$

$$R_E = 1 \text{ k}\Omega/16 = 62.5 \ \Omega \qquad \text{(Use 62 } \Omega.)$$

$$R_C = 15 \cdot R_E = 15 \cdot 62 \ \Omega = 930 \ \Omega \qquad \text{(Use 910 } \Omega.)$$

$$I_{C(Q)} = (V_{CC} - V_{CE(Q)})/(R_C + R_E) = 6 \text{ V}/972 \ \Omega = 6.16 \text{ mA}$$

$$V_E = V_{RE} = I_{C(Q)} \cdot R_E = 6.16 \text{ mA} \cdot 62 \ \Omega = 0.382 \text{ V}$$

$$V_{R2} \cong V_B = 0.7 \text{ V} + V_E = 0.7 \text{ V} + 0.382 \text{ V} = 1.082 \text{ V}$$

$$I_{B(Q)} \cong I_{C(Q)}/\beta_{DC(min)} = 6.16 \text{ mA}/100 = 61.6 \ \mu\text{A}$$

$$I_{R2} \geq 10 \cdot I_{B(Q)} = 10 \cdot 61.6 \ \mu\text{A} = 616 \ \mu\text{A}$$

$$R_2 \leq V_{R2}/I_{R2} = 1.082 \text{ V}/616 \ \mu\text{A} = 1756 \ \Omega \quad \text{(Use 1500 } \Omega.)$$

$$I_{R2} = 1.082 \text{ V}/1500 \ \Omega = 721 \ \mu\text{A}$$

$$R_1 = (V_{CC} - V_{R2})/(I_{R2} + I_B) = (12\text{V} - 1.082\text{V})/(721\mu\text{A} + 61.6 \ \mu\text{A})$$

$$= 10.92 \text{ V}/782.6 \ \mu\text{A} = 13,953 \ \Omega \qquad \text{(Use 14 k}\Omega, 2\%.)$$

VOLTAGE-DIVIDER BIAS TEMPERATURE STABILITY

Temperature and β_{DC}

The temperature stability of the voltage-divider design is not significantly affected by changes in beta as long as the Thevenized resistance of the voltage divider is very low. This is insured by making sure the voltage divider current is *at least* 10 times the base current.

As shown in Figure 5–12, we must Thevenize the voltage divider to form a base-circuit loop. From this, we can use Kirchoff's Voltage Law to derive a formula that shows the relationship between beta and collector current. We

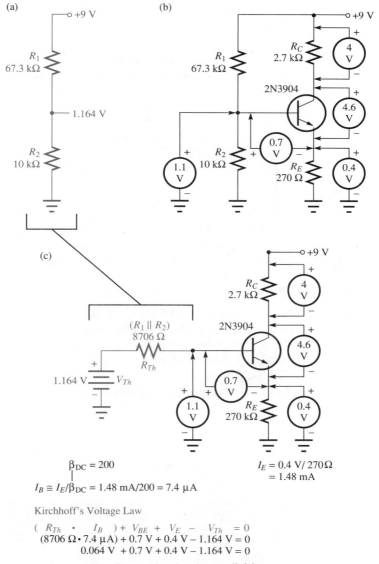

$$\beta_{DC} = 200$$
$$I_B \cong I_E / \beta_{DC} = 1.48 \text{ mA}/200 = 7.4 \text{ }\mu\text{A}$$

$$I_E = 0.4 \text{ V}/270\Omega$$
$$= 1.48 \text{ mA}$$

Kirchhoff's Voltage Law

$$(\quad R_{Th} \quad \cdot \quad I_B \quad) + V_{BE} + V_E - V_{Th} = 0$$
$$(8706 \text{ }\Omega \cdot 7.4 \text{ }\mu\text{A}) + 0.7 \text{ V} + 0.4 \text{ V} - 1.164 \text{ V} = 0$$
$$0.064 \text{ V} + 0.7 \text{ V} + 0.4 \text{ V} - 1.164 \text{ V} = 0$$

Figure 5–12   The Thevenized voltage divider.

should be able to show that beta has very little effect on collector current, thus making the amplifier very stable over a wide temperature range.

The base loop equation from Figure 5–12 is as follows:

$$(R_{Th} \cdot I_B) + V_{BE} + V_E - V_{Th} = 0$$

since $I_C \cong I_E$ and $I_B = I_C/\beta_{DC}$, we obtain the following by substitution:

$$(R_{Th} \cdot I_C/\beta_{DC}) + V_{BE} + (I_C \cdot R_E) - V_{Th} = 0$$

$$(I_C \cdot R_{Th}/\beta_{DC}) + (I_C \cdot R_E) = V_{Th} - V_{BE}$$

$$I_C \cdot [(R_{Th}/\beta_{DC}) + R_E] = V_{Th} - V_{BE}$$

therefore,

$$I_C = \frac{V_{Th} - V_{BE}}{(R_{Th}/\beta_{DC}) + R_E} \tag{5–20}$$

As you can see from Formula 5–20, beta has little effect on the collector current and the amplifier's temperature stability as long as R_{Th} is low. Applying Formula 5–20 to Figure 5–12, we see that if beta is 200, the collector current is 1.48 mA [(1.164 V − 0.7 V)/[(8,706 Ω/200) + 270 Ω] = 1.48 mA]. If beta increases to 250, the collector current increases to 1.52 mA, which represents no significant change [(1.164 V − 0.7 V)/[(8,706 Ω/250) + 270 ω] = 1.52 mA]. Also, if the transistor is replaced with another 2N3904, or a comparable transistor, the Q point will not change significantly, even if the beta of the new transistor differs greatly from that of the old one.

Formula 5–20 emphasizes the importance of R_{Th} being low. That means voltage-divider resistors R_1 and R_2 must be relatively low in value to insure that changes in β_{DC} with temperature are insignificant. That is why the design rule of thumb proposed is where $I_{R2} \geq 10I_B$. This ensures that the values of R_1 and R_2 will be low enough to provide good temperature stability.

Temperature and V_{BE}

As you have seen, the transistor's β_{DC} is directly related to the transistor's temperature. But that's not the total picture. Associated with an increase in β_{DC} and temperature is a *decrease* in base–emitter barrier potential. V_{BE} is nominally thought of as being 0.7 V. As temperature increases, V_{BE} will drop slightly, depending on the amount of increase in temperature. Example 5–10 illustrates the results of an increase in temperature in a poorly biased amplifier.

EXAMPLE 5–10 ▰▰▰▰▰▰▰▰▰▰▰▰

Calculate $I_{C(Q)}$ and $V_{CE(Q)}$ for Figure 5–13 when the transistor's β_{DC} is 180. Calculate these parameters again for a β_{DC} of 220—an increase in β_{DC} due to an increase in temperature. Assume V_{BE} is 0.7 V when β_{DC} is 180 and 0.67 V when β_{DC} is 220.

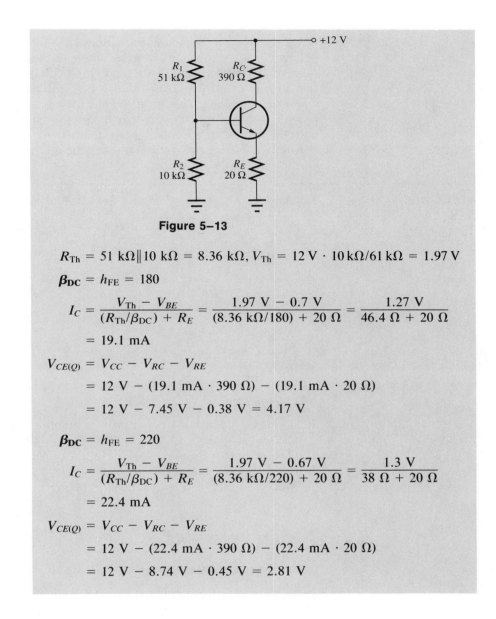

Figure 5-13

$R_{Th} = 51 \text{ k}\Omega \| 10 \text{ k}\Omega = 8.36 \text{ k}\Omega, V_{Th} = 12 \text{ V} \cdot 10 \text{ k}\Omega/61 \text{ k}\Omega = 1.97 \text{ V}$

$\beta_{DC} = h_{FE} = 180$

$$I_C = \frac{V_{Th} - V_{BE}}{(R_{Th}/\beta_{DC}) + R_E} = \frac{1.97 \text{ V} - 0.7 \text{ V}}{(8.36 \text{ k}\Omega/180) + 20 \text{ }\Omega} = \frac{1.27 \text{ V}}{46.4 \text{ }\Omega + 20 \text{ }\Omega}$$

$$= 19.1 \text{ mA}$$

$$V_{CE(Q)} = V_{CC} - V_{RC} - V_{RE}$$

$$= 12 \text{ V} - (19.1 \text{ mA} \cdot 390 \text{ }\Omega) - (19.1 \text{ mA} \cdot 20 \text{ }\Omega)$$

$$= 12 \text{ V} - 7.45 \text{ V} - 0.38 \text{ V} = 4.17 \text{ V}$$

$\beta_{DC} = h_{FE} = 220$

$$I_C = \frac{V_{Th} - V_{BE}}{(R_{Th}/\beta_{DC}) + R_E} = \frac{1.97 \text{ V} - 0.67 \text{ V}}{(8.36 \text{ k}\Omega/220) + 20 \text{ }\Omega} = \frac{1.3 \text{ V}}{38 \text{ }\Omega + 20 \text{ }\Omega}$$

$$= 22.4 \text{ mA}$$

$$V_{CE(Q)} = V_{CC} - V_{RC} - V_{RE}$$

$$= 12 \text{ V} - (22.4 \text{ mA} \cdot 390 \text{ }\Omega) - (22.4 \text{ mA} \cdot 20 \text{ }\Omega)$$

$$= 12 \text{ V} - 8.74 \text{ V} - 0.45 \text{ V} = 2.81 \text{ V}$$

Design Precautions

The changes in Q point due to an increase in temperature illustrated in Example 5-10 are obviously significant. What design precautions are necessary to avoid this? First, make sure that R_{Th}/β_{DC} is less than R_E. This is accomplished by making sure R_{Th} is low by using relatively low values for R_1 and R_2. Again, this is ensured by making $I_{R2} \geq 10 I_{B(Q)}$. More suitable values for R_1 and R_2 in Figure 5-13 would be $R_1 = 5.1 \text{ k}\Omega$ and $R_2 = 1 \text{ k}\Omega$, if it is desired that $V_{CE(Q)}$ be between 3 and 4 V over a wide temperature range. Second, V_{Th} should be greater than approximately 1.5 V_{BE} so slight decreases in V_{BE}, as temperature increases, will have little effect. The slight decrease in V_{BE} shown in Example 5–10 really has little effect because V_{Th} is relatively large compared to V_{BE}. V_{Th} is made relatively large by insuring that V_{RE} is not too small. V_{RE} should be greater than approximately 0.35 V whenever possible. This is accomplished by making R_E large enough to provide a voltage drop greater than 0.35 V for the desired quiescent collector current. The larger R_E and V_{RE} are, the better the temperature stability.

After reviewing this section, answer the questions of Self-Check 5–3.

Self-Check 5–3

1. Analyze the circuit of Figure 5–14 to find V_B, V_E, $I_{C(Q)}$, and $V_{CE(Q)}$.

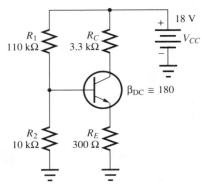

Figure 5–14

2. Design a voltage-divider transistor amplifier. The collector saturation current shall be 5 mA. V_{CC} is 12 V. $V_{CE(Q)}$ shall be 8 V. R_C shall be $10R_E$. The minimum transistor β_{DC} is 100.

3. Describe the extent to which the Q point of a voltage-divider biased transistor amplifier is dependent on β_{DC}.

5–4 EMITTER BIAS

EMITTER-BIAS ANALYSIS

Though not as common, emitter bias is a close cousin to voltage-divider bias. Shown in Figure 5–15, emitter bias requires a split supply instead of the voltage divider. The V_{EE} supply provides the emitter resistor and the base–emitter junction with the needed voltage drops with respect to ground. Notice that the base is close to ground potential (near 0 V). The base resistor is kept small to insure that the base is close to ground potential ($V_B = I_B \cdot R_B =$ near 0 V). This circuit functions the same and has nearly the same Q point as the circuit of Figure 5–9. The following analysis steps are applied to the circuit of Figure 5–15.

Emitter-Bias Analysis Steps

1. Draw the load line. Notice here that $V_{CE(cutoff)}$ is the sum of the two

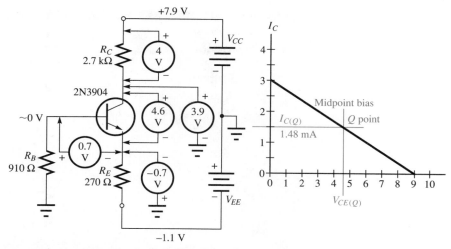

Figure 5-15 Emitter-bias circuit analysis.

supplies since they are series-aiding. Also, $I_{C(\text{sat})}$ is determined using the sum of the two supply voltages.

$$I_{C(\text{sat})} = (V_{CC} + V_{EE})/(R_C + R_E) \tag{5-21}$$

$$I_{C(\text{sat})} = (7.9 \text{ V} + 1.1 \text{ V})/(2.7 \text{ k}\Omega + 270 \text{ }\Omega) \cong 3 \text{ mA}$$

$$V_{CE(\text{cutoff})} = V_{CC} + V_{EE} \tag{5-22}$$

$$V_{CE(\text{cutoff})} = 7.9 \text{ V} + 1.1 \text{ V} = 9 \text{ V}$$

2. Calculate the emitter current using Ohm's Law, where

$$V_{RE} = V_E - V_{BE} \cong V_{EE} - 0.7 \text{ V}$$

$$I_C \cong I_E = V_{RE}/R_E \tag{5-23}$$

$$I_C \cong 0.4 \text{ V}/270 \text{ }\Omega = 1.48 \text{ mA}$$

3. Next, calculate the voltage across the collector resistor using Ohm's Law ($V_{RC} = I_C \cdot R_C$).

$$V_{RC} = 1.48 \text{ mA} \cdot 2.7 \text{ k}\Omega = 4 \text{ V}$$

4. Finally, calculate $V_{CE(Q)}$.

$$V_{CE(Q)} = V_{CC} + V_{EE} - V_{RC} - V_{RE} = V_C - V_E \tag{5-24}$$

$$V_{CE(Q)} = 7.9 \text{ V} + 1.1 \text{ V} - 4 \text{ V} - 0.4 \text{ V} = 4.6 \text{ V}$$

Notice that the collector of the transistor is at $+3.9$ V with respect to ground and the emitter of the transistor is at -0.7 V with respect to ground. The total voltage drop from collector to emitter is the total difference of potential [$+3.9 - (-0.7) = 4.6$ V]. Notice also that V_E and V_{RE} are not equal as they were in the voltage-divider design. Here, V_E is -0.7 V and V_{RE} is 0.4 V. Now, take time to carefully study Example 5-11.

EXAMPLE 5–11

Determine $I_{C(\text{at})}$, $V_{CE(\text{cutoff})}$, $I_{C(Q)}$, and $V_{CE(Q)}$ for Figure 5–16.

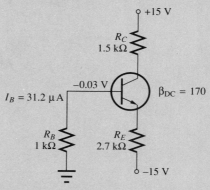

Figure 5–16

$$V_{CE(\text{cutoff})} = +15\ \text{V} - (-15\ \text{V}) = 30\ \text{V}$$

$$I_{C(\text{sat})} = 30\ \text{V}/4.2\ \text{k}\Omega = 7.14\ \text{mA}$$

$$I_{C(Q)} \cong I_{E(Q)} = V_{RE}/R_E = (15\ \text{V} - 0.7\ \text{V})/2.7\ \text{k}\Omega = 5.30\ \text{mA}$$

$$V_{CE(Q)} = V_C - V_E \cong (15\ \text{V} - (5.3\ \text{mA} \cdot 1.5\ \text{k}\Omega)) - (-0.7\ \text{V})$$
$$= 7.75\ \text{V}$$

Notice also that $I_{B(Q)} = I_{C(Q)}/\beta_{\text{DC}} = 5.30\ \text{mA}/170 = 31.2\ \mu\text{A}$ and $V_B = I_{B(Q)} \cdot R_B = 31.2\ \mu\text{A} \cdot 1\ \text{k}\Omega = 0.031\ \text{V} \cong 0\ \text{V}$.

Emitter-Bias Temperature Stability

The temperature stability and circuit reproducibility in the emitter-bias design are both as good or better than the voltage-divider design. Again, the minimal effects of changes in beta can be seen in a formula derived from Kirchoff's Voltage Law.

$$(R_B \cdot I_B) + V_{BE} + V_{RE} - V_{EE} = 0$$

Since $I_C \cong I_E$ and $I_B = I_C/\beta_{\text{DC}}$, we obtain the following by substitution.

$$(R_B \cdot I_C/\beta_{\text{DC}}) + V_{BE} + (I_C \cdot R_E) - V_{EE} = 0$$

$$(I_C \cdot R_B/\beta_{\text{DC}}) + (I_C \cdot R_E) = V_{EE} - V_{BE}$$

$$I_C \cdot [(R_B/\beta_{\text{DC}}) + R_E] = V_{EE} - V_{BE}$$

Therefore,

$$I_C = \frac{V_{EE} - V_{BE}}{(R_B/\beta_{\text{DC}}) + R_E} \tag{5–25}$$

As you can see from Formula 5–25, beta has virtually no effect on collector current because R_B/β_{DC} is very small compared to R_E. Also notice that changes in V_{BE} with temperature have virtually no effect on the collector current, because V_{EE} is normally very large compared to V_{BE}. Therefore, emitter bias is a very temperature-stable design.

Test your understanding with Self-Check 5–4.

**Self-Check
5–4**

Determine the following for Figure 5–17.

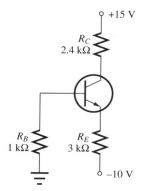

Figure 5–17

1. $V_{RE} =$
2. $I_{C(Q)} =$
3. $V_{RC} =$
4. $V_{CE} =$

5–5 TEMPERATURE-STABILITY FACTORS

BETA

We have already discussed the fact that beta changes with temperature and how it can continue to increase as transistor current and temperature increase. In power transistors this can be a severe problem as the collector current and temperature run away. As temperature increases, current increases, which further increases temperature. If precautions are not taken, collector current and device temperature can drive each other to destruction. This is often referred to as **thermal runaway.** The threat of thermal runaway is minimized with good biasing techniques such as voltage-divider or emitter bias and proper heat sinking. Naturally, we will pursue this further in a later chapter covering power amplifiers.

BASE–COLLECTOR LEAKAGE CURRENT—I_{CBO}

Another problem that is related to temperature and further aggravates thermal runaway is **base–collector leakage current,** known as I_{CBO}. You may recall this from an earlier discussion. This leakage current increases with temperature; under certain conditions it can cause the base-bias voltage to increase, which increases collector current. Though I_{CBO} does exist, it is usually not a problem in voltage-divider bias designs, where the voltage-divider current is so very great compared to base current and base–collector leakage current.

BASE–EMITTER VOLTAGE

Still another small contributor to the thermal problem is a slight decrease in base–emitter voltage as temperature increases. Interestingly, this actually causes the collector current to increase, though slightly. Consider this formula for the voltage-divider-biased circuit:

$$I_C = \frac{V_{\text{Th}} - V_{BE}}{(R_{\text{Th}}/\beta_{\text{DC}}) + R_E}$$

Note how the difference voltage in the numerator of this formula increases as V_{BE} decreases. This causes I_C to increase. The amount of increase in collector current largely depends on the value of V_{Th}. If V_{Th} is close to V_{BE} the increase in I_C can be significant. If V_{Th} is much greater than V_{BE}, the slight decrease in V_{BE} will have little effect.

Time for a self-check.

Self-Check 5–5

1. How can I_{CBO} affect bias temperature stability?
2. Explain how V_{BE} and temperature are related and how this affects bias temperature stability.
3. What is thermal runaway?

5–6 VARIATIONS IN SOURCE POLARITY AND GROUND

In this section, we illustrate different ways to apply DC source voltage to transistor amplifiers. Figure 5–18 illustrates some of the possible variations. Figures 5–18a and 5–18d are standard NPN and PNP configurations. Realize that all circuit calculations are the same for NPN and PNP transistors. Note that the proper polarity for each transistor type is maintained. Figures 5–18c and 5–18f are the same as Figures 5–18b and 5–18e respectively. The diagrams are simply inverted.

Figures 5–18 d, e, and f are complements of Figures 5–18a, b, and c. That is, the circuits function the same but are opposite in voltage polarities, current directions, and transistor type. Later, you will see how the NPN and PNP transistors can be placed in the same amplifier circuit to increase the efficiency of the circuit. It is said that they *complement* one another, forming a **complementary pair.** For example, the 2N3904 and 2N3906 are complementary, having very similar operating characteristics and ratings.

It might be a good idea to take time now to go back and review the various biasing techniques. You should be able to recognize many similarities in the way collector current and base current are determined in each design. Ohm's Law is used over and over again in many different ways. Also, make sure you understand the advantages and disadvantages of the various biasing schemes. Test your understanding with Self-Check 5–6.

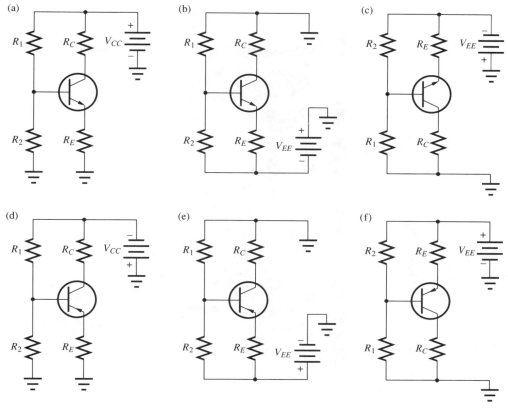

Figure 5–18 Variations in source polarity and ground for NPN and PNP circuits.

**Self-Check
5–6**

1. Explain how a PNP transistor amplifier can have a negative ground.
2. Explain how an NPN transistor amplifier can have a positive ground.

5–7 TRANSISTOR TESTING AND TROUBLESHOOTING

TRANSISTOR TROUBLES

Transistors first short, then burn open. Like diodes, transistors usually short internally when they fail. The short usually occurs between the collector and the base, because it is the collector that dissipates virtually all of the heat. This means the resistance from collector to base now has a very low fixed value. At the same time, the base–emitter junction burns open, which means it now has a very high fixed resistance. If the excessive current continues to flow in the shorted collector, it will eventually burn open.

TRANSISTOR TESTING

Transistors can be tested out-of-circuit using a transistor tester, a beta tester on some DMMs, the diode test function of some multimeters, or an analog

Figure 5–19 Using the h_{FE} test function of a multimeter to test a transistor. (Equipment courtesy of Beckman Industrial Corp.)

ohmmeter. Figure 5–19 demonstrates the use of the Circuitmate DM27 in testing a 2N3906 PNP transistor. This particular 2N3906 has a beta of 205 at room temperature.

Figure 5–20 shows the B&K 540 Component Tester being used to compare the collector characteristics of two 2N3904 transistors. The A or B button is pressed to quickly display the collector curves for the corresponding transistor. If a family of collector curves cannot be obtained, the transis-

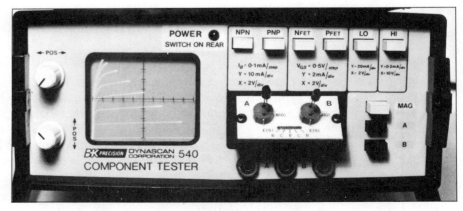

Figure 5–20 This B & K Precision 540 Component Tester is being used to display a family of collector curves for a 2N3904 NPN transistor. (Equipment courtesy of B & K Precision, a division of Maxtec International Corporation.)

tor is bad. The B&K 540 can also test field-effect transistors (FETs) and diodes.

If an analog ohmmeter is used, the leads must be tested to see which is positive and which is negative. Often, with analog multimeters, the black lead is connected to the positive side of the internal battery and the red lead to the negative side. In any case, the junctions of the transistor can be tested to see if they are shorted in both directions. In other words, if the resistance reading is low between any two transistor leads regardless of the test-lead polarity, the associated junction is shorted. A good junction allows current in only one direction. The collector-to-emitter test should indicate an open if the transistor is not shorted.

A quick test you can perform using the analog ohmmeter when testing NPN transistors is to clip the negative ohmmeter lead onto the emitter and the positive lead onto the base. The meter gives an up-scale reading since the base–emitter junction is now forward biased. Next, slide the positive ohmmeter lead over to touch the collector lead, so the ohmmeter lead contacts both the base and collector. If the transistor is good, the needle on the meter moves further up the scale indicating emitter–collector current and normal transistor action. For PNP transistors, simply reverse the ohmmeter test leads.

Figure 5–21 shows two very useful pieces of test equipment used to test and verify characteristics of bipolar transistors, diodes, and field-effect transistors. The LTC-906 of Figure 5–21a is an analog multimeter that permits

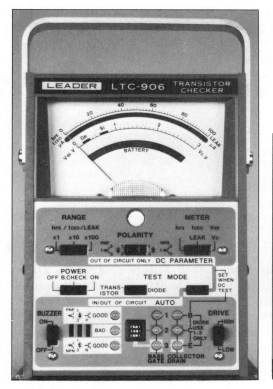

Figure 5–21 (a) The LTC-906 Transistor Checker. (b) The LTC-905 Curve Tracer. (Courtesy of Leader Instruments Corporation.)

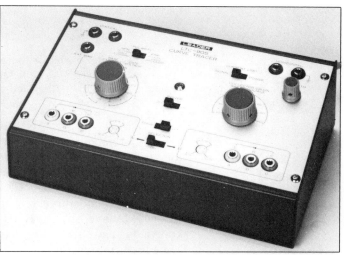

in- and out-of-circuit tests. As you can see, good/bad tests can be performed along with h_{FE}, I_{CEO} leakage, and forward V_{BE} measurements. The LTC-905 of Figure 5–21b is a useful companion for any oscilloscope. This is a curve tracer that generates characteristic curves (forward current vs voltage curves) for diodes, bipolar transistors, and field-effect transistors. Vertical and horizontal inputs on the oscilloscope are connected to the designated jacks on the LTC-905. Base current or gate voltage is selected using the left knob and the collector or drain sweep voltage is selected using the right knob. The device under test (DUT) may be plugged directly into the LTC-905 or clip leads may be used.

TRANSISTOR CIRCUIT TROUBLESHOOTING

Transistors can be tested in-circuit with special in-circuit transistor testers, or you can use your DVM and apply circuit theory with a little calculating. Figure 5–22 shows you how to apply your theoretical circuit analysis to actual troubleshooting. Consider the following:

If the	Then the	Because the
base voltage is high and almost equal to the collector voltage,	base–collector junction is probably shorted and the base–emitter junction may be open,	collector shorts and causes the base–emitter junction to burn open almost instantly.
base is externally shorted to ground,	emitter voltage will be very low and the collector voltage very high,	transistor acts as an open since the bias voltage is removed.
collector is externally shorted to the emitter,	collect-resistor and emitter-resistor voltages will be higher than normal,	short bridges the transistor connecting the collector resistor directly to the emitter resistor.
R_2 voltage divider resistor opens or is disconnected,	transistor will saturate, making V_{CE} close to 0 V, increasing both V_{RC} and V_{RE},	transistor acts as a short.
R_1 voltage divider opens or becomes disconnected,	transistor will be cut off, making V_{CE} close to V_{CC} and decreasing V_{RC} and V_{RE} to 0 V,	transistor acts as an open.

There are many other possible troubles involving open and shorted resistors and component leads, cold-solder joints, foil cracks, and temperature-related bad connections inside transistors. Naturally, we do not have the space here to cover them all. However, the solution to all of the possible troubles is found through a thoughtful application of the basic transistor theory we have covered thus far. How well you are able to apply basic knowledge and theory will determine how good you are at troubleshooting. Time for a self-check.

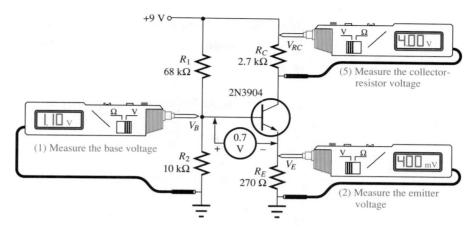

(5) Measure the collector-
resistor voltage

(1) Measure the base voltage

(2) Measure the emitter
voltage

(3) Calculate the emitter/collector current ($I_E \cong I_C \cong V_E/R_E$)
(4) Calculate the collector-resistor voltage ($V_{RC} = I_C \cdot R_C$)

Findings of steps 4 and 5 should be close to the same value

Figure 5–22   Transistor troubleshooting.

**Self-Check
5–7**

1. Transistors normally open when they first fail. True or false?
2. Describe how an analog ohmmeter is used to detect a shorted base–emitter junction (out-of-circuit test).
3. In a transistor amplifier circuit, if the base-bias voltage is increased, the collector–emitter voltage should do what?
4. Refer to the circuit of Figure 5–22. If V_B is normal and V_{RC} is higher than normal, what might be the trouble?
5. Refer to the circuit of Figure 5–22. Describe the voltage readings if the collector of the transistor becomes disconnected.

SUMMARY

FORMULAS

Base-Bias Analysis

(5–1) $I_{B(Q)} = (V_{CC} - 0.7 \text{ V})/R_B$

(5–2) $V_{CE(Q)} = V_{CC} - V_{RC} = V_{CC} - (I_{C(Q)} \cdot R_C)$

Base-Bias Design

(5–3) $R_C = V_{CC}/I_{C(\text{sat})}$

(5–4) $R_B = (V_{CC} - 0.7 \text{ V})/I_{B(Q)}$ (where $I_{B(Q)} = I_{C(Q)}/\beta_{DC}$)

Collector-Feedback-Bias Analysis

(5–5) $I_{C(Q)} = (V_{CC} - V_{CE(Q)})/R_C$

(5–6) $I_{B(Q)} = (V_{CE} - 0.7 \text{ V})/R_B$

Collector-Feedback-Bias Design

(5–7) $R_B = (V_{CE} - 0.7 \text{ V})/I_{B(Q)}$

(5–8) $R_B = \beta_{DC} \cdot (V_{CE} - 0.7 \text{ V})/I_{C(Q)}$

Collector-Feedback-Bias Temperature Stability

(5–9) $I_C = \dfrac{V_{CC} - V_{BE}}{R_C + (R_B/\beta_{DC})}$

Voltage-Divider-Bias Analysis

(5–10) $V_B = V_{R2} \cong V_{CC} \cdot R_2/(R_1 + R_2)$

(5–11) $V_E = V_{RE} = V_B - V_{BE} \cong V_B - 0.7 \text{ V}$ (where $V_B = V_{R2}$)

(5–12) $I_C \cong I_E = V_{RE}/R_E$

(5–13) $V_{CE} = V_{CC} - V_{RC} - V_{RE}$

Voltage-Divider-Bias Design

(5–14) $R_C + R_E = V_{CC}/I_{C(\text{sat})}$

(5–15) $I_{C(Q)} = (V_{CC} - V_{CE})/(R_E + R_C)$

(5–16) $V_E = V_{RE} = I_{C(Q)} \cdot R_E$

(5–17) $V_B = V_{R2} = V_{BE} + V_E \cong 0.7 \text{ V} + V_E$

(5–18) $R_2 \le V_B/10 I_B$

(5–19) $R_1 = V_{R1}/(I_{R2} + I_B)$ (where $V_{R1} = V_{CC} - V_{R2}$)

Voltage-Divider Bias Temperature Stability

(5–20) $I_C = \dfrac{V_{Th} - V_{BE}}{(R_{Th}/\beta_{DC}) + R_E}$

Emitter-Bias Analysis

(5–21) $I_{C(\text{sat})} = (V_{CC} + V_{EE})/(R_C + R_E)$

(5–22) $V_{CE(\text{cutoff})} = V_{CC} + V_{EE}$

(5–23) $I_C \cong I_E = V_{RE}/R_E$

(5–24) $V_{CE(Q)} = V_{CC} + V_{EE} - V_{RC} - V_{RE} = V_C - V_E$

Emitter-Bias Temperature Stability

(5–25) $I_C = \dfrac{V_{EE} - V_{BE}}{(R_B/\beta_{DC}) + R_E}$

CONCEPTS

■ These bias techniques are listed in the order of temperature stability from worst to the best: base bias, collector-feedback bias, voltage-divider bias and emitter bias.

- Transistor beta and collector-to-base leakage current increase with temperature and V_{BE} decreases with temperature. All cause collector current to increase contributing to the possibility of thermal runaway.
- Like diodes, transistors usually short when they fail.
- Amplifier troubleshooting involves comparing what should be (theory and calculations) with what is (actual measurements).

PROCEDURES

Voltage-Divider-Bias Analysis

1. Establish the load line, using $R_C + R_E$ to determine the saturation collector current.
2. Start at the voltage divider and calculate the base voltage ($V_{R2} = V_B$).
3. Next, calculate the emitter voltage ($V_E = V_{RE}$). According to Kirchhoff's Voltage Law, $V_E = V_{RE} \cong V_B - 0.7$ V.
4. Now, calculate the collector current using Ohm's Law. $I_C \cong I_E = V_{RE}/R_E$
5. Calculate V_{RC} using Ohm's Law, where $V_{RC} = I_C \cdot R_C$.
6. Determine the collector–emitter voltage according to Kirchhoff's Voltage Law, $V_{CE} = V_{CC} - V_{RC} - V_{RE}$.
7. Finally, if desired, crossplot the quiescent collector current and collector–emitter voltage on the load line to identify the Q point.

Voltage-Divider-Bias Design

1. Decide on a safe value of saturation current well below the maximum current rating of the transistor.
2. The sum of R_C and R_E is determined using Ohm's Law, $R_C + R_E = V_{CC}/I_{C(sat)}$.
3. Now decide on the relative sizes of R_E and R_C. The collector resistor may be anywhere between 1 and 30 times the emitter resistor.
4. Next, determine the desired quiescent collector–emitter voltage and collector current. $I_{C(Q)} = (V_{CC} - V_{CE})/(R_E + R_C)$
5. Use the quiescent collector current to calculate the emitter voltage. $V_E = V_{RE} = I_{C(Q)} \cdot R_E$
6. Determine the required base-bias voltage. $V_B = V_{R2} = V_{BE} + V_E \cong 0.7$ V $+ V_E$
7. Select a standard-value resistor for R_2 that will permit a voltage-divider current of at least 10 times the base current ($R_2 \leq V_B/10I_B$), where $I_B = I_C/\beta_{DC}$.
8. Finally, calculate the resistance of R_1. Ohm's Law is used here. $R_1 = V_{R1}/(I_{R2} + I_B)$ where $V_{R1} = V_{CC} - V_{R2}$

NEED-TO-KNOW SOLUTION

As you have discovered in this chapter, there are many biasing techniques that you can use. However, you should have discovered that emitter bias is the most temperature stable with voltage-divider bias running a close second. This is because I_{CBO} and I_B have little effect on the base bias voltage.

The emitter resistor keeps the quiescent collector current nearly constant; $I_C \cong (V_B - 0.7 \text{ V})/R_E$ for properly designed voltage-divider biasing, and $I_C \cong (V_{EE} - 0.7 \text{ V})/R_E$ for emitter bias.

QUESTIONS

5–1 BASE BIAS

1. What is the purpose for biasing a transistor?
2. What is a quiescent current or quiescent voltage?
3. What is an advantage of base bias?
4. What determines the amount of collector current in a base-biased amplifier?
5. Briefly explain what determines the Q point in a base-bias design.
6. What is the big disadvantage of base bias?

5–2 COLLECTOR-FEEDBACK BIAS

7. What factors must you know to design a collector-feedback amplifier for midpoint bias?
8. How is collector-feedback bias an improvement over base bias?
9. Is collector-feedback bias totally independent of beta? Explain.

5–3 VOLTAGE-DIVIDER BIAS

10. What is the purpose for the two voltage-divider resistors in a voltage-divider-biased amplifier?
11. What is the purpose for the emitter resistor (R_E) in a voltage-divider-biased amplifier?
12. Which of these is the most temperature stable and why: (a) base bias, (b) collector-feedback bias, (c) voltage-divider bias?
13. Which of the transistor circuit designs listed above is the most reliable as far as stability and reproducibility?

5–4 EMITTER BIAS

14. Does emitter biasing compare closely to (a) collector-feedback bias, or (b) voltage-divider bias?
15. What determines the collector current in an emitter-biased amplifier?
16. What is the approximate base voltage for an emitter-biased amplifier?

5–5 TEMPERATURE-STABILITY FACTORS

17. What is thermal runaway?
18. What effect does an increase in temperature have on β?
19. What is I_{CBO}?
20. How is I_{CBO} affected by an increase in temperature?
21. How is V_{BE} affected by an increase in temperature?
22. What effect does an increase in I_{CBO} and β have on collector current in a poorly biased amplifier design?
23. Why does collector current tend to increase slightly if V_{BE} decreases?

5–6 VARIATIONS IN SOURCE POLARITY AND GROUND

24. What is a complementary pair?
25. Is it possible for the common ground to be positive for an NPN transistor amplifier circuit? Explain.

5–7 TRANSISTOR TESTING AND TROUBLESHOOTING

26. What further damage may result when the base–collector junction shorts in a transistor?
27. Describe the effects on circuit parameters when the transistor fails as suggested in the question above.
28. Describe one method of testing a transistor out-of-circuit.

PROBLEMS

5–1 BASE BIAS

1. Calculate the collector current, the base current, and the collector–emitter voltage for Figure 5–23. Draw and label the load line and mark the Q point.

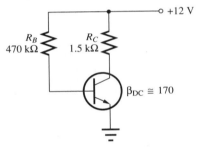

Figure 5–23

2. Calculate the collector current, the base current, and the collector–emitter voltage for Figure 5–24. Draw and label the load line and mark the Q point.

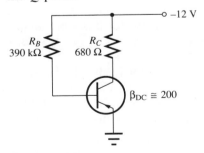

Figure 5–24

3. Design a base-biased amplifier from this data: NPN, $I_{C(sat)} = 50$ mA, $V_{CC} = 12$ V, $V_{CE} = 7$ V, $\beta_{DC} = 160$. Calculate R_C, $I_{B(Q)}$, and R_B.
4. Design a base-biased amplifier from this data: PNP, $I_{C(sat)} = 150$ mA, $V_{CC} = -18$ V, $V_{CE} = 10$ V, $\beta_{DC} = 90$. Calculate R_C, $I_{B(Q)}$, and R_B.

5–2 COLLECTOR-FEEDBACK BIAS

5. Calculate the collector current, the base current, and the collector–emitter voltage for Figure 5–25. Draw and label the load line and mark the Q point.

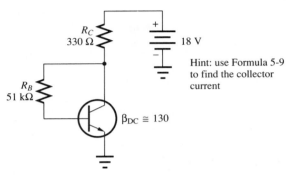

Hint: use Formula 5-9 to find the collector current

Figure 5–25

6. Calculate the collector current, the base current, and the collector-emitter voltage for Figure 5–26. Draw and label the load line and mark the Q point.

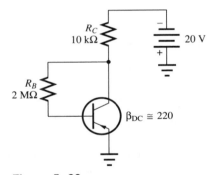

Figure 5–26

7. Design a collector-feedback bias amplifier from this data: NPN, $I_{C(\text{sat})} = 100$ mA, $V_{CC} = 15$ V, $V_{CE} = 8$ V, $\beta_{DC} = 110$. Calculate R_C, $I_{B(Q)}$, and R_B.

8. Design a collector-feedback bias amplifier from this data: PNP, $I_{C(\text{sat})} = 6$ mA, $V_{CC} = -9$ V, $V_{CE} = 4$ V, $\beta_{DC} = 230$. Calculate R_C, $I_{B(Q)}$, and R_B.

9. Calculate the power dissipated by the transistor in Problem 7.

10. Calculate the power dissipated by the transistor in Problem 8.

5–3 VOLTAGE-DIVIDER BIAS

11. Calculate the base voltage, emitter voltage, collector current, and collector–emitter voltage for Figure 5–27. Draw and label the load line and mark the Q point.

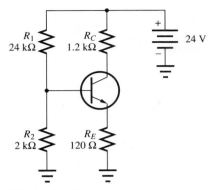

Figure 5–27

12. Calculate the base voltage, emitter voltage, collector current, and collector–emitter voltage for Figure 5–28. Draw and label the load line and mark the Q point.

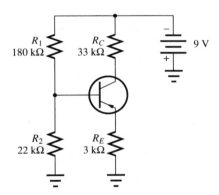

Figure 5–28

13. Design a voltage-divider-biased amplifier from this data: NPN, $I_{C(\text{sat})} = 25$ mA, $V_{CC} = 12$ V, $V_{CE(Q)} = 6$ V, $\beta_{DC} = 190$. The ratio of R_C to R_E shall be 15/1. Calculate R_C, R_E, R_1, R_2, and $I_{C(Q)}$.

14. Design a voltage-divider-biased amplifier from this data: PNP, $I_{C(\text{sat})} = 15$ mA, $V_{CC} = -24$ V, $V_{CE(Q)} = 15$ V, $\beta_{DC} = 160$. The ratio of R_C to R_E shall be 10/1. Calculate R_C, R_E, R_1, R_2, and $I_{C(Q)}$.

15. Calculate the power dissipated by the transistor in Problem 13.

16. Calculate the power dissipated by the transistor in Problem 14.

5–4 EMITTER BIAS

17. Calculate the collector current, and the collector–emitter voltage for Figure 5–29.

18. Calculate the collector current, and the collector-emitter voltage for Figure 5–30.

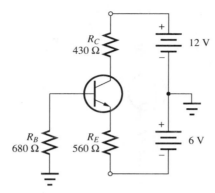

Figure 5–29

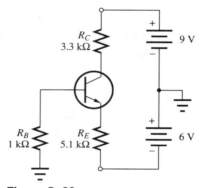

Figure 5–30

5–7 TRANSISTOR TESTING AND TROUBLESHOOTING

19. Refer to the circuit of Problem 6. Describe the effect on collector current and collector–emitter voltage for each of these circuit changes.
    (a) h_{FE} increases.
    (b) R_B increases in resistance.
    (c) R_B becomes shorted.

20. Refer to the circuit of Problem 11. Describe the effect on collector current and collector–emitter voltage for each of these troubles.
    (a) The base and emitter leads short together.
    (b) R_2 opens.
    (c) R_C opens.
    (d) R_E opens.
    (e) R_1 becomes shorted.
    (f) R_1 opens.

21. Refer to the circuit of Problem 12. Describe the effect on collector current and collector–emitter voltage for each of these circuit changes.
    (a) h_{FE} increases.
    (b) R_2 increases in resistance.
    (c) R_C decreases in resistance.
    (d) R_1 increases in resistance.
    (e) The ambient temperature increases.

ADDITIONAL PROBLEMS

22. Calculate the quiescent collector current, base current, and collector–emitter voltage for Figure 5–31. Draw and label the load line and mark the Q point.

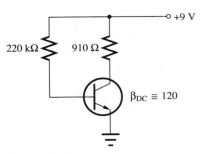

Figure 5–31

23. Calculate $I_{B(Q)}$, $I_{C(Q)}$, and $V_{CE(Q)}$ for Figure 5–32. Draw and label the load line and mark the Q point.

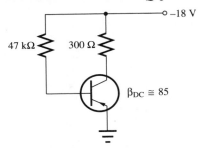

Figure 5–32

24. Design a base-biased amplifier from this data: NPN, $I_{C(sat)} = 15$ mA, $V_{CC} = 15$ V, $V_{CE} = 7$ V, $\beta_{DC} = 210$. Calculate R_C, $I_{B(Q)}$, $I_{C(Q)}$, and R_B.

25. Calculate $I_{B(Q)}$, $I_{C(Q)}$, and $V_{CE(Q)}$ for Figure 5–33. Draw and label the load line and mark the Q point.

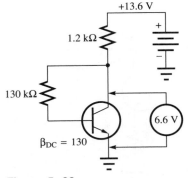

Figure 5–33

26. Calculate $I_{B(Q)}$, $I_{C(Q)}$, $V_{CE(Q)}$, and $P_{D(Q)}$ of the transistor for Figure 5–34.

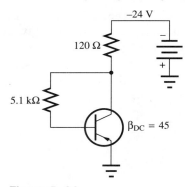

Figure 5–34

27. Design a collector-feedback-bias amplifier from this data: NPN, $I_{C(\text{sat})} = 80$ mA, $V_{CC} = 24$ V, $V_{CE(Q)} = 12$ V, $\beta_{DC} = 70$. Calculate R_C, $I_{B(Q)}$, $I_{C(Q)}$, and R_B.

28. Calculate V_B, B_E, $I_{C(Q)}$, $V_{CE(Q)}$, and $P_{D(Q)}$ for the transistor in Figure 5–35.

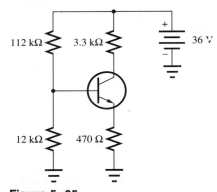

Figure 5–35

29. Calculate V_B, V_E, $I_{C(Q)}$, $V_{CE(Q)}$, and $P_{D(Q)}$ for the transistor in Figure 5–36.

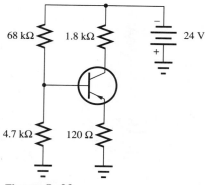

Figure 5–36

30. Design a voltage-divider-biased amplifier from this data: NPN, $I_{C(sat)}$ = 25 mA, V_{CC} = 12 V, $V_{CE(Q)}$ = 6 V, β_{DC} = 190. The ratio of R_C to R_E shall be approximately 12/1. Calculate R_C, R_E, R_1, R_2, and $I_{C(Q)}$.

31. Calculate $I_{C(Q)}$, $V_{CE(Q)}$, and $P_{D(Q)}$ for Figure 5–37.

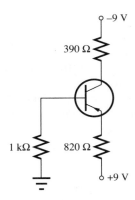

Figure 5–37

ANSWERS TO SELF-CHECKS

SELF-CHECK 5–1

1. Collector current is determined by transistor β_{DC} and base current.
2. V_{RB}, R_B, and β_{DC}
3. β_{DC}
4. R_B = 457.6 kΩ
5. Collector current increases with temperature.

SELF-CHECK 5–2

1. $I_{C(Q)}$ = 4.48 mA and $I_{B(Q)}$ = 35.8 μA.
2. R_B = 348.3 kΩ
3. As temperature increases, V_{CE} tends to decrease, which decreases V_{RB}, which decreases I_B, which decreases I_C and increases V_{CE}. Thus, the bias point is self-regulated.

SELF-CHECK 5–3

1. V_B = 1.5 V, V_E = 0.8 V, $I_{C(Q)}$ = 2.67 mA, and $V_{CE(Q)}$ = 8.39 V
2. R_C = 2.2 kΩ, R_E = 220 Ω, R_2 = 6,424 Ω, R_1 = 60,275 Ω
   $I_{C(Q)}$ = 1.65 mA, $I_{B(max)}$ = 1.65 mA/100 = 16.5 μA
   I_{R2} = 165 μA, V_{R2} = 0.7 V + 0.36 V = 1.06 V
3. As long as the voltage divider resistors are not too large, β_{DC} has little effect on the Q point. $R_2 \leq V_B/10I_B$

SELF-CHECK 5–4

1. $V_{RE} = 9.3$ V
2. $I_{C(Q)} = 3.1$ mA
3. $V_{RC} = 7.44$ V
4. $V_{CE} = 8.26$ V

SELF-CHECK 5–5

1. I_{CBO} increases with temperature and can cause the base-bias voltage to increase, which increases I_C.
2. V_{BE} decreases with temperature and causes I_B and I_C to increase.
3. A compounding effect in which increasing collector current and temperature are both cause and effect.

SELF-CHECK 5–6

1. The negative terminal of the DC supply is connected to the common ground and the positive terminal is connected to the PNP transistor's emitter resistor. The amplifier is connected as shown in Figure 5–12e and f.
2. The positive terminal of the DC supply is connected to the common ground and the negative terminal is connected to the NPN transistor's emitter resistor. The amplifier is connected as shown in Figure 5–12b and c.

SELF-CHECK 5–7

1. False
2. Test leads are placed across the base–emitter junction. If the same low reading is obtained when the leads are switched, the junction is shorted.
3. Decrease
4. The collector resistor may be open, in which case $V_{RC} = V_{CC}$, or may have increased in resistance due to heat or aging.
5. The base voltage is normal, the collector–emitter voltage is approximately equal to V_{CC}, and V_{RE} and V_{RC} are close to 0 V.

SUGGESTED PROJECTS

1. Add some of the main concepts, formulas, and procedures from this chapter to your Electronics Notebook.
2. Construct and test some of the circuits in this chapter. You may want to compare the temperature stability of the base-bias, collector-feedback-bias, and voltage-divider-bias designs. To do this, connect your voltmeter across the transistor to measure V_{CE}. Now, very carefully, use a low-wattage soldering iron to heat the transistor. Do not touch the hot iron to the transistor; just bring the hot tip close to the transistor without touching the transistor. This will heat it sufficiently so that you will see a change in V_{CE} in the base-bias and collector-feedback designs. However,

you should see very little change in V_{CE} in the voltage-divider design. You could also place an ammeter in series with the collector to observe collector current while heating.

3. Design a voltage-divider transistor amplifier circuit. You may want to use a 2N3904 transistor. Design your circuit for midpoint bias with $I_{C(Q)}$ in the area of 5 to 20 mA. Select R_E to be approximately equal to 0.1 R_C. Remember, the voltage-divider current should be about 10 times the base current for a good design (one where beta has little effect). Construct your design and measure V_{CE} to see if you are close to midpoint bias.

Common-emitter transistor amplifiers are used extensively in this stereo audio mixer from Radio Shack. This demonstrates that discrete transistor amplifiers are still used in electronic equipment. (Courtesy of Radio Shack, a division of Tandy Corporation)

6 Transistor Amplifier Configurations

OBJECTIVES

After studying this chapter, you will be able to

- analyze, design, and explain the characteristics of common-emitter (CE) amplifiers.
- analyze, design, and explain the characteristics of common-collector (CC) amplifiers.
- analyze and explain the characteristics of common-base (CB) amplifiers.
- troubleshoot amplifier stages and amplifier systems using a signal generator, oscilloscope, signal injector, and/or a signal tracer.

NEED TO KNOW

Suppose you have an audio mixer that has only high-level inputs (inputs intended for turntables and tape decks) and you want to add a low-level amplifier for a microphone input. You want to build a microphone preamplifier that will raise the microphone level to the level of the tape decks. The tape decks normally supply about 500 mVAC to the mixer input. The microphone only produces about 20 mVAC. Therefore, you need an amplifier that can provide an amplification factor of about 25(500 mV/20 mV = 25 = 28 dB) to raise the microphone level to the tape-deck level. The input impedance at the mixer is 50 kΩ. What type of amplifier configuration will you use and how will you go about designing it? Not sure? Keep this practical problem in mind as you study this chapter. The solution to this Need to Know will make more sense to you after you study this chapter. Try to design it yourself before you look at the solution.

Here are some guidelines to follow. Use the DC supply in the mixer to power your preamplifier. Assume it to be +18 V. Use a 10-kΩ resistor for the collector resistor in your amplifier circuit. Design your circuit so the quiescent V_{CE} is about 9 V. Use a 2N3904 transistor and assume the minimum AC beta to be 100. Determine coupling and bypass capacitor values for the lowest audio frequency (f_{low}) of 50 Hz.

INTRODUCTION

This chapter is a very practical one that covers the AC analysis of transistor amplifier circuits. You will learn to analyze and design useful single-stage amplifier circuits. You will also discover the three main amplifier configurations: common-emitter, common-collector, and common-base. Applications and characteristics for these very different configurations will be discussed. Finally, you will increase your knowledge of troubleshooting as new techniques and equipment are introduced. Enjoy!

6–1 COMMON-EMITTER AMPLIFIERS

INTRODUCTION TO COMMON-EMITTER (CE) AMPLIFIERS

The CE Configuration

The most frequent implementation of transistors in amplifier circuits is the **common-emitter (CE)** configuration. This is the configuration that you learned to bias in Chapter 3. It is so named because the emitter circuit is in common with the input and output (the base being the input terminal and the collector the output terminal). The main purpose for the CE amplifier is to provide voltage and power gain. In other words, CE amplifiers are able to multiply the AC input voltage and power manyfold.

Audio Amplifier Application

Figure 6–1 shows a simple four-stage audio amplifier circuit. The first three stages are common-emitter stages. Each of these CE stages is able to amplify (multiply) its input signal (AC voltage). This is necessary because a microphone, for example, is not able to drive a speaker directly. The audio voltage applied to the speaker is normally in a range greater than 1 V. Dynamic

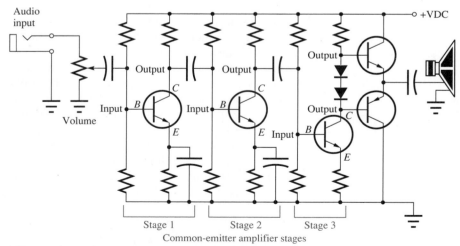

Figure 6–1   Common-emitter amplifiers in an audio amplifier system.

microphones, for example, are able to produce audio voltages in the range of 5 to 25 mV at a very low current. The first three CE stages of this amplifier circuit provide the voltage gain and the final stage provides the current gain to produce the power to drive the speaker. In many amplifier systems, voltage gain is obtained first through the use of CE amplifiers. Then the voltage gain is converted to a power gain using a current amplifier (more on this later). For the circuit of Figure 6–1, the overall voltage gain for the three CE stages is probably in the range of 60 to 80 dB (a range of amplification between 1,000 to 10,000).

You may have noticed that the CE amplifier stages are capacitor coupled. Recall that a capacitor blocks DC while passing AC. The capacitor prevents the higher DC collector voltage of Stage 1 from overbiasing the base of Stage 2. This allows each stage to be designed nearly independently and assembled as building blocks to provide the necessary overall AC voltage gain. We will discuss this further later.

Radio-Frequency Amplifier Application

Figure 6–2 illustrates how common-emitter amplifiers are also used in radio-frequency amplifier circuits. In this case the intermediate-frequency (IF) section of an AM or FM radio is shown. This is the middle section of radio receivers, where most of the amplification takes place. The overall voltage gain of this section is usually in the range of 80 to 100 dB (10,000 to 100,000 times).

Notice that the coupling between stages is provided by RF transformers. These transformers are tuned, and therefore resonant, at the intermediate frequency (typically 455 kHz for AM and 10.7 MHz for FM). This tuned-transformer coupling provides the necessary selectivity to reject unwanted

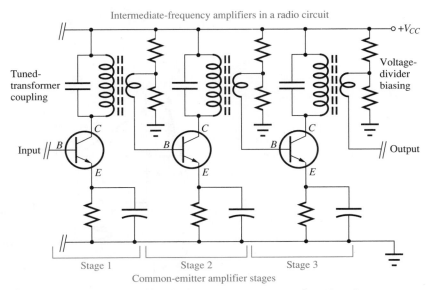

Figure 6–2 Common-emitter amplifiers in the intermediate-frequency section of a radio.

stations while the intended station is amplified. Naturally, the discussion of the overall theory of radio receivers is not our purpose here. The point is that CE amplifiers have the same basic purpose in radio-frequency amplifiers as they do in audio amplifiers—to provide voltage gain.

Now that you are aware of the great importance of CE amplifiers, let's begin a systematic study of their characteristics, analysis, and design from an AC viewpoint.

THE INPUT/OUTPUT PHASE RELATIONSHIP

One of the important characteristics of the CE amplifier is the out-of-phase relationship of the AC input signal and the output signal. This is illustrated in Figure 6–3. The output at the collector is 180° out of phase with the input at the base. This is not a disadvantage, simply a fact. The graph shows the cause and effect relationship between the AC input signal and the AC output signal. Notice that, as the AC at the input increases in the positive direction, the base-bias voltage increases, due to superposition. In other words, the base voltage is the *sum* of the DC bias voltage and the instantaneous signal voltage. As the bias increases with the positive-going AC, the collector

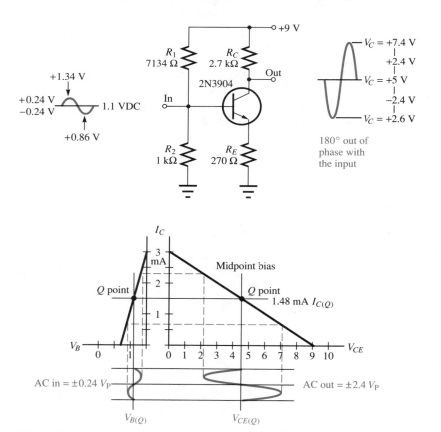

Figure 6–3 Input/output phase relationship of the common-emitter amplifier.

current increases. This causes the collector–emitter voltage to decrease, because the collector-resistor voltage increases with collector current ($\downarrow V_{CE} = V_{CC} - \uparrow V_{RC} - \uparrow V_{RE}$). Thus, as the base voltage increases, the collector voltage decreases, causing the output waveform to be 180° out of phase with the input ($\downarrow V_C = \downarrow\downarrow V_{CE} + \uparrow V_{RE}$). Study Figure 6–3 carefully so you can clearly see the relationship between the AC input voltage, collector current, and AC output voltage. The graph shows how the changing base voltage affects the collector current and the collector–emitter voltage.

AC TRANSISTOR PARAMETERS

AC Currents, Voltages, and Resistances

The AC analysis of CE amplifier circuits involves the use of AC parameters. When analyzing a transistor circuit, it is often necessary to distinguish between AC and DC currents, voltages, and resistances. AC parameters are designated as such with lowercase letters to clearly identify them apart from DC parameters. Here is a listing of some of the AC parameters we use.

i_b = AC base current = a change in I_B = ΔI_B

i_e = AC emitter current = a change in I_E = ΔI_E

i_c = AC collector current = a change in I_C = ΔI_C

$v_b = v_{in}$ = AC base voltage = a change in V_B = ΔV_B

v_{be} = AC base-emitter voltage = a change in V_{BE} = ΔV_{BE}

$v_c = v_{out}$ = AC collector voltage = a change in V_C = ΔV_C

v_{ce} = AC collector-emitter voltage = a change in V_{CE} = ΔV_{CE}

v_e = AC emitter voltage = a change in V_E = ΔV_E

r_c = a very large internal AC collector resistance

r_b = a very small internal AC base resistance

r'_e = a small but significant internal AC emitter resistance

r_C = the total external AC collector resistance, which includes $R_C \parallel R_L$ (R_L being a load resistance)

r_E = an external emitter resistor that opposes AC and DC

AC Current Gain (β, h_{fe})

AC current gain is designated as β or h_{fe} and is the ratio of AC collector current to AC base current. The AC collector current represents a change in DC collector current (ΔI_C) and the AC base current represents a change in DC base current (ΔI_B). Therefore,

$$\beta = h_{fe} = i_c/i_b = \Delta I_C/\Delta I_B \tag{6–1}$$

EXAMPLE 6–1

An AC input signal to a CE transistor amplifier causes a 10-μA change in base current, which results in a 2.2-mA change in collector current. What is the transistor's AC current gain (β) under these conditions?

$$\beta = h_{fe} = i_c/i_b = \Delta I_C/\Delta I_B = 2.2 \text{ mA}/10 \text{ } \mu\text{A} = 220$$

So, what is the difference between β_{DC} and β? Sometimes there is very little difference. For small-signal amplifiers, the AC collector current is very small compared to the DC quiescent current. The change in collector current is, say, $\frac{1}{10}$ of the quiescent collector current. In this case, the ratio of $i_c/i_b \cong I_C/I_B$. Thus, the change in base and collector currents does not vary significantly above or below the quiescent values, which keeps β close to β_{DC}. However, for large-signal applications, the AC current gain can differ from the DC current gain because the AC current varies over a larger portion of the I_C/I_B curve and this curve is nonlinear (not a straight-line graph). Also, the actual value of β depends on the amount of quiescent collector current, which means the position of the Q point on the curve. See Figure 6–4. Notice that the slope of the curve is less when close to cutoff and saturation than it is in the middle of the curve. The slope at any point on the curve is equal to the DC beta and affects the AC beta for AC currents varying up and down from that point. The distinction between AC beta and DC beta is usually relatively small and can be considered insignificant in many cases.

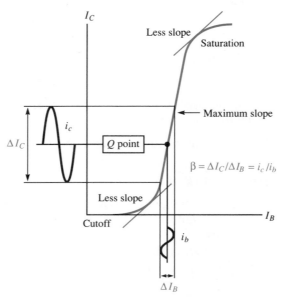

Figure 6–4   AC beta (β, h_{fe}).

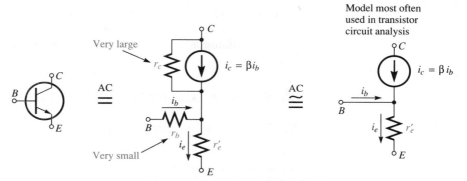

Figure 6–5 *R*-parameter equivalents for the bipolar transistor.

A TRANSISTOR MODEL

A Practical Model

Often, a model of the transistor helps us understand its function in a circuit such as the CE amplifier circuit. Figure 6–5 shows a current-source model of the transistor that is very helpful in understanding transistor circuit theory. The first model, to the right of the transistor symbol, is a complete model, showing the *r*-parameter equivalent of the transistor under AC operation. The AC collector resistance (r_c), paralleling the current-source symbol, is very large and normally has little effect on the operation of the transistor. Thus, from a practical standpoint, we can eliminate it from the model. The AC base resistance (r_b) is very small and has little attenuating effect on the applied AC voltage. Thus, it can be replaced with a short. The one internal AC resistance that we will leave in the model is the AC emitter resistance (r_e'). This is not a large resistance, yet it does have a significant effect on transistor circuit performance, as you will soon see.

AC Emitter Resistance (r_e')

The amount of internal AC emitter resistance of a transistor depends on the amount of DC emitter current. The higher the current, the lower the AC emitter resistance. A formula has been derived using calculus that shows this relationship.

$$r_e' \cong 25\ mV/I_E \qquad\qquad (6\text{–}2)$$

where 25 mV is a constant derived using calculus.

EXAMPLE 6–2

The base-bias voltage for a CE amplifier is 1.2 V and the emitter resistor R_E is 180 Ω. Calculate the approximate AC emitter resistance r_e'.
First calculate I_E.

$$I_E = V_{RE}/R_E \cong (1.2\ V - 0.7\ V)/180\ \Omega = 2.78\ mA$$

Now calculate r_e'.

$$r_e' \cong 25\ mV/I_E \cong 25\ mV/2.78\ mA = 8.99\ \Omega$$

Formula 6–2 is an approximation that depends on transistor design, temperature, and emitter current. This approximation is adequate for most transistor amplifier analysis or design. (See Appendix F for the derivation of this formula.)

COMMON-EMITTER AMPLIFIER VOLTAGE GAIN

The Voltage-Gain Relationship

You are already aware that the voltage gain of a CE amplifier is of great importance. But what determines the voltage gain of the CE amplifier? Recall that voltage gain is the ratio $v_{\text{out}}/v_{\text{in}}$. The symbol for voltage gain is A_V, for voltage amplification factor. Thus,

$$A_V = v_{\text{out}}/v_{\text{in}} \tag{6–3}$$

The General A_V Formula for CE Amplifier Analysis

Formula 6–3 assumes you have measured the input and output AC voltages and are using those values to determine the actual voltage gain. But suppose you want to determine the voltage gain from the schematic of a CE amplifier without building the circuit and experimenting with it. The voltage gain can be determined very closely using theoretical analysis. The exact formula you use will depend on the actual circuit design. However, all formulas for A_V are based on a simple relationship:

$$A_V = \text{AC collector resistance/AC emitter resistance} \tag{6–4}$$

Consider the three cases shown in Figure 6–6.

$A_V = R_C/r'_e$

Figure 6–6a indicates the voltage gain to be the ratio of R_C/r'_e. This conforms to the general formula, Formula 6–4. The collector resistor acts as the AC collector resistance and the internal emitter resistance is the AC emitter resistance. But what does R_C have to do with v_{out} and r'_e have to do with v_{in}? In other words, why is $v_{\text{out}}/v_{\text{in}} = R_C/r'_e$? In Figure 6–6a, v_{out} is developed across R_C and v_{in} is developed across r'_e. Consider the following:

AC base voltage = AC emitter voltage = AC emitter current · AC emitter resistance

$$v_b = v_e = i_e \cdot r'_e = v_{\text{in}}$$

$$i_e \cong i_c \quad \text{therefore} \quad v_c \cong i_e \cdot R_C = v_{\text{out}}$$

$$A_V = v_{\text{out}}/v_{\text{in}} = (i_e \cdot R_C)/(i_e \cdot r'_e) = R_C/r'_e$$

Why is the AC output voltage (v_{out}) developed across the collector resistor? This is important for you to understand. As far as AC is concerned, the top of the collector resistor is at ground potential. This is because the DC supply (V_{CC}) offers a very low impedance path to ground for the AC. This means that the output from collector to ground (v_c) is actually the AC voltage drop across the collector resistor. You'll see this again in a moment.

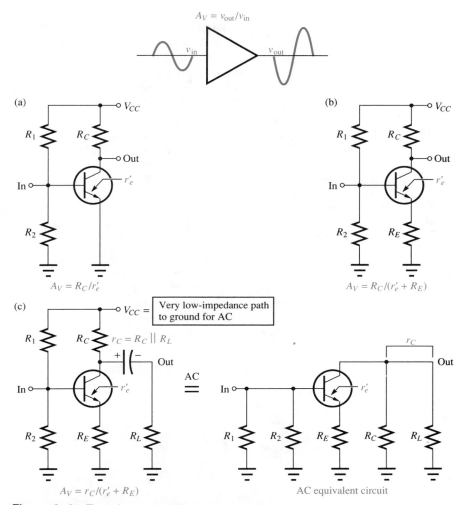

Figure 6–6 Transistor-amplifier voltage gain.

$A_V = R_C/(r'_e + R_E)$

Figure 6–6b has an additional emitter resistance (R_E). This resistor is called a **swamping resistor.** Recall that the value of r'_e is dependent on I_E. With an AC signal applied to the base, the emitter current is continually and rapidly changing value ($i_e = \Delta I_E$). Since I_E is changing, r'_e must also be changing ($\Delta r'_e = 25$ mV/ΔI_E). Finally, since r_e is changing, the voltage gain must be changing (for Figure 6–6a, $\Delta A_V = R_C/\Delta r'_e$). This is not good, because the constantly changing voltage gain of the amplifier causes undesirable changes in the output voltage waveform, changes that are referred to as **distortion.** In other words, the output voltage is not a faithful reproduction of the input voltage. The swamping resistor helps swamp out (nullify) the effects of the changing r'_e on the voltage gain. This is because, with the swamping resistor, the voltage gain formula now becomes the ratio of $R_C/(r'_e + R_E)$, where R_E is much greater than r'_e.

$$A_V = (R_C \parallel R_L)/(r'_e + R_E)$$

Figure 6–6c is a further, more practical, application of the general voltage gain formula (Formula 6–4). Notice that a load resistor is added. This is a practical consideration, since the amplifier must be connected to something. Now the AC collector resistance is not simply R_C. It is R_C in parallel with R_L. The AC equivalent circuit demonstrates this. Remember, V_{CC} acts as a near short to ground for the AC currents. As such, R_1 and R_C are tied to ground, as far as AC is concerned. Notice how R_C is in parallel with R_L. Also, the coupling capacitor is replaced with a short between R_C and R_L. This means the AC collector current ($i_c \cong i_e$) must flow through the parallel equivalent of $R_C \parallel R_L$. The output voltage (v_{out}) is developed across this parallel equivalent ($R_C \parallel R_L$) = r_C, $v_c = v_{out} = i_c \cdot r_C$. The AC resistance for the collector is r_C and the AC resistance for the emitter is $r'_e + R_E$. Therefore, the voltage gain for the circuit of Figure 6–6c is the ratio of $r_C/(r'_e + R_E)$.

Notice how the voltage gain was reduced by adding the swamping resistor (R_E) and the reduced again by adding the load resistor (R_L). The emitter resistor increases the resistance in the denominator and the load resistor decreases the resistance in the numerator of the voltage gain formula, decreasing the overall value of A_V. Examples 6–3, 6–4, and 6–5 illustrate voltage gain calculations.

EXAMPLE 6–3

Determine the voltage amplification factor and voltage gain in decibels for Figure 6–7.

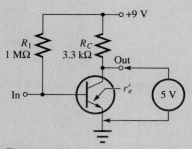

Figure 6–7

First determine I_E:

$$I_E \cong I_C = V_{RC}/R_C = (9 \text{ V} - 5 \text{ V})/3.3 \text{ k}\Omega = 1.21 \text{ mA}.$$

Next find r'_e:

$$r'_e \cong 25 \text{ mV}/I_E = 25 \text{ mV}/1.21 \text{ mA} = 20.7 \ \Omega.$$

Now calculate A_V:

$$A_V = R_C/r'_e = 3300 \ \Omega/20.7 \ \Omega = 159.$$

Gain in dB = $20 \log_{10}(159) = 44$ dB.

EXAMPLE 6–4

Determine the voltage amplification factor and voltage gain in decibels for Figure 6–8.

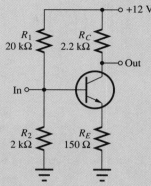

Figure 6–8

To determine I_E, we must first determine V_E and V_B, where $V_E \cong V_B - 0.7$ V.

Using the voltage-divider rule,

$V_B \cong 12$ V $\cdot$ 2 kΩ/22 kΩ = 1.09 V

$V_E \cong V_B - 0.7$ V = 1.09 V $-$ 0.7 V = 0.39 V

Now determine I_E:

$I_E = V_{RE}/R_E = 0.39$ V/150 Ω = 2.6 mA.

Next find r'_e:

$r'_e \cong 25$ mV/I_E = 25 mV/2.6 mA = 9.62 Ω.

Now calculate A_V:

$A_V = R_C/(r'_e + R_E)$

    = 2,200 Ω/(9.62 Ω + 150 Ω) = 13.8.

Gain in dB = 20 $\log_{10}$(13.8) = 22.8 dB.

EXAMPLE 6–5

Use a coupling capacitor to connect a 10-kΩ load resistor to the output of the amplifier in Figure 6–8. Now determine the voltage gain.

$A_V = (R_C \parallel R_L)/(r'_e + R_E) = r_c/(r'_e + R_E)$

    = (10 k$\Omega \parallel$ 2.2 $k\Omega$)/(9.62 Ω + 150 Ω) = 1,803 Ω/159.62 Ω = 11.3

Gain in dB = 20 $\log_{10}$(11.3) = 21.1 dB

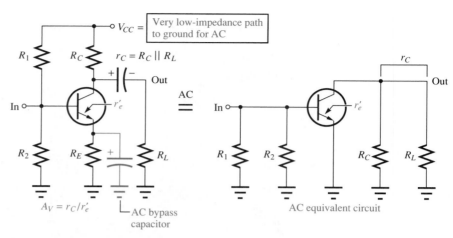

Figure 6–9   Bypassing the emitter resistor for more gain.

Example 6–5 clearly demonstrates the effect the load resistor has on the amplifier's voltage gain. As the load resistor is made lower in value, the gain decreases. The load resistor represents the input impedance of a consecutive (cascaded) amplifier stage. Thus, each consecutive stage affects the voltage gain of the previous stage. This must be taken into consideration when designing an amplifier system for a specific total gain.

Increasing A_V and A_V Stability

Figure 6–9 shows a very common form of the CE amplifier. A bypass capacitor is added across the emitter resistor to increase the voltage gain. This capacitor has a very low X_C at the lowest frequency the amplifier must amplify. In this way, the emitter of the transistor is tied (shorted) to ground as shown in the AC equivalent diagram. The voltage gain is once again very high, equal to approximately r_C/r_e'. The emitter resistor still provides some DC bias stability in the form of negative feedback against the base–emitter junction. However, the problem of distortion due to rapid changes in voltage gain has returned. This problem is not severe if the circuit is operated as a small-signal amplifier where $i_e < 0.1\,I_E$.

Figure 6–10 is a final effort to have the best of both worlds—high gain and good gain stability. A portion of R_E is used as r_E to help swamp out the effects of a changing r_e'. Notice the AC equivalent circuit diagram and the formula for A_V. The AC emitter resistance is the sum of r_e' and r_E. Thus, the voltage gain is the ratio of $r_C/(r_e' + r_E)$, which still conforms to our general formula for voltage amplification (total AC collector resistance divided by the total AC emitter resistance).

The Concept of A_V—A Summary

You may be wondering how you can possibly remember all the different formulas for A_V. The various formulas are not numbered because I want you to focus your understanding on Formula 6–4, $A_V = r_C/(r_e' + r_E)$. The voltage gain of any CE amplifier is always the ratio of the AC collector resistance to

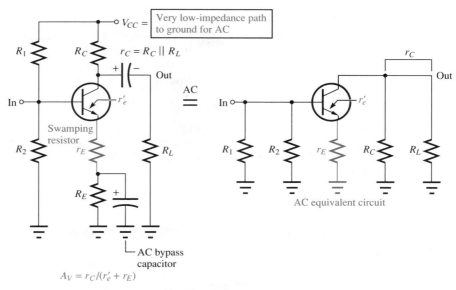

Figure 6–10   Adding a swamping resistor for gain stability.

the AC emitter resistance. The AC collector resistance is either R_C, with no load, or $R_C \parallel R_L$ when there is a load resistance. The AC emitter resistance always includes the internal emitter resistance (r_e') and any unbypassed emitter resistor. It's that simple. No formulas to memorize. Consider Example 6–6.

EXAMPLE 6–6

The circuit of Figure 6–10 has the following values: $R_C = 3.3$ kΩ, $R_L = 4.7$ kΩ, $r_E = 100$ Ω, $R_E = 250$ Ω, $I_E = 1.8$ mA.
Calculate the voltage amplification factor (A_V).
First calculate r_e':

$$r_e' \cong 0.025/1.8 \text{ mA} = 13.9 \text{ }\Omega$$

Next, calculate r_C:

$$r_C = R_C \parallel R_L = (3.3 \text{ k}\Omega \cdot 4.7 \text{ k}\Omega)/(3.3 \text{ k}\Omega + 4.7 \text{ k}\Omega)$$
$$= 1.94 \text{ k}\Omega$$

Now A_V:

$$A_V = r_C/(r_e' + r_E) = 1.94 \text{ k}\Omega/(13.9 \text{ }\Omega + 100 \text{ }\Omega) = 17$$

$$^\#\text{dB} = 20 \log(17) = 20 \cdot 1.23 = 24.6 \text{ dB}$$

Coupling Capacitors and Bypass Capacitors

The coupling capacitor between the collector of the transistor and the load resistor must not have a significant X_C at the frequency, or frequencies, that must be amplified. You do not want the coupling capacitor to drop a significant amount of the AC voltage across itself. As a general rule, the X_C of the coupling capacitor should be less than or equal to the load resistance at the lowest frequency that must be amplified. Therefore, from the X_C formula, we can derive the following:

$$C_C \geq 0.159/R_L f_{\text{low}} \tag{6-5}$$

The emitter bypass capacitor should act as a near short at the lowest frequency of operation. A suggested rule of thumb here is to make the bypass capacitor large enough so its X_C is 0.1 r_e' at the lowest frequency. Consider Example 6–7.

$$C_B \geq 0.159/0.1\, r_e' f_{\text{low}} = 1.59/r_e' f_{\text{low}} \tag{6-6}$$

EXAMPLE 6–7

The lowest frequency a CE amplifier is to amplify is 20 Hz. The load resistor is 10 kΩ and r_e' is 26 Ω. What is the minimum capacitance for the coupling capacitor and the bypass capacitor?

$$C_C \geq 0.159/R_L f_{\text{low}} = 0.159/(10 \text{ k}\Omega \cdot 20 \text{ Hz}) = 0.795 \ \mu\text{F} \qquad (\text{use } 1 \ \mu\text{F})$$

$$C_B \geq 1.59/r_e' f_{\text{low}} = 1.59/(26 \ \Omega \cdot 20 \text{ Hz})$$

$$= 3{,}058 \ \mu\text{F} \qquad (3{,}000 \ \mu\text{F or greater is OK})$$

COMMON EMITTER INPUT AND OUTPUT IMPEDANCE

In a multistage amplifier, it is important to know the input impedance to each amplifier stage, because it is this input impedance that acts as the load resistance for the previous stage. The stage input impedance affects both the gain of the previous stage and the value of the interstage coupling capacitor. Therefore, to determine the minimum value of coupling capacitance and the voltage gain of the previous stage, the input impedance must be calculated.

Base Input Impedance (Z_b)

Let's return to the practical transistor model as shown in Figure 6–11. The AC impedance looking into the base of the transistor itself is part of the total

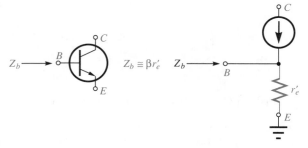

Figure 6–11   Base–emitter input impedance.

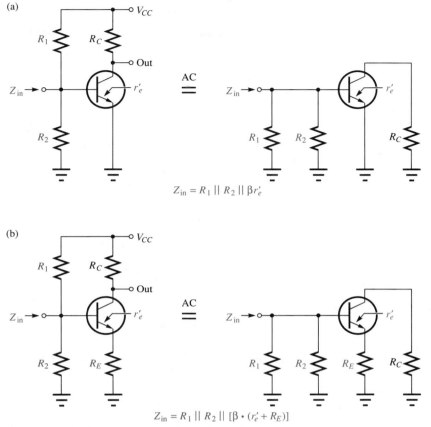

$$Z_{in} = R_1 \parallel R_2 \parallel \beta r'_e$$

$$Z_{in} = R_1 \parallel R_2 \parallel [\beta \cdot (r'_e + R_E)]$$

Figure 6–12 Amplifier stage input impedance.

input impedance for any CE amplifier. Here, we see that the input impedance to the base of the transistor itself is the product of the AC beta and the internal emitter resistance.

CE Stage Input Impedance (Z_{in})

Figure 6–12 illustrates stage input impedance calculations for two CE amplifiers. Here is what you need to realize: The stage input impedance (Z_{in}) for the voltage-divider-biased CE amplifier is always the parallel combination of $R_1 \parallel R_2 \parallel Z_b$.

$$Z_{in} = R_1 \parallel R_2 \parallel Z_b = 1/[(1/R_1) + (1/R_2) + (1/Z_b)] \tag{6–7}$$

where Z_b is always the product of β and any AC emitter resistances.

Carefully compare the CE amplifier circuits shown in Figures 6–12 and 6–13. Notice the input impedance calculations always include $R_1 \parallel R_2 \parallel Z_b$. It is the manner in which the base impedance (Z_b) is calculated for the different circuits that should concern you. However, realize that in every case, the base impedance is the product of β and the total AC emitter resistance. The total AC emitter resistance may be: just r'_e (Figure 6–12a and 6–13a), $r'_e + R_E$ (Figure 6–12b), or $r'_e + r_E$ (Figure 6–13b). As in voltage gain calculations,

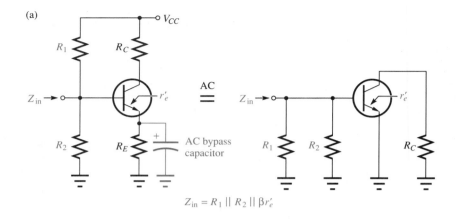

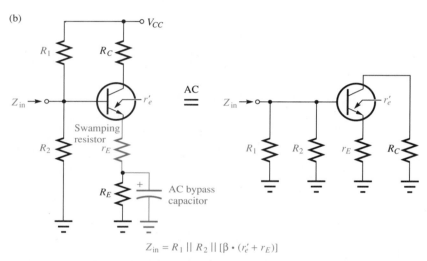

Figure 6-13 The emitter bypass capacitor and input impedance.

stage input impedance calculations are based on one basic formula—Formula 6-7. Consider the following examples.

EXAMPLE 6-8

Determine Z_{in} for Figure 6–14.

$Z_{in} = R_1 \parallel R_2 \parallel Z_b = R_1 \parallel R_2 \parallel [\beta \cdot (r'_e + r_E)]$

We know all values except r'_e. To find r'_e we must calculate I_E. To find I_E we must calculate V_B.

$V_B \cong V_{CC} \cdot R_2/(R_1 + R_2) = 12 \text{ V} \cdot 1 \text{ k}\Omega/(1 \text{ k}\Omega + 6.8 \text{ k}\Omega) = 1.54 \text{ V}$

$I_E \cong (V_B - V_{BE})/(r_E + R_E) = (1.54 \text{ V} - 0.7 \text{ V})/(120 \ \Omega + 330 \ \Omega)$

$\qquad = 1.87 \text{ mA}$

$r'_e \cong 0.025/I_E = 0.025/1.87 \text{ mA} = 13.4 \ \Omega$

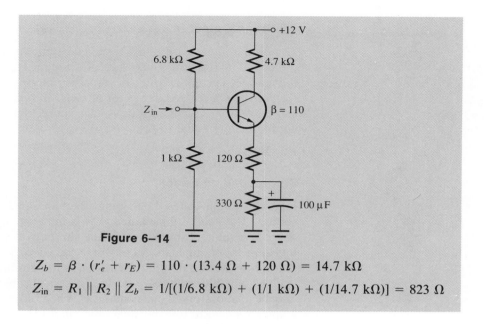

Figure 6–14

$$Z_b = \beta \cdot (r_e' + r_E) = 110 \cdot (13.4\ \Omega + 120\ \Omega) = 14.7\ \text{k}\Omega$$

$$Z_{in} = R_1 \parallel R_2 \parallel Z_b = 1/[(1/6.8\ \text{k}\Omega) + (1/1\ \text{k}\Omega) + (1/14.7\ \text{k}\Omega)] = 823\ \Omega$$

EXAMPLE 6–9

Determine Z_{in} for Figure 6–15.

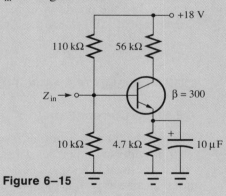

Figure 6–15

$$Z_{in} = R_1 \parallel R_2 \parallel Z_b = R_1 \parallel R_2 \parallel \beta r_e'$$

We know all values except r_e'. To find r_e' we must calculate I_E. To find I_E we must calculate V_B.

$$V_B \cong V_{CC} \cdot R_2/(R_1 + R_2) = 18\ \text{V} \cdot 10\ \text{k}\Omega/(10\ \text{k}\Omega + 110\ \text{k}\Omega) = 1.5\ \text{V}$$

$$I_E \cong (V_B - V_{BE})/R_E = (1.5\ \text{V} - 0.7\ \text{V})/4.7\ \text{k}\Omega = 0.17\ \text{mA}$$

$$r_e' \cong 0.025/I_E = 0.025/0.17\ \text{mA} = 147\ \Omega$$

$$Z_b = \beta r_e' = 300 \cdot 147\ \Omega = 44.1\ \text{k}\Omega$$

$$Z_{in} = R_1 \parallel R_2 \parallel Z_b = 1/[(1/110\ \text{k}\Omega) + (1/10\ \text{k}\Omega) + (1/44.1\ \text{k}\Omega)]$$

$$= 7.59\ \text{k}\Omega$$

CE Stage Output Impedance (Z_{out})

The output impedance of a CE stage is approximately equal to the value of the collector resistor. Thus, the collector resistor is shown in parallel with the load for current-source AC transistor models and in series with the load for voltage-source AC transistor models. In other words, the CE transistor stage acts as an AC current or voltage source that has an internal impedance approximately equal to R_C.

$$Z_{out} \cong R_C \tag{6-8}$$

Stage Loading Effect

Figure 6–16 illustrates the loading effect an amplifier has on the AC voltage source. The source impedance (Z_S) is in series with the stage input impedance. As such, it drops some of the source voltage across itself. The lower the stage input impedance, the worse the voltage drop and signal loss. Note that the total, or overall, system gain is the product of the source/load loss and the amplifier voltage gain. In a practical sense, the AC voltage source may be a laboratory signal generator. When the generator is connected to an amplifier stage, to test the stage, the input impedance of the stage loads the generator. Therefore, the voltage (v_{in}) should be set *after* the signal generator is connected and V_{CC} is applied.

The voltage source shown in Figure 6–11 may also be a previous transistor stage. Recall the three CE stages in Figure 6–1. Each consecutive stage acts as a load to the previous stage. In Figure 6–16, the voltage source can be considered a voltage-source AC model of a transistor stage where $Z_S = Z_{out} = R_C$.

COMMON-EMITTER AMPLIFIER CURRENT AND POWER GAIN

CE Stage Current Gain (A_i)

Though the main function of the CE stage is to provide voltage gain, it can also provide some current gain. As you know, the AC current gain of the transistor itself is β (h_{fe}). The entire stage current amplification factor (A_i) is not the same as β. It is the ratio of AC collector current to AC input current.

$$A_i = i_{out}/i_{in} = (v_{out}/Z_{out})/(v_{in}/Z_{in}) \tag{6-9}$$

$$= (v_{out} \cdot Z_{in})/(v_{in} \cdot Z_{out}) = A_V \cdot Z_{in}/Z_{out}$$

The stage current gain is much lower than β because the AC input current is much greater than i_b due to the current demanded by the voltage divider network. In other words, $i_{in} \gg i_b$.

CE Stage Power Gain (A_P)

The power gain for a CE stage can be very high and there are applications in which this is put to use, as we will discuss in more detail when we cover power amplifiers. For now, you should realize that, just as power is the product of current and voltage, the power amplification factor (A_P) is the

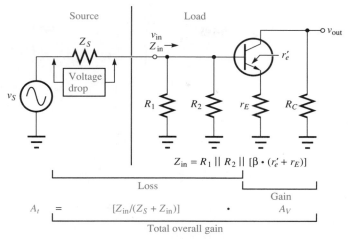

$$Z_{in} = R_1 \| R_2 \| [\beta \cdot (r'_e + r_E)]$$

$$A_t = [Z_{in}/(Z_S + Z_{in})] \quad \cdot \quad A_V$$

Figure 6–16   Input impedance loading effect.

product of the current and voltage amplification factors as follows:

$$A_P = A_i A_V = P_{out}/P_{in} = (v_{out}^2/Z_{out})/(v_{in}^2/Z_{in}) \tag{6–10}$$

$$= (v_{out}^2 \cdot Z_{in})/(v_{in}^2 \cdot Z_{out}) = A_V^2 \cdot Z_{in}/Z_{out}$$

Consider Example 6–10.

EXAMPLE 6–10 ▮▬▬▬▬▬▬▬▬▬▬▬▬▬▬▬▬▬▬▬▬▬▬▬▬▬▬▬▬▬▬

This is a continuation of Example 6–8. Z_{in} was calculated to be 823 Ω. $Z_{out} = R_C = 4.7$ kΩ. The stage voltage gain is calculated as follows:

$$A_V = R_C/(r'_e + r_E) = 4.7 \text{ k}\Omega/(13.4 \text{ }\Omega + 120 \text{ }\Omega) = 35.2$$

The stage current gain is

$$A_i = A_V \cdot Z_{in}/Z_{out} = 35.2 \cdot 823 \text{ }\Omega/4.7 \text{ k}\Omega = 6.16 \qquad \text{(Note that } \beta = 110\text{)}$$

The stage power gain is

$$A_P = A_i A_V = 6.16 \cdot 35.2 = 217$$

THE AC LOAD LINE

Determining the AC Load Line

An AC load line is very helpful in determining or demonstrating the range of **AC compliance** (maximum limits of peak-to-peak output voltage swing), also referred to as **dynamic headroom.** Figure 6–17 shows the DC load line and the AC load line for the CE amplifier shown. For the DC load line, all capacitors are removed and the line is defined as shown in box 1. (Review

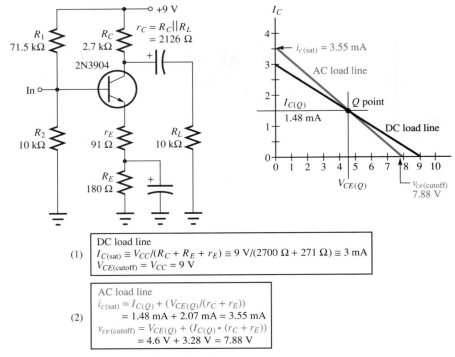

Figure 6–17 The AC load line.

DC load lines in the previous chapter if necessary.) For the AC load line, capacitors are included and the following formulas are used.

$$i_{c(\text{sat})} = I_{C(Q)} + [V_{CE(Q)}/(r_C + r_E)] \qquad (6\text{--}11)$$

$$v_{ce(\text{cutoff})} = V_{CE(Q)} + [I_{C(Q)} \cdot (r_C + r_E)] \qquad (6\text{--}12)$$

where r_C is the total AC collector resistance and r_E is the total AC emitter resistance.

Notice that the quiescent values of $I_{C(Q)}$ and $V_{CE(Q)}$ must be determined before the AC load line can be defined. Recall that $I_C \cong I_E = (V_B - 0.7 \text{ V})/$ (total DC emitter resistance), and $V_{CE(Q)} = V_{CC} - V_E - V_{RC}$. Also notice that the AC saturation current ($i_{c(\text{sat})}$) is the sum of the DC quiescent current and the maximum possible AC current $[V_{CE(Q)}/(r_C + r_E)]$. The maximum AC current is determined using the transistor voltage ($V_{CE(Q)}$) and the AC collector and emitter resistances. $V_{CE(Q)}$ is used because it is this voltage that is transferred to the AC resistances as the AC current is produced. When all of $V_{CE(Q)}$ is transferred to the AC resistances, the transistor is saturated and there is no further increase in AC current. Also, realize that the AC resistances are those resistances through which the AC current actually passes. In Figure 6–17, AC current is passed through R_C, R_L, and r_E. Note how R_E is bypassed—effectively shorted by the capacitor. Finally, the AC load line must pass through the Q point on the DC load line. If your calculations are correct, this will be so.

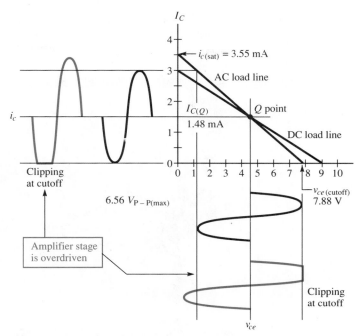

Figure 6–18   Maximum output voltage swing.

Maximum Output Voltage Swing

Once the AC load line is defined, you can easily see the maximum range of voltage swing that is possible at the output of the amplifier. Figure 6–18 illustrates this and the clipping that occurs when the transistor is overdriven. If the maximum voltage swing (AC compliance, dynamic headroom) is known, and the A_V for the stage is known, the maximum input signal voltage can be calculated. Consider Example 6–11.

EXAMPLE 6–11

For the circuit of Figure 6–17, the A_V is 19.7 and the maximum output swing is 6.56 $V_{P\text{-}P}$. Thus, the maximum input voltage is 6.56 $V_{P\text{-}P}/19.7 =$ 0.333 $V_{P\text{-}P}$ = 0.167 V_P = 0.118 V (RMS).

AC ANALYSIS OF A CE AMPLIFIER

Let's combine what you know about the analysis of voltage-divider-biased CE amplifiers in a step-by-step analysis procedure. To do so, we will follow the analysis steps provided in Example 6–12. Our purpose in analyzing this amplifier is to determine vital information such as input impedance, voltage gain, and maximum input voltage. Some of the analysis process involves the DC analysis formulas and procedures you learned in Chapter 5. Combining those with the AC analysis presented in this section will enable you to do a complete CE stage analysis.

EXAMPLE 6–12

Do a complete AC analysis of Figure 6–19.

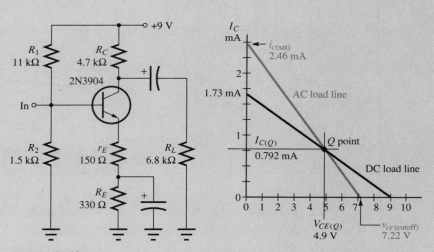

Figure 6–19

STEP 1   Determine and draw the DC load line.

$$I_{C(\text{sat})} \cong V_{CC}/(R_C + R_E + r_E) = 9 \text{ V}/5180 \ \Omega = 1.74 \text{ mA}$$

$$V_{CE(\text{cutoff})} = V_{CC} = 9 \text{ V}$$

STEP 2   Calculate the base voltage.

$$V_B \cong V_{CC} \cdot R_2/(R_1 + R_2) = 9 \text{ V} \cdot 1.5 \text{ k}\Omega/12.5 \text{ k}\Omega = 1.08 \text{ V}$$

STEP 3   Calculate the emitter voltage.

$$V_E \cong V_B - 0.7 \text{ V} = 1.08 \text{ V} - 0.7 \text{ V} = 0.38 \text{ V}$$

STEP 4   Determine the value of quiescent collector/emitter current.

$$I_{C(Q)} \cong I_{E(Q)} = V_E/(R_E + r_E) = 0.38 \text{ V}/480 \ \Omega = 0.792 \text{ mA}$$

STEP 5   Use $I_{C(Q)}$ to calculate the collector-resistor voltage.

$$V_{RC} = I_{C(Q)} \cdot R_C = 0.792 \text{ mA} \cdot 4.7 \text{ k}\Omega = 3.72 \text{ V}$$

STEP 6   Now you are ready to determine the quiescent collector–emitter voltage.

$$V_{CE(Q)} = V_{CC} - V_{RC} - V_E = 9 \text{ V} - 3.72 \text{ V} - 0.38 \text{ V}$$

$$= 4.9 \text{ V}$$

STEP 7   The approximate value of r'_e can now be determined.

$r'_e \cong 0.025/I_E = 0.025/0.792 \text{ mA} = 32 \ \Omega$

STEP 8   Next, the AC collector resistance can be calculated.

$r_C = R_C \parallel R_L = (4.7 \text{ k}\Omega \cdot 6.8 \text{ k}\Omega)/(4.7 \text{ k}\Omega + 6.8 \text{ k}\Omega)$

$= 2.78 \text{ k}\Omega$

STEP 9   Now that you know r'_e and r_C you can calculate the AC voltage gain.

$A_V = r_C/(r'_e + r_E) = 2.78 \text{ k}\Omega/182 \ \Omega = 15.3$

$^\#\text{dB} = 20 \log(15.3) = 20 \cdot 1.18 = 23.7 \text{ dB}$

STEP 10   Define and draw the AC load line.

$i_{c(\text{sat})} = I_{C(Q)} + [V_{CE(Q)}/(r_C + r_E)] = 0.792 \text{ mA} + 1.67 \text{ mA}$

$= 2.46 \text{ mA}$

$v_{ce(\text{cutoff})} = V_{CE(Q)} + [I_{C(Q)} \cdot (r_C + r_E)] = 4.9 \text{ V} + 2.32 \text{ V}$

$= 7.22 \text{ V}$

STEP 11   Calculate the maximum output voltage swing. The maximum output voltage swing is limited by the position of the Q point relative to the AC load line. In this case, the maximum swing is limited by the difference between $v_{ce(\text{cutoff})}$ and $V_{CE(Q)}$.

$v_{c(\text{out})} = (v_{ce(\text{cutoff})} - V_{CE(Q)}) \cdot 2 = (7.22 \text{ V} - 4.9 \text{ V}) \cdot 2$

$= 4.64 \ V_{\text{P-P}}$

STEP 12   Calculate the maximum input signal voltage.

$v_{b(\text{in})} = v_{c(\text{out})}/A_V = 4.64 \ V_{\text{P-P}}/15.3$

$= 0.303 \ V_{\text{P-P}} = 0.107 \text{ V (RMS)}$

STEP 13   Calculate the stage input impedance. Assume the data sheet indicates a minimum β (h_{fe}) of 100. Use this minimum value.

$Z_{\text{in}} = R_1 \parallel R_2 \parallel [\beta \cdot (r'_e + r_E)]$

$= 1/[(1/R_1) + (1/R_2) + (1/[\beta \cdot (r'_e + r_E)])]$

$= 1/[(1/11 \text{ k}\Omega) + (1/1.5 \text{ k}\Omega) + (1/18.2 \text{ k}\Omega)] = 1.23 \text{ k}\Omega$

STEP 14   Determine the stage output impedance.

$Z_{\text{out}} \cong R_C = 4.7 \text{ k}\Omega$

STEP 15   If desired, calculate the stage current gain and power gain.

$A_i = A_V \cdot Z_{\text{in}}/Z_{\text{out}} = 15.3 \cdot 1.23 \text{ k}\Omega/4.7 \text{ k}\Omega = 4$

$A_P = A_i A_V = 4 \cdot 15.3 = 61.2$

DESIGNING A STABLE COMMON-EMITTER AMPLIFIER

Where do you begin when you want to design a CE amplifier stage? Naturally, you must decide on the supply voltage (V_{CC}), the quiescent collector–emitter voltage ($V_{CE(Q)}$), and the desired voltage gain (A_V). The voltage gain should be between 1 and 30 to insure a good stable design—stable in terms of temperature, voltage gain, and immunity from oscillation (a problem to be discussed later). Also, you must decide on the value of the collector resistor and you must know the value of the load resistance the stage will drive. The collector resistance (R_C) should be equal to or less than the load resistance. A transistor must be selected that has maximum ratings well above those estimated for the design. From the transistor's data sheet, the minimum value of β (h_{fe}) can be obtained for use in some of the calculations. Finally, you must know the lowest frequency the amplifier must amplify. This is so the coupling and bypass capacitors can be calculated. Once all of this information is determined, the actual calculations can begin. Study Design Note 6–1 and Example 6–13 to see the steps involved in the total design.

EXAMPLE 6–13 ▮▮▮▮▮▮▮▮▮▮▮▮

Design an amplifier like that of Design Note 6–1 from the following information: $V_{CC} = 18$ V, $V_{CE} = 9$ V, $f_{low} = 40$ Hz, $\beta_{min} = 150$, $A_V = 20$, $R_C = 6.8$ kΩ, $R_L = 8.5$ kΩ.

STEP 1   Determine r_C.

$$r_C = R_C \parallel R_L = 6.8 \text{ k}\Omega \parallel 8.5 \text{ k}\Omega = 3.78 \text{ k}\Omega$$

STEP 2   Calculate the total DC emitter resistance.

$$R_E + r_E = R_C/10 = 6.8 \text{ k}\Omega/10 = 680 \ \Omega$$

STEP 3   Calculate the emitter current.

$$I_E = (V_{CC} - V_{CE})/(R_C + r_E + R_E)$$
$$= (18 \text{ V} - 9 \text{ V})/(6.8 \text{ k}\Omega + 680 \ \Omega) = 1.2 \text{ mA}$$

STEP 4   Calculàte r'_e.

$$r'_e \cong 25 \text{ mV}/I_E = 25 \text{ mV}/1.2 \text{ mA} = 20.8 \ \Omega$$

STEP 5   Calculate the base voltage.

$$V_B \cong 0.7 \text{ V} + [I_E \cdot (r_E + R_E)]$$
$$= 0.7 \text{ V} + (1.2 \text{ mA} \cdot 680 \ \Omega) = 1.52 \text{ V}$$

STEP 6   Determine the approximate base current.

$$I_B \cong I_E/\beta = 1.2 \text{ mA}/150 = 8 \ \mu\text{A}$$

STEP 7   Calculate the value for R_2.

$$R_2 = V_{R2}/I_{R2} = V_B/10I_B = 1.52 \text{ V}/80 \ \mu\text{A} = 19 \text{ k}\Omega$$

(Use 18 kΩ)

DESIGN NOTE 6–1 COMMON-EMITTER AMPLIFIER DESIGN

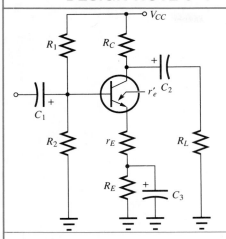

$r_C = R_C \parallel R_L = \text{RCO*}$
$r_e' = \text{REINT*}$
$r_E = \text{REUN*}$
$R_E = \text{REBYP*}$
$r_E + R_E = \text{REDC*}$
*Program variables

DESIGN APPROACH

$R_C/(r_E + R_E) = 10/1$
$1 \le A_V \le 30$
$I_{R2} = 10 I_B$
Z_{in} is an approximation
based on the minimum β.

BASIC PROGRAM

```
10 CLS
15 CLEAR
20 PRINT"COMMON-EMITTER AMPLIFIER
DESIGN PROGRAM"
30 PRINT""
40 INPUT"ENTER THE SUPPLY VOLTAGE -
VCC = ";VCC
50 INPUT"ENTER THE DESIRED
COLLECTOR-EMITTER VOLTAGE - VCE =
";VCE
60 INPUT"ENTER THE LOWEST FREQUENCY
TO BE AMPLIFIED - F = ";F
70 INPUT"ENTER THE MINIMUM AC BETA
FOR THE TRANSISTOR - B = ";B
80 INPUT"ENTER THE DESIRED VOLTAGE
GAIN (1 TO 30) - AV = ";A
90 INPUT"ENTER THE DESIRED COLLECTOR
RESISTOR - RC = ";RC
100 INPUT"ENTER THE LOAD RESISTANCE -
RL = ";RL
110 RM  ** CALCULATE THE AC COLLECTOR
RESISTANCE **
120 RCO = (RL * RC)/(RL + RC)
130 REM  ** CALCULATE THE TOTAL DC
EMITTER RESISTANCE **
140 REDC = RC/10
150 REM  ** CALCULATE THE
EMITTER/COLLECTOR CURRENT **
160 IE = (VCC - VCE)/(RC + REDC)
170 REM  ** CALCULATE THE INTERNAL
EMITTER RESISTANCE **
180 REINT = .025/IE
190 REM  ** CALCULATE THE BASE
VOLTAGE **
200 VB = (IE * REDC) + .7
210 REM  ** CALCULATE THE APPROXIMATE
BASE CURRENT **
220 IB = IE/B
230 REM  ** CALCULATE THE VALUE OF R2
**
240 R2 = VB/(10 * IB)
250 REM  ** CALCULATE THE VALUE OF R1
**
260 R1 = (VCC - VB)/(10 * IB + IB)
270 REM  ** CALCULATE THE VALUE OF
THE UNBYPASSED EMITTER RESISTANCE **
280 REUN = (RCO/A) - REINT
290 REM  ** CALCULATE THE VALUE OF
THE BYPASSED EMITTER RESISTOR **
300 REBYP = (RC/10) - REUN
305 IF REBYP < 0 THEN REBYP = 0
310 REM  ** CALCULATE THE APPROXIMATE
INPUT IMPEDANCE **
320 ZIN = 1 / ((1/R1) + (1/R2) +
(1/(B * (REINT + REUN))))
330 REM  ** CALCULATE THE VALUE OF
THE INPUT CAPACITOR **
340 C1 = .159/(F * ZIN)
350 REM  ** CALCULATE THE VALUE OF
THE OUTPUT CAPACITOR **
360 C2 = .159/(F * RL)
370 REM  ** CALCULATE THE VALUE OF
THE BYPASS CAPACITOR **
375 IF REBYP = 0 THEN GOTO 390
380 C3 = 1.59/(F * (REINT + REUN))
390 PRINT""
400 REM  ** OUTPUT SECTION **
410 PRINT"THE UNBYPASSED EMITTER
RESISTOR SHOULD BE ";REUN;" OHMS."
420 PRINT"THE BYPASSED EMITTER
RESISTOR SHOULD BE ";REBYP;" OHMS."
430 PRINT"RESISTOR R2 SHOULD BE
";R2;" OHMS."
440 PRINT"RESISTOR R1 SHOULD BE
";R1;" OHMS."
450 PRINT"THE INPUT CAPACITOR SHOULD
BE GREATER THAN ";C1;" F."
460 PRINT"THE OUTPUT CAPACITOR SHOULD
BE GREATER THAN ";C2;" F."
465 IF REBYP = 0 THEN PRINT"THERE IS
NO NEED FOR A BYPASS CAPACITOR.":GOTO
490
470 PRINT"THE BYPASS CAPACITOR SHOULD
BE GREATER THAN ";C3;" F."
490 PRINT""
500 INPUT"WOULD YOU LIKE TO DESIGN
ANOTHER AMPLIFIER?  (Y/N) ";A$
510 IF A$="Y" THEN GOTO 10
520 END
```

STEP 8   Calculate the value of R_1.

$$I_{R2} = V_B/R_2 = 1.52 \text{ V}/18 \text{ k}\Omega = 84.4 \ \mu\text{A}$$

$$R_1 = (V_{CC} - V_B)/(I_{R2} + I_B)$$

$$= (18 \text{ V} - 1.52 \text{ V})/(84.4 \ \mu\text{A} + 8 \ \mu\text{A})$$

$$= 16.5 \text{ V}/92.4 \ \mu\text{A} = 178.6 \text{ k}\Omega \qquad (\text{Use } 180 \text{ k}\Omega)$$

STEP 9   Determine the value of the unbypassed emitter resistor.

$$r_E = (r_C/A_V) - r_e' = (3.78 \text{ k}\Omega/20) - 20.8 \ \Omega = 168.2 \ \Omega$$

(Use 160 Ω)

STEP 10   Calculate the value of the bypassed emitter resistor.

$$r_E + R_E = R_C/10 = 680 \ \Omega$$

$$R_E = 680 \ \Omega - r_E = 680 \ \Omega - 160 \ \Omega = 520 \ \Omega$$

(Use 510 Ω)

STEP 11   Calculate the stage input impedance.

$$Z_{\text{in}} = R_1 \parallel R_2 \parallel Z_b = R_1 \parallel R_2 \parallel [\beta \cdot (r_e' + r_E)]$$

$$= 180 \text{ k}\Omega \parallel 18 \text{ k}\Omega \parallel [150 \cdot (20.8 \ \Omega + 160 \ \Omega)]$$

$$= 180 \text{ k}\Omega \parallel 18 \text{ k}\Omega \parallel 27.1 \text{ k}\Omega = 10.2 \text{ k}\Omega$$

STEP 12   Calculate the value of the input coupling capacitor.

$$C_1 = 0.159/(f_{\text{low}}Z_{\text{in}}) = 0.159/(40 \text{ Hz} \cdot 10.2 \text{ k}\Omega)$$

$$= 0.390 \ \mu\text{F} \qquad (\text{Use } 0.47 \text{ or } 0.5 \ \mu\text{F})$$

STEP 13   Calculate the value of the output capacitor.

$$C_2 = 0.159/(f_{\text{low}}R_L) = 0.159/(40 \text{ Hz} \cdot 8.5 \text{ k}\Omega)$$

$$= 0.468 \ \mu\text{F} \qquad (\text{Use } 0.5 \ \mu\text{F})$$

STEP 14   Calculate the value of the bypass capacitor.

$$C_3 = C_B = 10 \cdot 0.159/[f_{\text{low}} \cdot (r_e' + r_E)]$$

$$= 1.59/(40 \text{ Hz} \cdot 180.8 \ \Omega) = 1.59/7{,}232 = 220 \ \mu\text{F}$$

(Use any value equal to or greater than 200 μF)

Time for a self-check.

**Self-Check
6–1**

1. What is the main purpose for the common-emitter amplifier?
2. Describe the input/output voltage phase relationship of a CE amplifier.
3. Explain the effects of r_e' on A_V and Z_{in}.
4. What is the purpose for a swamping resistor (r_E)?

5. The circuit of Figure 6–10 has the following values: $R_C = 5.6$ kΩ, $R_L = 10$ kΩ, $r_E = 150$ Ω, $R_E = 330$ Ω, $I_E = 0.893$ mA. Calculate the voltage gain (A_V).

6. The lowest frequency a CE amplifier is to amplify is 50 Hz. The load resistor is 47 kΩ. What is the minimum value of capacitance for the output coupling capacitor?

7. Figure 6–13b has the following values: $R_1 = 33$ kΩ, $R_2 = 2.7$ kΩ, $R_C = 15$ kΩ, $r_E = 470$ Ω, $R_E = 680$ Ω, $\beta = 110$, $V_{CC} = 18$ V. Find Z_{in} and A_V.

8. Define the AC load line for Question 7. Find $i_{c(sat)}$ and $v_{ce(cutoff)}$.

9. Determine the maximum peak-to-peak voltage swing at the output of the amplifier described in Question 7.

6–2 COMMON-COLLECTOR AMPLIFIERS

INTRODUCTION TO COMMON-COLLECTOR (CC) AMPLIFIERS

CC for Power Requirements

The **common-collector (CC)** transistor amplifier stage is a very useful and needed amplifier configuration. While the CE amplifier provides necessary voltage gain to amplify very weak signals from microphones, tape heads, and phonograph cartridges, the common-collector amplifier provides a large current gain, which translates the amplified voltage, from CE stages, into power. In standard linear amplifier systems, the voltage is amplified first, then current is amplified using a CC amplifier. The amplified current times the already amplified voltage yields power sufficient to drive a loudspeaker or some other electromechanical device. Take a quick look back at Figure 6–1. The first three stages are CE amplifiers that provide voltage gain. The last stage is a complementary pair (NPN and PNP) that are configured as CC amplifiers. These CC transistors provide the current gain and power needed to drive the speaker.

Common Collector?

So why are these amplifiers called common collector (CC)? Look at the CC circuits of Figure 6–20. In each case, the output is taken from the emitter. The input is the base. Notice that the collector of the transistor is tied to V_{CC}. The V_{CC} DC source is a very-low-impedance path to ground. As far as circuit analysis is concerned, the collector is tied to ground and is in common with the input and output ground.

The Emitter Follows the Base

The common-collector amplifier is also very often called an **emitter-follower** amplifier. The reason for this is very simple. The output voltage, whether it be DC or AC, follows the input voltage at the base. Figure 6–20a is a DC emitter-follower (CC) circuit. The speed of the motor is controlled by the setting of the potentiometer. The series-pass transistor supplies the required current to the motor and is controlled by the potentiometer. When the wiper

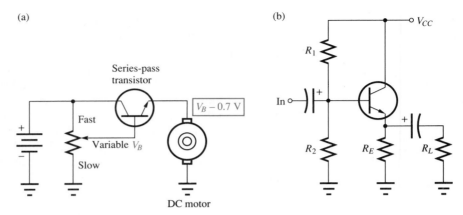

Figure 6–20 DC and AC common-collector circuits.

is moved up on the resistor element, the base voltage increases. The increased base voltage causes an increase in base current. The increased base current naturally causes the emitter and collector current to increase. As a result, the voltage across the motor increases, the motor current increases, and the motor speed increases. The motor voltage (V_E) tracks, or follows, the base voltage (V_B), maintaining a difference of about 0.7 V (for silicon transistors). The motor voltage (V_E) can never become greater than $V_B - 0.7$ V. Why? If the motor voltage could increase, it would shut the transistor down by reducing V_{BE} below 0.7 V. Thus, the emitter voltage follows the base voltage, maintaining a DC difference of 0.7 V.

CC and AC

Figure 6–20b shows a CC amplifier intended for AC current amplification. In this circuit, $V_E = V_B - 0.7$ V, as in the DC circuit. An AC voltage applied to the base is translated into a high-current AC voltage of the same amplitude at the emitter ($v_b = v_e$). We will investigate this further in a moment.

COMMON-COLLECTOR AMPLIFIER CHARACTERISTICS

Input/Output Phase Relationship

One of the primary characteristics of the CC amplifier is the in-phase relationship of the input AC and the output AC. Figure 6–21 illustrates why this is so. The AC input signal is superimposed on the DC base-bias voltage. As the AC heads in the positive direction, the base-bias voltage increases. This transient increase in base voltage results in a transient increase in base current, emitter current, and emitter voltage. Thus, the emitter voltage increases in step with the base voltage. Conversely, as the input AC heads in the negative direction, it has a canceling effect on some of the base-bias voltage, which reduces bias, reduces base current, reduces emitter current, and reduces emitter voltage. Figure 6–21 illustrates this graphically with changes in base voltage translated into changes in emitter current.

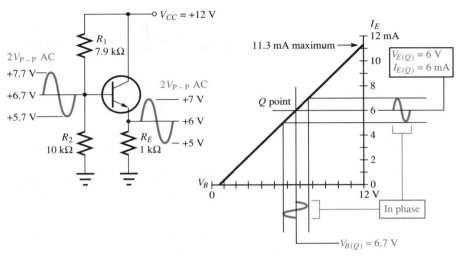

Figure 6–21 Input/output phase relationship of the common-collector amplifier.

Voltage Gain (A_V)

From Figure 6–21, you noticed there is no voltage gain for a common-collector amplifier. The emitter voltage simply follows the base input voltage and $v_{out} = v_{in}$ with $A_V = 1 = v_{out}/v_{in}$. In practice, there is a small AC voltage drop across the internal AC emitter resistance (r'_e) of the transistor. This drop is normally very insignificant and can usually be ignored. Thus, ideally $v_{out} = v_{in}$.

Current Gain (β and A_i)

The CC amplifier stage can provide a current gain approaching the AC beta (β) for AC circuits, or the DC beta (β_{DC}) for DC circuits. Recall that β (h_{fe}) is the ratio of $i_c/i_b \cong i_e/i_b$. The current gain for a particular stage (A_i) depends on the input impedance of the stage, where $A_i = i_e/i_{in}$ and $i_{in} = v_{in}/Z_{in}$. The total AC input current is greater than i_b due to AC currents in the base bias resistors. Since i_{in} is larger than i_b, A_i is less than β. Even so, the current gain of the CC stage is substantial, which also results in a high power gain (A_P).

Stage Input Impedance (Z_{in})

Figure 6–22 demonstrates how the stage input impedance is determined for a voltage-divider-biased CC amplifier. First, note the significance of the load resistance (R_L). As far as AC is concerned, the load resistor is in parallel with the emitter resistor. Therefore, the AC emitter resistance is $r_E = R_E \parallel R_L$. Naturally, if there is no load resistance, or if R_E is the load resistance, then $r_E = R_E$. As in CE amplifiers, the base input impedance (Z_b) is approximately βr_E (again we ignore r'_e since it is usually very small compared to r_E). The stage input impedance for CC amplifiers is calculated the same way as for voltage-divider-biased CE amplifiers.

$$Z_{in} = R_1 \parallel R_2 \parallel Z_b = 1/[(1/R_1) + (1/R_2) + (1/Z_b)]$$

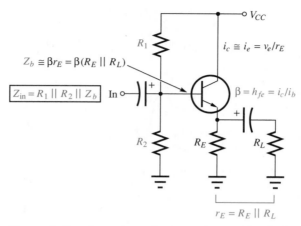

Figure 6–22 Input impedance and current gain for the common-collector amplifier.

Recall that R_1 appears in parallel with R_2 and Z_b because of the very low AC impedance of the DC source voltage (V_{CC}).

Stage Output Impedance (Z_{out})

Compared to the stage input impedance, the output impedance of the CC amplifier at the emitter is very low. This is a very useful and important characteristic of the CC amplifier stage. The entire stage acts as an impedance transformer that transfers voltage from a high-impedance circuit to a low-impedance load. At the same time, current and power are amplified.

Z_{out} is determined by looking back into the amplifier at the emitter. Figure 6–23 shows the AC equivalent of the voltage-divider-biased CC amplifier. Here we once again see the importance of β. Just as the base impedance is

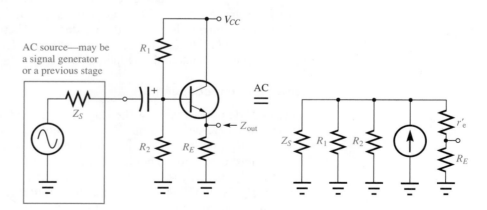

$$Z_{out} = R_E \ || \ [r_e' + ((Z_S \ || \ R_1 \ || \ R_2)/\beta)] \cong r_e' + [(Z_S \ || \ R_1 \ || \ R_2)/\beta]$$

Figure 6–23 Common-collector amplifier output impedance and AC beta.

the product of β and r_E (R_E if no load), the emitter impedance is the dividend of β. In other words, all parallel impedances on the base side are divided by β to yield the emitter impedance. Note Formula 6–13. All impedances at the base are divided by β. This includes $Z_S \parallel R_1 \parallel R_2$. As you can see, the impedance of the AC source (Z_S) has a definite effect on the stage output impedance. If the AC source is disconnected, the output impedance increases. If the AC source is connected and its internal impedance decreases, the output impedance of the CC amplifier will also decrease. Also, recognize the extreme dependance of input and output impedance on β. If temperature increases, so does β, causing Z_{in} to increase and Z_{out} to decrease. Finally, note that we may choose to ignore R_E since it is normally very large compared to r'_e. Thus,

$$Z_{\text{out}} \cong r'_e + [(Z_S \parallel R_1 \parallel R_2)/\beta]$$

$$Z_{\text{out}} \cong r'_e + \frac{1}{\beta[(1/Z_S) + (1/R_1) + (1/R_2)]} \tag{6–13}$$

where $r'_e \cong 0.025 \text{ V}/I_E$

Consider Example 6–14.

EXAMPLE 6–14 ▰▰▰

The following values are assigned to the CC amplifier of Figure 6–23: $Z_S = 1 \text{ k}\Omega$, $R_1 = 5.1 \text{ k}\Omega$, $R_2 = 6.8 \text{ k}\Omega$, $R_E = 330 \ \Omega$, $V_{CC} = 12 \text{ V}$, the minimum β from the data sheet is 100. Calculate the stage input and output impedances.

$$Z_{\text{in}} = 1/[(1/R_1) + (1/R_2) + (1/Z_b)]$$

$$= 1/[(1/5.1 \text{ k}\Omega) + (1/6.8 \text{ k}\Omega) + (1/(100 \cdot 330 \ \Omega))]$$

$$= 1/[(1.96 \text{ E-4}) + (1.47 \text{ E-4}) + (3.03 \text{ E-5})]$$

$$= 1/3.733 \text{ E-4} = 2679 \ \Omega$$

$$V_B = 12 \text{ V} \cdot 6.8 \text{ k}\Omega/(6.8 \text{ k}\Omega + 5.1 \text{ k}\Omega) = 6.86 \text{ V}$$

$$V_E = V_B - 0.7 \text{ V} = 6.86 \text{ V} - 0.7 \text{ V} = 6.16 \text{ V}$$

$$I_E = V_E/R_E = 6.16 \text{ V}/330 \ \Omega = 18.7 \text{ mA}$$

$$r'_e \cong 0.025 \text{ V}/I_E = 0.025 \text{ V}/18.7 \text{ mA} = 1.34 \ \Omega$$

$$Z_{\text{out}} \cong r'_e + \frac{1}{\beta[(1/Z_S) + (1/R_1) + (1/R_2)]}$$

$$= 1.34 \ \Omega + 1/[100 \cdot ((1/1 \text{ k}\Omega) + (1/5.1 \text{ k}\Omega) + (1/6.8 \text{ k}\Omega))]$$

$$= 1.34 \ \Omega + 7.45 \ \Omega = 8.79 \ \Omega$$

Significance of the Low Output Impedance

Notice the extreme difference between the input and output impedances of the amplifier in Example 6–14. The output impedance is very low. This means the transistor stage can supply its AC output voltage to a very-low-load impedance. In the case of Example 6–14, the 330-Ω emitter resistor acts as a load resistance. Naturally, virtually all of the output voltage will appear across the 330-Ω resistor instead of being dropped across the stage output impedance ($Z_{out} = 8.79\ \Omega$). You see, the stage output impedance is the same as a Thevenized source resistance (impedance). Thus, the 8.79-Ω output impedance of Example 6–14 is actually in series with the 330-Ω emitter resistor, as far as AC is concerned.

Stage Current and Power Gain

Consider these current amplification (A_i) and power amplification (A_P) relationships for the CC amplifier:

$$A_i = i_e/i_{in} = (v_{out}/r_E)/(v_{in}/Z_{in}) = (v_{out} \cdot Z_{in})/(v_{in} \cdot r_E)$$

Since $v_{in} \cong v_{out}$, then

$$A_i = Z_{in}/r_E \tag{6–14}$$

Also,

$$A_P = P_{out}/P_{in} = (v_{out}^2/r_E)/(v_{in}^2/Z_{in})$$

$$= (v_{out}^2 \cdot Z_{in})/(v_{in}^2 \cdot r_E) = Z_{in}/r_E$$

Therefore,

$$A_P = P_{out}/P_{in} = Z_{in}/r_E \tag{6–15}$$

For the CC amplifier of Example 6–14, the stage current gain and power gain is 2679 Ω/330 $\Omega \cong 8$, since $R_E = r_E$. This modest current and power gain can be increased by reducing R_E or by increasing R_1 and R_2. However, as stated earlier, A_i can never be greater than β.

An AC Model of the Common-Collector Amplifier

Figure 6–24 summarizes the CC amplifier stage with an equivalent AC model. The input is the base terminal and includes $R_1 \parallel R_2 \parallel Z_b$. The output is

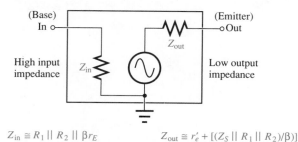

$Z_{in} \cong R_1 \parallel R_2 \parallel \beta r_E$ $Z_{out} \cong r_e' + [(Z_S \parallel R_1 \parallel R_2)/\beta)]$

Figure 6–24 AC model of a common-collector amplifier stage.

the emitter terminal. The emitter resistor (not shown) is considered to be an AC load resistance that is connected to the emitter. The model shows Z_{out} as a Thevenized equivalent resistance across which some voltage is dropped, though usually very little. The purpose of the model is to help you realize that the transistor stage acts as both a load to some source and a source to some load. The primary purpose of a CC amplifier is to transfer the voltage of a high-impedance source to a low-impedance load.

COMMON-COLLECTOR AMPLIFIER DESIGN

Design Note 6–2 provides one approach to designing a voltage-divider-bi-ased common-collector amplifier stage. The design procedure is very similar to that of CE amplifiers discussed in the previous section. Notice the design approach specified in the design note. R_E is considered to be the load device. The design process begins with given information regarding V_{CC}, R_E, β (minimum data sheet value), and quiescent V_E. Often, V_E is half of V_{CC}. In the computer program, I_{R2} is always $10 \cdot I_B$. The 10 times factor is arbitrary but does insure a fairly solid voltage-divider-bias scheme. Study the computer program to see the order and nature of the design steps. The overall purpose of the program is to determine values of R_1 and R_2 that will provide the desired quiescent emitter voltage, which is 0.7 V less than the base voltage. In the next chapter, you will discover how the voltage divider (R_1 and R_2) can be replaced with a CE transistor stage to greatly improve the current and power gain. In other words, the DC collector voltage of a CE stage will provide the needed DC base-bias voltage for a CC stage. This is called *direct coupling*. Now, take time to study Example 6–15.

EXAMPLE 6–15

Design a CC amplifier stage in which $V_{CC} = +13.6$ V, $R_E = 45$ Ω, $\beta_{min} = 70$, and $V_{E(Q)} = 6.8$ V.

Design

$I_E = V_E/R_E = 6.8$ V$/45$ $\Omega = 151$ mA

$I_B \cong I_E/\beta = 151$ mA$/70 = 2.16$ mA

$V_{R2} = 0.7$ V $+ V_{E(Q)} = 0.7$ V $+ 6.8$ V $= 7.5$ V

$I_{R2} = 10I_B = 10 \cdot 2.16$ mA $= 21.6$ mA

$R_2 = V_{R2}/I_{R2} = 7.5$ V$/21.6$ mA $= 347$ Ω (Use 330 Ω)

$I_{R2} = V_{R2}/R_2 = 7.5$ V$/330$ $\Omega = 22.7$ mA

$I_{R1} = I_{R2} + I_B = 22.7$ mA $+ 2.16$ mA $= 24.9$ mA

$R_1 = (V_{CC} - V_{R2})/I_{R1} = (13.6$ V $- 7.5$ V$)/24.9$ mA $= 245$ Ω

  (Use 249 Ω, 2%)

DESIGN NOTE 6-2 COMMON-COLLECTOR AMPLIFIERS

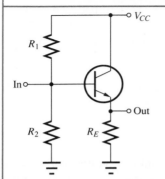

DESIGN APPROACH

V_{CC}, R_E, β, and V_E must be known or decided upon before the design begins.

$I_{R2} = 10 I_B$

where $I_B = I_E/\beta$

$\beta_{DC} \cong \beta$

BASIC PROGRAM

```
10 CLS
20 CLEAR
30 PRINT "COMMON-COLLECTOR AMPLIFIER DESIGN PROGRAM"
40 REM ** INPUT SECTION **
50 INPUT "ENTER THE VALUE OF VCC - ";VCC
60 INPUT "ENTER THE VALUE OF THE EMITTER RESISTOR - ";RE
70 INPUT "ENTER THE MINIMUM VALUE OF AC BETA - ";B
80 INPUT "ENTER THE DESIRED EMITTER VOLTAGE - ";VE
90 REM ** CALCULATION SECTION **
100 IE = VE/RE
110 REM ** IB IS NOW CALCULATED AS AN APPROXIMATION USING AC BETA **
120 IB = IE/B
130 IR2 = 10 * IB
140 VR2 = VE + .7
150 R2 = VR2/IR2
160 VR1 = VCC - VR2
170 R1 = VR1/IR2
180 PRE = IE * VE
190 PTRANS = IE * (VCC - VE)
200 PR2 = IR2 * VR2
210 PR1 = IR2 * VR1
220 REM ** OUTPUT SECTION **
230 PRINT""
240 PRINT "R2 = ";R2;" OHMS."
250 PRINT "R1 = ";R1;" OHMS."
260 PRINT "THE TRANSISTOR POWER DISSIPATION IS ";PTRANS;" WATTS."
270 PRINT "THE POWER RATING OF THE TRANSISTOR SHOULD BE GREATER THAN
";2 * PTRANS;" WATTS."
280 PRINT "THE EMITTER-RESISTOR POWER RATING SHOULD BE GREATER THAN
";2 * PRE;" WATTS."
290 PRINT "THE POWER RATING OF R2 SHOULD BE GREATER THAN ";2 * PR2;"
WATTS."
300 PRINT "THE POWER RATING OF R1 SHOULD BE GREATER THAN ";2 * PR1;"
WATTS."
310 PRINT""
320 INPUT "ANOTHER DESIGN PROBLEM? (Y/N?) ";A$
330 IF A$ = "Y" THEN GOTO 10
340 END
```

Analysis

$$Z_{in} = 249 \ \Omega \ \| \ 330 \ \Omega \ \| \ (\beta \cdot R_E) = 249 \ \Omega \ \| \ 330 \ \Omega \ \| \ 3{,}150 \ \Omega$$

$$= 136 \ \Omega$$

$$r'_e \cong 25 \ \text{mV}/I_E = 25 \ \text{mV}/151 \ \text{mA} = 0.166 \ \Omega$$

$$Z_{out} = r'_e + [(R_1 \ \| \ R_2)/\beta] = 0.166 \ \Omega + [(249 \ \Omega \ \| \ 330 \ \Omega)/70]$$

$$= 0.166 \ \Omega + 2.027 \ \Omega = 2.193 \ \Omega$$

$$\text{Transistor power dissipation} = P_{D(Q)} = I_{E(Q)} \cdot V_{CE(Q)}$$

$$= 151 \ \text{mA} \cdot 6.8 \ \text{V} = 1.03 \ \text{W}$$

THE DARLINGTON COMBINATION

Darlington Common-Collector Amplifier Analysis

Earlier it was stated that the current gain and power gain can be increased by increasing the values of R_1 and R_2. But how can that be done and still maintain a solid voltage-divider bias scheme? If R_1 and R_2 are too large, the temperature stability of the design will be forfeited. Figure 6–25 illustrates a popular solution to this problem. Figure 6–25a is what is known as a **Darlington pair**—two separate transistors in a piggyback arrangement. Figure 6–25b shows a Darlington transistor—two transistors fabricated on the same silicon chip and packaged as a single transistor. The Darlington pair and Darlington transistor form a supertransistor with a very high DC and AC β. When a pair is used, the total β is simply the product of the betas of the two transistors. For example, if $\beta_1 = 250$ and $\beta_2 = 100$, the total β is 25,000. Not bad, huh? Once the total β is known, the Darlington pair is treated as a single transistor with a very high β.

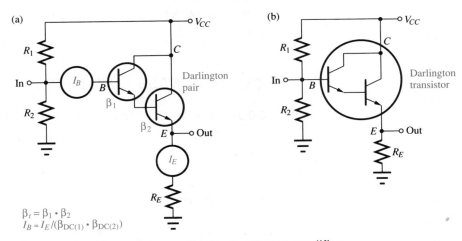

$$\beta_t = \beta_1 \cdot \beta_2$$
$$I_B = I_E/(\beta_{DC(1)} \cdot \beta_{DC(2)})$$

Figure 6–25   The common-collector Darlington amplifier.

But there is one other difference between a Darlington transistor, or pair, and a single transistor. The base–emitter voltage of a Darlington is approximately 1.4 V instead of 0.7 V because there are two base–emitter junctions in series.

The analysis of a Darlington CC stage is the same as that of a single-transistor CC stage except for the very high β and the approximate 1.4-V base–emitter voltage. Naturally, the Darlington stage has a much higher current and power gain and a much higher input impedance than a single-transistor CC stage.

Darlington Common-Collector Amplifier Design

Designing a CC stage with a Darlington transistor is basically the same as designing a single-transistor CC stage. Once again, the difference is the very high β and the 1.4-V base emitter voltage. Only line 140 of the computer program in Design Note 6–2 need be modified. For a Darlington design, line 140 should be: 140 VR2 = VE + 1.4. The β entered in line 70 is the β of the Darlington transistor or the total β for a Darlington pair ($\beta_t = \beta_1 \cdot \beta_2$).

Take a moment now to review this section and answer the questions of Self-Check 6–2.

Self-Check 6–2

1. Why are CC stages often called emitter followers?
2. If the base-bias voltage of a CC stage is 7.3 V, what is the emitter voltage? (Assume a silicon transistor.)
3. Describe the input/output voltage phase relationship for CC amplifiers.
4. What factors affect the input impedance of a CC stage?
5. Describe what design changes can be made to increase the power gain of a single-transistor CC stage.
6. The following values are assigned to the CC amplifier of Figure 6–18: $Z_S = 600\ \Omega$, $R_1 = 8.2\ k\Omega$, $R_2 = 10\ k\Omega$, $R_E = 680\ \Omega$, $I_E = 8.67$ mA, the minimum β from the data sheet is 180. Calculate the stage input and output impedances.
7. What are some benefits to using a Darlington transistor in a CC amplifier design?

6–3 COMMON-BASE AMPLIFIERS

INTRODUCTION TO COMMON-BASE (CB) AMPLIFIERS

The **common-base (CB) amplifier** is an interesting amplifier configuration, though not as common as CE or CC amplifiers. Shown in Figure 6–26, the CB amplifier is practically a complete opposite to the CC amplifier just covered. Instead of a very high input impedance, the CB amplifier has a very low input impedance. This is considered a big disadvantage for most applications because the very low input impedance heavily loads down the AC signal source. The CB amplifier provides a very large voltage gain but not current gain. This very high voltage gain capability is useful in overcoming the loss at the input caused by the very low input impedance. Finally, the CB amplifier has a relatively high output impedance. Compare that to the CC amplifier with its very low output impedance. Again, the biggest disadvantage of the CB amplifier is the very low input impedance.

Interestingly, for some specialized applications, the CB amplifier is an ideal choice because of the low input impedance. This sounds like a contradiction to what was stated in the previous paragraph, but consider this: If the AC signal source impedance is very low, the CB amplifier acts much like a step-up transformer—the voltage at the CB output is much greater than the voltage at the input. You will see this clearly in an example later in this section.

Figure 6–26 shows four common implementations of the common-base amplifier. As an aside, you should be aware that these circuits can be constructed with PNP transistors by reversing the polarity of the DC source(s). You should be able to recognize these as CB amplifier stages because, in each case, the base is in common with the input and output. This is because the base is at ground potential. In Figures 6–26a and 6–26b the base is at both DC and AC ground. In Figures 6–26c and 6–26d the base is at AC ground because of the bypass capacitors. Because of this base to ground arrangement, the CB amplifier is often called the **grounded-base** amplifier.

Emitter-biased common-base amplifiers

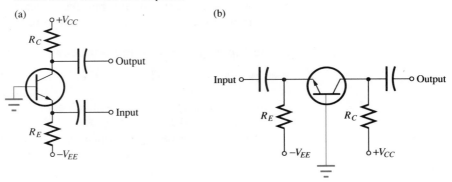

Voltage-divider biased common-base amplifiers

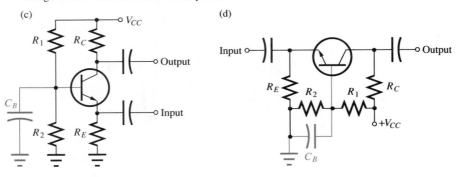

Figure 6–26 Common-base amplifier circuits.

Notice also that the input is at the emitter and the output is at the collector of the CB amplifier. It is the emitter that has the very low input impedance and the collector that has the relatively high output impedance.

Figures 6–26a and 6–26b are emitter-biased CB amplifiers. Obviously this requires a bipolar, or dual, DC power supply. If the dual DC supply is already available, this is the design to use because of the lower parts count. However, if only a single supply is available or intended for use, voltage-divider biasing can be used, as shown in Figures 6–26c and 6–26d.

COMMON-BASE AMPLIFIER CHARACTERISTICS

Input/Output Phase Relationship

For a CB amplifier, the input and output AC voltages are in phase with each other (recall that this is opposite to the CE amplifier). Let us see why. As you can see in Figure 6–27, the AC input signal is applied to the emitter. A transient increase on the positive alternation of an applied AC signal causes emitter current to decrease. Why? This is important for you to understand. Look at Figure 6–27. The input signal is applied to the emitter–base junction at the NPN transistor. An increase of voltage in the positive direction at the emitter causes the emitter–base junction to become less biased. This actually reduces emitter and collector current. This reduction in collector current causes the collector to become more positive. Therefore, the positive-going alternation at the input (emitter) causes a positive-going alternation at the output (collector). The inverse is true for the negative alternation.

Stage Input and Output Impedances

Earlier it was stated that the input impedance to the common-base amplifier is very low. This is because the AC impedance from the emitter to the grounded base is very low, approximately equal to the AC emitter resistance (r'_e). See Figure 6–27b. $Z_{in} \cong r'_e \cong 0.025 \text{ V}/I_E$.

The output impedance is approximately equal to the collector resistor (R_C). Since the V_{CC} side of the collector resistor is at AC ground, due to the

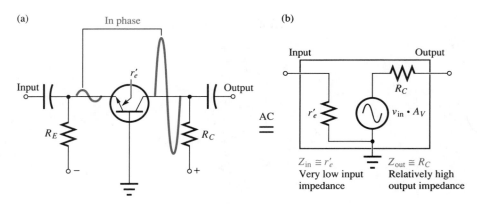

Figure 6–27 An AC model for the common-base amplifier.

very low internal AC impedance of the V_{CC} supply, the AC output voltage is developed across the collector resistor. In other words, any AC emitter current caused by the AC input voltage causes a corresponding AC collector current, which creates the AC voltage drop across the collector resistor. Therefore, $Z_{out} \cong R_C$.

Current Gain (A_i)

Current gain (A_i) is the ratio of i_{out}/i_{in}. In the case of CB amplifiers, $i_{in} = i_e$ and $i_{out} = i_c$. Since $i_e \cong i_c$, $i_{in} \cong i_{out}$ and the current gain is approximately unity. $A_i = i_c/i_e \cong 1$.

Voltage Gain (A_V)

The voltage gain for CB amplifiers is normally very high. Recall that $A_V = v_{out}/v_{in}$. Since $v_{out} = i_c \cdot R_C$ and $v_{in} = i_e \cdot r_e'$, the voltage amplification factor is R_C/r_e'. $A_V = v_{out}/v_{in} = (i_c \cdot R_C)/(i_e \cdot r_e') = R_C/r_e'$, since $i_e \cong i_c$.

$$A_V = v_{out}/v_{in} = R_C/r_e' \qquad (6\text{–}16)$$

Power Gain (A_P)

The power gain is equal to the voltage gain. $A_P = A_V$. Consider this: $A_P = P_{out}/P_{in} = (i_e \cdot v_{out})/(i_c \cdot v_{in}) = v_{out}/v_{in}$, since $i_e \cong i_c$.

$$A_P = P_{out}/P_{in} = v_{out}/v_{in} = R_C/r_e' \qquad (6\text{–}17)$$

Common-Base Amplifier Analysis

Figure 6–28 illustrates the analysis of an emitter-biased CB amplifier. In this case, the amplifier is analyzed as a complete system including the AC source and load. Of primary concern in the analysis process is the value of r_e', the AC emitter–base resistance. The quiescent DC emitter current is needed in order to calculate r_e' ($r_e' \cong 0.0025 \text{ V}/I_E$). The emitter current is calculated as follows:

$$I_E = (V_{EE} - 0.7 \text{ V})/R_E \qquad (6\text{–}18)$$

In Figure 6–28b, $I_E = (18 \text{ V} - 0.7 \text{ V})/12 \text{ k}\Omega = 1.44 \text{ mA}$. The emitter resistance is then found to be $r_e' \cong 0.025 \text{ V}/1.44 \text{ mA} = 17.4 \ \Omega$.

Using the AC model of Figure 6–28b, you can see the overall system gain is the combination of the input loss, the stage voltage gain, and the output loss. Notice that the stage input impedance (r_e') heavily loads the signal source, which has an internal impedance of 600 Ω. The voltage divider ratio of $r_e'/(r_e' + Z_S)$ indicates an input voltage gain of 0.028, which is actually a loss. The ratio of R_C/r_e' indicates a stage voltage gain of 391. Finally, the voltage divider ratio of $R_L/(R_C + R_L)$ indicates an output voltage gain of 0.595, which is a loss. The overall system gain is the product of these three gains: $A_t = 0.028 \cdot 391 \cdot 0.595 = 6.51$. In terms of decibels, the overall system gain is a little more than 16 dB ($^{\#}$dB $= 20 \cdot \log 6.51$). This means the source voltage is multiplied only about 6.5 times from source to load, even though the amplifier itself has a gain of 391. The indicated AC voltages are RMS values that reflect the losses and gain at key points in the system. As a final

(a)

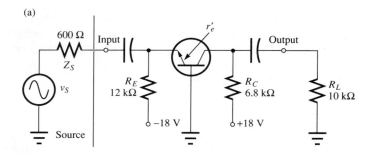

(b)

$A_V = R_C/r'_e = 6.8\text{ k}\Omega/17.4\ \Omega$
$= 391$

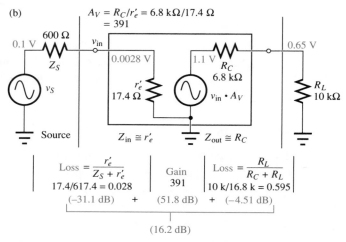

$$\left|\ \text{Loss} = \frac{r'_e}{Z_S + r'_e}\ \right|\ \text{Gain}\ \left|\ \text{Loss} = \frac{R_L}{R_C + R_L}\ \right|$$

17.4/617.4 = 0.028   391   10 k/16.8 k = 0.595

(−31.1 dB)   +   (51.8 dB)   +   (−4.51 dB)

(16.2 dB)

Overall gain from source to load = 0.028 • 391 • 0.595 = 6.51 (16.3 dB)

Figure 6–28   Common-base circuit analysis.

note, if the AC source impedance was much lower (much lower than 600 Ω), the overall system gain would be much higher. Take time to study Example 6–16.

EXAMPLE 6–16 ▰

Determine v_{in}, v_{out}, Z_{in}, Z_{out}, the CB stage voltage gain and the overall voltage gain for Figure 6–29.

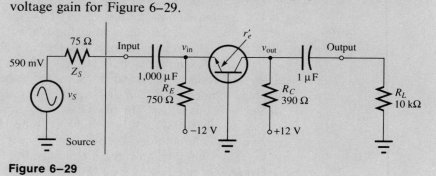

Figure 6–29

$$I_E = (V_{EE} - 0.7 \text{ V})/R_E = (12 \text{ V} - 0.7 \text{ V})/750 \text{ } \Omega = 15.1 \text{ mA}$$

$$Z_{\text{in}} \cong r_e' \cong 25 \text{ mV}/I_E = 25 \text{ mV}/15.1 \text{ mA} = 1.66 \text{ } \Omega$$

$$Z_{\text{out}} \cong R_C = 390 \text{ } \Omega$$

$$A_V \cong R_C/r_e' = 390 \text{ } \Omega/1.66 \text{ } \Omega = 235$$

$$\text{dB gain} = 20 \log_{10}(235) = 47.4 \text{ dB}$$

$$\text{Loss of input network} = r_e'/(Z_S + r_e')$$

$$= 1.66 \text{ } \Omega/(75 \text{ } \Omega + 1.66 \text{ } \Omega) = 0.0217$$

$$\text{dB gain of input network} = 20 \log_{10}(0.0217) = -33.3 \text{ dB}$$

$$\text{Loss of output network} = R_L/(R_L + R_C)$$

$$= 10 \text{ k}\Omega/(10 \text{ k}\Omega + 390 \text{ } \Omega) = 0.962$$

$$\text{dB gain of output network} = 20 \log_{10}(0.962) = -0.34 \text{ dB}$$

$$\text{Total system amplification factor} = A_t = 235 \cdot 0.0217 \cdot 0.962 = 4.91$$

$$\text{Overall system gain} = 47.4 \text{ dB} - 33.3 \text{ dB} - 0.34 \text{ dB} = 13.8 \text{ dB}$$

$$= 20 \log_{10}(4.91) = 13.8 \text{ dB}$$

$$v_{\text{in}} = v_S \cdot r_e'/(Z_S + r_e') = 590 \text{ mV} \cdot 0.0217 = 12.8 \text{ mV}$$

$$v_{\text{out}} = v_S \cdot A_t = 590 \text{ mV} \cdot 4.91 = 2.9 \text{ V}$$

Time for a self-check.

Self-Check 6–3

1. Describe the CB amplifier in terms of input impedance, output impedance, voltage gain, current gain, and power gain.
2. Explain why a low-impedance source should be connected to a CB amplifier.
3. What is the key, or most important, parameter needed in the analysis of a CB amplifier stage or system?

6–4 TROUBLESHOOTING

Safety first—Make sure you are aware of all lethal-voltage points while troubleshooting a powered-up system. Use one hand to maneuver the test probe and keep your body clear of the equipment. Never work alone on a high-voltage system. Think!

TROUBLESHOOTING A SINGLE STAGE

Troubleshooting an amplifier stage involves the application of basic amplifier theory. From a schematic, you must be able to recognize the type of configuration of the amplifier and apply the proper theory. If the amplifier stage is the common-emitter configuration, you should immediately remember that the purpose of that stage is to provide voltage gain. Therefore, using the oscilloscope, you will expect to see evidence of amplification when a signal is present at the amplifier's input. If the stage is a common-collector amplifier, you should realize that there is no voltage gain from input to output. Inspection of the input and output with an oscilloscope should reveal matching signals. For the common-base amplifier stage, you should remember that the stage itself provides a very large voltage gain from emitter to collector. Thus, you will expect to see a greatly amplified signal at the collector.

In any case, the amplifier should faithfully reproduce the input signal without modifying it. Any change in the waveform itself, other than amplification, is known as distortion and is generally undesirable. The distortion may be clipping of the waveform due to overdriving the stage, clipping on one alternation of the waveform due to overdriving or a severe shift in the bias Q point, or a change in the symmetry or shape of the waveform due to a shift in the bias Q point or slightly overdriving the stage. The input signal swing must stay clear of the saturation and cutoff regions for the transistor stage to avoid distortion. We will discuss distortion further later.

TROUBLESHOOTING A SYSTEM

A Standard Test Setup

System troubleshooting involves knowing what to expect from the overall system, what to expect from individual stages, and the proper use of test equipment. Figure 6–30 illustrates a test setup for a simple audio amplifier system. What should you expect from this system? You should expect to see evidence of voltage gain for every CE stage, Q_1, Q_2, and Q_3. You should expect Q_4 and Q_5 to provide current gain and have the same AC signal voltage at base and emitter.

As you can see, a signal generator can be used as a continuous signal source for the system. The signal generator should provide a low-distortion sine wave signal. Set it for an audio frequency between 400 Hz and 2 kHz (a standard test frequency in the United States is 1 kHz). If the amplifier system has a very high gain, such as a microphone amplifier, you may have to add an attenuator between the signal generator and the amplifier input as shown in Figure 6–30. Care must be taken not to overdrive the amplifier. The amplitude of the input signal should be comparable to the signals the amplifier sees in actual use.

Note also that the speaker has been temporarily replaced with a nonreactive load resistor, usually 8 Ω. Make sure the power rating of the resistor is sufficient to handle full-load testing of the amplifier. The use of the resistor eliminates the possibility of speaker damage or ear damage during testing.

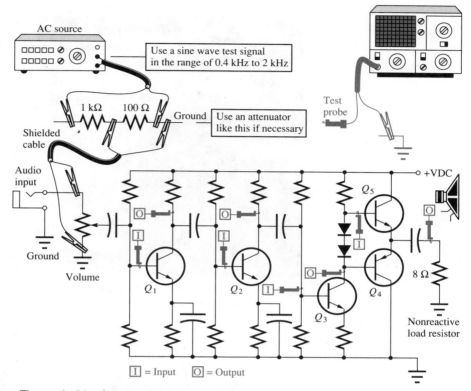

Figure 6–30 System troubleshooting.

Shown in Figure 6–31, the oscilloscope is a very valuable tool that allows you to look at the amplifier stage by stage. Naturally, you will use the oscilloscope to view the input and output signals of each stage, looking for the amount of amplification and visible distortion. A dual-trace oscilloscope is very useful for making direct comparisons between input and output signals. In a small system such as that of Figure 6–30, each stage can quickly be tested from beginning to end. In a larger system, you may want to use the "divide and conquer" method. The center stage of the system is tested to see if the problem is in the first half of the system or the last half, and so on.

The Signal Injector

The signal injector, shown in Figure 6-32, is a handy tool that permits stage-by-stage testing when a signal generator and oscilloscope are not available. The signal injector is a small audio oscillator circuit, often battery powered, that has an output amplitude control. In some cases, the entire signal injector circuit is built into a fat, hand-held, test-probe type of case. With the speaker connected to the amplifier system, the injector is used to inject a signal at the input of each stage in the amplifier, usually starting with the output stage and working back toward the input. The output level of the

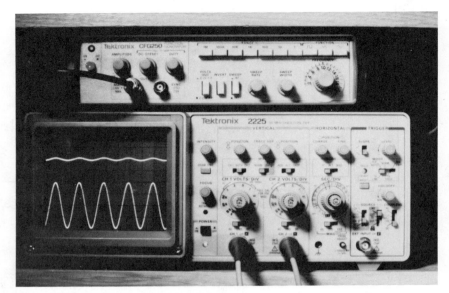

Figure 6–31   Using the oscilloscope to compare input and output signals for each amplifier stage. (Equipment courtesy of Tektronix.)

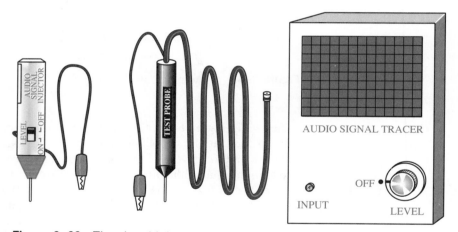

Figure 6–32   The signal injector and signal tracer.

injector is reduced more and more the farther back toward the system input you move. Extreme care must be taken not to overdrive the stages. When a bad stage is discovered, the sound at the speaker will be very low, nonexistent, and/or distorted. The signal injector is a bit crude, but it does serve a purpose when other equipment is not available.

The Signal Tracer

Another inexpensive piece of test equipment is the signal tracer. An audio signal tracer is a compact, battery-powered amplifier with an input volume control, a speaker, and a shielded test probe. While a signal source is still needed at the amplifier input, the signal tracer is an inexpensive substitute for the oscilloscope. The method here is simple. A test signal is applied at the system input and the signal tracer is used to test the input and output of each stage from input to final output. The ground clip on the tracer's probe is connected to a common ground point for the system and the probe is moved from stage to stage. A resistive load should be substituted for the amplifier's speaker so that the only speaker heard is the tracer's speaker. When using the tracer, you will be listening for the absence or loss of a signal and/or audible distortion. We will talk more about troubleshooting later. For now, take a moment to consider the questions of Self-Check 6–4.

Self-Check 6–4

1. Which of these instruments is used to generate a test signal: (a) signal generator, (b) oscilloscope, (c) signal injector, (d) signal tracer?
2. As far as input and output is concerned, what should you expect from a CC stage?
3. Describe a simple approach to troubleshooting a large amplifier system.
4. Briefly explain the use of a signal tracer.

SUMMARY

FORMULAS

Common-Emitter and General Formulas

(6–1) $\beta = h_{fe} = i_c/i_b = \Delta I_C/\Delta I_B$

(6–2) $r'_e \cong 25 \text{ mV}/I_E$

(6–3) $A_V = v_{out}/v_{in}$

(6–4) $A_V = $ AC collector resistance/AC emitter resistance

(6–5) $C_C \geq 0.159/R_L f_{low}$

(6–6) $C_B \geq 0.159/0.1 r'_e f_{low} = 1.59/r'_e f_{low}$

(6–7) $Z_{in} = R_1 \parallel R_2 \parallel Z_b = 1/[(1/R_1) + (1/R_2) + (1/Z_b)]$
where Z_b is always the product of β and any AC emitter resistances (for CE and CC amplifiers)

(6–8) $Z_{out} \cong R_C$ (for CE and CB amplifiers)

(6–9) $A_i = i_{out}/i_{in} = (v_{out}/Z_{out})/(v_{in}/Z_{in})$
$= (v_{out} \cdot Z_{in})/(v_{in} \cdot Z_{out}) = A_V \cdot Z_{in}/Z_{out}$

(6–10) $A_P = A_i A_V = P_{out}/P_{in} = (v_{out}^2/Z_{out})/(v_{in}^2/Z_{in})$
$= (v_{out}^2 \cdot Z_{in})/(v_{in}^2 \cdot Z_{out}) = A_V^2 \cdot Z_{in}/Z_{out}$

(6–11) $i_{c(sat)} = I_{C(Q)} + [V_{CE(Q)}/(r_c + r_E)]$

(6–12) $v_{ce(cutoff)} = V_{CE(Q)} + [I_{C(Q)} \cdot (r_c + r_E)]$

Common-Collector Formulas

(6–13) $Z_{out} \cong r'_e + \dfrac{1}{\beta[(1/Z_S) + (1/R_1) + (1/R_2)]}$

(6–14) $A_i = Z_{in}/r_E$

(6–15) $A_P = P_{out}/P_{in} = Z_{in}/r_E$ ($r_E = R_E$ when there is no R_L)

Common-Base Formulas

(6–16) $A_V = v_{out}/v_{in} = R_C/r'_e$

(6–17) $A_P = P_{out}/P_{in} = v_{out}/v_{in} = R_C/r'_e = A_V$

(6–18) $I_E = (V_{EE} - 0.7 \text{ V})/R_E$ (CB emitter biased)

CONCEPTS

COMPARING AMPLIFIER CONFIGURATIONS

Parameter	CE amplifier	CC amplifier	CB amplifier
I/O Phase	180°	0°	0°
Z_{in}	moderate	moderate	very low
Z_{out}	$\cong R_C$	low	$\cong R_C$
A_V	high	$\cong 1$	very high
A_i	low, $<\beta$	high, $<\beta$	$\cong 1$
A_P	very high	high	very high

■ The CE amplifier configuration is the most frequently used of the configurations. It is suitable for voltage and power amplification.
■ The CC configuration is used for current and power amplification applications.
■ The CB configuration is rarely used but can provide a very large voltage gain from very-low-impedance sources.
■ A signal injector is used to inject a test signal at the input of an amplifier stage to see if it is functional.
■ A signal tracer is used to listen to the output of amplifier stages to determine if they are working properly (amplification with no distortion).

PROCEDURES

Designing the Common-Emitter Amplifier

This procedure is employed in the program of Design Note 6–1.

1. Decide on V_{CC}, V_{CE} (usually about half of V_{CC}), the desired A_V, and the load resistance (R_L).

2. Choose a standard value of resistance for R_C. R_C is usually equal to or less than R_L.
3. Calculate $r_C = R_C \parallel R_L$.
4. Calculate the total DC emitter resistance: $R_{EDC} \cong R_C/10$.
5. Calculate $I_E = (V_{CC} - V_{CE})/(R_C + R_{EDC})$.
6. Calculate $r'_e = 0.025 \text{ V}/I_E$.
7. Calculate $V_B = (I_E \cdot R_{EDC}) + 0.7 \text{ V}$.
8. Calculate the approximate base current: $I_B \cong I_E/\beta$. (The minimum AC beta can be used here since $\beta_{DC} \cong \beta$.)
9. Calculate $R_2 = V_B/10 I_B$.
10. Calculate $R_1 = (V_{CC} - V_B)/(I_{R2} + I_B)$. (Choose standard values as close as possible to the calculated values for R_1 and R_2.)
11. Calculate $r_E = (r_C/A_V) - r'_e$. (This is the unbypassed emitter resistor.)
12. Calculate $R_E = R_{EDC} - r_E$. (This is the bypassed emitter resistor.)
13. Calculate $Z_{in} = 1/[(1/R_1) + (1/R_2) + (1/[\beta \cdot (r_e + r_E)])]$.
14. Use the lowest frequency that is to be amplified to calculate the input coupling capacitor: $C_C = 0.159/(f_{low} \cdot Z_{in})$.
15. Use the lowest frequency that is to be amplified to calculate the output coupling capacitor: $C_C = 0.159/(f_{low} \cdot R_L)$.
16. Use the lowest frequency that is to be amplified to calculate the emitter bypass capacitor: $C_B = 1.59/[f_{low} \cdot (r_E + r'_e)]$.
17. Select a transistor whose ratings are well above the current and power dissipation of the circuit. Minimum transistor ratings are

$$I_{C(max)} > 2 \cdot I_{C(sat)} \quad \text{and} \quad P_{D(max)} > 2 \cdot I_{C(Q)} \cdot V_{CE(Q)}$$

Designing the Common-Collector Amplifier

This procedure is employed in the program of Design Note 6–2.

1. Decide on V_{CC}, V_E (usually about half of V_{CC}), and the emitter resistor (R_E), which in many cases is the load resistance.
2. Calculate $I_E = V_E/R_E$.
3. Calculate the approximate base current: $I_B \cong I_E/\beta$. (The minimum AC beta can be used here since $\beta_{DC} \cong \beta$.)
4. Calculate $V_B = (I_E \cdot R_E) + 0.7 \text{ V}$.
5. Calculate $R_2 = V_B/10 I_B$. (A factor of 10 is used here to insure solid voltage-divider biasing.)
6. Calculate $R_1 = (V_{CC} - V_B)/(I_{R2} + I_B)$. (Choose standard values as close as possible to the calculated values for R_1 and R_2.)
7. Calculate $Z_{in} \cong 1/[(1/R_1) + (1/R_2) + (1/\beta R_E)]$.
8. Use the lowest frequency that is to be amplified to calculate the input coupling capacitor: $C_C = 0.159/(f_{low} \cdot Z_{in})$.
9. Select a transistor whose ratings are well above the current and power dissipation of the circuit. Minimum transistor ratings are

$$I_{C(max)} > 2 \cdot I_{C(sat)} \quad \text{and} \quad P_{D(max)} > 2 \cdot I_{C(Q)} \cdot V_{CE(Q)}$$

10. Make sure the power rating of all resistors is well above their actual dissipation.

NEED-TO-KNOW SOLUTION

Follow the common-emitter amplifier design procedure to verify the values in this circuit.

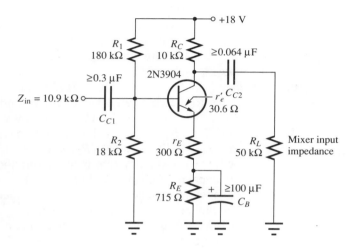

QUESTIONS

6–1 COMMON-EMITTER AMPLIFIERS

1. What is the main purpose for the CE amplifier?
2. List two general applications for CE amplifiers.
3. Describe the input/output voltage phase relationship of the CE amplifier.
4. How can you tell the difference between DC and AC transistor parameters?
5. Under what conditions is β almost exactly equal to β_{DC}?
6. What is the parameter r_e'?
7. Describe in general terms how the CE amplifier voltage amplification factor (A_V) is calculated.
8. What is a swamping resistor and why is it needed?
9. What is the purpose for an emitter-resistor bypass capacitor?
10. What is the purpose for a coupling capacitor?
11. What are the factors that are involved in determining the base impedance of a CE amplifier?
12. What are the factors that are involved in determining the total input impedance of a CE amplifier stage?
13. Describe the effect the input impedance of a stage has on the output of a previous stage.
14. CE amplifiers have no current gain. True or false?
15. CE amplifiers have very little power gain. True or false?
16. What is dynamic headroom?

6–2 COMMON-COLLECTOR AMPLIFIERS

17. What is the purpose for a CC amplifier?
18. Which of these does a CC amplifier *not* produce?
    (a) A_V,   (b) A_i (c) A_P
19. What is another name for the CC amplifier?
20. List two applications for the CC amplifier.
21. Describe the input/output voltage phase relationship for the CC amplifier.
22. What parameter limits the maximum possible current gain of a CC stage?
23. Is the output impedance of the CC amplifier (a) high, or (b) low? Explain why.
24. What does the impedance of a source connected to the input of a CC amplifier have to do with the output impedance of the amplifier?
25. Describe the Darlington pair in terms of base–emitter voltage and overall β.
26. List two benefits to using a Darlington transistor in a CC amplifier design.
27. What is the primary function of a CC amplifier?

6–3 COMMON-BASE AMPLIFIERS

28. How do the input and output impedances of a CB amplifier compare to those of a CC amplifier?
29. Under what circumstances is the CB amplifier a good choice?
30. Which of these does a CB amplifier not provide?
    (a) A_V (b) A_i (c) A_P
31. What is another name for the CB amplifier?
32. What is the input/output voltage phase relationship for a CB amplifier?
33. What determines the output impedance of a CB stage?
34. Why is the current gain of a CB stage approximately equal to 1?

6–4 TROUBLESHOOTING

35. What are some important safety considerations when troubleshooting a powered-up piece of equipment?
36. Any change in an amplified waveform, other than amplification and a possible 180° phase shift, is known as what?
37. Explain why it is helpful to identify the configuration of a stage when troubleshooting it.
38. Briefly explain how a bench signal generator and an oscilloscope might be used to troubleshoot an amplifier system.
39. What is the "divide and conquer" method of troubleshooting?
40. What is an audio signal injector?
41. Explain how you can troubleshoot an audio amplifier system with just a signal tracer. Assume you have a turntable or tape player you can use as an audio source.

PROBLEMS

6–1 COMMON-EMITTER AMPLIFIERS

Refer to Figure 6–33 for Problems 1 through 25.

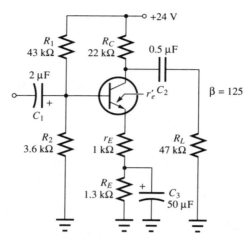

Figure 6–33

CE ANALYSIS

1. Calculate $I_{C(sat)}$ and $V_{CE(cutoff)}$. Then draw the DC load line graph. Use linear graph paper.
2. Calculate the base voltage V_B.
3. Calculate the emitter voltage V_E.
4. Calculate the quiescent collector current $I_{C(Q)}$.
5. Calculate the collector–emitter voltage $V_{CE(Q)}$.
6. Calculate the internal AC emitter resistance r'_e.
7. Calculate the AC voltage gain A_V.
8. Calculate $i_{c(sat)}$ and $v_{ce(cutoff)}$. Then draw the AC load line over the DC load line graph.
9. Determine the maximum output voltage swing.
10. Determine the maximum input voltage (V_{P-P}).
11. Calculate the stage input impedance Z_{in}.
12. Calculate the approximate output impedance Z_{out}.
13. Calculate the stage current gain A_i.
14. Calculate the stage power gain A_P.

CE DESIGN

Design a voltage-divider-biased CE amplifier stage like Figure 6–33 according to the following guidelines: (Problems 15 through 25) $R_L = 33$ kΩ, $R_C = 18$ kΩ, $V_{CC} = 12$ V, $V_{CE(Q)} \cong 6$ V, $\beta_{(min)} = 150$, $A_V \cong 20$. The lowest frequency to be amplified is 30 Hz. Calculate:

15. r_C, the AC collector resistance.
16. R_{EDC}, the total DC emitter resistance.

17. r_e', the internal AC emitter resistance.
18. R_2, the lower voltage divider resistor.
19. R_1, the upper voltage divider resistor.
20. r_E, the unbypassed emitter resistor.
21. R_E, the bypassed emitter resistor.
22. Z_{in}, the stage input impedance.
23. C_1, the minimum value of the input capacitor.
24. C_2, the minimum value of the output capacitor.
25. C_3, the minimum value of the bypass capacitor.

6–2 COMMON-COLLECTOR AMPLIFIERS

Refer to Figure 6–34 for problems 26 to 34.

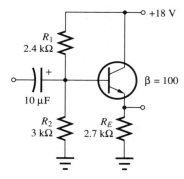

Figure 6–34

CC ANALYSIS

26. Calculate the stage input impedance Z_{in}.
27. Calculate the stage output impedance Z_{out}.
28. Calculate the stage current gain A_i.
29. Calculate the stage power gain A_P.

CC DESIGN

Design a voltage-divider-biased CC amplifier stage like Figure 6–34 according to the following guidelines: (Problems 30 through 34) $R_E = 1\ k\Omega$, $V_{CC} = 9\ V$, $V_E \cong 5\ V$, $\beta_{(min)} = 100$, the lowest frequency to be amplified is 50 Hz. Calculate

30. I_E, the DC emitter current.
31. R_2, the value of the lower voltage-divider resistor.
32. R_1, the value of the upper voltage-divider resistor.
33. Z_{in}, the stage input impedance.
34. the minimum value of the input capacitor.

DARLINGTON AMPLIFIER ANALYSIS

Refer to Figure 6–35 for Problems 35 through 41. Calculate

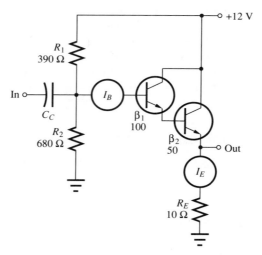

Figure 6–35

35. V_E, the DC emitter voltage.
36. I_E, the emitter current.
37. the total β.
38. I_B, the base current.
39. Z_{in}, the stage input impedance.
40. C_C, the minimum value of the coupling capacitor if $f_{low} = 30$ Hz.
41. A_i, the stage current amplification factor.

6–3 COMMON-BASE AMPLIFIERS

Refer to Figure 6–36 for Problems 42 through 50.

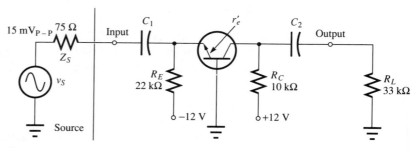

Figure 6–36

CB ANALYSIS

42. Calculate the DC emitter current I_E.
43. Calculate the internal AC emitter resistance r_e'.
44. Calculate the minimum value of the input capacitor (C_1) if $f_{\text{low}} = 50$ Hz.
45. Calculate the minimum value of the output capacitor (C_2) if $f_{\text{low}} = 50$ Hz.
46. Calculate the stage voltage amplification factor a_V. Express this factor in decibels.
47. Calculate the source to input loss factor and express it in decibels.
48. Calculate the output to load loss factor and express it in decibels.
49. Calculate the overall system gain and express it as a factor and in decibels.
50. Calculate the loaded AC output voltage $-v_{\text{out}}$.

ADDITIONAL PROBLEMS

Refer to Figure 6–37 for Problems 51 through 60.

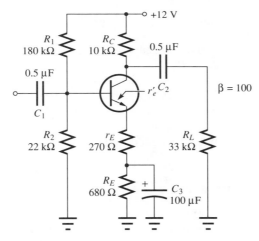

Figure 6–37

51. Calculate $I_{C(\text{sat})}$ and $V_{CE(\text{cutoff})}$. Then draw the DC load line graph. (Use linear graph paper.)
52. Calculate the base voltage V_B.
53. Calculate the emitter voltage V_E.
54. Calculate the quiescent collector current $I_{C(Q)}$.
55. Calculate the collector–emitter voltage $V_{CE(Q)}$.
56. Calculate the internal AC emitter resistance r_e'.
57. Calculate the AC voltage gain A_V.
58. Calculate $i_{c(\text{sat})}$ and $v_{ce(\text{cutoff})}$. Then draw the AC load line over the DC load line graph.
59. Determine the maximum output voltage swing.
60. Determine the maximum input voltage $(V_{\text{P-P}})$.

ANSWERS TO SELF-CHECKS

SELF-CHECK 6–1

1. To amplify voltage and power
2. 180° out of phase
3. The internal AC emitter resistance is a resistance that is included in the calculation of A_V and Z_{in}. It changes with changes in emitter current, which causes A_V and Z_{in} to change.
4. The swamping resistor greatly lessens the effect of changes in r'_e on A_V and Z_{in} since the swamping resistor is much greater than r'_e.
5. 20
6. $C \geq 0.07\ \mu F$
7. $Z_{in} \cong 2400\ \Omega$, $A_V \cong 29$
8. $i_{C(sat)} = 1.14\ mA$, $v_{ce(cutoff)} = 17.6\ V$
9. $2 \cdot 8.7\ V_P = 17.4\ V_{P\text{-}P}$

SELF-CHECK 6–2

1. The AC emitter voltage follows the base voltage in phase and amplitude.
2. 6.6 V
3. 0° out of phase, in phase
4. β, r'_e, R_E, R_2, R_1
5. Decrease r_E; use a transistor with a higher β; increase the values of the voltage divider resistors; use a different bias scheme, such as single-resistor base bias or collector-feedback bias.
6. $Z_{in} \cong 4350\ \Omega$, $Z_{out} \cong 5.8\ \Omega$
7. Higher input impedance, higher current gain, higher power gain

SELF-CHECK 6–3

1. Very low input impedance, high output impedance, very high voltage gain, no current gain, very high power gain.
2. To minimize the loading effect of the very low CB input impedance
3. The internal AC emitter resistance (r'_e)

SELF-CHECK 6–4

1. (a) and (c)
2. No voltage gain, no visible distortion.
3. Select a stage in the middle of the system and test its output. If the test signal is present and is not distorted, the problem is in the last half of the system. If the test signal is not present or is distorted, the problem is in the first half of the system.
4. Connect a signal source to the amplifier system. Use the signal tracer to listen to the output of each stage to see where the signal is lost or heavily distorted.

SUGGESTED PROJECTS

1. Add some of the main concepts, formulas, and procedures from this chapter to your Electronics Notebook.
2. Use a 2N3904 or a 2N2222 transistor to construct and test some of the circuits in this chapter.
3. Build and test some of your own designs. Be careful not to overdissipate your transistors.

Power transistors for heavy-duty power supplies and high-power amplifiers are mounted on large heat sinks to pass heat from the transistors to the air. A large heat sink like this one has a very low thermal resistance, or opposition to the transfer of heat to the air.

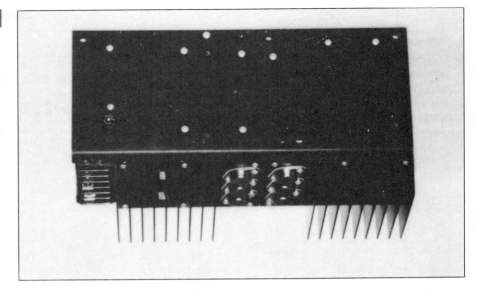

Power Amplifiers by Classification

CHAPTER OUTLINE

7–1 CLASS A AMPLIFIERS
7–2 CLASS B AMPLIFIERS
7–3 CLASS C AMPLIFIERS
7–4 CLASS D AMPLIFIERS
7–5 POWER AMPLIFIER CONSIDERATIONS
7–6 TROUBLESHOOTING

OBJECTIVES

After studying this chapter, you will be able to

- identify the class of biasing from an amplifier's schematic.
- describe each class of biasing in terms of duty cycle and power efficiency.
- calculate transistor power dissipation, total DC power, load power, and power efficiency for class A, B, and C amplifiers.
- list various applications for class A, B, C, and D amplifiers.
- explain the purpose for and ratings of heat sinks.
- calculate transistor case operating temperature and derated maximum power dissipation.
- explain various methods of bias stabilization at high temperatures.
- use the signal generator and oscilloscope to troubleshoot class A and B amplifiers.

NEED TO KNOW

Consider the following practical problems:

1. You want to design and build a power amplifier that can amplify a broad band of radio frequencies without the need for tuning. What kind and class of amplifier could this be?
2. You have an FM communications transmitter that you want to operate on a frequency of 144.64 MHz. The transmitter contains a frequency doubler and two triplers. What is the frequency of the master oscillator? (The master oscillator is the first stage of the FM transmitter.)
3. You need an amplifier to act as a digital line driver. Should this amplifier operate as (1) class A, (2) class B, (3) class C, or (4) class D?

4. A certain power transistor will dissipate 25 W in actual operation. The transistor will be mounted on a heat sink. The thermal resistance between the transistor's case and the heat sink will be about 0.5°C/W. The ambient temperature will never go above 40°C. What is the maximum acceptable thermal resistance rating ($R_{\Theta SA}$) for the heat sink to insure that the transistor case temperature never exceeds 100°C?

These are interesting problems, are they not? Can you solve them? At this point you probably cannot. However, when you finish this chapter, you should be able to solve these problems. The fact that you cannot do so now merely establishes your need to know. Have fun.

INTRODUCTION

This is a very practical chapter filled with information that you will use as a technician or engineer. You will learn much about power amplifiers and the different ways they are used. You will discover how amplifiers are classified according to their biasing and Q point. You will also learn that the power efficiency for different classes of amplifiers varies widely. Understanding of this is significant in helping you to understand the various applications for these amplifiers. Finally, you will explore power amplifier topics related to power dissipation and transistor heat dissipation. Keep in mind that the topics to be covered in this chapter are far more extensive than the space allowed for them. However, this chapter will provide you with a good foundation for future courses of study.

7–1 CLASS A AMPLIFIERS

INTRODUCTION TO CLASS A AMPLIFIERS

You have been reading and learning about class A amplifiers for some time now. Remember learning about midpoint bias, which allows for maximum AC compliance or dynamic headroom? Class A amplifiers are biased so that the entire input waveform is amplified without clipping. In other words, the DC bias and level of input signal are set so the output signal is unclipped and undistorted. Figure 7–1 should look familiar to you.

Both (a) and (b) of Figure 7–1 are class A amplifiers. Figure 7–1a is known as a small-signal amplifier because the circuit is biased low on the load line, permitting very little signal swing (headroom). Early stages in an amplifier system should be biased this way because the signal voltage swings are not great until later stages. Biasing in this way reduces the DC supply current and increases the efficiency of the entire system.

Figure 7–1b shows how the later stages of an amplifier system should be biased. Note that midpoint bias is used to allow maximum signal swing. Naturally, the DC current requirement is higher because of the higher quiescent collector current and a higher bias current.

In any case, small-signal and large-signal class A amplifiers operate at 100% duty cycle. This means the transistor is on all the time and is dissipating power in the form of heat. For this reason, the class A amplifier is the least efficient of all classes of amplifiers. You will see why as you read on.

(a) Small-signal class A amplifier

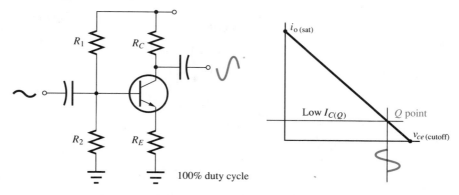

100% duty cycle

(b) Large-signal class A amplifier

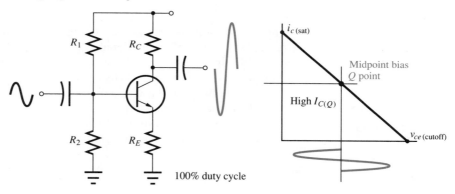

100% duty cycle

Figure 7–1   Class A biasing.

THE CLASS A Q POINT

Ideally, the Q point for a class A power amplifier should be in the middle of the AC load line. For the DC loadline, that is no problem. You can easily design the class A amplifier to have a Q point in the center of the DC load line. However, adding a load creates the AC load line superimposed over the DC Q point. As shown in Figure 7–2, the Q point is not in the center of the AC load line. This, of course, limits the amount of undistorted output voltage swing. In a moment, we will take time to analyze this amplifier in terms of DC power, transistor power dissipation, output power, and power efficiency.

CLASS A POWER CONSIDERATIONS

Class A Transistor Power Dissipation (P_D)

The power that the transistor dissipates (conducts to the air) in the form of heat is simply the quiescent collector current times the quiescent collector–emitter voltage.

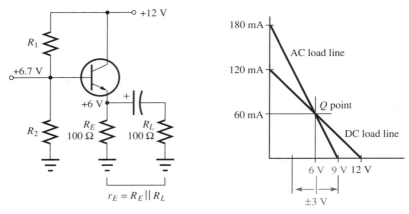

Figure 7–2   Common-collector class A power amplifier.

$$P_D = V_{CE(Q)} \cdot I_{C(Q)} \qquad\qquad (7\text{–}1)$$

This is the amount of power the class A biased transistor dissipates whether or not an AC input signal is present. In other words, the transistor will not dissipate any more power when the input signal is present and amplification is taking place. Why? Because the collector current and collector–emitter voltage increase and decrease by equal amounts with each alternation of the output signal. The average AC current is equal to $I_{C(Q)}$ and the average AC collector–emitter voltage is equal to $V_{CE(Q)}$. Thus, the maximum transistor dissipation is the product of the quiescent DC parameters. The transistor of Figure 7–2 is dissipating 6 V $\cdot$ 60 mA = 360 mW of power. The actual rating of the transistor should be at least twice this value. A 1-W transistor is best.

Class A Output Power ($P_{out} = P_L$)

The output power from any amplifier is the power that is delivered to the load device (resistance). This means the RMS AC load voltage squared divided by the load resistance. The maximum RMS load voltage is 0.707 $\cdot$ ($v_{\text{P-P(max)}}/2$).

$$P_{L(max)} = (0.707 \cdot v_{\text{P-P(max)}}/2)^2/R_L = 0.125 \cdot (v_{\text{P-P(max)}})^2/R_L$$

$$P_{L(max)} = (v_{\text{P-P(max)}})^2/8R_L \qquad\qquad (7\text{–}2)$$

For the circuit of Figure 7–2, the maximum output power is:

$$P_{L(max)} = (6\ V_{\text{P-P(max)}})^2/(8 \cdot 100\ \Omega) = 36\ V_{\text{P-P(max)}}/800\ \Omega = 45\ \text{mW}$$

Notice that the AC load line limits the maximum output voltage swing to ± 3 V. For any class A amplifier, the maximum AC output voltage is either

$$v_{\text{P-P(max)}} = 2 \cdot (v_{ce(\text{cutoff})} - V_{CE(Q)}) \qquad\qquad (7\text{–}3)$$

where $V_{CE(Q)} \geq 0.5\ V_{CC}$.

$$v_{\text{P-P(max)}} = 2 \cdot (V_{CE(Q)} - V_{CE(\text{sat})}) \qquad\qquad (7\text{–}4)$$

where $V_{CE(Q)} - V_{CE(\text{sat})} < v_{ce(\text{cutoff})} - V_{CE(Q)}$.

Class A DC Power (P_{DC})

The DC power is the amount of power delivered to the power amplifier from the DC supply (voltage-divider power excluded). Thus, the DC power is

$$P_{DC} = V_{CC} \cdot I_{C(Q)} \tag{7–5}$$

Again, for the circuit of Figure 7–2, the DC power supplied to the amplifier via the emitter and collector is 12 V · 60 mA = 720 mW. This is also the maximum power that is ever delivered to the amplifier, because when AC is applied, the average collector current is equal to $I_{C(Q)}$.

Class A Power Efficiency (η)

The efficiency factor for any amplifier is the ratio of actual output power to DC input power. It indicates how efficiently the DC power is converted to AC power in the load. The Greek letter η (eta) represents the efficiency factor.

$$\eta = P_L/P_{DC} \tag{7–6}$$

The percent efficiency is:

$$\% \text{ eff.} = \eta \cdot 100\% \tag{7–7}$$

Maximum efficiency occurs when the output voltage swing is maximum, which makes the load power maximum. For the circuit of Figure 7–2, the efficiency factor is 45 mW/720 mW = 0.063. The percent efficiency is 0.063 · 100% = 6.3%. This is very low but is typical for class A power amplifiers and makes them a very bad choice for power amplifier applications. As you read on, you will discover much more efficient power amplifier designs.

Theoretically, the maximum efficiency for class A amplifiers is 25%. This is a theoretical value that cannot easily be realized. If the amplifier of Figure 7–2 could deliver 12 V_{P-P} to the load resistor, which it cannot, the efficiency would reach 25% as follows:

$$P_{L(max)} = 12^2/(8 \cdot 100) = 144/800 = 0.18 \text{ W}$$

$$\eta_{(max)} = P_{L(max)}/P_{DC} = 0.18 \text{ W}/0.72 \text{ W} = 0.25$$

$$\% \text{ eff.} = \eta \cdot 100\% = 0.25 \cdot 100\% = 25\%$$

Once again, realize that it is not actually possible for the circuit of Figure 7–2 to attain an efficiency of 25%, since the maximum voltage swing is limited by the 9-V $v_{ce(cutoff)}$. Now, let us put all of this together in the analysis demonstrated in Example 7–1.

EXAMPLE 7–1 ▮▮▮▮▮▮

Determine the power efficiency for the class A amplifier of Figure 7–3.

1. Determine the DC load line.

$$I_{C(sat)} = V_{CC}/(R_C + R_E) = 12 \text{ V}/(100 \text{ } \Omega + 10 \text{ } \Omega) = 109 \text{ mA}$$

$$V_{CE(cutoff)} = V_{CC} = 12 \text{ V}$$

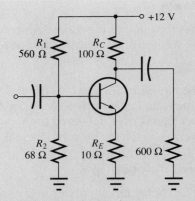
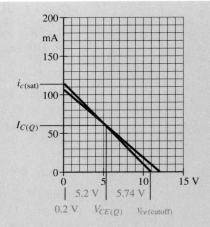

Figure 7–3

2. Determine the Q point.

$$V_B \cong V_{CC} \cdot R_2/(R_1 + R_2) = 12 \text{ V} \cdot 68 \text{ }\Omega/(560 \text{ }\Omega + 68 \text{ }\Omega)$$

$$= 12 \text{ V} \cdot 68 \text{ }\Omega/628 \text{ }\Omega = 1.3 \text{ V}$$

$$V_E \cong V_B - 0.7 \text{ V} = 1.3 \text{ V} - 0.7 \text{ V} = 0.6 \text{ V}$$

$$I_{C(Q)} \cong I_{E(Q)} = V_E/R_E = 0.6 \text{ V}/10 \text{ }\Omega = 60 \text{ mA}$$

$$V_{RC} = I_{C(Q)} \cdot R_C = 60 \text{ mA} \cdot 100 \text{ }\Omega = 6 \text{ V}$$

$$V_{CE(Q)} = V_{CC} - V_{RC} - V_E = 12 \text{ V} - 6 \text{ V} - 0.6 \text{ V} = 5.4 \text{ V}$$

3. Calculate transistor power dissipation.

$$P_D = V_{CE(Q)} \cdot I_{C(Q)} = 5.4 \text{ V} \cdot 60 \text{ mA} = 0.324 \text{ W}$$

The transistor is probably rated for 1 W or so.

4. Calculate the DC power supplied to the collector–emitter circuit.

$$P_{DC} = V_{CC} \cdot I_{C(Q)} = 12 \text{ V} \cdot 60 \text{ mA} = 0.72 \text{ W}$$

5. Determine the AC load line.

$$i_{c(\text{sat})} = I_{C(Q)} + [V_{CE(Q)}/(\text{AC collector resistance} + \text{AC emitter resistance})]$$

$$= 60 \text{ mA} + [5.4 \text{ V}/(100 \text{ }\Omega \parallel 600 \text{ }\Omega + 10 \text{ }\Omega)]$$

$$= 60 \text{ mA} + [5.4 \text{ V}/(85.7 \text{ }\Omega + 10 \text{ }\Omega)]$$

$$= 60 \text{ mA} + 56.4 \text{ mA} = 116.4 \text{ mA}$$

$$v_{ce(\text{cutoff})} = V_{CE(Q)} + [I_{C(Q)} \cdot (\text{AC collector resistance} + \text{AC emitter resistance})]$$

$$= 5.4 \text{ V} + [60 \text{ mA} \cdot (85.7 \text{ }\Omega + 10 \text{ }\Omega)]$$

$$= 5.4 \text{ V} + 5.74 \text{ V} = 11.14 \text{ V}$$

6. Determine the maximum compliance. Assume $V_{CE(\text{sat})}$ to be approximately 0.2 V.

$$u_{\text{P-P(max)}} = 2 \cdot (V_{CE(Q)} - V_{CE(\text{sat})}) = 2 \cdot (5.4 \text{ V} - 0.2 \text{ V})$$
$$= 2 \cdot 5.2 \text{ V} = 10.4 \; V_{\text{P-P}}$$

7. Calculate the maximum power delivered to the load.

$$P_{L(\text{max})} = (u_{\text{P-P(max)}})^2/8R_L$$
$$= 10.4^2/(8 \cdot 600 \; \Omega) = 108/4800 = 0.023 \text{ W}$$

8. Calculate the efficiency for the amplifier.

$$\eta = P_L/P_{\text{DC}} = 0.023 \text{ W}/0.72 \text{ W} = 0.032$$

$$\% \text{ eff.} = \eta \cdot 100\% = 0.032 \cdot 100\% = 3.2\%$$

Matching the Load for Maximum Power Transfer

The maximum power transfer theorem states that maximum power is delivered to a load only when the load impedance (resistance) is equal to the internal impedance of the source. We will prove this important theorem by considering three different loads for the amplifier of Figure 7–4. Note the three different AC load lines that correspond to the three different load resistances: (a) 500 Ω, (b) 1 kΩ, (c) 2 kΩ. These lines were defined from the formulas used in Chapter 6.

$$i_{c(\text{sat})} = I_{C(Q)} + [V_{CE(Q)}/(\text{AC collector resistance} + \text{AC emitter resistance})]$$

$$u_{ce(\text{cutoff})} = V_{CE(Q)} + [I_{C(Q)} \cdot (\text{AC collector resistance} + \text{AC emitter resistance})]$$

where the AC collector resistance $= r_C = R_C \parallel R_L$ and the AC emitter resistance $= R_E$.

Now, let's proceed and prove the maximum power transfer theorem. To do this, we simply calculate the load power (output power) for each of the

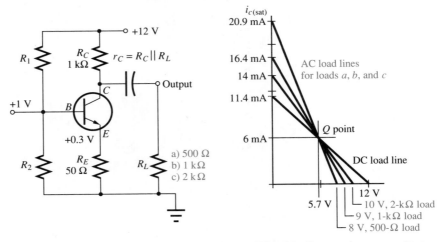

Figure 7–4 Common-emitter, class A amplifier loading and power efficiency.

loads. The 1-kΩ load resistor should receive the most power since it matches the output impedance ($Z_{out} \cong R_C = 1$ kΩ).

$$P_{L(a)} = (4.6\ V_{P\text{-}P(max)})^2/(8 \cdot 500\ \Omega) = 5.29\ mW$$

where $4.6\ V_{P\text{-}P} = 2 \cdot (8\ V - 5.7\ V)$

$$P_{L(b)} = (6.6\ V_{P\text{-}P(max)})^2/(8 \cdot 1\ k\Omega) = 5.44\ mW$$

where $6.6\ V_{P\text{-}P} = 2 \cdot (9\ V - 5.7\ V)$

$$P_{L(c)} = (8.6\ V_{P\text{-}P(max)})^2/(8 \cdot 2\ k\Omega) = 4.62\ mW$$

where $8.6\ V_{P\text{-}P} = 2 \cdot (10\ V - 5.7\ V)$

Since the maximum amount of power is delivered to the 1-kΩ load, the amplifier also operates at its highest efficiency. The maximum efficiency for the amplifier of Figure 7–4 is $\eta_{(max)} = P_{L(max)}/P_{DC} = 5.44$ mW/72 mW = 0.076. Note that $P_{DC} = 12\ V \cdot 6$ mA. The % eff. = $0.076 \cdot 100\% = 7.6\%$. Now consider Example 7–2.

EXAMPLE 7–2 ▬▬▬▬▬▬▬▬▬

Replace the 600-Ω load resistance of Example 7–1 with a 100-Ω resistance and recalculate power efficiency.

1. Determine the new AC load line.

    $i_{c(sat)} = I_{C(Q)} + [V_{CE(Q)}\ /$ (AC collector resistance
    $\qquad + $ AC emitter resistance)]

    $\qquad = 60$ mA $+ [5.4\ V/(100\ \Omega\ \|\ 100\ \Omega + 10\ \Omega)]$

    $\qquad = 60$ mA $+ [5.4\ V/(50\ \Omega + 10\ \Omega]$

    $\qquad = 60$ mA $+ 90$ mA $= 150$ mA

    $v_{ce(cutoff)} = V_{CE(Q)} + [I_{C(Q)} \cdot$ (AC collector resistance
    $\qquad + $ AC emitter resistance)]

    $\qquad = 5.4\ V + [60$ mA $\cdot (50\ \Omega + 10\ \Omega)]$

    $\qquad = 5.4\ V + 3.6\ V = 9\ V$

2. Determine the maximum compliance. Assume $V_{CE(sat)}$ to be approximately 0.2 V.

    $v_{P\text{-}P(max)} = 2 \cdot (v_{ce(cutoff)} - V_{CE(Q)}) = 2 \cdot (9\ V - 5.4\ V)$

    $\qquad = 2 \cdot 3.6\ V = 7.2\ V_{P\text{-}P}$

3. Calculate the maximum power delivered to the load.

    $P_{L(max)} = (v_{P\text{-}P(max)})^2/8R_L$

    $\qquad = 7.2^2/(8 \cdot 100\ \Omega) = 51.8/800 = 0.065\ W$

4. Calculate the efficiency for the amplifier.

$$\eta = P_L/P_{DC} = 0.065 \text{ W}/0.72 \text{ W} = 0.09$$

$$\% \text{ eff.} = \eta \cdot 100\% = 0.09 \cdot 100\% = 9\%$$

Summary

In summary, the load impedance must match the amplifier's output impedance and there must be maximum output voltage swing for maximum output power and efficiency. Also, the theoretical maximum efficiency for class A is 25%, which cannot be achieved in practice. Thus, the class A amplifier is a very poor choice for power amplification.

In the following sections, you will study more efficient amplifier designs. Before you go on, test your understanding with Self-Check 7–1.

Self-Check 7–1

1. How do small-signal and large-signal class A amplifiers differ?
2. Midpoint bias exists only on the DC load line. True or false?
3. For a class A power amplifier, does the transistor dissipate more power when an AC signal is applied to its input? Explain.
4. What is the maximum theoretical efficiency for class A amplifiers?
5. What changes must you make to the amplifier of Figure 7–4 to make it most efficient with a 500-Ω load?

7–2 CLASS B AMPLIFIERS

INTRODUCTION TO CLASS B AMPLIFIERS

Class B amplifiers are used widely in audio- and radio-frequency power amplifiers because of their high efficiency. Here, you will discover how the class B biased transistor functions only half of the time. Class B transistors operate at 50% duty cycle and amplify one complete alternation of a waveform—180°, no more, no less. The transistor works for half a cycle and rests for half a cycle. During the rest period, the transistor is nearly turned off. This means there is very little power demanded from the DC supply while the transistor is resting. During the rest period, a second transistor can turn on and amplify the other alternation. In the paragraphs ahead, you will see how this is done and why the class B amplifier is very much preferred over the class A amplifier for power applications.

THE CLASS B Q POINT

Figure 7–5 illustrates a simple and impractical class B amplifier. Notice that the output waveform is severely clipped. Only the negative-going alternation is present. The base bias voltage is right at 0.7 V, leaving the voltage across the emitter resistor at near 0 V. The transistor is biased right at the threshold

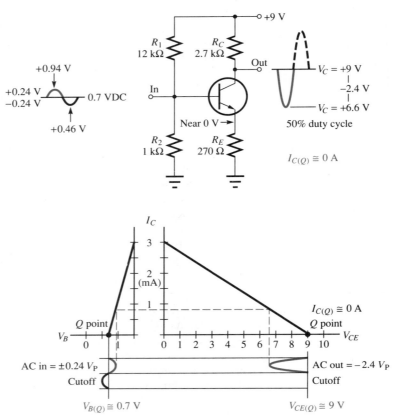

Figure 7–5   Class B biasing of the common-emitter transistor amplifier.

of turning on, which means the collector voltage is close to V_{CC} (+9 V). Note that the positive-going alternation of the input signal is able to turn the transistor on because it adds to the 0.7-V bias. During this input positive alternation, collector current is able to flow and the voltage drop across the collector resistor increases sinusoidally. As the voltage across the collector resistor increases, the transistor collector voltage decreases. Thus, the output voltage decreases from 9 V and returns to 9 V in concert with the positive alternation of the input signal. This is demonstrated by the graph of Figure 7–5. Obviously the transistor is completely cut off during the negative-going alternation of the input signal.

At this point, you may question the worth of an amplifier that is only able to amplify half of the input signal. You're right. Figure 7–5 grossly distorts the input signal, making the amplifier totally unacceptable. We could solve this problem if we had a second amplifier to take care of the negative-going alternation. Read on and see how.

CLASS B PUSH-PULL AND BIASING REQUIREMENTS

Theory of Class B Push-Pull

Figure 7–6 solves the problem previously discussed. Figure 7–6a is a common-collector class B amplifier using an NPN transistor. Since the base input and emitter output are in phase, this amplifier is able to amplify the positive alternation. Note that the transistor is biased at the threshold of turn-on ($V_B \cong 0.7$ V). Therefore, the quiescent collector current is very low (close to 0 A).

Figure 7–6b is a common-collector class B amplifier using a PNP transistor. Since the base input and emitter output are in phase, this amplifier is able to amplify the negative alternation. Note that the transistor is biased at the threshold of turn-on ($V_B = V_{R2} \cong -0.7$ V with respect to $+V_{EE}$). Therefore, the quiescent collector current is very low (close to 0 A). The negative-going alternation of an input signal adds to the -0.7-V bias and causes the transistor to turn on.

Figure 7–6c combines the circuits of 7–6a and 7–6b. In this way, the two amplifiers complement each other and permit the entire waveform to be amplified. The NPN transistor creates the positive alternation and the PNP transistor creates the negative alternation. For this reason, the amplifier is referred to as a **complementary push-pull amplifier.**

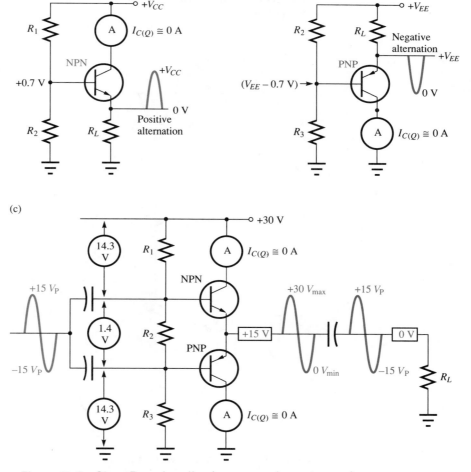

Figure 7–6 Class B push-pull using a complementary pair.

Notice that a capacitor is used to couple the load to the emitters. The coupling capacitor serves two very important functions. First, it blocks the DC voltage, present at the emitters, from getting to the load resistor. This prevents any DC current from flowing in the AC load. Second, the capacitor is charged and discharged via the two transistors. The load current is the charging and discharging capacitor current. The capacitor is charged via the NPN transistor and discharged via the PNP transistor.

R_1, R_2, and R_3 provide the bias required by the two transistors. The quiescent collector current is kept very low by selecting the proper value for R_2. The total voltage drop across R_2 should be approximately 1.4 volts, equal to the sum of the two base–emitter junction voltages. This sets both transistors right at the threshold of turn-on. In fact, there is some current flowing through the transistors, but it is small compared to the average collector current that exists when an AC signal is applied (when drive is applied). You might have guessed that R_1 is the same value as R_3.

Notice that the DC emitter voltage for the transistors is 15 V, half of the V_{CC} voltage. This represents the midpoint bias voltage and is only exactly half of V_{CC} if the transistors are a matched complementary pair and are both biased identically. Transistors are manufactured as complementary pairs for this purpose.

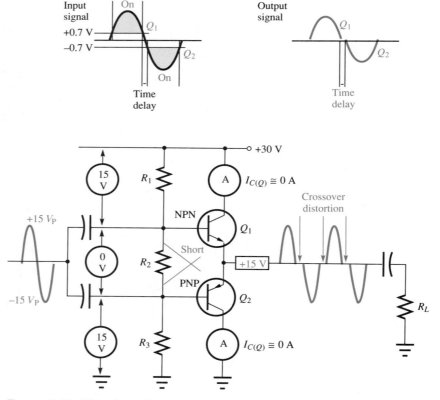

Figure 7–7   Class B power amplifier crossover distortion.

The Importance of Proper Biasing

Proper biasing for the class B amplifier is very important, to minimize waveform distortion and excessive power dissipation by the transistors. Figure 7–7 illustrates an extreme and very undesirable condition. R_2 has become shorted externally. This effectively removes the bias voltage from the transistors. Both transistors are completely cut off. The NPN transistor will only turn on when the positive alternation of the input signal rises above +0.7 V. The PNP transistor will turn on only when the negative alternation exceeds −0.7 V. For a short period of time, this causes a loss of output signal slightly above and below the zero-crossing point. The gap, or time delay, is known as **crossover distortion** and is quite audible in faulty audio amplifiers.

Diode Biasing

Using a resistor (R_2 of Figure 7–7) to provide bias for the transistors is not really practical. The resistor is not able to maintain a fixed 1.4-V drop for a stable bias point and quiescent collector current. If V_{CC} is not fixed or firmly regulated, it can increase or decrease and cause significant changes in the bias voltage. A far better method of biasing the class B transistors is with the use of diodes, as shown in Figure 7–8. Each diode provides an approximately 0.7-V drop to match the 0.7 V required for the base–emitter junction of each transistor. This places each transistor right at or near threshold. Figure 7–8 also emphasizes the symmetry of the complementary push-pull design, referred to as **complementary symmetry.**

The Current Mirror

Diode biasing is very well suited for class B amplifiers because the diode junction closely copies the characteristics of the transistor's base–emitter

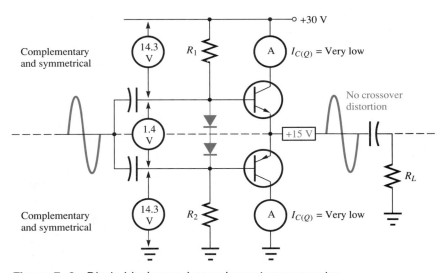

Figure 7–8   Diode biasing and complementary symmetry.

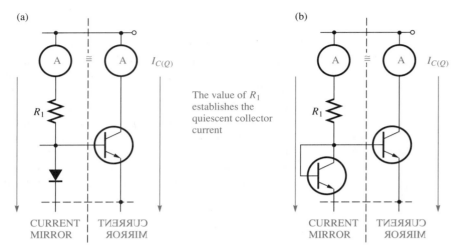

Figure 7–9 The current mirror.

junction. In fact, if the diode is closely matched to the transistor, the diode current is closely reflected, or mirrored, in the transistor as collected current, forming what is known as a **current mirror.** Current-mirror circuits are illustrated in Figure 7–9. A very close reflection of current can be obtained by using another transistor, of the same type, as a diode (by connecting the base and collector leads together as shown in Figure 7–9b). The value of R_1 determines the current through the diode. This establishes a diode voltage drop in the area of 0.7 V that biases the transistor to a low-current threshold point. The low quiescent current of the transistor is approximately equal to the diode and R_1 current. If R_1 is replaced with a rheostat, the quiescent collector current can be set to a specific value by adjusting the rheostat. Care must be taken in this adjustment. If the quiescent collector current is set too high, the transistor will begin to heat and thermally run away. The temperature and collector current continue to increase until the transistor self-destructs.

TYPES OF CLASS B AMPLIFIERS

Tuned Class B Amplifiers

A single transistor, biased class B, can be used to amplify a sinusoidal waveform without significant distortion. This can be done with the addition of a parallel resonant circuit (tank circuit) as shown in Figure 7–10. However, this design is only efficient for a very narrow band of frequencies centered around the resonant frequency of the tank. This design is used for radio-frequency (RF) amplification. It cannot be used to amplify the audio-frequency range because no tuned circuit can cover the entire audio range.

Let's see how this circuit functions. On the rising edge of the positive alternation of the input signal the transistor goes into conduction and the tank-circuit capacitor is fully charged. On the falling side of the positive alternation the capacitor begins to discharge through the parallel inductor.

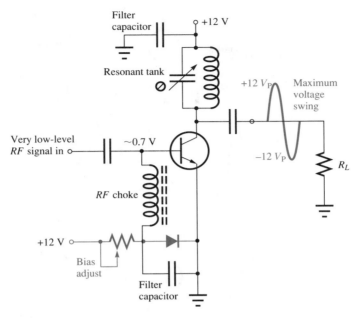

Figure 7–10   The tuned class B amplifier.

The magnetic field of the inductor builds up to maximum strength. During the time the transistor is off (during the negative alternation of the input signal), the inductor recharges the capacitor in the opposite polarity. Thus, the negative alternation for the output and load is formed. The exchange of energy between the inductor and capacitor continues back and forth at a rate equal to the resonant frequency [$f_r = 1/(2\pi \sqrt{LC})$]. During every positive alternation of the input signal, the transistor conducts and replaces energy to the tank that was lost in the windings of the inductor and to the load. As you can see in Figure 7–10, the maximum voltage swing is twice the DC supply voltage ($v_{\text{P-P(out)}} = 2V_{CC}$). The amplifier can be fine-tuned with a variable inductor or variable capacitor.

The bias to the transistor is provided by a rheostat/diode circuit. The rheostat is adjusted to set the desired quiescent collector current (recall our discussion of the current mirror). The RF choke and filter capacitor prevent the RF signal from getting back through the rheostat to the DC supply. The relatively high inductive reactance of the choke and very low capacitive reactance of the filter capacitor prevents this from happening.

Split-Supply Push-Pull Amplifiers

Figure 7–11 illustrates the split-supply complementary-symmetry push-pull amplifier. Instead of a single 30-V DC supply, this amplifier uses two 15-V supplies. Because the upper and lower halves of the circuit are exact complements, the amplifier circuit is symmetrical in a mirror-image sense. The center of the amplifier should be exactly at ground potential (0 V). This means the load can be connected directly to the emitters of the transistors without the need for an output coupling capacitor. When an AC signal is

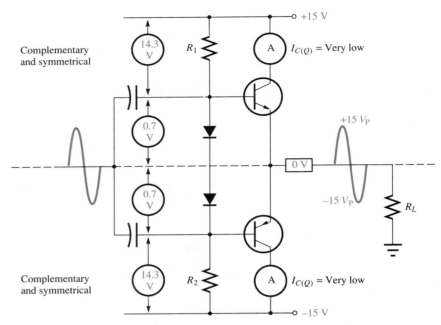

Figure 7–11 Split-supply class B push-pull power amplifier.

present at the input (drive), the NPN transistor will take the load toward the positive supply, then the PNP transistor will take the load toward the negative supply. As long as the bias diodes are closely matched to the base–emitter junctions of the transistors and R_1 and R_2 are chosen for a low threshold collector current, there will be very little crossover distortion (nothing visible using the oscilloscope and nothing audible).

Split-supply and single-supply push-pull amplifiers are suitable for audio and RF applications. They are very broad-banded (able to handle a wide frequency range) because there is no need for a tuned circuit.

Darlington-Pair Push-Pull Amplifiers

Figure 7–12 shows a push-pull amplifier suitable for high-power audio applications (able to drive a speaker system as the load). The high-power capability is obtained through the use of complementary Darlington pairs or Darlington transistors. This circuit is shown with a split supply but will also work well with a single supply, as long as a coupling capacitor is placed between the amplifier output and the load. Notice the biasing requirements for this circuit. Four diodes are needed—two diodes providing 1.4 V of bias for each Darlington pair. As before, $R_1 = R_2$ and is chosen to provide the desired, very low, quiescent collector current.

Direct-Drive Push-Pull Power Amplifiers

Figure 7–13 illustrates two very commonly used power amplifier designs. As you can see, these amplifiers use a direct-drive class A amplifier to provide DC bias and AC drive for the final Darlington pairs. The class A driver

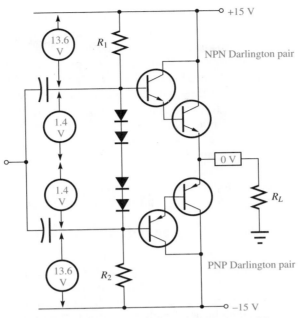

Figure 7–12 Darlington-pair push-pull amplifier.

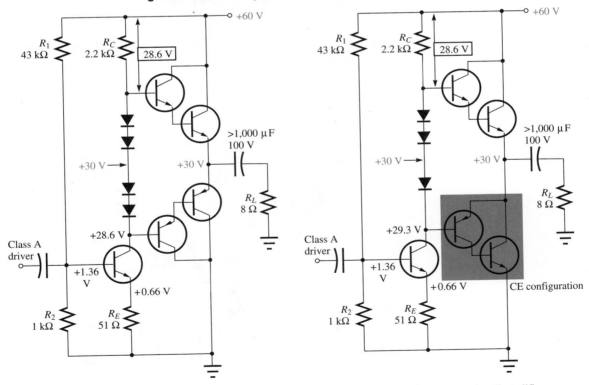

Complementary push-pull amplifier

Quasi-complementary push-pull amplifier

Figure 7–13 Complementary and quasi-complementary power amplifiers with class A drivers.

provides voltage and power gain. The value of R_1 in each circuit is critical in establishing the proper DC bias for the Darlington pairs. Usually, compensation circuits are added to the design to automatically control the bias voltages and currents. Without these special circuits, it is easy for high-power amplifiers to overheat and self-destruct.

Notice that the quasi-complementary power amplifier uses a complementary Darlington pair in a CE configuration at the output. In this case, a PNP transistor is piggybacked onto an NPN transistor. Both final output transistors are NPN. This permits the output transistors to be of the exact same type, having nearly identical operating characteristics. Also notice that only three bias diodes are needed. Whether the design is quasi-complementary or strictly complementary, additional compensation circuitry is needed to insure thermal stability and prevent self-destruction.

Transformer-Coupled Push-Pull Amplifiers

Figure 7–14 shows a very common design for broad-banded radio-frequency power amplifiers. This is a transformer-coupled push-pull amplifier. Both power transistors are matched NPN transistors. Bias is supplied from the rheostat/diode circuit through the secondary windings of the input transformer. The base of each transistor receives a DC bias of approximately 0.7 V along with the RF drive signal. As you can see in the diagram, the transistors are driven into conduction alternately. Each transistor is responsible for developing one alternation of the output waveform (50% duty cycle). This design provides very high power amplification (100- to 1,000-W output) and very low distortion. It also has the advantage of not being tuned. An ampli-

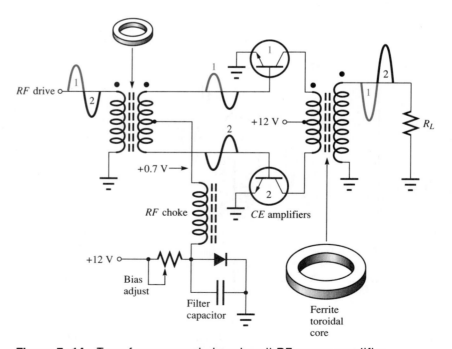

Figure 7–14   Transformer-coupled push-pull RF power amplifier.

fier such as this designed for the HF (high-frequency) band can cover a range of 1 MHz to 30 MHz.

CLASS B POWER CONSIDERATIONS

Class B Transistor Power Dissipation (P_D)

With no signal applied to the input of a class B amplifier, the transistor dissipates very little power. The power it does dissipate is the product of $V_{CE(Q)}$ and $I_{C(Q)}$. Since $I_{C(Q)}$ is set very low, the quiescent power dissipation is very low.

With an AC signal applied, the power dissipation of the transistor increases. The maximum power dissipation of each transistor in a push-pull amplifier is determined from the maximum average value of collector current ($i_{c(max\ avg)}$) and collector–emitter AC voltage ($v_{ce(max\ avg)}$). See Figure 7–15. The maximum peak AC current depends on the value of $V_{CE(Q)}$ and R_L.

$$i_{c(sat)} = V_{CE(Q)}/R_L \tag{7–8}$$

where $V_{CE(Q)}$ is half of the total supply voltage.

The maximum average current for each transistor is

$$i_{c(max\ avg)} = 0.318\ i_{c(sat)} = 0.318\ V_{CE(Q)}/R_L \tag{7–9}$$

where 0.318 is a constant used to find the average value of a 50% duty cycle sine wave.

The average maximum collector–emitter voltage for each transistor under full drive is

$$v_{ce(max\ avg)} = 0.318 \cdot V_{CE(Q)} \tag{7–10}$$

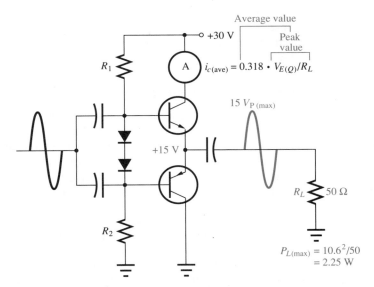

Figure 7–15   Class B power considerations.

Now the maximum power dissipation of each transistor can be calculated by finding the product of $i_{c(\text{max avg})}$ and $v_{ce(\text{max avg})}$.

$$P_{D(\text{max})} = i_{c(\text{max avg})} \cdot v_{ce(\text{max avg})}$$

$$= (0.318\ V_{CE(Q)}/R_L) \cdot (0.318\ V_{CE(Q)})$$

$$= (0.318\ V_{CE(Q)})^2/R_L \cong (V_{CE(Q)})^2/10\ R_L$$

$$P_{D(\text{max})} \cong (V_{CE(Q)})^2/10\ R_L \qquad (7\text{--}11)$$

For the circuit of Figure 7–15, the maximum power dissipation for each transistor is approximately $(15\ \text{V})^2/(10 \cdot 50\ \Omega) = 0.45$ W. 1-W transistors would be a wise choice for this amplifier.

Class B Output Power ($P_{\text{out}} = P_L$)

The maximum output power from a class B push-pull amplifier is equal to the square of the maximum RMS load voltage divided by the load resistance.

$$P_{L(\text{max})} = (v_{L(\text{max})})^2/R_L = (0.707\ V_{CE(Q)})^2/R_L \qquad (7\text{--}12)$$

For the circuit of Figure 7–15, the maximum load power is $(0.707 \cdot 15\ \text{V})^2/50\ \Omega = 2.25$ W. This, of course, assumes that the output voltage is able to swing a full 15 V in each direction. In practice, the maximum undistorted voltage swing across the load is slightly less than $V_{CE(Q)}$ because of the small voltage drop across the saturated transistor.

Class B DC Power (P_{DC})

The maximum DC power delivered to the push-pull amplifier from the DC source is the product of the maximum average AC current ($i_{c(\text{max avg})}$) and the DC source voltage (V_{CC}).

$$P_{\text{DC(max)}} = i_{c(\text{max avg})} \cdot V_{CC} \qquad (7\text{--}13)$$

where $i_{c(\text{max avg})} = 0.318\ i_{c(\text{sat})} = 0.318\ V_{CE(Q)}/R_L$.

The maximum DC power for the circuit of Figure 7–15 is 95.4 mA $\cdot$ 30 V = 2.86 W.

Class B Power Efficiency (η)

The efficiency for the class B push-pull amplifier is the ratio of output power to DC power ($\eta = P_L/P_{\text{DC}}$). Since the load power and the DC power are directly related, the percent efficiency remains fairly constant, close to an ideal value of about 78.7%. At low levels of drive and low output levels, the efficiency decreases slightly. Let us use the circuit of Figure 7–15 to verify the ideal 78.7% efficiency. For this circuit,

$$\eta = P_{L(\text{max})}/P_{\text{DC(max)}} = 2.25\ \text{W}/2.86\ \text{W} = 0.787$$

$$\%\ \text{eff.} = \eta \cdot 100\% = 0.787 \cdot 100\% = 78.7\%$$

The 78.7% value is ideal because it assumes the load voltage actually reaches a maximum peak equal to $V_{CE(Q)}$. In practice, the peak load voltage is slightly less than $V_{CE(Q)}$ and the actual efficiency is closer to about 75%

(still very good). Now take time to study Example 7–3 before answering the questions of Self-Check 7–2.

EXAMPLE 7–3 ▬▬▬▬▬▬▬▬

Perform a complete power and efficiency analysis on Figure 7–16.

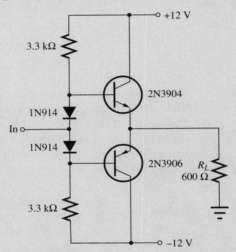

Figure 7–16

1. $i_{c(sat)} = V_{CE(Q)}/R_L = 12\ V/600\ \Omega = 20\ mA$
2. $i_{c(max\ avg)} = 0.318\ i_{c(sat)} = 0.318 \cdot 20\ mA = 6.36\ mA$
3. $v_{ce(max\ avg)} = 0.318 \cdot V_{CE(Q)} = 0.318 \cdot 12\ V = 3.82\ V$
4. $P_{D(max)} = i_{c(max\ avg)} \cdot v_{ce(max\ avg)} = 6.36\ mA \cdot 3.82\ V = 24.3\ mW$
   Maximum power dissipation for each transistor is 24.3 mW.
5. $P_{L(max)} = (0.707\ V_{CE(Q)})^2/R_L = (0.707 \cdot 12\ V)^2/600\ \Omega = 120\ mW$
6. $P_{DC(max)} = i_{c(max\ avg)}\ 2\ V_{CC} = 6.36\ mA \cdot 24\ V = 153\ mW$
   Total power supplied to both transistors is 153 mW.
7. $\eta = P_{L(max)}/P_{DC(max)} = 120\ mW/153\ mW = 0.784$
8. % eff. $= 0.784 \cdot 100\% = 78.4\%$

Self-Check 7–2

1. Describe a class B amplifier in terms of percent duty cycle.
2. What is the approximate value of the base-bias voltage for a class B amplifier?
3. Why is a diode better than a resistor for biasing a class B amplifier?
4. What causes crossover distortion?
5. How does a tuned class B amplifier differ from a push-pull class B amplifier?
6. When converting a split-supply push-pull amplifier to a single-supply amplifier, what important change in the circuit must you make?

7. What is the advantage of a transformer-coupled push-pull RF amplifier over a tuned class B amplifier?

8. A single-supply class B push-pull amplifier, such as the one shown in Figure 7–15, has the following values: $V_{CC} = +40$ V, $R_L = 100$ Ω. Calculate $i_{c(\text{max avg})}$, $P_{D(\text{max})}$, $P_{L(\text{max})}$, $P_{DC(\text{max})}$, and the percent efficiency.

7–3 CLASS C AMPLIFIERS

INTRODUCTION TO CLASS C AMPLIFIERS

Class C amplifiers have a very high power efficiency, ranging from about 80% to nearly 100%. They are most often used in FM (frequency modulated) communications and broadcasting equipment, particularly in FM transmitters. Their high efficiency enables them to convert nearly all of the DC Power to output power. The percent duty cycle (on time compared to cycle time) for class C amplifiers is usually far less than 50%. In other words, class C amplifiers are cut off most of the time. Since this is the case, the class C biased transistor dissipates very little power compared to the load.

Class C amplifiers have the further advantage of not requiring a special bias circuit. As shown in Figure 7–17, an input coupling capacitor and a resistor from base to ground are all that is needed. With no AC signal applied, the base of the transistor is at ground potential (0 V) and there is no collector current, except for a very small leakage current. Therefore, the class C amplifier is very temperature stable and there is no danger of thermal runaway (an increasing temperature and collector-current snowball effect). The advantages of class C are: very high power efficiency, circuit simplicity, and excellent temperature stability.

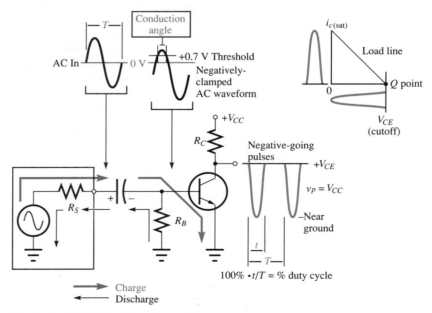

Figure 7–17 The class C amplifier.

In spite of the excellent advantages offered by class C amplifiers, they cannot be used for many applications. The very low percent duty cycle greatly distorts the applied signal. Far less than 50% of the input waveform is amplified. This means class C amplifiers cannot be used to amplify any waveform that contains complex variations in amplitude (voltage levels), such as audio signals (voice and music) and radio-frequency signals that are amplitude modulated.

THE CLASS C Q POINT

The Load Line

Figure 7–17 demonstrates the theory of operation for the class C amplifier. The output pulses are negative-going pulses that start at the V_{CC} voltage level and descend to near ground potential. During the time between pulses, the transistor is cut off. The load-line diagram shows the relationship between V_{CE} and I_C. As you can see, the narrow output pulses have no resemblance to the sine wave applied to the input. The only remaining similarity between the input and output is the cycle time or frequency.

Clamper Biasing

Why is the output waveform so badly distorted? Why is not at least half of the input waveform (one alternation) faithfully reproduced at the output? The answer has to do with clamper action (discussed in Chapter 3). Let's review that information to see how clamping action is at work in class C amplifiers. In Figure 7–17, the coupling capacitor is charged through the base–emitter junction diode. This charge builds up very quickly during the rising side of the positive alternation of the input signal. The capacitor holds that charge on the falling side of the positive alternation and for the entire negative alternation. The negative charge on the base side of the capacitor keeps the transistor in cutoff. In other words, the base is clamped to a negative potential that is almost equal to the peak input voltage.

Notice that R_B provides a discharge path for the capacitor. If it were not for R_B, the transistor would be forced into total cutoff for all input cycles after the first charging cycle and there would be no output. Because of R_B, there is a need restore lost charge on the capacitor with each positive alternation of the input signal. When the positive alternation exceeds the capacitor charge voltage by approximately 0.7 V, the transistor is turned on and saturates. The portion of the input signal over which the transistor conducts is known as the **conduction angle** and is measured in degrees (always less than 180°). The length of time (t) the output pulse exists is known as the **pulse duration.** Duty cycle is the ratio of pulse duration to period, where period = $T = 1/f$. The percent duty cycle is always less than 50% for class C amplifiers. For example, if the duration of the output pulse is 1 ms and the frequency of the applied signal is 100 Hz, the percent duty cycle is $100\% \cdot 1\text{ ms}/10\text{ ms} = 10\%$.

$$\% \text{ Duty Cycle} = 100\% \cdot t/T \qquad (7–14)$$

where t is the pulse duration and T is the period equal to $1/f$.

What determines the actual percent duty cycle or the duration of the output pulses? Basically, it is the value of R_B. R_B is normally very large compared to the internal resistance of the source (R_S, also designated as Z_S). Thus, the value of R_B can be changed to change the discharge time and the conduction angle. Larger values of R_B produce very low duty cycles (narrow output pulses) and lower values of R_B produce high duty cycles (wide output pulses) for a given value of input coupling capacitance.

CLASS C APPLICATIONS

Class C Tuned Amplifiers

The problem of severe waveform distortion at the output of class C amplifiers can be eliminated for narrow bands of frequencies. As shown in Figure 7–18, the output has been restored to a full sine wave using a parallel resonant circuit (tank circuit). As in class B amplifiers, the ringing tank current creates a sinusoidal output voltage. Near the peak of every positive alternation of the input signal, the transistor conducts and restores energy lost by the tank circuit to the load. Consequently, the output waveform is a sine wave of constant amplitude.

Like the class B tuned amplifier, the class C tuned amplifier is efficient over a narrow group (band) of frequencies. This narrow band of frequencies depends on the resonant frequency (f_r) of the tank and the Q (as in quality factor) of the entire output circuit (Q_{ckt}). The following formulas are true for tuned class B and class C amplifiers.

$$\text{Bandwidth} = BW = f_r/Q_{ckt} \tag{7–15}$$

$$f_r = 1/(2\pi\sqrt{LC}) = 0.159/\sqrt{LC} \tag{7–16}$$

$$Q_{ckt} = (Z_{tank} \parallel R_L)/X_L \tag{7–17}$$

$$Z_{tank} = X_L^2/R_W \tag{7–18}$$

where R_W is the DC resistance of the inductor's windings.

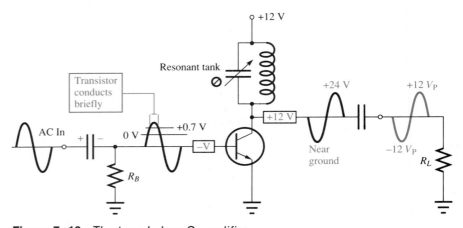

Figure 7–18   The tuned class C amplifier.

$$X_L = 2\pi f_r L \tag{7–19}$$

Consider Example 7–4.

EXAMPLE 7–4 ▮▬▬▬▬▬

Find f_r, X_L, Z_{tank}, Q_{ckt}, and BW for Figure 7–19.

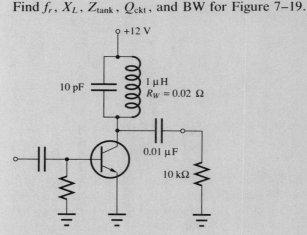

+12 V

10 pF

1 µH
$R_W = 0.02\ \Omega$

0.01 µF

10 kΩ

Figure 7–19

$$f_r = 0.159/\sqrt{LC} = 0.159/\sqrt{1\ \mu H \cdot 10\ pF} = 50.3\ \text{MHz}$$

$$X_L = 2\pi f_r L = 6.28 \cdot 50.3\ \text{MHz} \cdot 1\ \mu H = 316\ \Omega$$

$$Z_{\text{tank}} = X_L^2/R_W = 316^2/0.02 \cong 5\ \text{M}\Omega$$

$$Q_{\text{ckt}} = (Z_{\text{tank}} \parallel R_L)/X_L = (5\ \text{M}\Omega \parallel 10\ \text{k}\Omega)/316\ \Omega$$

$$= 9.98\ \text{k}\Omega/316\ \Omega = 31.6$$

$$BW = f_r/Q_{\text{ckt}} = 50.3\ \text{MHz}/31.6 = 1.59\ \text{MHz}$$

This class C amplifier will function efficiently over a bandwidth of 1.59 MHz centered on a frequency of 50.3 MHz. The actual range of frequencies, or bandpass, is 49.5 MHz to 51.1 MHz.

Class C Frequency Multipliers

Class C amplifiers can be tuned to a multiple of the input frequency and thereby multiply the input frequency. For example, the frequency multiplier/amplifier of Figure 7–20 produces an output signal at a frequency that is twice the input frequency. The tank circuit resonates (rings) at $2f$ and the input frequency (f) keeps the tank ringing. For every other output cycle the tank receives a "kick" from the positive alternation of the input cycle. The tank must ring on its own until the rising edge of the positive alternation of the next input cycle.

For efficient and distortion-free operation, the tank must be tuned to an exact multiple of the input frequency. If the tank is tuned to twice the input

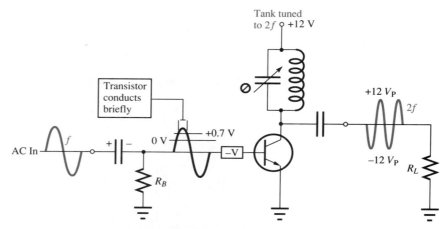

Figure 7–20 The class C frequency doubler.

frequency, the circuit is called a *doubler*. If the tank is tuned to three times the input frequency, the circuit is called a *tripler*. Four times is a *quadrupler*. Usually, the quadrupler is the highest multiplier factor used, because the ringing of the tank dampens out a little more with each ring (cycle) due to coil resistance and the drain caused by the load resistor. After the fourth output cycle, a kick from the input cycle is needed to recharge the tank and restore the peak-to-peak output to its maximum value.

Usually, doublers and triplers are linked together (cascaded) to produce the total desired multiplication factor. Such cascades are commonly used in FM transmitters to multiply a relatively low frequency to a much higher frequency. For example, a 12-MHz frequency can be tripled, doubled, and doubled again to arrive at a final transmitter frequency of 144 MHz. In the process of frequency multiplication, voltage and power amplification takes place.

CLASS C POWER CONSIDERATIONS

Class C Transistor Power Dissipation (P_D)

How much power does a class C biased transistor dissipate? Not much. When the transistor is ON, it is, for the most part, saturated. That means the power dissipated by the transistor is the product of $v_{ce(\text{sat})}$ and $i_{c(\text{sat})}$. However, the transistor is only saturated for a certain time (t). Therefore, the average power dissipation of the transistor is in proportion to the ratio of saturation time to total input cycle time (duty cycle).

$$P_D = i_{c(\text{sat})} \cdot v_{ce(\text{sat})} \cdot t/T \tag{7–20}$$

where t/T is the duty cycle of the class C amplifier as determined by the value of the input coupling capacitor and R_B.

$$i_{c(\text{sat})} = V_{CC}/(Z_{\text{tank}} \parallel R_L) \tag{7–21}$$

The AC collector–emitter saturation voltage is always very low, usually in the vicinity of 0.1 to 0.2 V. The actual value depends on the transistor type and saturation current.

For the circuit of Example 7–4, we will assume the ON time of the transistor to be 1 ns $(1 \cdot 10^{-9}$ s). The total cycle time is $1/50.3$ MHz = 19.9 ns. If the supply voltage is 12 V, the saturation current is

$$i_{c(\text{sat})} = V_{CC}/(Z_{\text{tank}} \parallel R_L) = 12 \text{ V}/(5 \text{ M}\Omega \parallel 10 \text{ k}\Omega)$$

$$= 12 \text{ V}/9.98 \text{ k}\Omega = 1.2 \text{ mA}$$

If we assume the saturated collector–emitter voltage to be 0.2 V, the transistor power dissipation is

$$P_D = i_{c(\text{sat})} \cdot v_{ce(\text{sat})} \cdot t/T = 1.2 \text{ mA} \cdot 0.2 \text{ V} \cdot 1 \text{ ns}/19.9 \text{ ns}$$

$$= 12.1 \ \mu\text{W}$$

Class C Output Power ($P_{\text{out}} = P_L$)

As with class A and B amplifiers, the maximum power delivered to the load resistor is simply the square of the RMS load voltage divided by the load resistance.

$$P_{L(\text{max})} = (0.707 \cdot V_{CC})^2/R_L = 0.5 \cdot V_{CC}^2/R_L \qquad (7\text{–}22)$$

where V_{CC} is the maximum peak voltage that appears across the load resistor.

Again, using Example 7–4, the maximum load power (output power) is

$$P_{L(\text{max})} = 0.5 \cdot V_{CC}^2/R_L = 0.5 \cdot 12^2/10{,}000 = 72/10{,}000 = 7.2 \text{ mW}$$

Class C DC Power (P_{DC})

The power supplied by the DC supply to the amplifier is the sum of the maximum load power, the transistor power dissipation, and the power dissipation of the tank circuit.

$$P_{\text{DC}} = P_L + P_D + P_{\text{tank}} \qquad (7\text{–}23)$$

Since the tank circuit has the same voltage as the load, the power dissipation of the tank is calculated as follows:

$$P_{\text{tank}} = (0.707 \cdot V_{CC})^2/Z_{\text{tank}} = 0.5 \cdot V_{CC}^2/Z_{\text{tank}} \qquad (7\text{–}24)$$

Again, for Example 7–4, the power dissipated by the tank is

$$P_{\text{tank}} = 0.5 \cdot V_{CC}^2/Z_{\text{tank}} = 0.5 \cdot 12^2/5{,}000{,}000 = 14.4 \ \mu\text{W}$$

The total DC power delivered to the amplifier circuit is

$$P_{\text{DC}} = P_L + P_D + P_{\text{tank}} = 7.2 \text{ mW} + 12.1 \ \mu\text{W} + 14.4 \ \mu\text{W} = 7.23 \text{ mW}$$

Class C Power Efficiency (η)

As stated earlier, the power efficiency of class C amplifiers is very high—ranging between 80% and nearly 100%. As with all classes of amplifiers, the efficiency is the ratio of output power to total DC input power, $\eta = P_L/P_{DC}$. The efficiency of the circuit in Example 7–4 is

$\eta = P_L/P_{DC} = 7.2 \text{ mW}/7.23 \text{ mW} = 0.996$

% eff. $= \eta \cdot 100\% = 0.996 \cdot 100\% = 99.6\%$ (Not bad!)

Now, take time to study Example 7–5.

EXAMPLE 7–5 ▮▮▮▮▮▮▮▮

Perform a complete bandwidth and power analysis on Figure 7–21. Transistor ON time is 5 ns. Assume $v_{ce(sat)}$ to be 0.1 V.

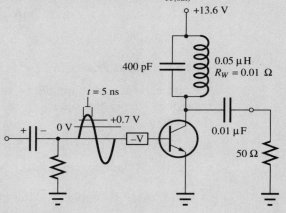

Figure 7–21

$$f_r = 0.159/\sqrt{LC} = 0.159/\sqrt{0.05\ \mu H \cdot 400\ pF} = 35.6 \text{ MHz}$$

$$X_L = 2\pi f_r L = 6.28 \cdot 35.6 \text{ MHz} \cdot 0.05\ \mu H = 11.2\ \Omega$$

$$Z_{\text{tank}} = X_L^2/R_W = 11.2^2/0.01 \cong 12.5 \text{ k}\Omega$$

$$Q_{\text{ckt}} = (Z_{\text{tank}} \parallel R_L)/X_L = (12.5 \text{ k}\Omega \parallel 50\ \Omega)/11.2\ \Omega$$
$$= 50\ \Omega/11.2\ \Omega = 4.5$$

$$BW = f_r/Q_{\text{ckt}} = 35.6 \text{ MHz}/4.5 = 7.91 \text{ MHz}$$

$$i_{c(sat)} = V_{CC}/(Z_{\text{tank}} \parallel R_L) = 13.6 \text{ V}/(12.5 \text{ k}\Omega \parallel 50\ \Omega) = 0.272 \text{ A}$$

$$T = 1/f_r = 1/35.6 \text{ MHz} = 28.1 \text{ ns}$$

$$P_D = i_{c(sat)} \cdot v_{ce(at)} \cdot t/T$$
$$= 0.272 \text{ A} \cdot 0.1 \text{ V} \cdot 5 \text{ ns}/28.1 \text{ ns} = 4.84 \text{ mW}$$

$$P_{L(max)} = 0.5 \cdot V_{CC}^2/R_L = 0.5 \cdot 13.6^2/50\ \Omega = 1.85 \text{ W}$$

$$P_{\text{tank}} = 0.5 \cdot V_{CC}^2/Z_{\text{tank}} = 0.5 \cdot 13.6^2/12.5 \text{ k}\Omega = 7.4 \text{ mW}$$

$$P_{DC} = P_L + P_D + P_{\text{tank}} = 1.85 \text{ W} + 4.84 \text{ mW} + 7.4 \text{ mW} = 1.86 \text{ W}$$

$$\eta = P_L/P_{DC} = 1.85 \text{ W}/1.86 \text{ W} = 0.995 = 99.5\% \text{ efficiency}$$

Summary

It is important for you to understand that class C efficiency depends on:

- duty cycle—the ratio of transistor on time to total cycle time (t/T)—which depends on the value of R_B and the value of the input coupling capacitor.
- the frequency of the applied signal.
- the power dissipated by the tank circuit.

The higher the duty cycle, the lower the efficiency. However, rarely will the class C efficiency drop below 80%.

**Self-Check
7–3**

1. Describe the output of an untuned class C amplifier.
2. What characteristic of the output waveform and the input signal remains the same?
3. List three advantages of the class C amplifier.
4. The output waveform of a tuned class C amplifier is what?
5. What is a basic limitation of a tuned class C amplifier?
6. What is a class C frequency multiplier?
7. The following information is known about a tuned class C amplifier: V_{CC} = +20 V, L_{tank} = 2 μH, the resistance of the inductor's windings R_W = 0.03 Ω, C_{tank} = 25 pF, R_L = 47 kΩ, the transistor conducts in 5-ns pulses, and $v_{ce(sat)}$ = 0.2 V. Find: f_r, X_L, Z_{tank}, Q_{ckt}, BW, $P_{L(max)}$, P_D, P_{DC}, and % eff.

7–4 CLASS D AMPLIFIERS

INTRODUCTION TO CLASS D AMPLIFIERS

Class D amplifiers are the most efficient of all amplifiers thus far discussed. They operate at very close to 100% efficiency. Figure 7–22 illustrates the simplicity of the class D amplifier. When a transistor is operated class D, it functions as a high-speed switch. The transistor is always in one of two states—saturated or cutoff. The rising and falling edges of the collector voltage and current waveforms are very steep, forming near-perfect square waves. Figure 7–22 emphasizes the 180° relationship between the output and

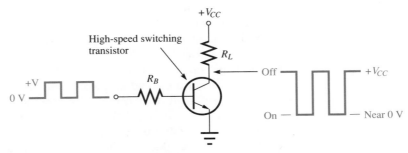

Figure 7–22 The class D amplifier.

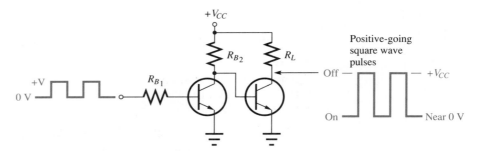

Figure 7–23 Cascaded class D common-emitter amplifiers for in-phase output.

input. This is exactly what you would expect from a common-emitter configuration. The common-collector configuration is rarely used for class D operation because the transistor will not saturate as completely as it does in the CE configuration. In the CE configuration, the collector–emitter voltage drops to near ground potential, in the vicinity of 0.1 V. In the CC configuration, approximately 0.7 V is the lowest possible V_{CE}. The CE configuration transfers more voltage to the load and the transistor dissipates far less power.

CLASS D APPLICATIONS

In-Phase Line Driver

Figure 7–23 demonstrates how two CE class D amplifiers (switches) can be cascaded to recover the original phase of the input signal. Each transistor provides a 180° phase inversion, which places the output in phase with the input. An arrangement such as this can be used as a digital line driver to transmit binary data over a bus wire (line).

Pulse Duration Modulation Amplifier

Figure 7–24 is a scaled-down model of a modulation technique used in some modern AM broadcast transmitters. This technique is known as **pulse duration modulation (PDM).** The audio signal is used to vary the duty cycle of a square-wave pulse train. As you can see, on positive audio peaks the duty cycle of the pulses is very high (ON much longer than it is OFF). On negative audio peaks, the duty cycle of the pulses is very low (OFF longer than it is ON). At points of zero crossing, the duty cycle is exactly 50%. This varying duty cycle pulse train is then used to drive the class D amplifier which acts as a switch.

As the transistor is turned on and off by the pulse train, the surges of collector current are filtered and averaged by the lowpass filter. The bandstop filter is used to further remove (block) the original pulse frequency. In many broadcast transmitters the frequency of the pulse train is about 80 kHz. Thus, the bandstop filter is tuned to 80 kHz to block and further eliminate any of the 80-kHz signal from getting to the load. Because of the lowpass filter, the bandstop filter, and the filter capacitor, the pulse train is

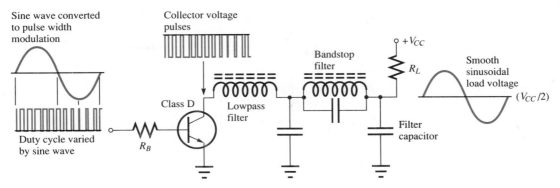

Figure 7–24 Class D pulse duration modulation amplifier.

turned back into the original sine wave signal, which is usually voice or music. The audio at the load is greatly amplified and rides on a DC voltage level that is half of V_{CC}. The DC to AC power conversion efficiency is nearly 100%.

CLASS D POWER CONSIDERATIONS

As stated earlier, the power efficiency of the class D amplifier is nearly 100%. Since the transistor is either saturated or cut off, it can never dissipate a significant amount of power. Power equals current times voltage. If the collector current is zero (cutoff) the power dissipation must be zero. If the collector–emitter voltage is zero (close to it when saturated), the power dissipation must be zero. Thus, the load is the only component that dissipates power. Nearly all DC source power is converted to load power: $\eta = 1 = P_L/P_{DC} = 100\%$ eff. Using the PDM technique, class D amplifiers can be used for extremely efficient high-power audio applications.

Self-Check 7–4

1. What are the two operating states of the class D amplifier?
2. To what device can a class D amplifier be compared?
3. List two applications for class D amplifiers.
4. What is the purpose for the filters of Figure 7–24?
5. What is the percent efficiency for class D amplifiers?

7–5 POWER AMPLIFIER CONSIDERATIONS

POWER RATING AND DERATING

Power transistors are rated to handle (dissipate) a specified amount of power with a case temperature (T_C) of 25°C. If the case temperature increases during operation, which of course it will, the transistor must be derated. It is assumed that the amplifier is designed properly and the temperature of the case of the transistor itself will level off at some operating temperature. If the operating temperature of the transistor case is known, or can be calcu-

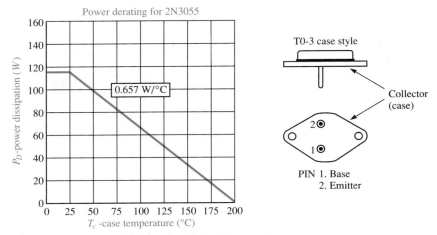

Figure 7–25   Derating the 2N3055 NPN transistor.

lated, the transistor can be derated according to the derating factor specified by the manufacturer. The **derating factor (D)** is specified as so many watts per degree centigrade (above 25°C).

$$P_{D(\text{max at operating temp})} = P_{D(\text{max at 25°C})} - [(T_C - 25°C) \cdot D] \qquad (7–25)$$

Consider Figure 7–25 and Example 7–6.

EXAMPLE 7–6 ▮▮▮▮▮▮▮▮▮▮▮▮▮▮▮▮▮▮

The 2N3055 is a very popular high-power NPN transistor. It is rated for a maximum power dissipation of 115 W at a case temperature of 25°C. The specified derating factor is 0.657 W/°C. If the transistor's case temperature reaches 65°C during operation, the transistor's power rating is reduced to 88.7 W.

$$P_{D(\text{max at operating temp})} = P_{D(\text{max at 25°C})} - [(T_C - 25°C) \cdot D]$$

$$P_{D(\text{max at 65°C})} = 115 \text{ W} - [(65°C - 25°C) \cdot 0.657 \text{ W/°C}]$$

$$= 115 \text{ W} - 26.3 \text{ W} = 88.7 \text{ W}$$

The 88.7-W power rating at 65°C can also be determined from the graph of Figure 7–25. Graphs such as these are provided in data sheets by the manufacturer.

HEAT SINKS FOR POWER TRANSISTORS

As you may already know, a heat sink is a thermally conductive mass that is used to transfer transistor heat to the air. Figures 7–26 and 7–27 illustrate heat sinks for medium- and high-power transistors. The purpose for using the heat sink is to remove dissipated power in the form of heat from the

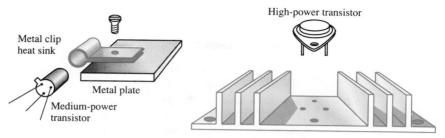

Figure 7–26   Some heat sinks for power transistors.

transistor case as quickly as possible. If large quantities of heat are rapidly removed from the transistor case, the temperature of the case will not rise severely. In other words, the better the heat sink, the lower the transistor case temperature. If the transistor case temperature is kept relatively low, the power rating will be closer to its maximum rated value.

Some transistors can be mounted in direct contact with the heat sink, thus providing maximum heat transfer from case to sink. In many applications, the transistor must be electrically insulated from the heat sink but not thermally insulated. In such a situation, the case of the transistor (usually the collector) is at a potential above ground while the heat sink is at ground potential. To insulate electrically but not thermally, a thin precut sheet of mica is placed between the transistor case and the heat sink. Also, heat sink compound (a greasy, nonconductive substance) is used on each side of the mica sheet to insure maximum heat transfer from transistor to sink. Teflon sleeves and washers are used to insulate the mounting screws from the heat sink so the transistor case is not shorted to the sink.

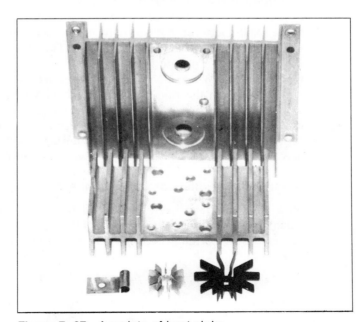

Figure 7–27   A variety of heat sinks.

THERMODYNAMICS

Ohm's Law of Thermodynamics

How can you determine what the case temperature (T_C) of the transistor will be in order to derate the transistor? How can you know that the power rating of the transistor during operation will be higher than the actual power the transistor is dissipating? You certainly do not want the transistors to overheat and burn up. The answers to these questions can be obtained by applying simple principles of thermodynamics. Sounds neat, huh? OK, let's see how.

Temperature and power dissipation are related in the same way voltage and current are related. Also, there is such a thing as thermal resistance, which is similar to electrical resistance. Ohm's Law of thermodynamics for power transistors is written like this:

$$P_D = (T_C - T_A)/R_\theta \qquad\qquad (7-26)$$

where T_C = case temperature, T_A = ambient temperature, and R_θ = thermal resistance from case to air.

This formula is similar to Ohm's Law: $I = E/R$. In this case, the power dissipation (P_D) is equal to the difference in temperature from case to air ($T_C - T_A$) divided by the thermal resistance (R_θ) from the transistor's case to the air. The difference in temperature is like a difference of potential. Without a difference in temperature between two points separated by thermal resistance, there is no power dissipation (transfer).

Thermal Resistance (R_θ)

The **thermal resistance (R_θ)** in Formula 7–26 is the total resistance to heat transfer that exists between the transistor's case and the air. Thermal resistance exists between the transistor's case and the heat sink ($R_{\theta CS}$) and between the heat sink and the air ($R_{\theta SA}$). Thermal resistance is expressed in units of °C/W. The thermal resistance between case and sink is usually between 0.5°C/W and 1.5°C/W. The thermal resistance between the sink and air is usually in the range of 2°C/W to 100°C/W. A thermal resistance of 0.5°C/W is very low and 100°C/W is very high. Heat sinks are rated according to their sink to air thermal resistance. For example, the large, finned heat sinks in Figures 7–26 and 7–27 have thermal resistances of about 5°C/W or less. The larger the heat sink, the lower the thermal resistance.

Determining Transistor Case Temperature (T_C)

Now that you have been introduced to a little thermodynamics, you can calculate the operating temperature of the transistor's case as it dissipates its power. First, Formula 7–26 must be rearranged to solve for case temperature.

$$P_D = (T_C - T_A)/R_\theta \quad \text{and} \quad P_D \cdot R_\theta = T_C - T_A$$

therefore,

$$T_C = (P_D \cdot R_\theta) + T_A \qquad\qquad (7-27)$$

where P_D is the actual power dissipated by the transistor and R_θ is the total thermal resistance ($R_{\theta CS} + R_{\theta SA}$).

Consider Example 7–7.

EXAMPLE 7–7

A 2N3055 power transistor dissipates 20 W during operation. The amplifier circuit is designed to operate over an ambient temperature range of 0 to 80°C. The worst case condition exists when the ambient temperature is 80°C. The transistor case to heat sink thermal resistance is 0.5°C/W and the heat sink is rated for a thermal resistance of 3°C/W. Calculate the case temperature of the transistor for worst-case operating conditions.

$$T_C = (P_D \cdot R_\theta) + T_A = (20 \text{ W} \cdot 3.5°\text{C/W}) + 80°\text{C}$$

$$= 70°\text{C} + 80°\text{C} = 150°\text{C}$$

Now, what is the derated power rating for the 2N3055 if the ambient temperature does reach 80°C?

$$P_{D(\text{max at operating temp})} = P_{D(\text{max at 25°C})} - [(T_C - 25°\text{C}) \cdot D]$$

$$P_{D(\text{max at 80°C})} = 115 \text{ W} - [(150°\text{C} - 25°\text{C}) \cdot 0.657 \text{ W/°C}]$$

$$= 115 \text{ W} - 82 \text{ W} = 33 \text{ W}$$

The transistor is actually dissipating 20 W, so the maximum of 33 W is a safe margin.

In Example 7–7, it is important for you to realize that an ambient temperature of 80°C is very high. In practice, the ambient temperature can be kept between 30 and 35°C using a cooling fan or placing the heat sink in the open air, not enclosed in a case. Proper ventilation is very important. Note that if the ambient temperature can be maintained at 35°C, the maximum derated power rating for the transistor would be about 62 W. You can also see that it is difficult to make use of the full power-handling capability of the transistor (115 W for the 2N3055). For maximum power-handling capability, the thermal resistance (case to sink and sink to air) must be kept very low and the ambient temperature must be kept low. Consider one more example—Example 7–8.

EXAMPLE 7–8

What size heat sink, in terms of °C/W, do you need for a 2N3055 if the power dissipation is 55 W, and the ambient air temperature is 35°C? Assume a case to sink thermal resistance of 0.8°C/W.

From the chart in Figure 7–25, at a maximum dissipation of 55 W the case temperature must be approximately 115°C.

$$T_C = (P_D \cdot R_\theta) + T_A$$

Therefore,

$$R_\theta = (T_C - T_A)/P_D = (115° - 35°)/55 \text{ W} = 80°/55 \text{ W} = 1.45°C/W$$

$$R_\theta (R_{\theta CS} + R_{\theta SA})$$

Therefore,

$$R_{\theta SA} = R_\theta - R_{\theta CS} = 1.45°C/W - 0.8°C/W = 0.65°C/W$$

So, the heat sink must not have a thermal resistance greater than 0.65°C/W.

BIAS STABILIZATION AT HIGH TEMPERATURES

As you can see, power transistors normally operate warm or even hot, because of the power that is being converted to heat and transferred to the air. The higher operating temperature causes some transistor parameters, such as β, r_e', and V_{BE}, to change. Collector current increases with temperature, which increases transistor power dissipation, which increases temperature, which further increases current . . . well, you get the point. This is the thermal runaway we have mentioned before. The problem is serious and must be addressed in the power amplifier design.

Figure 7–28 illustrates a minimum precaution that can be taken to help combat thermal runaway. Notice that the bias diodes are physically mounted on the heat sink close to the power transistor. This causes the temperature of the diodes to increase with the temperature of the transistor's case. As heating takes place, the diode junction voltage decreases slightly. The decrease in junction voltage reduces the bias on the power transistor, which helps control the collector current.

Another stabilization scheme involves the use of thermistors. Negative-temperature-coefficient thermistors may be used in place of the bias diodes. As temperature increases, the resistance of the thermistor(s) decreases, thus reducing base bias and collector current. However, the thermistor must be carefully chosen so that it does not overcompensate and thus create crossover distortion.

Using diodes and thermistors to bias the power transistors does work, but there is a better, though more complicated, method to obtain bias stabilization. This involves a secondary circuit that monitors and controls the DC collector current, which is accomplished by placing low resistances (about 0.2 Ω) in the emitter path of each final power transistor. The voltage across the small resistance is monitored by a special circuit that also controls the bias for the transistors. This special circuit is able to ignore AC voltage variations and respond only to the voltage drop that is created by the DC collector current. Thus, if the collector current attempts to increase due to increasing temperature, the emitter-resistor voltage drop increases, which

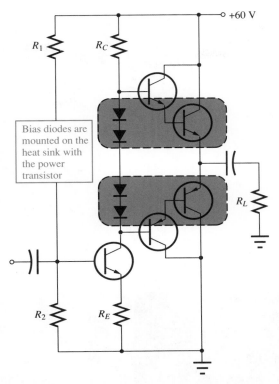

Figure 7–28   Temperature compensation.

signals the bias-control circuitry to reduce the bias. In this way, a closed loop is formed that constantly monitors collector current and adjusts the bias as needed.

Take a moment to review this section and test your understanding by answering the questions of Self-Check 7–5.

Self-Check 7–5

1. The derating factor for a power transistor is 0.5 W/°C. The transistor is rated for 60 W at $T_C = 25°C$. If the transistor operates at a case temperature of 100°C, what is the derated maximum power dissipation for the transistor?

2. If a heat sink has a thermal resistance rating of 50°C/W, is the heat sink a large one or a small one? Explain.

3. A 2N3055 power transistor dissipates 30 W during operation. The amplifier circuit is designed to operate over an ambient temperature range of 0 to 50°C. The transistor case to heat sink thermal resistance is 0.5°C/W and the heat sink is rated for a thermal resistance of 2°C/W. Calculate the case temperature of the transistor for worst-case operating conditions and the derated maximum power dissipation of the transistor ($D = 0.657$ W/°C).

4. Briefly explain how the thermistors can be used to help stabilize bias and compensate for increases in operating temperature.

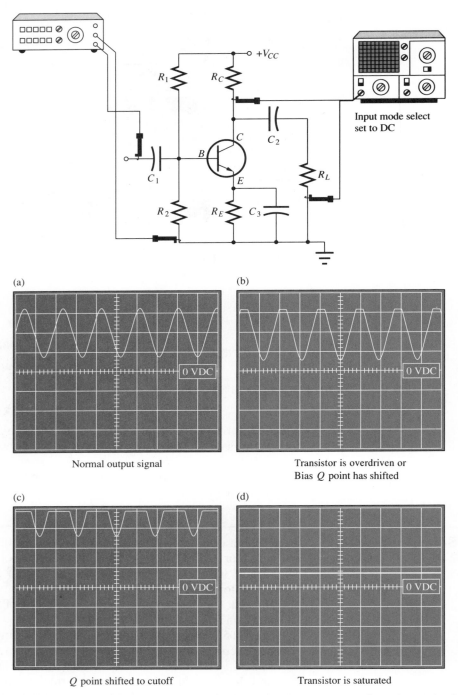

(a)

Normal output signal

(b)

Transistor is overdriven or
Bias Q point has shifted

(c)

Q point shifted to cutoff

(d)

Transistor is saturated

Figure 7–29 Troubleshooting class A amplifiers by observing the output waveform.

7–6 TROUBLESHOOTING

TROUBLESHOOTING CLASS A AMPLIFIERS

In this troubleshooting section, we investigate the use of the oscilloscope and signal generator in troubleshooting amplifiers. Specifically, we use the oscilloscope to observe the amplifier's output and apply theory to suggest reasons for what we see.

Figure 7–29 illustrates how the signal generator is used to inject a test signal (a 1- to 2-kHz sine wave). The oscilloscope is connected to the collector of the transistor to monitor both the AC signal and the DC collector voltage.

Figure 7–29a shows what you would expect to see at the output of a properly functioning class A amplifier. The output signal is riding on a positive DC reference voltage. There is no visible distortion. The waveform is not deformed or clipped.

Figure 7–29b shows a clipped output. However, this may be normal for this amplifier. The input signal might be too great in amplitude and the amplifier might be overdriven. The reason only the positive-going peaks are clipped is because the Q point is not in the center of the AC load line. You should know this is possible from your study of class A amplifiers. Another possibility is that the bias has shifted from its original design point. This can be caused by changes in the value of R_1 or R_2. However, this is not a common occurrence.

Figure 7–29c illustrates what would be observed if the Q point of the transistor were shifted radically to cutoff. Only a portion of the positive alternation of the input signal gets amplified. Between negative-going pulses at the output the transistor is cutoff. This problem may be caused by R_1 becoming disconnected (due to, say, a cold solder joint or a cracked foil). Thus, DC bias is removed and the transistor is cut off until the positive alternation of the input signal reaches about +0.7 V.

Figure 7–29d indicates that the transistor is either saturated or shorted collector to emitter. Notice that the DC level is very low and would be equal to the voltage drop across R_E. The transistor could be shorted externally from collector to emitter or R_2 may have become disconnected, causing the base-bias voltage to increase tremendously and saturate the transistor. If C_3 became shorted, a similar output would be observed but the DC level would be very low, probably less than 0.2 V. A shorted capacitor is a real possibility, especially if the capacitor is a tantalum capacitor. In my troubleshooting experience, I have found that tantalums tend to short and aluminum electrolytics become leaky. If C_1 becomes leaky, the bias and Q point will definitely shift.

TROUBLESHOOTING CLASS B PUSH-PULL AMPLIFIERS

You should recognize the circuit of Figure 7–30 as a Darlington class B push-pull amplifier. Since it is a single-supply amplifier, you would expect to observe a DC level at the output that is half of the DC source voltage.

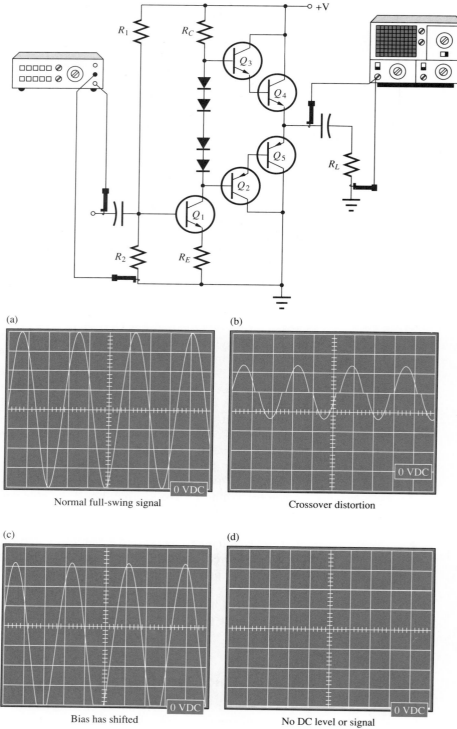

(a)

Normal full-swing signal

(b)

Crossover distortion

(c)

Bias has shifted

(d)

No DC level or signal

Figure 7–30 Troubleshootng push-pull amplifiers by observing the output waveform.

Figure 7–30a shows a normal full-swing signal at the amplifier's output. There is no visible crossover distortion or clipping. Notice the O-VDC reference is set at the bottom of the screen. The entire AC waveform is positive.

Figure 7–30b illustrates the very common crossover distortion problem that is characteristic for push-pull amplifiers. It is very likely that one or more of the diodes has become shorted internally.

Figure 7–30c demonstrates another common problem. The bias and Q point have shifted. As seen on the CRT, the shift is downward. This indicates that Q_5 is conducting a little more than Q_4. Q_1 is probably conducting more than it should, which increases the bias for Q_2 and decreases the bias for Q_3. This increase in conduction for Q_1 could be due to heat or to an increase in the resistance of R_2. The older carbon-composition resistors have been known to increase in resistance with age and exposure to heat. This problem is virtually extinct with the newer metal-film resistors. Another real possibility here is the input coupling capacitor has become leaky. If this happens, the signal source will either act as a load on the bias network for Q_1 or will contribute DC current to the bias of Q_1. An extreme-case possible cause for this shift in Q point is thermal runaway. If this is the case, you will see the output waveform continue to shift downward (or upward) over a short period of time until full saturation occurs and one or more of the power transistors destructs or a fuse blows.

Figure 7–30d illustrates what can be seen at the output of the push-pull amplifier at the conclusion of thermal runaway. The trace is at or near the 0-V line and there is no signal. If this is because a fuse has blown, there is probably a good reason why the fuse blew. If the fuse has not yet blown, the power transistors are probably hot and possibly shorted. It is apparent that Q_5 is conducting very hard. Another possibility is a short from emitter to ground of Q_5. If you have just installed a new Q_5, you may not have mounted it correctly in the heat sink. Care must be taken to ensure that the base and emitter leads are centered in the feed-through holes in the heat sink and that insulating hardware is used properly. We must also consider the fact that Q_1 might be saturated or shorted, which would cause Q_5 to conduct very hard. Use your voltmeter to check V_{R2} and V_{CQ1}.

We have not been able to cover all trouble scenarios here. However, we have covered some of the more common problems. Remember, the solution to any troubleshooting problem is the careful application of circuit theory and troubleshooting techniques. Time for a self-check.

Self-Check 7–6

1. Refer to the circuit of Figure 7–29. Describe what would be seen on the oscilloscope if the emitter of the transistor became shorted to ground.
2. Refer to the circuit of Figure 7–29. Describe what would be seen on the oscilloscope if the base of the transistor became shorted to ground.
3. Refer to the circuit of Figure 7–30. Describe what would be seen on the oscilloscope if R_1 became open.
4. Refer to the circuit of Figure 7–30. Describe what would be seen on the oscilloscope if R_C became open.

SUMMARY

FORMULAS

Class A Amplifiers

(7–1) $P_D = V_{CE(Q)} \cdot I_{C(Q)}$

(7–2) $P_{L(max)} = (v_{\text{P-P(max)}})^2/8R_L$

(7–3) $v_{\text{P-P(max)}} = 2 \cdot (v_{ce(\text{cutoff})} - V_{CE(Q)})$
(where $V_{CE(Q)} \geq 0.5\ V_{CC}$)

(7–4) $v_{\text{P-P(max)}} = 2 \cdot (V_{CE(Q)} - V_{CE(\text{sat})})$
(where $V_{CE(Q)} - V_{CE(\text{sat})} < v_{ce(\text{cutoff})} - V_{CE(Q)}$)

(7–5) $P_{DC} = V_{CC} \cdot I_{C(Q)}$

(7–6) $\eta = P_L/P_{DC}$

(7–7)   % eff. $= \eta \cdot 100\%$

Class B Amplifiers

(7–8) $i_{c(\text{sat})} = V_{CE(Q)}/R_L$

(7–9) $i_{c(\text{max avg})} = 0.318\ i_{c(\text{sat})} = 0.318\ V_{CE(Q)}/R_L$

(7–10) $v_{ce(\text{max avg})} = 0.318 \cdot V_{CE(Q)}$

(7–11) $P_{D(max)} \cong (V_{CE(Q)})^2/10R_L$

(7–12) $P_{L(max)} = (v_{L(max)})^2/R_L = (0.707\ V_{CE(Q)})^2/R_L$

(7–13) $P_{DC(max)} = i_{c(\text{max avg})} \cdot V_{CC}$

Class C Amplifiers

(7–14)   % Duty Cycle $= 100\% \cdot t/T$

(7–15)   Bandwidth $= BW = f_r/Q_{\text{ckt}}$

(7–16) $f_r = 1/(2\pi\sqrt{LC}) = 0.159/\sqrt{LC}$

(7–17) $Q_{\text{ckt}} = (Z_{\text{tank}} \parallel R_L)/X_L$

(7–18) $Z_{\text{tank}} = X_L^2/R_W$

(7–19) $X_L = 2\pi f_r L$

(7–20) $P_D = i_{c(\text{sat})} \cdot v_{ce(\text{sat})} \cdot t/T$

(7–21) $i_{c(\text{sat})} = V_{CC}/(Z_{\text{tank}} \parallel R_L)$

(7–22) $P_{L(max)} = (0.707 \cdot V_{CC})^2/R_L = 0.5 \cdot V_{CC}^2/R_L$

(7–23) $P_{DC} = P_L + P_D + P_{\text{tank}}$

(7–24) $P_{\text{tank}} = (0.707 \cdot V_{CC})^2/Z_{\text{tank}} = 0.5 \cdot V_{CC}^2/Z_{\text{tank}}$

Power Ratings and Thermodynamics

(7–25) $P_{C(\text{max at operating temp})} = P_{D(\text{max at 25°C})} - [(T_C - 25°C) \cdot D]$

(7–26) $P_D = (T_C - T_A)/R_\theta$

(7–27) $T_C = (P_D \cdot R_\theta) + T_A$

CONCEPTS

- Class A amplifiers operate at 100% duty cycle and have power efficiencies less than 25%, usually much less.
- Class B amplifiers operate at 50% duty cycle and are approximately 75% efficient.
- Class C amplifiers operate at much less than 50% duty cycle and have power efficiencies in the range of about 80% to near 100%.
- Class D amplifiers act more like switches and have efficiencies very close to 100%. Their duty cycle depends on the duty cycle of the drive signal (input square wave).
- Crossover distortion is common among class B push-pull amplifiers that are improperly biased.
- Tuned class B and C amplifiers are efficient over only a very narrow band of frequencies.
- Untuned class B amplifiers are very broad-banded.
- Power transistors are derated according to the derating factor and the temperature of the transistor's case while operating.
- A large heat sink has a low thermal resistance from sink to air.
- Power transistor bias can be temperature stabilized by mounting bias diodes, or thermistors, on the heat sink close to the power transistor.
- Power transistor bias can be temperature stabilized by using a secondary circuit that monitors the DC collector current of the final power transistors and corrects the bias as needed.

NEED-TO-KNOW SOLUTION

1. A class B push-pull transformer-coupled amplifier will provide high efficiency, low distortion, and broad-banded ratio-frequency performance.
2. The total frequency multiplication factor is $2 \cdot 3 \cdot 3 = 18$. The transmitted frequency is 144.64 MHz. Thus, the oscillator must operate at a frequency of $144.64/18 = 8.03555$ MHz.
3. The line driver should operate class D.
4. $P_D = (T_C - T_A)/(R_{\theta CS} + R_{\theta SA})$
   $(R_{\theta CS} + R_{\theta SA}) = (T_C - T_A)/P_D$
   $R_{\theta SA} = [(T_C - T_A)/P_D] - R_{\theta CS} = [(100° - 40°)/25 \text{ W}] - 0.5°\text{C/W}$
   $= [60°/25 \text{ W}] - 0.5°\text{C/W} = 2.4°\text{C/W} - 0.5°\text{C/W}$
   $= 1.9°\text{C/W}$

QUESTIONS

7–1 CLASS A AMPLIFIERS

1. Describe the position of the Q point on the load line for small-signal class A amplifiers.
2. Describe the position of the Q point on the load line for large-signal class A amplifiers.
3. What is the percent duty cycle for class A amplifiers?
4. Why will a class A amplifier dissipate the same amount of power whether or not a signal is applied?

5. Under what condition does maximum efficiency occur for class A amplifiers?

6. What is the theoretical maximum efficiency for class A amplifiers?

7. If it is desired to transfer maximum power to a load resistance from a class A common-emitter amplifier that has a 600-Ω collector-resistor, what should the value of the load resistor be?

8. Is the class A amplifier a good choice for power amplification? Explain.

7–2 CLASS B AMPLIFIERS

9. What is the percent duty cycle for class B amplifiers?

10. Can a single-transistor class B amplifier be used to amplify audio with satisfactory results? Explain.

11. Describe the Q point on the load line for class B amplifiers.

12. Briefly describe the operation of a class B push-pull amplifier.

13. What causes crossover distortion?

14. Why are the terms *complementary symmetry* used to describe the class B push-pull amplifier?

15. Explain how the quiescent collector current can be adjusted when a diode is used to bias a class B amplifier.

16. Identify an obvious limitation of the class B tuned amplifier.

17. Name a component that is eliminated in the split-supply push-pull amplifier circuit.

18. How does the quasi-complementary amplifier differ from the complementary push-pull amplifier?

19. Describe the advantages of the transformer-coupled push-pull power amplifier.

20. What values of current and voltage should you use to calculate the maximum power dissipation of a class B transistor?
    (a) peak values   (b) quiescent values   (c) average values

21. What is the approximate percent efficiency for class B amplifiers?

7–3 CLASS C AMPLIFIERS

22. What is the percent duty cycle for class C amplifiers?

23. Why are class C amplifiers unsuitable for voice and music amplification?

24. Explain how the severe waveform distortion is eliminated when class C amplifiers are used to amplify radio frequencies.

25. Briefly explain why the transistor of a class C amplifier conducts only for a very short time during each input cycle.

26. What two components determine the conduction angle for the transistor of a class C amplifier?

27. Explain the basic operation of a class C frequency tripler.

28. What is the range of percent efficiency for class C amplifiers?

7–4 CLASS D AMPLIFIERS

29. What determines the percent duty cycle for class D amplifiers?

30. What mechanical component does a class D amplifier simulate?
31. What is the approximate percent efficiency for class D amplifiers?
32. Can a class D amplifier be used to amplify voice or music directly? Explain.
33. Briefly explain PDM.
34. Explain why a class D amplifier dissipates very little power.

7–5 POWER AMPLIFIER CONSIDERATIONS

35. What does the transistor's case temperature have to do with its power rating?
36. What is the purpose for a heat sink?
37. What is thermal resistance?
38. Why would you want to mount bias diodes on a heat sink next to the power transistor(s)?
39. Explain how a thermistor can be used to temperature stabilize the bias of a power transistor.

7–6 TROUBLESHOOTING

40. For the circuit of Figure 7–29, explain what might cause the voltage gain of the amplifier to be much lower than it should be.
41. For the circuit of Figure 7–29, explain what might cause the transistor to stay in saturation.
42. For the circuit of Figure 7–30, explain what might cause the DC level at the emitter of Q_4 to be close to $+V$.
43. For the circuit of Figure 7–30, explain what would result if the emitter of Q_1 became shorted to ground.

PROBLEMS

7–1 CLASS A AMPLIFIERS

1. Calculate P_D for Figure 7–31.

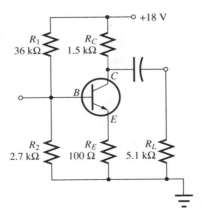

Figure 7–31

2. Calculate $P_{L(max)}$ for Figure 7–31.
3. Calculate P_{DC} for Figure 7–31.
4. Calculate % eff. for Figure 7–31.
5. Calculate P_D for Figure 7–32.

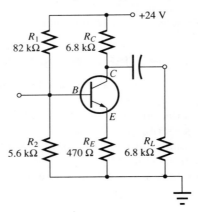

Figure 7–32

6. Calculate $P_{L(max)}$ for Figure 7–32.
7. Calculate P_{DC} for Figure 7–32.
8. Calculate % eff. for Figure 7–32.

7–2 CLASS B AMPLIFIERS

9. Calculate P_D for each final power transistor in Figure 7–33.

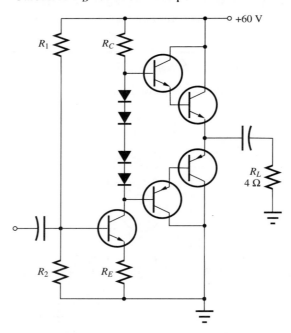

Figure 7–33

10. Calculate $P_{L(max)}$ for Figure 7–33.
11. Calculate P_{DC} for Figure 7–33.
12. Calculate % eff. for Figure 7–33.
13. Calculate $P_{D(max)}$ for each final power transistor in Figure 7–34.

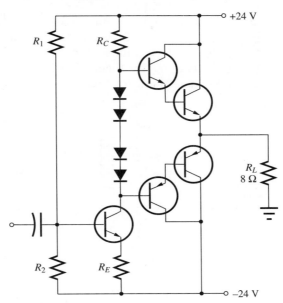

Figure 7–34

14. Calculate $P_{L(max)}$ for Figure 7–34.
15. Calculate $P_{DC(max)}$ for Figure 7–34.
16. Calculate % eff. for Figure 7–34.

7–3 CLASS C AMPLIFIERS

17. Calculate f_r for Figure 7–35.
18. Calculate BW for Figure 7–35.

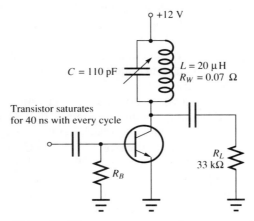

Figure 7–35

19. Calculate P_D for Figure 7–35. (Assume $V_{CE(sat)} = 0.2$ V).
20. Calculate $P_{L(max)}$ for Figure 7–35.
21. Calculate P_{DC} for Figure 7–35.
22. Calculate % eff. for Figure 7–35.
23. Calculate f_r for Figure 7–36.
24. Calculate BW for Figure 7–36.
25. Calculate P_D for Figure 7–36. (Assume $V_{CE(sat)} = 0.2$ V.
26. Calculate $P_{L(max)}$ for Figure 7–36.
27. Calculate P_{DC} for Figure 7–36.
28. Calculate % eff. for Figure 7–36.

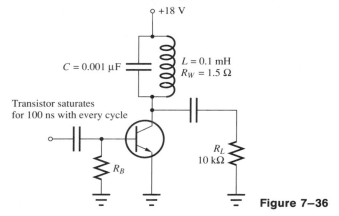

Figure 7–36

7–5 POWER AMPLIFIER CONSIDERATIONS

29. A power transistor has a power rating of 80 W at a case temperature of 25°C and has a derating factor of 0.38 W/°C. What is its power rating at a case temperature of 75°C?
30. A power transistor has a power rating of 45 W at a case temperature of 25°C and has a derating factor of 0.12 W/°C. What is its power rating at a case temperature of 35°C?
31. A power transistor has a power rating of 90 W at a case temperature of 25°C and has a derating factor of 0.55 W/°C. It dissipates 10 W during operation. The amplifier circuit is designed to operate over an ambient temperature range of 0 to 60°C. The transistor case to heat sink thermal resistance is 0.5°C/W and the heat sink is rated for a thermal resistance of 3°C/W. Calculate the case temperature of the transistor for worst-case operating conditions and the derated maximum power dissipation of the transistor.
32. A power transistor has a power rating of 50 W at a case temperature of 25°C and has a derating factor of 0.72 W/°C. It dissipates 12 W during operation. The amplifier circuit is designed to operate over an ambient temperature range of 0°C to 50°C. The transistor case to heat sink thermal resistance is 0.5°C/W and the heat sink is rated for a thermal resistance of 4 °C/W. Calculate the case temperature of the transistor for worst-case operating conditions and the derated maximum power dissipation of the transistor.
33. What size heat sink, in terms of °C/W, do you need for a 2N3055 if the power dissipation is 40 W and the ambient air temperature is 40°C? Assume a case to sink thermal resistance of 0.6°C/W.

34. What size heat sink, in terms of °C/W, do you need for a 2N3055 if the power dissipation is 36 W, and the ambient air temperature is 50°C? Assume a case to sink thermal resistance of 0.55°C/W.

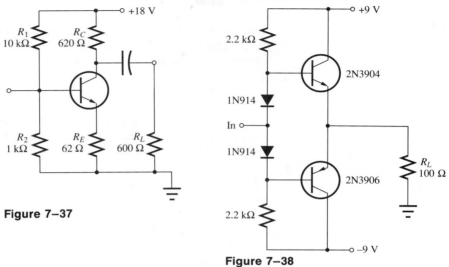

Figure 7–37

Figure 7–38

ADDITIONAL PROBLEMS

35. Calculate P_D for Figure 7–37.
36. Calculate $P_{L(max)}$ for Figure 7–37.
37. Calculate P_{DC} for Figure 7–37.
38. Calculate % eff. for Figure 7–37.
39. Calculate P_D for each final power transistor in Figure 7–38.
40. Calculate $P_{L(max)}$ for Figure 7–38.
41. Calculate P_{DC} for Figure 7–38.
42. Calculate % eff. for Figure 7–38.
43. Calculate f_r for Figure 7–39.
44. Calculate BW for Figure 7–39.
45. Calculate P_D for Figure 7–39. (Assume $v_{sat(CE)} = 0.2$ V.
46. Calculate $P_{L(max)}$ for Figure 7–39.
47. Calculate P_{DC} for Figure 7–39.
48. Calculate % eff. for Figure 7–39.

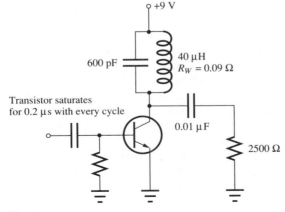

Figure 7–39

ANSWERS TO SELF-CHECKS

SELF-CHECK 7–1

1. The amplified waveform of a small-signal amplifier covers only a small portion of the load line. Small-signal amplifiers normally have a Q point that is low on the load line (closer to cutoff). Large-signal amplifiers are midpoint biased and use most of the load line.
2. True, if the AC and DC load lines are different and the Q point falls in the middle of the DC load line.
3. No. The quiescent power dissipation of the class A biased transistor is the same as when the transistor is being driven hard. This is because the average AC current is equal to $I_{C(Q)}$ and the average AC collector–emitter voltage is equal to $V_{CE(Q)}$.
4. 25%. However, this is nearly impossible to realize.
5. Change R_C to 500 Ω and adjust the bias and Q point by changing the value of R_1.

SELF-CHECK 7–2

1. 50% duty cycle
2. 0.7 V
3. The diode characteristics are similar to the base–emitter junction characteristics of the transistor. Also, the diode voltage drop will not change radically with variations in supply voltage as a resistor voltage drop may.
4. The class B bias voltage is too low or a bias diode is shorted.
5. The tuned amplifier uses only one transistor and is only functional over a narrow band of frequencies.
6. You must add an output coupling capacitor.
7. The transformer-coupled push-pull amplifier operates over a very wide band of frequencies. It also develops a higher output power.
8. $i_{c(\text{max avg})} = 63.6\,\text{mA}$, $P_{D(\text{max})} = 0.4\,\text{W}$, $P_{L(\text{max})} = 2\,\text{W}$, $P_{DC(\text{max})} = 2.54\,\text{W}$, % eff. $= 78.7\%$
   The efficiency of 78.7% is somewhat ideal because it assumes the peak load voltage to equal half the supply voltage ($V_{CE(Q)}$). In practice, the maximum peak load voltage is a little less than half the supply voltage.

SELF-CHECK 7–3

1. The output of an untuned class C amplifier is pulses with a duty cycle less than 50%.
2. The pulse frequency is the same as the frequency of the input signal.
3. The class C amplifier has very high efficiency, no need for a special bias circuit, and a very stable Q point with virtually no chance of thermal runaway.
4. A sine wave
5. Efficient over only a very narrow band of frequencies
6. A class C tuned amplifier whose tank circuit is tuned for a multiple of the input frequency

7. $f_r = 22.5$ MHz, $X_L = 283$ Ω, $Z_{tank} = 2.67$ MΩ, $Q_{ckt} = 163$, $BW = 138$ kHz, $P_{L(max)} = 4.26$ mW, $P_D = 9.74$ μW, $P_{DC} = 4.34$ mW, % eff. $= 98\%$

SELF-CHECK 7–4

1. Saturated and cutoff
2. A switch
3. Digital line drivers and PDM applications
4. To convert the pulsating DC of a varying duty cycle to an average current and voltage that has the same waveform as the original audio
5. Nearly 100%

SELF-CHECK 7–5

1. 22.5 W
2. The heat sink is small because the thermal resistance is high.
3. $T_C = 125°C$ and $P_{D(max\ at\ 50°C)} = 49.3$ W
4. The thermistor can be mounted next to the power transistor. As the transistor warms, the resistance of the thermistor decreases, causing the bias to decrease. Thus, thermal runaway cannot occur.

SELF-CHECK 7–6

1. A straight-line trace would be seen, indicating a very low DC voltage (close to ground potential). This is because the transistor would be fully saturated.
2. A straight-line trace would be seen indicating a very high DC voltage (close to V_{CC}). This is because the transistor would be fully cut off.
3. A straight-line trace would be seen indicating a very high DC voltage (close to $+V$). This is because Q_1 and Q_5 would be fully cut off as though they were open.
4. A straight-line trace would be seen indicating 0 VDC with no AC signal. This is because Q_3 and Q_4 are cut off.

SUGGESTED PROJECTS

1. Add some of the main concepts, formulas, and procedures from this chapter to your Electronics Notebook.
2. Construct and test the amplifier of Figure 7–30. Use 2N3904 transistors for Q_1, Q_3, and Q_4. Use 2N3906 transistors for Q_2 and Q_5. $V_{CC} = 9$ V (9-V battery), $R_1 = 25$-kΩ trim-pot wired as a rheostat, $R_2 = 2.2$ kΩ, $R_E = 510$ Ω, $R_C = 2.2$ kΩ, diodes $= 1$N914, $R_L = 100$ Ω, input and output coupling capacitors ≥ 1 μF. Apply a 1-kHz sine wave to the input while observing the output with the oscilloscope. Vary R_1 to adjust the bias for a Q_5 DC emitter voltage that permits a maximum output voltage swing. Replace R_C with a 10-kΩ resistor and look for some crossover distortion. Also, use a jumper wire to short one or more of the diodes and look for crossover distortion. Simulate other troubles and try to predict the results. Enjoy!

The transistors in this photograph look like medium-power BJTs, but they are not. These are enhancement-type TMOS power field-effect transistors. Their primary ratings are $V_{DSS} = 60$ V and I_D 12-A continuous. You will learn about FETs such as these in this chapter. (Courtesy of Motorola, Inc., Semiconductor Products Sector.)

JFETs and MOSFETs

OBJECTIVES

After studying this chapter, you will be able to

- Identify *n*-channel and *p*-channel JFETs and MOSFETs from schematic signals.
- identify D-type and E-type MOSFETs from schematic symbols.
- describe ON and OFF characteristics of JFETs, D MOSFETs, and E MOSFETs.
- explain the difference between VMOS, TMOS, and CMOS.
- describe bias requirements for JFETs and MOSFETs.
- analyze basic JFET and MOSFET amplifiers.
- design basic JFET and MOSFET amplifiers.
- discuss advantages of power MOSFETs over bipolar transistors.
- discuss some applications for FETs.
- troubleshoot FETs and FET amplifiers.

NEED TO KNOW

Let us suppose you have a high-impedance microphone, such as a crystal microphone, and you want to interface it with an amplifier that has a low input impedance. We'll say the output impedance of the microphone is 1 MΩ and the input impedance to the amplifier is 10 kΩ. If you connect the crystal microphone directly to the amplifier input, the input impedance of the amplifier will heavily load down the microphone (the 1-MΩ microphone in series with the 10-kΩ input).

Can you design a simple, single-stage, amplifier that will solve this interface problem? By the time you finish this chapter, you will be able to do just that.

INTRODUCTION

This chapter is an exploration of field-effect transistors (FETs) and their applications. You will discover the many advantages of field-effect transistors over bipolar transistors. Some of these advantages are: very high input impedances, simple circuit designs, low power consumption, and very-high and ultra-high operating speeds. The intent of this chapter is not to be exhaustive in the coverage of FETs but to give you a well-rounded understanding of operational theory, circuit analysis, amplifier design, and troubleshooting. You will be well equipped for further studies based on application.

8–1 JUNCTION FIELD-EFFECT TRANSISTORS

INTRODUCTION TO FIELD-EFFECT TRANSISTORS (FETs)

In this section, we begin the study of some very interesting and widely used devices known as **field-effect transistors (FETs).** Field-effect transistors have many advantages over the bipolar transistors you have just studied, some of which are: very high input impedance, ease of circuit design, low power consumption, and high package density in integrated circuits. There are also some general disadvantages, such as lower voltage gain and higher waveform distortion. These disadvantages are considered insignificant for the vast number of applications for which FETs are used.

There are many varieties of FETs. However, to begin our study of FETs, we will first investigate the very common **junction field-effect transistor (JFET).** JFETs are **unipolar** devices. That means the current through the device is of one type, either majority electron current or majority hole current. Recall that transistors are **bipolar** because the majority carriers are electrons in the *n* material and holes in the *p* material. Just as transistors are of two basic types, NPN and PNP, JFETs are of two basic types, *n* channel and *p* channel. Let's look at each of these two JFET types and examine their theory of operation.

n-CHANNEL JFETs

Figure 8–1 illustrates the *n*-channel and *p*-channel JFET in three different ways. Let's first consider the *n*-channel JFET. The layer diagram shows how the JFET is actually constructed. The *n* material is deposited on a *p*-material substrate. The *n* material is then etched to form a valley perimeter in which *p* material is deposited. Though not shown, a metalized layer is deposited on the surface of the chip and is etched to separate the three regions: source, gate, and drain. Ohmic contacts are then made for the terminal connections. Note the planar construction—all contacts on the surface of the chip.

For *n*-channel JFETs, conduction-band electrons are the majority carriers. As shown in the layer diagram, electrons enter the source and exit at the drain. The space between the *p*-type substrate and the *p*-type gate is the channel through which conduction takes place. The functional diagram shows this more clearly. Electrons enter the source and proceed through the channel to the drain. For *n*-channel JFETs, a negative potential is applied to

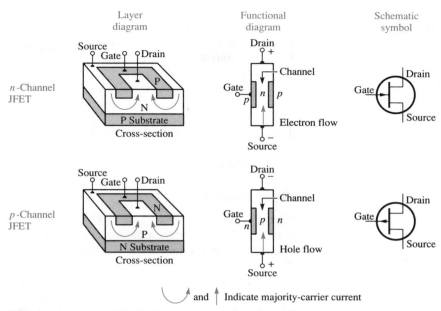

Figure 8–1   *n*-channel and *p*-channel JFETs.

the gate to control the electron flow in the channel. Thus JFETs are voltage controlled, unlike bipolar transistors, which are current controlled (I_B controls I_C).

The schematic symbol for the *n*-channel JFET is also shown in Figure 8–1. Notice the vertical line representing the channel and the gate arrow that is pointing toward the channel. This indicates that a *pn* junction is formed between the gate and the channel. The arrow points toward the *n* material, in this case the channel. The junction that is formed between the gate and channel is always reverse biased in actual operation. The only current that ever flows between the channel and gate is leakage current at a very low and insignificant level.

p-CHANNEL JFETs

The *p*-channel JFET is also shown in three ways in Figure 8–1. Note the similarities between the *p*-channel JFET and the *n*-channel JFET. The difference is the switch in materials. Current still flows from source to drain through the channel. However, this time the channel is *p* material and the majority carriers are valence-band holes. Also note the change in polarity on the source and drain terminals; *p*-channel JFETs require a negative drain potential and *n*-channel JFETs require a positive drain potential. Finally, note the gate arrow on the schematic symbol for *p*-channel JFETs. The arrow is pointing away from the channel, indicating that the gate is *n* material and the channel is *p* material.

To preserve space, we will emphasize only the *n*-channel JFET. What is presented about *n*-channel JFETs also applies to *p*-channel JFETs, except all voltage polarities are opposite. Before we continue, take a few minutes to test your understanding with Self-Check 8–1.

1. Why are JFETs unipolar?
2. What is the type of current that flows through *p*-channel JFETs?
3. Is the source to drain current in a JFET controlled by gate current or is it controlled by a gate voltage?
4. List two differences between JFETs and bipolar transistors.

8–2 JFET CHARACTERISTICS AND PARAMETERS

BASIC THEORY

Ohmic Region

Figure 8–2 shows an *n*-channel JFET test circuit using the functional diagram. Electron flow is indicated in the channel of the functional diagram since this is an *n*-channel JFET. The graph shows how drain current (I_D) is affected by drain to source voltage (V_{DS}) when the gate to source voltage is 0 V ($V_{GS} = 0$ V). Since the gate is shorted to the source, V_{GS} remains at 0 V. The source voltage (V_{DD}) is increased from 0 V, which increases V_{DS}. In what is called the **ohmic region,** the current increases linearly because the *n*-material channel acts as a fixed resistor. For this reason the ohmic region is also called the *linear region* and the *constant-resistance region*.

Saturation Region

At the top, or knee, of the linear rise in drain current, the FET begins to saturate. The V_{DS} at which this occurs is very low, usually in the range of 1 to 4 V, and is designated as $V_{DS(sat)}$ or $V_{pinch\text{-}off}$. This pinch-off point is the beginning of the saturation region. In the *saturation region,* the drain current is held nearly constant at a level designated as I_{DSS} (drain to source current with gate shorted to source). Notice, from the graph, that the drain current is held nearly constant even though V_{DD} and V_{DS} continue to increase. According to Ohm's Law, if voltage increases but current does not, the resistance

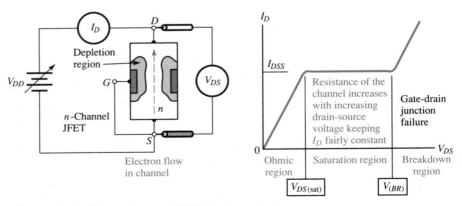

Figure 8–2   The n-channel JFET characteristic curve.

must be increasing with voltage, $\leftrightarrow I = \uparrow E/\uparrow R$. Thus, the resistance of the channel increases with V_{DS}.

How can the channel resistance increase automatically with V_{DS}? The n channel and the p gate form a *pn* junction. This junction is reverse biased because the gate is at a negative potential and the drain is at a positive potential. As a result, a depletion region is formed on all sides of the channel. The depletion region becomes significant and begins to limit channel current when V_{DS} approaches $V_{DS(\text{sat})}$. As you can see in the functional diagram, the depletion region pinches down on the channel, making it narrower. As V_{DS} continues to increase, the depletion region widens and the channel becomes more narrow. Thus, the channel resistance increases, maintaining channel current (drain current) fairly constant. Some would call the saturation region the pinch-off region. Using the term *pinch-off* is a misnomer since the current is not pinched off. Rather, the current is limited to a specific value as though the device were saturated and could produce no further increase in majority carriers.

Breakdown Region

Above the saturation region is the breakdown region. A V_{DS} is finally reached at which the reverse-biased gate to channel junction is overstressed and breaks down ($V_{(BR)}$). A permanent carbon path is formed between the gate and channel. The FET forever acts as a resistor and is no longer useful as an amplifier. Naturally, the maximum V_{DS} is specified on the FET's data sheet. A value of V_{DD} must be chosen that is below the specified maximum V_{DS}.

OPERATIONAL CHARACTERISTICS

Drain Curves

Notice that the test circuit of Figure 8–3 is accompanied by two sets of graphs. The family of drain curves on the right shows the drain current as a function of V_{DS} at specific values of gate to source voltage (V_{GS}). The gate to source voltage is set to a chosen voltage and V_{DS} is varied from 0 to, in this case, 25 V. The top curve is labeled as I_{DSS}. This is the maximum current for the JFET when V_{GS} is 0 V (gate shorted to source). As V_{GS} is set to more negative potentials, the maximum drain current, in saturation, is less and less. For example, when V_{GS} is set at -0.6 V, the drain current reaches a maximum saturation value of about 0.25 mA as V_{DS} is increased.

When V_{GS} is set to -1.2 V, the drain current is totally cut off regardless of the amount of drain to source voltage. This value of gate to source voltage is designated as $V_{GS(\text{OFF})}$ and is specified on the data sheet for the JFET. Naturally $V_{GS(\text{OFF})}$ is different for different JFETs. In fact, the value of $V_{GS(\text{OFF})}$ varies among FETs of the same type, as does I_{DSS} and other parameters. More on this later. Figure 8–4 demonstrates what happens when V_{GS} is increased to the cutoff potential. At $V_{GS(\text{OFF})}$, the channel is truly pinched off and drain current is cut off.

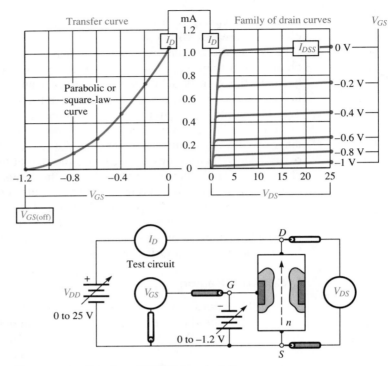

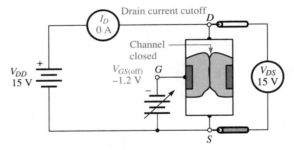

Figure 8–3 Plotting JFET characteristics.

Figure 8–4 Gate to source cutoff voltage.

Transfer Curve

Figure 8–3 also shows the transfer curve that relates to the family of drain curves. The transfer curve is a parabolic curve. It shows the relationship between gate voltage and drain current, drain current being a function of gate voltage, while V_{DS} is held constant at some voltage in the saturation region (i.e., 15 V). This function is also called a *square-law function* because the drain current is a function of the square of the gate to source voltage as follows:

$$I_D = I_{DSS} \cdot [1 - (V_{GS}/V_{GS(OFF)})]^2 \tag{8–1}$$

Values of I_{DSS} and $V_{GS(OFF)}$ can be taken from the data sheet of any JFET and placed in this formula to solve for I_D at any value of V_{GS}. Example 8–1 checks the transfer curve of Figure 8–3.

EXAMPLE 8–1 ▮▮▮▮▮▮▮▮▮▮▮▮▮▮▮▮▮▮▮

From the characteristic curves of Figure 8–3, $V_{GS(OFF)} = -1.2$ V and $I_{DSS} \cong 1.03$ mA. Calculate I_D for $V_{GS} = -0.8$ V and -0.4 V.

$I_D = 1.03$ mA $\cdot$ $[1 - (V_{GS}/-1.2 \text{ V})]^2$
$\quad = 1.03$ mA $\cdot$ $[1 - (-0.8 \text{ V}/-1.2 \text{ V})]^2 = 1.03$ mA $\cdot$ $[0.333]^2$
$\quad = 1.03$ mA $\cdot$ $0.111 = 0.114$ mA   (This checks with the graph.)

$I_D = 1.03$ mA $\cdot$ $[1 - (-0.4 \text{ V}/-1.2 \text{ V})]^2 = 1.03$ mA $\cdot$ $[0.667]^2$
$\quad = 1.03$ mA $\cdot$ $0.445 = 0.458$ mA   (This checks with the graph.)

Design Note 8–1 is provided as an aid to plot the transfer curve for any JFET when I_{DSS} and $V_{GS(OFF)}$ are known. I_{DSS} and $V_{GS(OFF)}$ can be obtained from data sheets or experimentally, using a test circuit.

TRANSCONDUCTANCE (g_m)

The transfer curve just discussed shows the drain current as a function of gate to source voltage. It shows how V_{GS} is transferred, or translated, to drain current. The curve can also be used to demonstrate the change in drain current that results from a change in V_{GS}. Mathematically, the relationship can be written as $\Delta I_D/\Delta V_{GS}$. This simply means that the change in drain current is a function of the change in gate to source voltage. Notice that this relationship of drain current over gate voltage is the formula for conductance (G), since $R = E/I$ and $1/R = G = I/E$. Because the relationship involves a change in current and voltage, we call this **transconductance (g_m).** Thus the transfer curve is also called the **transconductance curve.**

Figure 8–5 illustrates the concept of transconductance. Notice that the transconductance is also the slope of the curve surrounding some point on the curve. Thus, $g_m = \Delta I_D/\Delta V_{GS} = $ slope. Note that the slope, and transconductance, is highest at I_{DSS}, where $V_{GS} = 0$ V. This highest transconductance is designated as g_{m0}, the 0 indicating that $V_{GS} = 0$ V. On data sheets, g_{m0} is often designated as y_{fs}, which stands for forward admittance in the common-source configuration (similar to the common-emitter configuration for bipolar transistors). The lowest slope and transconductance is around $V_{GS(OFF)}$.

$$g_m = \Delta I_D/\Delta V_{GS} \tag{8–2}$$

Let's calculate the transconductance from the change in V_{GS} shown in Figure 8–5. The change is centered around a V_{GS} of -0.4 V. The change in V_{GS} is from -0.3 to -0.5 V. Thus, $\Delta V_{GS} = 0.2$ V. The corresponding change

DESIGN NOTE 8–1 TEN-POINT TRANSFER CURVE

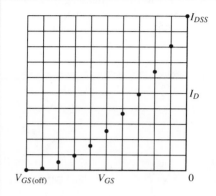

$V_{GS(OFF)}$ and I_{DSS} are obtained from the data sheet for the JFET.

$$I_D = I_{DSS} \cdot [1 - (V_{GS}/V_{GS(OFF)})]^2$$

BASIC PROGRAM

```
20 CLS
30 PRINT "-> TEN-POINT TRANSFER CURVE <-"
40 PRINT""
50 PRINT "THIS PROGRAM WILL PROVIDE YOU WITH TEN POINTS THAT CAN BE
PLOTTED TO"
60 PRINT "FORM THE TRANSFER CURVE FOR ANY JFET."
70 PRINT""
80 INPUT "ENTER THE VALUE OF IDSS FOR YOUR JFET. - IDSS = ";IDSS
90 INPUT "ENTER THE VALUE OF VGS(OFF) FOR YOUR JFET. - VGS(OFF) =
";VGSOFF
100 PRINT""
110 PRINT "VGS" TAB(15) "ID"
120 Y = VGSOFF/10
130 FOR X = 1 TO 10
140 VGS = VGSOFF - Y * X
150 ID = IDSS * (1 - (VGS/VGSOFF))^2
160 PRINT USING "+#.##^^^^";VGS;
165 PRINT USING "    ##.##^^^^";ID
170 NEXT X
180 PRINT""
190 INPUT "ANOTHER PROBLEM?  (Y/N)  ";A$
200 IF A$ = "Y" THEN CLEAR: CLS: GOTO 70
210 CLS: END
```

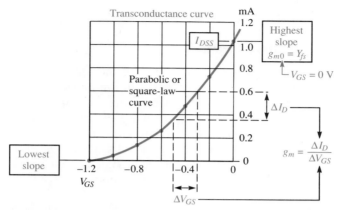

Figure 8–5 Transconductance (g_m).

in drain current is from 0.6 mA to about 0.35 mA. Thus, $\Delta I_D = 0.25$ mA. Therefore, $g_m = \Delta I_D/\Delta V_{GS} = 0.25$ mA/0.2 V $= 1.25$ mS $= 1250$ μS. Data sheets often use the mho (mmhos, μmhos) instead of the siemen (S) as the unit for transconductance or admittance.

The transconductance, or slope, at any point along the curve can be calculated if g_{m0} (y_{fs}) and $V_{GS(OFF)}$ are known using the following formula:

$$g_{m-VGS} = g_{m0} \cdot [1 - (V_{GS}/V_{GS(OFF)})] \tag{8–3}$$

For Figure 8–5, $g_{m0} = 1875$ μS and $V_{GS(OFF)} = -1.2$ V. Therefore, at $V_{GS} = -0.4$, $g_{m-0.4} = 1{,}875$ μS $\cdot [1 - (-0.4/-1.2)] = 1{,}250$ μS. Study Example 8–2.

EXAMPLE 8–2

From the data sheet for a 2N3822, the minimum g_{m0} (y_{fs}) is given as 3,000 μS (3,000 μmhos). $V_{GS(OFF)} = -6$ V. Calculate g_m at $V_{GS} = -4$ V, $V_{GS} = -2$ V, and $V_{GS} = -1$ V.

$g_{m-4} = g_{m0} \cdot [1 - (V_{GS}/V_{GS(OFF)})] = 3{,}000$ μS $\cdot [1 - (-4$ V$/-6$ V$)]$

$\quad = 3{,}000$ μS $\cdot 0.333 = 1{,}000$ μS

$g_{m-2} = g_{m0} \cdot [1 - (V_{GS}/V_{GS(OFF)})] = 3{,}000$ μS $\cdot [1 - (-2$ V$/-6$ V$)]$

$\quad = 3{,}000$ μS $\cdot 0.667 = 2{,}000$ μS

$g_{m-1} = g_{m0} \cdot [1 - (V_{GS}/V_{GS(OFF)})] = 3{,}000$ μS $\cdot [1 - (-1$ V$/-6$ V$)]$

$\quad = 3{,}000$ μS $\cdot 0.833 = 2{,}500$ μS

Later you will see how transconductance is related to amplifier gain. From this discussion, you can see how a higher transconductance means a greater change in drain current for a given change in V_{GS} ($\uparrow \Delta I_D = \uparrow g_m \cdot \Delta V_{GS}$). The greater the change in drain current, the greater the output voltage swing. Thus voltage gain is directly related to the JFET's transconductance.

OTHER JFET PARAMETERS

Maximum Ratings

Figure 8–6 is a data sheet for the Motorola 2N5457/8/9 JFETs. Notice the maximum ratings specified in the upper box. Some of the ratings are self-evident while others need some explaining. The specified 10-mA gate current is the maximum forward current before damage results. In practice, there is little or no forward gate current, since the gate junction is reverse biased. The maximum power dissipation is specified at an ambient temperature of 25°C, as it is for many bipolar transistors. Power derating is accomplished the same way as for bipolar transistors.

Off Characteristics

Notice that the electrical characteristics are divided into three main sections: OFF characteristics, ON characteristics, and small-signal characteristics. First, let's look at the OFF characteristics. Again, some are self-evident. Notice the reverse gate current rating (I_{GSS}). At 25°C, the 2N5457 is rated as having a maximum reverse (leakage) gate current of 1 nA with a V_{GS} of -15 V. This is an important parameter that lets you calculate the low-frequency input resistance at the gate. From Ohm's Law, the minimum gate resistance at 25°C is 15/1 nA = 15,000 MΩ = 15 GΩ. At 100°C, the reverse gate current increases to 200 nA, making the gate input resistance equal to 15/200 nA = 75 MΩ (still a very high value).

Also notice $V_{GS(OFF)}$. Notice the very wide range of $V_{GS(OFF)}$ specified for the 2N5457 (-0.5 V to -6.0 V). Unfortunately, this wide range is typical for most JFETs. You are probably wondering what value of $V_{GS(OFF)}$ to use in Formulas 8–1 and 8–3. That is the problem. The 2N5457 that you use will have a $V_{GS(OFF)}$ somewhere between -0.5 and -6.0 V. You can set up a test circuit like Figure 8–3 to determine the actual value or you can select a value in the middle of the extremes as a guess ($6 - 0.5 = 5.5$, $5.5/2 = 2.75$, $0.5 + 2.75 = 3.25$ V). A guess of -3.25 V for $V_{GS(OFF)}$ may still be way off.

On Characteristics

As stated earlier, I_{DSS} is the maximum saturation current that exists when the JFET is biased with a V_{GS} of 0 V (gate shorted to source). Notice the wide range of I_{DSS} given for the 2N5457, from 1 to 5 mA. Fortunately, a typical value of 3 mA is specified and can be used in Formula 8–1. Once again, an actual value of I_{DSS} for your FET can be determined experimentally, using the test circuit of Figure 8–2.

Small-Signal Characteristics

The forward transfer admittance for common-source (y_{fs}) is specified at a V_{GS} of 0 V. This is also known as the low-frequency transconductance, designated g_{m0}. As with other parameters, the range of transconductance is wide. For the 2N5457, g_{m0} ranges from 1,000 to 5,000 μS (μmhos). As before, a test circuit like Figure 8–3 can be used to determine the actual

**2N5457
thru
2N5459**

**CASE 29-04, STYLE 5
TO-92 (TO-226AA)**

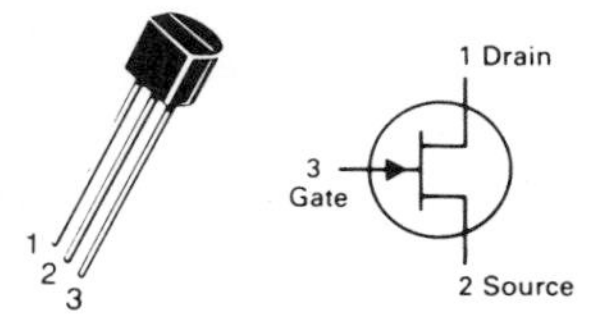

**JFETs
GENERAL PURPOSE**

N-CHANNEL — DEPLETION

Refer to 2N4220 for graphs.

MAXIMUM RATINGS

Rating	Symbol	Value	Unit
Drain-Source Voltage	V_{DS}	25	Vdc
Drain-Gate Voltage	V_{DG}	25	Vdc
Reverse Gate-Source Voltage	V_{GSR}	– 25	Vdc
Gate Current	I_G	10	mAdc
Total Device Dissipation @ $T_A = 25°C$ Derate above 25°C	P_D	310 2.82	mW mW/°C
Junction Temperature Range	T_J	125	°C
Storage Channel Temperature Range	T_{stg}	– 65 to + 150	°C

ELECTRICAL CHARACTERISTICS ($T_A = 25°C$ unless otherwise noted.)

Characteristic		Symbol	Min	Typ	Max	Unit
OFF CHARACTERISTICS						
Gate-Source Breakdown Voltage ($I_G = – 10\ \mu Adc$, $V_{DS} = 0$)		$V_{(BR)GSS}$	– 25	—	—	Vdc
Gate Reverse Current ($V_{GS} = – 15$ Vdc, $V_{DS} = 0$) ($V_{GS} = – 15$ Vdc, $V_{DS} = 0$, $T_A = 100°C$)		I_{GSS}	— —	— —	– 1.0 – 200	nAdc
Gate Source Cutoff Voltage ($V_{DS} = 15$ Vdc, $I_D = 10$ nAdc)	2N5457 2N5458 2N5459	$V_{GS(off)}$	– 0.5 – 1.0 – 2.0	— — —	– 6.0 – 7.0 – 8.0	Vdc
Gate Source Voltage ($V_{DS} = 15$ Vdc, $I_D = 100\ \mu Adc$) ($V_{DS} = 15$ Vdc, $I_D = 200\ \mu Adc$) ($V_{DS} = 15$ Vdc, $I_D = 400\ \mu Adc$)	2N5457 2N5458 2N5459	V_{GS}	— — —	– 2.5 – 3.5 – 4.5	— — —	Vdc
ON CHARACTERISTICS						
Zero-Gate-Voltage Drain Current* ($V_{DS} = 15$ Vdc, $V_{GS} = 0$)	2N5457 2N5458 2N5459	I_{DSS}	1.0 2.0 4.0	3.0 6.0 9.0	5.0 9.0 16	mAdc
SMALL-SIGNAL CHARACTERISTICS						
Forward Transfer Admittance Common Source* ($V_{DS} = 15$ Vdc, $V_{GS} = 0$, $f = 1.0$ kHz)	2N5457 2N5458 2N5459	Y_{fs}	1000 1500 2000	— — —	5000 5500 6000	μmhos
Output Admittance Common Source* ($V_{DS} = 15$ Vdc, $V_{GS} = 0$, $f = 1.0$ kHz)		Y_{os}	—	10	50	μmhos
Input Capacitance ($V_{DS} = 15$ Vdc, $V_{GS} = 0$, $f = 1.0$ MHz)		C_{iss}	—	4.5	7.0	pF
Reverse Transfer Capacitance ($V_{DS} = 15$ Vdc, $V_{GS} = 0$, $f = 1.0$ MHz)		C_{rss}	—	1.5	3.0	pF

*Pulse Test: Pulse Width $\leq$ 630 ms; Duty Cycle $\leq$ 10%.

Figure 8–6 Sample JFET data sheet. (Copyright, Motorola, Inc. Used by permission.)

value for your FET or a midpoint value, such as 3000 μS, can be chosen as a starting point for design or analysis work.

The output admittance (y_{os}) is also known as the *output conductance* (g_{os}). It is the ratio of the slight change in drain current over a corresponding change in drain to source voltage in the saturation region. Note that the characteristic drain curves are not exactly horizontal in the saturation region. As V_{DS} is increased, I_D increases slightly. Thus, $g_{os} = \Delta I_D/\Delta V_{DS}$. The reciprocal of g_{os} is r_{ds}, the dynamic drain to source resistance.

$$r_{ds} = \Delta V_{DS}/\Delta I_D = 1/g_{os} \qquad (8-4)$$

For the 2N5457, the maximum value of g_{os} is specified as 50 μS at $V_{GS} = 0$ V. This means the minimum drain to source resistance of the FET will be 1/50 μS = 20 kΩ. Typically, the actual value is much higher particularly at negative values of gate bias where the slope of the drain current curve in the saturation region is more horizontal.

The high-frequency effects of input capacitance (C_{iss}) and reverse transfer capacitance (C_{rss}) will be discussed in a later chapter. It's time now to pause for another self-check.

Self-Check 8–2

1. Describe I_{DSS}.
2. In what region of the drain curve is the resistance of the channel material constant?
3. What is $V_{GS(OFF)}$?
4. Describe how changes in V_{GS} are related to changes in I_D.
5. Determine the g_m of an FET if a change in gate to source voltage of 0.1 V causes a 1.5-mA change in drain current.

8–3 JFET BIASING

BIASING ON THE MOST LINEAR PORTION OF THE CURVE

From the previous section, you have been made aware that the transconductance of an FET changes significantly from one point on the curve to another. This means the amount of change in drain current is different at different points on the curve for the same amount of change in gate voltage. For this reason, we confront two serious problems when using FETs.

The First Problem

First, the AC input signal at the gate must not be too large, or the output signal will be heavily distorted. As the positive alternation of the input signal swings in the positive direction, it swings up on the higher end of the transconductance curve, where the g_m is greater. Thus, the drain current is greater for the positive alternation of the input signal. For the negative alternation of the input signal, the signal swings down on the lower end of the transconductance curve where the g_m is much less. Thus, the drain current is much less for the negative alternation. The overall result is a greatly distorted output voltage waveform that has an elongated negative alternation and a flattened positive alternation.

Consider Figure 8–7. In this example, the output distortion is not severe and noticeable because the swing of the input signal at the gate is not great ($v_{gs} = \pm 0.1$ V). The amplitude of the input signal must be kept small to avoid the severe distortion described above.

The Second Problem

The second problem is that of linearity. It is best to bias the FET high on the transconductance curve where the curve is most linear, offering the least change in g_m over the range of the signal swing. This, of course, is high on the curve, as shown in Figure 8–7. In addition to being more linear high on the curve, the amplifier has a higher gain when biased in that region. Notice $V_{GS(Q)}$ is just a fraction of $V_{GS(OFF)}$.

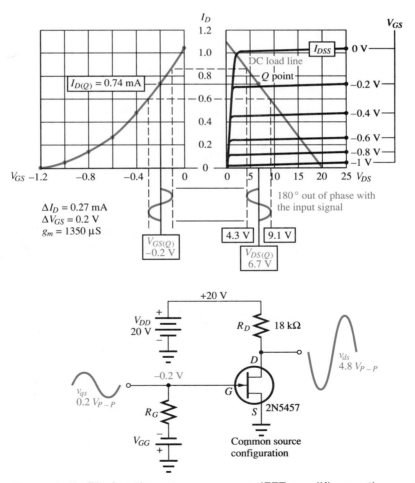

Figure 8–7 Biasing the common-source JFET amplifier on the most linear portion of the transconductance curve.

Other Observations

Notice the transconductance of the JFET at the -0.2-V bias point. From the transconductance curve, it appears that the change in drain current is about 0.27 mA from 0.61 to 0.88 mA. The change in gate voltage is 0.2 V. Therefore, the transconductance is 1,350 μS (0.27 mA/0.2 V = 1,350 μS).

Also, for the common-source configuration of Figure 8–7, there is a 180° phase relationship between the output and input signal. This is because drain voltage decreases as the FET conducts harder during the positive alternation of the input signal.

Finally, notice the DC load line, which in this case is also the AC load line. This load line is developed the same way as was done for bipolar transistors. The line extends from V_{DD} on the base line to V_{DD}/R_D on the vertical axis.

DC Load Line

$V_{DS} = V_{DD}$ where $I_D = 0$ A

$I_D = V_{DD}/R_D$ where $V_{GS} = 0$ V

SELF-BIASING

Theory

The method of biasing used in Figure 8–7 is neither necessary nor practical. There is a less costly and simpler way to bias the JFET at the desired point on the transconductance curve. That method is called *self biasing* and is shown in Figure 8–8. Notice the addition of the source resistor (R_S). This source resistor develops a voltage drop as determined by the drain current ($V_{RS} = I_D \cdot R_S$). As a result, the source is placed at a positive potential with respect to ground. In the case shown, the source is at $+0.2$ V. The gate is at ground potential because of R_G. This makes the gate look negative compared to the source. Therefore, the gate to source voltage is now -0.2 V. That's exactly what we want. The -0.2 V places the bias point on the transconductance curve, as shown in Figure 8–7.

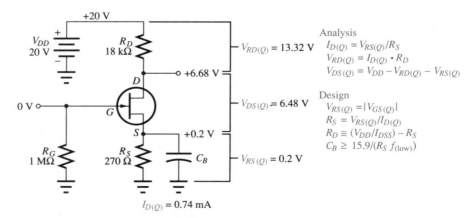

Figure 8–8   Self-biasing the JFET.

Analysis

How do you go about analyzing a circuit such as Figure 8–8? We will assume that $V_{GS(Q)}$ is known (-0.2 V). From this the quiescent drain current can be calculated. Since $V_{GS(Q)} = -0.2$ V, V_{RS} must be $+0.2$ V. From Ohm's Law,

$$I_{D(Q)} = |V_{GS(Q)}|/R_S = V_{RS(Q)}/R_S \tag{8–5}$$

For Figure 8–8, $I_{D(Q)} = 0.2$ V/270 Ω = 0.74 mA.

Next, the voltage drop across the drain resistor can be calculated.

$$V_{RD(Q)} = I_{D(Q)} \cdot R_D \tag{8–6}$$

For Figure 8–8, $V_{RD(Q)} = 0.74$ mA $\cdot$ 18 kΩ = 13.32 V.

Finally, the quiescent drain to source voltage can be determined.

$$V_{DS(Q)} = V_{DD} - V_{RD(Q)} - V_{RS(Q)} \tag{8–7}$$

For Figure 8–8, $V_{DS(Q)} = 20$ V $- 13.32$ V $- 0.2$ V $= 6.48$ V.

Design

Now, let's see how to design the same amplifier circuit Start with the transconductance curve on the data sheet for the FET. Choose a $V_{GS(Q)}$ that corresponds to the higher, more linear, portion of the curve. If the data sheet does not show a transconductance curve, a good design choice for $V_{GS(Q)}$ is about one fourth of $V_{GS(OFF)}$.

Once $V_{GS(Q)}$ is decided on, you must determine the quiescent drain current. This can be read from the transconductance curve or the family of drain curves, or calculated using Formula 8–1.

Now you are able to calculate the proper value for R_S.

$$R_S = V_{RS(Q)}/I_{D(Q)} \tag{8–8}$$

where $V_{RS(Q)} = |V_{GS(Q)}|$

For Figure 8–8, $R_S = 0.2$ V/0.74 mA $= 270$ Ω.

Next, determine a reasonable value for the drain resistor. There are several approaches to this, but I offer this one as more than adequate. The load line should extend all the way up to somewhere around I_{DSS}, as shown in Figure 8–7, to permit operation in the most linear portion of the transconductance curve. Therefore, R_D can be approximated as follows:

$$R_D \cong (V_{DD}/I_{DSS}) - R_S \tag{8–9}$$

For Figures 8–7 and 8–8, $R_D \cong (20$ V/1.05 mA$) - 270$ Ω = 18.8 kΩ. An 18-kΩ resistor is fine.

Finally, add a bypass capacitor across the source resistor to greatly increase voltage gain. The following formula insures that the X_C of the bypass capacitor at the lowest operating frequency is very low. This makes sure the source is very close to ground as far as the signal current is concerned. As a result, the AC load line is slightly steeper than the DC load line, since R_S is bypassed.

Formula 8–10 is derived from the capacitive-reactance formula by substituting $0.1 R_S$ for X_C. This formula insures that the X_C of the bypass capacitor is equal to or less than $R_S/10$, placing the source effectively at ground potential. This design rule of thumb is arbitrary but practical. We will investigate this further later.

$$C_B \geq 1.59/R_S f_{\text{low}} \qquad\qquad (8\text{--}10)$$

For Figure 8–8, we will assume the lowest frequency that is to be amplified is 30 Hz. $C_B \geq 1.59/(270 \cdot 30) \cong 200\ \mu\text{F}$. Review the design procedure by studying Design Note 8–2 and Example 8–3.

EXAMPLE 8–3

Design, then analyze, an FET amplifier like that of Figure 8–8. The FET that will be used has the following characteristics: $I_{DSS} = 10$ mA, $V_{GS(OFF)} = -4.6$ V. Design it for $V_{GS} = -1$ V. $V_{DD} = 9$ V. The lowest frequency to be amplified will be 40 Hz.

Design

First determine I_D when V_{GS} is -1 V.

$$I_D = I_{DSS} \cdot [1 - (V_{GS}/V_{GS(OFF)})]^2 = 10\ \text{mA} \cdot [1 -(-1\ \text{V}/-4.6\ \text{V})]^2$$

$$= 10\ \text{mA} \cdot [1 -(-1\ \text{V}/-4.6\ \text{V})]^2 = 10\ \text{mA} \cdot 0.612 = 6.12\ \text{mA}$$

Next calculate R_S.

$$R_S = |V_{GS(Q)}|/I_{D(Q)} = 1\ \text{V}/6.12\ \text{mA} = 163\ \Omega \qquad \text{(Use 160 } \Omega\text{)}$$

Now determine R_D.

$$R_D \cong (V_{DD}/I_{DSS}) - R_S = (9\ \text{V}/10\ \text{mA}) - 160\ \Omega = 740\ \Omega \qquad \text{(use 750 } \Omega\text{)}$$

Finally, calculate a practical value for C_B.

$$C_B \geq 1.59/R_S f_{\text{low}} = 1.59/(160\ \Omega \cdot 40\ \text{Hz}) = 248\ \mu\text{F} \qquad \text{(Use 250 } \mu\text{F)}$$

Analysis

Now, let us reverse the process and analyze our design. $V_{RS(Q)}$ is known to be 1 V.

$$I_{D(Q)} = V_{RS(Q)}/R_S = 1\ \text{V}/160\ \Omega = 6.25\ \text{mA}$$

$$V_{RD(Q)} = I_{D(Q)} \cdot R_D = 6.25\ \text{mA} \cdot 750\ \Omega = 4.69\ \text{V}$$

$$V_{DS(Q)} = V_{DD} - V_{RS(Q)} - V_{RD(Q)} = 9\ \text{V} - 1\ \text{V} - 4.69\ \text{V} = 3.31\ \text{V}$$

BIASING PROBLEMS

The problem you will run into in your design work is the wide range of critical parameters for a particular JFET. Recall our earlier discussion regarding the 2N5457. Figure 8–9 demonstrates that you cannot predict exactly what the quiescent drain current will be for the 2N5457 you want to

DESIGN NOTE 8–2 SELF-BIASED CS JFET AMPLIFIER

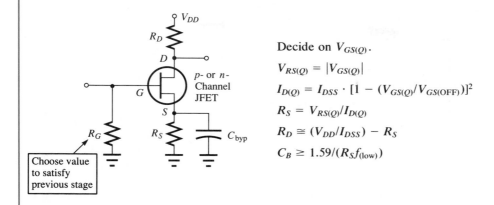

Decide on $V_{GS(Q)}$.

$$V_{RS(Q)} = |V_{GS(Q)}|$$

$$I_{D(Q)} = I_{DSS} \cdot [1 - (V_{GS(Q)}/V_{GS(OFF)})]^2$$

$$R_S = V_{RS(Q)}/I_{D(Q)}$$

$$R_D \cong (V_{DD}/I_{DSS}) - R_S$$

$$C_B \geq 1.59/(R_S f_{(low)})$$

BASIC PROGRAM

```
20 CLS
30 PRINT "-> SELF-BIASED CS JFET AMPLIFIER DESIGN <-"
40 PRINT""
50 PRINT "THIS PROGRAM WILL CALCULATE RS, RD, AND THE SOURCE BYPASS"
60 PRINT "CAPACITOR FOR ANY SELF-BIASED CS JFET AMPLIFIER."
70 PRINT""
80 INPUT "ENTER THE SUPPLY VOLTAGE. - VDD = ";VDD
90 INPUT "ENTER THE VALUE OF IDSS FOR YOUR JFET. - IDSS = ";IDSS
100 INPUT "ENTER THE VALUE OF VGS(OFF) FOR YOUR JFET. - VGS(OFF) =
";VGSOFF
110 INPUT "ENTER THE DESIRED VALUE FOR VGS(Q). - VGS(Q) = ";VGSQ
120 INPUT "ENTER THE LOWEST FREQUENCY TO BE AMPLIFIED. - F = ";F
125 PRINT""
130 ID = IDSS * (1 - (VGSQ/VGSOFF))^2
140 VRS = ABS(VGSQ)
150 RS = VRS/ID
160 RD = ABS((VDD/IDSS) - RS)
170 C = 1.59/(RS * F)
180 ID1 = IDSS * (1 - ((VGSQ + .1 * VGSQ)/VGSOFF))^2
190 ID2 = IDSS * (1 - ((VGSQ - .1 * VGSQ)/VGSOFF))^2
200 GM = ABS((ID1 - ID2)/(.2 * VGSQ))
210 AV = GM * RD
220 PRINT "RS = ";RS;" OHMS"
230 PRINT "RD = ";RD;" OHMS"
240 PRINT "ID(Q) = ";ID;" AMPS"
250 PRINT "C-BYPASS => ";C;" FARADS"
260 PRINT "THE TRANSCONDUCTANCE = ";GM;" SIEMENS'
270 PRINT "THE VOLTAGE GAIN = ";AV
280 PRINT""
290 INPUT "ANOTHER PROBLEM?  (Y/N) ";A$
300 IF A$ = "Y" THEN CLEAR:CLS:GOTO 80
310 CLS:END
```

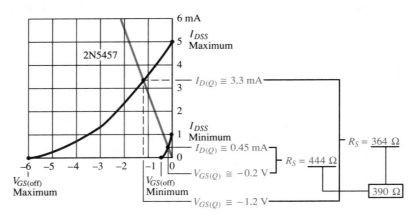

Figure 8–9   Using minimum and maximum values to determine a value for R_s.

use. From the data sheet, the extremes of I_{DSS} and $V_{GS(OFF)}$ are plotted and the transconductance curve for each is drawn. For the 2N5457, minimum values are $I_{DSS} = 1$ mA and $V_{GS(OFF)} = -0.5$ V, and the maximum values are $I_{DSS} = 5$ mA and $V_{GS(OFF)} = -6$ V. A design line is then drawn from the origin through the more linear portions of the transconductance curves. From the intersections of the design line and the curves, quiescent values of V_{GS} and I_D are obtained. R_S is calculated using the minimum, then the maximum, values of $V_{GS(Q)}$ and $I_{D(Q)}$. A standard value resistor somewhere between the two calculated values for R_S can be used in your design. In this case demonstrated in Figure 8–9, a 390-Ω resistor can be used. However, this does not solve the basic problem. We still do not know for sure what $I_{D(Q)}$ or $V_{GS(Q)}$ will be until we build the circuit and test it using different values for R_D. This is a real big problem in mass production where the same circuit must be duplicated predictably over and over again. If the drain current was always the same value, there would be no problem. The following is a viable solution to this problem.

CONSTANT-CURRENT-SOURCE BIASING

If we could predetermine the quiescent drain current so that it would be a specific value regardless of the characteristics of any FET, we could design a circuit that could be duplicated reliably in mass production. The idea is as shown in Figure 8–10. In this case, $I_{D(Q)}$ is predetermined to be 0.45 mA regardless of the transconductance curve of the FET being used. An immediate tradeoff to this approach is the increased distortion that must be accepted if the particular FET has $V_{GS(OFF)}$ and I_{DSS} values closer to the maximum values (−6 V and 5 mA). Note how low the Q point is on the transconductance curve. Keeping the input signal small will help reduce would-be distortion.

So, how do we design a circuit that will make sure the quiescent drain current is always 0.45 mA, as an example? The answer is to use a constant-current source. Shown in Figure 8–11, a transistor can be biased to provide a constant 0.45 mA of current to any FET that is placed in the circuit. Here is

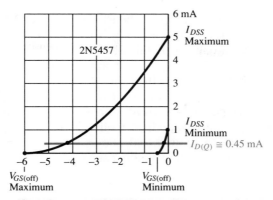

Figure 8–10   Keeping $I_{D(Q)}$ constant regardless of FET characteristics.

how it works. R_1 and R_2 provide a fixed 1.15 V to the base of the transistor. The emitter voltage is then 1.15 V − 0.7 V = 0.45 V. Since this 0.45 V appears across the 1-kΩ emitter resistor, the emitter current is a constant 0.45 mA. Thus, the collector current is approximately 0.45 mA, which means the drain current must be approximately 0.45 mA. The quiescent voltage drop across R_D will always be 10.8 V, since $I_{D(Q)}$ is a constant 0.45 mA (0.45 mA · 24 kΩ = 10.8 V). This means the quiescent DC voltage from the drain to ground will always be 13.2 V regardless of FET characteristics. The FET has no choice but to comply with the amount of drain current established by the constant-current source. Automatically, the gate to

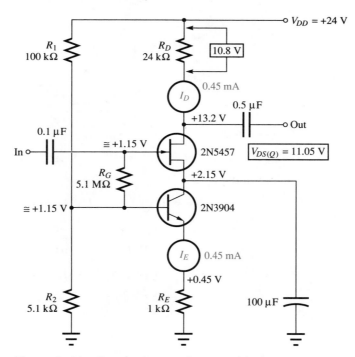

Figure 8–11   Constant-current-source biasing.

source voltage is set up for the FET to conduct 0.45 mA. In this case, for this particular FET, $V_{GS(Q)}$ is -1 V, the difference between the source voltage and the gate voltage. If this 2N5457 is replaced with another, $V_{GS(Q)}$ might change to -2 V, or -3 V, or any value between -0.25 V and -4.25 V. However, this has no effect on $I_{D(Q)}$ or V_D ($+13.2$ V). If you like, you can build the circuit of Figure 8–11 and test several 2N5457 or similar JFETs.

Since the constant-current source resists any changes in current, a bypass capacitor is necessary from collector to ground. This completes the AC current path to ground and allows the AC current to vary as needed to develop the AC output voltage across R_D. Consider Example 8–4.

EXAMPLE 8–4

Analyze Figure 8–12 to determine $I_{D(Q)}$ and $V_{D(Q)}$.
First calculate V_B:

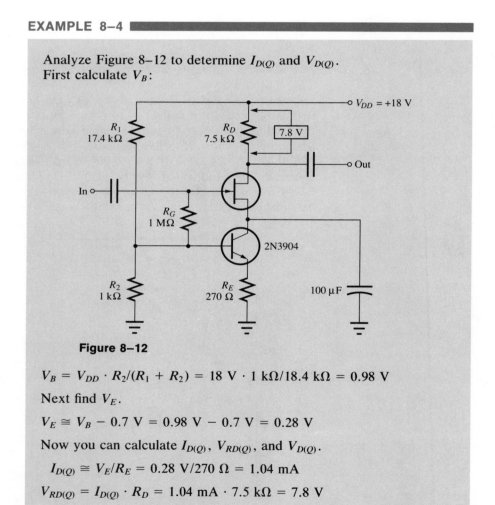

Figure 8–12

$V_B = V_{DD} \cdot R_2/(R_1 + R_2) = 18 \text{ V} \cdot 1 \text{ k}\Omega/18.4 \text{ k}\Omega = 0.98 \text{ V}$

Next find V_E.

$V_E \cong V_B - 0.7 \text{ V} = 0.98 \text{ V} - 0.7 \text{ V} = 0.28 \text{ V}$

Now you can calculate $I_{D(Q)}$, $V_{RD(Q)}$, and $V_{D(Q)}$.

$I_{D(Q)} \cong V_E/R_E = 0.28 \text{ V}/270 \text{ }\Omega = 1.04 \text{ mA}$

$V_{RD(Q)} = I_{D(Q)} \cdot R_D = 1.04 \text{ mA} \cdot 7.5 \text{ k}\Omega = 7.8 \text{ V}$

$V_{D(Q)} = V_{DD} - V_{RD(Q)} = 18 \text{ V} - 7.8 \text{ V} = 10.2 \text{ V}$

Time again for a self-check.

Self-Check 8–3

1. Using the graphs of Figure 8–7, determine the value of R_S needed to provide a $V_{GS(Q)}$ of -0.4 V.
2. If I_{DSS} is 8 mA and $V_{GS(OFF)}$ is -4 V for a particular JFET, what value of R_S do you need to bias the FET for a $V_{GS(Q)}$ of -1 V?
3. For a self-biased, common-source JFET amplifier, if $V_{GS(Q)}$ is known, explain how to find V_{RD}.
4. When designing a JFET amplifier, describe how the FET should be biased for minimum distortion and high gain.
5. Briefly explain a problem and a solution in mass-producing JFET amplifier circuits.
6. Given a circuit like Figure 8–11 with the following values: $R_1 = 43$ kΩ, $R_2 = 2.7$ kΩ, $R_E = 470$ Ω, $R_D = 8.2$ kΩ, $V_{DD} = 18$ V. Find $I_{D(Q)}$.

8–4 FET AMPLIFIER CONFIGURATIONS

THE COMMON-SOURCE (CS) CONFIGURATION

You are already somewhat familiar with the common-source (CS) configuration from the previous section. You know that the source is at AC ground potential and the output voltage, taken from the drain, is 180° out of phase with the input signal. Here, we will investigate input impedance, output impedance, and voltage gain for loaded, self-biased, CS amplifiers.

Input Impedance (Z_{in}) for CS Amplifiers

Figure 8–13 illustrates a typical CS amplifier and its AC equivalent circuit. The input signal ($v_{in} = v_{gs}$) is dropped across the input impedance of the amplifier stage. This input impedance is the parallel combination of R_G and R_{in} from gate to source. Normally R_{in} is very high—100 MΩ to over 1,000 MΩ. Recall that $R_{in} = V_{GS}/I_{GSS}$. Since R_G is normally chosen to be some value below 10 MΩ, the parallel effects of R_{in} can be ignored.

$$Z_{in} \cong R_G \qquad (8\text{–}11)$$

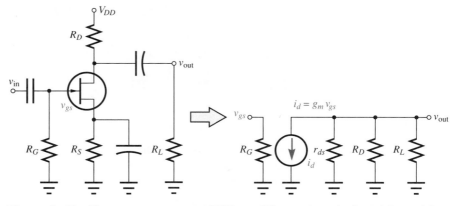

Figure 8–13 The common-source FET amplifier and equivalent AC model.

Output Impedance (Z_{out}) for CS Amplifiers

The output impedance is seen looking back into the amplifier circuit at the drain, load disconnected. As such, R_D is found to be in parallel with the dynamic drain to source resistance (r_{ds}). Recall that r_{ds} is the ratio of $\Delta V_{DS}/\Delta I_D$ in the saturation region. This means that r_{ds} is normally very large compared to R_D. Therefore, r_{ds} can be ignored and the output impedance is approximately R_D.

$$Z_{out} \cong R_D \qquad\qquad (8-12)$$

Voltage Gain (A_V) for CS Amplifiers

As you know, the voltage gain of any amplifier is the ratio of v_{out}/v_{in}. We can prove that the voltage gain is also the product of the FET's transconductance and the AC drain resistance ($R_D \| R_L$).

Recall that $g_m = \Delta I_D/\Delta V_{GS}$. Therefore, $g_m = i_d/v_{gs}$, where in this case $v_{gs} = v_{in}$. Solve for v_{gs}: $v_{gs} = v_{in} = i_d/g_m$. Next, we must express v_{out} in terms of AC drain current and resistance. $v_{out} = i_d \cdot (R_D \| R_L)$. Finally, expand then reduce the voltage gain expression.

$$A_V = v_{out}/v_{in} = \frac{i_d \cdot (R_D \| R_L)}{i_d/g_m} = g_m \cdot (R_D \| R_L)$$

$$A_V = v_{out}/v_{in} = g_m \cdot (R_D \| R_L) \qquad\qquad (8-13)$$

Consider Example 8–5.

EXAMPLE 8–5

The JFET of Figure 8–13 has a transconductance of 2600 μS. $R_D = 12$ kΩ and $R_L = 22$ kΩ. $v_{gs} = v_{in} = 40$ mV.
The loaded voltage gain is

$$A_V = g_m \cdot (R_D \| R_L) = 2{,}600 \ \mu\text{S} \cdot (12 \ \text{k}\Omega \| 22 \ \text{k}\Omega)$$

$$= 2{,}600 \ \mu\text{S} \cdot 7.76 \ \text{k}\Omega = 20.2 = 26.1 \ \text{dB}$$

$$v_{out} = A_V \cdot v_{in} = 20.2 \cdot 40 \ \text{mV} = 808 \ \text{mV}$$

The unloaded voltage gain is

$$A_V = g_m \cdot R_D = 2{,}600 \ \mu\text{S} \cdot 12 \ \text{k}\Omega = 31.2 = 29.9 \ \text{dB}$$

$$v_{out} = A_V \cdot v_{in} = 31.2 \cdot 40 \ \text{mV} = 1.25 \ \text{V}$$

The Bypass Capacitor (C_B)

Formula 8–13 assumes that the bypass capacitor for the source resistor is large enough so that its X_C is very low and the source is effectively at AC ground. Recall that it was suggested earlier that the X_C at the lowest frequency be $\frac{1}{10}$ of the value of R_S. Let us take a moment here to explore this subject again through mathematical analysis. When we say we want to bypass the source resistor, we actually mean that we want the source to be as close as is practical to AC ground. We want the source to see a very low X_C, so R_S has no effect on A_V. Our exploration begins with an expansion of the output/input amplification ratio. This time, we will assume the source resistor is unbypassed in order to demonstrate how to determine a practical value for C_B.

$A_V = v_{out}/v_{in}$

$v_{out} = v_{gs} \cdot g_m \cdot R_D = v_{gs}g_mR_D$

$v_{in} = v_{gs} + v_{RS}$

$v_{RS} = i_d \cdot R_S$

Now, $i_d = v_{gs} \cdot g_m$ since $g_m = i_d/v_{gs}$, so

$v_{RS} = v_{gs} \cdot g_m \cdot R_S = v_{gs}g_mR_S$

Therefore,

$v_{in} = v_{gs} + v_{gs}g_mR_S = v_{gs}(1 + g_mR_S)$

Now, we can substitute these expanded terms into the A_V formula.

$A_V = \dfrac{v_{out}}{v_{in}} = \dfrac{v_{gs}g_mR_D}{v_{gs}(1 + g_mR_S)} = \dfrac{g_mR_D}{1 + g_mR_S}$

When a bypass capacitor is used, we want its X_C to be low enough to nullify the effects of R_S in the formula above to the extent that X_C takes the place of R_S in the formula.

$A_V = \dfrac{v_{out}}{v_{in}} = \dfrac{g_mR_D}{1 + g_mX_C}$ (8–14)

How low should the X_C of the bypass capacitor be? In practical terms, the denominator of the formula should not be any higher than 1.1, where $g_mX_C \leq 0.1$. That insures that the X_C has less than a 10% effect on A_V. Therefore, since $g_mX_C \leq 0.1$, $X_C \leq 0.1/g_m$. What does this prove or demonstrate? It demonstrates that the bypass capacitor is actually selected in by considering g_m not R_S. With this in mind, we will re-evaluate Example 8–5 as shown in Example 8–6. First, let us derive a new formula for the bypass capacitor. From the X_C formula,

$C_B = 1/(2\pi f_{low}X_C) \cong 0.159/(f_{low}X_C)$

since $X_C \leq 0.1/g_m$, $C_B \geq 0.159/(f_{low}0.1/g_m)$. Therefore,

$C_B \geq 1.59\ g_m/f_{low}$ (8–15)

EXAMPLE 8–6

The JFET of Figure 8–13 has a transconductance of 2,600 μS. $R_D = 12$ kΩ and $R_L = 22$ kΩ, $R_S = 500\ \Omega$, $f_{low} = 20$ Hz. Determine a practical value for C_B so that $X_C \leq 0.1/g_m$. Then, calculate the voltage gain (A_V).

$X_C \leq 0.1/g_m = 0.1/2{,}600 \; \mu S = 38.5 \; \Omega$

$C_B \geq 1.59 \; g_m/f_{\text{low}} = 1.59 \cdot 2{,}600 \; \mu S/20 \; \text{Hz} = 207 \; \mu F \quad \text{(Use } 250 \; \mu F\text{)}$

For $X_C = 0 \; \Omega$, the *ideal* loaded voltage gain is

$A_V = g_m \cdot (R_D \| R_L) = 2{,}600 \; \mu S \cdot [12 \; k\Omega \| 22 \; k\Omega]$

$\qquad = 2{,}600 \; \mu S \cdot 7.76 \; k\Omega = 20.2 = 26.1 \; dB$

For $X_C = 38.5 \; \Omega$, the *practical* loaded voltage gain is:

$A_V = \dfrac{g_m(R_D \| R_L)}{1 + g_m X_C} = \dfrac{2{,}600 \; \mu S \cdot 7.76 \; k\Omega}{1 + (2{,}600 \; \mu S \cdot 38.5 \; \Omega)} = \dfrac{20.2}{1 + 0.1} = 18.4$

$\qquad = 20 \cdot \log(18.4) = 25.3 \; dB$

As you can see from Example 8–6, using a practical value for C_B where its $X_C \leq 0.1/g_m$ causes a reduction in gain of less than 1 dB from the ideal value. That is very acceptable. But what about the Formula 8–10 used earlier to quickly obtain a value for C_B where $C_B \geq 1.59/(R_S f_{\text{low}})$? Formula 8–10 is still adequate for selection of a "safe" value for C_B. Let us use the values in Example 8–6 in Formula 8–10 and compare. $C_B \geq 1.59/(R_S f_{\text{low}}) = 1.59/(500 \; \Omega \cdot 20 \; \text{Hz}) = 159 \; \mu F$. Notice that this value for C_B is less than that calculated in Example 8–6. Nonetheless, it will provide satisfactory performance in the circuit. You may use Formula 8–10 to obtain a safe approximation or you may use Formula 8–15 if g_m is known.

THE COMMON-DRAIN (CD) CONFIGURATION

You will recognize the common-drain (CD) amplifier of Figure 8–14 to be similar to the common-collector bipolar transistor amplifier. Like the common-collector amplifier, there is no phase difference between the output and input signals. Also, as we will demonstrate, the voltage gain of the CD FET amplifier is less than 1 (ideally 1 where $v_{\text{out}} = v_{\text{in}}$).

Input Impedance (Z_{in}) for CD Amplifiers

From the diagrams of Figure 8–14a and 8–14b, you can see that the input impedance of the CD amplifier is approximately equal to R_G since R_{GS} is very high (over 100 MΩ). Thus, like CS amplifiers, $Z_{\text{in}} \cong R_G$.

Output Impedance (Z_{out}) for CD Amplifiers

The output impedance is seen looking back into the amplifier at the source excluding the load. This includes R_S in parallel with $1/g_m$ as shown in Figure 8–14d.

$Z_{\text{out}} = (1/g_m \| R_S)$ \hfill (8–16)

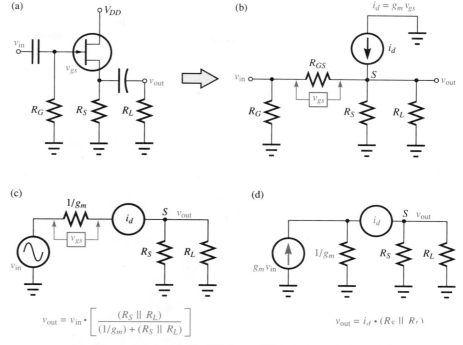

Figure 8–14 The common-drain FET amplifier and equivalent AC models.

Voltage Gain (A_V) for CD Amplifiers

From Figure 8–14b, notice that v_{in} is the sum of v_{gs} and v_{out} ; v_{out} is slightly less than v_{in} because v_{gs} is very small and $v_{out} = v_{in} - v_{gs}$. Since v_{out} is slightly less than v_{in}, the voltage gain is less than unity (1). But how much less is it? Is there so little difference between the input and output voltages that we can assume unity gain? The answers to these questions depend on the value of R_S and the actual g_m of the FET. This can be demonstrated by deriving a voltage gain formula for the CD amplifier.

$A_V = v_{out}/v_{in}$ and $i_d = g_m v_{gs}$

$v_{out} = i_d \cdot R_S = g_m v_{gs} R_S$

$v_{in} = v_{gs} + v_{out} = v_{gs} + g_m v_{gs} R_S = v_{gs}(1 + g_m R_S)$

Therefore,

$A_V = v_{out}/v_{in} = g_m v_{gs} R_S / v_{gs}(1 + g_m R_S) = g_m R_S/(1 + g_m R_S)$

$A_V = R_S/[(1/g_m) + R_S]$ (no load amplification)   (8–17)

Since $A_V = v_{out}/v_{in} = R_S/[(1/g_m) + R_S]$,

$v_{out} = v_{in} \cdot R_S/[(1/g_m) + R_S]$ (8–18)

You should recognize Formula 8–18 as the voltage-divider rule. This is illustrated in Figure 8–14c. With the load included, Formula 8–18 becomes:

$$v_{out} = \frac{v_{in} \cdot (R_S \| R_L)}{(1/g_m) + (R_S \| R_L)} \qquad \text{(loaded output)} \qquad (8\text{--}19)$$

Figure 8–14d shows the Norton equivalent of Figure 8–14c. Notice that v_{out} is the product of i_d and the parallel combination of R_S and R_L when R_L is connected to the source. Now let's look at Example 8–7 and put this all together.

EXAMPLE 8–7 ▪▪▪▪▪▪▪▪▪▪▪▪▪▪▪▪▪▪▪▪▪▪▪▪▪▪▪▪▪▪▪▪▪▪

The following values are known for the circuit of Figure 8–14a:

$v_{in} = 3$ V, $R_S = 2.7$ kΩ, $R_L = 4.7$ kΩ, and $g_m = 3,500$ μS.

Find Z_{out}, A_V, and v_{out} for loaded and unloaded conditions.

$Z_{out} = (1/g_m \| R_S) = (1/3,500 \text{ μS} \| 2.7 \text{ kΩ}) = 258$ Ω

The unloaded voltage gain is

$A_V = R_S/(1/g_m + R_S) = 2.7 \text{ kΩ}/[(1/3,500 \text{ μS}) + 2.7 \text{ kΩ}]$

$\quad = 2.7 \text{ kΩ}/[286 \text{ Ω} + 2.7 \text{ kΩ}] = 2.7 \text{ kΩ}/2,986 \text{ Ω} = 0.904$

$\quad = -0.877$ dB gain (a loss of 0.877 dB)

$v_{out} = A_V \cdot v_{in} = 0.904 \cdot 3 \text{ V} = 2.71$ V

To find the loaded voltage gain, first calculate the equivalent resistance of $R_S \| R_L$.

$R_{eq} = R_S \| R_L = 2.7 \text{ kΩ} \| 4.7 \text{ kΩ} = 1,715$ Ω

Now substitute R_{eq} for R_S in Formula 8–17.

$A_V = R_{eq}/(1/g_m + R_{eq}) = 1,715 \text{ Ω}/[(1/3,500 \text{ μS}) + 1,715 \text{ Ω}]$

$\quad = 1,715 \text{ Ω}/[286 \text{ Ω} + 1,715 \text{ Ω}] = 1,715 \text{ Ω}/2,001 \text{ Ω} = 0.857$

$\quad = -1.34$ dB gain (a loss of 1.34 dB)

$v_{out} = A_V \cdot v_{in} = 0.857 \cdot 3 \text{ V} = 2.57$ V

From Example 8–7 you should recognize that if $R_S \| R_L$ is much greater than $1/g_m$, the gain of the CD stage will be close to unity (1). For CD amplifiers, A_V will never be greater than or equal to unity. It should also be noted that the CD amplifier distorts the output signal far less than the CS or CG amplifier configurations because the output follows the input signal in a nearly 1/1 ratio. The distorting effect of the nonlinear transconductance curve is nullified dramatically.

Because of its very high input impedance, low output impedance, and low distortion characteristics, the CD JFET amplifier is commonly used as a buffer amplifier. This means the CD stage is used to separate one stage from the next while passing the AC signal. Some circuits, such as oscillators, are very sensitive to changes in load impedance or load reactance. The buffer amplifier provides the sensitive circuit with a constant high-impedance load and handles any variations in the next stage itself.

THE COMMON-GATE (CG) CONFIGURATION

The common-gate (CG) amplifier is shown in Figure 8–15. The output voltage is in phase with the input voltage as is true for CB bipolar transistor amplifiers. Also you will soon see that, like the CS amplifier, this amplifier has a voltage gain much greater than unity.

Input Impedance (Z_{in}) for CG Amplifiers

From Figure 8–15, you can see that the input impedance to the CG amplifier is equal to the parallel combination of the source resistor and $1/g_m$. Note that this is the same as the output impedance for CD stages. Since $1/g_m$ is relatively low, the input impedance for the CG amplifier is very low.

$$Z_{in} = R_S \| (1/g_m) \tag{8–20}$$

Output Impedance (Z_{out}) for CG Amplifiers

Looking back into the drain of the FET, the output impedance is very high and can be considered equal to R_D.

$$Z_{out} \cong R_D \tag{8–21}$$

Voltage Gain (A_V) for CG Amplifiers

The output voltage is developed across the drain resistor and is the product of drain current and drain resistance. Thus, $v_{out} = i_d \cdot R_D$. When a load is connected, $v_{out} = i_d \cdot (R_D \| R_L)$. Since i_d is still equal to $g_m v_{gs}$, the output voltage can be expressed as

$$v_{out} = g_m v_{gs}(R_D \| R_L) \qquad \text{(with load)} \tag{8–22}$$

The input voltage is simply v_{gs}.
Therefore, the voltage gain is

$$A_V = v_{out}/v_{in} = [g_m v_{gs}(R_D \| R_L)]/v_{gs} = g_m(R_D \| R_L)$$

$$A_V = g_m(R_D \| R_L) \qquad \text{(with load)} \tag{8–23}$$

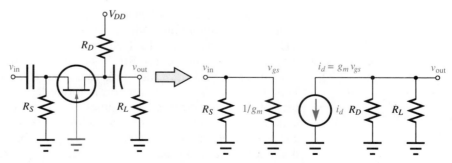

Figure 8–15   The common-gate FET amplifier and equivalent AC model.

Study Example 8–8.

EXAMPLE 8–8 ▬▬▬▬▬▬▬▬▬▬▬▬▬▬▬▬▬▬

For the circuit of Figure 8–15, $R_S = 470\ \Omega$, $R_D = 3.3\ k\Omega$, $R_L = 6.8\ k\Omega$, $g_m = 1,500\ \mu S$, and $v_{in} = 25\ mV$.
Find Z_{in}, Z_{out}, A_V, and v_{out} (loaded condition only).

$$Z_{in} = R_S \| (1/g_m) = 470\ \Omega \| 1/1,500\ \mu S = 470\ \Omega \| 667\ \Omega = 276\ \Omega$$

$$Z_{out} \cong R_D = 3.3\ k\Omega$$

$$v_{out} = g_m v_{gs}(R_D \| R_L) = 1,500\ \mu S \cdot 25\ mV \cdot (3.3\ k\Omega \| 6.8\ k\Omega)$$

$$= 37.5\ \mu A \cdot 2.22\ k\Omega = 0.0833\ V = 83.3\ mV$$

$$A_V = v_{out}/v_{in} = 83.3\ mV/25\ mV = 3.33$$

Also,

$$A_V = g_m(R_D \| R_L) = 1,500\ \mu S \cdot (3.3\ k\Omega \| 6.8\ k\Omega) = 3.33$$

Before continuing, test your knowledge with Self-Check 8–4.

Self-Check 8–4

1. The JFET of Figure 8–13 has a transconductance of 4,000 μS. $R_D = 10$ $k\Omega$ and $R_L = 33\ k\Omega$. $v_{in} = 5\ mV$. Calculate the loaded voltage gain and output voltage.
2. The JFET of Figure 8–13 has a g_{m0} of 4,000 μS and a $V_{GS(OFF)}$ of -3.4 V. $V_{GS(Q)} = -1$ V, $R_D = 36\ k\Omega$ and $R_L = 47\ k\Omega$. $v_{in} = 5\ mV$. Calculate the loaded voltage gain and output voltage.
3. The following values are known for the circuit of Figure 8–14a: $v_{in} = 2$ V, $R_S = 1.5\ k\Omega$, $R_L = 3.3\ k\Omega$, and $g_m = 2700\ \mu S$. Find Z_{out}, v_{out}, and A_V.
4. For the circuit of Figure 8–15, $R_S = 1\ k\Omega$, $R_D = 10\ k\Omega$, $R_L = 15\ k\Omega$, $g_m = 2,000\ \mu S$, and $v_{in} = 60\ mV$. Find Z_{in}, Z_{out}, v_{out}, and A_V.

8–5 MOSFETs

In this section, you will discover a very interesting family of field-effect transistors called **metal oxide semiconductor FETs (MOSFETs).** While these FETs have many of the JFET characteristics, they differ in a very significant way. The gate of the MOSFET is insulated from the channel. For this reason, MOSFETs are also referred to as *IGFETs* (insulated-gate FETs). Unlike the JFET, no *pn* junction is formed. This means the gate to source cannot be forward biased as a junction can. Therefore, the gate to channel leakage current (I_{GSS}) is very, very low, making the input resistance at the gate extremely high ($\gg 1,000\ M\Omega$). The two basic types of MOSFETs are depletion type and enhancement type. Let us examine the depletion type first.

DEPLETION-TYPE MOSFETs

Description

The **depletion-type (D-type) MOSFET** is very similar to the JFET, except for the insulated gate. Figure 8–16 illustrates the *n*-channel and *p*-channel D-type MOSFETs. Notice the layer of silicon dioxide between the gate metalization and the channel material. This layer, though very thin, insulates the gate from the channel. You should be able to recognize the difference between *n*-channel and *p*-channel MOSFETs from the schematic symbols. If the arrow in the symbol is pointing in toward the channel, the MOSFET is *n*-channel. If the arrow points away from the channel, the MOSFET is *p*-channel.

Handling

MOSFETs must always be handled carefully so the insulating layer is not damaged from static charges. Often, MOSFETs are shipped with a shorting strap (clip) in place, with instructions that the strap not be removed until the MOSFET is in the circuit. In any case, you should avoid touching the leads while the device is out-of-circuit. Always make sure your body is neutralized with the work area and common ground of the circuit. Place your hands on the work area and equipment before handling the MOSFET. While handling FETs, MOSFETs, and other sensitive ICs, technicians often wear a wrist strap that is electrically connected to bench ground. Important—this is not to say that you should ground yourself while working on equipment! Never ground your body while working on equipment that has lethal voltages present!

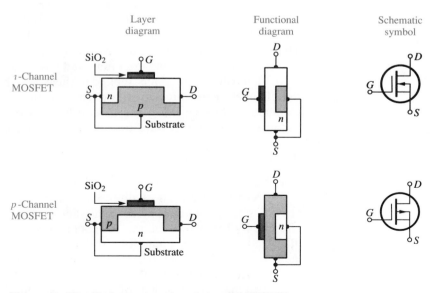

Figure 8–16 *N*-channel and *p*-channel MOSFETs.

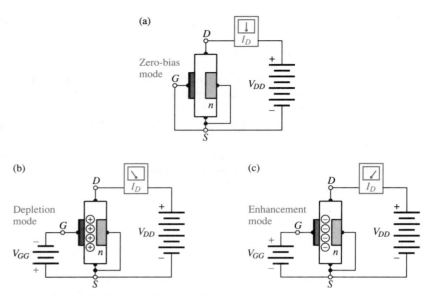

Figure 8–17 MOSFET bias modes.

Operating Characteristics

Unlike the JFET, the D-type MOSFET can be biased to operate in one of three modes. This is illustrated in Figure 8–17. The first mode is the **zero-bias mode** shown in Figure 8–17a. In this mode the difference of potential between the gate and source is 0 V. As you can see, the D-type MOSFET conducts just as a JFET does with zero bias. Often, D MOSFETs are called **normally ON MOSFETs** because they conduct with zero bias. The second mode is called the **depletion mode** as shown in Figure 8–17b. This mode is the same manner in which JFETs are biased. In this case, the negative potential applied to the gate repels electrons from the adjacent channel area. This creates a depletion region and reduces conduction through the channel. The third mode is the **enhancement mode** as shown in Figure 8–17c. In this mode, a positive potential is applied to the gate, which attracts electrons into the channel. This enhances the channel with free electrons and increases conduction through it. JFETs cannot be biased in the enhancement mode because this would forward bias the gate to source junction.

Biasing the D MOSFET

With three choices of biasing mode, how do we choose? As shown in Figure 8–18, zero biasing is most often chosen for the D MOSFET because the circuit is very simple and the amplifier performs adequately. Notice the circuit only has two resistors. The gate resistor is chosen to suit your particular need, serving as a load for a previous stage. The drain resistor is calculated very quickly from data sheet information. On the data sheet, you look for I_{DSS}. Recall that this is the saturation current that corresponds to a V_{GS} of 0 V. Assume V_{RD} to be half of V_{DD} and use Ohm's Law to calculate R_D.

$$R_D = (V_{DD}/2)/I_{DSS} = V_{DD}/2I_{DSS} \tag{8–24}$$

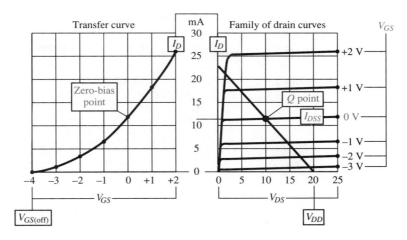

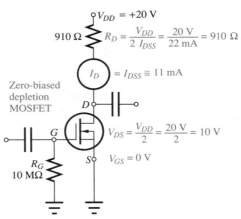

Figure 8–18   Zero biasing the D MOSFET.

From the graphs of Figure 8–18, you can see how zero bias places the Q point in the middle of the transfer (transconductance) curve. This point corresponds with I_{DSS} in the family of drain curves. The graphs also emphasize the choices in biasing; depletion, enhancement, or zero bias. Note the positive and negative values of V_{GS}. Also, note the load line drawn between V_{DD} and $I_{D(\text{sat})}$ ($I_{D(\text{sat})} = V_{DD}/R_D = 20 \text{ V}/910 \text{ }\Omega = 22 \text{ mA}$).

Analysis, design, and theory is very similar to JFETs. Formulas 8–1, 8–2, and 8–3 apply to D MOSFETs as well as to JFETs. Consider Examples 8–9 and 8–10.

EXAMPLE 8–9

A D MOSFET has an I_{DSS} of 15 mA. Design a zero-biased amplifier using a +24-V supply.

$R_D = (V_{DD}/2)/I_{DSS} = (24 \text{ V}/2)/15 \text{ mA} = 12 \text{ V}/15 \text{ mA} = 800 \text{ }\Omega$

R_G can be any value you want.

EXAMPLE 8–10 ▮▮▮▮▮▮▮▮▮▮▮▮▮▮▮▮▮▮▮▮▮▮▮▮▮▮▮

An n-channel D MOSFET has an I_{DSS} of 10 mA and a g_{m0} (y_{fs}) of 5,000 μS (5,000 μmhos). $V_{GS(off)} = -3$ V. Design an amplifier with a V_{GS} of $+1$ V. Determine the g_m at $V_{GS} = +1$ V. Use an $+18$-V supply. Also, determine A_V and v_{out} with a v_{in} of 50 mV.

$g_m = g_{m0} \cdot [1 - (V_{GS}/V_{GS(off)})] = 5,000 \ \mu S \cdot [1 - (+1 \ V/-3 \ V)]$

$= 5,000 \ \mu S \cdot 1.333 = 6,667 \ \mu S$

$I_D = I_{DSS} \cdot [1 - (V_{GS}/V_{GS(off)})]^2 = 10 \ mA \cdot [1 - (+1 \ V/-3 \ V)]^2$

$= 10 \ mA \cdot 1.78 = 17.8 \ mA$

$R_D = (V_{DD}/2)/I_D = (18 \ V/2)/17.8 \ mA$

$= 9 \ V/17.8 \ mA = 506 \ \Omega \ (510 \ \Omega \ is \ fine.)$

Use a voltage divider to provide the $+1$ V of bias at the gate. A 1.8-MΩ resistor in series with a 100-kΩ resistor would be fine or even 18 MΩ in series with 1 MΩ will work.

$A_V = g_m \cdot R_D = 6,667 \ \mu S \cdot 510 \ \Omega = 3.4 = 10.6 \ dB$

$v_{out} = A_V \cdot v_{in} = 3.4 \cdot 50 \ mV = 170 \ mV$

From Example 8–10, you may not think the MOSFET is of much use because the voltage gain is only 10.6 dB. But what about current gain and power gain? Think about it. There is no gate current. The only input current is the current in the gate resistor or voltage-divider network. If the gate resistor or voltage-divider resistors are high in resistance, which they can be, the AC input current and power is extremely small. Compared to this insignificant input current and power, the output current and power is very, very high. Therefore, P_{out}/P_{in} is very, very high! This is one reason why MOSFETs are important and useful devices. You will find that high-power MOSFETs are taking the place of power transistors in many applications because of their high input impedance and high power gain.

The Dual-Gate MOSFET

Figure 8–19 shows a dual-gate D-type MOSFET and common-source circuit. Data for this type of MOSFET is given with gate 2 at some specified positive bias voltage. In this case, the data sheet specified V_{GS2} at $+4$ V for the 3N201 MOSFET. Gate 1 is usually zero biased as shown. However, depletion biasing is sometimes used at gate 1 by adding a source resistor, as was done for self-biased JFETs.

As stated above, all data is specified at a particular gate 2 bias voltage. This means I_{DSS} and the entire family of drain curves is established at the specified value of V_{GS2}. This does not mean that gate 2 must always be at the specified voltage. For example, the voltage at gate 2 in Figure 8–18 could be $+5$ or $+3$. However, an increase in V_{GS2} from the specified value increases

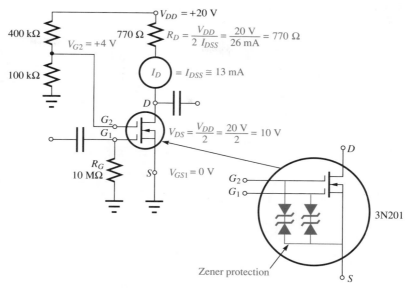

Figure 8–19 A dual-gate MOSFET circuit.

I_{DSS} and g_m and a decrease in V_{GS2} from the specified value causes a decrease in I_{DSS} and g_m. Very often, gate 2 is used to control the gain of the amplifier by varying its bias voltage. The design procedure is the same as for single-gate D MOSFETs.

Figure 8–19 also shows a more complete schematic symbol for the 3N201 dual-gate MOSFET. Note the zener diodes used to protect the gates from overvoltage and breakdown. These zener diodes are fabricated on the same chip as the FET. Many single-gate and dual-gate MOSFETs have this built-in protection. However, care must still be taken in handling any MOSFET.

ENHANCEMENT-TYPE MOSFETs

Symbol and Operation

The second basic type of MOSFET is the **enhancement-type (E-type) MOSFET.** These MOSFETs are sometimes called **normally OFF MOSFETs** because when $V_{GS} = 0$ V, there is no conduction. This type of MOSFET must be enhanced with a positive V_{GS} (for n-channel types) before conduction occurs. Figure 8–20a shows the schematic symbol for E-type MOSFETs. Notice the broken channel line in the symbol. This indicates the MOSFET is normally OFF and must be enhanced to conduct.

Conventional E MOSFETs

Figure 8–20b shows a layer diagram for conventional E-type MOSFETs of the low-current variety. Notice the n-type source region and the n-type drain region separated by a large p-type section just under the insulated gate. Normally, no current would flow from source to drain. However, when a positive potential is applied to the gate, free electrons in the p material are

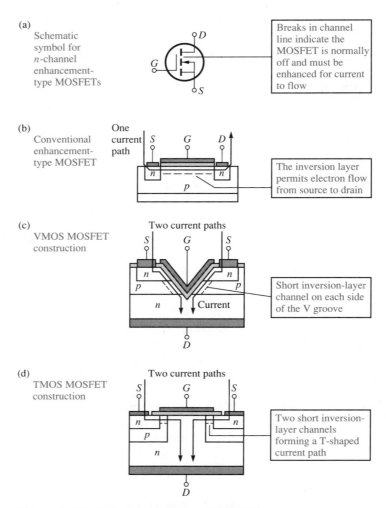

Figure 8–20 Enhancement-type MOSFETs.

attracted to a thin zone or layer adjacent to the gate. These electrons fill in the holes in this area of the *p* material and form an **inversion layer.** The inversion layer then begins to pass conduction-band electrons from source to drain. Thus, the channel is formed in the inversion layer only as long as a positive potential is applied to the gate. You might say the channel is enhanced. As you can see, the channel is relatively long, making channel resistance high and conduction low.

VMOS Construction

Shown in Figure 8–20c, the VMOS construction was developed to permit larger currents and a lower ON resistance from drain to source ($r_{DS(ON)}$). The VMOS design accomplishes this in two ways: by doubling the number of channels and by shortening each one. Carefully examine Figure 8–20c. Notice the short channels (inversion layers) on each side of the V groove. These layers are formed when a positive gate bias is provided. Electrons flow from the two sources (which are tied together) to the drain at the bottom. VMOS FETs are used in relatively high-power applications.

TMOS Construction

A more recent design for power MOSFETs is TMOS, by Motorola, Inc. As you can see in Figure 8–20d, two inversion layers are still used, as in VMOS. In this design, no V groove is needed. Manufacturing is less costly and packing density is higher.

Power MOSFET Advantages

In recent years, power MOSFETs have become more popular, taking the place of bipolar transistors for many high-power applications. These devices are simpler to design with and require fewer support parts than do bipolar transistors. For example, since a power MOSFET has an extremely high input impedance, there is no need for several stages of power amplification ahead of the MOSFET. A low-power source can drive the gate of the power MOSFET directly, thus eliminating intermediate stages and reducing cost.

Power MOSFETs are generally much faster devices than bipolar transistors. A charge stored in the base junction of a bipolar transistor slows down the turn-off time for the transistor. This type of charge, called a *storage charge,* does not exist in power MOSFETs. As an example, an IRF511 power MOSFET can switch 2 A of current on in less than 50 ns and off in less than 50 ns. A comparable power switching transistor such as the 2N5877 takes approximately 300 ns to switch 2 A of current on and 1,300 ns to turn off.

Another advantage of power MOSFETs over bipolar transistors is the lack of thermal runaway. Because they have a negative temperature coefficient, MOSFETs will not thermally run away and self-destruct. As temperature increases, drain current actually decreases, reducing power dissipation. This characteristic also permits the paralleling of power MOSFETs for increased load power. Any imbalance in the sharing of load current is equalized by an increase in temperature of the device that is conducting the most. This does not work with bipolar transistors.

Biasing the E-Type MOSFET

Figure 8–21 illustrates two methods for biasing E MOSFETs. Since the gate must be enhanced, a voltage divider or a drain-feedback resistor can be used. A Q point is selected from the transfer curve for the MOSFET and components are selected accordingly. In Figure 8–21c, the Q point is chosen to be $V_{GS} = +6$ V and $I_D \cong 61$ mA. A voltage divider is used in Figure 8–21a to provide the +6-V bias. The value of R_D is selected to place $V_{DS(Q)}$ somewhere around half of V_{DD}. In this case, $V_{DS} = 7$ V and $V_{RD} = 7$ V. Since the quiescent drain current is 61 mA, R_D must be 7 V/61 mA $\cong$ 115 Ω.

Drain-feedback biasing is shown in Figure 8–21b. The gate bias voltage is obtained from the drain. Since +6 V is needed at the gate, V_{RD} must be 8 V. With a V_{GS} of +6 V, the drain current is 61 mA. Therefore, R_D must be 8 V/61 mA $\cong$ 130 Ω. Simple, huh? Study Example 8–11.

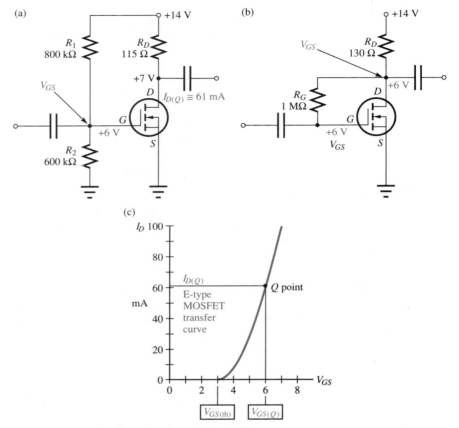

Figure 8–21 Biasing the E-type MOSFET.

EXAMPLE 8–11

From the transfer curve of Figure 8–21, design a MOSFET amplifier where $I_{D(Q)} = 40$ mA. Design it using (a) voltage-divider bias and (b) drain-feedback bias. Let $V_{DD} = +13.6$ V.

(a) Voltage-divider bias

From the transfer curve, $V_{GS(Q)} \cong 5.3$ V for $I_{D(Q)} = 40$ mA.

$R_D = (V_{DD}/2)/I_{D(Q)} = (13.6 \text{ V}/2)/40 \text{ mA} = 170 \ \Omega$ (Use 180 Ω)

R_2 = any value, say 1 MΩ

$R_1 = V_{R1}/I_{R1} = (V_{DD} - V_{GS(Q)})/(V_{GS(Q)}/R_2)$

$\quad = (13.6 \text{ V} - 5.3 \text{ V})/(5.3 \text{ V}/1 \text{ M}\Omega) = 8.3 \text{ V}/5.3 \ \mu\text{A}$

$\quad = 1.57 \text{ M}\Omega$ (Use 1.58 MΩ, 1%)

(b) Drain-feedback bias

$R_D = V_{RD}/I_{D(Q)} = (V_{DD} - V_{GS(Q)})/I_{D(Q)}$

$\quad = (13.6 \text{ V} - 5.3 \text{ V})/40 \text{ mA} = 8.3 \text{ V}/40 \text{ mA}$

$\quad = 208 \ \Omega$ (Use 210 Ω, 1%)

R_G = any value depending on desired input impedance

The Transconductance Curve

The transfer curve of Figure 8–21c is also the transconductance curve for the E MOSFET. Notice that $V_{GS(OFF)}$, for E MOSFETs, is now referred to as $V_{GS(th)}$, which is the gate to source threshold voltage. Conduction begins above $V_{GS(th)}$. The transconductance curve for E MOSFETs is still parabolic in shape and follows a square-law function. However, the formula for drain current is different than the drain current formula used for JFETs and D MOSFETs.

$$I_D = K(V_{GS} - V_{GS(th)})^2 \tag{8–25}$$

The K in the formula is a constant that depends on the particular E MOSFET design. K has units of A/V^2. Though not stated in the data sheet, K can be determined from values that are given. For example, the data sheet for a BS170 E MOSFET states that $r_{DS(ON)}$ is typically 1.8 Ω when I_D is 200 mA resulting from a V_{GS} of 10 V. It also indicates that $V_{GS(th)}$ is typically 2 V. Applying these values to Formula 8–25, we get:

$$200 \text{ mA} = K \text{ A/V}^2 \cdot (10 \text{ V} - 2 \text{ V})^2 = K \text{ A/V}^2 \cdot 64 \text{ V}^2$$

$$K = 0.2 \text{ A}/64 \text{ V}^2 = 0.00313 \text{ A/V}^2$$

Thus, for the BS170, $K = 0.00313 \text{ A/V}^2$. Now that K is known, other values of drain current can be calculated for different values of V_{GS}. Consider Example 8–12.

EXAMPLE 8–12

For the BS170, $K = 0.00313 \text{ A/V}^2$. Calculate I_D when $V_{GS} = 4$ V.

$$I_D = 0.00313 \text{ A/V}^2 \cdot (4 \text{ V} - 2 \text{ V})^2 = 0.00313 \text{ A/V}^2 \cdot 4 \text{ V}^2$$

$$= 0.0125 \text{ A} = 12.5 \text{ mA}.$$

Data sheets for some E MOSFETs specify $I_{D(ON)}$ for a certain value of V_{GS}. These values can be used to determine the K factor for the MOSFET. Look at Example 8–13.

EXAMPLE 8–13

The data sheet for the 2N7000 E MOSFET states that $I_{D(ON)}$ is a minimum of 75 mA with a V_{GS} of 4.5 V. $V_{GS(th)}$ is a minimum of 0.8 V. Calculate the K factor.

$$K = I_{D(ON)}/(V_{GS} - V_{GS(th)})^2 = 75 \text{ mA}/(4.5 \text{ V} - 0.8 \text{ V})^2 = 0.00548 \text{ A/V}^2$$

With this K factor and Formula 8–25, you can plot the transconductance curve for the 2N7000 using different values for V_{GS} and calculating I_D.

Take time to review this section. Then, test your knowledge with Self-Check 8–5.

1. Explain what it means to use the enhancement mode of biasing for a D MOSFET.
2. A D MOSFET is rated to have an I_{DSS} of 5 mA. If a 28-V DC supply is used, calculate the value of R_D needed for a zero-biased amplifier.
3. An n-channel D MOSFET has an I_{DSS} of 12 mA and a g_{m0} (y_{fs}) of 12,000 μS. $V_{GS(OFF)} = -4$ V. Design an amplifier with a V_{GS} of +2 V. Determine the g_m at $V_{GS} = +2$ V. Use a +20 V supply. Also, determine A_V and v_{out} with a v_{in} of 100 mV.
4. In Figure 8–19, describe the effect on g_m and A_V if the 400-kΩ resistor is replaced with a 510-kΩ resistor.
5. What is the basic operational difference between a D MOSFET and an E MOSFET?
6. Calculate the K factor for the E MOSFET of Figure 8–21.

8–6 FET APPLICATIONS

RADIO-FREQUENCY MIXERS

A JFET Mixer

Radio-frequency mixer circuits are very important in communications and broadcasting equipment. Figure 8–22 illustrates a JFET mixer circuit at the front end of an FM receiver. As you can see, the front-end tank circuit and the oscillator are gang-tuned and are both adjusted with the same knob. As the knob is adjusted, the tank circuit is tuned to a new station and the oscillator frequency tracks at a frequency that is 10.7 MHz above the station frequency. The selected station signal and the oscillator signal are mixed in the JFET. The output tank circuit is tuned to the 10.7 MHz intermediate

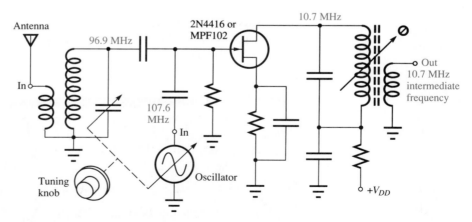

Figure 8–22 A JFET radio-frequency mixer.

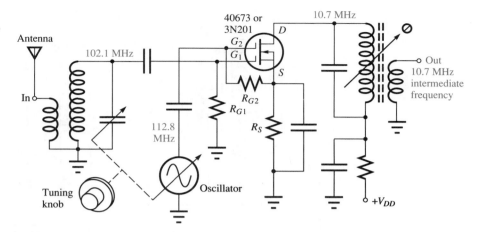

Figure 8–23 A dual-gate MOSFET mixer.

frequency (IF). The FET mixer amplifies the station frequency (96.9 MHz) and the oscillator frequency (107.6 MHz). The mixing action produces sum and difference frequencies, 107.6 MHz + 96.9 MHz = 204.5 MHz and 107.6 MHz − 96.9 MHz = 10.7 MHz. Since the output tank circuit at the drain is tuned only for 10.7 MHz, all other signals are greatly attenuated. Only a band of frequencies around 10.7 MHz is passed to the output. This band of frequencies contains the original information (voice and music). Several tuned amplifier stages following the mixer are used to greatly amplify the 10.7 MHz IF signal before the information is extracted and further amplified by an audio amplifier.

A MOSFET Mixer

A dual-gate MOSFET is very frequently used as a mixer/amplifier. This is illustrated in Figure 8–23. Notice gate 2 is used for the oscillator signal and gate 1 for the station signal. The self-bias scheme used here is very clever. The source resistor provides bias for both gates at the same time—a negative bias for gate 1 and a positive bias for gate 2. The station that is being received is at 102.1 MHz. The oscillator is set at 112.8 MHz. The difference between the two gate signals is 10.7 MHz, the IF frequency.

AUTOMATIC GAIN CONTROL (AGC)

Following the mixer in a radio receiver is the intermediate frequency section (IF section). This section is composed of two or three stages like that shown in Figure 8–24. In many receivers, the IF section is gain controlled with an automatic gain control circuit (AGC). A sample of the signal at the output of the final IF stage is rectified (peak detected) and filtered. A negative peak detector is used to create a negative DC control voltage (−AGC voltage). This control voltage is sent back to the IF stages to control their bias point and transconductance. A strong station produces a large negative control voltage, which reduces the gain of the IF amplifiers. Thus, the total gain of

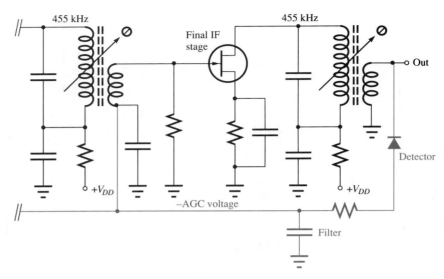

Figure 8–24 A gain-controlled IF stage.

the IF section is automatically controlled and the amplitude of the signal at the output of the IF section remains fairly constant.

POWER AMPLIFIERS

As we discussed earlier, MOSFETs are used for many power applications. Figure 8–25 is an example of a class C power amplifier. Notice the extreme simplicity of the circuit. The value of the gate resistor is chosen to satisfy the needs of the previous stage. V_{DD} is chosen not to exceed the V_{DS} maximum rating of the MOSFET. The impedance of the output tank circuit limits the maximum drain current. As for any class C amplifier, the MOSFET is cut off most of the time during each cycle. Only during a portion of the positive alternation of the input signal does the E MOSFET conduct.

Power MOSFETs are also used in class B push-pull amplifier circuits for audio and radio-frequency applications. As stated earlier, the advantages of high input impedance, no thermal runaway, simplicity of design, and paral-

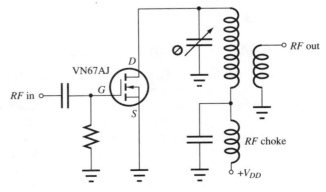

Figure 8–25 E MOSFET class C power amplifier.

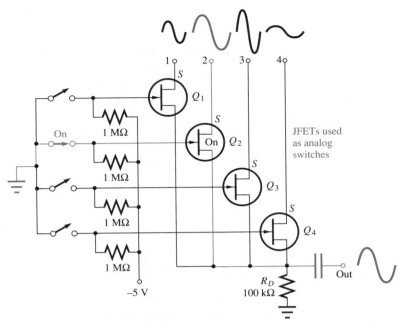

Figure 8–26   Analog multiplexing.

leling capability for higher load currents make power MOSFETs attractive choices. Most manufacturers' data books give details for power amplifier designs using MOSFETs.

ANALOG MULTIPLEXING

FETs are used in analog multiplexing circuits similar to that shown in Figure 8–26. The word multiplex means "many into one." Here, you see four analog signals being multiplexed, or routed, to one output. One or more of the analog signals will appear at the output, depending on the switch settings. As shown, Q_2 is on passing its signal to the output. The closed switch zero biases Q_2, which is a normally ON JFET. The ON resistance ($r_{DS(on)}$) of the JFET is very low, which means almost all of the input signal is passed to the output. The other JFETs are biased OFF by the −5 V. The OFF resistance of the JFETs is very high, blocking virtually all of the input signal from getting to the output.

In many real-world applications, the mechanical switches are replaced with digital switches that are computer controlled. Thus, a computer program can determine the signal source(s) sent to the output. The input signals that are to be multiplexed do not have to be sine waves. They can be any wave shape. Also, different DC levels can be multiplexed to the output.

CMOS INVERTERS

Complementary MOS (CMOS) inverters, such as those shown in Figure 8–27, are commonly used in digital circuitry. The complementary MOS-FETs are normally OFF, E-type MOSFETs. They offer very low current

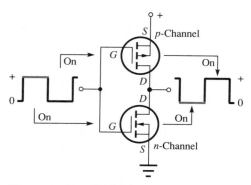

Figure 8–27   CMOS inverter.

drain, very low power consumption, and high switching speeds. As you can see in Figure 8–27, one of the MOSFETs is OFF while the other is ON, depending on the level of the input. The only current that actually flows through either MOSFET is load current and leakage current through the OFF MOSFET. If the load is the gate circuit of another MOSFET, there is very little current. Naturally, the power consumption is extremely low (in the nanowatts), making them very attractive for high-density packaging and battery-powered equipment.

DC-MOTOR SPEED CONTROL

Power MOSFETs are widely used in power-switching applications turning large amounts of current on and off at some frequency. One such application is shown in Figure 8–28. Here, an E-type MOSFET is used to control the speed of a DC motor. However, the MOSFET is either ON or OFF since it is driven at its gate by a square wave (pulsating DC). The speed of the DC motor depends on the average current that flows through its armature windings. If the duty cycle of the drive signal is low, the average armature current

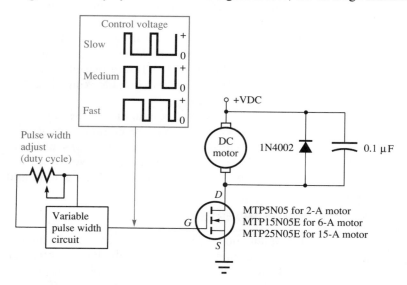

Figure 8–28   MOSFET motor speed control circuit.

is low because the MOSFET is ON for only a small portion of the complete cycle. As shown in the figure, a high duty cycle of the drive signal causes the motor to run at a high speed, because the average current is high, because the MOSFET conducts for most of the cycle. A potentiometer, or rheostat, is used to vary the duty cycle of the drive signal supplied by the variable-pulse-width circuit. The frequency of the drive signal remains constant at some frequency, usually between 400 Hz and 2 kHz. The MOSFET operates class D. This method of speed control is sometimes referred to as *pulse width modulation* (PWM) or *pulse duration modulation* (PDM).

Naturally there are many other applications for FETs. These have been just a few of the more common ones. You are at least aware of the tremendous importance of FETs in the world of electronics. Take time to review this section and answer the questions of Self-Check 8–6.

Self-Check 8–6

1. Briefly explain how a dual-gate MOSFET can be used in a radio-frequency mixer circuit.
2. Explain how a negative AGC voltage controls the gain of an *n*-channel JFET in the IF section of a receiver.
3. List three advantages power MOSFETs have over bipolar transistors.
4. Briefly describe a CMOS inverter.
5. What type MOSFET should you use in a PDM motor speed control circuit?
   (a) D-type MOSFET   (b) E-type MOSFET   (c) CMOS

8–7 TROUBLESHOOTING

JFETs

Ohmmeter Testing

JFETs can be checked with an ohmmeter when they are out-of-circuit. There are two checks that can be made. As you know, there is a *pn* junction between the gate and channel (drain/source). The gate to source should conduct somewhat when forward biased and act as an open when reverse biased. If the JFET is bad, it is possible that this junction may be shorted (shows conduction in both directions). The second check that can be made with the ohmmeter is from source to drain. Since the JFET is out-of-circuit, it has zero bias from gate to source. Therefore, a relatively low channel resistance from source to drain can be measured. This measured value should be within the range of the $r_{DS(ON)}$ value specified in the data sheet for the JFET.

> **Care must be taken in handling all types of FETs. Make sure all static charges on your body are neutralized with the work area before handling the FET. Make sure all pieces of test equipment are grounded to the same earth ground.**

Curve-Tracer Testing

Figure 8–29 shows the Tektronix 571 Curve Tracer being used to test an *n*-channel JFET that is plugged into a socket on the front panel (not shown). In Figure 8–29a, operating parameters are selected from the setup screen. Notice that the maximum drain current is set at 10 mA and the gate voltage is to be applied in 0.5-V steps from −3.0 V to −0.5 V. When the start button on the 571 is pressed, the test begins and the screen changes to the test screen shown in Figure 8–29b. As you can see, this FET is functioning normally. As the gate voltage (bias) is made less negative in 0.5-V steps, the drain saturation current increases.

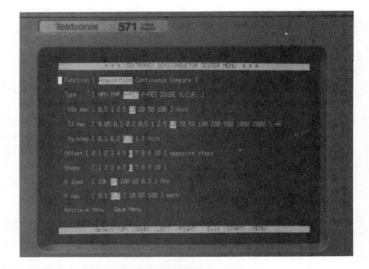

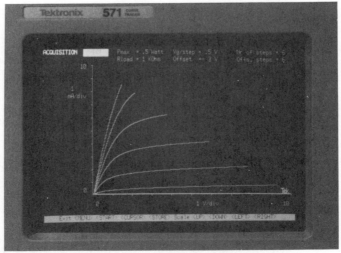

Figure 8–29 Using the Tektronix 571 curve tracer to test an *n*-channel JFET: (a) the setup screen, where operating parameters are selected, and (b) the test screen, where drain curves are displayed. (Equipment courtesy of Tektronix.)

Using a Test Circuit

The JFET can also be tested out of its original circuit, or permanent circuit, by placing it in a test circuit. The test circuit allows for simultaneous measurement of V_{GS}, V_{DS}, and I_D. Characteristic drain curves can be plotted manually for a good JFET. Also, a low-level sine wave can be applied and the amplifier tested for gain and distortion.

In-Circuit Voltmeter Testing

DC voltages can be measured and compared with values specified on a schematic. Often, DC values are specified in parentheses at key test points in the circuit (gate, source, and drain). If values are not specified on the schematic, at least you can determine the type of biasing that is being used and decide on reasonable estimated values based on theory. Do not try to carry this to an extreme. Checking the data sheet for the JFET and using calculations to predict DC values is not always accurate, due to extreme variations in JFET parameters. Use DC measurements mainly to identify shorts and opens in FET circuits.

Using the Signal Generator and Oscilloscope

The signal generator and oscilloscope are better tools for troubleshooting in-circuit JFETs. Be careful not to over-drive the gate of the JFET. The test signal should be the same amplitude as the normal operating signal. Use the schematic to determine the configuration of the amplifier stage (CD, CS, or CG). This way you will know if you should expect to see some voltage gain or a phase inversion from input to output.

MOSFETs

MOSFETs can be tested in much the same way as JFETs with some exceptions. Remember, the MOSFET has an insulated gate. Therefore, there should be no measurable conduction between gate and source when testing with the ohmmeter. Also, remember there are two general types of MOSFETs, normally ON (D-type) and normally OFF (E-type). The static drain to source ON resistance ($r_{DS(ON)}$) can be measured with the ohmmeter if the MOSFET is the D-type. Recall that the E-type must be enhanced (biased ON) before it conducts.

SYSTEMS

FET amplifier systems can be checked using a signal generator and oscilloscope. A schematic and general amplifier specifications are essential. You must know the type of input the system expects to see and the output the system is supposed to provide. The schematic allows you to determine input and output points for each stage. The oscilloscope probe should be used to test for amplification and distortion at the output of each stage. The faulty stage is identified by checking its input to determine if the stage is receiving a proper drive signal. Proper drive and poor output narrows the problem down to a few components in most cases. Besides faulty FETs, shorted or leaky couplings and bypass capacitors are also common problems. Don't forget to look for foil cracks, solder bridges, cold solder joints, and obvious overheating of components.

Time for a self-check.

Self-Check 8–7

1. You test an E-type MOSFET from source to drain with an ohmmeter. What would you expect to see?
2. How do the results of testing the gate to source junction of a JFET with an ohmmeter differ from those for a MOSFET?
3. If the output signal of a common-source amplifier is compared with the input signal, using a dual-trace oscilloscope, what would you expect to see?
4. When using a signal generator and an oscilloscope to troubleshoot an amplifier system, how do you know when you have located the faulty stage?

SUMMARY

FORMULAS

(8–1) $I_D = I_{DSS} \cdot [1 - (V_{GS}/V_{GS(OFF)})]^2$
(for JFETs and D-type MOSFETs)

(8–2) $g_m = \Delta I_D/V_{GS}$

(8–3) $g_{m\text{-}VGS} = g_{m0} \cdot [1 - (V_{GS}/V_{GS(OFF)})]$
(for JFETs and D-type MOSFETs)

(8–4) $r_{ds} = \Delta V_{DS}/\Delta I_D = 1/g_{os}$

Self-Bias Analysis

(8–5) $I_{D(Q)} = |V_{GS(Q)}|/R_S = V_{RS(Q)}/R_S$

(8–6) $V_{RD(Q)} = I_{D(Q)} \cdot R_D$

(8–7) $V_{DS(Q)} = V_{DD} - V_{RD(Q)} - V_{RS(Q)}$

Self-Bias Design

(8–8) $R_S = V_{RS(Q)}/I_{D(Q)}$ (where $V_{RS(Q)} = |V_{GS(Q)}|$)

(8–9) $R_D \cong (V_{DD}/I_{DSS}) - R_S$

(8–10) $C_B \geq 1.59/R_S f_{\text{low}}$

Common-Source Amplifier

(8–11) $Z_{\text{in}} \cong R_G$ (for CS and CD Amplifiers)

(8–12) $Z_{\text{out}} \cong R_D$

(8–13) $A_V = v_{\text{out}}/v_{\text{in}} = g_m \cdot (R_D \parallel R_L)$ (Ideal, with source at AC ground)

(8–14) $A_V = \dfrac{v_{\text{out}}}{v_{\text{in}}} = \dfrac{g_m R_D}{1 + g_m X_C}$ (Practical, consideration given to bypass capacitor.)

(8–15) $C_B \geq 1.59 \, g_m/f_{\text{low}}$

Common-Drain Amplifier

(8–16) $Z_{\text{out}} = [(1/g_m) \parallel R_S]$

(8–17) $A_V = R_S/[(1/g_m) + R_S]$ (no load)

(8–18) $v_{\text{out}} = v_{\text{in}} \cdot R_S/[(1/g_m) + R_S]$ (no load)

(8–19) $v_{\text{out}} = v_{\text{in}} \cdot (R_S \parallel R_L)/[(1/g_m) + (R_S \parallel R_L)]$ (with load)

Common-Gate Amplifier

(8–20) $Z_{\text{in}} = R_S \parallel (1/g_m)$

(8–21) $Z_{\text{out}} \cong R_D$

(8–22) $v_{\text{out}} = g_m v_{gs}(R_D \parallel R_L)$ (with load)

(8–23) $A_V = g_m(R_D \parallel R_L)$ (with load)

Zero-Biased D-Type MOSFET

(8–24) $R_D = (V_{DD}/2)/I_{DSS} = V_{DD}/2I_{DSS}$

E-Type MOSFET

(8–25) $I_D = K(V_{GS} - V_{GS(\text{th})})^2$

CONCEPTS

COMPARING COMMON-EMITTER AND COMMON-SOURCE AMPLIFIERS

Parameter	BJT	JFET	MOSFET
Z_{in}	very low $\cong R_1 \parallel R_2$	very high $\cong R_G$	very high $\cong R_G$
Z_{out}	$\cong R_C$	$\cong R_D$	$\cong R_D$
A_V (no load)	$\cong R_C/(r'_e + r_E)$	$\cong g_m R_D$	$\cong g_m R_D$

COMPARING CS, CD, AND CG AMPLIFIERS

Parameter	CS Amplifier	CD Amplifier	CG Amplifier
Z_{in}	very high $\cong R_G$	very high $\cong R_G$	very low $= R_S \parallel 1/g_m$
Z_{out}	$\cong R_D$	very low $= R_S \parallel 1/g_m$	$\cong R_D$
A_V	$<1, g_m \cdot (R_D \parallel R_L)$	$<1, R_S/(1/g_m + R_S)$	$>1, g_m \cdot (R_D \parallel R_L)$
Phase	180°	0°	0°
Application	voltage and power amplifier	buffer amplifier	voltage and power amplifier

- FETs are voltage-controlled devices; bipolar transistors are current controlled.
- JFETs and D-type MOSFETs are normally ON types of devices when zero biased.
- VMOS and TMOS are construction techniques used for power MOSFETs.
- CMOS inverters are complementary pairs of E MOSFETs in a push-pull arrangement used for high-speed, low-power switching.
- g_{m0} is the transconductance of a JFET or D MOSFET with zero bias.
- Compared to bipolar transistors, FETs have the advantages of very high input impedance, high-speed operation, simple circuit design, and low power consumption.
- Compared to bipolar power transistors, power MOSFETs have the further advantages of simpler circuitry, low-power bias requirements, no thermal runaway, and paralleling capability to deliver more load current.
- FETs have the disadvantage of high distortion for large-swing signals due to the parabolic transfer curve.
- Extreme care must be taken in handling FETs. Static charges can permanently damage the gate to channel area.

PROCEDURES

- DESIGN PROCEDURE FOR SELF-BIASED CS JFET AMPLIFIERS
    1. Use the transconductance curve to determine quiescent values of I_D and V_{GS} that place the Q point on the upper, more linear, portion of the curve.
    2. Use the quiescent values to calculate the value for R_S. $R_S = V_{RS(Q)}/I_{D(Q)}$, where $V_{RS(Q)} = |V_{GS(Q)}|$.
    3. Use a standard value for R_D that is close to $(V_{DD}/I_{DSS}) - R_S$.
    4. Bypass the source resistor for maximum gain. $C_B \geq 1.59/(R_S f_{low})$ or $C_B \geq 1.59\, g_m/f_{low}$ if g_m is known.
    5. R_G can be any value. It is usually determined by the needs of any previous stage.

NEED-TO-KNOW SOLUTION

This is the simplest solution to the interface problem—a CD stage.

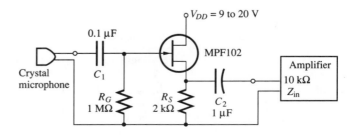

QUESTIONS

8–1 JUNCTION FIELD-EFFECT TRANSISTORS

1. List three advantages of FETs over bipolar transistors.
2. List two disadvantages of FETs compared to bipolar transistors.
3. What are the majority carriers in n-channel JFETs?
4. How can you tell the difference between an n-channel schematic symbol and a p-channel schematic symbol?
5. Are JFETs (a) current-controlled devices, or (b) voltage-controlled devices?

8–2 JFET CHARACTERISTICS AND PARAMETERS

6. Describe the characteristics of the JFET when operated in the ohmic region.
7. Define I_{DSS}.
8. Explain how different values of V_{GS} affect the amount of saturation current in a JFET.
9. Describe the drain current when V_{GS} is equal to $V_{GS(OFF)}$.
10. What is transconductance mathematically?
11. Is the transconductance the same for all points of the transfer curve? Explain.
12. What parameter can you calculate from the specified value of I_{GSS} at a specified value of V_{GS} for a JFET?
13. Explain g_{m0}.
14. What is g_{os}?

8–3 JFET BIASING

15. Briefly explain the two problems related to output signal distortion.
16. Where on the transconductance curve should the JFET be biased for maximum linearity and high transconductance?
17. Explain some problems you encounter when obtaining data from a data sheet for the purpose of biasing a particular JFET.
18. What is the purpose for constant-current-source biasing?

8–4 FET AMPLIFIER CONFIGURATIONS

19. For the CS configuration, what is the phase relationship between the output and input signal?
20. What three factors determine the voltage gain of a loaded CS amplifier?
21. Describe the CD amplifier in terms of voltage gain and input to output phase relationship.
22. How does the input impedance of the CG amplifier compare to the CS and CD amplifiers?

8–5 MOSFETs

23. What is one significant difference between a JFET and a MOSFET?

24. What has a higher gate resistance, (a) a JFET, or (b) a MOSFET?
25. Explain the zero-bias mode for D-type MOSFETs.
26. How does the schematic symbol for an E-type MOSFET differ from the symbol for a D-type MOSFET?
27. What is an inversion layer?
28. List three advantages of power MOSFETs over bipolar transistors.

8–6 FET APPLICATIONS

29. Briefly explain how a dual-gate MOSFET is used for a radio-frequency mixer.
30. Explain how the gain of a JFET amplifier can be controlled.
31. If it is desired to use zero bias, should an E MOSFET or a D MOSFET be used for a class C amplifier? Explain.
32. What is a CMOS inverter?
33. What are two big advantages to using CMOS instead of bipolar technology?
34. If you needed to design the final stage for a PDM motor speed control circuit for a $-$VDC system with positive ground, what type of power MOSFET would you choose?
    (a) n-channel D MOSFET   (b) p-channel D MOSFET
    (c) n-channel E MOSFET   (d) p-channel E MOSFET

8–7 TROUBLESHOOTING

35. Explain what to look for when testing a JFET out-of-circuit using an ohmmeter.
36. Why must you be careful when handling FETs?
37. Why is a schematic so important when it comes to troubleshooting a system?
38. The gate to source resistance for a MOSFET is measured with an ohmmeter and found to be 126.4 kΩ. Describe the condition of the MOSFET.

PROBLEMS

8–2 JFET CHARACTERISTICS AND PARAMETERS

1. Through the use of a test circuit, it is determined that $V_{GS(OFF)} = -2.4$ V and $I_{DSS} = 1.3$ mA for a particular JFET. Calculate I_D at a V_{GS} of -1 V.
2. From a data sheet, it is determined that $V_{GS(OFF)} = -4$ V and $I_{DSS} = 12$ mA for a particular JFET. Calculate I_D at a V_{GS} of -0.5 V.
3. Calculate the g_m for a JFET whose drain current varies from 1.32 mA to 1.54 mA when its gate to source voltage varies from -0.7 V to -0.6 V.
4. Calculate the g_m for a JFET whose drain current varies from 3.5 mA to 6.7 mA when its gate to source voltage varies from -2.2 V to -1.4 V.
5. The data sheet for a JFET specifies a typical value of g_{m0} to be 3,000 μmhos. $V_{GS(OFF)}$ is specified to be typically -6 V. Calculate g_m at a V_{GS} of -1.5 V.
6. The data sheet for a JFET specifies a typical value of g_{m0} to be 2.5

mmhos. $V_{GS(OFF)}$ is specified to be typically -3 V. Calculate g_m at a V_{GS} of -0.8 V.

7. Calculate the input resistance at the gate of a JFET for an I_{GSS} of 0.6 nA at a V_{GS} of -15 V.

8. Calculate the input resistance at the gate of a JFET for an I_{GSS} of 1.3 nA at a V_{GS} of -15 V.

9. Calculate the dynamic drain to source resistance (r_{ds}) when g_{os} is known to be 8.33 μS.

10. Calculate the dynamic drain to source resistance (r_{ds}) when g_{os} is known to be 3.25 μS.

8–3 JFET BIASING

11. Determine the following for the circuit of Figure 8–30: $I_{D(Q)}$, $V_{RD(Q)}$, and $V_{DS(Q)}$.

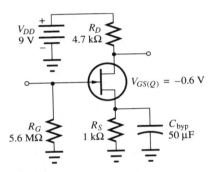

Figure 8–30

12. Determine the following for the circuit of Figure 8–31: $I_{D(Q)}$, $V_{RD(Q)}$, and $V_{DS(Q)}$.

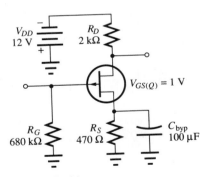

Figure 8–31

13. Given: $V_{GS(OFF)} = -4.5$ V, $I_{DSS} = 5.6$ mA, $V_{DD} = +12$ V, $V_{GS(Q)} = -1$ V, and $g_{m0} = 4,500$ μS. Design a common-source JFET amplifier by calculating the proper values for R_S and R_D from the given data. Also, calculate C_B for an f_{low} of 30 Hz.

14. Given: $V_{GS(OFF)} = -2$ V, $I_{DSS} = 14$ mA, $V_{DD} = +9$ V, $V_{GS(Q)} = -0.5$ V, and $g_{m0} = 3800$ μS. Design a common-source JFET amplifier by calculating the proper values for R_S and R_D from the given data. Also, calculate C_B for an f_{low} of 30 Hz.

8–4 FET AMPLIFIER CONFIGURATIONS

15. Calculate the approximate voltage gain for the amplifier of Problem 13. Express the gain in decibels.
16. Calculate the approximate voltage gain for the amplifier of Problem 14. Express the gain in decibels.
17. What is the approximate input and output impedance for the amplifier of Figure 8–30?
18. What is the approximate input and output impedance for the amplifier of Figure 8–31?
19. Calculate Z_{in}, Z_{out}, A_V, and v_{out} for the circuit of Figure 8–32. Also, express the voltage gain in decibels.

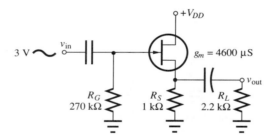

Figure 8–32

20. Calculate Z_{in}, Z_{out}, A_V, and v_{out} for the circuit of Figure 8–33. Also, express the voltage gain in decibels.

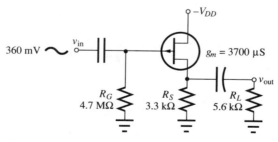

Figure 8–33

21. Calculate Z_{in}, Z_{out}, A_V, and V_{out} for a common-gate amplifier if $g_m = 2.4$ mS, $R_S = 820$ Ω, $R_D = 10$ kΩ, $R_L = 33$ kΩ, and $v_{in} = 30$ mV.
22. Calculate Z_{in}, Z_{out}, A_V, and V_{out} for a common-gate amplifier if $g_m = 3200$ μS, $R_S = 100$ Ω, $R_D = 1$ kΩ, $R_L = 4.7$ kΩ, and $v_{in} = 100$ mV.

8–5 MOSFETs

23. Calculate the value of R_D needed for a zero-biased, n-channel, common-source, D-type MOSFET amplifier if $V_{DD} = 20$ V and $I_{DSS} = 22$ mA.

24. Calculate the value of R_D needed for a zero-biased, p-channel, common-source, D-type MOSFET amplifier if $V_{DD} = -28$ V and $I_{DSS} = 40$ mA.

25. An n-channel D MOSFET has an I_{DSS} of 7 mA, and a g_{m0} of 7800 μS. $V_{GS(OFF)} = -3.6$ V. Design a CS amplifier like Figure 8–34 with a V_{GS} of $+0.8$ V. Use voltage-divider biasing for the gate. V_{DD} shall be $+24$ V. Determine g_m at $V_{GS} = +0.8$ V. Also, determine the no-load voltage gain and output voltage if $v_{in} = 85$ mV.

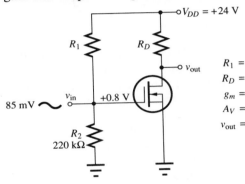

Figure 8–34

26. A p-channel D MOSFET has an I_{DSS} of 43 mA, and a g_{m0} of 11,500 μS. $V_{GS(OFF)} = +4.1$ V. Design a CS amplifier like Figure 8–35 with a V_{GS} of -0.5 V. Use voltage-divider biasing for the gate. V_{DD} shall be -18 V. Determine g_m at $V_{GS} = -0.5$ V. Also, determine the no-load voltage gain and output voltage if $v_{in} = 50$ mV.

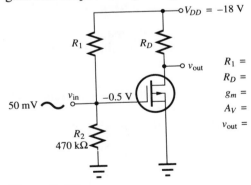

Figure 8–35

27. The data sheet for an E-type MOSFET specifies the following: $V_{GS(th)} = +2.8$ V, $I_{D(ON)} = 100$ mA at a V_{GS} of $+5$ V. Calculate I_D at a V_{GS} of 3.3 V.

28. The data sheet for an E-type MOSFET specifies the following: $V_{GS(th)} = +1.5$ V, $I_{D(ON)} = 70$ mA at a V_{GS} of $+6$ V. Calculate I_D at a V_{GS} of 3 V.

8–7 TROUBLESHOOTING

The following troubleshooting problems pertain to Figure 8–36.

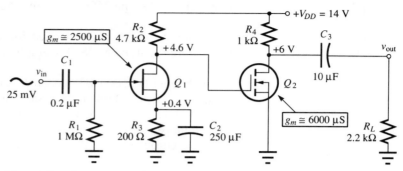

Figure 8–36

29. A 25-mV test signal is applied to the input of the amplifier in Figure 8–36. A 300-mV AC signal is measured at the drain of Q_1 and no signal is present across the load resistor at the output. What might be wrong?
30. The DC voltage at the drain of Q_2 is measured and found to be 14 V. What might be wrong?
31. A 25-mV test signal is applied to the gate of Q_1 and the signal at the gate of Q_2 is less than 200 mV. What might be wrong?
32. The DC voltage at the drain of Q_1 is found to be 14 V. What might be the trouble?
33. If the values for g_m specified in the schematic are fairly accurate, what should the signal voltage be at the load with a 25-mV test signal applied to the input of Q_1?
34. If the measured AC load voltage is a little more than 1 V when a 25-mV test signal is applied to Q_1, what might be wrong?

ADDITIONAL PROBLEMS

35. Which of the schematic symbols of Figure 8–37 is a *p*-channel JFET?
36. Which of the schematic symbols of Figure 8–37 is an E-type MOSFET?
37. Which of the JFET symbols in Figure 8–37 requires a positive V_{GS} for biasing?
38. Which of the MOSFETs in Figure 8–37 can have a positive or negative bias voltage?
39. A JFET has the following characteristics: $V_{GS(OFF)} = -2.5$ V, $I_{DSS} = 12$

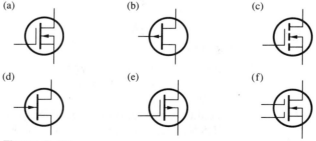

(a)   (b)   (c)

(d)   (e)   (f)

Figure 8–37

mA, and $g_{m0} = 6,000\ \mu S$. Use this JFET to design a common-source amplifier where $V_{DD} = +9$ V and $V_{GS(Q)} = -0.6$ V. Calculate the proper values for R_S, R_D, and C_B. Let $R_G = 2.5$ MΩ and $f_{low} = 40$ Hz.

40. What are the output and input impedances for the amplifier you designed in Problem 39?

41. What is the approximate A_V for the amplifier you designed in Problem 39 if it is connected to a 10-kΩ load resistance? Express the gain in decibels.

42. Calculate the voltage gain and output voltage for a common-gate JFET amplifier if $g_m = 4.8$ mS, $R_D = 18$ kΩ, and $R_L = 220$ kΩ and $v_{in} = 10$ mV.

43. Calculate the value of R_D needed for a zero-biased, n-channel, common-source, D-type MOSFET amplifier if $V_{DD} = 12$ V and $I_{DSS} = 30$ mA.

44. Determine the proper values for R_2 and R_3 from the information presented in Figure 8–38.

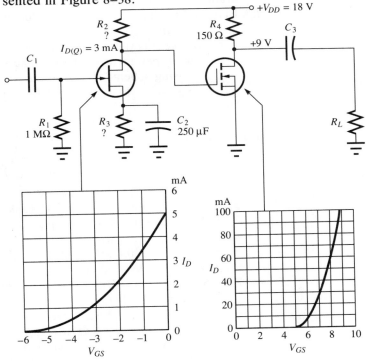

Figure 8–38

ANSWERS TO SELF-CHECKS

SELF-CHECK 8–1

1. JFETs are unipolar because there is only one type of majority-carrier current through the device from source to drain.

2. Valence-band hole flow

3. Gate voltage—there is no gate current except leakage current

4. JFETs are voltage controlled and are unipolar whereas bipolar transistors are current controlled and bipolar.

SELF-CHECK 8–2

1. I_{DSS} is the maximum saturation current for JFETs when $V_{GS} = 0$ V.
2. The ohmic region
3. The gate to source voltage needed to cut off current through the FET
4. The change in drain current as a result of a change in gate to source voltage is a square-law relationship. The graph of this relationship is parabolic.
5. 15 mmhos = 15 mS = 15,000 μS

SELF-CHECK 8–3

1. $R_S = V_{RS}/I_D = 0.4$ V/0.47 mA = 851 Ω
2. $I_D = I_{DSS} \cdot [1 - (V_{GS}/V_{GS(OFF)})]^2 = 8$ mA $\cdot [1 - (-1/-4)]^2 = 4.5$ mA
   $R_S = V_{RS}/I_D = 1$ V/4.5 mA = 222 Ω
3. First, calculate the drain current using $V_{GS(Q)}$ and R_S. Then, multiply drain current times R_D.
4. Bias the FET high on the transconductance curve for maximum linearity and high gain. $V_{GS(Q)} \cong V_{GS(OFF)}/4$
5. A big problem is the variations in drain current that exist due to large variations in parameters for the same type JFET. A constant-current-source biasing scheme is a solution.
6. $I_{D(Q)} = V_{RE}/R_E = (V_{R2} - 0.7$ V$)/R_E = (1.06$ V $- 0.7$ V$)/470$ Ω = 0.36 V/470 Ω = 766 μA

SELF-CHECK 8–4

1. $A_V = v_{\text{out}}/v_{\text{in}} = g_m \cdot (R_D \parallel R_L) = 4{,}000$ μS $\cdot (10$ k$\Omega \parallel 33$ k$\Omega)$
   $= 4{,}000$ μS $\cdot 7{,}674$ $\Omega = 30.7 = 29.7$ dB
   $v_{\text{out}} = 30.7 \cdot 5$ mV = 154 mV
2. $g_m = g_{m0} \cdot [1 - (V_{GS}/V_{GS(OFF)})] = 4{,}000$ μS $\cdot [1 - (-1$ V$/-3.4$ V$)]^2$
   $= 4{,}000$ μS $\cdot 0.498 = 1{,}992$ μS
   $A_V = v_{\text{out}}/v_{\text{in}} = g_m \cdot (R_D \parallel R_L) = 1{,}992$ μS $\cdot (36$ k$\Omega \parallel 47$ k$\Omega)$
   $= 1{,}992$ μS $\cdot 20.4$ k$\Omega = 40.6 = 32.2$ dB
   $v_{\text{out}} = 40.6 \cdot 5$ mV = 203 mV
3. $Z_{\text{out}} = (1/g_m \parallel R_S) = (1/2{,}700$ μS $\parallel 1.5$ k$\Omega)$
   $= (370$ $\Omega \parallel 1.5$ k$\Omega) = 297$ Ω
   $v_{\text{out}} = v_{\text{in}} \cdot (R_S \parallel R_L)/[1/g_m + (R_S \parallel R_L)]$
   $= 2$ V $\cdot (1.5$ k$\Omega \parallel 3.3$ k$\Omega)/[(1/2{,}700$ μS$) + (1.5$ k$\Omega \parallel 3.3$ k$\Omega)]$
   $= 2$ V $\cdot A_V = 2$ V $\cdot 1{,}031$ $\Omega/[370$ $\Omega + 1031$ $\Omega]$
   $= 2$ V $\cdot A_V = 2$ V $\cdot 0.736 = 1.47$ V
   $A_V = 0.736 = -2.66$ dB
4. $Z_{\text{in}} = R_S \parallel 1/g_m = 1$ k$\Omega \parallel 1/2{,}000$ μS = 333 Ω
   $Z_{\text{out}} \cong R_D = 10$ kΩ
   $v_{\text{out}} = g_m v_{gs}(R_D \parallel R_L) = 2{,}000$ μS $\cdot 60$ mV $\cdot (10$ k$\Omega \parallel 15$ k$\Omega)$
   $= 2{,}000$ μS $\cdot 60$ mV $\cdot 6$ k$\Omega = 0.72$ V = 720 mV
   $A_V = v_{\text{out}}/v_{\text{in}} = 720$ mV/60 mV = 12 = 21.6 dB

SELF-CHECK 8–5

1. A polarity of bias voltage is used that attracts majority carriers into the channel.

2. $R_D = (V_{DD}/2)/I_{DSS} = V_{DD}/2I_{DSS} = 28$ V$/(2 \cdot 5$ mA$) = 2{,}800$ Ω

3. $I_D = I_{DSS} \cdot [1 - (V_{GS}/V_{GS(OFF)})]^2 = 12$ mA $\cdot [1 - (2$ V$/-4$ V$)]^2$
   $= 12$ mA $\cdot 2.25 = 27$ mA
   $g_m = g_{m0} \cdot [1 - (V_{GS}/V_{GS(OFF)})] = 12{,}000$ μS $\cdot [1\ 2$ V$/-4$ V$)]$
   $= 12{,}000$ μS $\cdot 1.5 = 18{,}000$ μS
   $R_D = (V_{DD}/2)/I_D = (20$ V$/2)/27$ mA $= 10$ V$/27$ mA $= 370$ Ω
   If $R_2 = 200$ kΩ, $R_1 = 1.8$ MΩ.
   $A_V = g_m \cdot R_D = 18{,}000$ μS $\cdot 370$ $\Omega = 6.66 = 16.5$ dB
   $v_{out} = A_V \cdot v_{in} = 6.66 \cdot 100$ $mV = 666$ mV

4. V_{GS2} decreases, causing g_m to decrease and A_V to decrease.

5. The D MOSFET is normally on and the E MOSFET is normally off.

6. $K = I_D/(V_{GS} - V_{GS(th)})^2 = 61$ mA$/(6$ V $- 3$ V$)^2$
   $= 61$ mA$/9$ V$^2 = 0.00678$ A$/$V$^2 = 6.78$ mA$/$V^2

SELF-CHECK 8–6

1. The dual-gate MOSFET must be properly biased and the two radio-frequency signals applied one to each gate. The drain should be tuned to the desired output frequency (the sum or difference of the two input frequencies).
2. The negative AGC voltage increases the negative bias on the gate, which reduces the transconductance and gain of the amplifier.
3. No thermal runaway, simplicity of design, paralleling capability
4. A CMOS inverter is a push-pull arrangement of a p-channel and an n-channel E MOSFET.
5. (b) E-type MOSFET

SELF-CHECK 8–7

1. No conduction—looks open
2. The JFET shows conduction in one direction between gate and channel (source or drain). The MOSFET should show no conduction in either direction.
3. Some amplification and a 180° phase difference
4. A signal is present at the stage's input but not at its output, or the output signal is very low or heavily distorted.

SUGGESTED PROJECTS

1. Add some of the main concepts, formulas, and procedures from this chapter to your Electronics Notebook.
2. Obtain one or more of the following FETs with data sheets and construct and test some of the circuits in this chapter: 2N5457, 2N4416, MPF102, 3N201, 40673, 3N128, 2N7000.
3. Construct a self-biased CS amplifier with a 2N5457 JFET. Measure and record all DC voltages. Apply a 50-mV, 1-kHz test signal and measure the output signal. Replace the 2N5457 with a second 2N5457 and redo your measurements. Compare the results to see how close they are.

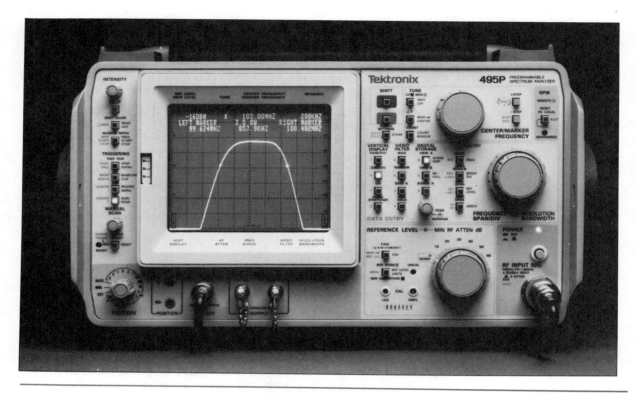

This spectrum analyzer is displaying the frequency response of an amplifier tuned for a center frequency of 100 MHz. The lower and upper cutoff frequencies are indicated with markers. The spectrum analyzer is a valuable test instrument used in the field of electronic communications. Portable Spectrum Analyzer. (Courtesy of Tektronix.)

9 Amplifier Frequency Response

OBJECTIVES

After studying this chapter, you will be able to

- define and explain key terms that pertain to the frequency response of an amplifier.
- describe highpass and lowpass frequency response in terms of cutoff frequency and slope of rolloff.
- explain how phase shift is related to frequency.
- explain what reactances affect the low-end frequency response of an amplifier.
- calculate the cutoff frequency for each of the highpass networks of an amplifier and determine which is dominant.
- explain what reactances affect the high-end frequency response of an amplifier.
- calculate the cutoff frequency for each of the lowpass networks of an amplifier and determine which is dominant.
- explain the cumulative effects of highpass and lowpass networks associated with amplifier circuits.
- discuss the phase response of amplifiers and the detrimental effects of phase shift.
- explain and use Miller's Theorem regarding amplifier capacitances.
- explain the advantage of using a cascade amplifier.
- describe the effects of stray capacitance and lead inductance on amplifier frequency response.
- calculate amplifier bandwidth using cutoff frequencies or the gain-bandwidth product relationship.
- use test equipment to determine the frequency response of an amplifier.

NEED TO KNOW

Calculate the dominant upper cutoff frequency for this amplifier. Then, describe how to use a signal generator and oscilloscope to verify your calculations.

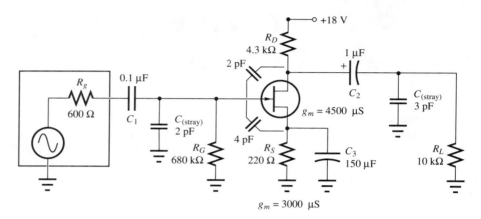

Are you having some difficulty? Are you not quite sure how to begin? Is it because you aren't sure what an upper cutoff frequency is? Is it because you don't know what values to use or what formulas to use? Well, maybe, just maybe, you have a need to know. By the time you finish this chapter, you will be able to solve this problem. As always, a solution is also provided at the end of the chapter.

INTRODUCTION

From previous chapters, you learned how to calculate the voltage gain of BJT and FET amplifiers. However, this voltage gain is accurate only for a specific range of frequencies. Above or below this range of frequencies, the voltage gain drops off. In this chapter, you will discover the practical frequency limitations of amplifiers and the factors that create those limitations. This will help you develop an understanding of the realistic capabilities of amplifiers.

We will begin with a general discussion of highpass and lowpass filters and later apply that information to the highpass and lowpass input and output networks of amplifiers. You will also gain an understanding of overall amplifier frequency response and amplifier testing using the signal generator and oscilloscope. Enjoy your exploration.

9–1 FREQUENCY RESPONSE

VOLTAGE GAIN AND FREQUENCY

In the previous chapters, you learned how to calculate voltage gain (A_V) for bipolar junction transistor (BJT) and field-effect transistor (FET) amplifiers. There was very little indication that voltage gain depends on the frequency

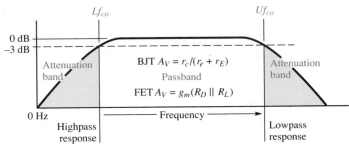

Figure 9–1 Amplifier frequency response.

of the applied signal. The only hint of this was the brief discussion on selecting coupling and bypass capacitors. Recall that these capacitors were selected for the lowest frequency that the amplifier must amplify. It is important for you to realize that the calculated voltage gain applies only to a certain range, or band, of frequencies. This range is called the **passband** of the amplifier. As shown in Figure 9–1, this passband is bordered by a highpass filter response and a lowpass filter response. These areas are known as **attenuation bands** or **stopbands.** In the highpass and lowpass attenuation bands, the voltage gain of the amplifier is caused to drop off due to the filtering effects of circuit capacitances. Circuit inductances also participate in this but only at very high frequencies.

Before we launch forward to analyze amplifier frequency response and all contributing factors, let's take time to review basic filter concepts and terminology. We will do this by reviewing highpass and lowpass filters.

HIGHPASS FILTERS

RL Highpass Filters

As shown in Figure 9–2, a series RL circuit forms a simple highpass filter. The voltage at the output terminals (V_L) changes with frequency since X_L changes with frequency ($X_L = 2\pi fL$). The top graph in the example is a Bode plot of the filter's frequency response. The **Bode plot** is a frequency response graph plotted on a semilog graph system that utilizes decibels. The filter output voltage is converted to decibels using an insertion loss formula (attenuation formula) that includes the voltage divider formula for the filter. The filter has a different insertion loss, measured in decibels, for each frequency applied to the filter since X_L is different for each frequency.

As you can see, the graph for this highpass filter is sloped. The **slope** of the graph is measured in decibels per octave (dB/octave) or decibels per decade (dB/decade) of frequency change (one **octave** is twice a reference frequency and one **decade** is ten times a reference frequency). The slope of the bode plot is said to **roll off** at so many dB/octave or dB/decade. For any simple RL or RC filter, the *ideal* slope is 6 dB/octave, which is equal to 20 dB/decade. Notice that the slope of rolloff for the filter of Figure 9–2 is actually about 18.5 dB/decade from 10 kHz to 100 kHz.

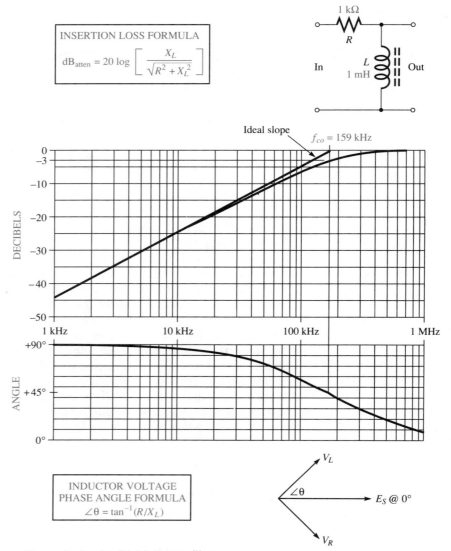

Figure 9–2 An *RL* highpass filter.

The **passband** of the filter consists of all frequencies whose voltage at the filter output is greater than −3 dB. The **stopband,** or **attenuation band,** of the filter consists of all frequencies whose voltage is less than −3 dB. For Figure 9–2, the passband includes all frequencies above 159 kHz and the attenuation band includes all frequencies below 159 kHz. The 159-kHz frequency is known as the *cutoff frequency*. The **cutoff frequency (f_{co})** for any filter is the frequency whose voltage is −3 dB in amplitude at the filter output. This is also known as the *half-power point,* or *half-power frequency,* since −3 dB represents a drop in power by half [dB = 10 log(1/2) = −3 dB]. The actual signal voltage of the cutoff frequency at the filter output is 0.707 times the input voltage [dB = 20 log(V_{out}/V_{in}) = 20 log(0.707) = −3 dB].

The lower graph of Figure 9–2 shows the filter's phase response. Recall how the phase angles between V_R, V_L, and E_S change with frequency in a series RL circuit. Notice that the phase angle between V_L and E_S, and E_S and V_R, is $+45°$ at the cutoff frequency. This is because $X_L = R$ and $V_L = V_R$ at the cutoff frequency, where $\angle +45° = \tan^{-1}(V_L/V_R) = \tan^{-1}(1) = 0.707$. Notice also that the highpass filter is a voltage-lead network where the output voltage leads the input (source) voltage (indicated by positive phase angles).

Since $X_L = R$ at the cutoff frequency, a formula to determine the cutoff frequency can be easily derived from the X_L formula. $X_L = R$ and $X_L = 2\pi fL$, so $R = 2\pi fL$. Evaluating this expression for f we see that $f = f_{co} = R/(2\pi L)$. Look at Example 9–1.

$$f_{co} = R/(2\pi L) = 0.159 \, R/L \tag{9–1}$$

EXAMPLE 9–1 ▉▉▉▉▉▉▉▉▉▉▉▉

Determine the cutoff frequency for an RL highpass filter in which $L = 350 \, \mu\text{H}$ and $R = 12 \, \text{k}\Omega$.

$f_{co} = 0.159 \, R/L = 0.159 \cdot 12 \, \text{k}\Omega/350 \, \mu\text{H} = 5.45 \, \text{MHz}$

RC Highpass Filters

A series RC circuit can also function as a highpass filter. Notice the circuit of Figure 9–3. A capacitor is placed in series with a load resistor. The higher the frequency, the lower the $X_C [X_C = 1/(2\pi fC)]$ and more current is passed on to the load resistor. It is important for you to realize that the Bode and phase plots for this filter are identical to those of the RL highpass filter of Figure 9–2. Thus, a highpass filter having all of the same characteristics as any RL filter can be made using a capacitor in series. The rolloff is still at the rate of about 18.5 dB/decade (ideally 20 dB/decade).

At the cutoff frequency, $X_C = R_L$. Thus, a formula to calculate the cutoff frequency can be derived from the X_C formula as follows: $X_C = R_L$ and $X_C = 1/(2\pi fC)$, so $R_L = 1/(2\pi fC)$. Thus, $f = f_{co} = 1/(2\pi CR_L)$. See Example 9–2.

$$f_{co} = 1/(2\pi CR_L) = 0.159/CR_L \tag{9–2}$$

EXAMPLE 9–2 ▉▉▉▉▉▉▉▉▉▉▉▉

Determine the cutoff frequency for an RC highpass filter in which $C = 0.022 \, \mu\text{F}$ and $R = 4.7 \, \text{k}\Omega$.

$f_{co} = 0.159/CR_L = 0.159 / (0.022 \, \mu\text{F} \cdot 4.7 \, \text{k}\Omega) = 1.54 \, \text{kHz}$

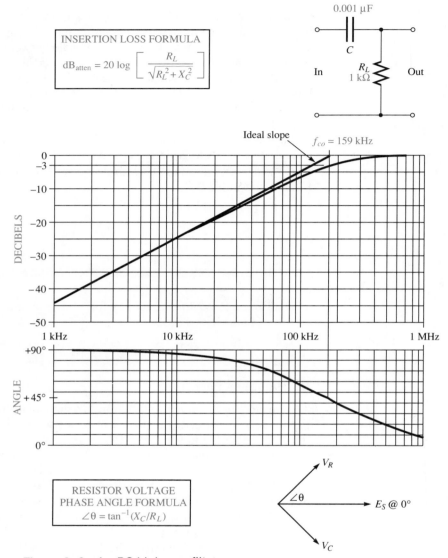

Figure 9–3 An *RC* highpass filter.

RCL Highpass Filters

Often, inductors and capacitors are used together to complement one another and improve the frequency response of the filter. Figure 9–4 is a case in point. Here, the inductor is placed in parallel with the load resistor and a capacitor is placed in series. As frequency is increased, the capacitor's reactance decreases and the inductor's reactance increases. Finally, a practical point is reached where X_C is insignificant compared to R_L, and X_L is very large, no longer having any effect in parallel with the load resistor. The push-pull effect of the inductor and capacitor working together provides a much steeper slope in the attenuation band than is possible using only a

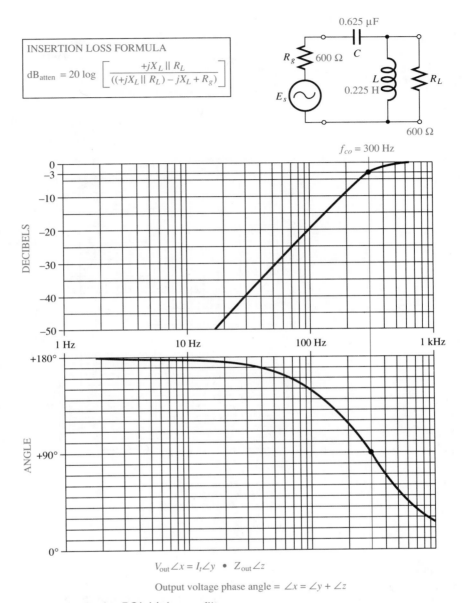

INSERTION LOSS FORMULA

$$dB_{atten} = 20 \log \left[\frac{+jX_L \parallel R_L}{((+jX_L \parallel R_L) - jX_L + R_g)} \right]$$

Figure 9–4 An *RCL* highpass filter.

capacitor or inductor. In fact, the slope now approaches an *ideal* 12 dB/octave, equal to 40 dB/decade. Notice, from the phase plot, that the *RCL* highpass filter is a voltage-lead network, as are all highpass filters.

LOWPASS FILTERS

RL Lowpass Filters

By switching the position of the inductor and resistor, a highpass filter becomes a lowpass filter. In Figure 9–5, the inductor is now in series with

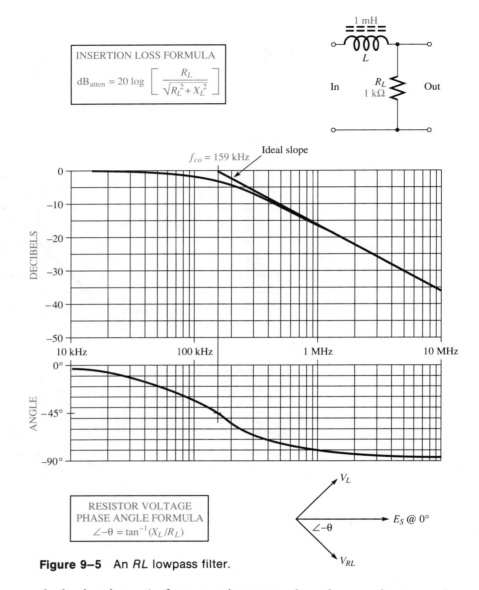

Figure 9–5 An *RL* lowpass filter.

the load resistor. As frequency increases, the voltage at the output (across the load resistor) decreases, because the X_L of the series inductor increases ($X_L = 2\pi fL$). Low frequencies, including DC (0 Hz), pass through the filter with little or no attenuation. The passband lies below 159 kHz and the stopband lies above 159 kHz. As you can see from the Bode plot, the slope is about 18 dB/decade between 200 kHz and 2 MHz. Again, the *ideal* slope is 20 dB/decade for simple *RL* or *RC* filters.

If you compare the filters of Figures 9–2 and 9–5, you will see they both use the same components and have the same cutoff frequency. Notice the phase response. The lowpass filter is a voltage-lag network and the highpass filter is a voltage-lead network. In Figure 9–5, the output voltage lags the input voltage by 45° ($\angle -45°$) at the cutoff frequency where $X_L = R$. Formula 9–1 is used to calculate the cutoff frequency for both highpass and lowpass *RL* filters.

EXAMPLE 9–3 ▰▰▰▰▰▰▰▰▰▰▰

Determine the cutoff frequency for an *RL* lowpass filter in which $L =$ 2.6 mH and $R = 560\ \Omega$.

$f_{co} = 0.159\ R/L = 0.159 \cdot 560\ \Omega/2.6\ \text{mH} = 34.2\ \text{kHz}$

RC Lowpass Filters

Just as the inductor and resistor can be switched, the capacitor and resistor can be switched to form an *RC* lowpass filter. Figure 9–6 uses the same components as Figure 9–3 to illustrate how a lowpass filter of the same cutoff frequency, can be formed by placing the capacitor in parallel with the

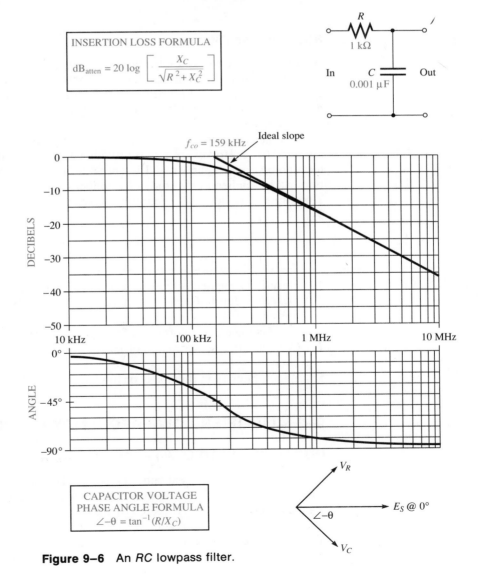

Figure 9–6 An *RC* lowpass filter.

output (output voltage = V_C). The output voltage decreases as the frequency increases since X_C decreases [$X_C = 1/(2\pi fC)$]. As with the RL lowpass filter, the passband lies below 159 kHz and the attenuation band lies above 159 kHz. As with all passive lowpass filters, the output voltage lags the input voltage in phase and time. Formula 9–2 is used to calculate the cutoff frequency for lowpass as well as highpass RC filters.

EXAMPLE 9–4

Determine the cutoff frequency for an RC lowpass filter in which $C = 0.47~\mu F$ and $R = 1~k\Omega$.

$f_{co} = 0.159/CR_L = 0.159/(0.47~\mu F \cdot 1~k\Omega) = 338~Hz$

RCL Lowpass Filters

Again, the inductor and capacitor can work together to improve the frequency response of the filter. Figure 9–7 shows an RCL lowpass filter with a cutoff frequency of 1 kHz and a rolloff slope approaching the ideal 40 dB/decade (12 dB/octave). Notice, from the phase plot, that output voltages for all frequencies lag the source voltage.

The material presented in this section is by no means complete nor is it intended to be. However, it does provide you with a basic foundation in filter terminology and highpass and lowpass filter characteristics. This information will be applied in the study of amplifier frequency response that follows. Take time to review this section by answering the questions of Self-Check 9–1.

Self-Check 9–1

1. Describe a highpass filter in terms of frequency response.
2. Describe cutoff frequency in terms of decibels, output voltage, and power.
3. What is the ideal rolloff slope for RC and RL highpass or lowpass filters?
4. Compare the performance of an RC lowpass filter to an RCL lowpass filter.
5. Which filter type (highpass or lowpass) is a voltage-lag network?

9–2 AMPLIFIER LOW-FREQUENCY RESPONSE

INTRODUCTION TO LOW-FREQUENCY RESPONSE

In this section, we will examine the reactances that affect the low-end frequency response of an amplifier. As shown in Figure 9–8, the low-end highpass filter response is created by the change in reactance of coupling and bypass capacitors. The reactance of these capacitors is very low and insignificant in the passband region of the amplifier's response. However, for frequencies below the lower cutoff frequency (Lf_{co}), the capacitive reac-

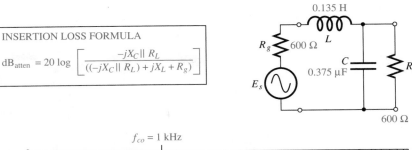

INSERTION LOSS FORMULA

$$dB_{atten} = 20 \log \left[\frac{-jX_C \| R_L}{((-jX_C \| R_L) + jX_L + R_g)} \right]$$

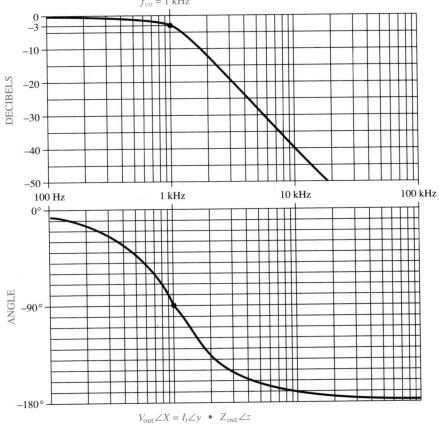

$$V_{out} \angle X = I_t \angle y \bullet Z_{out} \angle z$$

Output voltage phase angle $= \angle x = \angle y + \angle z$

Figure 9–7   An *RCL* lowpass filter.

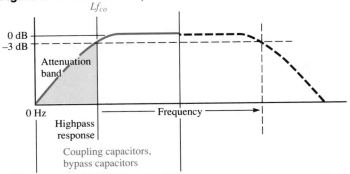

Figure 9–8   Low-frequency attenuation caused by coupling and bypass capacitors.

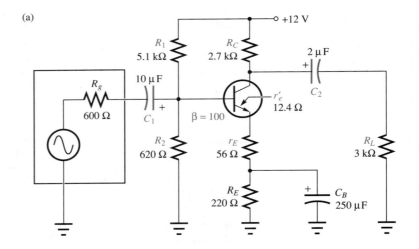

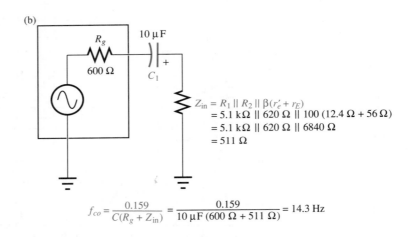

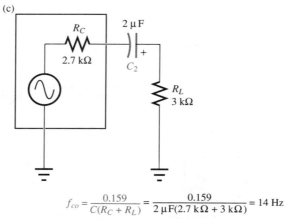

Figure 9–9   Coupling capacitors in BJT amplifiers.

tance is significant compared to circuit resistances. The lower the frequency, the greater the X_C and the greater the signal attenuation. In other words, the lower the frequency, the greater the reduction in amplifier gain.

The slope of the rolloff in the highpass attenuation band is at the idealized rate of 20 dB per decade for each highpass network. Here, we will study three such networks: the capacitor-coupled input network, the capacitor-coupled output network, and the emitter, or source, bypass network. The effect of these three networks is cumulative. That is, at some point on the curve, the slope will be 60 dB/decade.

COUPLING CAPACITORS AND LOW-END RESPONSE

The Input Coupling Network of BJT Amplifiers

Let's begin with the input coupling network of a bipolar junction transistor amplifier (BJT). In Figure 9–9a, a 10-μF capacitor is used to block any DC and pass AC from a signal source to the input of the transistor stage. The internal resistance of this signal source is 600 Ω. Once the input impedance to the stage is determined, the actual cutoff frequency of the input network can be determined. From previous study, you know that the input impedance to this CE stage is the parallel combination of R_1, R_2, and Z_b, which is $\beta(r'_e + r_E)$. The calculation is simple and straightforward. $Z_{in} = 511$ Ω, as shown in Figure 9–9b. The cutoff frequency is calculated by applying the sum of the generator resistance and the input impedance to Formula 9–2. The cutoff frequency is a very low 14.3 Hz and the slope of rolloff is 20 dB/ decade.

The Output Coupling Network of BJT Amplifiers

The output coupling network is shown in Figure 9–9c. The collector resistor is the output impedance (resistance) of the amplifier and is in series with the 2-μF coupling capacitor and load resistance. Realize that this load resistance may also be the input impedance of a second stage (a cascaded stage). In any case, the cutoff frequency is calculated by applying the sum of R_C and R_L to Formula 9–2. Here again, the cutoff frequency is found to be 14 Hz and the slope of rolloff is 20 dB/decade. The cumulative effect of the input and output highpass coupling networks is a slope of 40 dB/decade below approximately 14 Hz. Take a moment now to study Example 9–5.

EXAMPLE 9–5 ▉▉▉▉▉▉▉▉▉▉▉▉▉▉▉▉▉▉▉▉▉

Determine the cutoff frequency for the input and output coupling networks of Figure 9–10.

Input network

1. Determine the input impedance Z_{in}.

$$Z_{in} = R_1 \parallel R_2 \parallel \beta(r'_e + r_E) \cong R_1 \parallel R_2 \parallel \beta R_E$$

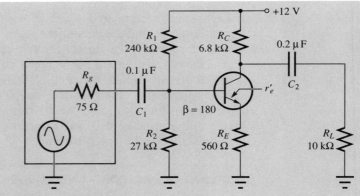

Figure 9–10

In this case r_e' can be ignored because of the large swamping resistor R_E.

$$Z_{in} \cong R_1 \parallel R_2 \parallel \beta R_E = 240 \text{ k}\Omega \parallel 27 \text{ k}\Omega \parallel 180 \cdot 560 \ \Omega$$

$$= 240 \text{ k}\Omega \parallel 27 \text{ k}\Omega \parallel 101 \text{ k}\Omega = 19.6 \text{ k}\Omega$$

2. Calculate f_{co}.

$$f_{co} = 0.159/RC = 0.159/C(R_g + Z_{in})$$

$$= 0.159/[0.1 \ \mu\text{F} \cdot (75 \ \Omega + 19.6 \text{ k}\Omega)]$$

$$= 0.159/0.00197 = 80.7 \text{ Hz}$$

Output network

1. $Z_{out} = R_C = 6.8 \text{ k}\Omega$

2. $f_{co} = 0.159/RC = 0.159/C(R_C + R_L)$

$$= 0.159/[0.2 \ \mu\text{F} \cdot (6.8 \text{ k}\Omega + 10 \text{ k}\Omega)]$$

$$= 0.159/0.00336 = 47.3 \text{ Hz}$$

The Input Coupling Network of FET Amplifiers

Figure 9–11a illustrates a CS JFET amplifier with a capacitor-coupled input and output. The analysis here is simplified because the input impedance is approximately equal to the value of the gate resistor (R_G). Notice how this very high input impedance allows the use of a relatively low-value coupling capacitor. The calculations for the cutoff frequency in Figure 9–11b reveal a very low cutoff of 1.6 Hz. This suggests that the coupling capacitor could be even smaller if desired. The cutoff frequency would be 16 Hz using a 0.01- coupling capacitor.

The Output Coupling Network for FET Amplifiers

The output highpass network is shown in Figure 9–11c. Since R_D is the output impedance of the stage, it appears in series with the coupling capaci-

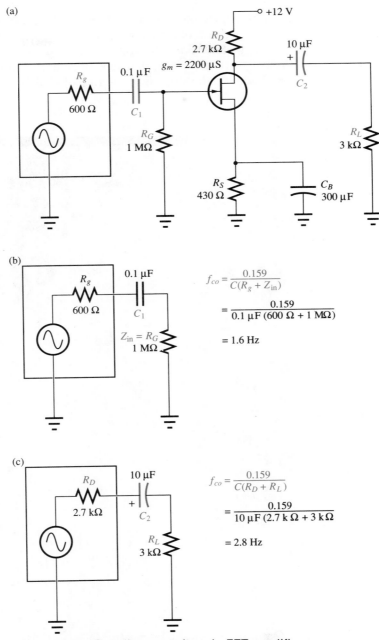

Figure 9–11 Coupling capacitors in FET amplifiers.

tor and the load resistance. From Formula 9–2, the cutoff frequency is calculated to be a very low 2.8 Hz. Again, a smaller coupling capacitor could be used if desired. A 1-μF coupling capacitor would provide a cutoff frequency of 28 Hz.

As for BJT amplifiers, the effect of the input and output coupling networks for FET amplifiers is cumulative. Since the output coupling network has a cutoff of 2.8 Hz it is called the **dominant cutoff frequency.** It dominates over the 1.6-Hz cutoff of the input network because, as frequency is lowered from the passband region, the rolloff begins with the 2.8-Hz cutoff frequency. From 2.8 Hz to 1.6 Hz, the slope of rolloff is an ideal 20 dB/decade. From 1.6 Hz down, the slope is at the rate of 40 dB/decade. Study Example 9–6.

EXAMPLE 9–6

Determine the cutoff frequency for the input and output coupling networks of Figure 9–12.

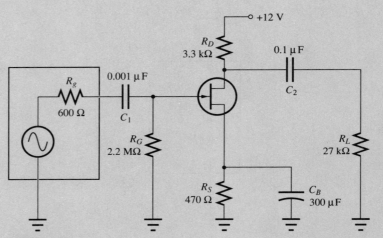

Figure 9–12

Input network

1. $Z_{in} = 2.2 \ \text{M}\Omega$
2. Calculate f_{co}.

$$f_{co} = 0.159/RC = 0.159/C(R_g + Z_{in})$$

$$= 0.159/[0.001 \ \mu\text{F} \cdot (600 \ \Omega + 2.2 \ \text{M}\Omega)]$$

$$= 0.159/0.0022 = 72.3 \ \text{Hz} \qquad \text{(Dominant cutoff frequency)}$$

Output network

1. $Z_{out} = R_D = 3.3 \ \text{k}\Omega$
2. $f_{co} = 0.159/RC = 0.159/C(R_D + R_L)$

$$= 0.159/[0.1 \ \mu\text{F} \cdot (3.3 \ \text{k}\Omega + 27 \ \text{k}\Omega)]$$

$$= 0.159/0.00303 = 52.5 \ \text{Hz}$$

BYPASS CAPACITORS AND LOW-END RESPONSE

The Emitter-Bypass Network for BJT Amplifiers

Now, let's go back to the BJT amplifier and consider the effects of the emitter bypass capacitor. As seen in Figure 9–13, the impedance seen at the point labeled Z_e is effectively shorted to ground for all passband frequencies. This insures the accuracy of the voltage gain formula for all passband frequencies, where $A_V = r_C/(r_e' + r_E)$. The cutoff frequency for the bypass network is the frequency at which $X_C = Z_e$. Thus, Z_e can be placed in Formula 9–2 to calculate the cutoff frequency. As you can see, Z_e is an extensive combination of circuit values.

$$Z_e = R_E \parallel [r_E + r_e' + ((R_g \parallel R_1 \parallel R_2)/\beta)] \tag{9–3}$$

(If r_E does not exist in the circuit, simply remove it from the formula.)

$$f_{co} = 0.159/(C_B Z_e) \tag{9–4}$$

where $C_B = 0.159/(f_{co}Z_e)$ at a specific cutoff frequency.

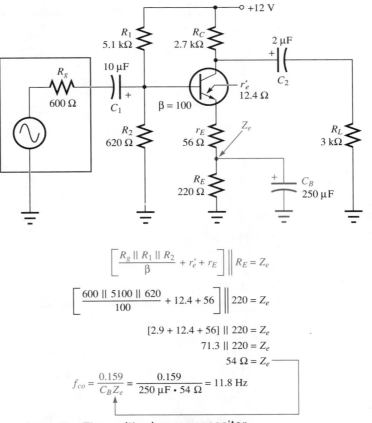

$$\left[\frac{R_g \parallel R_1 \parallel R_2}{\beta} + r_e' + r_E \right] \bigg\| R_E = Z_e$$

$$\left[\frac{600 \parallel 5100 \parallel 620}{100} + 12.4 + 56 \right] \bigg\| 220 = Z_e$$

$$[2.9 + 12.4 + 56] \parallel 220 = Z_e$$

$$71.3 \parallel 220 = Z_e$$

$$54\ \Omega = Z_e$$

$$f_{co} = \frac{0.159}{C_B Z_e} = \frac{0.159}{250\ \mu F \cdot 54\ \Omega} = 11.8\ \text{Hz}$$

Figure 9–13 The emitter-bypass capacitor.

At this point you may be a little confused about the proper formula to use to determine the value for the bypass capacitor, since a different formula was given in an earlier chapter $[C_B \geq 1.59/(r'_e f_{low})]$. The earlier formula was not intended to set a specific lower cutoff frequency but to ensure that the emitter was very near AC ground at the lowest desired frequency. Using the earlier formula $[C_B \geq 1.59/(r'_e f_{low})]$ to determine a value for C_B results in an actual cutoff frequency (f_{co}) that is much lower than the lowest desired frequency (f_{low}). Therefore, if it is a specific cutoff frequency that you want, use $C_B = 0.159/(f_{co} Z_e)$. If you simply want to ensure that the lowest frequency that passes through the amplifier will be amplified the maximum amount, use $C_B \geq 1.59/(r'_e f_{low})$ or $C_B \geq 1.59/[(r_E + r'_e)f_{low}]$. Consider Example 9–7.

EXAMPLE 9–7

Determine the cutoff frequency caused by the emitter bypass capacitor in Figure 9–14.

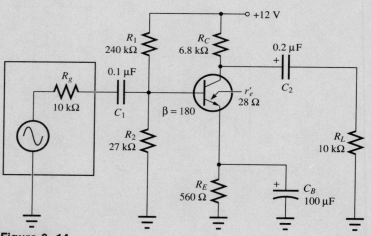

Figure 9–14

1. First calculate r'_e.
   To determine r'_e you must calculate I_E using V_E and R_E, where

   $V_E \cong V_B - 0.7$ V.

   $V_B \cong 12$ V $\cdot$ 27 kΩ/(27 kΩ + 240 kΩ) $\cong 1.2$ V

   $V_E \cong V_B - 0.7$ V $= 1.2$ V $- 0.7$ V $= 0.5$ V

   $I_E = 0.5$ V/560 $\Omega = 893$ μA

   $r'_e \cong 25$ mV/893 μA $= 28$ Ω

2. Now calculate Z_e.

$$Z_e = R_E \parallel [r_E + r_e' + ((R_g \parallel R_1 \parallel R_2)/\beta)]$$

$$= 560 \ \Omega \parallel [28 \ \Omega + ((10 \ k\Omega \parallel 240 \ k\Omega \parallel 27 \ k\Omega)/180)]$$

$$= 560 \ \Omega \parallel [28 \ \Omega + (7.08 \ k\Omega/180)]$$

$$= 560 \ \Omega \parallel [28 \ \Omega + 39.3 \ \Omega] = 560 \ \Omega \parallel 67.3 \ \Omega = 60 \ \Omega$$

3. Now determine the cutoff frequency.

$$f_{co} = 0.159/(C_B Z_e) = 0.159/(100 \ \mu F \cdot 60 \ \Omega) = 26.5 \ \text{Hz}$$

The Source Bypass Network for FET Amplifiers

As you can see in Figure 9-15, the cutoff frequency of the source-bypass network is found in similar fashion as for emitter-bypass networks. The source output impedance must first be determined, then applied to the cutoff-frequency formula.

$$Z_S = 1/g_m \parallel R_S \tag{9-5}$$

$$f_{co} = 0.159/(C_B Z_s) \tag{9-6}$$

where $C_B = 0.159/(f_{co} Z_s)$ at a specific cutoff frequency.

The cutoff frequency for the source-bypass network of Figure 9-12 is found to be 2.4 Hz. This is very low. If desired, a bypass capacitor of lower

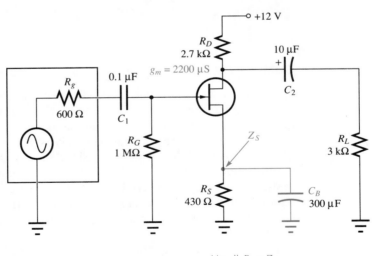

$$1/g_m \parallel R_S = Z_S$$

$$455 \ \Omega \parallel 430 \ \Omega = 221 \ \Omega = Z_S$$

$$f_{co} = \frac{0.159}{C_B Z_S} = \frac{0.159}{300 \ \mu F \cdot 221 \ \Omega} = 2.4 \ \text{Hz}$$

Figure 9-15   The source-bypass capacitor.

value can be used. For example, a 30-μF bypass capacitor would provide a cutoff frequency of 24 Hz. Study Example 9–8.

EXAMPLE 9–8

Determine the cutoff frequency created by the source bypass capacitor in Figure 9–16.

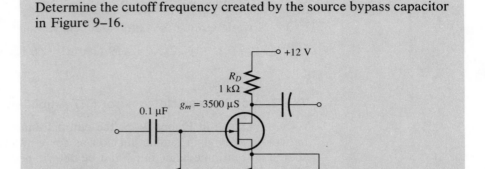

Figure 9–16

First determine Z_S.

$Z_S = 1/g_m \parallel R_S = (1/3{,}500\ \mu S) \parallel 220\ \Omega = 286\ \Omega \parallel 220\ \Omega = 124\ \Omega$

$f_{co} = 0.159/(C_B Z_S) = 0.159/(50\ \mu F \cdot 124\ \Omega) = 25.6\ Hz$

CUMULATIVE EFFECTS OF COUPLING AND BYPASS CAPACITORS

Figure 9–17 shows the cumulative effects of the coupling and bypass capacitors of the BJT amplifier in Figure 9–13. Slope A represents the cumulative effects of the input and output coupling networks. Both coupling networks have a cutoff frequency of approximately 14 Hz, making the combined slope of rolloff an ideal 40 dB/decade. Since the emitter-bypass network has a cutoff frequency of 11.8 Hz, the 14-Hz cutoff is dominant (begins attenuation first, as frequency is lowered from the passband down into the attenuation band). Below 11.8 Hz, the slope of rolloff is at the combined rate of an ideal 60 dB/decade. Slope B is the actual, though idealized, low-end rolloff for this amplifier.

The two cutoff frequencies are often referred to as **break frequencies,** since the rate of attenuation changes dramatically at these frequencies. The first break frequency is the dominant cutoff frequency. If the input cutoff frequency differed from the output cutoff frequency, there would be three break frequencies. For example, if the cutoff frequency for the input network was 20 Hz, and the cutoff frequency for the output network was 14 Hz, and the cutoff frequency for the emitter-bypass network was 8 Hz, there would be three distinct break frequencies (the 20-Hz cutoff being dominant).

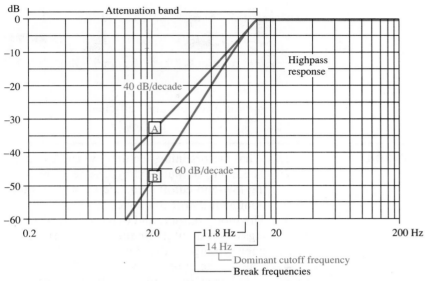

Figure 9–17 Cumulative effects of coupling and bypass capacitors.

PHASE RESPONSE

From your study of Section 9–1, you learned that highpass filter networks are also called voltage-lead networks, or just lead networks. This is because the output voltage leads the input voltage in phase angle and time. For frequencies in the passband, the phase shift is very little, since the X_C of the capacitor is very small compared to resistance(s). However, for frequencies in the attenuation band, the phase shift is great, greater than 45° (at f_{co}, $\angle \theta = 45° = \arctan(X_C/R)$, where $X_C = R$). This can cause phase distortion of the lower frequencies of a broad-banded signal. For example, if an audio frequency range of 80 Hz to 12 kHz (music) is applied to an amplifier that has a lower cutoff frequency of 100 Hz, all frequencies at and below 100 Hz will be severely phase shifted as compared to the original audio signal. This is a form of undesirable distortion. The solution is to make sure the low-end cutoff frequency of the amplifier is much lower than the actual lowest signal frequency. In this case, much lower than 80 Hz. Also, just as slope is cumulative, phase shift is cumulative for the coupling and bypass networks of an amplifier. This is even more reason to make the lower cutoff frequency as low as possible.

$$\angle \theta = \arctan(X_C/R) \qquad \text{(for each highpass network)} \qquad (9\text{–}7)$$

EXAMPLE 9–9

Determine the phase shift caused by the output coupling network of Figure 9–13 at a frequency of 10 Hz.

$$R = R_C + R_L = 2.7 \text{ k}\Omega + 3 \text{ k}\Omega = 5.7 \text{ k}\Omega$$

$$X_C = 0.159/fC = 0.159/(10 \text{ Hz} \cdot 2 \text{ } \mu\text{F}) = 7{,}950 \text{ } \Omega$$

$$\angle\theta = \arctan(X_C/R) = \arctan(7{,}950 \text{ } \Omega/5{,}700 \text{ } \Omega) = 54.4°$$

Time for a review and self-check.

Self-Check 9–2

1. What factors influence the low-end frequency response of an amplifier?
2. The input, output, and bypass networks of an amplifier have the following low-end cutoff frequencies: 45 Hz, 60 Hz, and 20 Hz. Which is the dominant cutoff frequency?
3. The input, output, and bypass networks of an amplifier have the following low-end cutoff frequencies: 30 Hz, 50 Hz, and 20 Hz. In what frequency range is the slope of rolloff 40 dB/decade?
4. Change the capacitor values of Figure 9–13 to the following values and calculate all low-end cutoff frequencies: $C_1 = 0.1 \text{ } \mu\text{F}$, $C_2 = 0.047 \text{ } \mu\text{F}$, $C_3 = 2 \text{ } \mu\text{F}$.
5. For Problem 4, calculate the phase shift caused by the input coupling network at a frequency of 500 Hz.

9–3 AMPLIFIER HIGH-FREQUENCY RESPONSE

INTRODUCTION TO HIGH-FREQUENCY RESPONSE

In this section, we discuss the factors that affect the high-frequency response of amplifiers. These factors are the reactances that become significant at some high frequency. For the most part, these are capacitive reactances internal to the active devices. These internal capacitances are continually decreasing in reactance as frequency increases. At some high frequency, these reactances become very low in value compared to circuit resistance. This effectively bypasses the signal to ground both at the input and output of the amplifier.

Figure 9–18 illustrates the upper cutoff frequency (Uf_{co}) that results from these internal reactances. The gain of the amplifier is overcome by their attenuating effects. As indicated in the figure, internal capacitances are not the only contributors to the attenuation band. Stray capacitance and lead inductance can also add to the attenuation if the frequency is high enough. Let's begin now with a discussion of a very important theorem that will help us understand the effects of internal capacitance on high-end frequency response.

MILLER'S THEOREM

Miller's Theorem is a very handy means by which the high-end frequency response of an amplifier can be analyzed. The theorem relates the gain of the amplifier to the effective input and output shunting capacitance of the ampli-

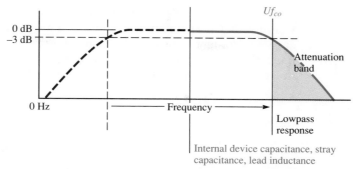

Figure 9–18 High-frequency attenuation caused by internal and stray reactances.

fier. It transforms internal feedback capacitance into equivalent input and output capacitance, as is illustrated in Figure 9–19.

All amplifiers have some internal feedback capacitance. This capacitance causes the output of the amplifier to be transferred back to the input in significant amounts above the upper cutoff frequency. In a CE BJT amplifier, the high-frequency collector signal is transferred back to the base. In a CS FET amplifier the high-frequency drain signal is transferred back to the gate. In each case, the output is 180° out of phase with the input signal, which causes the input signal to be partially canceled, or reduced in amplitude. Naturally, this reduces the effective gain of the amplifier, and, because the input signal is effectively loaded down, also makes the input impedance to the amplifier look much lower than it is for passband frequencies. In other words, it is as though a relatively large amount of capacitance appears from base to ground or gate to ground. At high frequencies the reactance of this shunting capacitance is very low and loads down the input network.

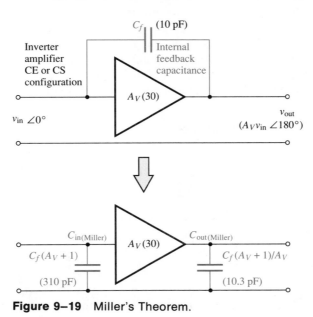

Figure 9–19 Miller's Theorem.

So, how can we determine the amount of shunting capacitance? That's where Miller's Theorem comes in. It simply states that internal feedback capacitance can be converted to equivalent input and output shunting capacitances for the purpose of circuit analysis. Though not difficult, the derivation of the theorem formulas is left to Appendix C, "Formula Derivations."

$$C_{\text{in(Miller)}} = C_f(A_V + 1) \tag{9-8}$$

$$C_{\text{out(Miller)}} = C_f(A_V + 1)/A_V \tag{9-9}$$

In the formulas above, C_f is the internal feedback capacitance of the amplifier. As you can see, this internal capacitance is seen greatly magnified in the input, and also appears across the output of the amplifier.

As demonstrated in Figure 9–15, the gain of the amplifier is a major factor in determining the effective input capacitance (Miller input capacitance). The higher the amplifier gain, the greater the Miller effect. In this case, the gain is 30 and the feedback capacitance is 10 pF. This results in an effective input shunting capacitance of 310 pF (10 pF · 31 = 310 pF). In the output, an effective shunting capacitance appears that is only slightly greater than the internal feedback capacitance.

BJT AND FET INTERELECTRODE CAPACITANCES

Now that you have a general idea of the effects of internal device capacitances, let's take a look at the BJT and FET in Figure 9–20. Here, we see these internal capacitances identified. Since they are capacitances that exist between the terminals of the devices (internally), they are often referred to as **interelectrode capacitances.**

BJT Interelectrode Capacitances

Notice the logical subscripting for these capacitances. Unfortunately, data sheets do not use the same subscripting. If you want to know the value of collector to base capacitance (C_{cb}) you look for the C_{obo} parameter on the data sheet. The subscripting obo indicates the manner in which the capacitance was obtained: $o$utput capacitance at the collector with the $b$ase grounded and emitter $o$pen. The base to emitter capacitance (C_{be}) is desig-

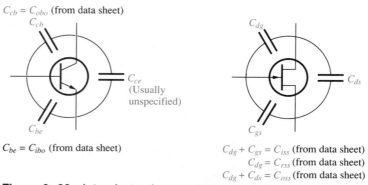

Figure 9–20   Interelectrode capacitance in BJTs and JFETs.

nated as C_{ibo} on the data sheet. The *ibo* subscript means: *i*nput capacitance at the emitter with the *b*ase grounded and the collector *o*pen. You knew that, right? The output capacitance (C_{ce}) is designated C_{oeo}. The *oeo* subscript means *o*utput capacitance at the collector with the *e*mitter grounded and the base *o*pen.

FET Interelectrode Capacitances

For the FET, data sheets specify lumped capacitances. C_{iss} is the combination of C_{dg} and C_{gs}, and C_{oss} is the combination of C_{dg} and C_{ds}. This is because the measurement is performed under short-circuit conditions. For C_{iss}, the input capacitance from gate to source is measured with the drain shorted to the source. This places C_{dg} and C_{gs} in parallel. For C_{oss}, the output capacitance from drain to source is measured with the gate shorted to the source. This places C_{dg} and C_{ds} in parallel. The reverse transfer capacitance (C_{rss}) is specified on the data sheet and is equal to C_{dg}.

The feedback capacitances that are applied to Miller's Theorem are C_{cb} (C_{obo}) and C_{dg} (C_{rss}). Now, let us see how the BJT and FET amplifiers are analyzed for high-frequency response using the information discussed thus far.

HIGH-FREQUENCY RESPONSE OF BJT AMPLIFIERS

The High-Frequency Input Network of the BJT Amplifier

Let's begin with the BJT amplifier circuit of Figure 9–21. Notice that C_{cb} (C_{obo}) is specified as 4 pF and C_{be} (C_{ibo}) is specified as 8 pF. To determine the upper cutoff frequency of the amplifier, we must know the total equivalent resistance of the input network and the total shunt capacitance. Then, these values can be applied to Formula 9–2 to determine the upper cutoff frequency (Uf_{co}).

Figure 9–21b shows the input network of the amplifier with all of the resistive and capacitive components. At the high end of the passband, all coupling and bypass capacitors act as shorts. The network is further reduced (Thevenized) to the circuit of Figure 9–21c. Note that R_g is considered in parallel with R_1, R_2, and $\beta r'_e$ to find the Thevenized value (R_{Th}) equal to 422 Ω.

Notice also that the total input capacitance is the sum of C_{be} and the Miller capacitance. The Miller capacitance at the input is found as follows: $C_{in(Miller)} = C_{cb} \cdot (A_V + 1)$, where $A_V = (R_C \parallel R_L)/r'_e = 3{,}701/25 = 123$. Therefore, $C_{in(Miller)} = 4 \text{ pF} \cdot (123 + 1) = 496 \text{ pF}$. The total capacitance shunting the base to ground is 8 pF + 496 pF = 504 pF.

Now we are able to determine the cutoff frequency by applying R_{Th} and $C_{in(total)}$ to Formula 9–2.

$$f_{co} = 0.159/(R_{Th}C_{in(total)}) = 0.159/(422 \text{ Ω} \cdot 504 \text{ pF}) = 747.6 \text{ kHz}$$

Notice two important facts. First, the upper cutoff frequency can be increased (raised) by reducing amplifier gain. If A_V is reduced, $C_{in(Miller)}$ will decrease. Second, the upper cutoff frequency can be increased by reducing

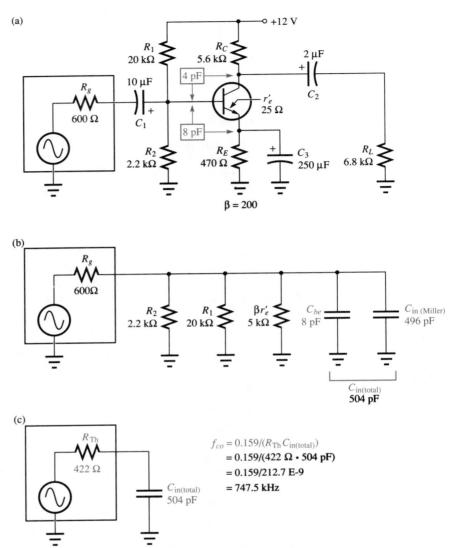

Figure 9–21 High-frequency response for a BJT common-emitter amplifier.

R_{Th} in Figure 9–17c. This can be reduced in a practical way by reducing the values of R_1, R_2, and/or R_g. Keep these important facts in mind.

The High-Frequency Output Network of the BJT Amplifier

What about the output network of the amplifier? Does it have any effect on the upper cutoff frequency? Though not shown in Figure 9–21, the output network at high frequencies consists of $R_C \parallel R_L$ shunted by the total output capacitance. So, what is the total output capacitance? The output capacitance is a combination of $C_{out(Miller)}$ and any stray capacitance (capacitance between wire leads and ground). The stray capacitance is hard to determine and can range from 0.2 to 2 or more pF. On the other hand, Formula 9–9 is used to determine $C_{out(Miller)}$.

$$C_{out(Miller)} = C_{cb}(A_V + 1)/A_V = 4 \text{ pF} \cdot (123 + 1)/123 = 4.03 \text{ pF}$$

Let's assume 1 pF of stray capacitance. The total output capacitance is then 5.03 pF. Since $R_C \| R_L = 5.6 \text{ k}\Omega \| 6.8 \text{ k}\Omega = 3{,}071 \text{ }\Omega$, the cutoff frequency for the output network is

$$f_{co} = 0.159/(3071 \text{ }\Omega \cdot 5.03 \text{ pF}) = 10.3 \text{ MHz}$$

Cumulative Effects of the Lowpass Networks

The high-end lowpass network at the input and the high-end lowpass network at the output do have some cumulative effect, the extent of which depends on the separation of the input and output cutoff frequencies. For the circuit of Figure 9–21, the input lowpass filter network is very dominant, with a low cutoff frequency of 747.5 kHz. While 747.5 kHz is the first break point, the output lowpass network provides a second break point of 10.3 MHz. Thus, between 747.5 kHz and 10.3 MHz the slope of rolloff is about 20 dB/decade. Above 10.3 MHz the slope of rolloff becomes 40 dB/decade because of the cumulative effect of the two networks. Obviously, if it is desired to increase the high-end frequency response, you must first improve the input network as discussed earlier. The dominant network must be improved first. Take time to carefully study Example 9–10.

EXAMPLE 9–10

Determine the high-end frequency response for Figure 9–22.

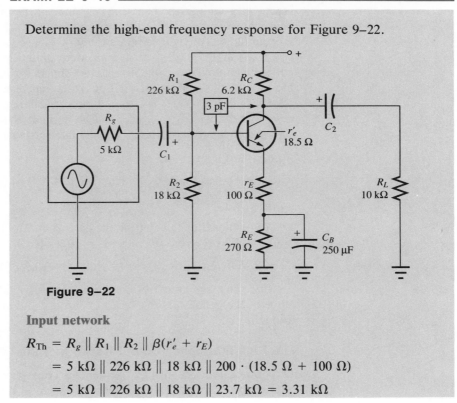

Figure 9–22

Input network

$$R_{Th} = R_g \| R_1 \| R_2 \| \beta(r'_e + r_E)$$
$$= 5 \text{ k}\Omega \| 226 \text{ k}\Omega \| 18 \text{ k}\Omega \| 200 \cdot (18.5 \text{ }\Omega + 100 \text{ }\Omega)$$
$$= 5 \text{ k}\Omega \| 226 \text{ k}\Omega \| 18 \text{ k}\Omega \| 23.7 \text{ k}\Omega = 3.31 \text{ k}\Omega$$

$$A_V = (R_C \parallel R_L)/(r_e' + r_E) = (6.2 \text{ k}\Omega \parallel 10 \text{ k}\Omega)/(18.5 \ \Omega + 100 \ \Omega)$$

$$= 3.83 \text{ k}\Omega/118.5 \ \Omega = 32.3$$

$$C_{\text{in(Miller)}} = C_{cb} \cdot (A_V + 1) = 3 \text{ pF} \cdot 33.3 = 100 \text{ pF}$$

$$f_{co} = 0.159/RC = 0.159/(R_{\text{Th}} C_{\text{in(total)}})$$

$$= 0.159/(3.31 \text{ k}\Omega \cdot 100 \text{ pF}) = 480 \text{ kHz} \quad \text{(dominant)}$$

Output network

$$R = R_C \parallel R_L = 6.2 \text{ k}\Omega \parallel 10 \text{ k}\Omega = 3.83 \text{ k}\Omega$$

$$C_{\text{out(Miller)}} = C_{cb}(A_V + 1)/A_V = 3 \text{ pF} \cdot 33.3/32.3 = 3.1 \text{ pF}$$

$$C_{\text{out(total)}} \cong 3.1 \text{ pF} + 1 \text{ pF stray capacitance} = 4.1 \text{ pF}$$

$$f_{co} = 0.159/RC = 0.159/(RC_{\text{out(total)}})$$

$$= 0.159/(3.83 \text{ k}\Omega \cdot 4.1 \text{ pF}) = 10.13 \text{ MHz}$$

HIGH-FREQUENCY RESPONSE OF FET AMPLIFIERS

High-Frequency Input Network of the FET Amplifier

Next, let's analyze the high-end response of the input and output of an FET amplifier. The analysis is very much the same, though simpler than for the BJT amplifier. We will use the circuit of Figure 9–23a. From the data sheet, C_{dg} (C_{rss}) and C_{gs} ($C_{iss} - C_{rss}$) are determined to be 1.5 pF and 3 pF. All coupling and bypass capacitors act as shorts for high-frequency analysis. In Figure 9–23b, the Thevenized input resistance is approximately 600 Ω, since 1 M$\Omega \parallel 600 \ \Omega \cong 600 \ \Omega$. The total input capacitance from gate to ground is the combination of C_{gs}, $C_{\text{in(Miller)}}$, and an estimated 1 pF of stray capacitance. The Miller input capacitance is calculated using Formula 9–8.

$$C_{\text{in(Miller)}} = C_{dg}(A_V + 1)$$

where $A_V = g_m(R_D \parallel R_L) = 2200 \ \mu\text{S} \cdot 1421 \ \Omega = 3.13$. Therefore,

$$C_{\text{in(Miller)}} = 1.5 \text{ pF} \cdot (3.13 + 1) = 6.2 \text{ pF}$$

The total capacitance shunting the gate to ground is $C_{\text{in(total)}} = C_{gs} + C_{\text{in(Miller)}} + C_{\text{stray}} = 3 \text{ pF} + 6.2 \text{ pF} + 1 \text{ pF} = 10.2 \text{ pF}$.

$$f_{co} = 0.159/(R_{\text{Th}} C_{\text{in(total)}}) = 0.159/(600 \ \Omega \cdot 10.2 \text{ pF}) = 26 \text{ MHz}$$

Notice that the cutoff frequency is very dependent on the internal resistance of the generator. $R_{\text{Th}} \cong R_g$. A larger value of R_g means a lower cutoff frequency.

The High-Frequency Output Network of the FET Amplifier

The output network at high frequencies consists of $R_D \parallel R_L$ shunted by the total output capacitance. So, what is the total output capacitance? As for

(a)

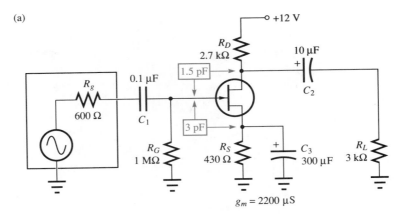

(b)

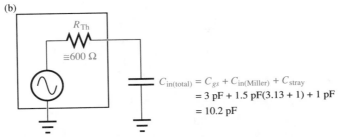

Figure 9–23 High-frequency response for an FET common-source amplifier.

BJT amplifiers, the output capacitance is a combination of $C_{out(Miller)}$ and any stray capacitance. Formula 9–9 is used to determine $C_{out(Miller)}$.

$$C_{out(Miller)} = C_{dg}(A_V + 1)/A_V = 1.5 \text{ pF} \cdot (3.13 + 1)/3.13 = 2 \text{ pF}$$

Assume 1 pF of stray capacitance. The total output capacitance is then 3 pF. Since $R_D \| R_L = 2.7 \text{ k}\Omega \| 3 \text{ k}\Omega = 1{,}421 \text{ }\Omega$, the cutoff frequency for the output network is

$$f_{co} = 0.159/(1{,}421 \text{ }\Omega \cdot 3 \text{ pF}) = 37.3 \text{ MHz}$$

Again we see the input network is the dominant lowpass network with a cutoff frequency of 28.8 MHz. The slope of rolloff is an ideal 20 dB/decade to 37.3 MHz, where it becomes 40 dB/decade due to cumulative effects. Notice that the dominant cutoff frequency for the FET amplifier is much higher than was obtained from the BJT amplifier. Because of their lower internal feedback capacitance and lower amplifier gain, FET amplifiers generally do have a higher upper cutoff frequency and consequently a wider passband than do BJT amplifiers. Now take time to study Example 9–11.

EXAMPLE 9–11

Determine the upper cutoff frequency for the input coupling network and the upper cutoff frequency for the output coupling network of Figure 9–24.

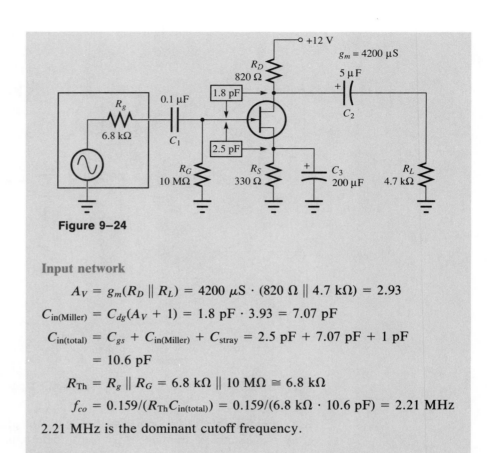

Figure 9–24

Input network

$$A_V = g_m(R_D \parallel R_L) = 4200 \ \mu S \cdot (820 \ \Omega \parallel 4.7 \ k\Omega) = 2.93$$

$$C_{in(Miller)} = C_{dg}(A_V + 1) = 1.8 \ pF \cdot 3.93 = 7.07 \ pF$$

$$C_{in(total)} = C_{gs} + C_{in(Miller)} + C_{stray} = 2.5 \ pF + 7.07 \ pF + 1 \ pF$$

$$= 10.6 \ pF$$

$$R_{Th} = R_g \parallel R_G = 6.8 \ k\Omega \parallel 10 \ M\Omega \cong 6.8 \ k\Omega$$

$$f_{co} = 0.159/(R_{Th}C_{in(total)}) = 0.159/(6.8 \ k\Omega \cdot 10.6 \ pF) = 2.21 \ MHz$$

2.21 MHz is the dominant cutoff frequency.

Output network

$$C_{out(Miller)} = C_{dg}(A_V + 1)/A_V = 1.8 \ pF \cdot 3.93/2.93 = 2.41 \ pF$$

$$C_{out(total)} = C_{out(Miller)} + C_{stray} = 2.41 \ pF + 1 \ pF = 3.41 \ pF$$

$$R = R_D \parallel R_L = 820 \ \Omega \parallel 4.7 \ k\Omega = 698 \ \Omega$$

$$f_{co} = 0.159/(RC_{out(total)}) = 0.159/(698 \ \Omega \cdot 3.41 \ pF)$$

$$= 66.8 \ MHz$$

THE CASCODE AMPLIFIER

The Input Network

Figure 9–25 shows a widely-used method of increasing the upper cutoff frequency of an amplifier. The circuit is a **cascode** FET amplifier. The lower FET (Q_1) is a common-source amplifier with a very low drain resistance. In this case, r_d for Q_1 is the input source impedance of Q_2, which is approximately $1/g_{m(Q2)}$. Since the transconductance for both FETs is the same, the

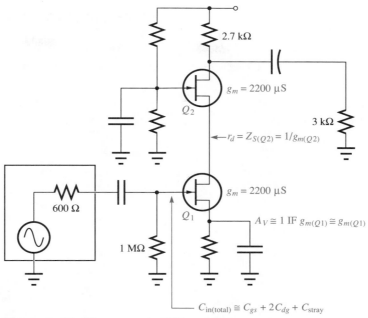

Figure 9–25   The cascode FET amplifier.

voltage gain of Q_1 is approximately unity ($A_V = g_{m(Q1)}r_d \cong g_{m(Q1)} \cdot 1/g_{m(Q2)} = g_{m(Q1)}/g_{m(Q2)} \cong 1$). Therefore, since the gain of Q_1 is unity, the Miller input capacitance at the gate of Q_1 must be $2C_{dg}$ ($C_{\text{in(Miller)}} \cong C_{dg}(A_V + 1) = C_{dg}(1 + 1) = 2C_{dg}$). Therefore, for cascode FET amplifier,

$$C_{\text{in(total)}} \cong C_{gs} + 2C_{dg} + C_{\text{stray}} \tag{9–10}$$

where $g_{m(Q1)} \cong g_{m(Q2)}$.

If Q_1 of Figure 9–25 has 1.5 pF of feedback capacitance (C_{dg}), C_{gs} is 3 pF, and C_{stray} is 1 pF, the total input capacitance shunting the gate of Q_1 to ground is 3 pF + 2(1.5 pF) + 1 pF = 7 pF. Notice that the cutoff frequency is

$$f_{co} = 0.159/(R_{\text{Th}} \cdot C_{\text{in(total)}}) = 0.159/(600 \ \Omega \cdot 7 \ \text{pF}) = 37.9 \ \text{MHz}.$$

This is much higher than the 26-MHz cutoff frequency of Figure 9–23. Thus, the cascode amplifier has improved the high-end frequency response.

The Output Network

The overall gain of the cascode amplifier is determined by Q_2 where $A_V = g_m(R_D \parallel R_L)$. The gain of Figure 9–25 is the same as the gain of Figure 9–23 ($A_V = 2200 \ \mu\text{S} \cdot 1,421 \ \Omega = 3.13$).

The output capacitance of the cascode amplifier is the same as for a single-FET amplifier. Thus, the output lowpass network is now the dominant network. The 37.3-MHz cutoff frequency of the output network is now the dominant frequency, since it is the first break point at the high end of the overall amplifier frequency response. Consider Example 9–12.

EXAMPLE 9–12

Determine the upper cutoff frequency for the input coupling network and the upper cutoff frequency for the output coupling network of Figure 9–26.

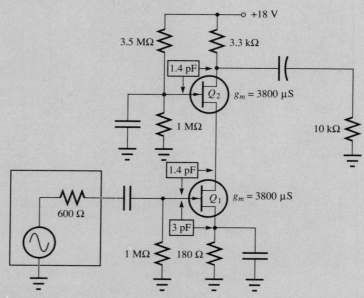

Figure 9–26

Input network

$$A_V = 1$$

$$C_{in(Miller)} = C_{dg}(A_V + 1) = 1.4 \text{ pF} \cdot 2 = 2.8 \text{ pF}$$

$$C_{in(total)} = C_{gs} + C_{in(Miller)} + C_{stray} = 3 \text{ pF} + 2.8 \text{ pF} + 1 \text{ pF} = 6.8 \text{ pF}$$

$$R_{Th} = R_g \parallel R_G = 600 \ \Omega \parallel 1 \text{ M}\Omega \cong 600 \ \Omega$$

$$f_{co} = 0.159/(R_{Th}C_{in(total)}) = 0.159/(600 \ \Omega \cdot 6.8 \text{ pF}) = 39 \text{ MHz}$$

Output network

$$A_V = g_m(R_D \parallel R_L) = 3,800 \ \mu\text{S} \cdot (3.3 \text{ k}\Omega \parallel 10 \text{ k}\Omega) = 9.4$$

$$C_{out(Miller)} = C_{dg}(A_V + 1)/A_V = 1.4 \text{ pF} \cdot 10.4/9.4 = 1.55 \text{ pF}$$

$$C_{out(total)} = C_{out(Miller)} + C_{stray} = 1.55 \text{ pF} + 1 \text{ pF} = 2.55 \text{ pF}$$

$$R = R_D \parallel R_L = 3.3 \text{ k}\Omega \parallel 10 \text{ k}\Omega = 2.48 \text{ k}\Omega$$

$$f_{co} = 0.159/(RC_{out(total)}) = 0.159/(2.48 \text{ k}\Omega \cdot 2.55 \text{ pF}) = 25.1 \text{ MHz}$$

25.1 MHz is dominant.

BJT Cascode Amplifiers

Bipolar transistors can also be cascoded for improved frequency response. We will not take the time to evaluate that here, but the principles are the same as for FET cascode amplifiers.

The Dual-Gate MOSFET Amplifier

Shown in Figure 9–27, the dual-gate MOSFET amplifier has a very, very low reverse transfer capacitance ($C_{rss} = C_{dg1}$). This internal feedback capacitance is usually less than 0.05 pF. For the 3N201, C_{rss} is less than 0.03 pF. Naturally, this makes the Miller input capacitance very low. Notice that g_m is also very high (12,800 μS). The g_m for dual-gate MOSFETs is typically much higher than individual JFETs. Consequently, the dual-gate MOSFET can provide a higher gain and higher frequency response than a single JFET. Is the dual-gate MOSFET amplifier a cascode amplifier? Yes.

STRAY CAPACITANCE AND LEAD INDUCTANCE

Stray Capacitance

Stray capacitance that exists between wire leads and ground can affect the high-end frequency response of the amplifier. However, the effect it has depends on the amount of stray capacitance compared to the other shunting capacitances such as $C_{in(Miller)}$, C_{be}, C_{gs}, and $C_{out(Miller)}$. If the shunting capacitances are low, the stray capacitance will have a significant effect. In general, stray capacitance has less effect on the high-end response of BJT amplifiers than FET amplifiers, since the upper cutoff frequency for BJT amplifiers is lower and the amount of shunting capacitance is higher than FET amplifiers. Also, the higher the upper cutoff frequency, the greater the effect stray capacitance has on frequency response. Again, generally speaking, stray capacitance has more effect above 30 MHz than below.

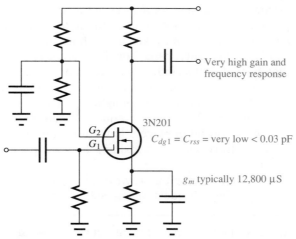

Figure 9–27 The dual-gate MOSFET has high gain and high frequency response.

Lead Inductance

The leads of transistors and other components have inductance. Even a straight piece of wire has some inductance. Fortunately, it is very small (in the picohenries). The effects of lead inductance, sometimes called stray inductance, are almost nil at frequencies below about 30 MHz. Above 30 MHz, lead inductance begins to develop an X_L in series with the AC signal path. This series inductive reactance works with the shunting capacitances to further attenuate very high frequencies. However, in the frequency range where lead inductance can have an effect, the amplifiers are usually tuned with resonant circuits that include lead inductance and stray capacitance in a controlled manner through careful design and layout.

PROBLEMS IN DESIGN AND ANALYSIS

Many engineers have said, "Designing a circuit on paper and actually building it are two different things!" What do they mean by that? They simply mean there are too many variables to include in the design in a controlled manner. Data sheets provide information on electronic devices but this information is usually very broad. The circuit must be built and tested before actual results can be known. For example, the frequency response calculations we have just discussed are correct in theory but the actual frequency response depends on actual values of internal capacitance and amplifier gain under actual operating conditions. These cannot be predicted with accuracy. The data sheet specifies reverse transfer capacitance and other capacitances to be within a certain range under specific test conditions. This does not tell you exactly what these values are for the device you are going to use and for the circuit in which it is placed. You must take an educated guess, build the circuit, and test it to see if it is close to what is needed or desired. You are always working in the ballpark but not necessarily on the base you want.

Also, the analysis we have just discussed is somewhat idealized. We assume that capacitors always act as capacitors. We assume that the coupling and bypass capacitors continue to decrease in reactance as frequency increases or that they act as a short in and above the passband of the amplifier. In reality, capacitors have a self-resonant frequency beyond which they begin to act as inductors. For example, an aluminum electrolytic capacitor may act as a capacitor only up to about 500 kHz. Often, tantalum capacitors are used as coupling and bypass capacitors because they have a much higher self-resonant frequency than do aluminum electrolytics. Also, designers will often place a low-value capacitor (10 to 1,000 pF) in parallel with electrolytics and tantalums to swamp out any inductance at higher frequencies.

Take time to carefully review this section. Then, test your understanding by answering the questions of Self-Check 9–3.

Self-Check 9–3

1. List the reactances that affect the high-end frequency response of amplifiers.
2. How does Miller's Theorem help us analyze the high-end frequency response of amplifiers?

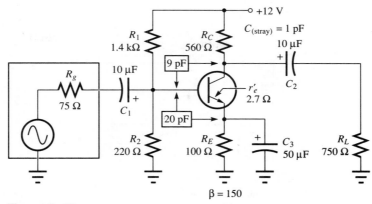

Figure 9–28

3. Determine the dominant lower cutoff frequency and dominant upper cutoff frequency for the amplifier of Figure 9–28.
4. Briefly explain how a cascode amplifier can have an upper cutoff frequency higher than that of a single-transistor amplifier.
5. What are some of the problems that we face in designing, building, and analyzing amplifiers?

9–4 TOTAL AMPLIFIER FREQUENCY RESPONSE

TOTAL BANDWIDTH (*BW*)

The DC Amplifier

Let us summarize what we have discussed thus far with another look at the overall frequency response of an amplifier and an amplifier system. Figure 9–29 illustrates the overall frequency response of a DC amplifier (a) and an AC amplifier (b). Since the DC amplifier is direct-coupled and uses no by-pass capacitors, the low-end response is flat all the way down to 0 Hz (DC). The high-end response is still affected by input and output shunting capacitances such as internal device capacitances, Miller capacitances, and even stray capacitances. Notice the cumulative effects of the input and output capacitances in the attenuation band. The overall bandwidth, in other words the width of the passband, is equal to the dominant cutoff frequency

$(BW = f_{co(\text{dominant})})$.

The AC Amplifier

Figure 9–29b demonstrates the overall frequency response of an AC amplifier. The AC amplifier uses coupling and bypass capacitors which create a highpass filter response on the low-end of the passband. Notice once again the cumulative effects of the highpass networks. The bandwidth in this case is the difference between the dominant upper cutoff frequency and the dominant lower cutoff frequency.

$$BW = Uf_{co(\text{dominant})} - Lf_{co(\text{dominant})} \qquad (9\text{–}11)$$

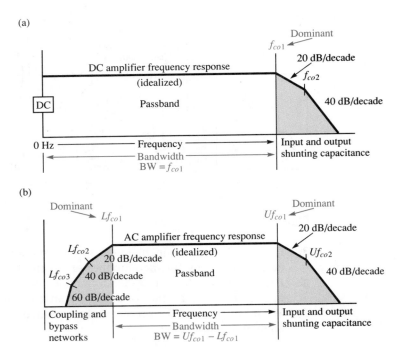

(a)

Figure 9–29 Amplifier bandwidth.

The Amplifier System

What happens to the overall bandwidth when amplifier stages are cascaded together to form an amplifier system? As you know, the overall amplification factor is the product of individual stage factors ($A_{V1} \cdot A_{V2} \cdot A_{V3} \cdots = A_{V(total)}$). Also, recall that decibel gains add. If the gain of stage 1 is 20 dB and the gain of stage 2 is 30 dB, the overall gain is 50 dB. So, what about the overall bandwidth? Is the overall bandwidth greater than the bandwidth of an individual stage? No. In fact, the overall bandwidth of cascaded stages is less than the bandwidth of any single stage. This is because of the cumulative effect of the highpass and lowpass networks from stage to stage. The input capacitance of the second stage becomes part of the output capacitance of the first stage, and so on. The overall result is a reduction in bandwidth. If two stages are identical and have the same dominant upper cutoff frequency, that cutoff frequency will be at −3 dB for each amplifier. The cumulative effect is that the cutoff frequency of the individual stages is down a total of 6 dB after the second stage. This means there must be a new, lower, cutoff frequency at −3 dB for both stages. Thus, the overall bandwidth is narrowed.

GAIN-BANDWIDTH PRODUCT (GBP)

Data sheets for BJTs and FETs specify a maximum upper frequency limit for the device, symbolized as f_T. This upper frequency limit is the frequency at which the amplifier will most likely have a gain of unity (1). It takes into account the typical internal capacitances of the device but ignores stray capacitances. In any case, this parameter is useful because it allows you to

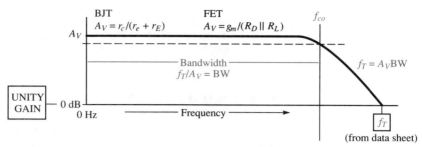

Figure 9–30   The gain-bandwidth product (GBP).

estimate the bandwidth of your amplifier from the gain of the amplifier. Here's how.

As shown in Figure 9–30, the upper frequency limit (f_T) is referred to as the gain-bandwidth product (GBP). This means the gain of the amplifier times the bandwidth of the amplifier should equal f_T.

$$f_T = A_V BW \tag{9–12}$$

From this we see that

$$BW = f_T/A_V \tag{9–13}$$

Once you calculate the gain of your amplifier and read the value of f_T from the data sheet of the device you are using, you can use Formula 9–13 to calculate the approximate bandwidth. This gives you a ballpark idea of the upper limit of your amplifier. The low-end response is still determined by coupling and bypass capacitors (highpass networks). See Example 9–13.

EXAMPLE 9–13 ▮

The data sheet for a transistor indicates its f_T is 450 MHz. If a common-emitter amplifier is made with this transistor and the amplifier's A_V is 18, what is its approximate bandwidth?

$$BW = f_T/A_V = 450 \text{ MHz}/18 = 25 \text{ MHz}$$

Time to check out.

Self-Check 9–4

1. The dominant upper cutoff frequency of a DC amplifier is 1.4 MHz. What is the amplifier's bandwidth?
2. The dominant lower cutoff frequency of an amplifier is 300 Hz and the dominant upper cutoff frequency is 860 kHz. What is the bandwidth of the amplifier?
3. The dominant lower cutoff frequency of an amplifier is 140 kHz and the dominant upper cutoff frequency is 2.1 MHz. What is the bandwidth of the amplifier?

4. A 2N3904 is used in a CE amplifier that has an $A_V = 26$. The data sheet for the transistor specifies f_T to be 300 MHz. What is the approximate upper cutoff frequency for the amplifier?

9–5 AMPLIFIER TESTING

AMPLIFIER TESTING USING SINE WAVES

In this section, we will discuss the use of test equipment in determining the overall frequency response of an amplifier. The main objective is to determine the actual upper and lower cutoff frequencies through experimentation. The first method we will consider is using a sine wave signal source.

The Test Setup

Figure 9–31 illustrates the test setup. A variable-frequency generator (signal generator or function generator) is connected to the input of the amplifier. Ideally, the output impedance should match that of the normal, or usual, signal source for the amplifier. A resistor can be placed in series with the signal generator or in parallel to obtain the proper source impedance. This simulates the operational input network, so the highpass and lowpass cutoff frequencies of the input network are close to actual.

The amplifier must be loaded with a resistance that is the same as the amplifier's normal load resistance. This ensures that the output network responds to a broad range of frequencies as it would under normal operating conditions. The oscilloscope test probe must be of the low-capacitance type (10 : 1 probe). Otherwise, the test probe and cable will contribute an additional 100 to 150 pF of shunting capacitance to the output network. In many cases, this will greatly reduce the high-end frequency response of the amplifier. A low-capacitance probe contributes only 10 to 20 pF to the circuit. Thus, there is very little reduction in the upper cutoff frequency.

Test Procedure

To begin the test, power up the test equipment and amplifier circuit. Make sure the amplitude control on the signal generator is preset to minimum so the amplifier is not overdriven when power is applied. Preset the frequency of the signal generator to a mid-band frequency. Slowly increase the amplitude control on the generator until a large undistorted signal is present in the output. If the amplifier is a power amplifier, keep the drive level low to keep the power dissipation low. Adjust the volts/division control on the oscilloscope and the amplitude control on the generator to display an output signal that is 6 or 8 divisions high, as shown in Figure 9–31b. Rock the frequency adjust knob on the generator back and forth to make sure you are in the passband of the amplifier where the output signal is maximum.

Now you are ready to determine the lower cutoff frequency (Lf_{co}). Observe the output on the oscilloscope as you reduce the frequency of the generator while checking that the voltage output from the generator stays constant. When the output amplitude drops to 0.707 of maximum, the lower

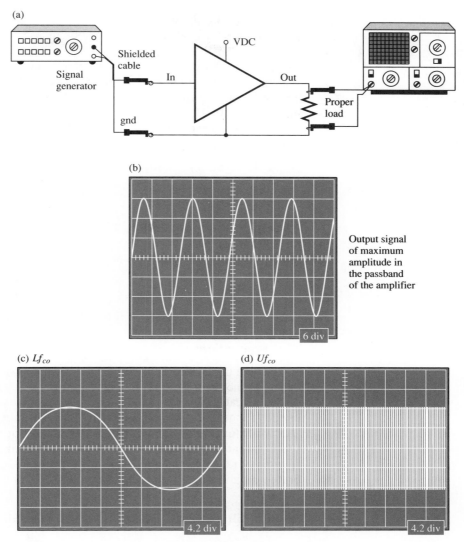

Figure 9–31 Using the signal generator and the oscilloscope to measure amplifier frequency response.

cutoff frequency has been found. In Figure 9–31c, the amplitude of the displayed signal is $0.707 \cdot 6$ div $= 4.2$ div. Now you can measure the time for one complete cycle and divide that into one (1) to determine the frequency ($f = 1/T$). Don't expect extreme accuracy. However, your determination for the lower cutoff frequency will be close enough for all practical needs. Accuracy can be increased by paralleling a frequency counter with the oscilloscope input, or the signal-generator output. Use a BNC T-connector and BNC jumper cable to the frequency counter.

The upper cutoff frequency (Uf_{co}) is determined in a similar manner. Set the frequency of the generator back at midband. Make sure the displayed signal once again covers 6 or 8 vertical divisions. Now, increase the frequency of the signal generator until the amplitude once again drops to 0.707

of maximum, as shown in Figure 9–31d. Reduce the time/division control until the time for one cycle can easily be measured. Calculate frequency as before, $f = 1/T$.

The slope of rolloff can also be determined if desired. This is done by comparing the amplitude of two decade frequencies (i.e., 100 Hz down to 10 Hz, and 300 kHz up to 3 MHz). Say the upper cutoff frequency of your amplifier is 240 kHz and you want to determine the slope of rolloff in the first decade. Record the amplitude at 240 kHz, then set the generator frequency to 2.4 MHz and record its amplitude. The slope is calculated as follows:

$$\text{Slope(dB/decade)} = 20 \log(V_{Ufco}/V_{10Ufco}) \tag{9–14}$$

$$\text{Slope(dB/decade)} = 20 \log(V_{Lfco}/V_{0.1Lfco}) \tag{9–15}$$

EXAMPLE 9–14

If the amplitude at 240 kHz is 4.2 $V_{\text{P-P}}$ and the amplitude at 2.4 MHz is 0.45 $V_{\text{P-P}}$, calculate the slope of rolloff in dB/decade.

$$\text{Slope} = 20 \log(4.2\ V_{\text{P-P}}/0.45\ V_{\text{P-P}}) = 19.4 \text{ dB/decade}$$

Test Precautions

Before you begin your amplifier frequency response test, make sure you test the frequency response of the signal generator itself. The output amplitude of the signal generator should not vary significantly over the needed frequency range. Also, you may have to change frequency ranges on the generator while testing for the upper cutoff frequency or slope of rolloff. Check to see if the amplitude of the generator signal jumps in amplitude from one frequency range to the next. If it does, the signal generator should be calibrated on all ranges so test measurements are not affected.

AMPLIFIER TESTING USING SQUARE WAVES

Using the Square Wave to Determine the Uf_{co}

As shown in Figure 9–32a, a pulsating DC square wave (CH-A) can be applied to an amplifier to determine its high-frequency response. The frequency of the square wave should be in the upper end of the passband of the amplifier so a very distinct rise and fall time is displayed (CH-B). This rising and falling transient response is caused by the charging and discharging shunt capacities at the input and output of the amplifier. Notice in Figure 9–32a, the rise time of the output pulse can easily be measured. Rise and fall times are always measured between the 10% and 90% amplitude points as shown. The time/division control can be further reduced to stretch the rise time over more of the screen to obtain a more accurate rise-time reading. Once the rise time (t_r) is measured, it is placed in the following formula to determine the upper cutoff frequency. (For a derivation of this formula see Appendix C, "Formula Derivations.")

$$Uf_{co} = 0.35/t_r \tag{9–16}$$

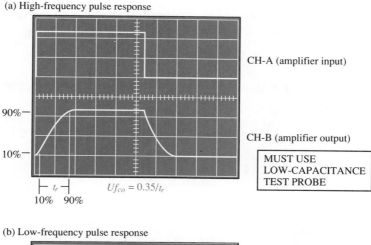

(a) High-frequency pulse response

CH-A (amplifier input)

CH-B (amplifier output)

MUST USE
LOW-CAPACITANCE
TEST PROBE

90%

10%

t_r

$10\%\quad 90\%$

$Uf_{co} = 0.35/t_r$

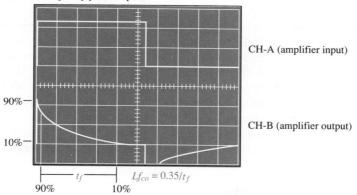

(b) Low-frequency pulse response

CH-A (amplifier input)

CH-B (amplifier output)

90%

10%

t_f

$90\%\quad 10\%$

$Lf_{co} = 0.35/t_f$

Figure 9–32 Using a square wave to determine the upper and lower cutoff frequencies.

EXAMPLE 9–15

In Figure 9–32a, we will assume that the time/division control is set on 2 μs/div. Determine the rise time and the upper cutoff frequency.

$t_r = 1.4$ div $\cdot$ 2 μs/div $= 2.8$ μs

$U_{fco} = 0.35/2.8$ μs $= 125$ kHz

Using the Square Wave to Determine the Lf_{co}

As shown in Figure 9–32b, a pulsating DC square wave (CH-A) can be applied to an amplifier to determine its low-frequency response. The frequency of the square wave should be low enough to allow the coupling and bypass capacitors to fully charge and discharge (CH-B). The resulting differentiated transient waveform is caused by charging and discharging coupling and bypass capacitors. Notice, in Figure 9–32b (CH-B), that the fall time of the output pulse can easily be measured. Rise and fall times are always measured between the 10% and 90% amplitude points as shown. Once the fall time (t_f) is measured, it is placed in the following formula to determine the lower cutoff frequency.

$$Lf_{co} = 0.35/t_f \tag{9–17}$$

EXAMPLE 9–16 ▮

If the time/division control is set to 1 ms/div, determine the fall time and lower cutoff frequency from Figure 9–32b.

$t_f = 3.8 \text{ div} \cdot 1 \text{ ms/div} = 3.8 \text{ ms}$

$Lf_{co} = 0.35/3.8 \text{ ms} = 92 \text{ Hz}$

Time for a self-check.

Self-Check 9–5

1. If the frequency response of an amplifier is from 30 Hz to 3 MHz and the amplitude of a 5-kHz test signal at the amplifier's output is 5.5 $V_{\text{P-P}}$, what is the output amplitude of a 30-Hz or 3-MHz test signal?
2. Why should a low-capacitance 10 : 1 test probe be used when measuring the high-frequency response of an amplifier?
3. If a pulsating DC square wave is used to determine the upper cutoff frequency of an amplifier and the rise time of the output signal is measured to be 3.4 μs, what is the cutoff frequency?

SUMMARY

FORMULAS

(9–1) $f_{co} = R/(2\pi L) = 0.159\, R/L$ (for RL highpass or lowpass filters)

(9–2) $f_{co} = 1/(2\pi CR_L) = 0.159/CR_L$ (for RC highpass or lowpass filters)

(9–3) $Z_e = R_E \parallel [r_E + r_e + ((R_g \parallel R_1 \parallel R_2)/\beta)]$ (emitter impedance for CE amplifiers)

(9–4) $f_{co} = 0.159/(C_B Z_e)$

(9–5) $Z_S = 1/g_m \parallel R_S$ (source impedance for CS amplifiers

(9–6) $f_{co} = 0.159/(C_B Z_S)$

(9–7) $\angle\theta = \arctan(X_C/R)$ (for highpass RC filters)

(9–8) $C_{\text{in(Miller)}} = C_f(A_V + 1)$ (for inverting amplifiers)

(9–9) $C_{\text{out(Miller)}} = C_f(A_V + 1)/A_V$ (for inverting amplifiers)

(9–10) $C_{\text{in(total)}} \cong C_{gs} + 2C_{dg} + C_{\text{stray}}$ (for cascode FET amplifiers where $g_{m(Q1)} \cong g_{m(Q2)}$)

For All Amplifiers

(9–11) $BW = Uf_{co(\text{dominant})} - Lf_{co(\text{dominant})}$

(9–12) $f_T = A_V BW$

(9–13) $BW = f_T/A_V$

(9–14)   Slope (dB/decade) = $20 \log(V_{Ufco}/V_{10Ufco})$

(9–15)   Slope (dB/decade) = $20 \log(V_{Lfco}/V_{0.1Lfco})$

(9–16) $Uf_{co} = 0.35/t_r$

(9–17) $Lf_{co} = 0.35/t_f$

CONCEPTS

■ Coupling capacitors and bypass capacitors form highpass filter networks with circuit resistances. This causes low-frequency attenuation, or reduction in gain for all frequencies below the dominant lower cutoff frequency.

■ All highpass networks are voltage-lead networks, where output voltage leads the input voltage in phase and time.

■ Internal device capacitances, stray capacitances, and lead inductances form lowpass filter networks with circuit resistances. This causes high-frequency attenuation, or reduction in gain for all frequencies above the dominant upper cutoff frequency.

■ All lowpass networks are voltage-lag networks, where output voltage lags the input voltage in phase and time.

■ Each stage of a cascaded amplifier system contributes to the reduction of the overall bandwidth of the amplifier.

■ Amplifier gain times amplifier bandwidth equals a frequency known as the gain-bandwidth product frequency (f_T).

■ Bandwidth and cutoff frequency calculations are only precise if all specified data is exact and all variables are known.

■ A low-capacitance, 10 : 1 probe must be used for all high-frequency measurements to prevent probe and cable capacitance from adding to output capacitance, greatly reducing the upper cutoff frequency.

■ The relative amplitude of upper and lower cutoff frequencies compared to maximum-amplitude mid-band frequencies is 0.707 or 70.7%.

PROCEDURES

Using the Signal Generator and Oscilloscope to Test Amplifier Frequency Response

1. Provide proper loading at the input and output of the amplifier in order to duplicate actual operating conditions.

2. Use a low-capacitance, 10 : 1 probe for the oscilloscope.

3. Apply a passband test frequency (sine wave) to the amplifier input at a level that drives the amplifier to a moderate output level.

4. Adjust the generator amplitude control and oscilloscope volts/division control for a display that covers 6 or 8 vertical divisions.

5. Reduce the generator frequency until the amplitude of the displayed signal drops by about 30%. This means 4.24 vertical divisions if you started with 6 divisions, and 5.66 divisions if you started with 8. $V_{fco} = 0.707 \cdot V_{\text{mid-band(max)}}$.

6. Measure the time for one cycle (period) and calculate the frequency ($f = 1/T$).

7. In a similar manner, increase the generator frequency to find the upper cutoff frequency.

8. The overall bandwidth is the difference between the upper and lower cutoff frequencies.

NEED-TO-KNOW SOLUTION

Output network

$$r_d = R_{Th} = R_D \parallel R_L = 4.3 \text{ k}\Omega \parallel 10 \text{ k}\Omega = 3 \text{ k}\Omega$$

$$A_V = g_m r_d = 3{,}000 \ \mu\text{S} \cdot 3 \text{ k}\Omega = 9$$

$$C_{out(Miller)} = C_{dg}(A_V + 1)/A_V = 2 \text{ pF} (9 + 1)/9 = 2.22 \text{ pF}$$

$$C_{out(total)} = C_{out(Miller)} + C_{stray} = 2.22 \text{ pF} + 3 \text{ pF} = 5.22 \text{ pF}$$

$$f_{co} = 0.159/(R_{Th} C_{out(total)}) = 0.159/(3 \text{ k}\Omega \cdot 5.22 \text{ pF}) = 10.2 \text{ MHz}$$

Input network

$$R_{Th} \cong 600 \ \Omega$$

$$C_{in(Miller)} = C_{dg}(A_V + 1) = 2 \text{ pF} (9 + 1) = 20 \text{ pF}$$

$$C_{in(total)} = C_{in(Miller)} + C_{stray} + C_{gs} = 20 \text{ pF} + 2 \text{ pF} + 4 \text{ pF} = 26 \text{ pF}$$

$$f_{co} = 0.159/(R_{Th} C_{in(total)}) = 0.159/(600 \ \Omega \cdot 26 \text{ pF}) = 10.2 \text{ MHz}$$

Neither the input nor the output lowpass network is dominant. However, when a test probe is connected across the load resistor, the output network will become dominant because of the severe capacitive loading caused by the probe/cable. Thus, the dominant lower cutoff frequency will be well below 10.2 MHz, due to the addition of the probe/cable capacitance. If the probe contributes an additional 10 pF of capacitance to the output network, the dominant upper cutoff frequency of the amplifier will appear to be about 3.5 MHz.

$$f_{co} = 0.159/(R_{Th}(C_{out(total)}) + C_{probe}) = 0.159/(3 \text{ k}\Omega \cdot 15.22 \text{ pF})$$

$$= 3.48 \text{ MHz}$$

QUESTIONS

9–1 FREQUENCY RESPONSE

1. In reference to frequency response, what are attenuation bands?
2. For highpass filters, all frequencies above the cutoff frequency are attenuated. True or false?
3. What is a Bode plot?
4. What are two units of measurement for slope of rolloff?

5. Describe cutoff frequency in terms of decibels, voltage amplitude, and power.
6. For an RC highpass or lowpass filter, what is the relationship between X_C and R at the cutoff frequency?
7. What is the output vs input voltage phase relationship for an RC or RL, highpass or lowpass, filter at the cutoff frequency?
8. What is the ideal slope of rolloff for an RCL highpass or lowpass filter?
9. Which filter type is a voltage-lag network, the highpass filter or the lowpass filter?

9–2 AMPLIFIER LOW-FREQUENCY RESPONSE

10. Which reactances of an amplifier circuit affect the low-end frequency response?
11. What is the ideal slope of rolloff for the input coupling network of an amplifier?
12. What is a dominant cutoff frequency?
13. Does the emitter, or source, bypass capacitor form (a) a highpass filter or (b) a lowpass filter?
14. Use the term "break frequency" to describe the cumulative effects of coupling and bypass networks.
15. Describe the undesirable condition that results if the lower cutoff frequency of an audio amplifier is higher than the lowest audio frequencies that must be amplified. (Hint: It has something to do with phase response.)

9–3 AMPLIFIER HIGH-FREQUENCY RESPONSE

16. Describe the reactances that affect the high-end frequency response of an amplifier.
17. What is the purpose of, or use for, Miller's Theorem?
18. Is the amount of Miller capacitance greatest (a) at the input of the amplifier or (b) at the output of the amplifier? Why?
19. What information do you need from the data sheet of a BJT to determine high-end frequency response by using Miller's Theorem?
20. For a BJT amplifier, which is the dominant lowpass network?
21. Which type amplifier generally has the highest upper cutoff frequency? (a) BJT   (b) FET
22. Why is the input capacitance of a cascode FET amplifier so low compared to single-FET amplifiers?
23. What are two advantages to using a dual-gate FET as an amplifier?
24. What effect does stray capacitance have on high-end frequency response?
25. What effect does lead inductance have on high-end frequency response?
26. What are some practical problems we face when using data sheet information to design an amplifier for a specific frequency response?

9–4 TOTAL AMPLIFIER FREQUENCY RESPONSE

27. How many dominant cutoff frequencies does a DC amplifier have?
28. What information must you have in order to determine the bandwidth of an AC amplifier?
29. What is the difference between a DC and an AC amplifier?
30. How do many cascaded stages in an amplifier system affect the overall bandwidth?
31. Explain gain-bandwidth product.
32. Explain how amplifier gain and amplifier bandwidth are related.

9–5 AMPLIFIER TESTING

33. When checking the frequency response of an amplifier, why must the input and output be loaded as they are in normal operation?
34. Why should you use a low-capacitance probe when testing the high-frequency response of an amplifier?
35. Briefly explain how you would use a sine-wave generator and an oscilloscope to determine the lower cutoff frequency of an amplifier.
36. When using a square wave to test the high-frequency response of an amplifier, should the frequency of the square wave be (a) in the upper end of the passband or (b) in the low-end attenuation band?
37. When you use a square wave to test the frequency response of an amplifier, why does the square wave become curved on the rising and falling edges or the upper and lower crowns?

PROBLEMS

9–1 FREQUENCY RESPONSE

1. A 4.7-kΩ resistor and 10-mH inductor form a highpass filter. What is its cutoff frequency?
2. A 330-kΩ resistor and a 500-μH inductor form a highpass filter. What is its cutoff frequency?
3. A 10-kΩ resistor and a 0.22-μF capacitor form a highpass filter.
4. A 56-kΩ resistor and a 0.047-μF capacitor form a highpass filter. What is its cutoff frequency?
5. A 22-kΩ resistor and a 40-mH inductor form a lowpass filter. What is its cutoff frequency?
6. A 150-Ω resistor and a 100-mH inductor form a lowpass filter. What is its cutoff frequency?
7. A 560-Ω resistor and a 0.022-μF capacitor form a lowpass filter. What is its cutoff frequency?
8. An 18-kΩ resistor and a 0.03-μF capacitor form a lowpass filter. What is its cutoff frequency?

9–2 AMPLIFIER LOW-FREQUENCY RESPONSE

9. Determine the cutoff frequency for the highpass input network of Figure 9–33.

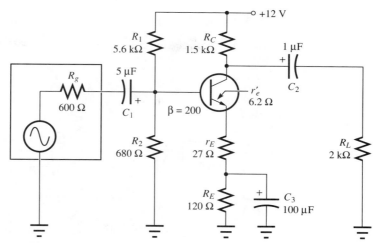

Figure 9–33

10. Determine the cutoff frequency for the highpass output network of Figure 9–33.
11. Determine the cutoff frequency for the highpass emitter-bypass network of Figure 9–33.
12. Which of the highpass cutoff frequencies for Figure 9–33 is dominant?
13. Determine the cutoff frequency for the highpass input network of Figure 9–34.

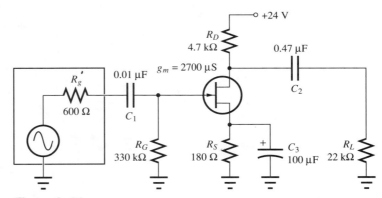

Figure 9–34

14. Determine the cutoff frequency for the highpass output network of Figure 9–34.
15. Determine the cutoff frequency for the highpass source-bypass network of Figure 9–34.
16. Which of the highpass cutoff frequencies for Figure 9–34 is dominant?
17. Calculate the phase shift of the highpass input network of Figure 9–34 at a frequency one octave below the cutoff frequency (one octave below $f_{co} = f_{co}/2$).

9–3 AMPLIFIER HIGH-FREQUENCY RESPONSE

18. Determine the cutoff frequency for the lowpass input network of Figure 9–35.

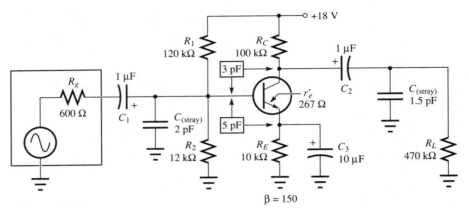

Figure 9–35

19. Determine the cutoff frequency for the lowpass output network of Figure 9–35.
20. Which of the lowpass cutoff frequencies for Figure 9–35 is dominant?
21. Determine the cutoff frequency for the lowpass input network of Figure 9–36.

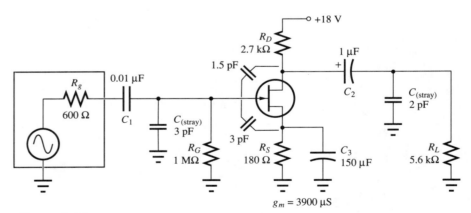

Figure 9–36

22. Determine the cutoff frequency for the lowpass output network of Figure 9–36.
23. Which of the lowpass cutoff frequencies for Figure 9–36 is dominant?
24. Calculate the phase shift of the lowpass input network of Figure 9–36 at a frequency one octave above the cutoff frequency (one octave above $f_{co} = 2f_{co}$).
25. Calculate the upper cutoff frequency of the lowpass input network for Figure 9–37.

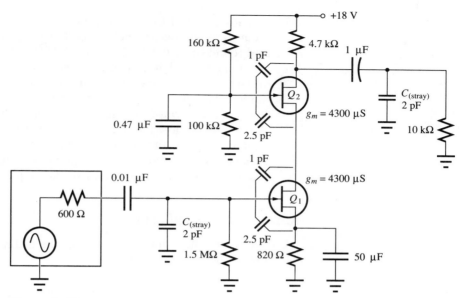

Figure 9–37

26. Calculate the upper cutoff frequency of the lowpass output network for Figure 9–37.
27. Which of the two upper cutoff frequencies for Figure 9–37 is dominant?

9–4 TOTAL AMPLIFIER FREQUENCY RESPONSE

28. The upper cutoff frequency of a DC amplifier is 4.25 MHz. How wide is its bandwidth?
29. The dominant lower cutoff frequency of an amplifier is 500 Hz and the dominant upper cutoff frequency is 50 kHz. How wide is its bandwidth?
30. The data sheet for an FET specifies $f_T = 450$ MHz. What is the approximate bandwidth of a single-stage amplifier using that FET if the gain of the amplifier is 20 dB?
31. The data sheet for a BJT specifies $f_T = 100$ MHz. What is the approximate bandwidth of a single-stage amplifier using that BJT if the gain of the amplifier is 50?

9–5 AMPLIFIER TESTING

32. A sine wave displayed on an oscilloscope covers 4.4 horizontal divisions. The time/div control is set at 10 μs/div. What is the frequency of the displayed signal?
33. A sine wave displayed on an oscilloscope covers 6.8 horizontal divisions. The time/div control is set at 0.5 ms/div. What is the frequency of the displayed signal?
34. The upper cutoff frequency at the output of an amplifier is 3.2 V_{P-P}. A frequency one decade above the upper cutoff frequency is measured and found to be 0.05 V_{P-P}. Calculate the slope of rolloff.

35. The lower cutoff frequency at the output of an amplifier is 2.6 $V_{P\text{-}P}$. A frequency one decade below the lower cutoff frequency is measured and found to be 0.033 $V_{P\text{-}P}$. Calculate the slope of rolloff.

36. An amplifier's high-frequency response is tested using a pulsating DC square wave. At the output of the amplifier the pulse rise time is measured between the 10% and 90% points and found to be 1.3 μs. Calculate the upper cutoff frequency of the amplifier.

37. An amplifier's low-frequency response is tested using a pulsating DC square wave. At the output of the amplifier the pulse fall time is measured between the 90% and 10% points and found to be 0.23 ms. Calculate the lower cutoff frequency of the amplifier.

ADDITIONAL PROBLEMS

38. Determine the cutoff frequency for the highpass input network of Figure 9–38.

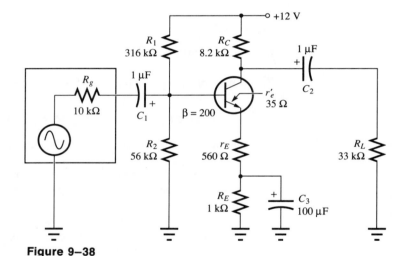

Figure 9–38

39. Determine the cutoff frequency for the highpass output network of Figure 9–38.

40. Determine the cutoff frequency for the highpass emitter-bypass network of Figure 9–38.

41. Which of the highpass cutoff frequencies for Figure 9–38 is dominant?

42. Determine the cutoff frequency for the lowpass input network of Figure 9–39.

43. Determine the cutoff frequency for the lowpass output network of Figure 9–39.

44. Which of the lowpass cutoff frequencies for Figure 9–39 is dominant?

45. Calculate the phase shift of the lowpass input network of Figure 9–39 at a frequency one octave above the cutoff frequency (one octave above $f_{co} = 2f_{co}$).

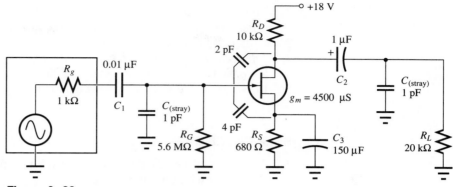

Figure 9–39

46. Calculate the upper cutoff frequency of the lowpass input network for Figure 9–40.

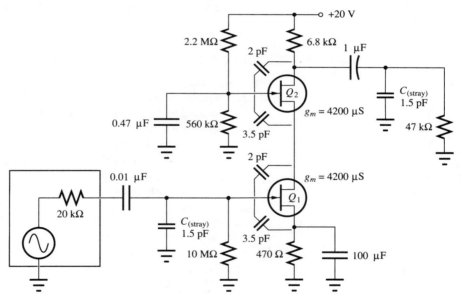

Figure 9–40

47. Calculate the upper cutoff frequency of the lowpass output network for Figure 9–40.

ANSWERS TO SELF-CHECKS

SELF-CHECK 9–1

1. For the highpass filter, all frequencies below the cutoff frequency are attenuated and all frequencies above the cutoff frequency are passed without attenuation.

2. The cutoff frequency is at -3 dB, which is a voltage level that is 0.707 times the maximum passband voltage at half the power.
3. 6 dB/octave, equal to 20 dB/decade
4. The *RCL* lowpass filter has an ideal slope of 40 dB/decade and the *RC* lowpass filter has an ideal slope of 20 dB/decade.
5. Lowpass filters are voltage-lag networks.

SELF-CHECK 9–2

1. The value of the input and output coupling capacitors and bypass capacitor, along with circuit resistances
2. 60 Hz
3. 30 Hz down to 20 Hz
4. Input network: Lf_{co} = 1,431 Hz. Output network: Lf_{co} = 594 Hz. Bypass network: Lf_{co} = 1,472 Hz (dominant).
5. $X_C = 0.159/fC = 0.159/(500 \text{ Hz} \cdot 0.1 \text{ } \mu\text{F}) = 3,180 \text{ }\Omega$
   $\angle\theta = \arctan(X_C/R) = \arctan[3,180/(600 + 511)] = 70.7°$

SELF-CHECK 9–3

1. Internal device capacitances, stray capacitances, lead inductances
2. Miller's Theorem enables us to convert the feedback capacitance to an effective shunting capacitance at the amplifier's input and output. This forms a simple *RC* lowpass filter network where $f_{co} = 0.159/RC$.
3. Highpass networks: input, Lf_{co} = 78 Hz; output, L_{fco} = 12 Hz; bypass, Lf_{co} = 1,060 Hz (dominant). Lowpass networks: input, Uf_{co} = 3.04 MHz (dominant); output, Uf_{co} = 49.1 MHz.
4. The input capacitance of a cascode amplifier is very low because $C_{in(Miller)}$ is very low. $C_{in(Miller)}$ is very low because the gain of the input device is approximately 1. Thus, since the total input capacitance is very low, the upper cutoff frequency is very high.
5. Data sheet parameter values are typical or approximate values. The actual parameter values may be greater or less than the typical values specified. Predicted frequency response is usually not precise, nor should we expect it to be. Also, we assume that capacitors will always act as capacitors as frequency is increased, when, in fact, they begin to look like inductors past their self-resonant frequency.

SELF-CHECK 9–4

1. 1.4 MHz
2. $\cong$860 kHz (860 kHz $-$ 300 Hz = 859.7 kHz)
3. 1.96 MHz
4. 11.5 MHz

SELF-CHECK 9–5

1. 3.9 $V_{\text{P-P}}$
2. The low-capacitance probe has less capacitance and has less effect on the frequency response of the output lowpass network.
3. 103 kHz

SUGGESTED PROJECTS

1. Add some of the main concepts, formulas, and procedures from this chapter to your Electronics Notebook.
2. Design your own single-stage CE amplifier using a 2N3904 or similar transistor. Predict the gain and frequency response of the amplifier. Test your amplifier to see how close your predictions are to actual measured values of gain, lower cutoff frequency, and upper cutoff frequency. Remember, due to stray capacitance and probe/cable capacitance, the high-frequency response will probably be way off from predicted response. Monitoring a circuit without the test equipment affecting the operation of the circuit has always been a challenge for engineers.

Operational amplifiers (op-amps) are small analog integrated circuits, used for audio amplifiers and a multitude of other applications. They are manufactured on wire-frame structures as shown. Individual wire frames are separated, trimmed, and hermetically sealed in plastic or ceramic cases.

10 Operational Amplifiers

OBJECTIVES

After studying this chapter you should be able to

- describe the operating and electrical characteristics of op-amps.
- explain the operation of the differential amplifier in terms of input and output modes and voltage gain.
- explain, analyze, and design negative-feedback op-amp circuits.

NEED TO KNOW

After the BJT and FET circuits you have just studied, you're going to think you're dreaming as you read the following assignment. If you had already studied this chapter, you would be able to accomplish this easily.

Design a single-stage amplifier that has a voltage gain of 100, an input impedance greater than 10 MΩ, and an output impedance less than 1Ω. Use only three components in your design (one active device and two resistors)!

It sounds impossible doesn't it? Using a single BJT or FET, it is! But there is something you need to know. Actually, there are many interesting things you need to know. Read on and enjoy.

INTRODUCTION

I remember back in the early 1970s when I first began using a remarkable little device called an *operational amplifier*. This is a small integrated-circuit amplifier. I was amazed to discover how easy it was to build a complex system using these infinitely versatile building blocks. I didn't have to worry about biasing or bias stability or gain stability, or even coupling and bypass capacitors. All I had to do was convert my system block diagram to an actual circuit using an operational amplifier for each block. The overall system had far less parts, took up less space, used less power, and cost less than if I had used BJT or FET amplifiers. Wow!

Today, a great selection of these marvelous devices is available from many manufacturers. Engineers and technicians the world over are using them for limitless applications. In this chapter, and chapters to follow, you will also become amazed at this remarkable device called the operational amplifier. This chapter is the foundation chapter upon which you will later build. You're going to like this one!

10–1 INTRODUCTION TO OPERATIONAL AMPLIFIERS (OP-AMPS)

A VERSATILE BUILDING BLOCK

Versatility

Wouldn't it be great to have a basic amplifier circuit that could easily be adapted to perform a wide variety of operations or functions? In other words, a basic building block that could be used over and over again to develop any number of different systems. Well, that is exactly what the **operational amplifier,** abbreviated **op-amp,** is. The op-amp is defined in some electronics dictionaries as ''an analog computer.'' This is because the op-amp can be used to perform basic analog operations with voltages, such as addition, subtraction, integration, and differentiation. With a few external components added, the same op-amp can be made to perform these and many other operations. As you will soon discover in this chapter and chapters to follow, the op-amp is the most flexible and exciting analog electronic building block available to the engineer and technician today.

Popularity

Why is the op-amp so popular? Because it has operating characteristics that are superior to discrete-component amplifiers, so you do not have to be concerned about biasing schemes and bias stability. So why did you have to learn how to bias discrete BJT and FET amplifiers in previous chapters? Because you will always find special needs for discrete amplifiers. They are not yet totally obsolete. As you study this chapter, you will discover the tremendous advantages of the operational amplifier and will probably resolve to use it whenever you can.

Cost

What about cost? Good question. The answer is surprising. Compared to a discrete amplifier that performs the same operation, the op-amp is less costly. Why? Because the op-amp is an almost totally self-contained integrated-circuit amplifier in a small package that is mass-produced and in high demand. Thus, the cost is relatively low. For example, the very common 741 op-amp can be purchased for 50¢ or less.

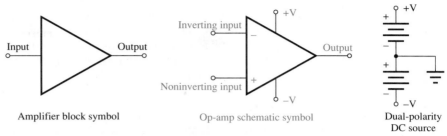

Figure 10–1   The operational amplifier (op-amp).

Schematic Symbol or Block Symbol?

Figure 10–1 shows the block symbol for an amplifier and the schematic symbol for the op-amp. The similarity between the two is obvious. In a sense, the op-amp symbol is a block symbol as well as a schematic symbol because the op-amp contains many transistors and transistor stages that are not shown. There is no need to show them. The op-amp functions as a versatile building block that can greatly simplify the design of a large electronic system. The same op-amp, used throughout a large system, can provide a voltage gain, current gain, voltage-level comparisons, all types of filtering, and more.

Figure 10–1 shows the various terminal designations for the op-amp. Many op-amps, but not all, require a positive and negative DC supply such as ±12 V, ±15 V, ±18 V, or ±22 V. All op-amps have two inputs, an inverting input (−) that causes the output to be 180° out of phase with the input and a noninverting input (+) that causes no phase shift. Thus, the op-amp can function like either a common-emitter amplifier or a common-collector amplifier.

THE IDEAL VS THE PRACTICAL OP-AMP

The Ideal

Shown in Figure 10–2, the ideal op-amp is one that has an infinite input impedance and a 0-Ω output impedance. The infinite input impedance would not load down any previous stage and the 0-Ω output impedance would not

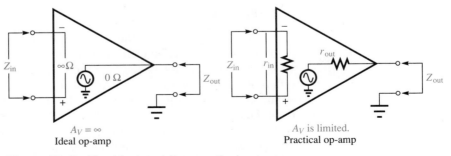

Figure 10–2   The ideal and the practical op-amp.

drop any output voltage across itself when a load is connected. Thus, the voltage gain would not be affected by loading effects. The ideal amplifier also has an infinite voltage gain and an output voltage of 0 V when the input is 0 V. The desirability of this is not evident to you at this point but it will become clear later.

The Practical

Also shown in Figure 10–2 is the practical, or real, op-amp. The practical op-amp has a finite input impedance (r_{in}) and an output impedance (r_{out}). However, the input impedance is very high and the output impedance is relatively low. As an example, the 741 op-amp (LM741, MC1741, etc.) has a specified input resistance of 2 MΩ and an output resistance of 75 Ω. For many applications these values are very satisfactory, causing minimum loading, voltage drop, and gain reduction. As you continue through these pages, you will see that although these values are not ideal, they can be greatly improved through the use of negative feedback, so the op-amp can be made nearly ideal.

Also, a practical op-amp does not have an infinite voltage gain. However, real op-amps do have very high gains. Typically, the gain of an op-amp is between 100,000 and 200,000 (100 to 106 dB). That is a much higher gain than can be obtained with a single-stage BJT or FET amplifier. This high gain is provided by several stages of amplification within the op-amp. As you will see later, this high voltage gain is the reason why the op-amp exhibits some nearly ideal characteristics.

Op-amps are also not ideal in other areas such as frequency response (amplification at any frequency regardless how high), signal distortion, and noise level. However, today's op-amps have very low distortion and noise characteristics, which satisfy most applications.

Before you hurry on, take time for Self-Check 10–1.

Self-Check 10–1

1. Why is the operational amplifier so named?
2. What is the difference between the two inputs of an op-amp?
3. In what ways is a real op-amp not ideal?

10–2 THE DIFFERENTIAL AMPLIFIER (DIFF-AMP)

THE DIFF-AMP

The heart of the op-amp is the **differential amplifier (diff-amp).** It is the diff-amp that provides the inverting and noninverting inputs. As shown in Figure 10–3, the diff-amp itself has two inputs and two outputs. The inputs and outputs are differential. In other words, a difference of potential can be applied to the two inputs and a large difference of potential can be obtained from the two outputs. The input signal is the difference voltage applied to the two input terminals. The output signal is the difference between the two output signals. To understand the op-amp, you must first understand the diff-amp. Therefore, this section is dedicated to the investigation of the differential amplifier.

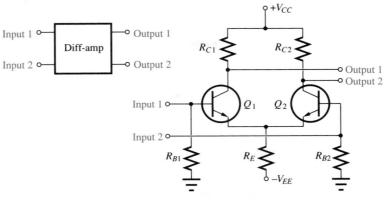

Figure 10–3   The differential amplifier (diff-amp).

DC DIFF-AMP OPERATION

Balanced Condition

Consider the diff-amp of Figure 10–4. The first thing you should notice is the emitter-bias scheme. A dual-polarity DC supply is used (± 12 V). The sum of the two emitter currents is the current through R_E labeled I_E. Notice how the amplifier is perfectly balanced (including component values, base voltages, emitter currents, collector currents, and collector voltages). Note that the base voltage of each transistor is approximately 0 V. Why? Let's assume the DC beta of each transistor is 200. That means the base current must be 1/200 of the collector current. $I_B = I_C/\beta_{DC} = 0.56$ mA/200 = 2.8 μA. The actual voltage dropped across the base resistors due to this very low current is only 1 k$\Omega \cdot 2.8$ μA = 2.8 mV.

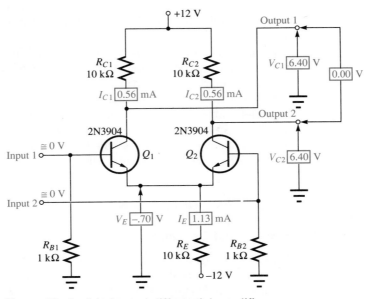

Figure 10–4   A balanced differential amplifier.

If all the matching resistors are in fact matched and the two transistors are identical, the base currents will be the same, the collector currents will be the same, and the collector voltage of each transistor will be the same. In this case, $I_{C1} = I_{C2} = 0.56$ mA $\cong I_E/2$ and $V_{C1} = V_{C2} = 12$ V $- (0.56$ mA $\cdot 10$ k$\Omega) = 6.40$ V. Note that the difference between the two output voltages is 0.00 V. This is ideal. In practice, there is usually a slight difference between the two collector voltages due to differences in transistor beta or resistor values. We will return to this discussion later.

Unbalanced Condition

Now let's see what happens when we apply a small positive voltage to one of the inputs. Figure 10–5a demonstrates the effects. A voltage of $+0.12$ V is applied to input 1 using a 100-kΩ pull-up resistor. Now carefully consider the results. Transistor Q_1 is almost saturated, having a high collector current and low collector voltage. Transistor Q_2 is almost cut off, having a low collector current and high collector voltage. But how is Q_2 affected by the input at Q_1? The $+0.12$ V applied to the base of Q_1 is transferred to its emitter where the voltage is added to the original -0.7 V provided by emitter bias. (This is due to the increased conduction of Q_1.) The result is an emitter voltage of $-0.7 + 0.12 = -0.58$ V. This means the emitter to base bias voltage for Q_2 is now only -0.58 V causing Q_2 to be nearly completely cut off. These voltage values are somewhat idealized for this discussion but they do represent what really happens. Notice the resulting difference of potential that exists at the two outputs. Notice also that the total emitter current ($I_E = 1.14$ mA) is virtually unchanged from the balanced condition. The total emitter current is simply divided between Q_1 and Q_2 depending on their state of conduction.

Figure 10–5b illustrates what happens when the 100-kΩ pull-up resistor is changed to the base of Q_2. As you would expect, Q_2 conducts heavily and Q_1 is nearly cut off. The difference of potential between the two outputs is still approximately 10.8 V, but the polarity is reversed. Again, the total emitter current is still 1.14 mA. You can construct this circuit and prove the results yourself.

In each case, Figures 10–5a and 10–5b, a difference of potential applied to the inputs is amplified and appears between the two outputs. The input difference of potential is very small (0.12 V) and the output is very large (10.8 V). This demonstrates the extreme gain or sensitivity of the differential amplifier and the need for all circuit parameters to be perfectly balanced. An imbalance in base resistances, base currents, base voltages, transistor beta, and/or collector resistances can make it impossible for a diff-amp to be perfectly balanced as in Figure 10–4.

AC DIFF-AMP OPERATION

Single-Input Operation

Now, let's consider the operation of a diff-amp when an AC signal is applied. This is demonstrated in Figure 10–6. A 13.2-mV AC signal is applied to input 1 and no signal is applied to input 2. This is known as *single-input* operation.

(a)

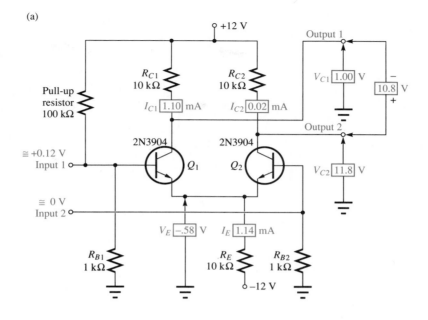

(b)

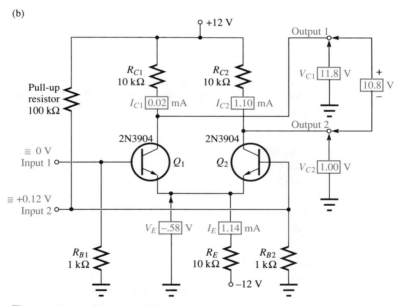

Figure 10–5 The unbalanced differential amplifier.

Consider the circuit operation very carefully. First, the amplification factor of Q_1 and Q_2 is very high. This is because A_V is determined by the value of R_C and AC emitter resistance r'_e. But wait. This is very important for you to realize. The emitter of Q_1 is connected to the emitter input impedance of Q_2. This means the emitter resistance of Q_1 is in series with the emitter input impedance of Q_2 ($r'_{e1} + Z_{e2}$). Since the base of Q_2 is nearly at ground potential, the emitter impedance of Q_2 is approximately equal to r'_{e2}. Therefore,

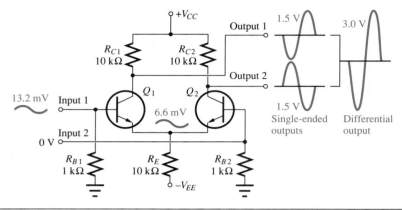

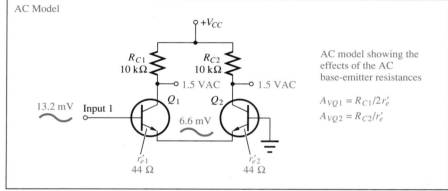

Figure 10-6 Single-input operation of the diff-amp.

the total AC emitter resistance for Q_1 is $r'_{e1} + r'_{e2}$. Assuming identical transistors, $r'_{e1} + r'_{e2} = 2r'_{e1}$. The voltage gain for Q_1 is $R_{C1}/2r'_{e1}$. If we assume $r'_{e1} = 44\Omega$, the voltage gain for Q_1 is $10 \text{ k}\Omega/88 \text{ }\Omega = 1.5 \text{ V}/13.2 \text{ mV} = 114$.

Why is the AC emitter voltage only 6.6 mV? Again r'_{e1} is in series with r'_{e2} and they are equal. Thus, the 13.2-mV signal applied to the base of Q_1 is divided between r'_{e1} and r'_{e2}.

Now we can calculate the voltage gain for Q_2. Q_2 is acting as a common-base amplifier. The voltage gain is the ratio of R_{C2}/r'_{e2}. Thus, $10 \text{ k}\Omega/44 \text{ }\Omega = 227$ and $6.6 \text{ mV} \cdot 227 = 1.5 \text{ V}$ at the collector of Q_2.

Naturally, the same theory and reasoning is applied no matter which input is used. If the 13.2-mV signal is applied to input 2, Q_2 will have a gain of 114 and Q_1 will have the gain of 227, and so on. Whichever input is used, however, the overall input to either output voltage amplification factor is $R_C/2r'_e$.

$$A_V = R_C/2r'_e \tag{10-1}$$

As you can see, the single-ended output of each transistor is 1.5 VAC with respect to ground. The differential output is the difference between the two single-ended outputs. For the negative alternation we have $-1.5 \text{ V} - (+1.5 \text{ V}) = -3.0 \text{ V}$ and for the positive alternation we have $+1.5 \text{ V} - (-1.5 \text{ V}) =$

+3 V. Thus, the differential output voltage is twice each single-ended output (3 V instead of just 1.5 V).

What about phase relationships? Notice that output 1 is 180° out of phase with input 1. Output 2 is in phase with input 1 because Q_1 acts as an emitter-follower supplying Q_2, which acts as a common-base amplifier. There is no phase shift for either the emitter-follower or the common-base configurations. Therefore, the collector of Q_2 must be in phase with the base signal of Q_1. Consider Example 10–1 before continuing.

EXAMPLE 10–1 ▮▮▮▮▮▮▮▮

The collector resistors of a differential amplifier are 18 kΩ. The internal emitter resistance (r_e') of each transistor is 75 Ω. A 5-mV signal is applied to one input. Calculate the voltage gain, the single-ended output voltage, and the differential output voltage.

$$A_V = R_C/2r_e' = 18 \text{ k}\Omega/150 \text{ }\Omega = 120$$

$$v_{\text{out(single)}} = v_{\text{in}} \cdot A_V = 5 \text{ mV} \cdot 120 = 0.6 \text{ V}$$

$$v_{\text{out(diff)}} = 2 \cdot v_{\text{out(single)}} = 1.2 \text{ V}$$

Differential-Input Operation

Figure 10–7 illustrates the operation of the diff-amp with a differential input. Immediately you notice the larger output signal swing. Both transistors are being driven at the same time with signals that are equal in amplitude but 180° out of phase. As a result, the signals that would otherwise appear at the emitters are 180° out of phase with each other and cancel. In other words, at the emitter of Q_1 we would have a positive-going 6.6-mV signal while at the

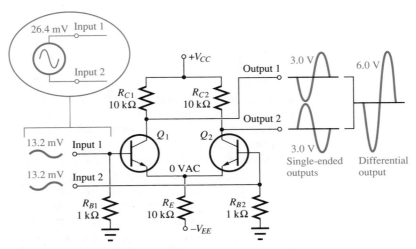

Figure 10–7 Differential-input operation of the diff-amp.

emitter of Q_2 we would have negative-going 6.6-mV signal. Since the emitters are tied together, these signals cancel, leaving 0 VAC. This means the emitters are virtually at ground potential. Therefore, the gain of each transistor is $R_C/r'_e = 10 \text{ k}\Omega/44 \text{ }\Omega = 227$ and the AC collector voltage of each transistor must be $13.2 \text{ mV} \cdot 227 = 3 \text{ V}$.

The differential input causes the two transistors to function independently as two separate common-emitter amplifiers each having an A_V of R_C/r'_e. However, the total voltage differential between input 1 and input 2 of Figure 10–7 is twice each input. In other words, the differential input voltage is actually 26.4 mV. Thus, the single-output with differential-input voltage amplification factor is $v_{out}/v_{in} = 3 \text{ V}/26.4 \text{ mV} = 114$. This means $A_{V(\text{diff})} = R_C/2r'_e$. The single-output with differential-input voltage gain is the same as the single-input voltage gain (Formula 10–1).

As before, if the output is taken differentially between output 1 and output 2, the signal is doubled in amplitude. Incidentally, many automotive stereo system amplifiers use this technique to drive speakers. Peak voltage is doubled and power is quadrupled. These are referred to as *biphase amplifiers*— two amplifiers 180° out of phase, each driving one end of the same load (speaker).

$$A_V = 2 \cdot R_C/2r'_e = R_C/r'_e \qquad \text{(differential output)} \qquad (10\text{–}2)$$

EXAMPLE 10–2 ▮▬▬▬▬▬▬▬▬▬▬▬▬▬▬▬▬▬▬

The collector resistors of a differential amplifier are 1 kΩ. The internal emitter resistance (r'_e) of each transistor is 4 Ω. An 8-mV signal is applied differentially. Calculate the voltage gain, the single-ended output voltage, and the differential output voltage.

$$A_{V(\text{diff})} = R_C/2r'_e = 1 \text{ k}\Omega/(2 \cdot 4 \text{ }\Omega) = 125$$

$$v_{out(\text{single})} = v_{in} \cdot A_V = 8 \text{ mV} \cdot 125 = 1 \text{ V}$$

$$v_{out(\text{diff})} = 2 \cdot v_{out(\text{single})} = 2 \text{ V}$$

Common-Mode Operation of the Diff-Amp

Figure 10–8 illustrates one of the very important advantages of using a diff-amp instead of a single common-emitter amplifier. That advantage is **common-mode rejection. Common mode** exists when both inputs of the diff-amp receive the same signal (same in amplitude and phase). The result is cancelation or rejection.

Common-mode rejection is used in most professional recording studios and public address systems. Long runs of microphone cable can pick up electrical noise in the form of 60-Hz hum and possibly radio interference. In a professional system, the microphone and cable are balanced, meaning the two microphone wires are floating above ground and feed a differential amplifier (an op-amp). All interfering common-mode signals are canceled and effectively rejected by the diff-amp.

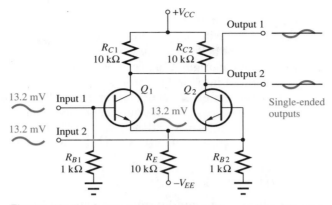

Figure 10–8   Common-mode operation of the diff-amp.

Let's begin to see how this works by examining Figure 10–8. Each 13.2-mV input signal produces a 6.6-mV signal at the emitter. Since these signals are in phase with each other, they add together. Thus, a 13.2-mV signal appears at the emitter of each transistor in phase with the two 13.2-mV inputs. This is exactly what you would expect from a single emitter-biased transistor amplifier. In fact, as shown in Figure 10–9, each transistor acts as an independent emitter-biased amplifier.

Common-Mode Gain ($A_{V(com)}$)

As you can see in Figure 10–9, the amplification factor for each amplifier is $R_C/(r'_e + R_E)$. Because r'_e is very small compared to R_E, it can be ignored. Therefore, the amplification factor under common-mode conditions is approximately R_C/R_E and is referred to as the **common-mode gain** ($A_{V(com)}$). In this case, $A_{V(com)} \cong 10 \text{ k}\Omega/20 \text{ k}\Omega = 0.5$, which of course is a loss, not a gain. Therefore, the output voltage from each collector is half of the input ($0.5 \cdot 13.2 \text{ mV} = 6.6 \text{ mV}$). Since the two outputs are in phase, the differential

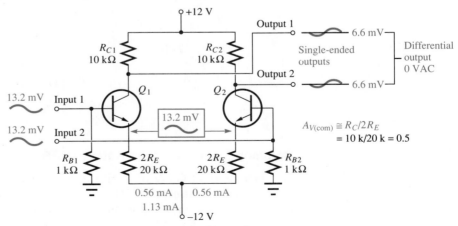

Figure 10–9   Common-mode gain ($A_{V(com)}$).

output is near 0 VAC. Thus, the common-mode signal is nearly totally rejected by using a differential output.

You might be wondering why each emitter resistor in Figure 10–9 is 20 kΩ instead of the original 10 kΩ shown in Figure 10–8. When the emitter resistor is separated into two resistors, the resistance of each must be doubled to ensure the same quiescent emitter and collector current. For example, going back to Figure 10–4, the quiescent emitter and collector current for each transistor is 0.56 mA with $V_{EE} = -12$ V. The emitter resistors in the model circuit of Figure 10–9 must be 20 kΩ to maintain the same quiescent current.

$$I_E \cong (V_{EE} - 0.7 \text{ V})/R_E = (12 \text{ V} - 0.7 \text{ V})/20 \text{ k}\Omega$$
$$= 11.3 \text{ V}/20 \text{ k}\Omega = 0.565 \text{ mA}$$

Going back to our differential amplifier of Figure 10–8, the common-mode gain is expressed as the ratio of $R_C/2R_E$ where R_E is the common emitter resistor for both sides of the differential amplifier. Look at Example 10–3.

$$A_{V(\text{com})} \cong R_C/2R_E \tag{10–3}$$

EXAMPLE 10–3

Determine the common-mode gain and the single-ended output voltage for the differential amplifier of Figure 10–10.

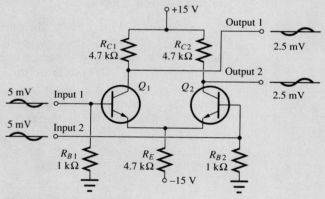

Figure 10–10

$$A_{V(\text{com})} \cong R_C/2R_E = 4.7 \text{ k}\Omega/(2 \cdot 4.7 \text{ k}\Omega) = 0.5$$

$$v_{\text{out}} = 0.5 \cdot v_{\text{in}} = 0.5 \cdot 5 \text{ mV} = 2.5 \text{ mV} \qquad \text{(from each collector)}$$

Common-Mode Rejection Ratio (CMRR)

A very important figure of merit for diff-amps and op-amps is the **common-mode rejection ratio (CMRR)**. This is the ratio of differential voltage gain ($A_{V(\text{diff})}$) to common-mode voltage gain ($A_{V(\text{com})}$).

$$\text{CMRR} = A_{V(\text{diff})}/A_{V(\text{com})} \tag{10–4}$$

For example, the circuit we have been discussing has a differential gain of 3 V/26.4 mV = 114 (Figure 10–7) and a common-mode gain of 6.6 mV/13.2 mV = 0.5 (Figure 10–9). The common-mode rejection ratio is 114/0.5 = 228 = 47.2 dB. Most op-amps have a CMRR of 70 to 110 dB ($\cong$3,000 to 300,000). Consider Example 10–4.

EXAMPLE 10–4 ▮

A differential amplifier has 22-kΩ collector resistors, a common 22-kΩ emitter resistor, and $r'_e = 40\ \Omega$. A 14.3-mV common-mode signal is present at its inputs. Calculate the differential gain, the common-mode gain, the single-ended output voltage, and the common-mode rejection ratio.

$$A_{V(\text{diff})} = R_C/2r'_e = 22\ \text{k}\Omega/(2 \cdot 40\ \Omega) = 22\ \text{k}\Omega/80\ \Omega = 275$$

$$A_{V(\text{com})} \cong R_C/2R_E = 22\ \text{k}\Omega/(2 \cdot 22\ \text{k}\Omega) = 0.5$$

$$v_{\text{out}} = 0.5 \cdot v_{\text{in}} = 0.5 \cdot 14.3\ \text{mV} = 7.15\ \text{mV}$$

$$\text{CMRR} = A_{V(\text{diff})}/A_{V(\text{com})} = 275/0.5 = 550$$

$$\text{CMRR (dB)} = 20 \cdot \log_{10}(\text{CMRR}) = 20 \cdot \log_{10}(550) = 54.8\ \text{dB}$$

What Does It All Mean?

In Example 10–4, the CMRR was found to be 550. That means a desired differential input signal will be amplified 550 times greater than will the undesired common-mode signal, assuming the desired input signal is equal in amplitude to the common-mode signal. Say the desired differential input signal is a 14.3-mV, 1-kHz sine wave and the undesired signal is a 14.3-mV, 60-Hz common-mode signal. At a single-ended output, the 1-kHz signal will be 14.3 mV · 275 = 3.93 V and the 60-Hz signal will be 7.15 mV. The ratio of these two signal voltages is 3.93 V/7.15 mV = 550, which is the CMRR.

A BASIC OP-AMP

Figure 10–11 shows the schematic of a working op-amp model. This model exhibits all of the characteristics of a typical op-amp and is suitable for use or experimentation. Notice the terminal connections corresponding to the schematic symbol for an op-amp, +V, −V, output, inverting input (−), and noninverting input (+). This model includes the differential amplifier at the inputs, a buffer and high-gain stage, and a push-pull output—all very similar to an actual op-amp. You may want to build this model to experiment with the behavior of the diff-amp and other features. This amplifier is able to drive relatively low-impedance loads and has an overall gain of about 1000 (60 dB).

Notice the offset null trim-pot. This trim-pot is wired and used as a rheostat to adjust the emitter current of Q_3. In this way, the base-bias voltage of Q_4 is adjusted, which sets the bias for Q_5 and Q_6. The trim-pot must be

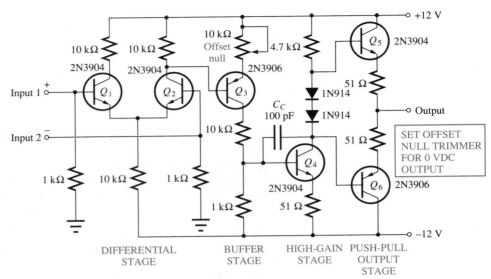

Figure 10–11 A working op-amp model.

carefully adjusted to set the DC level at the output to 0 V. Any DC voltage appearing at the output is due to an imbalance between Q_5 and Q_6 and is known as an *offset voltage*. An output offset voltage is undesirable because it will produce a continuous direct current in a load or be amplified by the next op-amp, if there is one.

Also, notice the single capacitor in the entire circuit. This capacitor is called a compensation capacitor (C_C). Later we will discuss this in detail in regard to stabilizing op-amps. For now, it is enough for you to realize that the amplifier circuit would be unstable without it. In other words, the amplifier would oscillate at some frequency. If an oscillator is not what you want, then this instability is undesirable, and it is prevented with the use of the compensation capacitor.

This model, like all op-amps, is totally direct-coupled. That simply means the amplifier circuit can amplify DC and AC. Thus, the low-frequency response is not limited by coupling and bypass capacitors. Frequency response is limited only on the high end. Again, it is advisable that you build and test this op-amp circuit. In doing so you will learn much.

Take time for Self-Check 10–2 before continuing.

Self-Check 10–2

1. Describe the currents and voltages of a balanced diff-amp.
2. Briefly explain how the collector voltage of one transistor is affected by a DC voltage on the base of the other transistor of a diff-amp.
3. A diff-amp has 6.8-kΩ collector resistors and r'_e for each transistor equals 30 Ω. If a 5-mV signal is applied to one of the inputs what is the total differential output voltage?
4. A diff-amp has 4.7-kΩ collector resistors and r'_e for each transistor equals 35 Ω. If a 10-mV signal is applied differentially to the inputs what is the total differential output voltage?
5. If the common-mode gain is 0.5, what is the CMRR for Problem 4?

10–3 OP-AMP ELECTRICAL CHARACTERISTICS

In this section we discuss some of the more important op-amp characteristics and parameters. The MC1741 data sheets are provided as an example of op-amp data so you can see the parameters as they are listed by the manufacturer. As parameters are discussed, you will want to locate them on the data sheets. Make note of the IC packages in which the 741 is manufactured. The pin-out designations are common to a wide variety of op-amps that are manufactured as direct pin-for-pin replacements for the 741.

Also, read over the maximum ratings section. You will notice that the 741 is available in two power supply voltage ratings, ±18 V and ±22 V. Notice also the continuous-short-circuit rating for the 741. Short-circuit protection of the output is a standard feature for most op-amps. Temperature range is also important. The 741 is available for general-purpose applications in the 0 to +70°C range or for more demanding applications with ambient temperatures ranging from −55 to +150°C.

As you can see from information on the data sheet, the 741 is internally compensated to prevent oscillation. No external frequency compensation is required. If you look near the center of the 741 schematic, you will see the 30-pF compensation capacitor. We will talk more about compensation later.

Let's begin now to identify and discuss some of the important characteristics listed in the electrical characteristics tables. The upper table, on page 2 of the 741 data sheets, shows characteristics specified at an ambient temperature of +25°C. The lower table contains the same characteristics specified over the complete temperature range, 0 to +70° for the MC1741C and −55 to +150°C for the MC1741.

VOLTAGE AND CURRENT OFFSETS

Input Offset Voltage (V_{IO})

The input offset voltage (V_{IO}) is defined as the differential voltage at the two inputs that is required to zero, or null, the output of the op-amp. The data sheet specifies the typical and maximum values. The greatest concern here is the output offset voltage (V_{OO}). Consider Figure 10–12. The output offset voltage should be as close to 0 VDC as possible to prevent a continuous direct current through a load and to prevent needless DC amplification in

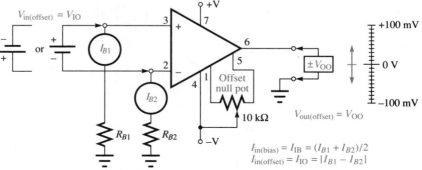

Figure 10–12 Op-amp offsets and correction.

ORDERING INFORMATION

Device	Alternate	Temperature Range	Package
MC1741CD	—	0°C to +70°C	SO-8
MC1741CG	LM741CH, μA741HC	0°C to +70°C	Metal Can
MC1741CP1	LM741CN, μA741TC	0°C to +70°C	Plastic DIP
MC1741CU	—	0°C to +70°C	Ceramic DIP
MC1741G	—	−55°C to +125°C	Metal Can
MC1741U	—	−55°C to +125°C	Ceramic DIP

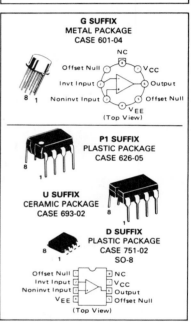

MC1741
MC1741C

OPERATIONAL AMPLIFIER
SILICON MONOLITHIC
INTEGRATED CIRCUIT

INTERNALLY COMPENSATED, HIGH PERFORMANCE OPERATIONAL AMPLIFIERS

. . . designed for use as a summing amplifier, integrator, or amplifier with operating characteristics as a function of the external feedback components.

- No Frequency Compensation Required
- Short-Circuit Protection
- Offset Voltage Null Capability
- Wide Common-Mode and Differential Voltage Ranges
- Low-Power Consumption
- No Latch Up

MAXIMUM RATINGS (T_A = +25°C unless otherwise noted)

Rating	Symbol	MC1741C	MC1741	Unit
Power Supply Voltage	V_{CC}	+18	+22	Vdc
	V_{EE}	−18	−22	Vdc
Input Differential Voltage	V_{ID}	±30		Volts
Input Common Mode Voltage (Note 1)	V_{ICM}	±15		Volts
Output Short Circuit Duration (Note 2)	t_S	Continuous		
Operating Ambient Temperature Range	T_A	0 to +70	−55 to +125	°C
Storage Temperature Range Metal and Ceramic Packages Plastic Packages	T_{stg}	−65 to +150 −55 to +125		°C

Note 1. For supply voltages less than +15 V, the absolute maximum input voltage is equal to the supply voltage.
Note 2. Supply voltage equal to or less than 15 V.

EQUIVALENT CIRCUIT SCHEMATIC

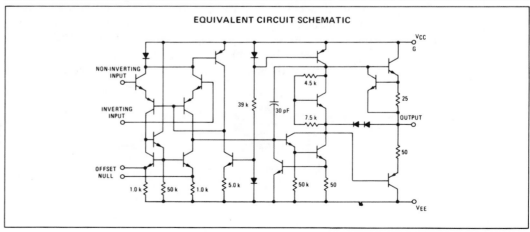

MC1741, MC1741C

ELECTRICAL CHARACTERISTICS (V_{CC} = +15 V, V_{EE} = –15 V, T_A = 25°C unless otherwise noted).

Characteristic	Symbol	MC1741			MC1741C			Unit
		Min	Typ	Max	Min	Typ	Max	
Input Offset Voltage ($R_S \leqslant$ 10 k)	V_{IO}		1.0	5.0	–	2.0	6.0	mV
Input Offset Current	I_{IO}		20	200	–	20	200	nA
Input Bias Current	I_{IB}	–	80	500	–	80	500	nA
Input Resistance	r_i	0.3	2.0		0.3	2.0	–	MΩ
Input Capacitance	C_i	–	1.4	–	–	1.4	–	pF
Offset Voltage Adjustment Range	V_{IOR}	–	±15	–	–	±15	–	mV
Common Mode Input Voltage Range	V_{ICR}	±12	±13		±12	±13	–	V
Large Signal Voltage Gain (V_O = ±10 V, $R_L \geqslant$ 2.0 k)	A_v	50	200	–	20	200	–	V/mV
Output Resistance	r_o	–	75		–	75	–	Ω
Common Mode Rejection Ratio ($R_S \leqslant$ 10 k)	CMRR	70	90		70	90	–	dB
Supply Voltage Rejection Ratio ($R_S \leqslant$ 10 k)	PSRR		30	150		30	150	μV/V
Output Voltage Swing ($R_L \geqslant$ 10 k) ($R_L \geqslant$ 2 k)	V_O	+12 +10	±14 +13	– –	±12 ±10	±14 ±13	– ––	V
Output Short-Circuit Current	I_{os}		20		–	20	–	mA
Supply Current	I_D		1.7	2.8	–	1.7	2.8	mA
Power Consumption	P_C		50	85		50	85	mW
Transient Response (Unity Gain – Non-Inverting) (V_I = 20 mV, $R_L \geqslant$ 2 k, $C_L \leqslant$ 100 pF) Rise Time	t_{TLH}		0.3		––	0.3	–	μs
(V_I = 20 mV, $R_L \geqslant$ 2 k, $C_L \leqslant$ 100 pF) Overshoot	os		15			15	–	%
(V_I = 10 V, $R_L \geqslant$ 2 k, $C_L \leqslant$ 100 pF) Slew Rate	SR		0.5		–	0.5	–	V/μs

ELECTRICAL CHARACTERISTICS (V_{CC} = +15 V, V_{EE} = –15 V, T_A = T_{low} to T_{high} unless otherwise noted).

Characteristic	Symbol	MC1741			MC1741C			Unit
		Min	Typ	Max	Min	Typ	Max	
Input Offset Voltage ($R_S \leqslant$ 10 kΩ)	V_{IO}		1.0	6.0	––	–	7.5	mV
Input Offset Current (T_A = 125°C) (T_A = –55°C) (T_A = 0°C to +70°C)	I_{IO}		7.0 85	200 500	– – –	– – –	– – 300	nA
Input Bias Current (T_A = 125°C) (T_A = –55°C) (T_A = 0°C to +70°C)	I_{IB}		30 300	500 1500	– – –	– – –	– – 800	nA
Common Mode Input Voltage Range	V_{ICR}	+12	+13	–	–	–	–	V
Common Mode Rejection Ratio ($R_S \leqslant$ 10 k)	CMRR	70	90	–	–	–	–	dB
Supply Voltage Rejection Ratio ($R_S \leqslant$ 10 k)	PSRR	–	30	150	–	–	–	μV/V
Output Voltage Swing ($R_L \geqslant$ 10 k) ($R_L \geqslant$ 2 k)	V_O	+12 +10	+14 ±13	– –	±10	±13	– –	V
Large Signal Voltage Gain ($R_L \geqslant$ 2 k, V_{out} = +10 V)	A_v	25		–	15	–		V/mV
Supply Currents (T_A = 125°C) (T_A = –55°C)	I_D		1.5 2.0	2.5 3.3			–	mA
Power Consumption (T_A = +125°C) (T_A = –55°C)	P_C		45 60	75 100		–– –	–	mW

*T_{high} = 125°C for MC1741 and 70°C for MC1741C
T_{low} = –55°C for MC1741 and 0°C for MC1741C

succeeding stages. This can be accomplished through the use of a null-pot. Many op-amps have offset null pins that can be used for output offset correction. Figure 10–12 illustrates how this is commonly done. Other schemes involve a potentiometer and voltage-divider network at one of the op-amp inputs (depending on the op-amp and the manufacturer's recommendation). Incidentally, manufacturers' data books provide, in the form of data sheets and application notes, all the information you need to make full use of their products.

Input Bias Current (I_{IB}) and Input Offset Current (I_{IO})

Input bias current (I_{IB}) is the very small amount of current that is needed to bias the differential transistor ON. The input bias current specified on data sheets is the average of the two input bias currents.

$$I_{IB} = (I_{B1} + I_{B2})/2 \qquad\qquad (10\text{--}5)$$

The data sheet for the 741 specifies the input offset current as typically 80 nA. This is a very small amount of current. However, some op-amps have JFET or MOSFET inputs with input currents of 0.05 nA and less.

The input offset current (I_{IO}) is the difference between the two input bias currents, as illustrated in Figure 10–12.

$$I_{IO} = |I_{B1} - I_{B2}| \qquad\qquad (10\text{--}6)$$

The input offset current creates an input offset voltage that causes an output offset voltage. Here's how.

$$V_{IO} = (I_{B1} \cdot R_{B1}) - (I_{B2} \cdot R_{B2}) \qquad\qquad (10\text{--}7)$$

If $R_{B1} = R_{B2} = R_B$, then

$$V_{IO} = I_{IO} \cdot R_B \qquad\qquad (10\text{--}8)$$

$$V_{OO} = A_{OL} \cdot V_{IO} \qquad\qquad (10\text{--}9)$$

where A_{OL} is the open-loop voltage gain of the op-amp.

For the 741, the input offset current is typically 20 nA. If the input resistors are each 10 kΩ, the input offset voltage would be 20 nA $\cdot$ 10 kΩ = 0.2 mV. This offset voltage may add to an input offset voltage that already exists between the base-emitter voltages of the two input transistors. On the other hand, it may help cancel the input offset voltage of the base-emitter junctions. In any case, the input offset voltage caused by the input offset current can be corrected, if need be, by increasing or decreasing the value of either of the input ground-return resistors (R_{B1} or R_{B2}) according to Formula 10–7. As stated earlier, the output offset voltage can always be corrected, by using an offset null-pot as shown in Figure 10–12.

INPUT AND OUTPUT RESISTANCE

Op-Amp Input Resistance (r_{in})

Illustrated in Figure 10–13, the input resistance (r_{in}) of an op-amp is an AC parameter specified on the data sheet. **Input resistance** is defined as the ratio of the change in input voltage to the change in input current on either input

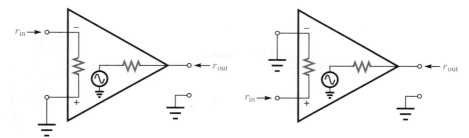

Figure 10–13   Input and output resistance.

of the op-amp with the other input grounded. This resistance is usually high or very high. Notice for the 741 the input resistance is typically 2 MΩ. For JFET- and MOSFET-input op-amps, such as the LF356, the input resistance is very high in the range of 10^{12} Ω or greater. We will discuss this further later.

Op-Amp Output Resistance (r_{out})

Also illustrated in Figure 10–13 is the op-amp **output resistance (r_{out}).** This is an AC parameter defined as the small-signal resistance seen at the output of the op-amp. For the 741 op-amp, this is specified as 75 Ω. However, this is an open-loop value. That means the amplifier is functioning without feedback (yet to be discussed). As you will soon see, adding a negative-feedback network to the op-amp will greatly reduce this output resistance to values less than 1 Ω.

SIGNAL CHARACTERISTICS

Open-Loop Voltage Gain (A_{OL})

The **open-loop voltage gain (A_{OL}),** sometimes called the large-signal voltage gain, is the maximum possible voltage gain of the op-amp. The open-loop voltage gain is usually 100,000 to 200,000 or so for most op-amps (100 to 106 dB). This parameter is symbolized on data sheets with any of the following: A_{OL}, A_V, A_{VOL}, A. On the data sheet, the open-loop gain may be expressed as a number (100,000), in decibels (100 dB), or in volts per millivolt (V/mV) where 100,000 = 100 V/mV. You will see how very important this parameter is later.

Output Voltage Swing (V_O)

The **output voltage swing (V_O)** of an op-amp is the maximum unclipped peak output voltage that can be obtained with a specified ±DC supply. This is illustrated in Figure 10–14. Notice the output swing cannot reach all the way to ±V. The waveform becomes clipped within a volt or so of the DC supply voltage. The 741 data sheet indicates a V_O of ±14 V when a ±15-V DC supply is used. Thus, the output signal compliance is somewhat less than the ±DC supply voltage.

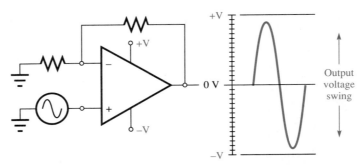

Figure 10–14   Maximum output voltage swing.

Common-Mode Rejection Ratio (CMRR)

Recall that we said the CMRR was the ratio of differential gain to common-mode gain ($A_{V(\text{diff})}/A_{V(\text{com})}$). For the entire op-amp, the CMRR is the ratio of open-loop gain to common-mode gain:

$$\text{CMRR} = A_{OL}/A_{V(\text{com})} \qquad\qquad (10\text{–}10)$$

Consider this simple example.

EXAMPLE 10–5 ▮

An op-amp has an open-loop gain of 200,000 and a common-mode gain of 6.4. What is the common-mode rejection ratio?

$$\text{CMRR} = A_{OL}/A_{V(\text{com})} = 200{,}000/6.4 = 31{,}250 = 90 \text{ dB}$$

A CMRR of 90 dB is typical for 741 op-amps and others.

CMRR is not a constant as far as frequency is concerned. As frequency is increased CMRR decreases. This is because the open-loop gain decreases with increasing frequency. More on this in a moment.

Slew Rate (*SR*)

One of the most important characteristics of an op-amp is its slew rate (*SR*). Shown in Figure 10–15, the **slew rate** is the highest rate at which the output voltage of the op-amp is able to increase. The slew rate is determined experimentally by applying a step voltage (pulsating DC square wave) to the noninverting input while the output is jumpered back to the inverting input. The output tries to keep up with the input but cannot because internal capacitances are in the process of charging. If the input step voltage is +10 V and it takes the output 1 μs to reach +10 V, the slew rate is 10 V/μs. The 741 has a slew rate of 0.5 V/μs, which is considered to be low. It takes the 741 about 20 μs to reach +10 V.

The rise time (t_{TLH}) of the output signal is measured from low to high between the 10% and 90% points on the slope as indicated. In some cases, such a delay is referred to as **propagation delay**. Consider Example 10–6.

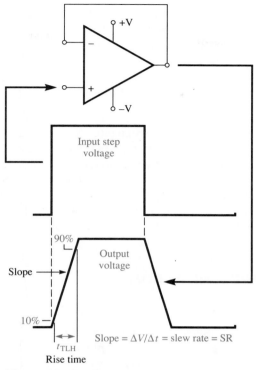

Figure 10–15 Slew rate.

EXAMPLE 10–6

The low to high rise time for an op-amp is 1.2 μs. During this time, the output voltage changes by 8.4 V in response to a square-wave input pulse. Express the slew rate in V/s and V/μs.

$SR = 8.4 \text{ V}/1.2 \ \mu s = 7 \text{ MV/s} = 7 \text{ V}/\mu s$

Take time now to review this section. Before continuing to the next section, test your understanding by answering the questions of Self-Check 10–3.

Self-Check 10–3

1. Why is a DC offset in the output of an op-amp undesirable?
2. How might the input offset current affect the output offset voltage of an op-amp circuit?
3. How can input offset currents be compensated for?
4. Explain open-loop voltage gain of an op-amp.
5. If the DC supply for an op-amp is ±20 V, what might the maximum output voltage swing be?

6. A certain op-amp has an open-loop gain of 150,000 and a common-mode gain of 2. Calculate the CMRR.
7. What is slew rate (*SR*)?

10–4 OP-AMP PERFORMANCE WITH NEGATIVE FEEDBACK

In this section we will investigate the theory and operation of the op-amp through the analysis of practical op-amp circuits. In each case, you will see the importance of negative feedback in the overall performance and characteristics of the circuits. You will see how a sample of the output, brought back to the inverting input, is able to greatly modify and enhance the performance of the op-amp. In general, you will see how this negative feedback affects amplifier gain, input impedance, output impedance, and signal distortion.

NONINVERTING AMPLIFIER WITH VOLTAGE FEEDBACK

An Overview

We begin our investigation with one of the most common implementations of the op-amp, the noninverting amplifier. Notice the simplicity of the circuit in Figure 10–16. There are only two resistors, feedback resistor R_F and inverting input resistor R_I. The op-amp shown here is a 741 that has an open-loop gain of 100 dB. The overall closed-loop gain of this amplifier circuit is set by the ratio $(R_I + R_F)/R_I$. If this ratio is 10/1, the A_V of the amplifier circuit is 10 (1 V in produces 10 V out). By adjusting the values of R_F and R_I, the amplifier voltage gain can be made any value from 1 to 100,000. The output of the amplifier (pin 6) is in phase with the input (pin 3). The entire amplifier functions as an emitter-follower that has voltage gain. The input impedance is very high and can be made any value you like by adding a resistor of the desired value from pin 3 to ground. If you desire a 10-kΩ input impedance,

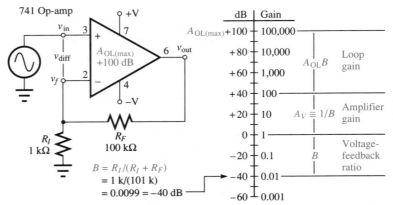

Figure 10–16   The noninverting amplifier with negative voltage feedback.

simply place a 10-kΩ resistor from pin 3 to ground. It's that simple. You don't worry about bias voltages or any such calculations. Now that you have the basic idea, let's take a closer look.

The Difference Voltage (v_{diff})

It is important for you to realize that the op-amp itself always has a voltage gain equal to A_{OL}. The 741 of Figure 10–16 has an A_{OL} of 100 dB. This means the difference voltage between the two inputs (pin 3 and pin 2) is always amplified 100,000 times. If $v_{\text{diff}} = 0.1$ mV, the output will be 10 V.

$$v_{\text{out}} = A_{\text{OL}}v_{\text{diff}} \tag{10–11}$$

The difference voltage is the difference between the input voltage (v_{in}) and the feedback voltage (v_f).

$$v_{\text{diff}} = v_{\text{in}} - v_f \tag{10–12}$$

Notice that the feedback voltage is actually the voltage drop across R_I where $v_f = v_{RI}$. The output voltage is divided down according to the ratio of $R_I/(R_I + R_F)$. This is called the **voltage-feedback ratio (B)**.

$$B = R_I/(R_I + R_F) \tag{10–13}$$

Therefore,

$$v_f = v_{\text{out}} \cdot R_I/(R_I + R_F) = Bv_{\text{out}} \tag{10–14}$$

and

$$v_{\text{diff}} = v_{\text{in}} - Bv_{\text{out}} \tag{10–15}$$

Overall Amplifier Voltage Gain (A_V)

From the relationships we have identified, we can derive a formula for the overall amplifier voltage gain known as the **closed-loop voltage gain (A_V)**. We begin with the relationship expressed in Formula 10–11 and expand from there.

$$v_{\text{out}} = A_{\text{OL}}v_{\text{diff}} \tag{10–16}$$

$$v_{\text{out}} = A_{\text{OL}}(v_{\text{in}} - v_f) \quad \text{since } v_{\text{diff}} = (v_{\text{in}} - v_f)$$

$$v_{\text{out}} = A_{\text{OL}}v_{\text{in}} - A_{\text{OL}}v_f$$

$$v_{\text{out}} = A_{\text{OL}}v_{\text{in}} - A_{\text{OL}}Bv_{\text{out}} \quad \text{since } v_f = Bv_{\text{out}}$$

$$v_{\text{out}} + A_{\text{OL}}Bv_{\text{out}} = A_{\text{OL}}v_{\text{in}}$$

$$v_{\text{out}}(1 + A_{\text{OL}}B) = A_{\text{OL}}v_{\text{in}}$$

$$v_{\text{out}}(1 + A_{\text{OL}}B)/v_{\text{in}} = A_{\text{OL}}$$

$$v_{\text{out}}/v_{\text{in}} = A_{\text{OL}}/(1 + A_{\text{OL}}B)$$

$$A_V = v_{\text{out}}/v_{\text{in}} = A_{\text{OL}}/(1 + A_{\text{OL}}B)$$

Since A_{OL} is very large, the voltage gain can be closely approximated as

$$A_V \cong 1/B = (R_I + R_F)/R_I \tag{10–17}$$

It is important for you to recognize here that the closed-loop voltage gain (A_V) of the amplifier is nearly completely independent of the open-loop gain (A_{OL}). This is very desirable because the open-loop voltage gain may vary among op-amps of the same type. Since the closed-loop voltage gain is largely dependent on R_F and R_I, the circuit can be mass-produced with little or no gain variations. Consider Example 10–7.

EXAMPLE 10–7 ▐▬▬▬▬▬▬▬▬▬▬▬▬▬

An op-amp has an open-loop voltage gain of 200,000 and is used to make a noninverting amplifier. R_F is 100 kΩ and R_I is 4.7 kΩ. If v_{in} is 30 mV, what is the amplitude of v_{out} and v_{diff}?

First calculate the voltage feedback ratio (B).

$B = R_I/(R_I + R_F) = 4.7\ k/(4.7\ k + 100\ k) = 0.045$

Next calculate A_V.

$A_V = A_{OL}/(1 + A_{OL}B) = 200,000/(1 + 200,000 \cdot 0.045) = 22.2$

$\cong 1/B = 1/0.045 = 22.2$

Now calculate v_{out}.

$v_{out} = A_V \cdot v_{in} = 22.2 \cdot 30\ mV = 666\ mV$

Calculate v_f.

$v_f = Bv_{out} = 0.045 \cdot 666\ mV = 30\ mV$

Finally, calculate v_{diff}.

$v_{diff} = v_{in} - v_f = 30\ mV - 30\ mV = 0\ V$

What happened here? How can the difference be 0 V? Because we rounded out numbers in the calculations, the very small difference voltage was lost.

$v_{diff} = v_{out}/A_{OL} = 666\ mV/200,000 = 3.33\ \mu V$

From this you can see that v_{in} and v_f are nearly equal.

Loop Gain ($A_{OL}B$)

The feedback loop starts at the output, comes back through the resistor voltage divider to the inverting input, then through the op-amp back to the output. The loop is composed of a voltage-divider loss (B) and the open-loop amplifier gain (A_{OL}). Loop gain is the product of the voltage-feedback ratio and the open-loop gain.

Loop gain = $A_{OL}B$ (10–18)

Look once again at Figure 10–16. The voltage-feedback ratio is 0.0099 (−40 dB) and the open-loop gain is 100,000 (+100 dB). Therefore, the loop gain is 0.0099 · 100,000 = 990 = 60 dB. Also, 100 dB − 40 dB = 60 dB. The vertical scale of Figure 10–16 illustrates the relationship between loop gain, amplifier gain, and voltage-feedback ratio. For the moment, this is what you should understand. As the feedback ratio $B = R_I/(R_I + R_F)$ becomes larger, the closed-loop gain $A_V = (R_I + R_F)/R_I$ becomes lower, and the loop gain $A_{OL}B$ becomes larger. We will make use of this later.

EXAMPLE 10–8 ▮▮▮▮▮▮▮▮

An op-amp has an open-loop gain of 150,000 and is used as a noninverting amplifier. R_F is chosen to be 47 kΩ and R_I is 3.3 kΩ. Determine the loop gain.

loop gain = $A_{OL}B$ = 150,000 · 3.3 kΩ/(3.3 kΩ + 47 kΩ) = 9841

$^{\#}$dB = 20 log (9841) = 79.9 dB

Also,

150,000 = 103.5 dB   and   3.3 kΩ/(3.3 kΩ + 47 kΩ) = −23.7 dB

Therefore,

dB loop gain = 103.5 dB + (−23.7 dB) = 79.8 dB

Input Impedance of the Noninverting Amplifier

The input impedance at the noninverting input of the op-amp is very high for the circuit shown in Figure 10–17. Basically, the input impedance is a prod-

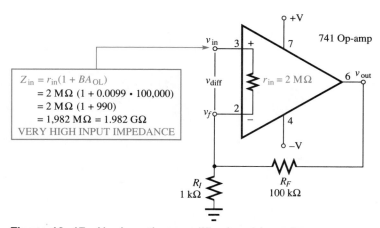

$Z_{in} = r_{in}(1 + BA_{OL})$
$= 2\ M\Omega\ (1 + 0.0099 \cdot 100,000)$
$= 2\ M\Omega\ (1 + 990)$
$= 1,982\ M\Omega = 1.982\ G\Omega$
VERY HIGH INPUT IMPEDANCE

Figure 10–17 Noninverting-amplifier input impedance.

uct of loop gain (BA_{OL} or $A_{OL}B$) and input resistance (r_{in}). But why? Let's see.

$$v_{in} = v_{diff} + v_f$$

$$v_{in} = v_{diff} + Bv_{out} \quad \text{since } v_f = Bv_{out}$$

$$v_{in} = v_{diff} + Bv_{diff}A_{OL} \quad \text{since } v_{out} = v_{diff}A_{OL}$$

$$v_{diff} = i_{in} \cdot r_{in}$$

so,

$$v_{in} = i_{in}r_{in} + Bi_{in}r_{in}A_{OL}$$

$$v_{in} = i_{in}r_{in} (1 + BA_{OL})$$

$$v_{in}/i_{in} = r_{in} (1 + BA_{OL}) = Z_{in}$$

$$Z_{in} = r_{in} (1 + BA_{OL}) \tag{10–19}$$

Output Impedance of the Noninverting Amplifier

The output impedance of the noninverting amplifier, as shown in Figure 10–18, is very low due to the effects of negative feedback. Again, the loop gain is a major determining factor. The AC output impedance is nearly the ratio of output resistance to loop gain. The derivation of this formula is left to Appendix C, "Formula Derivations."

$$Z_{out} = r_{out}/(1 + BA_{OL}) \tag{10–20}$$

Conceptually, here's what happens. If the load at the output is increased (smaller load resistor), the output voltage would tend to drop (be loaded down) somewhat. This means v_f is smaller and v_{diff} is greater for a fixed input voltage. The larger v_{diff} is amplified by A_{OL} and immediately compensates for the would-be drop in output voltage. This is the same effect as the internal output resistance becoming smaller as the load increases. Thus, the compensating feedback effectively causes the output impedance to be less than r_{out}.

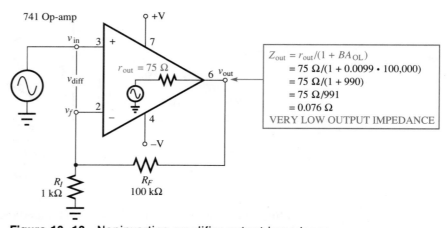

Figure 10–18 Noninverting-amplifier output impedance.

As you can see in Figure 10–16, an effective output impedance of 0.076 Ω is much, much less than the 75-Ω r_{out}. Without feedback, the output impedance would always be 75 Ω and the output could easily be loaded down by low-impedance loads. Does this mean the op-amp can supply any amount of current to any load? No. The op-amp has a current-limiting circuit at its output that prevents damage due to short-circuiting the output. The output current is often limited to 20 or 30 mA maximum.

EXAMPLE 10–9

Determine the input and output impedance for Figure 10–19 in which r_{in} = 5 MΩ, r_{out} = 50 Ω, and A_{OL} = 200,000.

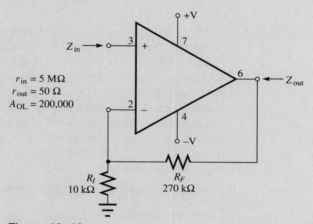

r_{in} = 5 MΩ
r_{out} = 50 Ω
A_{OL} = 200,000

R_I
10 kΩ

R_F
270 kΩ

Figure 10–19

$$B = R_I/(R_I + R_F) = 10\ \text{k}\Omega/(10\ \text{k}\Omega + 270\ \text{k}\Omega) = 0.0357$$

$$1 + BA_{OL} = 1 + (0.0357 \cdot 200{,}000) = 7{,}141$$

$$Z_{in} = r_{in}(1 + BA_{OL}) = 5\ \text{M}\Omega \cdot 7{,}141 = 35.7\ \text{G}\Omega$$

$$Z_{out} = r_{out}/(1 + BA_{OL}) = 50\ \Omega/7{,}141 = 7\ \text{m}\Omega \qquad (0.007\ \Omega)$$

The Unity-Gain Voltage-Follower Amplifier

Figure 10–20 shows a very useful and special op-amp circuit, the unity-gain voltage follower. This is used as a buffer amplifier and has an extremely high input impedance and extremely low output impedance. The amount of feedback is maximum because the voltage-feedback ratio is one (1). The output voltage is a faithful in-phase reproduction of the input voltage. In many ways, this amplifier is nearly ideal—extremely high input impedance, extremely low output impedance, and virtually no distortion. Although voltage gain is equal to one (1), the current and power gain of this amplifier is extremely high due to the high input impedance and low output impedance.

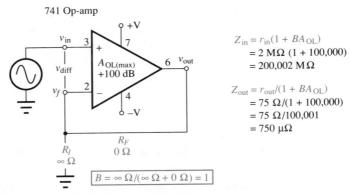

741 Op-amp

$$Z_{in} = r_{in}(1 + BA_{OL})$$
$$= 2\ M\Omega\ (1 + 100{,}000)$$
$$= 200{,}002\ M\Omega$$

$$Z_{out} = r_{out}/(1 + BA_{OL})$$
$$= 75\ \Omega/(1 + 100{,}000)$$
$$= 75\ \Omega/100{,}001$$
$$= 750\ \mu\Omega$$

$$\boxed{B = \infty\ \Omega/(\infty\ \Omega + 0\ \Omega) = 1}$$

Figure 10–20   The unity-gain voltage follower.

Why virtually no distortion? Negative feedback corrects any would-be distortion. Say the output has a little crossover distortion, common to push-pull amplifiers. This distortion is not part of the input voltage. Therefore, it becomes part of the difference voltage, because the output is fed back to the inverting input. Thus, the distortion is greatly amplified and inverted. This instantly cancels the distortion in the output signal. Say the open-loop distortion is 1% (the total of all distortion voltages is 1/100 of the output voltage). With maximum feedback, as in Figure 10–17, the distortion is reduced to $10 \cdot 10^{-6}\%$ (1%/100,000). This is virtually ideal.

NONINVERTING AMPLIFIER WITH CURRENT FEEDBACK

Figure 10–21 illustrates another type of noninverting amplifier that uses negative current feedback. This is often called a **transconductance amplifier** or a **voltage-to-current converter** because the output current is a function of

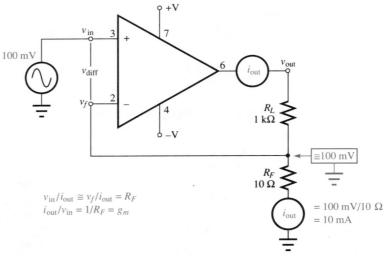

$$v_{in}/i_{out} \cong v_f/i_{out} = R_F$$
$$i_{out}/v_{in} = 1/R_F = g_m$$

Figure 10–21   The transconductance amplifier.

input voltage ($g_m = i_{out}/v_{in}$). Notice that the load resistor, or load device, is in series with the feedback network. Thus, the output current flows through the load resistance (R_L) and the feedback resistor (R_F). This output current is held constant as long as the input voltage is constant (AC or DC). Any would-be change in output current causes the voltage across R_F to change. Because v_{RF} and v_f are the same, if v_f does change, v_{diff} will change. The change in v_{diff} is amplified by A_{OL} and immediately adjusts the output voltage to restore the output current to its original value.

In Figure 10–21, the output current is 10 mA. This current will not change even if the load resistance changes. Why? This is because the output voltage is instantly changed to correct the current. If the load resistance decreases, the output voltage must decrease to maintain the current at a fixed value. Effectively, the output impedance of the op-amp increases. (This is the opposite of voltage feedback.) The *only way* the output current can be changed is by changing v_{in} or R_F.

Consider the following: $R_F = v_{RF}/i_{out} = v_f/i_{out}$. Since v_{diff} is very small, $v_{in} \cong v_f$. Therefore, $R_F = v_{in}/i_{out}$ and $1/R_F = g_m = i_{out}/v_{in}$.

$$g_m = i_{out}/v_{in} = 1/R_F \qquad (10\text{–}21)$$

If you decide that i_{out} will be 2 mA when v_{in} is 50 mV, then R_F must be 50 mV/2 mA = 25 Ω and the amplifier has a transconductance of 1/(25 Ω) = 40,000 μS = 40 mS. Remember, however, that the maximum output current is limited by the op-amp.

EXAMPLE 10–10 ■

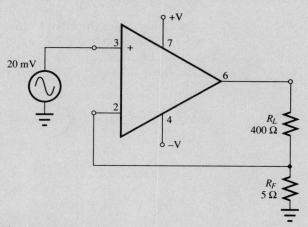

Determine the load (current) and transconductance for Figure 10–22.

Figure 10–22

$i_{out} \cong$ 20 mV/5 Ω = 4 mA

$g_m = i_{out}/v_{in} = 1/R_F$ = 4 mA/20 mV = 1/(5 Ω) = 0.2 S

Important Facts

- v_{diff} is very small ($v_{\text{out}}/A_{\text{OL}}$).
- $v_{\text{in}} \cong v_f$
- A_{OL} is very large (usually 100,000 or more).
- All functions such as A_V and g_m are virtually independent of A_{OL}.

INVERTING AMPLIFIER WITH VOLTAGE FEEDBACK

The Current-to-Voltage Converter

Figure 10–23 illustrates a very interesting and useful amplifier called a **transresistance amplifier** or a **current-to-voltage converter**, in which output voltage is a function of input current ($V_{\text{out}}/I_{\text{in}} = R$, the transresistance). An AC or DC current fed into the inverting input (pin 2) creates a proportionate output voltage. In this case, there is 1 V of output voltage for every 10 mA of input current. As you can see, the oscilloscope can now be used to measure current using the current-to-voltage converter.

The theory behind this amplifier is very interesting and important. It centers on what is called a **virtual ground,** a point in a circuit that acts like ground because it has a very low voltage. In Figure 10–21, pin 2 is a virtual ground. The voltage at this point is very low. We already know this voltage as V_{diff}. It is very low because $V_{\text{diff}} = V_{\text{out}}/A_{\text{OL}}$. As you can see, if the output voltage is 1 V, the difference voltage must be 10 μV (1 V/100,000 = 10 μV). The input impedance at the inverting input is calculated to be a mere 0.001 Ω, since the input current is 10 mA and the input voltage is 10 μV (10 μV/10 mA = 0.001 Ω). This impedance is virtually a short to ground—another reason for the name *virtual ground*.

$$Z_{\text{in}} = V_{\text{diff}}/I_{\text{in}} = V_{\text{out}}/A_{\text{OL}}I_{\text{in}} \tag{10–22}$$

Now, where does the 10-mA input current go? Does it go into the op-amp at pin 2? No. Recall that the input resistance of a 741, for example, is 2 MΩ. Thus, the 10 mA of current cannot go into the op-amp. Instead, the input current flows through the feedback resistor (R_F) due to the 1-V difference of

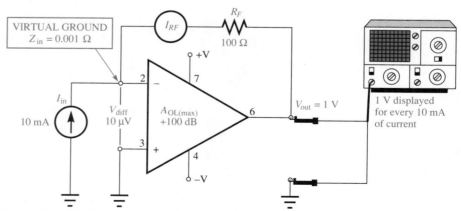

Figure 10–23   The transresistance amplifier.

potential that exists across R_F. Note that the output voltage is across R_F since the input is at virtual ground. Thus $I_{RF} = 1\ \text{V}/100\ \Omega = 10\ \text{mA} = I_{\text{in}}$.

$$R_F = V_{\text{out}}/I_{\text{in}} \tag{10–23}$$

If it is desired to have a 1-V output voltage for a 10-mA input current the transresistance must be $100\ \Omega = R_F = 1\ \text{V}/10\ \text{mA}$. Since $Z_{\text{in}} = V_{\text{out}}/A_{\text{OL}}I_{\text{in}}$,

$$Z_{\text{in}} = R_{\text{in(Miller)}} = R_F/A_{\text{OL}} \tag{10–24}$$

The input impedance at virtual ground is also called the **Miller input resistance** because it is the result or effect of the negative feedback resistance and amplifier gain. The **Miller output resistance** is equal to R_F because the input end of R_F is at virtual ground.

$$R_{\text{out(Miller)}} = R_F \tag{10–25}$$

This Miller output resistance is in parallel with the output impedance of the op-amp, which, with negative voltage feedback, is very low. As a result, the Miller output resistance is of little significance.

EXAMPLE 10–11

Determine the input impedance for Figure 10–24. Also determine the input and output voltages.

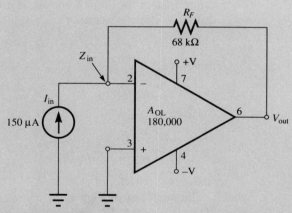

Figure 10–24

$$Z_{\text{in}} = R_{\text{in(Miller)}} = R_F/A_{\text{OL}} = 68\ \text{k}\Omega/180{,}000 = 0.378\ \Omega$$

$$V_{\text{out}} = I_{\text{in}} \cdot R_F = 150\ \mu\text{A} \cdot 68\ \text{k}\Omega = 10.2\ \text{V}$$

$$V_{\text{in}} = V_{\text{out}}/A_{\text{OL}} = 10.2\ \text{V}/180{,}000 = 56.7\ \mu\text{V}$$

The Inverting Voltage Amplifier

Figure 10–25 shows a voltage amplifier design that is very popular. Since the inverting input is used, this is an inverting amplifier. As we have just dis-

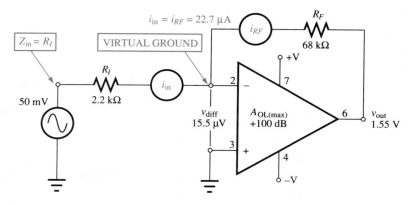

$$v_{out}/v_{in} = R_F/R_I = A_V = 68\ k\Omega/2.2\ k\Omega = 31 = 29.8\ dB$$

Figure 10–25 The inverting voltage amplifier.

cussed, the inverting input is at virtual ground due to the negative feedback of R_F. The voltage at pin 2 is near 0 V—in this case, 15.5 μV (1.55 V/ 100,000). The theory here is very similar to that of the current-to-voltage converter (transresistance amplifier). The input current (i_{in}) and the feedback current (i_{RF}) are the same. What we are doing here is driving a current-to-voltage converter with a voltage source. In this case, the voltage source has an internal resistance of 2.2 kΩ. Since the inverting input (pin 2) is at virtual ground, all of the source voltage is dropped across R_I, $Z_{in} = R_I$, and all of the output voltage is across R_F.

$$i_{in} = i_{RF}, \qquad i_{in} = v_{in}/R_I, \qquad i_{RF} = v_{out}/R_F$$

therefore,

$$v_{in}/R_I = v_{out}/R_F \tag{10-26}$$

$$R_F v_{in}/R_I = v_{out}$$

$$v_{out}/v_{in} = R_F/R_I$$

$$A_V = v_{out}/v_{in} = R_F/R_I$$

where $A_V = 1/B$ and $B = R_I/R_F$.

The amplifier of Figure 10–25 has a closed-loop voltage gain of 68 kΩ/2.2 kΩ = 31 = 29.8 dB, and $v_{out} = v_{in} \cdot A_V = 50$ mV $\cdot$ 31 = 1.55 V.

EXAMPLE 10–12

Determine the following for Figure 10–26: Z_{in}, Z_{out}, i_{in}, A_V, v_{out}, and v_{diff}.

$$Z_{in} = R_I = 22\ k\Omega$$

$$A_V = R_F/R_I = 150\ k\Omega/22\ k\Omega = 6.82$$

$$B = 1/A_V = 1/6.82 = 0.147$$

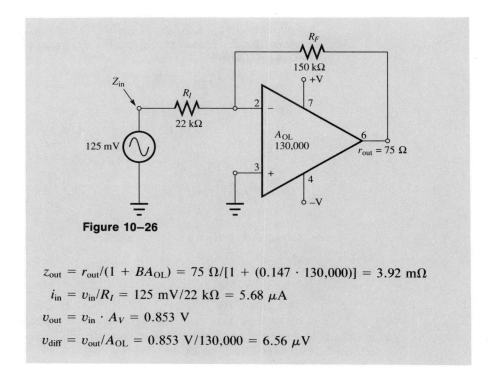

Figure 10–26

$$z_{out} = r_{out}/(1 + BA_{OL}) = 75\ \Omega/[1 + (0.147 \cdot 130,000)] = 3.92\ m\Omega$$

$$i_{in} = v_{in}/R_I = 125\ mV/22\ k\Omega = 5.68\ \mu A$$

$$v_{out} = v_{in} \cdot A_V = 0.853\ V$$

$$v_{diff} = v_{out}/A_{OL} = 0.853\ V/130,000 = 6.56\ \mu V$$

INVERTING AMPLIFIER WITH CURRENT FEEDBACK

The circuit of Figure 10–27 is a current amplifier for AC or DC. This circuit can be used to increase the sensitivity of an ammeter. In this example, the 1-mA ammeter now has a sensitivity of only 50 μA. The current gain for this

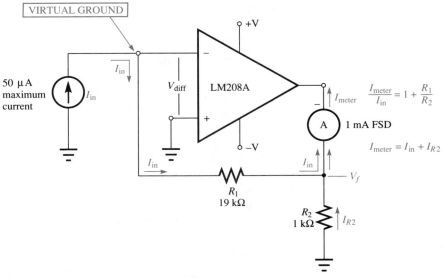

Figure 10–27 The current amplifier.

amplifier is simply $I_{out}/I_{in} = I_{meter}/I_{in}$. Values for R_1 and R_2 must be chosen to provide the desired current gain. We derive a formula suitable for this purpose as follows:

$$I_{meter} = I_{in} + I_{R2}$$

$$I_{meter} = I_{in} + (V_f/R_2)$$

Since the left end of R_1 is at virtual ground, R_1 and R_2 are effectively in parallel. This means that $V_f = I_{in} \cdot R_1$. Therefore,

$$I_{meter} = I_{in} + (I_{in} \cdot R_1/R_2)$$

$$I_{meter} = I_{in} (1 + R_1/R_2)$$

$$I_{meter}/I_{in} = 1 + R_1/R_2 = I_{out}/I_{in}$$

$$I_{out}/I_{in} = 1 + R_1/R_2 \qquad (10\text{--}27)$$

and

$$R_1 = R_2 [(I_{out}/I_{in} - 1)] \qquad (10\text{--}28)$$

For Figure 10–27, $R_1 = 1 \text{ k}\Omega \cdot [(1 \text{ mA}/50 \text{ }\mu\text{A}) - 1)] = 19 \text{ k}\Omega$. R_2 is usually 1 kΩ or less. You can design your own current amplifiers. Simply start with the ammeter you have on hand and decide how sensitive you want it to be. Consider Example 10–13.

EXAMPLE 10–13 ▨▨▨▨▨▨▨▨▨▨▨▨▨▨▨▨▨▨▨▨▨▨▨▨▨▨

Use an op-amp to increase the sensitivity of a current meter from 1 mA to 25 μA. Let $R_2 = 500 \text{ }\Omega$.

$$I_{meter} = 1 \text{ mA} \qquad I_{in} = 25 \text{ }\mu\text{A}$$

$$R_1 = R_2 [(I_{out}/I_{in}) - 1] = 500 \text{ }\Omega \cdot [(1 \text{ mA}/25 \text{ }\mu\text{A}) - 1] = 19,500 \text{ }\Omega$$

Take time to carefully review this section before continuing.

Self-Check 10–4

1. If an op-amp has an open-loop gain of 150,000 and its output voltage is 2.5 V, calculate the difference voltage between its two inputs.
2. Calculate the voltage feedback ratio (B) of a noninverting amplifier when R_F is 220 kΩ and R_I is 47 kΩ.
3. Calculate the input and output impedance for a noninverting amplifier when $A_{OL} = 120,000$, $r_{in} = 3 \text{ M}\Omega$, $r_{out} = 50 \text{ }\Omega$, $R_F = 82 \text{ k}\Omega$, and $R_I = 10 \text{ k}\Omega$.
4. Calculate the closed-loop voltage gain (A_V), and the loop gain for Problem 3 above. Express answers in decibels.
5. Describe an op-amp circuit that will produce 5 mA of output current for an input voltage of 50 mV. Calculate R_F.

6. Describe an op-amp circuit that can be used to convert 1 mA of current to 100 mV for display on the oscilloscope. Calculate R_F.

7. What is *virtual ground* and what input of the op-amp is at virtual ground for inverting amplifiers?

8. What determines the closed-loop voltage gain of an inverting voltage amplifier?

SUMMARY

FORMULAS

Differential Amplifiers

(10–1) $A_V = R_C/2r_e'$ (single output)

(10–2) $A_V = R_C/r_e'$ (differential output)

(10–3) $A_{v(com)} \cong R_C/2R_E$ (common-mode gain)

(10–4) $\text{CMRR} = A_{V(diff)}/A_{V(com)}$

Op-Amp Electrical Characteristics

(10–5) $I_{IB} = (I_{B1} + I_{B2})/2$

(10–6) $I_{IO} = |I_{B1} - I_{B2}|$

(10–7) $V_{IO} = (I_{B1} \cdot R_{B1}) - (I_{B2} \cdot R_{B2})$

(10–8) $V_{IO} = I_{IO} \cdot R_B$

(10–9) $V_{OO} = A_{OL} \cdot V_{IO}$

(10–10) $\text{CMRR} = A_{OL}/A_{V(com)}$

(10–11) $v_{out} = A_{OL}v_{diff}$

(10–12) $v_{diff} = v_{in} - v_f$

Noninverting Amplifiers

(10–13) $B = R_I/(R_I + R_F)$

(10–14) $v_f = v_{out} \cdot R_I/(R_I + R_F) = Bv_{out}$

(10–15) $v_{diff} = v_{in} - Bv_{out}$

(10–16) $A_V = v_{out}/v_{in} = A_{OL}/(1 + A_{OL}B)$

(10–17) $A_V \cong 1/B = (R_I + R_F)/R_I$

(10–18) $\text{Loop Gain} = A_{OL}B$

(10–19) $Z_{in} = r_{in}(1 + BA_{OL})$

(10–20) $Z_{out} = r_{out}/(1 + BA_{OL})$ (inverting and noninverting)

(10–21) $g_m = i_{out}/v_{in} = 1/R_F$

Inverting Amplifiers

(10–22) $Z_{in} = V_{diff}/I_{in} = V_{out}/A_{OL}I_{in}$ (at inverting input of op-amp)

(10–23) $R_F = V_{out}/I_{in}$

(10–24) $Z_{in} = R_{in(Miller)} = R_F/A_{OL}$ (at inverting input of op-amp)

(10–25) $R_{out(Miller)} = R_F$

(10–26) $A_V = v_{out}/v_{in} = R_F/R_I$

(10–27) $I_{out}/I_{in} = 1 + R_1/R_2$ (current feedback)

(10–28) $R_1 = R_2[(I_{out}/I_{in}) - 1]$ (current feedback)

CONCEPTS

- The input resistance of an op-amp is very high and the output resistance is very low.
- The input and output impedances of an op-amp circuit can be made much higher or lower depending on the circuit configuration.
- The open-loop gain of the op-amp is very high (100,000 or more).
- The voltages that appear at the two inputs to an op-amp are nearly the same. The difference between them depends on open-loop gain.
- The noninverting input always has a very high impedance.
- The inverting input always has a very low impedance, called *virtual ground*.
- Op-amp circuit functions such as A_V and g_m are virtually independent of open-loop gain.

COMPARING OP-AMP CONFIGURATIONS

Circuit Type	Figure	Function	Z_{in}	Z_{out}	Purpose
NONINVERTING					
Voltage feedback	10–16	v_{out}/v_{in}	$\gg r_{in}$	$\ll r_{out}$	In-phase voltage amplifier
Current feedback	10–21	i_{out}/v_{in}	$\gg r_{in}$	$> r_{out}$	Constant-current source
INVERTING					
Voltage feedback	10–23	v_{out}/i_{in}	$\ll r_{in}$	$\ll r_{out}$	Convert current to voltage
Voltage feedback	10–25	v_{out}/v_{in}	$< r_{in}$	$\ll r_{out}$	Inverting voltage amplifier
Current feedback	10–27	i_{out}/i_{in}	$\ll r_{in}$	$> r_{out}$	Current amplifier

NEED-TO-KNOW SOLUTION

See Figures 10–16, 17, and 18. It's that simple.

QUESTIONS

10–1 INTRODUCTION TO OPERATIONAL AMPLIFIERS (OP-AMPS)

1. Why are op-amps so popular?
2. Why is the schematic symbol for an op-amp also a block symbol?
3. Briefly describe the ideal amplifier.
4. Describe the practical op-amp.

10–2 THE DIFFERENTIAL AMPLIFIER (DIFF-AMP)

5. Given a diff-amp like that of Figure 10–3, if a small positive DC voltage is applied to the base of Q_2, what happens to the collector voltage of Q_1? Explain why.

6. Which of the following produces the largest output voltage from a diff-amp?
    (a) single input and single output
    (b) single input and differential output
    (c) differential input and single output
    (d) differential input and differential output

7. What does common-mode rejection mean?

8. Why is the common-mode gain of a diff-amp less than one (1)?

9. Give a simple definition for CMRR in reference to diff-amps.

10. Describe an application where the common-mode rejection characteristic of a diff-amp or op-amp is very helpful.

11. What is the purpose for the trim-pot in the working op-amp model of Figure 10–11?

10–3 OP-AMP ELECTRICAL CHARACTERISTICS

12. In an op-amp circuit, how can an output offset voltage be corrected?

13. What is a method of correcting an input offset current?

14. How can you determine the input resistance and output resistance of a particular type of op-amp?

15. Explain open-loop voltage gain.

16. Is the maximum output voltage swing of an op-amp always equal to the $\pm$VDC supply values? Explain.

17. Expressed in decibels, what is a typical value for the CMRR of op-amps?

18. What is slew rate and how is it determined?

10–4 OP-AMP PERFORMANCE WITH NEGATIVE FEEDBACK

19. Is the input impedance of a noninverting amplifier very high or is it very low?

20. What does negative feedback have to do with the input impedance of a noninverting amplifier?

21. Why is the difference in voltage between the two inputs of an op-amp circuit always very small?

22. What does the voltage feedback ratio of a noninverting amplifier circuit have to do with the amplifier's closed-loop gain?

23. Explain loop gain.

24. How does negative voltage feedback affect the output impedance of the op-amp?

25. How does negative current feedback affect the output impedance of the op-amp?

26. Explain virtual ground in reference to inverting amplifiers.

27. Is the Miller input resistance of an inverting amplifier very high, or is it very low?
28. Describe an op-amp circuit that can be used to increase the sensitivity of an analog ammeter.

PROBLEMS

10–2 THE DIFFERENTIAL AMPLIFIER (DIFF-AMP)

1. The collector resistors of a differential amplifier are 22 kΩ. The DC emitter current of each transistor is 257 μA. A 1-mV signal is applied to one input. Calculate the voltage gain, the single-ended output voltage, and the differential output voltage.
2. The collector resistors of a differential amplifier are 8.2 kΩ. The DC emitter current of each transistor is 689 μA. A 3-mV signal is applied to one input. Calculate the voltage gain, the single-ended output voltage, and the differential output voltage.
3. The collector resistors of a differential amplifier are 3.3 kΩ. The internal emitter resistance (r_e') of each transistor is 14.6 Ω. A 5-mV signal is applied differentially to both inputs. Calculate the voltage gain, the single-ended voltage, and the differential output voltage.
4. The collector resistors of a differential amplifier are 5.6 kΩ. The DC emitter current of each transistor is 1 mA. A 7-mV signal is applied differentially to both inputs. Calculate the voltage gain, the single-ended output voltage, and the differential output voltage.
5. A diff-amp has a common-mode gain of 0.08 and a differential gain of 250. Calculate the CMRR.
6. A diff-amp has a common-mode gain of 0.12 and a differential gain of 312. Calculate the CMRR.

10–3 OP-AMP ELECTRICAL CHARACTERISTICS

7. If the bias current for one input of an op-amp is 90 nA and the bias current for the other input is 100 nA, what is the average bias current and the input offset current?
8. If the bias current for one input of an op-amp is 60 nA and the bias current for the other input is 90 nA, what is the average bias current and the input offset current?
9. If the bias current for one input of an op-amp is 70 nA, the bias current for the other input is 80 nA, and the input bias resistor for each input is 4.7 kΩ, calculate the input offset voltage.
10. If the bias current for one input of an op-amp is 0.3 nA, the bias current for the other input is 0.28 nA, and the input bias resistor for each input is 100 kΩ, calculate the input offset voltage.
11. Express an open-loop gain of 175,000 in decibels.
12. Express an open-loop gain of 240,000 in decibels.
13. An op-amp has an open-loop gain of 110 dB and a common-mode gain of 6.5. Calculate its CMRR.
14. An op-amp has an open-loop gain of 106 dB and a common-mode gain of 18 dB. Calculate its CMRR.

10–4 OP-AMP PERFORMANCE WITH NEGATIVE FEEDBACK

15. The open-loop gain of an op-amp is 106 dB. If the output voltage is 2.6 V, what is the value of the difference voltage between the two inputs?

16. The open-loop gain of an op-amp is 80,000. If the output voltage is 4.2 V, what is the value of the difference voltage between the two inputs?

17. Calculate B, A_V, v_{diff}, v_{in}, loop gain, Z_{in}, and Z_{out} for Figure 10–28. For the op-amp shown, $r_{in} = 3$ MΩ and $r_{out} = 80$ Ω.

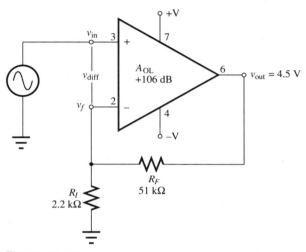

Figure 10–28

18. Calculate B, A_V, v_{diff}, v_{in}, loop gain, Z_{in}, and Z_{out} for Figure 10–29. For the op-amp shown, $r_{in} = 2$ MΩ and $r_{out} = 50$ Ω.

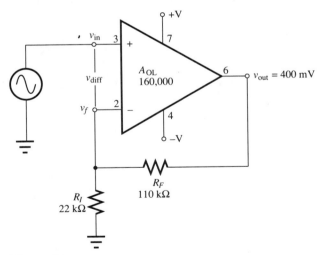

Figure 10–29

19. Given a noninverting amplifier with current feedback (Figure 10–21), if the load is 5 mA for an input voltage of 150 mV, what is the value of R_F? What is the value of g_m for the amplifier?

20. Given a noninverting amplifier with current feedback (Figure 10–21). If the load is 10 mA for an input voltage of 200 mV, what is the value of R_F? What is the value of g_m for the amplifier?

21. Given an inverting amplifier with voltage feedback and an open-loop gain of 130,000 (Figure 10–23). If the input current is 5 mA for an output voltage of 100 mV, what is the value of R_F and Z_{in}?

22. Given an inverting amplifier with voltage feedback and an open-loop gain of 200,000 (Figure 10–23). If the input current is 20 mA for an output voltage of 500 mV, what is the value of R_F and Z_{in}?

23. Calculate A_V, v_{diff}, v_{out}, and Z_{in} for Figure 10–30 if $R_F = 220$ kΩ and $R_I = 4.7$ kΩ.

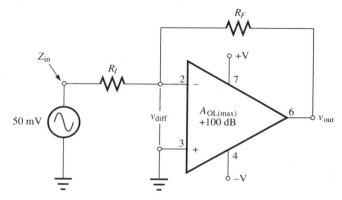

Figure 10–30

24. Calculate A_V, d_{diff}, v_{out}, and Z_{in} for Figure 10–30 if $R_F = 150$ kΩ and $R_I = 10$ kΩ.

25. Calculate the proper value for R_1 in Figure 10–31 if R_2 is 820 Ω, I_{meter} is

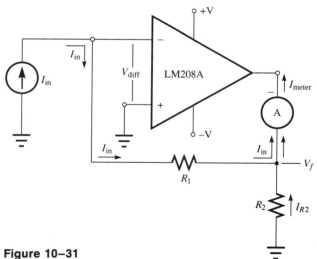

Figure 10–31

250 μA for full-scale deflection, and I_{in} is 50 μA.

26. Calculate the proper value for R_1 in Figure 10–31 if R_2 is 560 Ω, I_{meter} is 1 mA for full-scale deflection, and I_{in} is 100 μA.

ADDITIONAL PROBLEMS

27. An op-amp has an open-loop gain of 140,000 and a common-mode gain of 8. What is the common-mode rejection ratio?

28. The low to high rise time for the output pulse from an op-amp is 2.7 μs. During this time, the output voltage rises 11.3 V in response to a square-wave input pulse. Express the slew rate in V/s and V/μs.

29. An op-amp has an open-loop voltage gain of 100,000 and is used to make a noninverting amplifier. R_F is 330 kΩ and R_I is 20 kΩ. If v_{in} is 15 mV, what is the amplitude of v_{out} and v_{diff}?

30. An op-amp has an open-loop gain of 170,000 and is used as a noninverting amplifier. R_F is chosen to be 51 kΩ and R_I is 10 kΩ. Determine the loop gain.

31. Determine the input and output impedance for Figure 10–32 in which $r_{in} = 2$ MΩ, $r_{out} = 60$ Ω, and $A_{OL} = 145,000$.

32. Determine the load (current) and transconductance for Figure 10–33.

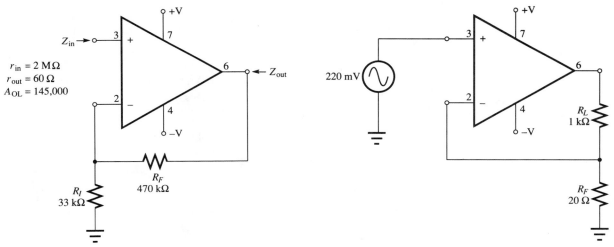

Figure 10–32

Figure 10–33

33. Determine the input impedance for Figure 10–34. Also determine the input and output voltages.

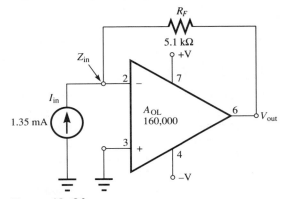

Figure 10–34

34. Determine the following for Figure 10–35: Z_{in}, Z_{out}, i_{in}, A_V, v_{out}, and v_{diff}.

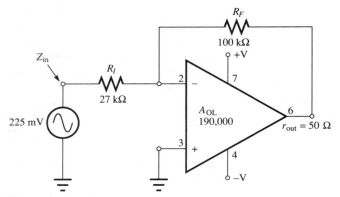

Figure 10–35

35. Determine the following for Figure 10–36: Z_{in}, Z_{out}, i_{in}, A_V, v_{out}, and v_{diff}.

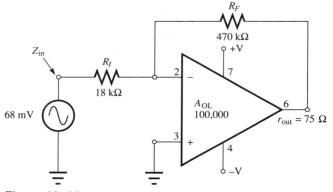

Figure 10–36

36. Use an op-amp to increase the sensitivity of a current meter from 500 μA to 50 μA. Let $R_2 = 1 \text{ k}\Omega$.

ANSWERS TO SELF-CHECKS

SELF-CHECK 10–1

1. The op-amp can perform many different analog operations such as addition, subtraction, integration, and differentiation. It can also be used for filtering and voltage and current amplification.
2. One input is an inverting input and the other is a noninverting input.
3. For a real op-amp, the voltage gain is high but not infinite, the input resistance is high but not infinite, and the output resistance is low but not exactly 0 Ω. Also, a real op-amp's frequency response and distortion characteristics are good but not perfect.

SELF-CHECK 10–2

1. For a perfectly balanced diff-amp, the bias currents are equal, the input voltages are equal, and the differential output voltage is 0 V.
2. A +DC input voltage of the first transistor appears at the emitter of both transistors. This reduces the bias on the second transistor, which conducts less. Thus, the collector voltage of the second transistor increases.
3. $v_{out(diff)} = 2 \cdot (v_{in} \cdot R_C/2r'_e) = v_{in} \cdot R_C/r'_e$
$\qquad = 2 \cdot (5 \text{ mV} \cdot 6.8 \text{ k}\Omega/60 \text{ }\Omega) = 1.13 \text{ V}$
4. $v_{out(diff)} = 2 \cdot (v_{in} \cdot R_C/2r'_e) = v_{in} \cdot R_C/r'_e$
$\qquad = 2 \cdot (10 \text{ mV} \cdot 4.7 \text{ k}\Omega/70 \text{ }\Omega) = 1.34 \text{ V}$
5. $A_{V(diff)} = 4.7 \text{ k}\Omega/70 \text{ }\Omega = 67.1$, CMRR $= 67.1/0.5 = 134 = 42.5 \text{ dB}$

SELF-CHECK 10–3

1. A DC output offset voltage creates a continuous load current and may be amplified by a succeeding stage.
2. The input offset current may increase or decrease the output offset voltage.
3. The input offset current can be corrected by adjusting the values of the input resistors or the effects of the input offset current can be canceled using an offset null-pot.
4. The open-loop voltage gain is the wide-open gain with no negative feedback.
5. Maximum output voltage swing $\cong \pm 18$ V to ± 19 V
6. CMRR $= 150,000/2 = 75,000 = 97.5$ dB
7. Slew rate is the rate of rise of the output pulse as a result of a square-wave input pulse. The slew rate is measured in V/μs.

SELF-CHECK 10–4

1. 16.7 μV
2. $B = 0.176$
3. $Z_{in} = 39,133$ MΩ, $Z_{out} = 3.83$ mΩ
4. $A_V = 9.2 = 19.3$ dB, loop gain $= 13,034 = 82.3$ dB
5. This is a noninverting amplifier with current feedback. $R_F = 10$ Ω
6. This is an inverting amplifier. $R_F = 100$ Ω
7. The inverting input is considered to be a virtual ground because the voltage at that input is always very low and current appears to flow into it.
8. $A_V = R_F/R_I$.

SUGGESTED PROJECTS

1. Add some of the main concepts, formulas, and procedures from this chapter to your Electronics Notebook.
2. Construct and test the circuit of Figure 10–11.
3. Using a 741 or LF356, construct and test some of the op-amp circuits in this chapter.

The oscilloscope display shows the slew response of a 741 op-amp. The upper trace is the input signal and the lower trace is the delayed output signal. The slow rise and fall of the output square wave is due to internal capacitance. This capacitance limits the small-signal and power bandwidth of the amplifier. (Courtesy of Tektronix)

11 Op-Amp Frequency Response and Troubleshooting

OBJECTIVES

After studying this chapter, you will be able to

- explain the relationship between large-signal bandwidth and slew rate.
- explain the relationship between closed-loop gain and op-amp frequency response.
- explain the need for compensation to prevent amplifier oscillation.
- explain the difference between the unity-loop-gain frequency and the critical frequency.
- explain the difference between an unconditionally stable op-amp and a conditionally stable op-amp.
- troubleshoot op-amps.

NEED TO KNOW

Many different op-amps have the same pin assignments, or designations, to make it easy to substitute one op-amp type for another in a circuit. They are said to be pin-for-pin compatible. Yet, when you substitute one op-amp type for another in an existing circuit, you may discover some interesting operational characteristics or problems. With one op-amp, amplified music or voice may sound clean and crisp, indicating a generous frequency response. With another op-amp, the sound may be "muddy," having a poor high-frequency response. Also, with high-level audio signals, one op-amp may introduce noticeable distortion while another op-amp does not. Another problem you may run into is an op-amp that turns into an oscillator instead of an amplifier. In other words, the op-amp generates a constant signal on its own. Why is there such a difference in performance for so called pin-for-pin compatible op-amps? That's a very good question and it's something you definitely have a need to know. By the time you finish this chapter, you will know.

INTRODUCTION

By now you are aware that electronic devices all have frequency-response limitations due to internal and external reactances. In this chapter, you will explore the frequency-related limitations of the op-amp. You will see why these limitations exist and how they are compensated for. This exploration will include a discussion of op-amp slew rate, overall frequency response, op-amp stability (preventing oscillations), and basic troubleshooting. This information is essential to your successful implementation of op-amps to fulfill specific design requirements. Enjoy!

11–1 OP-AMP SLEW RATE AND BANDWIDTH

POWER BANDWIDTH AND SLEW-RATE DISTORTION

The Importance of Slew Rate (*SR*)

Slew rate is important because it effects frequency response, waveform distortion at higher frequencies, and power bandwidth. Look at Figure 11–1. Note the obvious distortion in the output waveform. The output should be a

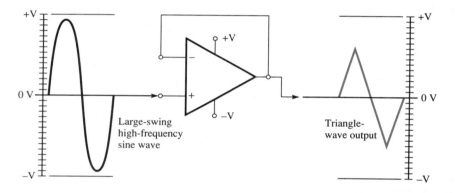

Large-swing high-frequency sine wave

Triangle-wave output

SLEW RATE IS TOO LOW FOR THE
HIGH-AMPLITUDE, HIGH-FREQUENCY
SINE WAVE INPUT SIGNAL

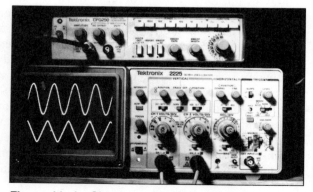

Figure 11–1 Slew-rate signal distortion.

sine wave. Instead, it is a triangle wave and it is reduced in amplitude. The output signal should be the same amplitude as the input signal with the op-amp configured as shown. What's happening here? The sine wave input voltage is changing at a higher rate than the internal capacitance of the op-amp can charge or discharge. Thus, the sine wave input reaches a positive peak before the output is much over half of its peak value. There just isn't enough time for the output signal to reach maximum value. The triangle-wave output must follow the charging and discharging internal capacitances and cannot follow the input sine wave.

Reducing Slew-Rate Distortion

How can this output distortion be reduced or avoided? First, reduce the amplitude of the input signal. If the amplitude of the input sine wave is reduced significantly, the rate of change in its voltage will be reduced. For example, a 20-kHz sine wave has a 12.5-μs positive-peak rise time from 0° to +90° ($t_{(0° \text{ to } 90°)} = 1/(4 \cdot 20 \text{ kHz}) = 12.5 \mu s$). Let's assume the input peak voltage is +14 V. The rate of change in input voltage is 14 V/12.5 μs = 1.12 V/μs. If the op-amp is a 741, the slew rate is 0.5 V/μs. As you can see, the rate of change in input voltage is greater than the 0.5-V/μs slew rate. By reducing the input amplitude, the rate of change in input voltage can be reduced to, or below, the 0.5-V/μs slew rate. If the input is reduced to a maximum peak of 5 V, the input rate of change is reduced to 5 V/12.5 μs = 0.4 V/μs. This is less than the 0.5-V/μs slew rate and the output should now be an undistorted 5-V_p sine wave.

A second cure for slew-rate distortion is to reduce the frequency of the input sine wave. Let's go back to the 14-V_p, 20-kHz sine wave. Now, let's reduce the frequency to 5 kHz but keep the amplitude at 14 V_p. The rate of change in input voltage from 0° to +90° is now 14 V/50 μs = 0.28 V/μs. The rate of change in voltage of the input sine wave is now less than the 0.5-V/μs slew rate. The output signal should now be an undistorted 14-V_p sine wave.

The last way we can reduce slew-rate distortion is to use an op-amp with a higher slew rate. An LF356 has a slew rate of 12 V/μs, an MC1741S has a slew rate of 12 V/μs, and a LF357 has a slew rate of 50 V/μs. Any of these op-amps, and many others, can provide undistorted higher-amplitude, higher-frequency output signals.

EXAMPLE 11–1

An op-amp has a slew rate of 2.5 V/μs. The op-amp is configured and tested as a unity-gain noninverting amplifier. The input signal is a 20-V_{P-P} sine wave at a frequency of 25 kHz. Calculate the rate of rise of input voltage and determine if the output voltage will be distorted.

$t_{(0° \text{ to } 90°)} = 1/(4 \cdot 25 \text{ kHz}) = 10 \mu s$

The input rise rate is 10 V/10 μs = 1 V/μs.
This is less than the op-amp's slew rate. Therefore, there should be no noticeable distortion.

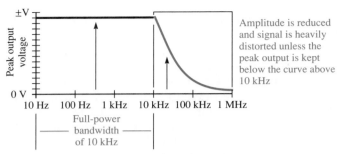

Figure 11–2   Power bandwidth limitations.

Full-Power Bandwidth Graphs and Calculations

Figure 11–2 is a graph that shows the relationship between frequency and amplitude for large signals (signals that are close to maximum output swing). Often these graphs are provided on the data sheets for op-amp. Notice that the amplitude of the output signal for this particular op-amp is not reduced until the frequency is increased above approximately 10 kHz. Along with the reduction in amplitude comes the slew-rate distortion. Above 10 kHz, the amplitude of the input signal must be reduced to avoid slew-rate distortion in the output. The full-power, full-signal-swing bandwidth is only approximately 10 kHz in this case.

The full-power bandwidth (BW_p) can also be calculated when slew rate (SR) and desired peak output voltage (V_p) are known. Consider Examples 11–2 and 11–3.

$$BW_p = SR/(2\pi V_p) = 0.159 \cdot SR/V_p \tag{11–1}$$

where slew rate (SR) is expressed in volts per second.

$$V_P = SR/(2\pi BW_p) = 0.159 \cdot SR/BW_p \tag{11–2}$$

EXAMPLE 11–2

Determine the power bandwidth for a 741 op-amp having a slew rate of 0.5 V/μs at an input and output amplitude of 14 V_P (noninverting, unity-gain configuration).

$BW_p = 0.159 \cdot SR/V_p = 0.159 \cdot 500{,}000$ V/s/14 $V_p = 5.68$ kHz

EXAMPLE 11–3

What is the largest undistorted output amplitude of a 10-kHz sine wave that can be obtained from a 741 op-amp having a 0.5 V/μs slew rate? In other words, the desired power bandwidth is 10 kHz.

$$V_P = 0.159 \cdot SR/BW_p = 0.159 \cdot \frac{500{,}000 \text{ V/s}}{10 \text{ kHz}} \cong 8 \ V_P$$

Formula 11–2 can be used to graph the power-bandwidth response of any op-amp when its slew rate is known (like that of Figure 11–2).

Review this section before continuing to the next section. Test your understanding by answering the questions of Self-Check 11–1.

Self-Check 11–1

1. What causes slew-rate distortion?
2. What is the power bandwidth of an op-amp that has a slew rate of 1.5 V/μs if the desired output amplitude is 10 V_P?
3. What is the maximum peak voltage of a 25-kHz sine wave at the output of an op-amp that has a slew rate of 0.75 V/μs?

11–2 OP-AMP FREQUENCY RESPONSE

In this section, you will explore the frequency response characteristics of the op-amp as related to amplifier gain and bandwidth. You will see how closed-loop gain and bandwidth are inversely related. The desire for amplifier gain and bandwidth is a tradeoff. More gain means less bandwidth. Let's see how and why.

OPEN-LOOP FREQUENCY RESPONSE

Figure 11–3 illustrates an internally compensated op-amp and its open-loop frequency response. The op-amp diagram shows the internal amplifier and equivalent lowpass filter created by internal resistance and a compensation capacitor (C_C). Many, but not all, op-amps are internally compensated. The 741 is a classic example. Data sheets indicate whether the op-amp is internally compensated or needs external compensation. If external compensa-

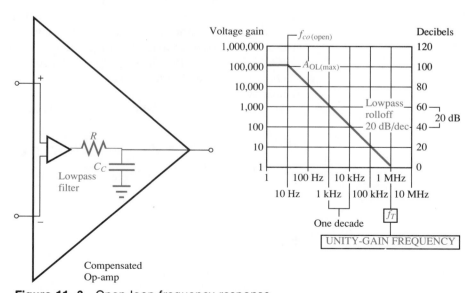

Figure 11–3 Open-loop frequency response.

tion is needed, the data sheet will suggest values to use and/or provide diagrams and formulas to accomplish this.

As you can see in Figure 11–3, the *RC* lowpass filter produces a rolloff in gain that starts at 10 Hz. The slope of rolloff is 20 dB/dec as would be expected for a simple *RC* filter. At 1 MHz, the open-loop gain has dropped to unity (1). The frequency at which the open-loop gain is unity (1) is known as the **unity-gain frequency (f_T).** The graph indicates that if the amplifier is operated open-loop (no feedback network), the gain will be maximum (100,000) only below 10 Hz. The gain drops at the rate of 20 dB/dec until the gain is one (1) at the unity-gain frequency. Needless to say, this is very poor. For most audio applications, we would like to have a flat response at least to 10 kHz, and preferably to 20 kHz. This can be done by sacrificing gain. Let's see how.

CLOSED-LOOP FREQUENCY RESPONSE

Gain-Bandwidth Product (*GBW* or *GBP*)

The **gain-bandwidth product (*GBP*)** is the product of amplifier gain and amplifier bandwidth and is always equal to the unity-gain frequency (f_T). (You probably recall this from our discussion of transistor-amplifier bandwidth.) This indicates that the frequency response of the op-amp can be extended by sacrificing gain, as demonstrated in Figure 11–4. As you can see, a voltage-feedback network (R_F and R_I) is used to provide a closed-loop gain that is much lower than the open-loop gain. In this case, the closed-loop voltage gain is set at 100, or 40 dB. As a result, the bandwidth has increased from 10 Hz to 10 kHz. The gain-bandwidth product is always equal to f_T, which is 1 MHz = 100 · 10 kHz.

The bandwidth can be set to any value up to the unity-gain frequency simply by setting the gain to the value that corresponds to the desired cutoff frequency. For example the bandwidth could be extended to 100 kHz by dropping the closed-loop gain to 10 (20 dB) or the bandwidth could be limited to 100 Hz by setting the closed-loop gain to 10,000, as shown in Figure 11–5. Therefore, you must first decide the bandwidth you want, then set the gain accordingly.

Here are some mathematical relationships of which you should be aware.

$$GBP = f_{co(\text{open})} \cdot A_{\text{OL(max)}} = f_T \qquad (11\text{–}3)$$

$$GBP = f_{co(\text{closed})} \cdot A_V = f_T \qquad (11\text{–}4)$$

$$A_V = f_T/f_{co(\text{closed})} \qquad (11\text{–}5)$$

$$f_{co(\text{open})} \cdot A_{\text{OL(max)}} = f_{co(\text{closed})} \cdot A_V = f_T$$

therefore,

$$f_{co(\text{closed})} = f_{co(\text{open})} \cdot A_{\text{OL(max)}}/A_V \qquad (11\text{–}6)$$

$$A_V = A_{\text{OL(max)}} \cdot f_{co(\text{open})}/f_{co(\text{closed})} \qquad (11\text{–}7)$$

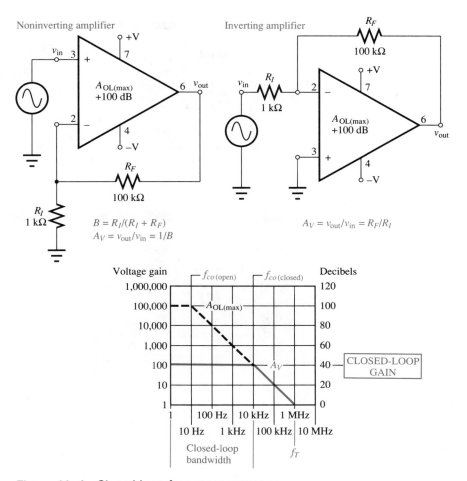

$$B = R_I/(R_I + R_F)$$
$$A_V = v_{out}/v_{in} = 1/B$$

$$A_V = v_{out}/v_{in} = R_F/R_I$$

Figure 11–4 Closed-loop frequency response.

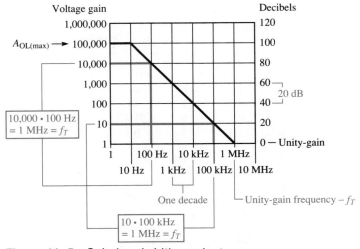

Figure 11–5 Gain-bandwidth product.

EXAMPLE 11–4 ▦

An op-amp has a bandwidth of 32 kHz with a closed-loop gain of 15.
(a) What is its *GBP*? (b) If the closed-loop gain is increased to 20, what
is the bandwidth? (c) What is the closed-loop gain if the desired bandwidth is 100 Hz?

(a) $GBP = f_{co(closed)} \cdot A_V = f_T = 32 \text{ kHz} \cdot 15 = 480 \text{ kHz}$
(b) $f_{co(closed)} = f_T/A_V = 480 \text{ kHz}/20 = 24 \text{ kHz}$
(c) $A_V = f_T/f_{co(closed)} = 480 \text{ kHz}/100 \text{ Hz} = 4{,}800 = 73.6 \text{ dB}$

EXAMPLE 11–5 ▦

An op-amp has an open-loop gain of 150,000 below a cutoff frequency
of 12 Hz. (a) Determine the *GBP*. (b) What is the closed-loop gain if the
desired cutoff frequency is 20 kHz?

(a) $GBP = f_T = f_{co(open)} \cdot A_{OL(max)} = 12 \text{ Hz} \cdot 150{,}000 = 1.8 \text{ MHz}$
(b) $A_V = A_{OL(max)} \cdot f_{co(open)}/f_{co(closed)} = f_T/f_{co(closed)}$
         $= 1.8 \text{ MHz}/20 \text{ kHz} = 90$

If the closed-loop gain A_V is set at 90, the bandwidth will be 20 kHz.

Comparing Popular Op-Amps

Table 11–1 is a listing and comparison of basic parameters for a variety of
popular op-amps. All of the parameters listed have been covered in this
chapter and the previous chapter. Take time to compare these op-amps and
review the parameters as needed. You will notice that some of the listed op-
amps have very high slew rates and gain-bandwidth products.

TABLE 11–1   POPULAR OP-AMPS

Type	A_{OL}	GBP	SR	V_{IO}	I_{IO}	CMRR
MC1741	200 k	1 MHz	0.5 V/μs	1 mV	20 nA	90 dB
MC1741S	200 k	1 MHz	12 V/μs	1 mV	30 nA	90 dB
LM11	300 k	600 kHz*	0.25 V/μs*	0.1 mV	0.5 pA	130 dB
LM301A	160 k	6 MHz*	9 V/μs*	2 mV	3 nA	90 dB
LM108A	300 k	2.5 MHz*	0.9 V/μs*	0.3 mV	0.05 nA	110 dB
LF351	100 k	4 MHz	13 V/μs	5 mV	25 pA	100 dB
LF356	200 k	5 MHz	12 V/μs	3 mV	3 pA	100 dB
MC34071†	100 k	4.5 MHz	10 V/μs	1 mV	6 nA	97 dB
MC34181	60 k	4 MHz	10 V/μs	0.5 mV	0.001 nA	86 dB
LM6361	2,900	50 MHz	300 V/μs	5 mV	150 nA	94 dB
LM6365	38 k	725 MHz	300 V/μs	1 mV	150 nA	102 dB

* Depends on value of external compensation capacitor.
† Single-supply op-amp.

Time once again for a self-check.

---

1. For a compensated op-amp, explain how gain and bandwidth are related.
2. If the closed-loop gain of an op-amp is 150 at a frequency of 80 kHz, what is its unity-gain frequency?
3. If an op-amp has an f_T of 2.5 MHz and the closed-loop gain is set at 60 dB, what is the resulting bandwidth?
4. If a certain op-amp has an open-loop gain of 200,000 and an open-loop cutoff frequency of 8 Hz, what is its unity-gain frequency?
5. When using an op-amp for a particular application, what is the first thing you must decide?

11–3 PREVENTING OSCILLATIONS IN OP-AMP CIRCUITS

Since the op-amp is a very high-gain device, it is easy for some op-amps to begin oscillating on their own. This means the op-amp produces an AC frequency at its output with or without an input signal. This is not good, since the purpose of the amplifier is to amplify only those signals intentionally placed at its input. Steps must be taken to ensure that the op-amp is stable and will not oscillate.

What makes the op-amp oscillate? There are two conditions that must exist for oscillation to occur. First, the frequency at which the op-amp oscillates must be fed back in-phase at the inverting input. What does that mean? As you know, the output is 180° out of phase with the inverting input of the op-amp. In addition to this 180° there is phase shift created by internal stage capacitances. If preventive steps are not taken, at some high frequency the total phase shift will be 360° = 0° and oscillation may take place. Oscillation will take place if, in addition to the 360° phase shift, the loop gain is greater than one (1), for it is the loop that is being used to create the oscillations. Recall that loop gain is $A_{OL}B$, the product of open-loop gain and the voltage-feedback ratio. Now, let's see how all of this is put together.

CUMULATIVE PHASE SHIFT FOR UNCOMPENSATED OP-AMPS

Earlier, you may have wondered why the 741 op-amp is so severely compensated (internally) that the open-loop cutoff frequency is only 10 Hz. Here, you will discover the reason. We will begin by examining the performance of an uncompensated op-amp.

Lag Networks

Figure 11–6 shows data for a hypothetical op-amp. Its open-loop gain is 100,000 (100 dB). The internal stages of this op-amp contain RC lowpass filter networks (lag networks) that produce three cutoff frequencies, sometimes called **break frequencies.** For our example, these frequencies are 100

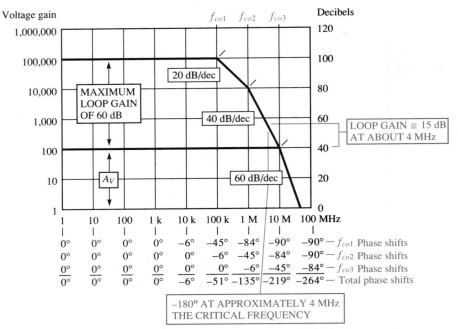

Figure 11–6 Cumulative phase shift for the uncompensated op-amp.

kHz, 1 MHz, and 10 MHz. Each of these lowpass networks contributes a phase lag (Φ) that increases with frequency to a maximum of $-90°$.

$$\Phi = -\arctan(R/X_C) \tag{11-8}$$

As you can see in Formula 11–8, as frequency changes so does capacitive reactance and phase angle. We can use Formula 11–8 to derive another formula that will allow us to determine phase angle for any frequency (f) based on the network's cutoff frequency (f_{co}). First, at f_{co}, $X_C = R = 1/(2\pi f_{co}C)$. Therefore, $1/(2\pi f_{co}C)$ can be substituted for R in Formula 11–8.

$$\Phi = -\arctan[(1/(2\pi f_{co}C))/X_C]$$

$$X_C = 1/(2\pi fC)$$

By substitution,

$$\Phi = -\arctan[(1/(2\pi f_{co}C))/(1/(2\pi fC))]$$

$$\Phi = -\arctan[(2\pi fC)/(2\pi f_{co}C)]$$

As you can see, $2\pi C$ cancels, leaving

$$\Phi = -\arctan(f/f_{co}) \tag{11-9}$$

Using Formula 11–9, the phase angle at any frequency can quickly be determined. Consider the first row of phase shifts just below the graph of Figure 11–6. This row is labeled f_{co1} phase shifts. At 10 kHz, the phase shift is $-\arctan(10 \text{ kHz}/100 \text{ kHz}) = -5.7° \cong -6°$. At 100 kHz, which is f_{co1}, the phase angle must be $-45°$. At 1 MHz, the phase shift is $-\arctan(1 \text{ MHz}/100$

kHz) $= -84.3° \cong -84°$. At 10 MHz and above the phase shift is effectively $-90°$.

Cumulative Lag

Each cutoff frequency contributes a phase shift as indicated in Figure 11–6. The total, or cumulative, phase shift is simply the sum of all phase shifts.

$$\Phi_t = -\arctan(f/f_{co1}) - \arctan(f/f_{co2}) - \arctan(f/f_{co3}) \tag{11-10}$$

EXAMPLE 11–7

An uncompensated op-amp has three break frequencies, which are 50 kHz, 400 kHz, and 1.3 MHz. What is the total output voltage phase lag if the applied frequency is (a) 30 kHz, (b) 300 kHz, (c) 3 MHz?

$$\Phi_t = -\arctan(f/f_{co1}) - \arctan(f/f_{co2}) - \arctan(f/f_{co3})$$

(a) $\Phi_t = -\arctan(30\text{ kHz}/50\text{ kHz}) - \arctan(30\text{ kHz}/400\text{ kHz})$
     $\qquad -\arctan(30\text{ kHz}/1.3\text{ MHz})$
     $\qquad = -31° - 4.3° - 1.3° = -36.6°$

(b) $\Phi_t = -\arctan(300\text{ kHz}/50\text{ kHz}) - \arctan(300\text{ kHz}/400\text{ kHz})$
     $\qquad -\arctan(300\text{ kHz}/1.3\text{ MHz})$
     $\qquad = -80.5° - 36.9° - 13° = -130.4°$

(c) $\Phi_t = -\arctan(3\text{ MHz}/50\text{ kHz}) - \arctan(3\text{ MHz}/400\text{ kHz})$
     $\qquad -\arctan(3\text{ MHz}/1.3\text{ MHz})$
     $\qquad = -89° - 82.4° - 66.6° = -238°$

Critical Frequency

The frequency at which the total phase shift is $-180°$ is called the **critical frequency.** If the loop gain is greater than one (1) at the critical frequency, the op-amp will oscillate. Consider the case of an op-amp circuit that has a closed-loop voltage gain (A_V) of 100 (40 dB). This is illustrated in Figure 11–6. The maximum loop gain is 100 dB − 40 dB = 60 dB, where the loop gain is the difference in decibels between open-loop gain and closed-loop gain. Recall also that loop gain $= A_{OL}B = A_{OL}/A_V$.

Now, this is important. Notice how the loop gain ($A_{OL}B$) decreases above 100 kHz. The open-loop gain (A_{OL}) is decreasing due to internal capacitances. At approximately 4 MHz, the critical frequency is reached. In order for the amplifier *not* to oscillate, the loop gain must be less than one (1 = 0 dB). As you can see, the loop gain is about 15 dB at 4 MHz and the op-amp will surely oscillate.

To insure that this op-amp does not oscillate, the closed-loop voltage gain (A_V) must be *increased*. Say we adjust the values of R_F and R_I to give us a gain of 1,000 (60 dB). Draw a straight line across the graph at $A_V = 1,000$. Notice the loop gain is now less than one (1 = 0 dB) at the critical frequency ($\cong 4$ MHz) where loop gain is 55 dB − 60 dB = −5 dB. The op-amp is now **conditionally stable.** This means as long as the closed-loop gain is greater than about 60 dB, the op-amp will not oscillate. Consider Example 11–8.

EXAMPLE 11–8

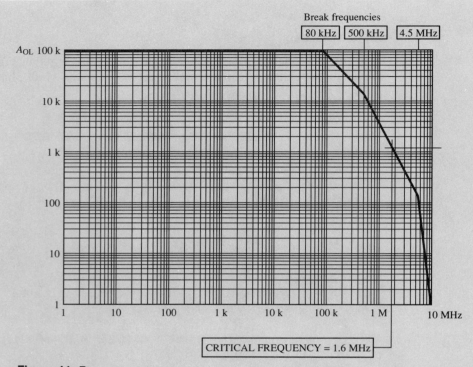

Figure 11–7

From Figure 11–7, determine the following:

(a) Is the op-amp conditionally stable if the closed loop gain is set at 1,000?

(b) For what values of closed-loop gain is this op-amp conditionally stable?

(a) From Figure 11–7, the loop gain is slightly greater than 1 at the critical frequency when the closed-loop gain is 1,000. Therefore, the op-amp is not stable and will oscillate near 1.6 MHz.

(b) The op-amp is conditionally stable for any closed-loop gain greater than approximately 1,100 or so. It is best to say that this op-amp will not be operated with a closed-loop gain less than 2,000. This will ensure stability since the loop gain would definitely be less than one near the critical frequency.

Worst Case

What happens if we use maximum voltage feedback, as in a unity-gain noninverting amplifier? Will the op-amp be stable or will it oscillate? Look once again at the graph of Figure 11–6. Unity gain is along the baseline. If the closed-loop gain is one (1), the loop gain at the critical frequency will be 55 dB. There is no doubt that this circuit will oscillate. Thus, the worst-case condition for oscillations is with unity-closed-loop gain. The unity-gain amplifier is the worst for stability.

How can we insure that the op-amp is **unconditionally stable** regardless of the closed-loop gain, even down to unity gain? Compensation is the cure. Let's see how.

CUMULATIVE PHASE SHIFT FOR COMPENSATED OP-AMPS

Compensated Response

Figure 11–8 shows the frequency response of our hypothetical op-amp after compensation has been added (solid graph). The additional capacitance causes the first cutoff frequency to be very low ($f_{co(dominant)}$ = 10 Hz). As you can see, the open-loop gain of the op-amp now rolls off at the rate of 20 dB/dec starting at 10 Hz. Notice that the total phase shift is only −141° all the way up to 100 kHz. The critical frequency is now somewhere around 300 kHz, where the open-loop gain is one (1). This op-amp may be unstable as a unity-gain amplifier because the loop gain is one (1) at or near the critical frequency where the total phase shift is −180°.

Phase Margin (Φ_{PM})

It is safe to say that the compensated amplifier of Figure 11–8 is *conditionally* stable for all closed-loop gains greater than 10. If $A_V = 10$ (20 dB), the loop gain will be unity at 100 kHz, where the total phase angle is −141° (loop

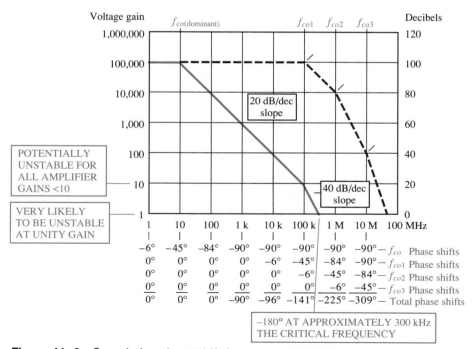

Figure 11–8 Cumulative phase shift for a compensated op-amp.

gain $= A_{OL(dB)} - A_{V(dB)} = 20$ dB $- 20$ dB $= 0$ dB $=$ unity loop gain) and 100 kHz is well below the critical frequency (300 kHz), where the phase angle is $-180°$. The difference in phase angle between $-180°$ and the phase angle of the frequency at unity loop gain is called the **phase margin** (Φ_{PM}).

$$\Phi_{PM} = |-180 - \Phi_{t(\text{unity loop gain})}| \tag{11–11}$$

In this case, when $A_V = 10$, the phase margin is $|-180 - (-141°)| = |-39°| = 39°$.

Slope and Phase Margin

Many designers maintain a safe phase margin by setting the op-amp closed-loop gain (A_V) at a level that intersects the open-loop gain rolloff only where the slope is 20 dB/dec. This means, for conditional stability, the closed-loop gain (A_V) of the compensated op-amp of Figure 11–8 can be anywhere between 10 and 100,000. This op-amp is considered to be potentially unstable for all closed-loop gains less than 10, since the phase margin is less than 45°. Designers like to use a phase margin close to or greater than 45° to absolutely insure stability. If you are using the 741 op-amp, you do not have to worry about phase margin because the internal compensation makes the 741 unconditionally stable even as a unity-gain amplifier.

External Compensation

Shown in Figure 11–9, the LM101A series of op-amps are externally compensated. Op-amps such as these let you determine the unity-gain frequency (f_T) by selecting the value of capacitance used for compensation. Notice the two rolloff slopes shown for the LM101A. The 3-pF capacitor gives you a higher frequency response than the 30-pF capacitor does. However, the op-amp is potentially unstable for closed-loop gains less than approximately three (3) when the 3-pF capacitor is used. Using the 30-pF capacitor, the op-amp is unconditionally stable (stable for all closed-loop gains). If the amplifier gain will be greater than three ($3 \cong 10$ dB), use a 3-pF capacitor for a wider bandwidth. However, you cannot operate the LM101A as a unity-gain amplifier if you use the 3-pF capacitor. You may also use other values of capacitance, such as 10 pF.

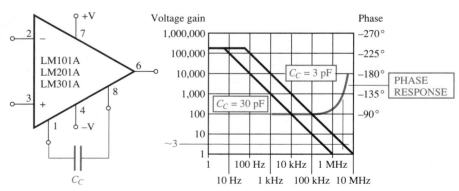

Figure 11–9 Compensation using a single external capacitor.

The data sheets for uncompensated op-amps usually show other methods of compensation and provide you with a circuit diagram and any necessary formulas.

Summary

- Internally compensated op-amps such as the 741 are unconditionally stable.
- Op-amps are stable as long as the unity-loop-gain frequency is well below the critical frequency where there is adequate phase margin (45° or so).
- For externally compensated op-amps, an adequate phase margin is ensured by setting the closed-loop gain at a level that intersects the 20 dB/dec slope of open-loop gain rolloff.
- The unity-gain op-amp circuit provides worst-case conditions because the loop gain is greater than 1 up to the unity-gain frequency (f_T).

It might be a good idea to reread this section. Take time to think everything through. Make sure you understand what the unity loop-gain frequency is and the concept of phase margin. Make sure you understand the summary. Test your understanding with Self-Check 11-3.

Self-Check 11-3

1. What are the two conditions that together cause oscillation?
2. Referring to Figure 11-6, why must the closed-loop gain be set at some value greater than 60 dB?
3. Explain critical frequency.
4. Referring to Figure 11-8, calculate the total phase shift at 200 kHz. (Hint: Use Formula 11-10 for each cutoff frequency.)
5. What does it mean for an op-amp circuit to be conditionally stable?
6. Explain the unity-loop-gain frequency.
7. Why does the unity-gain amplifier provide the worst-case conditions for instability?

11-4 TROUBLESHOOTING OP-AMPS

In most cases there isn't much to an op-amp circuit. Most of what can go bad is inside the op-amp and repair is accomplished through replacement. However, if the op-amp circuit does fail, there are some simple tests that can be performed to restore its operation. We will consider the use of the ohmmeter, DC voltmeter, and oscilloscope in op-amp troubleshooting.

USING THE OHMMETER

With power off, the ohmmeter can be used to measure continuity from the output back through the feedback resistors. This is illustrated in Figure 11-10. An open indicates that a break exists somewhere in the resistor line. A low reading indicates a short at the output or the inverting input.

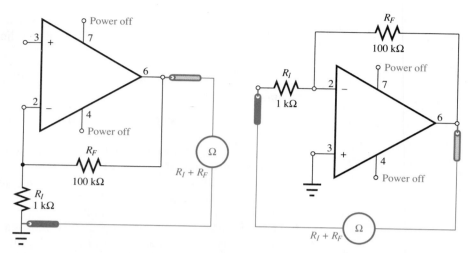

Figure 11–10 Simple power-off op-amp amplifier test using the ohmmeter.

USING THE DC VOLTMETER AND OSCILLOSCOPE

Figure 11–11 lists the checks that you need to make with power on. The DC voltages should be checked with power on and no input signal. Make sure the DC voltages are present at each supply pin (usually pins 7 and 4). A DC voltage measurement at the output will reveal the presence of an output offset voltage. If an extreme offset voltage is present, the op-amp may need to be replaced or circuit wiring carefully checked for shorts. If the offset is not severe, compensation can be added or the op-amp can be replaced.

With DC power applied and an input signal present, an oscilloscope can be used to check the amplifier for AC performance. The AC voltages at the two inputs (pins 2 and 3) should be nearly equal (recall that the difference voltage is very small). The output AC voltage should reflect the closed-loop gain of the amplifier circuit, where $v_{out}/v_{in} = (R_F + R_I)/R_I$.

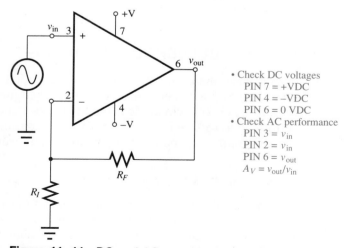

- Check DC voltages
  - PIN 7 = +VDC
  - PIN 4 = −VDC
  - PIN 6 = 0 VDC
- Check AC performance
  - PIN 3 = v_{in}
  - PIN 2 = v_{in}
  - PIN 6 = v_{out}
  - $A_V = v_{out}/v_{in}$

Figure 11–11 DC and AC op-amp circuit checks

If the circuit is malfunctioning, look for shorts, opens, cold-solder joints, and broken wires. Make sure the DC voltages are present at each supply pin. Also make sure an input signal is present. Replace the op-amp if necessary.

Self-Check 11–4

1. List some tests that can be made with a DC voltmeter when troubleshooting or testing an op-amp circuit.
2. List some tests that can be made with an oscilloscope when troubleshooting or testing an op-amp circuit.

SUMMARY

FORMULAS

(11–1) $BW_p = SR/(2\pi V_p) = 0.159 \cdot SR/V_p$

(11–2) $V_p = SR/(2\pi BW_p) = 0.159 \cdot SR/BW_p$

(11–3) $GBP = f_{co(open)} \cdot A_{OL(max)} = f_T$

(11–4) $GBP = f_{co(closed)} \cdot A_V = f_T$

(11–5) $A_V = f_T/f_{co(closed)}$

(11–6) $f_{co(closed)} = f_{co(open)} \cdot A_{OL(max)}/A_V$

(11–7) $A_V = A_{OL(max)} \cdot f_{co(open)}/f_{co(closed)}$

(11–8) $\Phi = -\arctan(R/X_C)$

(11–9) $\Phi = -\arctan(f/f_{co})$

(11–10) $\Phi_t = -\arctan(f/f_{co1}) - \arctan(f/f_{co2}) - \arctan(f/f_{co3})$

(11–11) $\Phi_{PM} = |-180 - \Phi_{t(unity\ loop\ gain)}|$ (phase margin)

CONCEPTS

- Slew rate and power bandwidth are directly related and depend on the amount of internal capacitance and compensation capacitance.
- Op-amp gain and bandwidth are inversely related.
- Op-amp gain must be sacrificed to obtain a wider bandwidth.
- The product of op-amp gain and bandwidth is always equal to the unity-gain frequency (f_T).
- Op-amps begin to oscillate if the loop gain is greater than one (1) at a frequency (critical frequency) whose total phase shift back to the inverting input is 360° (0° phase margin).
- Designers like to set the closed-loop gain so the phase margin between the unity loop-gain frequency and the critical frequency is in the area of 45°.

PROCEDURES

Op-Amp Troubleshooting

1. With power off, use the ohmmeter to measure the combined resistance of R_F and R_I to verify continuity and no shorts.

2. With power on and no input signal, use the DC voltmeter to check DC voltages.

   ■ 0 VDC at the output and both inputs
   ■ ± VDC at the DC supply pins

3. With power on and an input signal applied, use the oscilloscope to check AC performance.

   ■ AC voltages should be nearly equal at the two input pins.
   ■ Voltage gain should be consistent with the gain ratio of R_F and R_I.

NEED-TO-KNOW SOLUTION

By now you are aware that among the many pin-for-pin compatible op-amps there is great variation in slew rate, unity-gain frequency, and open-loop gain. Also, some op-amps are internally compensated, predetermining the open-loop frequency response, while others must be externally compensated and can be tailored to match a particular application. In terms of power bandwidth, small-signal bandwidth, and slew rate, the very popular 741 op-amp is very limited to many other op-amps available for substitution. This is not to say the 741 should not be used. The 741 is unconditionally stable and very desirable for many low-bandwidth applications. For large-signal and wide-bandwidth applications, you will want to use high-slew rate, high-f_T op-amps, which, in most cases, are externally compensated.

QUESTIONS

11–1 OP-AMP SLEW RATE AND BANDWIDTH

1. Why is the slew rate of an op-amp so important?
2. What is slew-rate distortion?
3. What causes slew-rate distortion?
4. How is slew rate related to large-signal or power bandwidth?
5. List three ways slew-rate distortion can be avoided.

11–2 OP-AMP FREQUENCY RESPONSE

6. Does the internal capacitance of an op-amp form (a) a highpass filter, or (b) a lowpass filter with internal resistance?
7. What is the slope or rate of rolloff for the frequency response of internally compensated op-amps?
8. What is the name given to the frequency at which the gain is one (1 = 0 dB)?
9. Which is greater for an op-amp circuit, the open-loop bandwidth or the closed-loop bandwidth? Explain.
10. What is the gain-bandwidth product?

11. Explain how closed-loop gain is related to bandwidth or frequency response.
12. What actually determines the closed-loop gain of an op-amp?
13. What does the impulse rise time for an op-amp have to do with the frequency response and f_T?

11–3 PREVENTING OSCILLATIONS IN OP-AMP CIRCUITS

14. What are the two requirements for an amplifier to oscillate?
15. How does compensation prevent oscillation problems?
16. What is the critical frequency?
17. What does *conditionally stable* mean?
18. Which is better, a phase margin of 10°, or a phase margin of 50°? Why?
19. What is the unity-loop-gain frequency?
20. Is the 741 op-amp unconditionally stable? Explain.
21. As far as oscillation is concerned, what is the worst-case op-amp circuit? Why?

11–4 TROUBLESHOOTING OP-AMPS

22. If there is no output signal from your op-amp when you think there should be, what oscilloscope test(s) can you perform to investigate the problem?
23. If you do not have access to an oscilloscope to test an op-amp circuit, what test(s) can you perform using a multimeter?
24. List four possible troubles and resulting symptoms for an op-amp amplifier circuit.

PROBLEMS

11–1 OP-AMP SLEW RATE AND BANDWIDTH

1. An op-amp has a slew rate of 1.5 V/μs. What is the power bandwidth if the output voltage is to be 8 V_P?
2. An op-amp has a slew rate of 12 V/μs. What is the power bandwidth if the output voltage is to be 14 V_P?
3. An op-amp has a slew rate of 10 V/μs. What is the maximum undistorted peak voltage at the output for a power bandwidth of 150 kHz?
4. An op-amp has a slew rate of 4 V/μs. What is the maximum undistorted peak voltage at the output for a power bandwidth of 50 kHz?

11–2 OP-AMP FREQUENCY RESPONSE

5. An op-amp has an open-loop gain of 90,000 and a unity-gain frequency of 1.5 MHz. Calculate the open-loop cutoff frequency.
6. An op-amp has an open-loop gain of 110,000 and an open-loop cutoff frequency of 9 Hz. Calculate the unity-gain frequency.

7. An op-amp circuit has an open-loop gain of 120,000, a closed-loop gain of 300, and an open-loop cutoff frequency of 12 Hz. Calculate the closed-loop cutoff frequency.

8. An op-amp circuit has an open-loop gain of 260,000, a closed-loop gain of 150, and an open-loop cutoff frequency of 7 Hz. Calculate the closed-loop cutoff frequency.

9. An op-amp has an open-loop gain of 140,000 and an f_T of 1.5 MHz. Determine the closed-loop gain needed for a cutoff frequency of 200 kHz.

10. An op-amp has an open-loop gain of 103 dB and an f_T of 2 MHz. Determine the closed-loop gain needed for a cutoff frequency of 30 kHz.

11. An op-amp has an f_T of 800 kHz and an open-loop cutoff frequency of 11 Hz. What is the op-amp's open-loop gain below 11 Hz?

12. An op-amp has an f_T of 1.2 MHz and an open-loop cutoff frequency of 20 Hz. What is the op-amp's open-loop gain below 20 Hz?

11–3 PREVENTING OSCILLATIONS IN OP-AMP CIRCUITS

13. An uncompensated op-amp has the following cutoff frequencies: f_{co1} = 240 kHz, f_{co2} = 3 MHz. Calculate the total phase shift (lag) at 500 kHz and 5 MHz.

14. An uncompensated op-amp has the following cutoff frequencies: f_{co1} = 300 kHz, f_{co2} = 1 MHz. Calculate the total phase shift (lag) at 500 kHz and 2 MHz.

15. Estimate the critical frequency for Problem 13.

16. Estimate the critical frequency for Problem 14.

17. From the graphs of Figure 11–12, what is the approximate unity-loop-gain frequency?

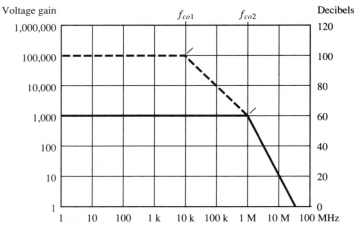

Figure 11–12

18. Will the op-amp circuit represented by the graphs of Figure 11–12 be unstable (oscillate)? Why?
19. If the total phase shift at the unity-loop-gain frequency is $-148°$, what is the phase margin?
20. If the phase margin at the unity loop-gain frequency is 35°, what is the total phase shift?

ADDITIONAL PROBLEMS

21. An op-amp has a slew rate of 1.8 V/μs. What is the power bandwidth if the output voltage is to be 11 V_P?
22. An op-amp has a slew rate of 17 V/μs. What is the maximum undistorted peak voltage at the output for a power bandwidth of 80 kHz?
23. An op-amp has an open-loop gain of 110,000 and a unity-gain frequency f_T of 1.2 MHz. Calculate the open-loop cutoff frequency.
24. An op-amp circuit has an open-loop gain of 105,000, a closed-loop gain of 450, and an open-loop cutoff frequency of 14 Hz. Calculate the closed-loop cutoff frequency.
25. An op-amp has an open-loop gain of 98,000 and an f_T of 950 kHz. Determine the closed-loop gain needed for a cutoff frequency of 55 kHz.
26. An op-amp has an f_T of 1.6 MHz and an open-loop cutoff frequency of 8 Hz. What is the op-amp's open-loop gain below 8 Hz?
27. An uncompensated op-amp has the following cutoff frequencies: $f_{co1} = 120$ kHz, $f_{co2} = 1.2$ MHz, $f_{co3} = 6.2$ MHz. Calculate the total phase shift (lag) at 200 kHz and 2 MHz.
28. Estimate the critical frequency for Problem 27.
29. If the total phase shift at the unity-loop-gain frequency is $-163°$, what is the phase margin?
30. If the phase margin at the unity-loop-gain frequency is 54°, what is the total phase shift?

ANSWERS TO SELF-CHECKS

SELF-CHECK 11–1

1. Slew-rate distortion is caused by circuit capacitance. This capacitance is unable to charge and discharge fast enough to keep up high-frequency large signals.
2. $BW_p = 0.159 \cdot SR/V_p = 0.159 \cdot 1.5$ V/μs/10 V_p = 23,850 Hz
3. $V_P = 0.159 \cdot SR/BW_p = 0.159 \cdot 0.75$ V/μs/25 kHz = 4.77 V_P

SELF-CHECK 11–2

1. Gain and bandwidth are inversely related—more gain, less bandwidth and vice versa.

2. $f_T = 150 \cdot 80 \text{ kHz} = 12 \text{ MHz}$
3. $60 \text{ dB} = 1,000, f_{co(\text{closed})} = 2.5 \text{ MHz}/1,000 = 2,500 \text{ Hz}$
4. $f_T = 200,000 \cdot 8 \text{ Hz} = 1.6 \text{ MHz}$
5. The required bandwidth or closed-loop cutoff frequency

SELF-CHECK 11–3

1. Loop gain must be greater than one (1) and the output must be fed back in phase with the input, meaning a total loop phase shift of 360° must take place.
2. When the closed-loop gain of the amplifier is equal to or greater than 60 dB, the loop gain is less than 0 dB (<1) for frequencies at and near the critical frequency. Thus, the amplifier is conditionally stable for all frequencies as long as the closed-loop gain is ≤60 dB.
3. The critical frequency is the frequency at which the total phase shift, or lag, is −180°, making the total loop phase shift equal to 360°. Oscillation will take place at the critical frequency if the loop gain is ≥0 dB.
4. $\Phi_t = -\arctan(f/f_{co}) - \arctan(f/f_{co1}) - \arctan(f/f_{co2}) - \arctan(f/f_{co3})$
   $= -\tan^{-1}(200 \text{ kHz}/10 \text{ Hz}) - \tan^{-1}(200 \text{ kHz}/100 \text{ kHz})$
   $\quad -\tan^{-1}(200 \text{ kHz}/1 \text{ MHz}) - \tan^{-1}(200 \text{ kHz}/10 \text{ MHz})$
   $= -90° - 63.4° - 11.3° - 1.15° = -165.9°$
5. An op-amp is conditionally stable if it is necessary for the closed-loop gain to be maintained above a specific amount to ensure freedom from oscillation.
6. The unity-loop gain frequency is the frequency at which the loop gain is equal to one (1 = 0 dB). The loop gain is the difference between the open-loop gain and the closed-loop gain at any frequency. Loop gain = A_{OL}/A_V and loop gain (dB) = $A_{OL(dB)} - A_{V(dB)}$
7. The unity-gain configuration provides the worst-case conditions for oscillation because the loop gain is greater than one (1) all the way up to the unity-gain frequency (f_T). If the critical frequency is lower than f_T, the amplifier will surely oscillate.

SELF-CHECK 11–4

1. The DC voltmeter can be used to check the supply voltages at the supply pins on the op-amp. Also, the quiescent DC output voltage can be measured to see if it is at 0 V when a dual supply is used or ½ E_S when a single supply is used. When the single supply is used, the DC output voltage should match the DC bias voltage at the noninverting input.
2. Use the oscilloscope to ensure that a signal is present at the input, observe the signal at the output, observe distortion, observe nonsymmetrical clipping on a large-signal output (which indicates a severe DC offset), and test the frequency response of the op-amp circuit.

**SUGGESTED
PROJECTS**

1. Add some of the main concepts, formulas, and procedures from this chapter to your Electronics Notebook.
2. Test the frequency response of a 741 op-amp at different gain settings as determined by R_F and R_I. In each case, calculate f_T. Recall that f_T should be the same for all gain settings.
3. Compare the frequency response of an LF356 to an LM741 at a gain setting of 40 dB ($A_V = 100$).

This photo shows rack-mounted audio mixers used for multi-channel recordings. Operational amplifiers are at the heart of audio systems such as this. Barbara Alper/STOCK.

12 Op-Amp Applications

OBJECTIVES

After studying this chapter, you will be able to

- operate op-amps from a single DC supply.
- identify, explain the operation of, and design a variety of
  Summing amplifier circuits
  Gain-controlled op-amp circuits
  Op-amp power amplifier circuits
  Balanced input and output op-amp circuits
  Comparator circuits
  Op-amp precision rectifier circuits
  Op-amp limiter and clamper circuits
  Op-amp integrators and differentiators
  Sample and hold circuits

NEED TO KNOW

Suppose you are troubleshooting a large electrical system in which the AC current periodically surges to an abnormally high level. The current surges are short-lived and you would like to know just how much of a surge occurs. You need to design a circuit that will constantly monitor the AC line and remember any current surge that occurs. Assume the AC current, including surges, is in the range of 1 to 30 A. Can you design a circuit to capture those surges? Well, believe it or not, by the time you finish this chapter, you will.

INTRODUCTION

This chapter will be interesting to you. Here, you will discover just a handful of the many applications for which op-amps can be used. This chapter should open a whole world of possibilities for you as you begin to realize how powerful and versatile the op-amp really is. Using these application circuits as building blocks, you will be able to understand and design many electronic systems, some of your own creation. Enjoy!

12–1 SINGLE-SUPPLY OP-AMP CIRCUITS

THE SINGLE-SUPPLY NONINVERTING AMPLIFIER

The Single Supply and AC Compliance

As you may have already discovered, the requirement for a dual DC supply for your op-amp circuits is often an inconvenience and extra technical and financial burden. Fortunately, your favorite op-amp can be operated using a single supply. The data sheet for a 741, for example, may indicate a maximum DC supply voltage of ±18 V. This is equivalent to a single ground-referenced supply of 36 V. However, this maximum value of 36 V need not be used. A single 18-V or 12-V supply, or even a 9-V transistor radio battery, may be adequate. The determining factor in selecting the single-supply voltage requirement is the amount of needed AC compliance or dynamic headroom. If the maximum amplified signal will never exceed approximately ±3.5 V_P, a single 9-V battery will suffice. If the maximum output signal is greater, a higher DC supply voltage is needed.

As a rule of thumb, make sure the DC supply voltage is at least 2 V higher than the maximum desired peak-to-peak voltage swing.

Biasing for Single-Supply Operation

Figure 12–1 illustrates how simple it is to adapt an op-amp for single-supply operation. In this case, the op-amp is set up as a noninverting amplifier. The AC gain (A_V) is still determined by the ratio $(R_I + R_F)/R_I$. The voltage divider composed of resistors R_D is used to establish the DC quiescent operating point at the output. The quiescent point is set at VDC/2 to permit maximum $\pm V_P$ in the output. Naturally, the R_D resistors are equal and determine the input impedance to the amplifier where $Z_{in} = R_D/2$.

$$Z_{in} = R_D/2 \tag{12–1}$$

$$R_D = 2Z_{in} \tag{12–2}$$

Since the input impedance at the noninverting input is very, very high, the value for R_D can be selected from a very wide range (into the megohms when a JFET or MOSFET op-amp is used).

Low-Frequency Considerations

One obvious disadvantage to using the single DC supply is the need for coupling capacitors. These limit the low-frequency response of the amplifier

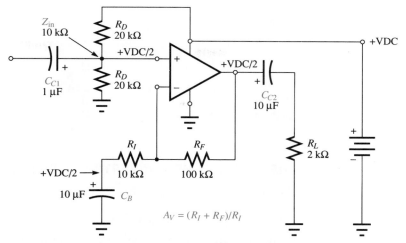

Figure 12–1 The single-supply noninverting amplifier.

since X_C is higher at lower frequencies. The amplifier is not a DC amplifier because the capacitors block DC. If you do not need to amplify DC, there is no real problem here. The rule of thumb that we used for transistor-amplifier coupling and bypass capacitors applies here as well. The X_C of the coupling capacitors should equal the input impedance ($R_D/2$) or the load impedance (R_L) at the lowest frequency that is to be amplified. The X_C of C_B in Figure 12–1 should be 1/10 of R_I at the lowest frequency. This will insure a fixed gain over the entire frequency range as determined by the coupling capacitors and the high-end response of the amplifier. Thus, the coupling capacitors determine the dominant lower cutoff frequency (f_{low}).

$$C_C \geq 0.159/(f_{low}R) \qquad \text{(Coupling)} \tag{12–3}$$

where R is the resistance the AC is being coupled into.

$$C_B \geq 1.59/(f_{low}R) \qquad \text{(Bypass)} \tag{12–4}$$

where R is the resistance that must be tied to ground.

EXAMPLE 12–1

Design a noninverting op-amp amplifier using a single DC supply. Maximum output voltage swing will be ± 5 V_P. The input impedance will be 50 kΩ. The load resistance will be 5 kΩ. Amplifier gain in the passband will be 10. The lower cutoff frequency will be 30 Hz. Use standard-value 5% resistors.

$$\text{VDC} \geq 2V_P + 2\text{ V} = (2 \cdot 5\text{ }V_P) + 2\text{ V} = 12\text{ V}$$

$$C_C \geq 0.159/(f_{low}Z_{in}) = 0.159/(30\text{ Hz} \cdot 50\text{ k}\Omega) = 0.11\text{ }\mu\text{F}$$

Each voltage-divider resistor $R_D = 2Z_{in} = 2 \cdot 50\text{ k}\Omega = 100\text{ k}\Omega$.

$$(R_I + R_F)/R_I = 10$$

Let $R_I = 10 \text{ k}\Omega$.

$(10 \text{ k}\Omega + R_F)/10 \text{ k}\Omega = 10$

$10 \text{ k}\Omega + R_F = 10 \cdot 10 \text{ k}\Omega$

$R_F = 100 \text{ k}\Omega - 10 \text{ k}\Omega = 90 \text{ k}\Omega$ (Use 91 kΩ)

$C_B \geq 1.59/(f_{\text{low}}R_I) = 1.59/(30 \text{ Hz} \cdot 10 \text{ k}\Omega) = 5.3 \ \mu\text{F}$

THE SINGLE-SUPPLY INVERTING AMPLIFIER

Figure 12–2 demonstrates how the inverting amplifier is biased for single-supply operation. The voltage-divider resistors are equal and can be any value desired up to about 1 MΩ for JFET and MOSFET op-amps. The gain of the amplifier is as expected, the ratio of R_F/R_I. Also, the input impedance is determined by the value of R_I. Coupling and bypass capacitors are determined using Formulas 12–3 and 12–4.

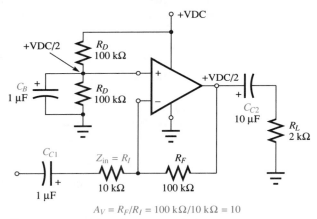

$A_V = R_F/R_I = 100 \text{ k}\Omega/10 \text{ k}\Omega = 10$

Figure 12–2   The single-supply inverting amplifier.

EXAMPLE 12–2

Design an inverting op-amp amplifier using a single DC supply. Maximum output voltage swing will be $\pm 3 \text{ V}_P$. The input impedance will be 33 kΩ. The load resistance will be 10 kΩ. Amplifier gain in the passband will be 20. The lower cutoff frequency will be 40 Hz. Use standard-value 5% resistors.

$\text{VDC} \geq 2 \, V_P + 2\text{V} = (2 \cdot 3 \, V_P) + 2 \text{ V} = 8 \text{ V}$
     (Use a 9-V battery or source.)

$Z_{\text{in}} = R_I = 33 \text{ k}\Omega$

$C_C \geq 0.159/(f_{\text{low}}R_I) = 0.159/(40 \text{ Hz} \cdot 33 \text{ k}\Omega) = 0.12 \ \mu\text{F}$

Each voltage-divider resistor R_D = any standard value from 10 kΩ to 1 MΩ. Use 100-kΩ resistors.

$$C_B \geq 1.59/(f_{low}R_D) = 1.59/(40 \text{ Hz} \cdot 100 \text{ k}\Omega) = 0.4 \ \mu\text{F}$$

$$R_F/R_I = 20 \qquad R_I = 33 \text{ k}\Omega$$

$$R_F/33 \text{ k}\Omega = 20$$

$$R_F = 20 \cdot 33 \text{ k}\Omega = 660 \text{ k}\Omega \qquad (\text{Use } 680 \text{ k}\Omega)$$

SINGLE-SUPPLY OP-AMPS

While dual-supply op-amps function well from a single DC supply, there are many op-amps that have been designed specifically for single-supply operation. A few of these are the low-noise LM381 and LM387, used frequently as microphone and stereo preamplifiers, the LM383 and LM384 power amplifiers, and the high-slew-rate MC34071 low-power op-amp.

Self-Check 12–1

1. Design a noninverting single-supply amplifier like that in Figure 12–1 to meet the following requirements: $A_V \cong 20$, $f_{low} \leq 30$ Hz, $Z_{in} = 10$ kΩ. Let $R_I = 15$ kΩ. The maximum peak-to-peak output voltage swing will be 9 V.
2. Explain why the voltage-divider resistors are equal in Figures 12–1 or 12–2.

12–2 SUMMING AMPLIFIER CIRCUITS

THE BASIC ADDER

Summing DC and AC

In this section, you will discover a very interesting and useful op-amp application referred to as the **summing amplifier** or **adder.** The concept and theory is very simple. Consider Figure 12–3. This is an inverting amplifier with three inputs. Any number of inputs can be used. The gain from each input to the output is determined by the ratio of R_F to each of the input resistances

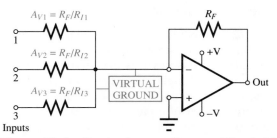

Figure 12–3   The basic summing amplifier (adder).

($R_{I\#}$). Furthermore, due to virtual ground, all inputs are isolated from each other. In other words, a 2-V signal at input 3 cannot appear at input 1 or 2. Neither will any of the inputs act as a load on the others. All of the inputs are independent and appear at the output as an inverted composite or sum.

Consider the following examples.

EXAMPLE 12–3 ▮▮▮▮▮▮▮▮▮▮▮▮▮▮▮▮▮▮▮▮▮▮▮▮▮▮▮▮▮▮▮▮

For these examples, assume all resistors are the same value and the A_V for each input is 1.

	Input 1	Input 2	Input 3	Output
1.	+1 VDC	+2 VDC	+3 VDC	−6 VDC
2.	+2 VDC	−1 VDC	−4 VDC	+3 VDC
3.	−3 VDC	−1 VDC	−5 VDC	+9 VDC

As you might guess, the resistors do not all have to be the same values. You can select the value of input resistors as needed. Consider Example 12–4.

$$R_I = R_F/A_V = R_F/(v_{out}/v_{in}) = R_F v_{in}/v_{out} \tag{12–5}$$

EXAMPLE 12–4 ▮▮▮▮▮▮▮▮▮▮▮▮▮▮▮▮▮▮▮▮▮▮▮▮▮▮▮▮▮▮▮▮

Suppose you want to mix three separate audio sources together: source 1 = 50 mV, source 2 = 100 mV, and source 3 = 200 mV. Also, assume you want all sources to be the same level at the output, say 1 V. If R_F is 100 kΩ, what must the value of each input resistor be?

$$R_I = R_F v_{in}/v_{out} = 100 \text{ k}\Omega \cdot v_{in}/v_{out}$$

$$R_{I1} = 100 \text{ k}\Omega \cdot 50 \text{ mV}/1 \text{ V} = 5 \text{ k}\Omega$$

$$R_{I2} = 100 \text{ k}\Omega \cdot 100 \text{ mV}/1 \text{ V} = 10 \text{ k}\Omega$$

$$R_{I3} = 100 \text{ k}\Omega \cdot 200 \text{ mV}/1 \text{ V} = 20 \text{ k}\Omega$$

A Practical Audio Mixer

Figure 12–4 illustrates a very popular application for the adder circuit, the audio mixer. This simple circuit is at the heart of even the most expensive audio mixing consoles found in the best recording studios. It is used to combine several high-level audio sources, such as prerecorded voice and music, onto one line. Though only three inputs are shown here, you may have any number of inputs. The virtual ground at the inverting input keeps all inputs isolated. When the input level of one input is adjusted, it has no

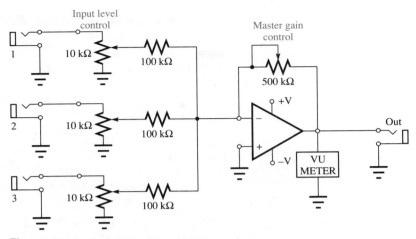

Figure 12–4 A simple line-level audio mixer.

effect on the other inputs. There is no cross-loading effect. Master gain control can be obtained as shown, using a variable R_F. The VU meter is a decibel volume-unit meter used to monitor the output level.

THE AVERAGER

The averaging amplifier of Figure 12–5 acts as an analog computer. It produces the arithmetic average of all input voltages. The first stage is the **averager** and the second is simply a unity-gain inverter. Notice that all input resistors are the same value. The feedback resistor (R_F) is determined by the number of inputs (N). Look at Example 12–5.

$$R_F = R_I/N \qquad\qquad (12\text{–}6)$$

where N is the number of inputs.

$$V_{\text{out}} = (V_1 + V_2 + V_3 + \cdots + V_N)/N \qquad\qquad (12\text{–}7)$$

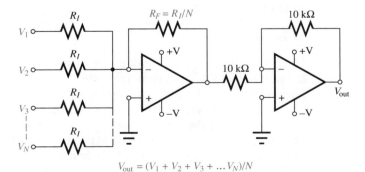

$$V_{\text{out}} = (V_1 + V_2 + V_3 + \ldots V_N)/N$$

Figure 12–5 The averaging amplifier (averager).

EXAMPLE 12–5

Consider an averager in which all input resistors are 10 kΩ and there are 3 inputs. What is the needed value for R_F?

$R_F = 10 \text{ k}\Omega/3 = 3.3 \text{ k}\Omega$

$A_V = 3.3 \text{ k}\Omega/10 \text{ k}\Omega = 0.33$

Now, say the input voltages are input 1 = 3 V, input 2 = 1 V, and input 3 = 5 V. The average of 3 V, 1 V, and 5 V is $V_{\text{avg}} = (3 \text{ V} + 1 \text{ V} + 5 \text{ V})/3 = 9 \text{ V}/3 = 3 \text{ V}$. Let's see if the output of the averager circuit is +3 V. The output is the sum of the inputs times the gain of each input. We know that the gain of each input is 0.33. Thus,

$V_{\text{out}} = (3 \text{ V} \cdot 0.33) + (1 \text{ V} \cdot 0.33) + (5 \text{ V} \cdot 0.33)$
$= 1 \text{ V} + 0.33 \text{ V} + 1.67 \text{ V} = 3 \text{ V}$

The input voltages to the averager could be from temperature, humidity, speed, or pressure sensors, or any parameters whose average may be significant.

A DIGITAL-TO-ANALOG CONVERTER (DAC)

Weighted Inputs

One other very common application for the adder is the **digital-to-analog converter (DAC).** The DAC is able to convert digital binary numbers into analog voltages. This is illustrated in Figure 12–6. First, notice the input resistors. These resistors are **weighted** in value. That means each resistor has a specific value that determines the output voltage from a given input voltage. Notice also that all input voltages are either +5 V or 0 V. These two voltage levels are provided by digital circuitry. A level of +5 V is considered a binary 1 and a level of 0 V is a binary 0. Each input is a **bit** of an eight-bit binary **word.** The **least significant bit (LSB)** has the least weight ($R_F/R_I = 1 \text{ k}\Omega/128 \text{ k}\Omega$) and is applied to the 128-kΩ resistor. The **most significant bit (MSB)** has the greatest weight ($R_F/R_I = 1 \text{ k}\Omega/1 \text{ k}\Omega$) and is applied to the 1-kΩ resistor.

Resolution

There are 256 ($2^8 = 256$) possible combinations of ones and zeros (highs and lows, +5 V and 0 V) starting from all zeros 00000000 to all ones 11111111. The weight of the LSB determines the smallest increment of output voltage, referred to as its **resolution.** In this case, the resolution is approximately 39 mV since, when the LSB is high (+5 V) and all other inputs are low, the output voltage is $+5 \text{ V} \cdot 1 \text{ k}\Omega/128 \text{ k}\Omega = 39 \text{ mV}$. Note that the 64-kΩ input is weighted at $1 \text{ k}\Omega/64 \text{ k}\Omega$, which yields a 78-mV output, the 32-kΩ input produces a 156-mV output, and so on, with each input, or bit, becoming more significant.

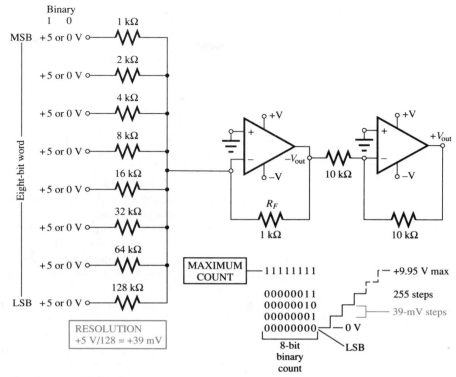

Figure 12–6 A digital-to-analog converter.

Digitized Sound Reproduction

The combination of the high inputs caused by any 8-bit word determines the output voltage. If the first 8-bit word is all zeros 00000000 and is incremented upward, the analog output voltage will be a staircase of 255 steps of 39 mV each, not including the 0-V level. Thus, any 8-bit word is translated into an analog voltage between 0 V and 9.95 V. In this way, digitized sound is rapidly clocked onto an 8-bit bus and fed into the DAC. With the arrival of each new 8-bit word, the output voltage either increases or decreases, recreating the original audio sound. In other words, the voltage at V_{out} is a jagged reproduction of the original audio waveform. The jaggedness is due to the steps and is removed with a lowpass filter.

Time for a self-check.

Self-Check 12–2

1. Which of the two op-amp inputs is used for summing? Why is this the best input to use for summing?
2. Design an averager that has 5 inputs, with the input resistor of each being 100 kΩ.
3. What is the maximum number of inputs an adder can have?
4. What do we mean when we say an adder has weighted inputs?
5. If a DAC circuit has a 1-kΩ feedback resistor and the input resistor for the LSB is 256 kΩ, what is the weight of the LSB input? What is the resolution of the DAC if a binary 1 is +5 V?

12–3 GAIN-CONTROLLED OP-AMP CIRCUITS

In this section, we explore various methods of controlling the overall gain of the operational amplifier. We begin with manual gain control, and later discuss automatic gain control.

MANUAL GAIN CONTROL

What is the best way to control the overall gain of an op-amp circuit? That's a good question. Figure 12–7 identifies the possibilities. When we talk about op-amp gain, we first think about the feedback resistor and the inverting input resistor (R_F and R_I). We know that the relative values of these resistors determines the closed-loop gain (A_V). Naturally, the gain of the amplifier can be varied by making one of these components variable. However, recall how the closed-loop gain and bandwidth are related. As the closed-loop gain is increased, the bandwidth is decreased. Thus, the bandwidth is varied with the gain. This may not be a problem, depending on bandwidth requirements. The bandwidth must remain wide enough to meet application needs at the highest gain setting.

Another method of gain control is to use fixed values for R_F and R_I to establish a fixed closed-loop gain while using a variable voltage divider at the noninverting input. One fixed and one variable resistor can be used to vary the signal level applied to the op-amp. The best method for manual control is to use a potentiometer. The total resistance of the potentiometer determines the input impedance and the position of the wiper determines the signal level. Varying the overall amplifier gain in this manner has no effect on bandwidth because the closed-loop gain remains fixed.

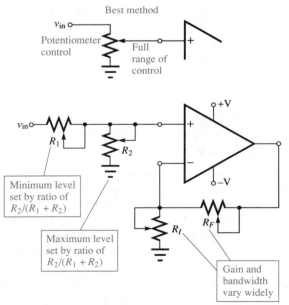

Figure 12–7 Possible methods of gain control.

AUTOMATIC GAIN CONTROL (AGC)

Automatic gain control (AGC), sometimes referred to as **automatic level control (ALC),** is a means by which the gain is automatically and electronically controlled to maintain the output at a generally constant level over a wide range of input levels. Circuits of this nature are used in recording studios to prevent tape saturation and in radio and television stations to prevent under- or over-modulation of transmitters. Most commonly, AGC is used in AM radio receivers to keep the sound at a fairly constant level even though stations of different strength are received.

Photoresistor Control

Figure 12–8 is an example of a simple, yet effective, audio AGC circuit using a Raytheon Raysistor®. The Raysistor® is a light-tight package that includes an LED facing a cadmium-sulfide photoresistor. The closed-loop gain of the op-amp is set at 11 ($A_V = (1 \text{ k}\Omega + 10 \text{ k}\Omega)/1 \text{ k}\Omega = 11$). The bandwidth is also fixed. The signal at the noninverting input is controlled through the use of a cadmium-sulfide (CdS) photoresistor. A voltage divider is formed between the 47-kΩ resistor and the CdS photoresistor. The dark resistance of the photoresistor may be anywhere from 500 kΩ to 50 MΩ and the minimum resistance with light is usually in the low hundreds of ohms, depending on photoresistor type. For the CK2145, the dark resistance is approximately 500 kΩ and the bright-light resistance is approximately 250 Ω. Depending on the brightness of the neighboring LED, the resistance of the photoresistor can be anywhere between 250 Ω and 500 kΩ. The brightness of the LED is controlled by the emitter current of the transistor, which is controlled by the audio level at the output.

Note that before the LED comes on, a signal threshold must first be reached. The negative peak output voltage must reach a threshold of approximately -1.5 to -3 V, depending on the forward voltage of the LED, before gain control begins. Once LED current is caused to flow, the resistance of

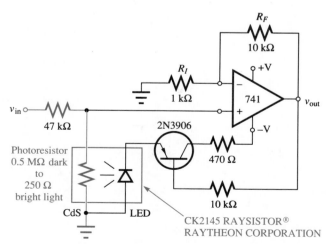

Figure 12–8 CdS/LED automatic gain control (AGC).

the photoresistor decreases and the input signal is reduced. Thus, the output signal level is maintained fairly constant for all input signal levels great enough to cause an output voltage that exceeds the threshold voltage of the LED.

Dynamic Range and Sensitivity

Since the range of resistance for the photoresistor is great, the dynamic range of gain control is great. If the threshold voltage for the circuit of Figure 12–8 is an output of $-2\ V_P$, gain control will begin with an input signal of $\pm 182\ mV_P$ ($2\ V_P/11 = 182$ mV). For any input signals greater than $\pm 182\ mV_P$, the signal voltage at the noninverting input pin will be maintained at slightly greater than ± 182 mVp and the output will be maintained slightly greater than $\pm 2\ V_P$. If the minimum resistance of the photoresistor is 250 Ω, the signal voltage at the nonvinerting input pin will be maintained at slightly greater than $\pm 182\ mV_P$ for an input signal as high as ± 34.4 Vp ($34.4\ V_P \cdot 250\ \Omega/(47\ k\Omega + 250\ \Omega) = 182$ mVp). Therefore, the so-called dynamic range of this AGC system is 34.4 V/182 mV = 189 $\cong$ 45.5 dB. The sensitivity of the circuit can be increased by increasing the closed-loop gain of the op-amp (make R_F larger in value). Changing R_F to a 100-kΩ resistor lowers the noninverting-input-pin voltage to a little over $\pm 18\ mV_P$ and the maximum input level to approximately $\pm 3.44\ V_P$ or 6.88 $V_{P\text{-}P}$. Consider Example 12–6.

EXAMPLE 12–6 ▐▬▬▬▬▬▬▬

At what value of input voltage will limiting begin for the circuit of Figure 12–9? What is the dynamic range of the AGC system?

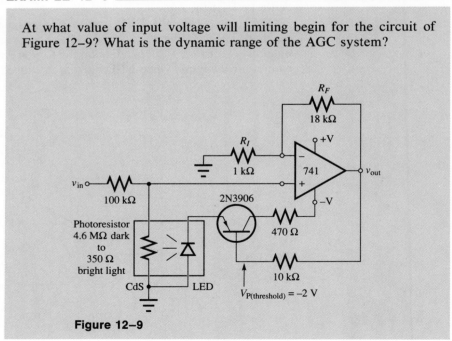

Figure 12–9

$$A_V = 19 \text{ k}\Omega/1 \text{ k}\Omega = 19$$

$$v_{\text{P(output maximum)}} \cong 2 \; V_P$$

$$v_{\text{P(input threshold)}} = v_{\text{P(output threshold)}}/A_V = 2 \; V_P/19 = 105 \text{ mV}_P$$

$$
\begin{aligned}
v_{\text{P(input maximum)}} &= i_{\text{P(in)}} \cdot Z_{\text{in}} \\
&= (105 \text{ mVp}/350 \; \Omega) \cdot 100{,}350 \; \Omega \\
&= 30 \; V_P
\end{aligned}
$$

$$
\begin{aligned}
\text{Dynamic range (dB)} &= 20 \log \left(v_{\text{P(input maximum)}}/v_{\text{P(input threshold)}} \right) \\
&= 20 \log(30 \text{ Vp}/105 \text{ mVp}) = 49.1 \text{ dB}
\end{aligned}
$$

Response Time

The LED response time is nearly instantaneous, whereas the photoresistor's response time is much slower. The time it takes for the photoresistor to decrease in resistance from maximum to minimum when light is applied is called its **attack time.** The time it takes for the photoresistor to increase in resistance from minimum to maximum when the light is removed is called its **recovery time.** For the CK2145, the attack time is 3 ms and the recovery time is 900 ms. For AGC applications, the photoresistor should have the fastest possible attack time for quick control of strong signal bursts and a moderate to slow recovery time. The slower recovery time maintains control during the half-cycle the LED is OFF. For the circuits of Figures 12–8 and 12–9, the LED is ON for all negative alternations above threshold and OFF for all positive alternations of the output signal.

FET Automatic Gain Control

Figure 12–10 is an FET AGC circuit. The 5.6-kΩ input resistor and the FET Q_1 form a voltage divider. The dynamic small-signal drain to source resistance (r_{ds}) of the FET is controlled by its gate voltage. This dynamic resistance may vary from 100 Ω when V_{GS} is 0 V to many megohms when V_{GS} is very negative (FET cutoff). With no input signal, Q_1 is cutoff (r_{ds} very high) and Q_2 is off. Since Q_2 is off, $-V$ is present at the gate of Q_1 via the 100-kΩ resistor, holding the FET deep into cutoff. When a signal is first applied, there is no attenuation contributed by the input voltage divider, because Q_1 is off and r_{ds} is very high. The signal reaches the noninverting input of the op-amp and is amplified by a factor of 11. If the negative peak value of the resulting output signal is equal to or greater than approximately 0.7 V, Q_2 will conduct and charge the 1-μF capacitor. The charge on the capacitor is positive at the gate and works against the $-V$ supply voltage. Thus, the FET Q_1 is biased ON to some degree. This reduces r_{ds} and works with the 5.6-kΩ input resistor to attenuate the input signal. Very quickly, a balance is reached between the attenuation factor of the input voltage divider and the gain of the op-amp, maintaining the output signal at approximately 0.7 V_P or 1.4 $V_{\text{P-P}}$. Automatic gain control does not begin until the input signal is at least 127 mV$_{\text{P-P}}$ (1.4 $V_{\text{P-P}}$/11 = 127 mV$_{\text{P-P}}$).

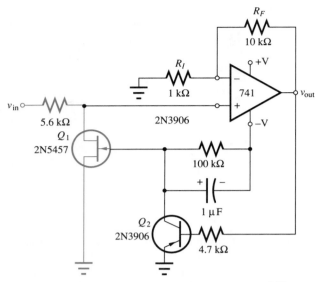

Figure 12–10   FET automatic gain control (AGC).

The attack time for Figure 12–10 is largely determined by the conduction of Q_2 and the 1-μF capacitor. Recovery time is determined by the RC time constant established by the 100-kΩ resistor and the 1-μF capacitor. Recovery time can be adjusted by substituting another value for the 100-kΩ resistor and/or changing the value of the capacitor.

If you construct and test the circuit of Figure 12–10, you will discover some distortion on the negative alternations of the output signal. This is due mainly to the fact that the capacitor receives a refresh charge only during the peak of the negative alternations. This distortion can be greatly reduced by inserting a precision negative rectifier between the output of the op-amp and the 4.7-kΩ resistor. This type of rectifier circuit inverts the positive alternation to provide full-wave negative pulsating DC. Thus, Q_2 conducts with both alternations of the signal and the capacitor is more consistently charged. The precision rectifier may also be used with the circuit of Figure 12–8. You will learn about precision rectifiers in a later section of this chapter.

Other AGC Circuits

As you have seen in Figure 12–10, some AGC systems use the charge time of a capacitor to determine the attack time and the discharge time to determine the recovery time. Usually, the capacitor's charge voltage is used to control the conduction of a transistor or FET that acts as the gain-control device. Many AGC integrated-circuit amplifiers have a gain-control pin (terminal) that is used to control the amplifier's gain. Normally, an increase in voltage at this pin decreases amplifier gain. A typical AGC control loop includes a rectifier (diode) to convert a sample of the output signal to pulsating DC, a filter capacitor that is rapidly charged for fast attack, a discharge resistor to determine the recovery time, and a gain-control device that responds to the filter-capacitor voltage. AGC circuits are not only used in audio circuits but are found in all AM receivers and television sets and some FM radio receivers.

Time once again for a quick self-check.

Self-Check 12–3

1. Why is a potentiometer at the noninverting input of Figure 12–7 the best method of manual gain control?
2. Explain AGC in general terms.
3. Briefly explain how a CdS/LED combination can be used to control the gain of an op-amp circuit.
4. Briefly explain what determines the attack time and the recovery time for the AGC circuit of Figure 12–10.
5. What determines the AGC input voltage threshold for the circuit of Figure 12–10?

12–4 POWER AMPLIFIER CIRCUITS

FULL-WAVE BOOSTING

Power and Current Limitations

Some applications require more current and power than the standard op-amp is able to deliver. Most common op-amps have internal current limiting of 20 to 50 mA and maximum power dissipation ratings less than 1 W. There are dual- and single-supply op-amps available for high-power requirements and these should be used where possible. However, you may not be satisfied with the input impedances or input offsets of some of these high-power op-amps or you may simply want to use what you have on hand. In any case, here you will see how the power-handling capability of any op-amp can be increased with the addition of a few external components.

Full-Wave Booster

Consider Figure 12–11. Here we see a 741 op-amp driving a push-pull complementary pair. This op-amp by itself is able to deliver a maximum of approximately 20 mA and dissipate approximately 500 mW. This is fine for many applications where the load resistance is greater than 1 kΩ. But suppose you need to drive a 100-Ω or 50-Ω load over a large voltage swing. The output of this op-amp must be boosted.

Figure 12–11 can be called a full-wave booster since it is designed to handle both alternations of an AC signal. This circuit can easily drive a 100-Ω load resistance to full voltage swing. If we assume a ±18-V DC supply, the peak output voltage swing should be approximately ±16 V. The RMS value of the peak voltage is used to calculate the power delivered to the load. In this case, $P_{L(max)} = (16 \; V_P \cdot 0.707)^2/R_L = 128/100 = 1.28$ W. The power dissipated by each transistor is the product of average current and voltage. The average voltage for each transistor is $18 \; V_P \cdot 0.318 = 5.72$ V.

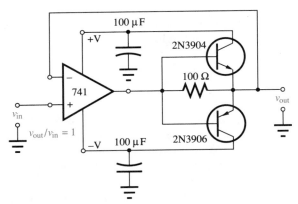

Figure 12–11   An op-amp with power-boosted output.

The average current is 5.72 V/100 Ω = 57.2 mA. The power dissipated in each transistor is 57.2 mA · 5.72 V = 327 mW. This may be a good time to review Section 7–2, which covers class B power amplifiers.

Crossover Distortion

But wait a minute. The circuit of Figure 12–11 has no biasing scheme for the push-pull transistors. With no input signal, the transistors are totally cut off. What about crossover distortion when a signal is applied? Good question. Notice that the transistors are included in the feedback loop. When a signal is first applied to the input, the loop appears to be open because the transistors are off. This means the overall gain of the amplifier is maximum, equal to A_{OL}. Therefore, as the input signal just begins to leave zero-crossing, this small voltage is very greatly amplified, causing one of the output transistors to come ON and close the loop. Thus, each transistor is automatically biased ON only when it is needed. There is still a very, very slight amount of crossover distortion, which is of no concern for most applications. However, this slight amount of crossover distortion is further reduced by the 100-Ω resistor shown in Figure 12–11. This resistor supplies the load current slightly above and below zero-crossing and shares some of the load current with the transistors. The bulk of the load current is still supplied via the transistors. The power-handling capability of a circuit such as this can be further increased by using Darlington transistors or Darlington pairs, as shown in Figure 12–12.

DC BOOSTING

Medium-Power Current Boosting

Figure 12–13 illustrates a single-supply constant-current source. The voltage set by the 10-kΩ potentiometer determines the amount of load current, which is held constant for a wide range of load resistance—including a shorted load. The emitter current of the output transistor is approximately equal to the load current. If the emitter current is held constant, the load current must be constant. Notice that the negative voltage feedback is taken

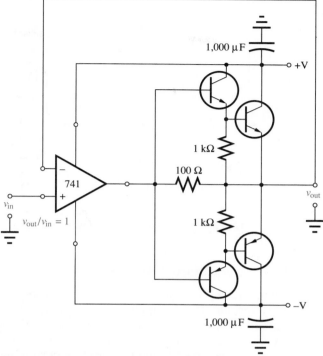

Figure 12–12 Darlington push-pull output.

from the emitter. Since the difference voltage between the inverting and noninverting inputs is near zero, V_{RE} must equal V_X. As an example, if $V_X = 3$ V, then V_{RE} must be 3 V and the load current must be 3 V/10 Ω = 0.3 A. As the wiper arm on the potentiometer is moved down, V_X and V_{RE} increase. Thus, the emitter current and load current increase. The only way load current can be changed is by adjusting the potentiometer. If the load becomes shorted, V_{RE} does not change—rather, V_{CE} increases.

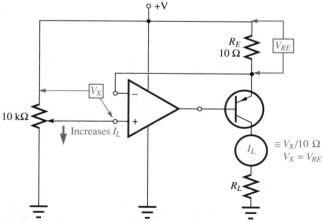

Figure 12–13 Single-supply, current-boosted, voltage-to-current converter.

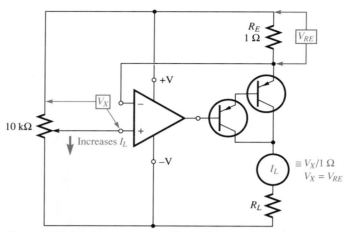

Figure 12–14   Dual-supply, high-power, voltage-to-current converter.

High-Power Current Boosting

Figure 12–14 illustrates a higher-power version that makes use of both the plus and minus DC supplies. The theory is the same as what we just discussed. Notice the emitter resistor is now 1 Ω and a Darlington pair is being used. This circuit acts as a high-power, constant-current source. If V_X is 2 V, then V_{RE} must be 2 V and the constant current must be 2 V/1 Ω = 2 A. Such would be the case if +V = 12 V and the voltage from the wiper arm of the potentiometer to ground is +10 V.

Fixed and Stabilized Current Source

In either Figure 12–13 or 12–14, if a fixed load current is desired, the potentiometer can be replaced with two fixed resistors or a fixed resistor and a zener diode. The zener diode would supply a fixed value of V_X even if the DC supply voltage varied (zener connected to a +V and series resistor to ground or −V). This insures a constant load current regardless of variations in supply voltage or load resistance.

Time for a self-check.

Self-Check 12–4

1. Explain how a 741, which is current limited at 20 mA, can be used to drive a 100-mA AC load.
2. Design a 1-A constant-current source using a 741 as the heart of the circuit.

12–5 BALANCED AMPLIFIER CIRCUITS

Balanced amplifiers are op-amp circuits that take advantage of the differential mode. The differential mode permits maximum voltage and power gain along with maximum common-mode signal rejection. Often, these amplifiers are called *instrumentation amplifiers* since they offer the qualities desired in

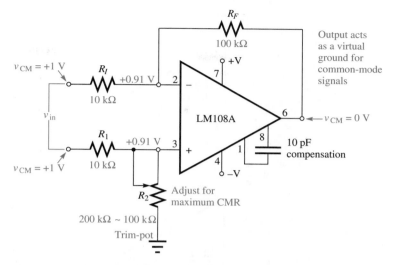

Figure 12–15 Differential input balanced for high common-mode rejection.

sensitive electronic instruments. Here, we will investigate some of these circuits and their qualities.

BALANCED FOR COMMON-MODE REJECTION

One of the most desirable qualities of an instrumentation amplifier is that of common-mode rejection. Common-mode noise must be suppressed as much as possible so legitimate parameters can be monitored and measured. Figure 12–15 is a standard circuit used to optimize common-mode rejection. This circuit has a differential input and a single-ended output and uses the LM108A, which has a CMRR of 110 dB. Any common-mode signals v_{CM} arriving at the two inputs must be canceled in the op-amp. The only way maximum cancelation can occur is if the common-mode signals at pins 2 and 3 are identical in amplitude. To insure that this is so, a trim-pot (R_2) is connected as shown and carefully adjusted for maximum CMR. The common-mode signal developed across R_F must match the common-mode signal across R_2. Therefore, the ratio of R_I/R_F should equal the ratio of R_1/R_2. In most cases this is satisifed by making $R_1 = R_I$ and $R_2 = R_F$. For example, $R_1 = R_I = 10$ kΩ and $R_2 = R_F = 100$ kΩ. If R_2 is variable, as shown in Figure 12–11, it should be 200 kΩ to allow for high- and low-side adjustment. The differential gain of the amplifier is the ratio of R_F/R_I.

Adjustment of this circuit for maximum CMR is very simple. A jumper wire is temporarily placed between the two inputs and an AC signal, acting as a common-mode signal, is applied between the jumper and ground. Variable resistor R_2 is carefully adjusted for minimum output.

IMPEDANCE-BALANCED INPUTS

Figure 12–16 illustrates a balanced amplifier with excellent CMR characteristics and a balanced floating input. Unlike that in the circuit of Figure 12–15, the balanced input impedance in this circuit can be any value up to millions

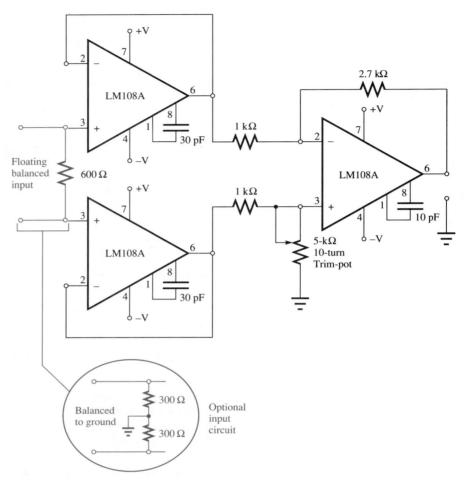

Figure 12–16 Impedance-balanced amplifier with optimized common-mode rejection.

of ohms. That makes this circuit nearly ideal for very sensitive instrumentation applications in which high-impedance sources must be monitored.

As shown in Figure 12–16, the input impedance of this balanced amplifier is only 600 Ω as determined by the resistor bridging the two noninverting inputs. This amplifier is found in many pieces of studio equipment, such as audio mixing consoles and tape machines, and is used as a line input amplifier. The 600-Ω input impedance is a standard in the recording industry and is the basis for the 0 dBm standard where the milliwatt is used as a reference for all audio power levels. Zero dBm is equal to 1 mW of power dissipated in a 600-Ω load having a difference of potential of 0.775 V_{RMS}.

The balanced input to the amplifier can be either floating or balanced to ground. A floating balanced input is one in which neither end of the input impedance is connected to ground and each input line is at a very high impedance above ground. The balanced-to-ground method, also shown in Figure 12–16, still provides the needed 600-Ω input impedance with each input balanced and tied to ground. Since each input line is loaded with 300 Ω

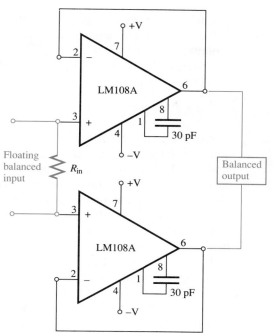

Figure 12–17 Balanced input and output amplifier.

to ground, there is less common-mode signal induced on each line and less for the op-amps to handle. The 300-Ω resistors should be identical in value for maximum CMR. In any case, the 5-kΩ, 10-turn trim-pot must be adjusted for maximum CMR.

BALANCED INPUT AND OUTPUT AMPLIFIERS

The balanced input and output amplifier of Figure 12–17 is also known as a *balanced line driver*. The overall gain of this amplifier is unity (1). You already know this as a differential output. The input to this amplifier is balanced and floating above ground. The actual input impedance is determined by the value of R_{in}. A balanced-to-ground input may also be used (and may be a better choice to reduce common-mode signals on the two input lines, since this circuit offers no means of common-mode rejection adjustment). Common-mode signals will appear on the output lines but will be rejected at the other end, where receiving amplifiers such as Figure 12–16 are used.

Self-Check 12–5

1. Which of these statements is true for Figure 12–15?
    (a) Maximum CMR is obtained when $R_1 = R_I$ and $R_2 = R_F$.
    (b) Maximum CMR is obtained when the common-mode voltage at pin 2 equals the common-mode voltage at pin 3.
    (c) Maximum CMR is obtained when $R_1/R_2 = R_I/R_F$.
    (d) All of the above are true.

2. What is one advantage of Figure 12–16 compared to Figure 12–15?
3. What is the advantage to using a balanced-to-ground input as compared to the floating balanced input?
4. Does the circuit of Figure 12–17 provide CMR? Explain.

12–6 COMPARATORS

In many electronic and electromechanical systems it is necessary to continually monitor a voltage that represents some function. This voltage may indicate a limit, such as temperature or mechanical travel, has been reached and/or exceeded. The system may be designed to remedy itself, or to activate a light or alarm to alert an operator. In any case, a voltage is monitored and action is taken when a predetermined level is reached or exceeded.

How does the system know the voltage has reached a certain level? This is accomplished with the use of comparators. A **comparator** is a high-gain amplifier that has a differential input and uses no negative feedback. Op-amps can be used as comparators. Since they are operated with no negative feedback, $A_V = A_{OL}$ and the slightest difference voltage between the two inputs will saturate the output either plus or minus. Let's explore a variety of comparator circuits.

BASIC COMPARATORS

The Zero-Reference Comparator

Figure 12–18 is a zero-reference comparator. Note that the inverting input is grounded and the noninverting input is used to monitor a DC voltage V_{in}. The open-loop gain of this op-amp is 100 dB. As you know, that means that V_{in} is amplified 100,000 times. To saturate the output at ± 10 V, the input voltage only needs to be ± 0.1 mV. Thus, an input voltage of $\geq +0.1$ mV causes the output to jump to $+10$ V and an input of ≥ -0.1 mV causes the output to jump to -10 V. A practical use for a comparator such as this is a polarity detector to indicate when a voltage has crossed zero and in what direction.

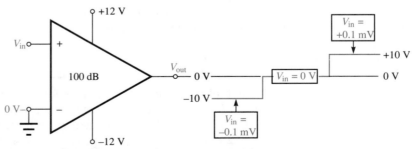

Figure 12–18   The zero-reference comparator.

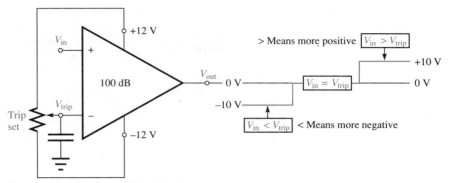

Figure 12–19   The dual-polarity comparator.

The Dual-Polarity Comparator

The comparator of Figure 12–19 has an adjustable reference point, or trip point, set by the potentiometer. Notice that the potentiometer is tied between both the positive and negative DC supplies. The wiper can be set negative or positive, allowing the trip point to be set anywhere in the range of ± 12 V. If the trip point is set at -5 V, the output will be 0 V for $V_{in} = -5$ V, -10 V for $V_{in} < -5$ V, and $+10$ V for $V_{in} > -5$ V. The capacitor at the wiper arm helps prevent false tripping due to noise or incomplete filtering on the DC supply lines.

Single-Supply Comparators

Figure 12–20 is a single-supply comparator using a general-purpose op-amp. Notice that the output is limited to the region of 0 V to $+10$ V. In practice, using an op-amp as a comparator, the low state is actually about $+1$ or $+2$ V. The output of this comparator circuit will not go high until V_{in} is more positive than V_{trip}.

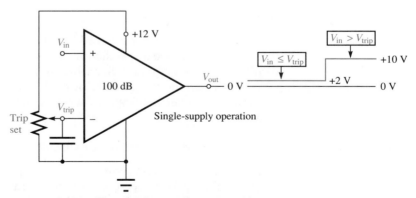

Figure 12–20   The single-supply comparator.

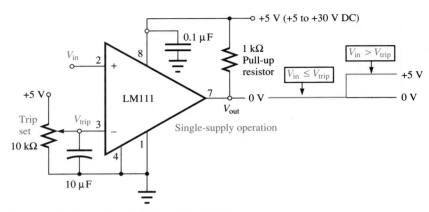

Figure 12–21   The LM111 comparator.

The LM111 Comparator

The LM111 shown in Figure 12–21 is a high-speed comparator. It is designed specifically for comparator operation and is found in the comparator section of data books. The output, at pin 7, is the collector of an output transistor. This comparator has an open-collector output and a pull-up resistor is needed to complete the output circuit. The LM111 and others like it are able to switch from low to high and vice versa at very high speeds. Recall that the switching time of an op-amp is limited by its slew rate. Where internal capacitor compensation is used, the slew rate is usually very slow (such as 0.5 V/μs for the 741) and switching is relatively slow. Comparator ICs are designed without capacitor compensation and other internal capacitances that would slow down the switching time.

Like op-amps, the LM111 may also be used with a dual DC supply. In such a case, pin 4 is tied to $-$VDC. The output can be made to swing from $-$VDC to $+$VDC and vice versa if desired. See a manufacturer's data book for more circuit details.

WINDOW COMPARATORS

Purpose

The window comparator of Figure 12–22 is used to determine if a voltage is either within or outside a specific range. This circuit can be used to monitor the voltage from a temperature-sensing circuit or a fluid-level circiut, to alert an operator when the temperature or fluid level is too high or too low, or in any number of other applications where a specific parameter range is important.

The LM339 Window Comparator Circuit

For this circuit, the very popular and inexpensive LM339 is used. The LM339 is actually four open-collector comparators in one dual-in-line package. Two of the comparators are used for this circuit. Note that the outputs

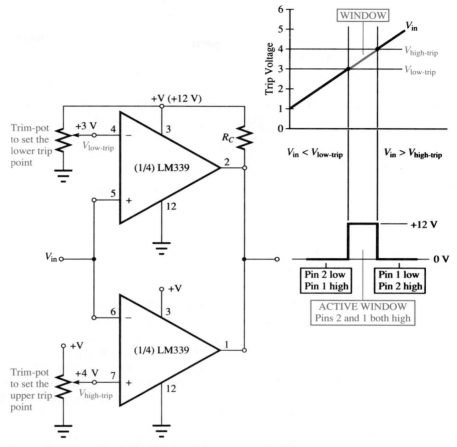

Figure 12–22 The adjustable window comparator.

are paralleled to the same pull-up resistor. Either comparator can pull the output to ground. Notice also that V_{in} is applied to the inverting input of one comparator and to the noninverting input of the second. Since the trip voltage is set at the inverting input of the upper comparator, the upper comparator is normally ON (pin 2 is low). Since the trip voltage is set at the noninverting input of the lower comparator, it is normally OFF (pin 1 is high). Since pins 1 and 2 are tied together, the output is normally low.

The only way the output will go high is if the input voltage is within the active window as set by the trim-pots. Say the trip voltage set by the upper trim-pot is +3 V and the trip voltage set by the lower trim-pot is +4V. If V_{in} is +3.1 V, pin 2 will be high because $V_{in} > V_{low-trip}$. Pin 1 is still high since $V_{in} < V_{high-trip}$. Since pins 1 and 2 are both high, the output is high at +12 V, assuming no load. Now, if V_{in} increases to +4.1 V, pin 1 will go low since $V_{in} > V_{high-trip}$. As you can see, the only time the output is high is when V_{in} is within the range of the active window. The active window can be as wide or as narrow as you like, since it depends on the settings of the trim-pots.

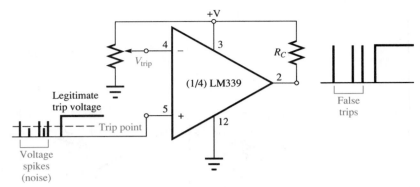

Figure 12–23   False tripping due to input noise.

SCHMITT TRIGGERS

Noise Problems

Comparators can be plagued by noise on the input line that causes false trips. Figure 12–23 illustrates the problem noise can cause. The input line contains narrow voltage pulses, or spikes, that will cause the output to switch if the input spikes are high enough in amplitude. If the peak of the noise spike is greater than the trip point, the output will switch. If the legitimate control voltage is greater than the noise spikes, the trip point can be set higher above the heads of the spikes. Otherwise, the line noise must be removed on-line with filters and/or by isolating the line from the source using shielded cables and other techniques.

Noise Riding on an AC Signal

Figure 12–24 shows a basic comparator that is being used to convert a sine wave to a pulsating DC square wave. This type of conversion is used at the input of digital frequency counters to convert each sine wave cycle into a single square-wave pulse that can be counted by the digital circuitry. Any noise on the line with the sinusoidal signal can cause false trips and an erroneous count. As shown in Figure 12–24, there are three output pulses when there should be just one. Noise pulses riding on the input signal often cause false trips near the trip point. This is a real and common problem that can be cured using a special comparator circuit called a Schmitt trigger.

The Schmitt Trigger

The Schmitt trigger type of comparator is shown in Figure 12–25. The noise pulses riding on the input signal now have no effect on the output. The output is a clean single pulse for each cycle of the input waveform. This is accomplished by designing the circuit for separated ON and OFF trip points. The difference in voltage between these two trip points is called the **hysteresis voltages.** *Hysteresis* means "to lag behind." In a sense, the OFF trip point lags behind the ON trip point. This separation of trip points ensures that normal noise pulses cannot cause repeated false tripping.

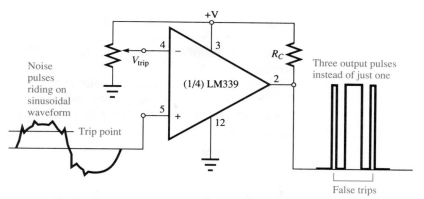

Figure 12–24 False tripping on sinusoidal waveforms.

Let's see how the circuit works. The ON trip point is set by the voltage divider R_1 and R_2. In this case, the trip point is +0.45 V. This +0.45 V at the inverting input holds pin 2 low. When the input waveform exceeds +0.45 V, the output goes high and the right end of R_3 goes high as well. R_3 and R_4 form a voltage divider that places +0.24 V at pin 5. This is the hysteresis voltage (V_H) and represents positive feedback. This positive hysteresis voltage must now be overcome by the input signal before the output can be returned to the low state (OFF). Thus, as the positive peak of the input signal decreases back toward zero-crossing, it is not enough that it fall below +0.45 V. It must drop down below +0.21 V to overcome the hysteresis voltage, since

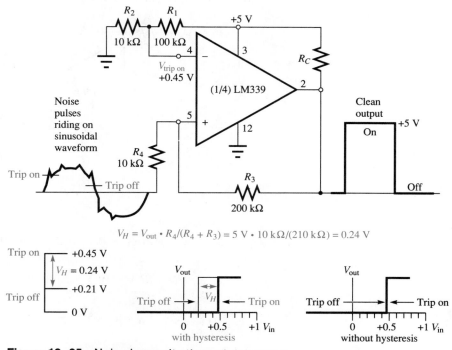

$$V_H = V_{out} \cdot R_4/(R_4 + R_3) = 5\text{ V} \cdot 10\text{ k}\Omega/(210\text{ k}\Omega) = 0.24\text{ V}$$

Figure 12–25 Noise immunity through hysteresis.

+0.21 V + 0.24 V = +0.45 V, which is the trip setting established by R_1 and R_2. Once the positive alternation of the input drops below +0.21 V, the output returns to 0 V, where it stays until the next positive alternation exceeds +0.45 V.

As stated earlier, the ON trip point is established by the ratio of $R_2/(R_2 + R_1)$. The hysteresis voltage is the difference between the ON and OFF trip points and is determined by the ratio $R_4/(R_4 + R_3)$. Thus, $V_{\text{trip OFF}} < V_{\text{trip ON}} - V_H$.

$$V_{\text{trip ON}} > +\text{VDC} \cdot R_2/(R_2 + R_1) \tag{12–8}$$

$$V_H = V_{\text{out}} \cdot R_4/(R_4 + R_3) \tag{12–9}$$

where V_{out} is the actual output voltage with or without a load.

$$V_{\text{trip OFF}} < V_{\text{trip ON}} - V_H \tag{12–10}$$

One final observation. Pin 2 is normally low and the right end of R_3 is at ground potential. This means that R_4 and R_3 form a voltage divider at the input, where the voltage at pin 5 is $V_{\text{in}} \cdot R_3/(R_3 + R_4)$. Therefore, the input voltage must be slightly higher than +0.45 V for the output to trip ON. The slight increase required in input voltage is not significant as long as R_3 is much larger than R_4. In any case, the difference in trip voltages is widened, further improving noise immunity. Now look at Example 12–7.

EXAMPLE 12–7

Determine $V_{\text{trip ON}}$, $V_{\text{trip OFF}}$, and V_H for Figure 12–26.

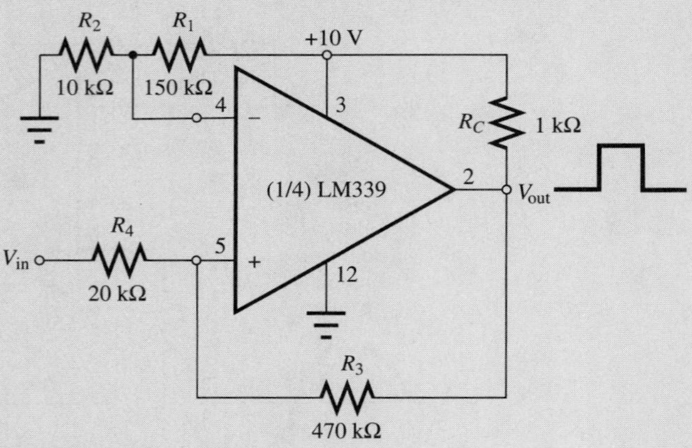

Figure 12–26

$$V_{\text{trip ON}} > +\text{VDC} \cdot R_2/(R_2 + R_1) = 10 \text{ V} \cdot 10 \text{ k}\Omega/(10 \text{ k}\Omega + 150 \text{ k}\Omega)$$
$$> 0.625 \text{ V}$$

$$V_H = V_{\text{out}} \cdot R_4/(R_4 + R_3) = 10 \text{ V} \cdot 20 \text{ k}\Omega/(20 \text{ k}\Omega + 470 \text{ k}\Omega)$$
$$= 0.408 \text{ V}$$

$$V_{\text{trip OFF}} < V_{\text{trip ON}} - V_H = 0.625 \text{ V} - 0.408 \text{ V}$$
$$< 0.217 \text{ V}$$

Time for another self-check.

---

1. Explain how the LM111 or LM339 is better than a 741 as a comparator.
2. Refer to Figure 12–22. What is the setting of the trim-pots if the active window is from +2 V to +2.25 V?
3. Again, refer to Figure 12–22. If the active window is from +2 V to +2.25 V and the input voltage is +3 V, which output pin is high and which is low?
4. Explain why a basic comparator is not reliable in converting noisy sine-wave cycles to square-wave pulses.
5. Referring to Figure 12–25, calculate the ON and OFF trip points when $R_2 = 10$ kΩ, $R_1 = 68$ kΩ, $R_4 = 4.7$ kΩ, and $R_3 = 150$ kΩ.

12–7 PRECISION RECTIFIERS

As you know, diode rectifiers drop a small voltage across themselves when they are forward biased (conducting), approximately 0.7 V for silicon diodes and 0.3 V for germanium. Suppose you want to rectify a sine wave that is 2 $V_{\text{P-P}}$. If silicon diodes are used, the rectified output voltage is only 0.3 V_P. Most of the voltage is dropped across the diodes. Even worse, suppose you want to rectify an AC signal that is only 100 m$V_{\text{P-P}}$. The diodes will not even begin to conduct and the output is 0 V. What to do? The answer is precision rectifiers using op-amps. These simple circuits are able to rectify very-low-level signals.

Why would you want to rectify very-low-level signals? Say you wanted to monitor the level of an audio signal. If the audio signal is converted to a DC level, using a precision rectifier and filter, it can be used to drive a meter or trip a comparator or control the gain of a stage in an AGC system. In this section, you will see how very-low-level signals are converted to DC using precision rectifiers.

PRECISION HALF-WAVE RECTIFIER

The Basic Precision Half-Wave Rectifier

The precision half-wave rectifier, shown in Figure 12–27, is the simplest of the precision rectifiers—only an op-amp and a diode are needed. As you can see, the output is taken after the diode. Normally this would allow the diode to take a 0.7-V drop. However, notice the feedback line from the diode to the inverting input. This places the diode within the feedback loop. With no signal applied, the diode is OFF and the feedback loop is open. When a signal is present at the input, the diode is forced to conduct during the positive alternations (negative alternations if you reverse the diode). The diode still gets a 0.7-V drop and the full peak voltage appears in the output. Why?

Recall that the difference voltage between the inverting and noninverting inputs is very small, near 0 V. That means, when a positive peak is applied to

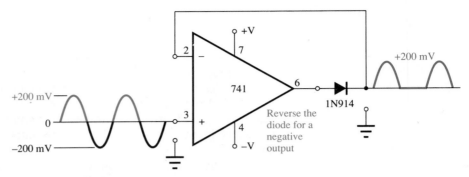

Figure 12–27   Precision half-wave rectifier.

pin 3 a nearly identical positive peak must appear at pin 2 and pin 2 is tied to the output. Remember, the op-amp has a tremendous open-loop gain. As the input signal first begins to increase in the positive direction from zero-crossing, the slightest positive voltage is amplified 100,000 to 200,000 times. The voltage at pin 6 is almost instantly large enough to forward bias the diode. Thus, very little of the input signal is sacrificed to cause the diode to conduct (0.7 V/100,000 = 7 μV). For all negative alternations, the diode is OFF and pin 6 is pinned to $-V$, since the loop is open for all negative alternations. Another diode can be placed in the feedback loop to prevent this (see Figure 12–29).

The Precision Positive-Peak Detector

Figure 12–28 illustrates the positive-peak detector. This is a precision half-wave rectifier with a filter capacitor. The filter capacitor is charged almost instantly by the precision rectifier, which appears to have a very low output impedance. Between positive alternations, the capacitor holds its charge, losing only what the load resistor demands. The load resistor should be very large and the RC time constant very long if a smooth DC output is desired.

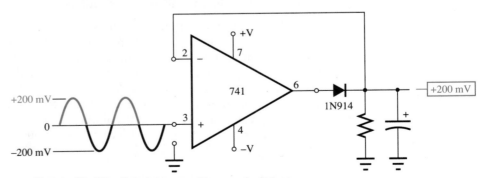

Figure 12–28   Precision positive-peak detector.

PRECISION FULL-WAVE RECTIFIER

The Circuit

The precision full-wave rectifier is shown in Figure 12–29. This circuit has two stages. The first stage is a precision negative half-wave rectifier. The second stage is a summing amplifier (adder). The signals at A and B are being added together. The signal at A is the AC input signal and the signal at B is the negative half-wave rectified signal. Notice the A and B inputs to the adder are weighted differently. The gain for input A is 1 ($R_4/R_5 = 20$ k/20 k = 1) and the gain for input B is 2 ($R_4/R_3 = 20$ k/10 k = 2).

Positive Alternations

Now, let's follow the signals to see the purpose for the weighted inputs, A and B. For each positive alternation at the input, a negative alternation appears at B (shaded alternations). These A and B alternations have the same peak value because the gain of the precision rectifier is 1 ($R_2/R_1 = 20$ k/20 k = 1). The negative alternations at B are doubled in amplitude and appear at pin 6 of the adder as positive alternations. At the same time, the positive alternations at A, the input, appear at pin 6 of the adder as negative alternations that cancel half the amplitude of the positive alternations created by input B. So, for all positive alternations at the input, the output is

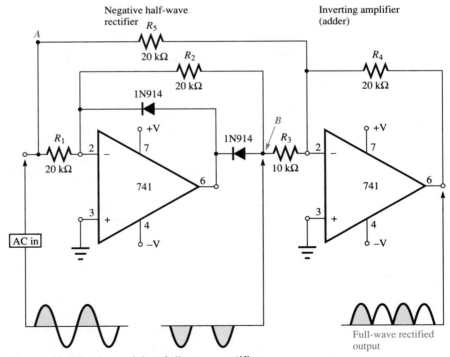

Figure 12–29 A precision full-wave rectifier.

$2V_P - V_P = V_P$ where $2V_P$ is caused by the B input and $-V_P$ is from the A input.

Negative Alternations

The explanation for the negative alternations at the input is easy. For all negative alternations, there is no output from the precision rectifier at point B. The feedback diode conducts and limits the voltage at pin 6 to $+0.7$ V. This allows the rectifier op-amp to quickly switch in the negative direction when positive alternations appear at the input. Otherwise, the op-amp would be saturated in the positive direction and have to swing all the way down to the negative rectified voltage.

The only circuit that is active during negative alternations is the adder. The negative alternations at A appear as positive alternations, of the same peak voltage, at the output. Thus, precision full-wave rectification is accomplished. Note: The entire circuit is converted to a negative precision-full-wave rectifier by simply reversing both diodes.

Self-Check 12–7

1. There is no 0.7-V diode drop across the diodes of precision rectifiers. True or false?
2. Explain how a precision rectifier is able to produce a rectified output that is nearly exactly the same amplitude as the peak input voltage.
3. What is the purpose for the feedback diode (between pins 2 and 6) of Figure 12–29?

12–8 LIMITERS AND CLAMPERS

LIMITERS

Voltage limiters, using op-amps, have the advantage of providing voltage gain with limiting. Figure 12–30 illustrates two limiter circuits that suggest many possibilities. Figure 12–30a is a simple diode-drop limiter. The small-signal closed-loop gain of the op-amp is set by R_F and R_I, which is normal for any inverting amplifier. Any signal that appears at pin 6 greater than ± 0.7 V is limited to approximately ± 0.7 V. This is because any signal at pin 6 greater than ± 0.7 V causes the diodes to conduct, providing a large amount of negative feedback. The diodes act as bypasses to R_F. The larger the would-be output signal, the more the diodes conduct, further reducing closed-loop gain. Diode D_2 conducts for positive output alternations and D_1 conducts during the negative output alternations when their 0.7-V barrier potential is approached and exceeded.

The gain of the op-amp should be adjusted to accommodate the level of input signal. If the output is to reach limiting when the input is 100 mV$_{P-P}$, the closed-loop gain must be set at 0.7 V/50 mV = 14. If the output is to reach limiting when the input is 30 mV$_{P-P}$, the closed-loop gain must be set at 0.7 V/15 mV = 47.

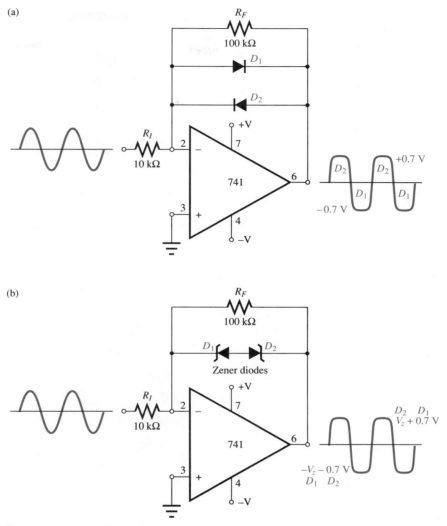

Figure 12–30   Voltage-limiter circuits.

Diodes can be placed in series to increase the threshold of limiting by factors of 0.7 V or zener diodes can be used as shown in Figure 12–30b. Notice the zener diodes are placed in series anode to anode as shown or cathode to cathode. One zener will operate in the zener breakdown region while the other is forward biased as a regular diode. Thus, the total limiting threshold for each output alternation is the sum of a forward diode drop (0.7 V) and a zener voltage. If both diodes are 6.2-V zeners, the total threshold voltage is ±6.9 V. This is known as **symmetrical limiting.**

The zeners do not have to be the same value. For example, one could be 3.6 V and the other 4.3 V. Depending on the series arrangement of these diodes, the output would be limited to either +4.3 V and −5 V or +5 V and −4.3 V. This is known as **asymmetrical limiting.**

EXAMPLE 12–8 ▰▰▰▰▰▰▰▰▰▰▰▰▰▰▰▰▰▰▰

Determine the input and output, positive and negative, limiting thresholds for Figure 12–31.

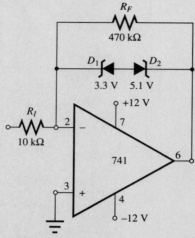

Figure 12–31

Maximum positive output voltage = 5.1 V + 0.7 V = 5.8 V_P

Maximum negative output voltage = −0.7 V + (−3.3 V) = −4 V_P

A_V = 470 kΩ/10 kΩ = 47

Maximum positive input voltage = $|-4\ V_P|/A_V$

$$= |-4\ V_P|/47 = +85\ mV_P$$

Maximum negative input voltage = $-5.8\ V_P/A_V$

$$= -5.8\ V_P/47 = -123\ mV_P$$

CLAMPERS

Figure 12–32 shows a precision clamper circuit. As you know, the problem with basic clamper circuits is the ±0.7-V diode drop, which causes 0.7 V of one peak to be over the zero-line (see Section 3–4 for a review). The precision negative clamper of Figure 12–32 overcomes this problem by using a precision rectifier. During the first positive alternation, capacitor charge current flows, causing a positive potential at the inverting input that instantly forces the output pin negative. This causes the diode to conduct, to assist the charging of the capacitor. After that first positive alternation, from 0° to 90°, the capacitor is fully charged to actual peak voltage. With the capacitor charged to peak value as shown, the inverting input sees the negative plate of the capacitor and is forced into positive saturation at its output pin. This means the diode is now reverse biased and cut off. The diode and op-amp are effectively removed from the circuit, leaving the charged capacitor in series

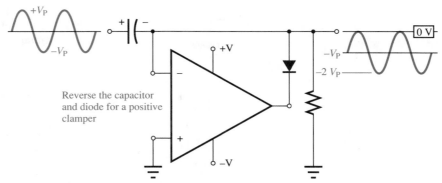

Figure 12–32 A precision clamper.

with the load resistor. The charge on the capacitor provides a negative reference voltage equal to $-V_P$ for the incoming AC signal.

Naturally, some of the charge voltage will be lost through the load. Say the peak voltage and capacitor charge voltage are 10 V. During a cycle we will say the capacitor discharges by 0.1 V, leaving a 9.9-V charge. When the next positive alternation arrives at the positive plate of the capacitor and reaches near peak voltage ($+10$ V) the capacitor charge current will flow, causing the output pin of the op-amp to swing negative, forward biasing the diode and quickly restoring the charge on the capacitor. The charge time is the same as the time it takes for the positive alternation to go from $+9.9$ V to $+10$ V. Thus, the capacitor's charge is precisely restored to peak value.

A positive clamper can be made simply by reversing the capacitor and by reversing the diode. Time for a self-check.

Self-Check 12–8

1. Describe the output waveform of Figure 12–30a if D_2 were removed.
2. Suggest values for R_F and R_I if it is desired to amplify and limit a 20-mV$_P$ signal using the circuit of Figure 12–30a.
3. What is the difference between symmetrical and asymmetrical limiting?
4. What is the advantage of a precision clamper over a basic clamper?
5. During what portion of an input cycle does the diode of Figure 12–32 conduct?

12–9 INTEGRATORS AND DIFFERENTIATORS

INTEGRATORS

The Basic Concept of Integration

Perhaps you recall integrators from your circuit-theory course. An integrator is a lowpass filter to which pulsating DC is applied. The output of the integrator is usually the average voltage of the input pulses. Here, you will discover a little more about these circuits as we consider op-amp integrators.

As you consider Figure 12–33, you will begin to see why these circuits are called *integrators*. Technically, an integrator is an analog computer circuit

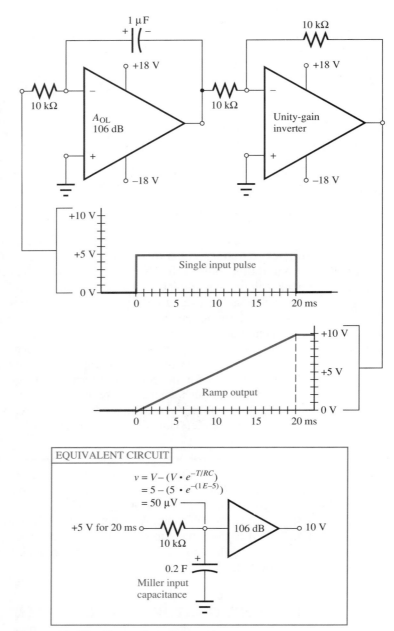

Figure 12–33 The voltage integrator.

that is able to create the integral of an input waveform. Mathematically, the integral of a waveform represents the area under the waveform. In Figure 12–33, the input waveform is a square pulse. The integral of this pulse is a rising slope that represents the increasing area of the pulse with time. Starting at time 0, the area under the square pulse is 0. As time increases to the right, the slope increases, representing the increasing area of the square pulse. At the end of the pulse, at $T = 20$ ms, the integration process is finished and the total area under the square pulse is stored on the capacitor as a charge of $+10$ V.

How does the circuit of Figure 12–33 accomplish this operation? Recall that the inverting input pin is at virtual ground. The input voltage is across the 10-kΩ input resistor. Since the input voltage is constant at +5 V, the resistor current is constant at 5 V/10 kΩ = 0.5 mA. This current is also the capacitor charge current. Thus, the capacitor is charging at the rate of 0.5 mA = 0.5 mC/s. After 20 ms, the total quantity of charge on the capacitor is 0.5 mC/s · 0.02 s = 0.01 mC. Therefore, the final charge voltage after 20 ms must be 0.01 mC/1 μF = 10 V since V = Q/C = quantity of charge/capacitance.

$$Q = T \cdot V_{in}/R \qquad (12\text{–}11)$$

where T is the length of time V_{in} is applied to R.

$$V = Q/C \qquad (12\text{–}12)$$

where V is the capacitor voltage, Q is the quantity of charge, and C is the capacitance of the capacitor.

The inset box of Figure 12–30 shows the equivalent circuit. Note that the Miller input capacitance is the product of feedback capacitance and open-loop gain. In this case, the feedback capacitance is 1 μF and the open-loop gain is 106 dB = 200,000. Thus, the Miller input capacitance is 1 μF · 200,000 = 0.2 F. The input resistor is in series with this very large capacitance. During the 20 ms the +5 V is applied, this huge capacitance charges to only +50 μV. The output voltage is the product of input voltage and open-loop gain, V_{out} = +50 μV · 200,000 = +10 V.

$$C_{in(Miller)} \cong CA_{OL} \qquad (12\text{–}13)$$

$$v = V - (V \cdot e^{-T/RC}) \qquad (12\text{–}14)$$

where v is the charge voltage at time T.

EXAMPLE 12–9

Determine the output voltage from the integrator of Figure 12–34 after a 6-V input pulse has been applied for 5 ms.

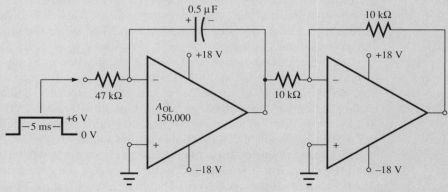

Figure 12–34

$$Q = T \cdot V_{\text{in}}/R = 5 \text{ ms} \cdot 6 \text{ V}/47 \text{ k}\Omega = 0.638 \ \mu\text{C}$$

$$V = Q/C = 0.638 \ \mu\text{C}/0.5 \ \mu\text{F} = 1.28 \text{ V}$$

Also,

$$C_{\text{in(Miller)}} \cong CA_{\text{OL}} = 0.5 \ \mu\text{F} \cdot 150{,}000 = 0.075 \text{ F}$$

$$v = V - (V \cdot e^{-T/RC}) = 6 \text{ V} - (6 \text{ V} \cdot e^{-5 \text{ ms}/(47\text{k}\Omega \cdot 0.075\text{F})})$$

$$= 6 \text{ V} - (6 \text{ V} \cdot e^{-1.4184\text{E}-6}) = 6 \text{ V} - (6 \text{ V} \cdot 0.999998581)$$

$$= 6 \text{ V} - 5.99999149 \text{ V} = 8.51 \ \mu\text{V}$$

$$V_{\text{out}} = 8.51 \ \mu\text{V} \cdot 150{,}000 = 1.28 \text{ V}$$

The Average-Value Integrator

Figure 12–35 illustrates a practical integrator circuit that includes a feedback resistance to stabilize the output offset voltage. Integrators such as these compute the average DC voltage of a complete cycle of an input waveform. Naturally, the average depends on the peak pulse amplitude and the duty cycle. As shown in Figure 12–35, the average voltage of a 100-mV, 50%-duty-cycle square wave is 50 mV. Since the gain of the integrator is 100, the average output voltage is +5 VDC. If the duty cycle were 30%, the average output would be +3 VDC, if the duty cycle were 70%, the average output would be +7 VDC and so on.

The average value is obtained at the output because the capacitor is able to discharge somewhat through the feedback resistor during the pulse-off time. To understand this better, consider the equivalent circuits in the inset box of Figure 12–35. First, the circuit is drawn showing the 10-kΩ input resistor and the Miller input capacitance and resistance. The Miller input resistance equals feedback resistance divided by open-loop gain. In this case, $R_{\text{in(Miller)}} \cong 1 \text{ M}\Omega/200{,}000 = 5 \ \Omega$.

$$R_{\text{in(Miller)}} \cong R_F/A_{\text{OL}} \tag{12–15}$$

Notice that the 10-kΩ input resistance and the Miller resistance form a voltage divider, and the peak pulse amplitude of 100 mV is divided down to +50 μV$_P$. Let's go one step further now and Thevenize the voltage divider. As you can see, we get $V_{\text{Th}} = +50 \ \mu\text{V}_P$ and $R_{\text{Th}} = 5 \ \Omega$. The Thevenin equivalent circuit shows us that the 0.2-F capacitor is being charged and discharged through the same 5-Ω resistance. When the capacitor charges and discharges through the same resistance, the capacitor holds the average voltage after five time constants. Five time constants is $5RC = 5 \cdot 5 \ \Omega \cdot 0.2 \text{ F} = 5 \text{ s}$. After 5 s, the voltage is held constant at an average value of +25 μV which is amplified 200,000 times for an output of +5 V.

The average value of any waveform at any duty cycle will be computed by the integrator. For a smooth DC output, the $R_F C$ time constant should be ≥100 times the input cycle time. The integrator of Figure 12–35 provides a smooth DC output for pulse rates as low as 100 pps (Hz).

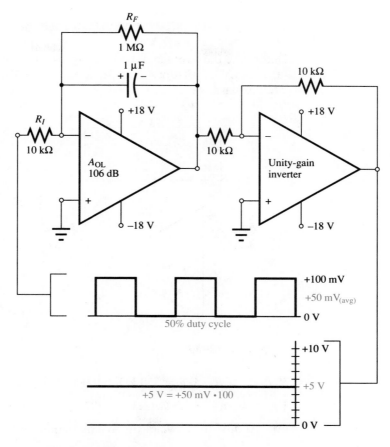

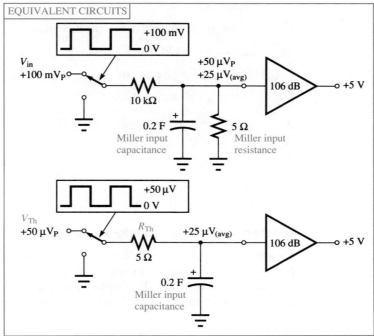

Figure 12–35   Average value integrator.

EXAMPLE 12–10 ▰▰▰▰▰▰▰▰▰▰▰▰▰▰▰▰▰

Determine the average output voltage for Figure 12–36 if the input is: (a) a 40-mV$_P$, 50%-duty-cycle square wave, or (b) a 40-mV$_P$, 10%-duty-cycle square wave.

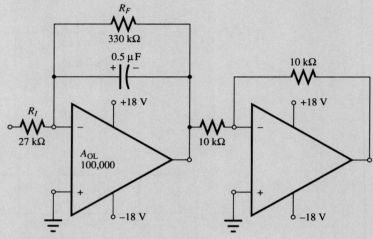

Figure 12–36

$R_{in(Miller)} \cong R_F/A_{OL} = 330 \text{ k}\Omega/100{,}000 = 3.3 \ \Omega$

$V_{Th} = 40 \text{ mV}_P \cdot 3.3 \ \Omega/(3.3 \ \Omega + 27 \text{ k}\Omega) = 4.888 \ \mu V_P$

(a) At 50% duty cycle, the average input voltage is

$4.888 \ \mu V_P \cdot 0.5 = 2.444 \ \mu V$

Therefore, the average output voltage must be

$2.444 \ \mu V \cdot 100{,}000 = 0.2444 \ V$

(b) At 10% duty cycle, the average input voltage is

$4.888 \ \mu V_P \cdot 0.1 = 0.4888 \ \mu V$

Therefore, the average output voltage must be

$0.4888 \ \mu V \cdot 100{,}000 = 0.04888 \ V$

DIFFERENTIATORS

Differentiation of a Triangle Wave

Figure 12–37 illustrates the differentiator. Differentiation is a mathematical process that is opposite to integration. It is used to compute the rate of change of a waveform. This implies that the waveform must be changing in amplitude over time ($\Delta V/\Delta t$), otherwise the output of the differentiator is zero.

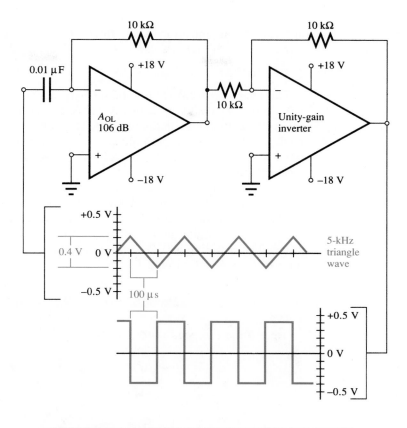

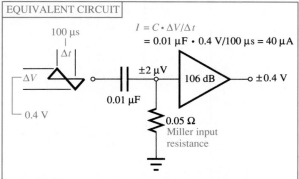

Figure 12–37 The differentiator.

As you can see in Figure 12–37, the input waveform is a triangle wave. The differentiator computes the slope, or rate of change, of this triangle wave. Since the slope of the triangle wave is either rising or falling, the output of the differentiator must switch between a positive level (+0.4 V), representing the positive-going slope, and a negative level (−0.4 V), representing the negative-going slope.

Why does the output switch between +0.4 V and −0.4 V? Since the slopes of the triangle wave are linear, the rate of change in capacitor charge voltage, $\Delta V/\Delta t$, is constant. Also, since $Q = CV$, then $\Delta Q/\Delta t = C \cdot \Delta V/\Delta t$. Because $I = \Delta Q/\Delta t$, we can substitute I for $\Delta Q/\Delta t$ and get

$$I = C \cdot \Delta V/\Delta t \qquad (12\text{--}16)$$

The charge current (I) for the 0.01-μF capacitor of Figure 12–37 is 0.01 μF $\cdot$ $\pm$0.4 V/100 μs = $\pm$40 μA. This charge current is also the current through the 10-kΩ feedback resistor. The voltage developed across the feedback resistor is the output voltage where $V_{out} = I \cdot R_F = \pm$40 μA $\cdot$ 10 kΩ = $\pm$0.4 V. Note that R_F can be selected to scale the output voltage to any desired level.

From Formula 12–16, you can see that if the input voltage is not changing, there is no charge current and the output of the differentiator must be 0 V.

The inset box of Figure 12–37 shows the equivalent circuit. Notice that the capacitor is charging and discharging through a 0.05-Ω Miller input resistance. The resulting $\pm$2-μV drop is amplified 200,000 times to $\pm$0.4 V at the output. Consider Example 12–11.

EXAMPLE 12–11

Determine the peak output voltage for Figure 12–38.

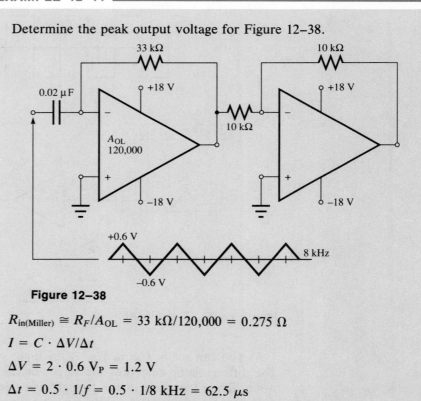

Figure 12–38

$R_{in(Miller)} \cong R_F/A_{OL} = 33$ kΩ/120,000 = 0.275 Ω

$I = C \cdot \Delta V/\Delta t$

$\Delta V = 2 \cdot 0.6$ V$_P$ = 1.2 V

$\Delta t = 0.5 \cdot 1/f = 0.5 \cdot 1/8$ kHz = 62.5 μs

$I = C \cdot \Delta V/\Delta t = 0.02$ μF $\cdot$ 1.2 V/62.5 μs = 384 μA

$V_{in} = 384$ μA $\cdot$ 0.275 Ω = $\pm$105.6 μV$_P$

$V_{out} = \pm$105.6 μV $\cdot$ 120,000 = $\pm$12.7 V$_P$

Differentiation of a Square Wave

Figure 12–39 illustrates a practical short-time-constant differentiator. This circuit is used to convert square-wave pulses to very narrow voltage spikes. Either the positive or the negative spikes can be used for timing pulses or trigger pulses in special circuits.

The output spikes only exist when the input square wave changes level. Notice that the output is 0 V during the time the input is either high or low. When the input pulse goes high, the capacitor charges rapidly through the 220-Ω resistor and the 10-kΩ feedback resistor. This charge current is short-lived and develops a voltage spike across the feedback resistor which is the output voltage.

The charge current at the first instant of time is V_{in}/R_I. Assume the peak pulse amplitude of the applied square wave is 100 mV. The charge current when the input pulse first goes positive is 100 mV/220 Ω = 0.455 mA. This initial current surges through the 10-kΩ feedback resistor, developing an output voltage of 0.455 mA · 10 kΩ = 4.55 V. The initial surge current is also 0.455 mA when the capacitor discharges through the 220-Ω resistor. Therefore, the voltage spikes at the output reach peaks of ±4.55 V. Also, the closed-loop gain of the inverting amplifier is R_F/R_I. In this case, the closed-loop gain is 10 k/220 = 45.5. Since the capacitor acts like a short when the input pulse first rises or falls, $V_{out} = V_{in} · 45.5 = 100$ mV $· 45.5 = 4.55$ V.

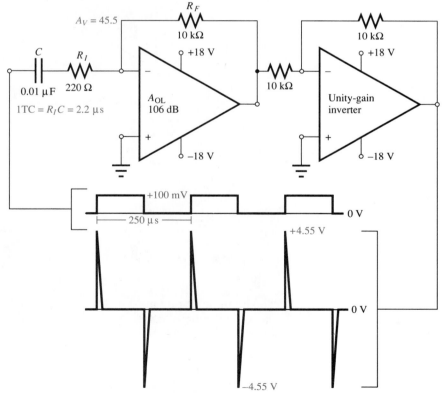

Figure 12–39   The short-time-constant differentiator.

Thus, the amplitude of the output spikes is determined by the peak voltage of the input square wave and the ratio of R_F/R_I. Keep the closed-loop gain less than 100 or the output will contain intolerable oscillations.

The $R_I C$ time constant must be very short compared to the input-pulse cycle time. For clean, narrow output pulses, the $R_I C$ time constant should be less than or equal to the input-cycle time divided by 100. For the circuit of Figure 12–39, the $R_I C$ time constant is $220\ \Omega \cdot 0.01\ \mu F = 2.2\ \mu s$. This combination of R_I and C will produce clean, narrow pulses for all input-cycle times greater than approximately $220\ \mu s$ (frequencies less than about 4.5 kHz).

EXAMPLE 12–12

Determine the output pulse amplitude and the highest input pulse rate for Figure 12–40.

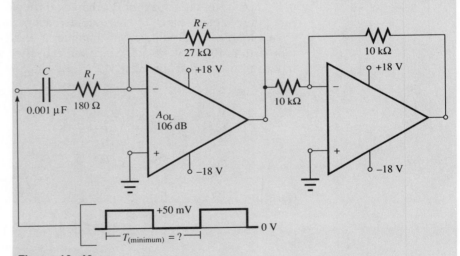

Figure 12–40

$A_V = R_F/R_I = 27\ k\Omega/180\ \Omega = 150$

$V_{P(out)} = V_{P(in)} \cdot A_V = 50\ mV \cdot 150 = 7.5\ V_P$

$1TC = R_I C = 180\ \Omega \cdot 0.001\ \mu F = 180\ ns$

$T_{(min)} = 100 \cdot 1TC = 100 \cdot 180\ ns = 18\ \mu s$

$f_{(max)} = 1/T_{(min)} = 1/18\ \mu s = 55.6\ kHz$

The input pulse rate must be less than 55.6 kHz for relatively sharp and narrow output pulses.

Time for a self-check.

**Self-Check
12–9**

1. An integrator is an analog computer that computes what?
2. Describe the output waveform of an integrator when a single square-wave pulse is applied to its input.
3. Describe the output waveform of an integrator when a continuous string of square-wave pulses is applied to its input.
4. The output of a differentiator circuit is 0 V under what circumstances?
5. Describe the output waveform of a differentiator when a continuous string of square-wave pulses is applied to its input.

12–10 SAMPLE AND HOLD CIRCUITS

Many electronic systems contain circuits that are able to snatch a sample of voltage from any point on an AC waveform or from a DC level. This sample is then stored as a charge on a capacitor. The purpose for this operation may be to remember a voltage level as a reference voltage or to convert the voltage to a digital binary word.

Analog to digital conversion (ADC) is a very common application for sample and hold circuits. The sampling is done at a very high rate, usually 20 kHz to 50 kHz. The sample circuit activates for a brief moment to capture the voltage level at a point on the analog signal. Instantly, this voltage sample charges a holding capacitor. The capacitor voltage is then almost instantly converted to a digital binary word that is shuffled out to a memory location in RAM (random access memory). The capacitor is then quickly discharged and another sample is taken, stored, converted, and stored in RAM. If the sample rate is 40 kHz, each sample, hold, and conversion process takes only 25 μs. Therefore, every 25 μs a sample of the analog waveform is processed. The digitized information can be converted back to analog using a DAC (digital to analog converter).

SAMPLE AND HOLD

A typical sample and hold circuit is shown in Figure 12–41. The circuit uses an op-amp as an input buffer amplifier, a low-leakage JFET to select samples, a capacitor to store the samples, a JFET to discharge the capacitor (reset), and an output buffer amplifier. As you can see, a clock pulse is used to turn on the JFET to allow a sample to pass. This sample time may be very short, just a few microseconds. The capacitor is a low-leakage film capacitor. Its value is usually very low, such as 0.005 to 0.001 μF or less. The capacitor charge voltage is instantly available at the output of the buffer. The analog to digital conversion is very fast. Once it is completed, a reset pulse is applied to the JFET to discharge the capacitor. After the reset pulse, another sample pulse is applied and the process starts again.

Offset-null adjustment is provided on each buffer to set pin 6 at exactly 0 V with no signal applied and no sample on hold. LF356 op-amps are a good choice here due to their very high input impedance (JFET inputs) and high slew rate (12 V/μs). Alternately, the LF357, which boasts a slew rate of 50 V/μs, can be used.

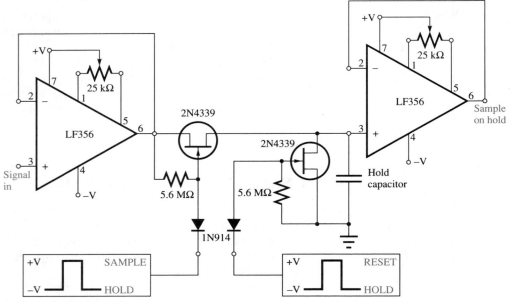

Figure 12–41 A sample and hold circuit.

PRECISION PEAK DETECTOR WITH HOLD

Some applications require that an AC signal be converted to a DC level where the DC level is the peak AC value. Such an application might be to monitor an AC line to capture and hold voltage surges. Figure 12–42 is a circuit that can be used for such applications. It is designed to remember (hold) the highest peak value that appears at the input.

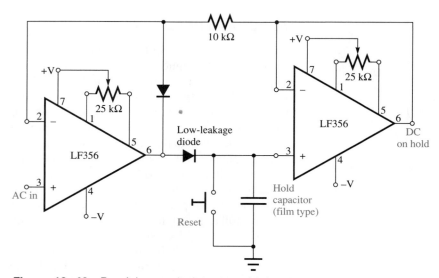

Figure 12–42 Precision peak detector with hold.

This circuit consists of a precision positive peak detector that includes a holding capacitor. The output op-amp is included in the feedback loop. As you can see, a 10-kΩ resistor connects the output of the second op-amp back to the inverting input of the first op-amp. This ensures that the sample is precise and does not suffer from the would-be diode drop. Also, the capacitor cannot discharge back through the diode. The series diode must be a low-leakage diode to prevent slow discharge of the holding capacitor. The output op-amp must be a JFET-input type, such as the LF356, to prevent premature discharge of the holding capacitor. Naturally, the capacitor should be a low-leakage film type.

Self-Check
12--10

1. What is one common application for a sample and hold circuit?
2. Briefly explain the operation of the circuit of Figure 12–41.
3. What is the overall purpose for the circuit of Figure 12–42?
4. How can the circuit of Figure 12–42 be converted to a negative peak detector with hold?

SUMMARY

FORMULAS

Single-Supply Op-Amp Circuits

(12–1) $Z_{in} = R_D/2$

(12–2) $R_D = 2Z_{in}$

(12–3) $C_C \geq 0.159/(f_{low}R)$

(12–4) $C_B \geq 1.59/(f_{low}R)$

Summing Op-Amp Circuits

(12–5) $R_I = R_F/A_V = R_F/(v_{out}/v_{in}) = R_F v_{in}/v_{out}$

(12–6) $R_F = R_I/N$ (for averaging adders)

(12–7) $V_{out} = (V_1 + V_2 + V_3 + \cdots + V_N)/N$

Op-Amp Schmitt Triggers

(12–8) $V_{trip\ ON} > +VDC \cdot R_2/(R_2 + R_1)$

(12–9) $V_H = V_{out} \cdot R_4/(R_4 + R_3)$

(12–10) $V_{trip\ OFF} < V_{trip\ ON} - V_H$

Op-Amp Integrators

(12–11) $Q = T \cdot V_{in}/R$

(12–12) $V = Q/C$

(12–13) $C_{in(Miller)} \cong CA_{OL}$

(12–14) $v = V - (V \cdot e^{-T/RC})$

(12–15) $R_{\text{in(Miller)}} \cong R_F/A_{\text{OL}}$

Op-Amp Differentiators

(12–16) $I = C \cdot \Delta V/\Delta t$

CONCEPTS

Circuit Type	Figure Number	Suggested Op-Amps	Suggested Applications
Single-Supply	12–1, 2	General*	Portable and single-supply circuits
Adder	12–3, 4	General*	AC or DC addition and averaging, Audio mixers, DACs
AGC	12–8	General*	Audio level control
Power-boost	12–9, 10	General*	AC and DC power boosting
Balanced	12–11 to 13	General*	Instrumentation, recording studios (provides high CMR and balanced input impedance)
Comparator	12–14 to 19	LM111 LM339	AC and DC level detection, sine wave to square wave conversion
Precision rectifier	12–20 to 22	LF356/7	AC to DC conversion of low-level signals (no voltage loss due to diodes)
Limiter	12–23	General*	Prevent the overdriving of sensitive circuits and equipment
Precision clamper	12–24	General*	Shift entire AC signal above or below ground reference without loss due to diode voltage drop
Integrator	12–25, 26	General*	Compute area under a waveform (used to convert any waveform to its average value)
Differentiator	12–27, 28	General*	Compute rate of change (used to convert triangle waves to square waves and square waves to narrow positive and negative pulses)
Sample and hold	12–29, 30	LF356/7	Hold a signal sample for observation or conversion (used in ADC systems)

* General = 741, LM301, LM307, LM308, LF356, LF357, LM11, etc.

NEED-TO-KNOW SOLUTION

Block Diagram

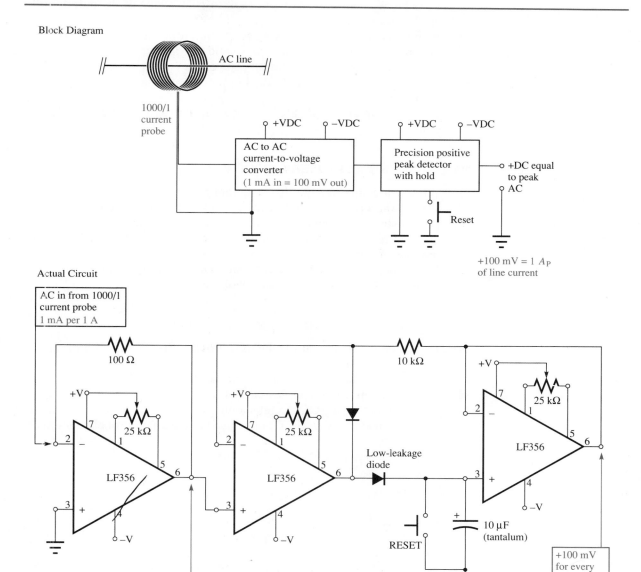

QUESTIONS

12–1 SINGLE-SUPPLY OP-AMP CIRCUITS

1. If an op-amp circuit is to be operated from a single supply and the maximum output-voltage swing is ±15 V, which of these single-supply voltages is best?

   (a) +9 V   (b) +15 V   (c) +20 V   (d) +28 V   (e) +36 V

2. As a rule, the single DC supply voltage should be at least how many volts higher than the maximum peak-to-peak swing of the output voltage?

3. If the quiescent operating voltage at the output is to be centered for maximum AC compliance, how should the DC voltage at the noninverting input compare to the supply voltage?

4. Why are most single-supply op-amp circuits not considered to be DC amplifiers?

5. List some op-amps that are designed specifically for single-supply operation.

12–2 SUMMING AMPLIFIER CIRCUITS

6. What is a common name for a summing amplifier?

7. Why is the inverting input used for summing-amplifier circuits?

8. Demonstrate mathematically that a summing amplifier is an averager if all input resistances are the same value and $R_F = R_I/N$, where N is the number of inputs.

9. What does it mean when we say an adder has weighted inputs?

10. What is a DAC and how does it work?

12–3 GAIN-CONTROLLED OP-AMP CIRCUITS

11. List three methods that can be used to vary the overall gain of an op-amp circuit.

12. Which method of manual gain control is best and why?

13. Briefly explain the principles of AGC.

14. Attack time for an AGC circuit should be slow. True or false? Explain.

15. Briefly explain how an FET can be used as a gain control element in an AGC circuit.

16. List the basic parts of the AGC control loop.

12–4 POWER AMPLIFIER CIRCUITS

17. Briefly explain why there is little or no crossover distortion at the output of a power-boosted op-amp circuit that has a complementary push-pull output.

18. What is the only way the output current of Figure 12–13 can be changed?

19. Describe what results if the load resistance in the circuit of Figure 12–14 becomes shorted.

12–5 BALANCED AMPLIFIER CIRCUITS

20. Explain why the variable resistor R_2 must be adjusted for maximum CMR in Figure 12–15.

21. What is the difference between a floating balanced input and a balanced-to-ground input?

22. What is the advantage of a balanced output like that of Figure 12–17?
23. Why does the circuit of Figure 12–17 not provide CMR?

12–6 COMPARATORS

24. Briefly describe a comparator.
25. What is a trip point?
26. How is the trip point of a basic comparator set?
27. How does the LM111 differ from a 741?
28. What is an LM339?
29. For what purpose might a window comparator be used?
30. What determines the width of the window for a window comparator?
31. How does a Schmitt trigger prevent false tripping?
32. What is the hysteresis voltage?

12–7 PRECISION RECTIFIERS

33. What determines the polarity of the pulses at the output of a precision half-wave rectifier?
34. What is the advantage of a precision rectifier over a conventional diode circuit?
35. Describe an application for which a precision rectifier might be used?

12–8 LIMITERS AND CLAMPERS

36. Placing a diode in the negative-feedback path of an op-amp has what effect on the output signal?
37. What is the maximum output voltage swing from an op-amp that has two parallel diodes of opposite polarity in the negative feedback path?
38. Explain asymmetrical limiting.
39. How does the performance of a precision clamper differ from that of a conventional diode clamper circuit?

12–9 INTEGRATORS AND DIFFERENTIATORS

40. The integral of a single positive square-wave pulse is a rising slope. What does this rising slope represent?
41. A practical op-amp integrator circuit performs what task or function?
42. What does the differentiator compute?
43. Describe the differentiator output with a triangle input.
44. What condition is required to obtain an output other than 0 V from a differentiator?
45. To obtain narrow positive and negative voltage spikes at the output of a practical differentiator, what should the relationship of the RC time constant $(R_I C)$ to the input square-wave cycle time be?

12–10 SAMPLE AND HOLD CIRCUITS

46. What is an ADC?

47. What role does a sample and hold circuit play in an ADC system?
48. Explain the purpose and sequence of the sample and reset pulses that control a sample and hold circuit.
49. For what purpose or application might a precision peak detector with hold be used?

PROBLEMS

12–1 SINGLE-SUPPLY OP-AMP CIRCUITS

1. Design a single-supply noninverting amplifier with the following specifications: $A_V \cong 15$, $f_{low} = 50$ Hz, $Z_{in} \cong 40$ kΩ. Let $R_I = 10$ kΩ. The maximum output voltage swing will be 6 V_{P-P}. Specify the DC supply voltage. Calculate all coupling and bypass capacitors.

2. Design a single-supply inverting amplifier with the following specifications: $A_V \cong 25$, $f_{low} = 40$ Hz, $Z_{in} \cong 10$ kΩ. Let $R_D = 100$ kΩ. The maximum output voltage swing will be 12 V_{P-P}. Specify the DC supply voltage. Calculate all coupling and bypass capacitors.

12–2 SUMMING AMPLIFIER CIRCUITS

3. Design a three-input audio mixer. The closed-loop gain for each input shall be 20 dB. The input impedance for each input shall be 10 kΩ. No level control shall be provided.

4. Given a basic three-input adder circuit in which $R_{I\#} = R_F = 10$ kΩ, determine the output for the following inputs:
   (a) +1 V, −2 V, −2 V
   (b) −5 V, −3 V, +6 V

5. Given a basic three-input adder circuit in which $R_F = 10$ kΩ, $R_{I1} = 10$ kΩ, $R_{I2} = 20$ kΩ, and $R_{I3} = 5$ kΩ, determine the output for the following inputs: (input 1, input 2, input 3)
   (a) +1 V, −1 V, −1 V
   (b) +4 V, −3 V, +2 V

6. If the input impedance for each input of a four-input averager is 100 kΩ, what value should R_F be?

7. If the 8-bit word at the input of the DAC in Figure 12–6 is MSB→01001101←LSB, what is the output voltage?

8. If the 8-bit word at the input of the DAC in Figure 12–6 is MSB→11000100←LSB, what is the output voltage?

12–3 GAIN-CONTROLLED OP-AMP CIRCUITS

9. If the output threshold of limiting voltage for the circuit of Figure 12–8 is −2.5 V, at what value of input voltage will limiting begin? $R_F = 10$ kΩ, $R_I = 1$ kΩ, and the input resistor is 47 kΩ. If the bright-light resistance of the photoresistor is 500 Ω, what is the dynamic range of the AGC system in dB?

10. If the output threshold of limiting voltage for the circuit of Figure 12–8 is −2 V, at what value of input voltage will limiting begin? $R_I = 2.7$ kΩ, $R_F = 47$ kΩ, and the input resistor is 22 kΩ. If the bright-light resistance

of the photoresistor is 200 Ω, what is the dynamic range of the AGC system in dB?

12–4 POWER AMPLIFIER CIRCUITS

11. If the output current of an op-amp is limited to 30 mA peak and the op-amp drives the base of a power transistor that has a beta of 70, what is the maximum peak output current (collector current)?

12. If the output current of an op-amp is limited to 25 mA peak and the op-amp drives the base of a power transistor that has a beta of 120, can the circuit drive a full load of 4 A peak? Explain.

13. Referring to Figure 12–13, if $+V = 12$ V and the voltage at the *noninverting input* to ground is 10 V, what is the value of constant current in the load resistor?

14. Referring to Figure 12–14, if $\pm V = \pm 15$ V and the voltage at the noninverting input to ground is $+12$ V, what is the value of constant current in the load resistor?

12–5 BALANCED AMPLIFIER CIRCUITS

15. Since it is not essential that $R_1 = R_I$ and $R_2 = R_F$ but it is essential that $R_I/R_F = R_1/R_2$ in Figure 12–15, what values should these resistors be to provide a total balanced input impedance of 600 Ω?

16. If the circuit of Figure 12–16 is to have a total balanced-to-ground input impedance of 200 kΩ, what is the value of each input resistor?

12–6 COMPARATORS

17. Refer to Figure 12–25. Calculate the ON and OFF trip points when $R_2 = 2.7$ kΩ, $R_1 = 33$ kΩ, $R_4 = 3.3$ kΩ, and $R_3 = 100$ kΩ. The supply voltage is $+5$ V as shown.

18. Refer to Figure 12–25. Calculate the ON and OFF trip points when $R_2 = 4.7$ kΩ, $R_1 = 6.8$ kΩ, $R_4 = 5.6$ kΩ, and $R_3 = 68$ kΩ. The supply voltage is $+5$ V as shown.

12–8 LIMITERS AND CLAMPERS

19. If it is desired to limit the peak output voltage of an op-amp to ± 0.7 V for a peak input voltage equal to or greater than ± 100 mV, what must the closed-loop gain of the op-amp be?

20. If it is desired to limit the peak output voltage of an op-amp to $+0.7$ V and -1.4 V for a peak input voltage equal to or greater than ± 40 mV$_P$, what must the closed-loop gain of the op-amp be?

12–9 INTEGRATORS AND DIFFERENTIATORS

21. Given an integrator circuit like Figure 12–33, if a single 200 mV square-wave pulse of 50 ms duration is applied to an input resistance of 4.7 kΩ and the feedback capacitor is 0.5 μF, what is the maximum output voltage?

22. Calculate the value of Miller input capacitance for Problem 21.
23. Use Formula 12–14 to check the answer for Problem 21. Show your work.
24. For the circuit of Figure 12–35, what is the output voltage if the duty cycle of the square-wave input is 10%? (All component values are as shown.)
25. Referring to Figure 12–35, what value should the negative feedback resistor R_F be to have a DC output voltage of +3 V for a 50%-duty-cycle, +200-mV$_P$ square-wave input? (The input resistor is 10 kΩ.)
26. For the circuit of Figure 12–37, if a 2-kHz, 1-V$_{P\text{-}P}$ triangle wave is applied to the input, what is the peak-to-peak output voltage?
27. For the circuit of Figure 12–37, if a 10-kHz, 0.5-V$_{P\text{-}P}$ triangle wave is applied to the input, what is the peak-to-peak output voltage?
28. Given a circuit like Figure 12–39 in which $R_I = 1$ kΩ, $R_F = 56$ kΩ, and $C = 0.1$ μF, if the peak square-wave voltage at the input is +0.15 V, what is the peak output voltage?
29. Given a circuit like Figure 12–39 in which $R_I = 470$ Ω, $R_F = 100$ kΩ, and $C = 0.002$ μF, if the peak square-wave voltage at the input is +0.05 V, what is the peak output voltage?
30. The circuit described in Problem 29 will produce narrow output pulses for input pulse rates all the way up to approximately what frequency?

ADDITIONAL PROBLEMS

31. Design a noninverting op-amp amplifier using a single DC supply. Maximum output voltage swing will be ±7.5 V$_P$. The input impedance will be 100 kΩ. The load resistance will be 3 kΩ. Amplifier gain in the passband will be 15. The lower cutoff frequency will be 25 Hz. Use standard-value 5% resistors. Let $R_I = 100$ kΩ.
32. Suppose you want to mix the following four separate audio sources: source 1 = 10 mV, source 2 = 40 mV, source 3 = 300 mV, and source 4 = 180 mV. If R_F is 220 kΩ, what must the value of each input resistor be so all inputs are amplified to 2 V at the output?
33. The input impedance for each input of a five-input averager is 4.7 kΩ. What is the needed value for the feedback resistor R_F?
34. At what value of input voltage will limiting begin for the circuit of Figure 12–43? What is the dynamic range of the AGC system? The minimum AC drain to source resistance when Q_1 is conducting heavily is 60 Ω. Threshold voltage for Q_2 is 0.7 V.
35. Determine the amount of load current for Figure 12–44.
36. Determine the active window for Figure 12–45.
37. Determine $V_{\text{trip ON}}$, $V_{\text{trip OFF}}$, and V_H for Figure 12–46.
38. Determine the input and output, positive and negative, limiting thresholds for Figure 12–47.
39. Determine the output voltage from the integrator of Figure 12–48 after

a 5-V input pulse has been applied for 30 ms. Also, determine the Miller input capacitance.

40. Determine the output pulse amplitude and the highest input pulse rate for Figure 12–49.

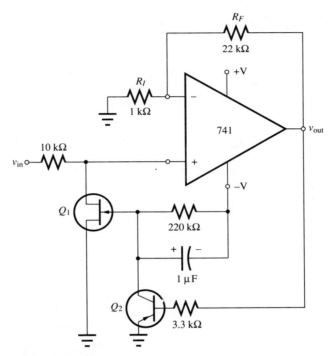

Figure 12–43

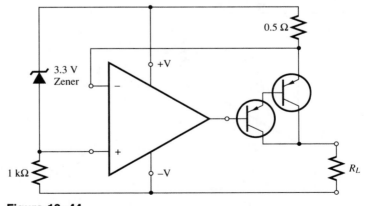

Figure 12–44

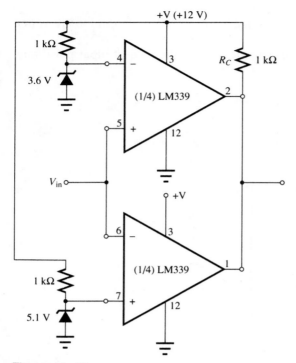

Figure 12–45

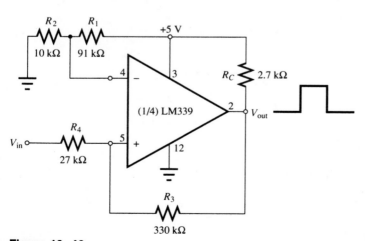

Figure 12–46

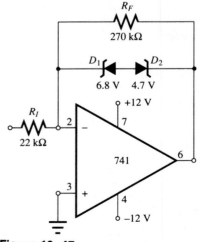

Figure 12–47

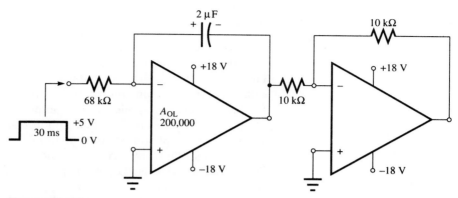

Figure 12–48

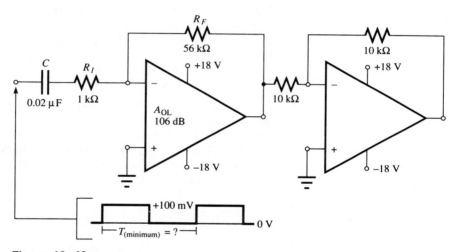

Figure 12–49

ANSWERS TO SELF-CHECKS

SELF-CHECK 12–1

1. $R_D = 20 \text{ k}\Omega$, $R_F = 285 \text{ k}\Omega$, $+\text{VDC} = 12 \text{ V}$, $C_{C(\text{in})} \geq 0.5 \mu\text{F}$, $C_{C(\text{out})} \geq 3 \mu\text{F}$ (assuming $R_L = 2 \text{ k}\Omega$), $C_{\text{bypass}} \geq 3.5 \mu\text{F}$
2. To bias the output to VDC/2.

SELF-CHECK 12–2

1. The inverting input is used for summing since it is a virtual ground and all inputs are isolated from each other.
2. $R_F = 20 \text{ k}\Omega$
3. No limit
4. The closed-loop gain is different for each input since the input resistors are different values.
5. Weight of LSB = $1 \text{ k}\Omega/256 \text{ k}\Omega$; resolution = $19.53 \mu\text{V}$

SELF-CHECK 12–3

1. Bandwidth is not affected and a full range of level control is possible, from 0 V to maximum.
2. The output signal is sampled and used to control the gain of the amplifier with some type of gain control device such as a CdS/LED optoisolator.
3. The input signal is applied to the amplifier through a voltage divider composed of a series resistor and a photoresistor to ground. The voltage drop across the photoresistor is held fairly constant, since, for strong input signals, the resistance of the photoresistor is caused to decrease. The output signal is used to drive an LED, which controls the resistance of the photoresistor.
4. The attack time is determined by the conduction of Q_2 and the 1-μF capacitor. Recovery time is determined by the discharge time of the 1-μF capacitor through the 100-kΩ resistor.
5. The input voltage threshold is determined by the conduction voltage threshold for Q_2 ($\cong -0.7$ V_P) and the gain of the op-amp is determined by R_F and R_I.

SELF-CHECK 12–4

1. Power boost the output of the 741 with a push-pull complementary pair. See Figure 12–11.
2. See Figure 12–10. The emitter resistor can be 2 Ω. Adjust the potentiometer for 2 V across the emitter resistor. The transistor must have a DC beta greater than 50 (1 A/20 mA(max) = 50) and be able to handle more than 1 A of current. A heat sink will be required.

SELF-CHECK 12–5

1. (d)
2. Figure 12–16 offers the possibility for an extremely high input impedance.
3. There is less induced common-mode voltage on the input lines of a balanced-to-ground input.
4. No. Common-mode voltage arriving at the two inputs is passed on to the two outputs.

SELF-CHECK 12–6

1. The LM111 and LM339 are much faster than the 741 op-amp.
2. The upper trim-pot is set at +2 V and the lower trim-pot is set at +2.25 V.
3. Pin 1 is low and pin 2 is high.
4. A basic single-trip-point comparator is susceptible to false tripping due to input line noise.
5. $V_{\text{trip on}} > +0.64$ V and $V_{\text{trip off}} < +0.49$ V

SELF-CHECK 12–7

1. False. There is, but the op-amp makes up for it.
2. The very high open-loop gain of the op-amp amplifies the slightest change above or below zero-crossing, which instantly forward biases the

output diode to close the loop.

3. This diode prevents the output of the op-amp from saturating in the opposite direction.

SELF-CHECK 12–8

1. Positive alternations at the output would be full amplitude (unclipped).
2. $A_V = 0.7$ V/20 mV$_P$ = 35, $R_F = 35R_I$, $R_I = 10$ kΩ, and $R_F = 350$ kΩ
3. Symmetrical limiting maintains the positive and negative alternations of the output at the same level. Asymmetrical limiting means the alternations are not the same amplitude.
4. With a precision clamper, the entire waveform is above or below the 0-V center line since there is no diode drop when the capacitor charges.
5. In the area of the positive peak just before and up to approximately 90°

SELF-CHECK 12–9

1. The area under a waveform
2. The output is a slope that continues to rise, or fall, until the input pulse returns to 0.
3. The integrator computes the average value of the input signal.
4. When there is no change in input voltage
5. Positive and negative voltage spikes, assuming a short time constant.

SELF-CHECK 12–10

1. Analog to digital conversion.
2. A sample is captured when the series JFET is ON. The capacitor holds the sample. The sample is erased when desired by activating the parallel JFET.
3. To store the last highest positive voltage peak on the capacitor.
4. Reverse the polarity of both diodes.

SUGGESTED PROJECTS

1. Add some of the main concepts and formulas from this chapter to your Electronics Notebook.
2. Construct and experiment with the circuits in this chapter.
3. Construct and experiment with the Need to Know circuit. You will need a 1000 : 1 current probe. Another possibility is to convert the circuit to a voltage monitor by replacing the current probe with a 1-kΩ resistor. The input current will be 1 mA$_P$ for every 1 V$_P$ of AC voltage being monitored. The output of the circuit will provide 100 mVDC for every 1 V$_P$ AC input voltage. However, the maximum current the LF356 can supply is between 20 mA and 30 mA. This means the maximum peak input voltage (voltage that is being monitored) must be below 30 V$_P$. You can modify the circuit to handle higher input voltages. You might consider using a 10-kΩ input resistor so it will take 10 V$_P$ input to produce 100 mVDC in the output. As always, be careful when measuring dangerous voltages.

Active filters are found in many different places within the control room of a radio station. They are used for turntable equalization, tape machine equalization, and channel equalization for the main audio console (mixer). © Tyrone Hall/Stock.

13 Active Filters

OBJECTIVES

After studying this chapter, you will be able to

- discuss the differences between Chebyshev, Butterworth, and Bessel frequency response.
- explain damping factor and its effect on active-filter frequency response.
- explain the meaning of poles and order in regard to active filters.
- analyze and design active highpass and lowpass filters.
- analyze and design a variety of active bandpass and bandstop filters.
- use a dual-polarity DC supply, a low-distortion variable sine wave generator, and a variety of meters and the oscilloscope to determine the frequency response of an active filter.
- use active filters in a variety of practical applications.

NEED TO KNOW

Many folks today have stereo television sets. Don't you? No? Well, why not design a circuit that will synthesize stereo by creating two different-sounding outputs from a single input? The synthesizer circuit is connected between the mono output on your TV (headphone or external speaker jack) and the stereo inputs on your stereo system. The basic idea is to separate high-range and low-range audio frequencies. Mid-range and low-range frequencies will come out the left speaker and mid-range and high-range frequencies will come out the right speaker. Let's say frequencies below 5 kHz go to the left channel and frequencies above 500 Hz go to the right channel. Can you design an active-filter circuit that can accomplish this?

Believe it or not, by the time you finish this chapter you will be able to do this. This is only one of hundreds of applications to which you will be able to apply active filters throughout your career.

INTRODUCTION

In this chapter, you will discover an extremely versatile building block, the active filter. You will learn how to design and analyze active filters and apply them to many interesting applications. We begin with a general discussion of active filters by way of introduction. Next, you will learn how to design and analyze active highpass and lowpass filters followed by bandpass and bandstop filters. Then, you will learn how to test active filters to verify performance. Finally, a few interesting active filter applications will be discussed. Though we just begin to scratch the surface on active filters, you will gain very valuable and practical knowledge about them. Enjoy your exploration!

13–1 INTRODUCTION TO ACTIVE FILTERS

Take some time to review basic filter concepts in Section 9–1 before continuing here.

THE ACTIVE FILTER

The **active filter** is one that includes an active device in the design. In most cases, that active device is an operational amplifier such as the 741, LF356, or any of the popular op-amps. Active filters offer the following advantages over passive filters: no insertion loss due to cascaded filter sections, voltage gain, modular (or building-block) construction, low output impedance to drive a load, and simple design.

There are many kinds of active filters that are variations of the basic highpass, lowpass, bandpass, and bandstop types of filters. Of the many kinds, the **constant-K active filter** is the most common. The constant-K active filters are also referred to as voltage-controlled voltage source (VCVS) filters and Sallen and Key active filters in honor of the inventors. Figure 13–1 illustrates the basic constant-K configuration. Constant-K active filters are recognized as noninverting amplifiers with an RC filter network at the noninverting input. The filter network determines whether the filter is of the highpass, lowpass, bandpass, or bandstop type. The K in constant-K is actually the voltage gain of the op-amp circuit (A_V). As can be seen in Figure 13–1:

$$K = A_V = (R_I + R_F)/R_I \tag{13-1}$$

The K of the active filter is very important because the frequency response characteristics can be modified by changing K. For a particular frequency response characteristic, K must be a constant or specific value. This leads us to a discussion of active-filter frequency response and damping.

FREQUENCY RESPONSE AND DAMPING

K and Damping

The frequency response of an active filter can be modified as shown in Figure 13–2 by adjusting the value of K and the **damping factor (*DF*).** The

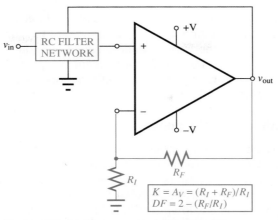

Figure 13–1 The constant-*K* active filter.

damping factor is related to *K* in the following manner:

$$DF = 2 - (R_F/R_I) = 3 - K \qquad\qquad (13–2)$$

If *K* is increased, by adjusting the ratio of R_F/R_I, the damping factor decreases and vice versa.

Chebyshev Response

The Chebyshev response (also spelled Tschebyscheff and Tchebsheff) is shown in Figure 13–2a. The ripple contained in the passband is caused by underdamping. In this case, the ripple being referred to is a single peak in

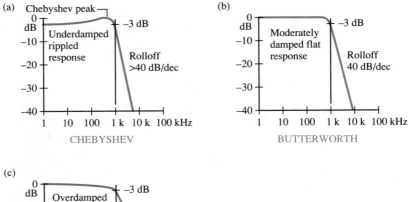

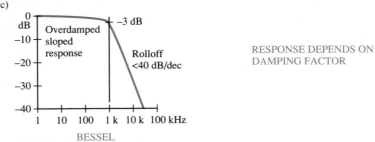

Figure 13–2 Frequency response and damping.

output voltage as frequency through the filter is increased toward the cutoff frequency. A simple filter, such as that of Figure 13–1, can produce such a response if the filter is underdamped. In some applications, the passband ripple is tolerated to obtain a steeper slope of rolloff in the stopband. The amount of passband ripple and the slope of rolloff are determined by the value of K and DF.

Butterworth Response

The Butterworth response, shown in Figure 13–2b, is often called a *maximally flat* response and results from moderate damping. As you can see, the passband response is virtually flat until the cutoff frequency is approached. The 40-dB/dec rolloff shown in the Butterworth Bode plot is typical for a two-section RC lowpass filter. Most of the filters we discuss in this chapter will have a Butterworth response which is desirable for most filtering applications because of the flat response in the passband.

Bessel Response

The Bessel Response of Figure 13–2c is overdamped. This means K is lower and DF higher than what is needed for the Butterworth and Chebyshev response. The result is a passband that slopes downward and a more gradual rolloff in the stopband. Because of these passband and stopband characteristics, the Bessel response is not desirable for most applications. However, the Bessel response is used in cases where voltage pulses must be filtered. The voltage pulses cause severe overshoot and ringing at the output of Chebyshev filters and moderate overshoot at the output of Butterworth filters. With Bessel filters there is no overshoot. Also, the Bessel filter is said to have a linear phase response—meaning the amount of phase shift increases linearly with frequency. This maintains a uniform time delay for all frequencies, which prevents overshoot due to disarrayed frequency components in the output.

POLES AND ORDER

As you have seen, active filters are described by a variety of terms, such as *highpass, lowpass, bandpass, bandstop, constant-K, Chebyshev, Butterworth,* and *Bessel.* Active filters are further described in terms of **poles** and **order.** Figure 13–3 illustrates two single-pole passive filters. They are described as single-pole because there is only one reactive component in

Figure 13–3   Single-pole, first-order networks.

each filter. These filters are also described as first-order. A first-order filter has one pole and a typical rolloff of 20 dB/dec (6 dB/octave). Higher-order filters are made by combining sections to increase the number of poles and slope of rolloff. For example, a third-order filter has three poles and a slope of rolloff of 60 dB/dec. This will be made clear to you as we begin our discussion of active highpass and lowpass filters.

Time for a self-check.

Self-Check 13–1

1. What are some of the advantages of active filters over passive filters?
2. What is a constant-K filter?
3. Which of these has a maximally flat response?
   (a) Chebyshev filter   (b) Butterworth filter   (c) Bessel filter
4. How many poles does a second-order filter have? How many dB/dec is the slope of rolloff for a second-order filter?

13–2 ACTIVE HIGHPASS AND LOWPASS FILTERS

SINGLE-POLE, FIRST-ORDER FILTERS

Figures 13–4a and 13–5a respectively illustrate the single-pole (first-order) highpass and lowpass constant-K filters. The extremely high input impedance of the op-amp has virtually no loading effect on the RC network. Therefore, the slope of rolloff is nearly the ideal 20 dB/dec and the cutoff frequency is the frequency at which $X_C = R = 1/(2\pi f_{co} C)$.

$$f_{co} = 1/(2\pi RC) \cong 0.159/RC \tag{13–3}$$

The very low output impedance of the op-amp allows the filter to drive almost any load (depending on the op-amp). The op-amp acts as a buffer amplifier between the filter network and load. The load cannot affect the filter's characteristics. For first-order active filters, the gain can be any value desired: $K = A_V =$ any desired value.

As you might have thought, the upper limit of all active highpass filters is determined by the frequency response of the chosen op-amp. In practice, all active highpass filters are actually very-wide-band bandpass filters. For lowpass filters, the maximum cutoff frequency is once again limited by the frequency response of the chosen op-amp—which, as you know, is determined by f_T and A_V.

TWO-POLE, SECOND-ORDER FILTERS

Second-order highpass and lowpass filters are shown in Figures 13–4b and 13–5b respectively. Notice that these are two-pole filters. The expected slope of rolloff for these filters is 40 dB/dec, assuming they are damped for a Butterworth response. The cutoff frequency for these filters is determined by Formula 13–3, where the two capacitors are the same value and the two resistors are the same value. Consider Example 13–1.

(a) Single-pole (first-order) highpass filter

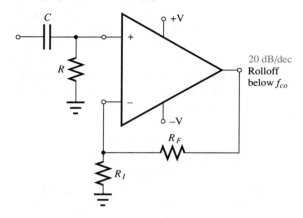

(b) Two-pole (second-order) highpass filter

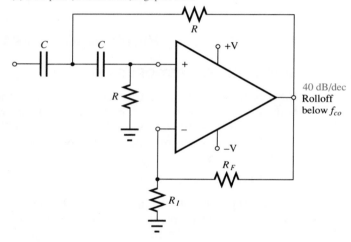

(c) Three-pole (third-order) highpass filter

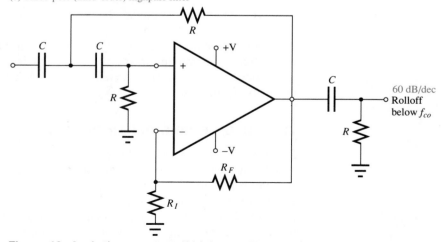

Figure 13–4   Active constant-K highpass filters.

(a) Single-pole (first-order) lowpass filter

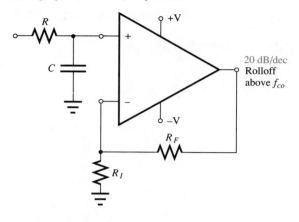

(b) Two-pole (second-order) lowpass filter

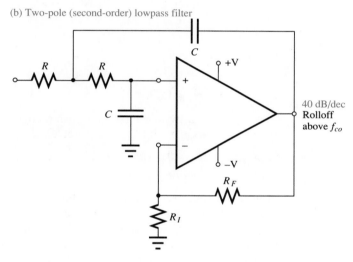

(c) Three-pole (third-order) lowpass filter

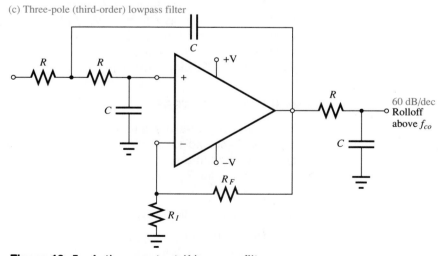

Figure 13–5   Active constant-*K* lowpass filters.

EXAMPLE 13–1

Determine the cutoff frequency and slope of rolloff for the active filter of Figure 13–6.

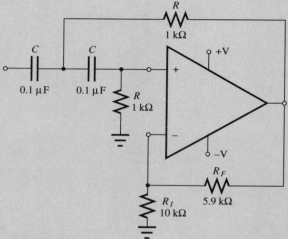

Figure 13–6

Figure 13–6 is a two-pole (second-order) highpass filter having a slope of rolloff of approximately 40 dB/decade.

$$f_{co} = 0.159/RC = 0.159/(1 \text{ k}\Omega \cdot 0.1 \text{ } \mu\text{F}) = 1{,}590 \text{ Hz}$$

As you can see, second-order constant-K active filter stages use positive feedback. At some frequency, the phase shift from output to noninverting input will be 0°. This sets the stage for instability or oscillations to occur. In other words, the circuit functions as an oscillator instead of a filter. To prevent this, the damping factor must be kept high by keeping the K factor low. Thus the damping factor (DF) prevents oscillation and determines if the frequency response is Chebyshev, Butterworth, or Bessel. For a second-order Butterworth filter (either highpass or lowpass) the K factor must be close to 1.586 and the damping factor is 1.414, where R_I might be 10 kΩ and R_F is 5.9 kΩ (2% film resistor).

MULTI-POLE FILTERS

Third- and higher-order filters are made by cascading sections or stages. Figures 13–4c and 13–5c illustrate third-order, three-pole filters. Each pole provides an additional 20 dB/dec of rolloff in the stopband. All C values are the same and all R values are the same, as determined by rearranging Formula 13–3.

$$R = 1/(2\pi f_{co}C) \cong 0.159/f_{co}C \tag{13–4}$$

$$C = 1/(2\pi f_{co}R) \cong 0.159/f_{co}R \tag{13–5}$$

To maintain the Butterworth response and exact cutoff frequency, the damping factor must be adjusted. The K factor must be 2 and the damping factor 1 for third-order active filters. A noninverting op-amp of any gain can be added to the output as a buffer stage between the filter output and load. Also, a first-order stage, such as Figure 13–4a, can be placed in front of the second-order stage of Figure 13–4b to form a third-order filter. The K factor for the first-order stage can be any desired value but the K factor for the second-order stage must be 2 when forming a third-order filter.

You can continue to cascade second-order stages until the desired slope of rolloff is obtained. However, the damping factors of the cascaded second-order stages must be fine-tuned to maintain the Butterworth response. Table 13–1 is provided as a guide in designing up to sixth-order highpass and lowpass filters.

TABLE 13–1

Order (Poles)	First Stage K	First Stage DF	Second Stage K	Second Stage DF	Third Stage K	Third Stage DF	Rolloff dB/dec	Total A_V
1	X						20	X
2	1.586	1.414					40	1.586
3	X		2	1			60	$2 \cdot X$
4	1.152	1.848	2.235	0.765			80	2.575
5	X		1.382	1.618	2.382	0.618	100	$3.292 \cdot X$
6	1.068	1.932	1.586	1.414	2.482	0.518	120	4.204

Note: X indicates a single-pole stage of any desired gain.

Table 13–2 suggests resistor values that can be used to design up to sixth-order highpass and lowpass filters.

TABLE 13–2

Order (Poles)	First Stage R_I	First Stage R_F	Second Stage R_I	Second Stage R_F	Third Stage R_I	Third Stage R_F	Rolloff dB/dec	Total A_V
1	10 kΩ	10 kΩ					20	2
2	10 kΩ	5.9 kΩ					40	1.59
3	10 kΩ	10 kΩ	10 kΩ	10 kΩ			60	4
4	10 kΩ	1.54 kΩ	10 kΩ	12.4 kΩ			80	2.58
5	10 kΩ	10 kΩ	10 kΩ	3.83 kΩ	10 kΩ	13.7 kΩ	100	6.56
6	10 kΩ	680 Ω	10 kΩ	5.9 kΩ	10 kΩ	14.7 kΩ	120	4.19

Take time to consider the following design examples.

EXAMPLE 13–2

Design a four-pole lowpass active Butterworth filter with a cutoff frequency of 800 Hz.

Figure 13–7 is the circuit we want. The slope of rolloff for this filter is a

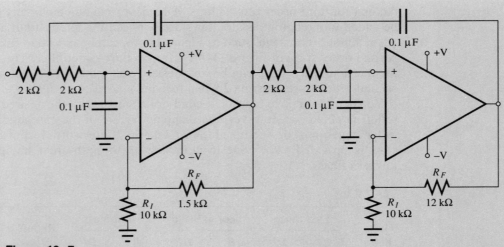

Figure 13-7

very steep 80 dB/dec. Standard 5%-tolerance resistors are used for R_F but greater precision can be realized by using 1% or 2% film resistors.

$$R = 0.159/Cf_{co} = 0.159/(0.1 \ \mu F \cdot 800 \ Hz) = 1,988 \ \Omega \cong 2 \ k\Omega$$

and

$$C = 0.159/Rf_{co} = 0.159/(2 \ k\Omega \cdot 800 \ Hz) = 0.099 \ \mu F \cong 0.1 \ \mu F$$

Usually a standard capacitor value is chosen and the needed resistor value is calculated.

EXAMPLE 13-3

Design a three-pole highpass active Butterworth filter that has a cutoff frequency of 8 kHz.

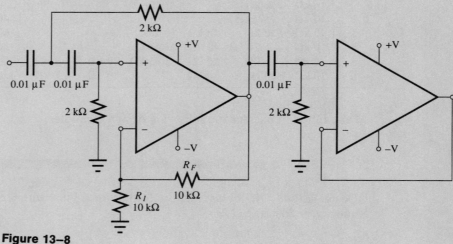

Figure 13-8

Figure 13–8 is a third-order, 8-kHz, highpass filter. The slope of rolloff for this filter is approximately 60 dB/dec. R_F and R_I are selected from Table 13–2. C is chosen to be 0.01 μF.

$$R = 0.159/Cf_{co} = 0.159/(0.01\ \mu\text{F} \cdot 8\ \text{kHz}) = 1,988\ \Omega \cong 2\ \text{k}\Omega$$

Take a few minutes to study Design Note 13–1. This will help you visualize the design process for constant-K highpass and lowpass filters.

**Self-Check
13–2**

1. Design a highpass active filter that has a cutoff frequency of 4 kHz and a rolloff of 100 dB/dec. Let $C = 0.01\ \mu$F.
2. Design a lowpass active filter that has a cutoff frequency of 500 Hz and a rolloff of 60 dB/dec. Let $C = 0.047\ \mu$F.
3. If an active filter has a rolloff of 140 dB/dec, how many RC networks does it have? What order is this filter?

13–3 ACTIVE BANDPASS AND BANDSTOP FILTERS

ACTIVE BANDPASS FILTERS

As you probably already know, bandpass filters are designed to pass a specific band of frequencies that exists between two cutoff frequencies. All frequencies below the lower cutoff frequency are rejected and all frequencies above the upper cutoff frequency are rejected. Here you will become familiar with a variety of active bandpass filters.

The Wide-Band Bandpass Filter

The bandpass filter shown in Figure 13–9 is one with which you are already familiar. It is made of a highpass constant-K filter and a lowpass constant-K filter. This kind of filter offers an adjustable bandwidth while maintaining the slope of the skirts (rolloff) at 40 dB/dec (higher if higher-order filters are used). It does not matter which filter is placed first. In this case, the signal first passes through the highpass filter. However, the filter will function just as well if the circuit is arranged so the signal passes through the lowpass filter first. Bandpass filters such as this are used in graphic equalizers and other audio circuits where it is desired to segment the audio spectrum. The highpass and lowpass sections are designed separately, using the procedures discussed in the previous section.

The Constant-K Bandpass Filter

A constant-K bandpass filter is shown in Figure 13–10. The filter network at the noninverting input is composed of a lowpass and a highpass filter. The bandpass is thus created in much the same way as in the filter of Figure 13–9. Note that the network capacitors (each labeled C) are the same value and the network resistors (each labeled R) are the same value. The formulas for this

DESIGN NOTE 13–1   HIGHPASS AND LOWPASS FILTERS

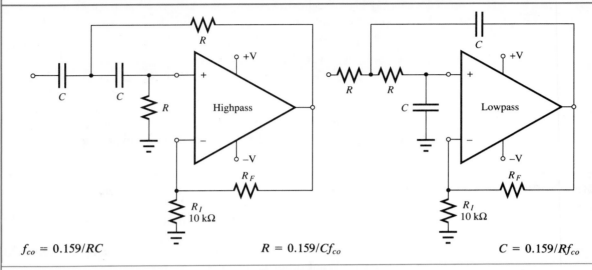

$$f_{co} = 0.159/RC$$

$$R = 0.159/Cf_{co}$$

$$C = 0.159/Rf_{co}$$

BASIC PROGRAM

```
10 REM * ACTIVE HIGHPASS AND LOWPASS FILTER DESIGN *
20 REM    THIS PROGRAM WILL CALCULATE R, C, AND RF FOR TWO TO SIX
POLE
30 REM    ACTIVE HIGHPASS AND LOWPASS FILTERS.
40 CLS
50 CLEAR
60 PRINT "ACTIVE HIGHPASS OR LOWPASS FILTER DESIGN PROGRAM"
70 PRINT ""
80 INPUT "ENTER THE DESIRED CUTOFF FREQUENCY - ";F
85 PRINT "ENTER CAPACITANCE IN FARADS - EXAMPLE: 0.01 MICROFARAD =
0.01E-6"
90 INPUT "ENTER A STANDARD CAPACITOR VALUE - ";C
100 INPUT "ENTER THE NUMBER OF DESIRED POLES FROM 2 TO 6 - ";N
110 R = .159/(C * F)
120 IF N = 2 THEN S = 1:RF(1) = 5900
130 IF N = 3 THEN S = 2:RF(1) = 10000:RF(2) = 10000
140 IF N = 4 THEN S = 2:RF(1) = 1540:RF(2) = 12400
150 IF N = 5 THEN S = 3:RF(1) = 10000:RF(2) = 3830:RF(3) = 13700
160 IF N = 6 THEN S = 3:RF(1) = 680:RF(2) = 5900:RF(3) = 14700
170 REM  OUTPUT SECTION
180 FOR X = 1 TO S
185 PRINT ""
190 PRINT "STAGE -";X
200 PRINT "C  = ";C;" F"
210 PRINT "R  = ";R;" OHMS"
215 PRINT "RI =  10000  OHMS"
220 PRINT "RF = ";RF(X);" OHMS"
230 NEXT X
240 PRINT ""
250 INPUT "DESIGN ANOTHER FILTER? (Y/N) ";A$
260 IF A$ = "Y" THEN 50
270 END
```

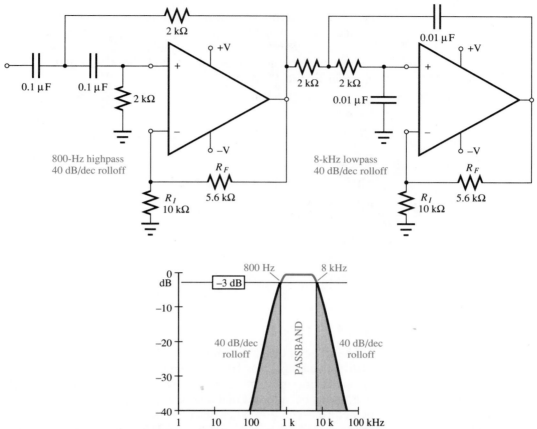

Figure 13–9 An 800-Hz to 8-kHz bandpass filter with wide bandwidth and steep rolloff.

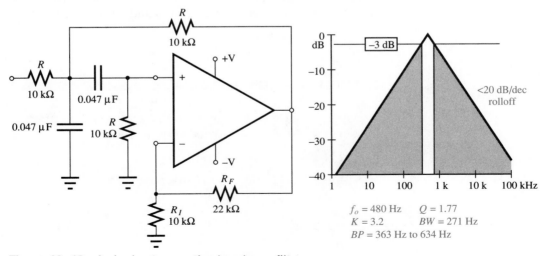

Figure 13–10 A single-stage active bandpass filter.

filter are very straightforward. As in passive resonant circuits, we are concerned with finding the center frequency (f_c), or the frequency of operation (f_o), and the bandwidth (BW). In this case, as in passive circuits, the bandwidth is determined by circuit Q. Use these formulas to verify the values given in Figure 13–10.

Analysis

$$f_o = 0.225/RC \tag{13–6}$$

$$Q = 1.414/(4 - K) \tag{13–7}$$

where K is the A_V in the passband.

$$BW = f_o/Q \tag{13–8}$$

Design

$$R = 0.225/Cf_o \tag{13–9}$$

$$C = 0.225/Rf_o \tag{13–10}$$

$$Q = f_o/BW \tag{13–11}$$

$$K = 4 - (1.414/Q) \tag{13–12}$$

The slope of the skirts for this bandpass filter (Figure 13–10) is less than 20 dB/dec, making it less effective than most other bandpass filters. Also, the Q of this circuit must be set lower than 10 to ensure circuit stability. In practice, it has been found that a Q of approximately 7 is about as high as Q can be before oscillation takes place. To keep the Q in the stable range, the gain of the amplifier ($K = A_V = (R_F + R_I)/R_I$) must be no higher than 3.8. Using Formula 13–7,

$$Q = 1.414/(4 - K) = 1.414/(4 - 3.8) = 1.414/0.2 = 7.07$$

As you can see, this type of active bandpass filter, though very simple, is unable to provide a narrow bandwidth and steep rolloff. Consider Example 13–4.

EXAMPLE 13–4 ▆▆▆▆▆▆▆▆▆▆▆▆▆▆▆▆▆▆▆▆

Design a single-stage, constant-K, bandpass filter with a center frequency of 20 kHz and a bandwidth of 4 kHz.

$Q = f_o/BW = 20 \text{ kHz}/4 \text{ kHz} = 5$

$K = 4 - (1.414/Q) = 4 - (1.414/5) = 3.72$

Let $C = 0.0022 \ \mu\text{F}$. Then

$R = 0.225/Cf_o = 0.225/(0.0022 \ \mu\text{F} \cdot 20 \text{ kHz}) = 5.1 \text{ k}\Omega$

The Multiple-Feedback Bandpass Filter

The multiple-feedback bandpass filter of Figure 13-11 permits a slightly higher Q than does the constant-K circuit. As you can see, the inverting input is used and there are two feedback paths via C_1 and R_2. The bandpass response is created by the R_1C_1 lowpass network and the C_2R_2 highpass network. While the capacitors are the same value, the resistors are not. The calculations for this bandpass filter are a little more involved than those for the previous filters. In each case, $C_1 = C_2 = C$.

Analysis

$$f_o = (0.159/C) \cdot \sqrt{(R_1 + R_3)/R_1R_2R_3} \tag{13–13}$$

$$Q = \pi CR_2f_o = 0.5 \cdot \sqrt{R_2/R_1} \cdot \sqrt{1 + (R_1/R_3)} \tag{13–14}$$

$$A_o = R_2/2R_1 = \text{gain at the frequency of operation} \tag{13–15}$$

$$BW = f_o/Q = 0.318/CR_2 \tag{13–16}$$

As you can see in Formula 13–15, R_3 has no effect on amplifier gain at the frequency of operation. Thus, R_3 can be adjusted to set the Q independent of gain. However, adjusting R_3 does have an effect on the frequency of operation. Thus, C must be changed to compensate for the adjustment of R_3.

Use Formulas 13–13 to 13–16 to verify the values shown in Figure 13–11.

Design

$$R_2 = Q/\pi Cf_o = 0.318/(BW \cdot C) \tag{13–17}$$

$$R_1 = R_2/2A_o \tag{13–18}$$

$$R_3 = R_2/(4Q^2 - 2A_o) \tag{13–19}$$

These design formulas indicate that the design process starts with the desired frequency of operation and bandwidth. Then a standard capacitor

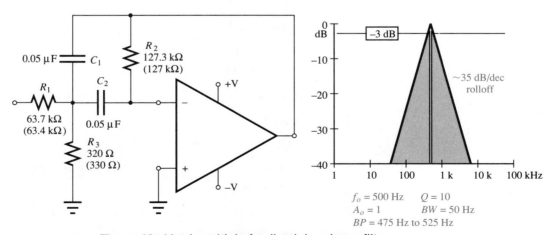

Figure 13–11 A multiple-feedback bandpass filter.

value is chosen for C_1 and C_2. R_2 is calculated first. Once the desired gain is determined, R_1 may be calculated. To calculate R_3, the Q must be known from $Q = f_o/BW$. Consider Examples 13–5 and 13–6.

EXAMPLE 13–5 ▰

Design a multiple-feedback bandpass filter for a center frequency of 2 kHz and a bandwidth of 100 Hz. Let $C_1 = C_2 = C = 0.047\ \mu\text{F}$. The gain at the frequency of operation shall be 10.

1. Determine Q.

   $Q = 2\ \text{kHz}/100\ \text{Hz} = 20$

2. Calculate R_2.

   $R_2 = Q/\pi C f_o = 20/(\pi \cdot 0.047\ \mu\text{F} \cdot 2\ \text{kHz}) = 67.7\ \text{k}\Omega\ (68\ \text{k}\Omega)$

3. Calculate R_1.

   $R_1 = R_2/2A_o = 67.7\ \text{k}\Omega/(2 \cdot 10) = 3.385\ \text{k}\Omega\ (3.3\ \text{k}\Omega)$

4. Calculate R_3.

   $R_3 = R_2/(4Q^2 - 2A_o) = 67.7\ \text{k}\Omega/(4 \cdot 20^2 - 2 \cdot 10)$

   $\quad = 67.7\ \text{k}\Omega/(1,600 - 20) = 42.8\ \Omega\ (43\ \Omega)$

The parameters specified in Example 13–5 are confirmed in Example 13–6.

EXAMPLE 13–6 ▰

Analyze the filter of Example 13–5 to verify your calculations for R_1, R_2, and R_3. Use the practical values for R_1, R_2, and R_3 given in parenthesis.

1. Calculate the frequency of operation.

   $f_o = (0.159/C) \cdot \sqrt{(R_1 + R_3)/R_1 R_2 R_3}$

   $\quad = (0.159/0.047\ \mu\text{F}) \cdot \sqrt{(3.3\ \text{k}\Omega + 43\ \Omega)/(3.3\ \text{k}\Omega \cdot 68\ \text{k}\Omega \cdot 43\ \Omega)}$

   $\quad = (0.159/0.047\ \mu\text{F}) \cdot 5.89 \cdot 10^{-4} = 1,993\ \text{Hz} \cong 2\ \text{kHz}$

2. Calculate the Q.

   $Q = \pi C R_2 f_o = \pi \cdot 0.047\ \mu\text{F} \cdot 68\ \text{k}\Omega \cdot 2\ \text{kHz} \cong 20$

3. Calculate the voltage gain at the frequency of operation.

   $A_o = R_2/2R_1 = 68\ \text{k}\Omega/(2 \cdot 3.3\ \text{k}\Omega) = 10.3$

4. Calculate the bandwidth.

   $BW = f_o/Q = 2\ \text{kHz}/20 = 100\ \text{Hz}$

The State-Variable (SV) Bandpass Filter

The state-variable (SV) bandpass filter shown in Figure 13–12 is superior in performance to the constant-K and multiple-feedback filters discussed thus far. This design provides a high Q and narrow bandwidth. The center frequency is determined by the values of R and C independent of Q and bandwidth: $f_o = 1/(2\pi RC) = 0.159/RC$. This is the same formula used for highpass and lowpass constant-K filters. Also, $R = 0.159/Cf_o$, when C is selected first.

The Q is adjusted by adjusting the ratio of R_A and R_B.

$$Q = 0.333 + (R_A/3R_B) \tag{13–20}$$

and

$$R_A = R_B(3Q - 1) \tag{13–21}$$

where R_B is selected first.

Let's see how this interesting filter operates. Notice that stage 1 is an adder. The lowpass output is being added to the input. The second and third stages are integrators acting as lowpass filters, since the negative feedback is greatest at the higher frequencies. If you consider the Miller input capacitance at the inverting input of stages 2 and 3, you will realize a $-90°$ phase shift is created at the inverting input. This is because the X_C of the capacitor is very large compared to R and $\angle\theta = \arctan(X_C/R)$. Since the inverting input is used, the op-amp provides an additional $-180°$ of phase shift. Therefore, the signal at the output of stage 2 is at $-270° = +90°$. The third stage provides an additional $+90°$ phase shift. The lowpass output is thus $180°$ out of phase with the input at stage 1. In this way, the first stage is turned into a highpass filter because the low frequencies are returned to the first stage $180°$ out of phase. The returned low frequencies cancel the incoming low frequen-

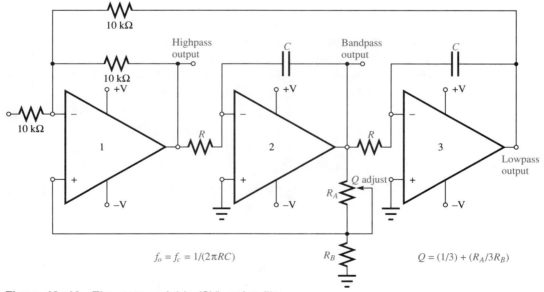

Figure 13–12 The state-variable (SV) active filter.

cies. At high frequencies, the lowpass output at stage 3 is very low in amplitude. In other words, the high frequencies are greatly attenuated by the third stage. These weak high frequencies are returned to the first stage and have little canceling effect on the incoming high-frequency signals. Thus, high frequencies appear at the output of stage 1.

So, why is the output of stage 2 a bandpass output? The answer is simple. A highpass filter (stages 1 and 3 working together) is feeding a lowpass filter (stage 2). The cutoff frequency for each is the same. Thus, the bandpass response is simply the result of cascading a highpass and lowpass filter.

Consider the following examples.

EXAMPLE 13–7 ▬▬▬▬▬▬▬▬▬▬▬▬▬▬▬

Design an SV bandpass filter for a center frequency of 18 kHz and a bandwidth of 400 Hz. Let $C = 0.001 \ \mu F$ and $R_B = 10 \ k\Omega$.

1. Calculate Q.

$$Q = f_o/BW = 18 \text{ kHz}/400 \text{ Hz} = 45$$

2. Calculate the value of R.

$$R = 0.159/Cf_o = 0.159/(0.001 \ \mu F \cdot 18 \text{ kHz}) = 8{,}833 \ \Omega \ (8.87 \ k\Omega, 1\%)$$

3. Calculate R_A.

$$R_A = R_B(3Q - 1) = 10 \ k\Omega \cdot (135 - 1) = 1.34 \text{ M}\Omega \ (1.33 \text{ M}\Omega)$$

All resistors for the first stage are the same value (such as 10 kΩ).

EXAMPLE 13–8 ▬▬▬▬▬▬▬▬▬▬▬▬▬▬▬

Analyze the SV filter of Example 13–7 to verify calculations. Use actual resistor values as given in parentheses.

1. Calculate f_o.

$$f_o = 0.159/RC = 0.159/(8.87 \ k\Omega \cdot 0.001 \ \mu F)$$
$$= 17{,}926 \text{ Hz} \cong 18 \text{ kHz}$$

2. Calculate the Q.

$$Q = 0.333 + (R_A/3R_B) = 0.333 + (1.33 \text{ M}\Omega/30 \ k\Omega) = 44.7 \cong 45$$

As you have seen, the SV bandpass filter is an easily designed filter that provides a narrow bandwidth and steep skirts. Gain can be varied, independent of all other parameters, by changing the value of the feedback resistor of stage 1. A dual potentiometer can be used for R in stages 2 and 3 to permit variable-frequency adjustment. The variable R_A permits easy bandwidth adjustment.

ACTIVE BANDSTOP FILTERS

The Twin-Tee Constant-K Notch Filter

Figure 13–13 illustrates a constant-K bandstop filter, also known as a notch filter. The center frequency lies at the bottom of the notch. The bandstop bandwidth of the filter is defined as those frequencies that lie between the lower and upper cutoff frequencies at the -3 dB points on the notch skirts. The circuit Q determines the bandstop bandwidth. Analysis and design of these filters is very simple. As for other constant-K filters, $f_c = f_o = 1/2\pi RC \cong 0.159/RC$. The circuit Q is very dependent on the K established by R_F and R_I.

$$Q = 1/(4 - 2K) \tag{13–22}$$

and

$$K = 2 - (1/2Q) \tag{13–23}$$

According to Formula 13–22, K can never be greater than 2. For a Q between 1 and infinity, K must be between 1.5 and 2. As you can see, slight changes in K cause great changes in Q. This notch filter is intended for low-Q applications where K is near 1.75 or so. If R_I is 10 kΩ, a 10-turn, 10-kΩ potentiometer, or trim-pot, wired as a rheostat can be used for R_F to provide variable Q. Fine adjustment of the center notch frequency can be obtained by slight variations of $R/2$ and $2C$. Consider Example 13–9.

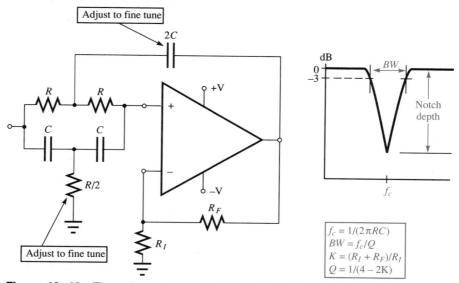

Figure 13–13   The twin-tee constant-K bandstop filter (notch filter).

EXAMPLE 13–9

Design a twin-tee constant-K notch filter for a center frequency of 120 Hz and a bandstop bandwidth of 60 Hz. Let $R_I = 10$ kΩ and $C = 0.1$ μF.
1. $R = 0.159/Cf_o = 0.159/(0.1\ \mu\text{F} \cdot 120\ \text{Hz}) = 13.25$ kΩ (13.3 kΩ)
2. $Q = f_o/BW = 120\ \text{Hz}/60\ \text{Hz} = 2$
3. $K = 2 - (1/2\ Q) = 2 - (1/4) = 1.75$
4. $R_F = R_I \cdot (K - 1) = 10$ k$\Omega \cdot (1.75 - 1) = 10$ k$\Omega \cdot 0.75 = 7.5$ kΩ

A Multiple-Feedback Bandstop Filter

You should recognize the first stage of the circuit of Figure 13–14. It's the multiple-feedback bandpass filter of Figure 13–11. The addition of the unity-gain adder provides a bandstop output. At the center frequency, the bandpass output is 180° out of phase with the filter input. Since the bandpass filter has unity gain and a 180° phase shift, the two inputs to the adder cancel, creating a notch at the center frequency. Resistors R_4 and R_6 for the unity-gain adder are the same value (your choice). To allow you to balance the bandpass output against the filter input, the variable resistor R_5 should be twice R_4. This will enable you to obtain a maximum notch depth at the bandstop output. R_6 can be greater than R_4 if gain is needed. All design and analysis formulas are the same as for the bandpass filter.

The State-Variable Bandstop Filter

A bandstop filter can be created from any active bandpass filter by adding an adder stage as was done in Figure 13–14. Figure 13–15 is another example of this. The state-variable filter is now a high-Q bandstop filter as well as a highpass, lowpass, and bandpass filter. Since the lowpass output and the

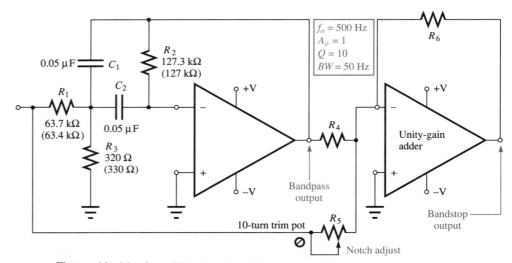

Figure 13–14 A multiple-feedback bandstop filter.

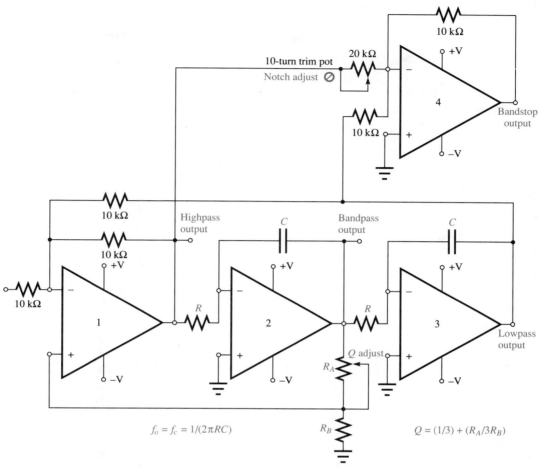

Figure 13–15 The state-variable bandstop filter.

highpass output are 180° out of phase and equal in amplitude at the center frequency, cancelation takes place at the adder, creating a bandstop output. The 20-kΩ, 10-turn trimmer provides an adjustment to obtain a maximum notch depth. If precision resistors are used, the trimmer may not be needed. All design and analysis formulas are the same as for the SV bandpass filter.

Design Note 13–2 is provided to assist you in designing a variety of bandpass and bandstop active filters. You may want to study the computer program to review the design steps for each type. Before continuing, test your understanding by answering the questions of Self-Check 13–3.

Self-Check 13–3

1. Describe a bandpass filter that can have a very wide bandwidth yet very steep skirts.
2. Which of the bandpass filters discussed in this section has the highest Q capability?
3. What is one disadvantage of the constant-K bandpass filter?
4. What is one disadvantage of the twin-tee constant-K bandstop filter?

DESIGN NOTE 13-2 BANDPASS AND BANDSTOP FILTERS

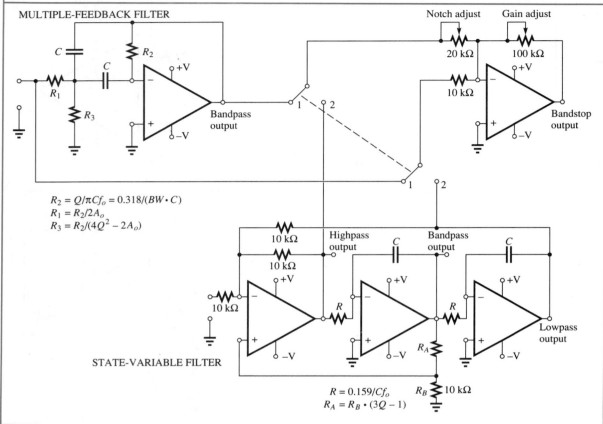

MULTIPLE-FEEDBACK FILTER

$R_2 = Q/\pi C f_o = 0.318/(BW \cdot C)$
$R_1 = R_2/2A_o$
$R_3 = R_2/(4Q^2 - 2A_o)$

STATE-VARIABLE FILTER

$R = 0.159/C f_o$
$R_A = R_B \cdot (3Q - 1)$

BASIC PROGRAM

```
10 REM  * ACTIVE BANDPASS AND BANDSTOP
FILTER DESIGN *
20 CLS
30 PRINT "BANDPASS AND BANDSTOP ACTIVE
FILTERS PROGRAM"
40 PRINT ""
50 CLEAR
60 PRINT "(1) MULTIPLE-FEEDBACK BANDPASS/
STOP FILTER"
70 PRINT "(2) STATE-VARIABLE BANDPASS/
STOP FILTER"
75 PRINT "(3) END"
80 PRINT ""
90 INPUT "WHICH FILTER TYPE? (1 OR 2) - ";CH
100 IF CH < 1 OR CH > 3 THEN GOTO 20
110 ON CH GOTO 200,400,600
200 PRINT ""
210 PRINT "MULTIPLE-FEEDBACK FILTER DESIGN"
220 PRINT ""
230 INPUT "ENTER THE FREQUENCY OF OPERATION
- ";F
240 INPUT "ENTER THE DESIRED BANDWIDTH - "
;BW
250 Q = F/BW
260 PRINT "THE GAIN MUST BE LESS THAN ";2
* Q^2
280 INPUT "ENTER THE DESIRED CENTER-
FREQUENCY GAIN - ";A
```

```
280 IF A >= 2 * Q^2 THEN PRINT "GAIN
IS TOO HIGH!":GOTO 260
290 INPUT "ENTER A STANDARD VALUE FOR
THE CAPACITORS - ";C
300 R2 = .318/(BW * C)
310 R1 = R2/(2 * A)
320 R3 = R2/(4 * Q^2 - 2 * A)
330 PRINT ""
340 PRINT "R1 = ";R1;" OHMS"
350 PRINT "R2 = ";R2;" OHMS"
360 PRINT "R3 = ";R3;" OHMS"
370 GOTO 40
400 PRINT ""
410 PRINT "STATE-VARIABLE FILTER DESIGN"
420 PRINT ""
430 INPUT "ENTER THE FREQUENCY OF
OPERATION - ";F
440 INPUT "ENTER THE DESIRED BANDWIDTH
- ";BW
450 Q = F/BW
460 INPUT "ENTER A STANDARD VALUE FOR
THE CAPACITORS - ";C
470 R = .159/(C * F)
480 RA = 10000 * (3*Q-1)
490 PRINT ""
500 PRINT "R= ";R;" OHMS"
510 PRINT RA = ";RA;" OHMS"
520 PRINT "RB = 10000 OHMS"
530 GOTO 40
600 CLS:END
```

5. Explain how an adder circuit can create a bandstop output from a band-pass active filter.

6. Design an SV active filter circuit for a center frequency of 5 kHz and a bandwidth of 200 Hz. Let $R_B = 10 \ k\Omega$ and $C = 0.01 \ \mu F$.

13–4 FILTER FREQUENCY-RESPONSE TESTING

TEST INSTRUMENTS

The Setup

Once you have designed a filter, you will want to test it to see if the actual frequency response matches your design criteria. As shown in Figure 13–16, you will need a variable-frequency generator—more specifically, a low-distortion sine wave generator (because the distortion in the waveform is actually higher-frequency components). Using a sine wave source that has significant distortion will not allow you to determine the true rolloff of highpass and bandpass filters. This is because the highpass slope of the filter will attenuate the fundamental signal much more than it will the higher-frequency distortion components. For example, let's say a 1-kHz sine wave contains a 10-kHz distortion product (in reality, the distortion is composed of a large number of harmonics of the fundamental frequency). The slope of a highpass filter will attenuate the 1-kHz sine wave more than it will the 10-

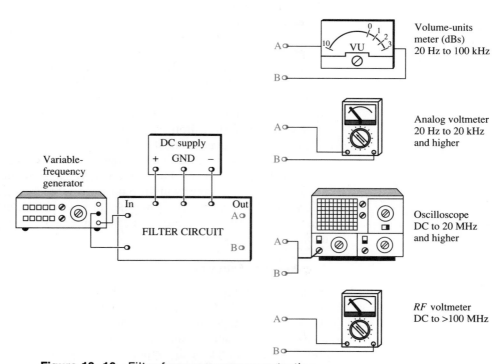

Figure 13–16 Filter frequency-response testing.

kHz distortion. The test equipment will measure the distortion products, producing readings higher than they would be if the distortion did not exist. For laboratory testing, the signal generator should produce less than 0.1% total harmonic distortion (THD) plus noise. That means that the sum of all harmonic components, or distortion products, plus any device noise must be less than 0.1% (-60 dB) of the test signal. Even this is a modest requirement.

In addition to the low-distortion frequency generator, you will need a dual-polarity power supply. This supply should be well filtered and regulated so that the plus and minus voltages are clean and equal in amplitude. Additional filter capacitors may have to be placed on the circuit board as close as possible to the power pins of the op-amp(s). This is especially true for high-performance op-amps such as the LF356 and LF456. High-performance op-amps tend to make use of the inductance of the interconnecting DC supply wires and begin to oscillate. The addition of 0.01-μF capacitors paralleled with 50-μF capacitors between each DC supply line and ground [right on the circuit board close to the op-amp(s)] will cure this problem.

Obviously, you will need some type of measuring equipment to monitor the output of your filter. Let's consider a variety of instruments that can be connected to output terminals A and B, as shown in Figure 13–16.

The VU Meter

A volume-units (VU) meter can be connected across the output of your filter to determine the cutoff frequency and the slope of rolloff over the first octave from cutoff. The analog VU meter may be accurate up to as high as 100 kHz.

To use the VU meter, set the frequency generator to a frequency well into the passband of the filter. Adjust the generator's amplitude control so the VU meter indicates $+3$ dB. Slowly rotate the frequency-adjust knob on the generator until the VU indicates 0 dB. This is the cutoff frequency. The frequency can be read from the dial on the generator, or you can use a digital frequency counter to monitor the signal-generator output and more accurately determine the cutoff frequency.

Rotate the frequency-adjust knob further to a frequency that is one octave away from cutoff. One octave is either twice or half of the cutoff frequency (i.e., 500 Hz is one octave below 1 kHz and 2 kHz is one octave above). The pointer on the VU meter will drop down to some reading such as -6 or $\div 10$ dB. From this reading, the slope per decade can be estimated as approximately $3.3 \cdot \#\text{dB/octave}$ (i.e., -6 dB/octave $= 3.3 \cdot -6$ dB/octave $\cong 20$ dB/dec).

The Analog Multimeter

An analog multimeter on the AC-volts ranges can be used in place of a VU meter. In fact, the faces of many analog meters are calibrated in dB for this purpose. The range switch gives a little more flexibility to the range of your measurements than the simple VU meter. The manual for the analog meter should be consulted for the upper frequency limit of the meter. Most analog meters are accurate at least to 20 kHz.

If the analog meter face is not marked in dB, you will have to translate voltage readings to dB (-3 dB $= 0.707 \cdot V_{max}$, $- 6$ dB $= 0.5 \cdot V_{max}$, -10 dB $= 0.316 \cdot V_{max}$, -20 dB $= 0.1 \cdot V_{max}$, etc.).

The Oscilloscope

The oscilloscope is one of the best instruments to use to check frequency response. It allows you to view the output as you measure it and has a much higher frequency response than most instruments do. However, depending on the oscilloscope, it is limited to signals greater than about 1 mV or so. We will discuss the use of the oscilloscope further later.

The RF Voltmeter

An RF voltmeter is another analog piece of equipment that can be used over very wide frequency and amplitude ranges. This meter contains wide-band amplifiers and rectifiers that convert high-frequency, low-level AC to DC. Measurements down to the microvolts are usually possible. A dB scale is provided to make filter testing easy. A range switch is used to permit mid- or upper-scale readings for nearly any signal level.

The Digital Voltmeter?

The DMM or DVM is usually of little use in filter frequency-response testing for two reasons: (1) These meters normally have a very low frequency response, in most cases less than 500 Hz. (2) Relatively slow update of display digits makes it difficult to follow amplitude changes as frequency is changed.

USING THE OSCILLOSCOPE

The oscilloscope is probably the instrument you will use most often to test active-filter frequency response. Figure 13–17 illustrates how to determine the cutoff frequencies of a bandpass filter. In this case, channel 1 is being used with the V/div control set at 1 V/div. The main point for you to realize here is that the cutoff frequencies will have a voltage that is 0.707 times the maximum passband voltage. As shown in the figure, the voltage at center frequency is first set at 6 V_{P-P}. The frequency knob on the generator is adjusted above or below the center frequency until the voltage drops to 4.2 V_{P-P}, which is $0.7 \cdot 6 \; V_{P-P} \cong -3$ dB. Alternatively, you could start with 8 V_{P-P} at the center frequency and adjust to 5.6 V_{P-P}, which is $0.7 \cdot 8 \; V_{P-P} \cong -3$ dB. In either case, the frequency of the displayed signal is determined by dividing period into one ($f = 1/T$ where T = the number of horizontal divisions for one cycle times the Time/div control setting). For Figure 13–17, if the Time/div control is set at 20 μs/div, the lower cutoff frequency is $1/(3.1 \cdot 20 \; \mu s) =$ 16.1 kHz and the upper cutoff frequency is $1/(2.6 \cdot 20 \; \mu s) =$ 19.2 kHz, with a center frequency of $1/(2.8 \cdot 20 \; \mu s) =$ 17.9 kHz.

Time for a self-check.

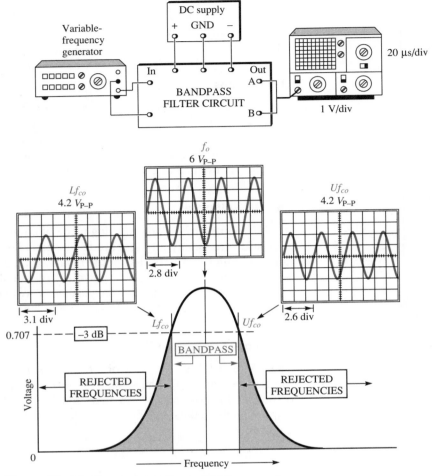

Figure 13–17 Determining the cutoff frequencies.

**Self-Check
13–4**

1. Describe a setup for active-filter frequency-response testing.
2. Why should the sine wave generator have a very-low-distortion output for testing filters?
3. What are the advantages to using an oscilloscope to determine filter frequency response instead of an analog voltmeter?
4. When using the oscilloscope, how do you know when you have found the −3 dB cutoff frequency?

13–5 ACTIVE-FILTER APPLICATIONS

In this section, we will cover only a couple of the many popular applications for active filters. The purpose here is to demonstrate their building-block flexibility.

THREE-BAND AUDIO TONE CONTROL

Figure 13–18 illustrates the use of second-order highpass and lowpass active filters in a three-band audio system. Each of the two-pole sections provides a

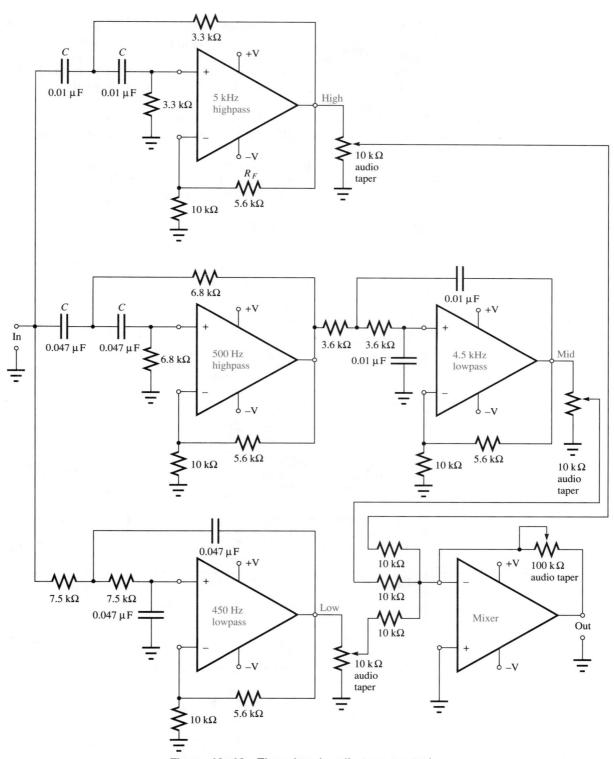

Figure 13–18 Three-band audio tone control.

rolloff of 40 dB/dec. They are designed using the formulas presented in Section 13–2. The mixer is an adder that is supplied with audio information from three separate frequency bands (<450 Hz, 500 Hz to 4.5 kHz, and >5 kHz). The potentiometers allow you to mix these bands as desired. The feedback potentiometer, wired as a rheostat, provides master gain control at the mixer stage.

Three-band circuits such as this are used in stereo systems and in each channel of a multichannel audio mixing console, providing modest equalization for each channel.

This circuit can also be used to synthesize stereo. Two adders are used instead of one. The first is fed from the lowpass filter and the bandpass filter, the second from the highpass filter and the bandpass filter. Thus, low and

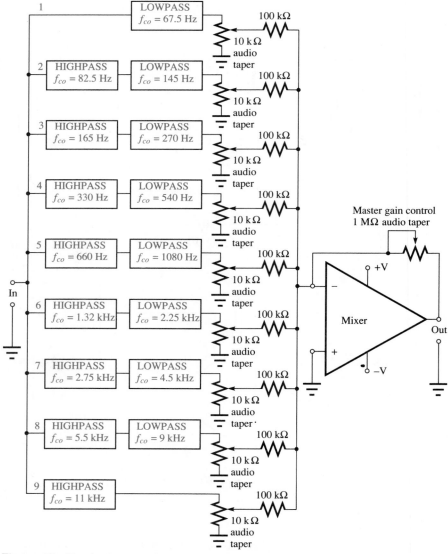

Figure 13–19   A nine-octave graphic equalizer.

mid-range frequencies are sent to the right channel from the output of the first adder and high and mid-range frequencies are sent to the left channel from the second adder. When listening, you get the feeling of bass instruments on the right and high-pitched instruments on the left.

NINE-OCTAVE GRAPHIC EQUALIZER

Figure 13–19 illustrates the block layout of a nine-band graphic equalizer. The nine audio bands are mixed together using a nine-input adder circuit. They are centered at the following approximate frequencies: <75 Hz, 100 Hz, 200 Hz, 400 Hz, 800 Hz, 1700 Hz, 3500 Hz, 7kHz, >10 kHz. Notice that the lowpass cutoff frequency of all previous bands is lower than the highpass frequency of all consecutive bands. For example, the lowpass cutoff for band 4 is 540 Hz and the highpass cutoff for band 5 is 660 Hz. You might assume that both should have a cutoff of 600 Hz but this would cause a +3 dB bump at 600 Hz in the overall output. This is because the mixer adds bands 4 and 5 together. At 600 Hz, the output of band 4 would be 0.7 and the output of band 5 would be 0.7, totaling 1.4 at 600 Hz. The total at the overlap frequency should equal 1. If the cutoff frequencies between bands are separated, the overlap frequency is attenuated by more than 0.7 at the output of each band. Ideally, the overlap frequency should be at 0.5, making the total of the two adjacent bands 1.

Band 5 is shown schematically in Figure 13–20, which demonstrates the simple, straightforward, design of each band. The highpass and lowpass

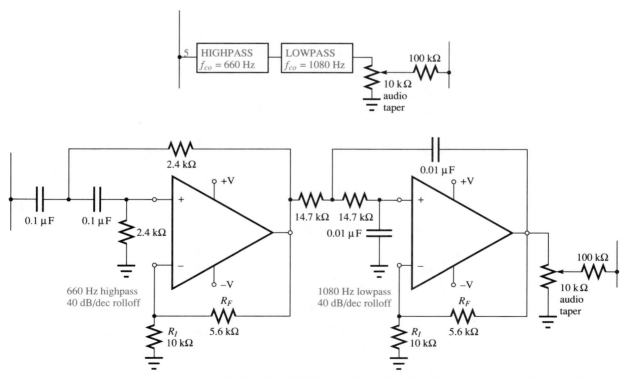

Figure 13–20 The fifth-band circuit for the nine-octave graphic equalizer.

sections are designed independently as discussed in Section 13–2. Film capacitors, such as polystyrene, should be used, along with precision resistors (1% or 2%). Use your calculator to verify the values shown in the circuit.

You will find many other applications for active filters as time goes on, for the active filter is a versatile building block that can be used in any electronic system.

Self-Check 13–5

1. Design band 2 of the graphic equalizer in Figure 13–19.
2. Design band 8 of the graphic equalizer in Figure 13–19.
3. Calculate the exact cutoff frequencies for the two highpass and two lowpass filters of Figure 13–18.

SUMMARY

FORMULAS

Constant-K Highpass and Lowpass Active Filters

(13–1) $\quad K = A_V = (R_I + R_F)/R_I$

(13–2) $\quad DF = 2 - (R_F/R_I) = 3 - K$

(13–3) $\quad f_{co} = 1/(2\pi RC) \cong 0.159/RC$

(13–4) $\quad R = 1/(2\pi f_{co}C) \cong 0.159/f_{co}C$

(13–5) $\quad C = 1/(2\pi f_{co}R) \cong 0.159/f_{co}R$

Constant-K *Bandpass Active Filters*

(13–6) $\quad f_o = 0.225/RC$

(13–7) $\quad Q = 1.414/(4 - K)$

(13–8) $\quad BW = f_o/Q$

(13–9) $\quad R = 0.225/Cf_o$

(13–10) $\quad C = 0.225/Rf_o$

(13–11) $\quad Q = f_o/BW$

(13–12) $\quad K = 4 - (1.414/Q)$

Multiple-Feedback Bandpass Active Filters

(13–13) $\quad f_o = (0.159/C) \cdot \sqrt{(R_1 + R_3)/R_1R_2R_3}$

(13–14) $\quad Q = \pi CR_2f_o = 0.5 \cdot \sqrt{R_2/R_1} \cdot \sqrt{1 + (R_1/R_3)}$

(13–15) $\quad A_o = R_2/2R_1 = $ gain at the frequency of operation

(13–16) $\quad BW = f_o/Q = 0.318/CR_2$

(13–17) $\quad R_2 = Q/\pi Cf_o = 0.318/(BW \cdot C)$

(13–18) $\quad R_1 = R_2/2A_o$

(13–19) $\quad R_3 = R_2/(4Q^2 - 2A_o)$

State-Variable Filters

(13–20) $Q = 0.333 + (R_A/3R_B)$

(13–21) $R_A = R_B(3Q - 1)$

Twin-Tee Notch Filters

(13–22) $Q = 1/(4 - 2K)$

(13–23) $K = 2 - (1/2Q)$

CONCEPTS

- Compared to passive filters, active filters have these advantages: no insertion loss due to cascaded filter sections, voltage gain provided in the passband, modular or building-block construction possible, low output impedance to drive a load (so load does not affect filter response), and simple design procedures.
- Constant-K filters require a specific voltage gain, which determines the damping factor.
- The amount of damping determines the type of frequency response: Chebyshev (underdamped), Butterworth (moderately damped), or Bessel (overdamped).
- The number of capacitors or RC networks determines the number of poles (or the order) of the filter.
- The slope of rolloff for active highpass or lowpass filters is 20 dB/dec per pole.
- Active highpass and lowpass filters can be cascaded to form bandpass filters.
- The constant-K bandpass filter is for low-Q applications where Q is less than approximately 7.
- The multiple-feedback bandpass filter can operate with a higher Q than the constant-K bandpass filter can and also has steeper skirts (rolloff).
- The state-variable (SV) filter has the advantage of very-high-Q capability, where Q is easily adjusted independent of frequency of operation.
- Active bandpass filters can be converted to bandstop filters by using an additional adder stage where the filter's input and output are added together and cancel each other at the center frequency.
- A filter's cutoff frequency is the frequency at which the AC voltage at the filter's output drops to $0.707 \cdot V_{max}$, where V_{max} is the maximum passband voltage. The maximum passband voltage is considered as 0 dB and the cutoff frequency is at -3 dB.

PROCEDURES

Designing Constant-K Highpass and Lowpass Active Filters

1. Decide on the cutoff frequency and the amount of stopband rolloff.
2. Select a standard value for C and calculate R. Use precision film capacitors, such as polystyrene or polyester capacitors, and precision film resistors.

3. Determine the number of poles needed (one pole for every 20 dB/dec of rolloff).
4. Use Tables 13–1 and 13–2 to determine the values for R_I and R_F for each stage.

Designing Bandpass or Bandstop Filters

1. Start with the desired center frequency and bandwidth.
2. Determine the required circuit Q, where $Q = f_c/BW$.
3. Decide on a filter type that will satisfy the Q requirements.
4. Choose a standard capacitor value. Use precision film capacitors, such as polystyrene or polyester capacitors, and precision film resistors.
5. Use the appropriate formulas from Section 13–3 to calculate component values.

NEED-TO-KNOW SOLUTION

One solution to this problem would be to design and construct a 5-kHz lowpass filter whose output is connected to the left channel input of your stereo system, and a 500-Hz highpass filter whose output is connected to the right channel input of your stereo system. The mono source is connected to the input of both filters. Thus, only frequencies lower than 5 kHz come out the left speaker and only frequencies higher than 500 Hz come out the right speaker—the bass is on the left and the highs are on the right. I would use fourth-order filters for this.

Another solution, shown on the facing page, is a slightly modified version of the circuit of Figure 13–18. This solution allows you to boost the highs and lows to your taste.

QUESTIONS

13–1 INTRODUCTION TO ACTIVE FILTERS

1. What is an active filter?
2. How are active filters better than passive filters?
3. What are constant-K active filters?
4. What are two other names for constant-K active filters?
5. What type of filter response has a peak before it rolls off?
6. What type of filter response has the most gradual rolloff?
7. What type of filter response is maximally flat?
8. A fifth-order active filter has how many RC networks?
9. What is the slope of rolloff for a fourth-order highpass filter?

13–2 ACTIVE HIGHPASS AND LOWPASS FILTERS

10. To prevent a constant-K filter from oscillating, the damping factor must be _____ and the K factor must be _____.
11. What is the value of damping factor for a two-pole active filter?
12. For a sixth-order active filter, what is the value of R_F for the third stage if R_I is 10 kΩ?

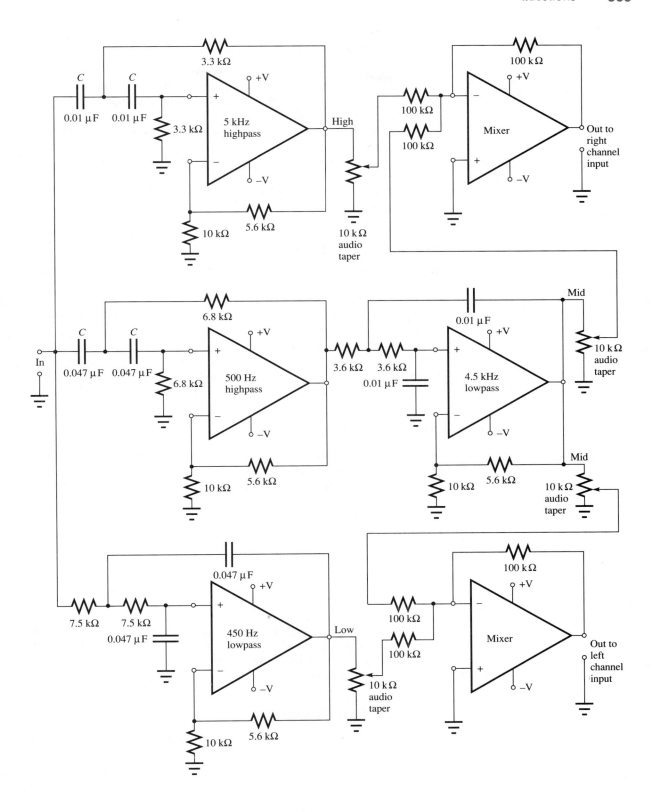

13–3 ACTIVE BANDPASS AND BANDSTOP FILTERS

13. Describe a bandpass filter that has a wide bandwidth yet steep rolloff.
14. Name two disadvantages of the constant-K bandpass filter.
15. How does the multiple-feedback bandpass filter compare in performance to the constant-K bandpass filter?
16. Compare the SV bandpass filter to the multiple-feedback bandpass filter.
17. Discuss the relationship between K and Q of the twin-tee bandstop filter.
18. Explain the theory of how an adder converts a bandpass filter to a bandstop filter.

13–4 FILTER FREQUENCY-RESPONSE TESTING

19. Why should the output of a variable sine wave generator be as clean as possible (low distortion and noise) if it is to be used for testing filters, especially highpass filters?
20. When testing an active filter circuit, why might it be necessary to place filter capacitors on each DC line close up to the op-amps?
21. How is a VU meter marked (units)?
22. What is the practical frequency limitation of many digital voltmeters?
23. Briefly explain how to identify a cutoff frequency using an oscilloscope.

13–5 ACTIVE FILTER APPLICATIONS

24. Briefly explain how the audio spectrum can be divided into small bands and remixed to the desired blend of highs and lows.
25. What are some common uses for a three-band audio tone-control circuit?
26. Why should the overlap frequencies between bands of an equalizer circuit have a relative amplitude of 0.5?

PROBLEMS

13–1 INTRODUCTION TO ACTIVE FILTERS

1. The resistors in the voltage-divider feedback network of a constant-K active filter are as follows: $R_I = 8.2$ kΩ, $R_F = 5.6$ kΩ. What is the value of the K factor and the damping factor?
2. What is the slope of rolloff for a five-pole active filter?

13–2 ACTIVE HIGHPASS AND LOWPASS FILTERS

3. Design a constant-K highpass filter to have a cutoff frequency of 3 kHz and a rolloff of 60 dB/dec. Use 0.05-μF capacitors.
4. Design a constant-K lowpass filter to have a cutoff frequency of 1 kHz and a rolloff of 80 dB/dec. Use 0.1-μF capacitors.

5. A constant-K highpass filter has four 0.02-μF capacitors and four 27-kΩ resistors. Calculate the cutoff frequency and determine the slope of rolloff.

6. A constant-K lowpass filter has three 0.001-μF capacitors and three 3.9-kΩ resistors. Calculate the cutoff frequency and determine the slope of rolloff.

13–3 ACTIVE BANDPASS AND BANDSTOP FILTERS

7. Determine the frequency of operation, Q, and bandwidth for the constant-K bandpass filter shown in Figure 13–21.

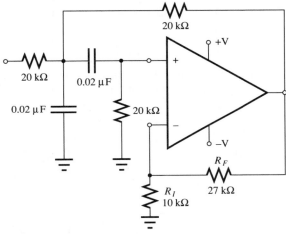

Figure 13–21

8. Design a constant-K bandpass filter to have a 25-kHz frequency of operation and a 10-kHz bandwidth. Let $C = 0.001 \ \mu$F.

9. Determine the frequency of operation, Q, bandwidth, and gain for the multiple-feedback bandpass filter shown in Figure 13–22.

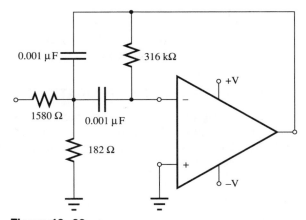

Figure 13–22

10. Design a multiple-feedback bandpass filter to have a 10-kHz frequency of operation and a 500-Hz bandwidth. Let $C = 0.002\ \mu F$. The gain at the frequency of operation shall be 100.

11. Design a multiple-feedback bandpass filter to have a 350-Hz frequency of operation and a 20-Hz bandwidth. Let $C = 0.05\ \mu F$. The gain at the frequency of operation shall be 50.

12. An SV bandpass filter has the following component values: $R_A = 150$ kΩ, $R_B = 10$ kΩ, $R = 6.8$ kΩ, and $C = 0.03\ \mu F$. Calculate the frequency of operation, Q, and bandwidth.

13. An SV bandpass filter has the following component values: $R_A = 270$ kΩ, $R_B = 22$ kΩ, $R = 27$ kΩ, and $C = 0.002\ \mu F$. Calculate the frequency of operation, Q, and bandwidth.

14. Design an SV bandpass filter for a 15-kHz frequency of operation and a bandwidth of 500 Hz. Let $C = 0.005\ \mu F$ and $R_B = 10$ kΩ.

15. Design an SV bandstop filter for a 120-Hz center frequency and a bandwidth of 10 Hz. Let $C = 0.1\ \mu F$ and $R_B = 10$ kΩ.

16. Determine the center frequency, Q, and bandstop bandwidth for the twin-tee notch filter shown in Figure 13–23.

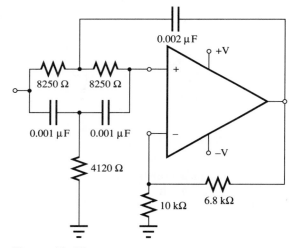

Figure 13–23

17. Determine the center frequency, Q, and bandstop bandwidth for the twin-tee notch filter shown in Figure 13–24.

13–5 ACTIVE FILTER APPLICATIONS

18. Design band 3 of the graphic equalizer of Figure 13–19.
19. Design band 7 of the graphic equalizer of Figure 13–19.
20. Design a high-Q notch filter to remove 60-Hz hum from an audio source.

Additional Problems

21. Design a constant-K highpass filter to have a cutoff frequency of 2.5 kHz and a rolloff of 40 dB/dec. Use 0.05-μF capacitors.

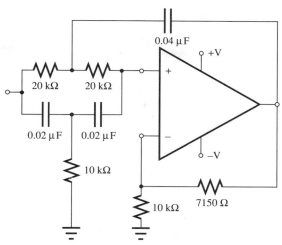

Figure 13–24

22. Design a constant-K lowpass filter to have a cutoff frequency of 400 Hz and a rolloff of 60 dB/dec. Use 0.1-μF capacitors.

23. A constant-K highpass filter has four 0.05-μF capacitors and four 10-kΩ resistors. Calculate the cutoff frequency and determine the approximate slope of rolloff.

24. A constant-K lowpass filter has three 0.01-μF capacitors and three 5.1-kΩ resistors. Calculate the cutoff frequency and determine the approximate slope of rolloff.

25. Design a constant-K bandpass filter to have a 15-kHz frequency of operation and a 4-kHz bandwidth. Let $C = 0.002$ μF.

26. Design a multiple-feedback bandpass filter to have a 5-kHz frequency of operation and a 500-Hz bandwidth. Let $C = 0.02$ μF. The gain at the frequency of operation shall be 20.

27. Design a multiple-feedback bandstop filter to have a 19-kHz center frequency and a 1-kHz bandstop bandwidth. Let $C = 0.022$ μF. Let $A_o = 50$.

28. Design an SV bandpass filter for a 1-kHz frequency of operation and a bandwidth of 100 Hz. Let $C = 0.05$ μF and $R_B = 10$ kΩ.

29. Design an SV bandstop filter for a 60-Hz center frequency and a bandwidth of 5 Hz. Let $C = 0.1$ μF and $R_B = 10$ kΩ.

30. Design band 2 of the graphic equalizer of Figure 13–19.

ANSWERS TO SELF-CHECKS

SELF-CHECK 13–1

1. No insertion loss due to cascaded filter sections, passband voltage gain, modular construction, low output impedance, simple design
2. An active filter that has a fixed gain and a filter network at the noninverting input
3. (b)
4. 2; 40 dB/dec

SELF-CHECK 13–2

1. Stage 1: $C = 0.01 \mu F$, $R = 3,975 \Omega$ (3,920 Ω, 1%), $R_I = 10 k\Omega$, $R_F = 10 k\Omega$
   Stage 2: $C = 0.01 \mu F$, $R = 3,975 \Omega$, $R_I = 10 k\Omega$, $R_F = 3,830 \Omega$ (1%)
   Stage 3: $C = 0.01 \mu F$, $R = 3,975 \Omega$, $R_I = 10 k\Omega$, $R_F = 13.7 k\Omega$ (1%)
2. Stage 1: $C = 0.047 \mu F$, $R = 6,766 \Omega$ (6.8 $k\Omega$), $R_I = 10 k\Omega$, $R_F = 10 k\Omega$
   Stage 2: $C = 0.047 \mu F$, $R = 6,766 \Omega$, $R_I = 10 k\Omega$, $R_F = 10 k\Omega$
3. 7; seventh

SELF-CHECK 13–3

1. A bandpass filter formed by cascading a highpass and a lowpass active filter
2. State-variable type
3. Low Q, gradual rolloff
4. Slight changes in K cause great changes in Q.
5. At the center frequency, the output of the bandpass filter is 180° out of phase with its input. If the input and output are added, they cancel (assuming they are equal in amplitude).
6. $R = 3,180 \Omega$ and $R_A = 740 k\Omega$

SELF-CHECK 13–4

1. A $\pm DC$ supply is needed along with a low-distortion, low-noise variable sine wave generator. A meter or oscilloscope is needed to monitor the filter's output.
2. Distortion and noise products cause stopband readings at the filter's output to be higher than they would otherwise be. This is especially severe when testing highpass filters, because distortion products are higher-frequency harmonics and pass to the filter's output.
3. The waveform can be observed and the oscilloscope has a higher frequency response than does a VU meter or analog voltmeter.
4. The peak-to-peak amplitude of the cutoff frequency will be 0.707 times the maximum passband amplitude.

SELF-CHECK 13–5

1. Highpass section: if $C = 0.1 \mu F$ then $R = 19.3 k\Omega$ (19.1 $k\Omega$, 1%).
   Lowpass section: if $C = 0.1 \mu F$ then $R = 11 k\Omega$ (1%).
   $R_F = 5.6 k\Omega$ when $R_I = 10 k\Omega$.
2. Highpass section: if $C = 0.005 \mu F$ then $R = 5,790 \Omega$ (5,760 Ω, 1%).
   Lowpass section: if $C = 0.005 \mu F$ then $R = 3,540 \Omega$ (3,570 Ω, 1%).
   $R_F = 5.6 k\Omega$ when $R_I = 10 k\Omega$.
3. For the 5-kHz highpass filter, $f_{co} = 4,823$ Hz.
   For the 500-Hz highpass filter, $f_{co} = 498$ Hz.
   For the 4.5-kHz lowpass filter, $f_{co} = 4,421$ Hz.
   For the 450-Hz lowpass filter, $f_{co} = 452$ Hz.

SUGGESTED PROJECTS

1. Add some of the main concepts, formulas, and procedures from this chapter to your Electronics Notebook.
2. Build and test some of the example circuits from this chapter.
3. Design, build, and test an SV filter with bandpass and bandstop capability. Use a potentiometer, wired as a rheostat, to vary the Q of the filter. Use Figure 13–15 as a model. Design it for any frequency you want between 10 Hz and 20 kHz. Use LF356 op-amps.

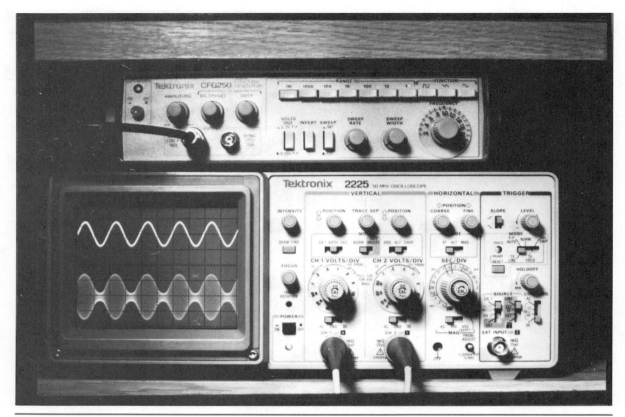

A radio frequency (RF) and an audio frequency (AF) are applied to a nonlinear mixer to produce the amplitude-modulated (AM) signal shown here. The upper trace is the audio signal and the lower trace is the AM envelope—the modulated signal. The AM envelope is composed of three distinct frequencies: the radio frequency and sum and difference frequencies (RF, RF−AF, RF + AF).

14 Mixers

OBJECTIVES

After studying this chapter, you will be able to

■ explain the difference between linear and nonlinear mixers.
■ list applications for linear and nonlinear mixers.
■ calculate products resulting from nonlinear mixing.
■ explain the purpose for the converter in a heterodyne receiver.
■ describe how to troubleshoot a nonlinear mixer.
■ explain the theory of amplitude modulation in terms of mixing and mixing products.

NEED TO KNOW

What is a mixer, or mixer circuit? Perhaps you have worked with audio mixers such as microphone mixers or mixing consoles. Have you ever heard anyone talk about mixers that are in radio receivers and television sets? Are audio mixers, radio mixers, and television mixers all basically the same circuit? Do they all operate the same? What is the purpose for these different mixers? How are they made?

When you are an electronics technician or engineer, it will be assumed that you know the answers to these questions. Your need to know will be satisfied as you study this chapter. Enjoy your exploration.

INTRODUCTION

In this chapter, you will be introduced to the world of mixers. You will discover the two basic types of mixers, linear and nonlinear, and be exposed to a variety of mixer circuits. This chapter builds upon your knowledge of diodes, BJTs, FETs, and op-amps as you see these devices used in mixer circuits. As a bonus, you will gain a basic understanding of audio mixing consoles, AM radio receivers, and AM transmitters—along with AM theory. So as not to cloud the concepts and theory of linear and nonlinear mixing, the use of math is greatly minimized. Any math that is performed will be simple addition or subtraction. To take care of the heavy math, three design notes with computer programs are included. Time to begin your exploration into the world of mixers.

14–1 LINEAR MIXERS

INTRODUCTION TO LINEAR MIXING

This section covering linear mixing is a supplement to Section 12–2, "Summing Amplifier Circuits." Here we take another look at adder circuits as linear mixers.

What is a linear mixer? A linear mixer is an adder circuit. It is a circuit in which voltages, both AC and DC, are added together much as positive and negative numbers are added. Figure 14–1 shows a common block symbol for a linear adder. This symbol represents any number of circuits that mix voltages linearly.

Perhaps the simplest of linear mixers is the resistive mixer, also shown in Figure 14–1. Notice that voltages V_1 and V_2 are added at the output junction and the weight of each input is taken into consideration. What do I mean by the weight of each input? Each input resistor forms a voltage divider with the load resistor and the other input resistor. The voltage-divider ratio, designated with a K, is the weight of the input. For K_1, R_2 is in parallel with R_L and the voltage divider ratio is $(R_2 \| R_L)/[R_1 + (R_2 \| R_L)]$. For K_2, R_1 is in parallel with R_L and the voltage-divider ratio is $(R_1 \| R_L)/[R_2 + (R_1 \| R_L)]$. The total voltage at the output is the superimposed sum of the two weighted input voltages. In other words, the output is determined by applying the Superposition Theorem.

$$K_1 = (R_2 \| R_L \| \cdots \| R_N)/(R_1 + (R_2 \| R_L \| \cdots \| R_N)) \qquad (14\text{–}1)$$

where all inputs other than the input being analyzed are in parallel with the load.

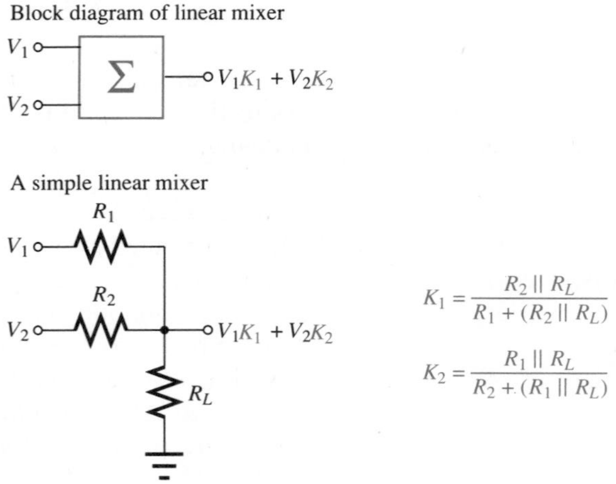

Block diagram of linear mixer

A simple linear mixer

$$K_1 = \frac{R_2 \| R_L}{R_1 + (R_2 \| R_L)}$$

$$K_2 = \frac{R_1 \| R_L}{R_2 + (R_1 \| R_L)}$$

Figure 14–1   The linear mixer.

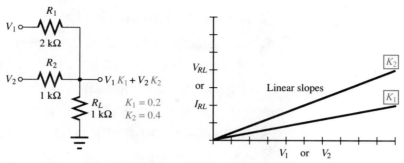

Figure 14–2 The linear relationships between input and output voltages of a resistive mixer.

Figure 14–2 is an example of what we have discussed. First, let's verify the weights given as $K_1 = 0.2$ and $K_2 = 0.4$.

$$K_1 = (R_2 \| R_L)/[R_1 + (R_2 \| R_L)] = (1 \text{ k}\Omega \| 1 \text{ k}\Omega)/[2 \text{ k}\Omega + (1 \text{ k}\Omega \| 1 \text{ k}\Omega)]$$

$$= 500 \ \Omega/2.5 \text{ k}\Omega = 0.2$$

$$K_2 = (R_1 \| R_L)/[R_2 + (R_1 \| R_L)] = (2 \text{ k}\Omega \| 1 \text{ k}\Omega)/[1 \text{ k}\Omega + (2 \text{ k}\Omega \| 1 \text{ k}\Omega)]$$

$$= 667 \ \Omega/1{,}667 \ \Omega = 0.4$$

Note the linear graphs in Figure 14–2. These graphs represent the resistive weighting of each input and demonstrate the linear relationship between the output and the inputs of the summing network. That is why this is called a *linear mixer*. The slope of each line is the weighting factor. For the K_1 line, there are 2 V out for every 10 V in. For the K_2 line, there are 4 V out for every 10 V in. The total output voltage is the simple arithmetic sum of the weighted input voltages. Study Example 14–1.

$$V_{\text{out}} = V_1 K_1 + V_2 K_2 + \cdots + V_N K_N \tag{14–2}$$

EXAMPLE 14–1

Determine the weight of each input and the final output voltage for Figure 14–3.

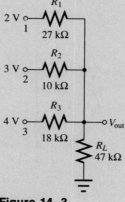

Figure 14–3

First determine all K values.

$$K_1 = (R_2 \parallel R_3 \parallel R_L)/[R_1 + (R_2 \parallel R_3 \parallel R_L)]$$
$$= (10 \text{ k}\Omega \parallel 18 \text{ k}\Omega \parallel 47 \text{ k}\Omega)/(27 \text{ k}\Omega + [10 \text{ k}\Omega \parallel 18 \text{ k}\Omega \parallel 47 \text{ k}\Omega])$$
$$= 5.66 \text{ k}\Omega/(27 \text{ k}\Omega + 5.66 \text{ k}\Omega) = 0.173$$

$$K_2 = (R_1 \parallel R_3 \parallel R_L)/[R_2 + (R_1 \parallel R_3 \parallel R_L)]$$
$$= (27 \text{ k}\Omega \parallel 18 \text{ k}\Omega \parallel 47 \text{ k}\Omega)/[10 \text{ k}\Omega + (27 \text{ k}\Omega \parallel 18 \text{ k}\Omega \parallel 47 \text{ k}\Omega)]$$
$$= 8.78 \text{ k}\Omega/(10 \text{ k}\Omega + 8.78 \text{ k}\Omega) = 0.468$$

$$K_3 = (R_1 \parallel R_2 \parallel R_L)/[R_3 + (R_1 \parallel R_2 \parallel R_L)]$$
$$= (27 \text{ k}\Omega \parallel 10 \text{ k}\Omega \parallel 47 \text{ k}\Omega)/[18 \text{ k}\Omega + (27 \text{ k}\Omega \parallel 10 \text{ k}\Omega \parallel 47 \text{ k}\Omega)]$$
$$= 6.32 \text{ k}\Omega/(18 \text{ k}\Omega + 6.32 \text{ k}\Omega) = 0.260$$

Now you can calculate the output voltage.

$$V_{\text{out}} = V_1 K_1 + V_2 K_2 + V_3 K_3$$
$$= (2 \text{ V} \cdot 0.173) + (3 \text{ V} \cdot 0.468) + (4 \text{ V} \cdot 0.260)$$
$$= 0.346 \text{ V} + 1.404 \text{ V} + 1.04 \text{ V} = 2.79 \text{ V}$$

THE OP-AMP LINEAR MIXER

Figure 14–4 is a linear mixer that you have seen before, in Section 12–2. As it is for simple resistive mixers, the output vs input relationship is linear for the op-amp mixer. This is an active linear mixer that provides voltage gain, unlike the passive resistive mixer that provides attenuation (loss). In this case, the weight of each input is a voltage gain where $K_N = A_{V(N)} = R_F/R_{I(N)}$. As before, the total DC output voltage is the sum of the weighted inputs ($V_{\text{out}} = -(V_1 K_1 + V_2 K_2)$, the negative sign simply indicates a 180° phase (polarity) reversal).

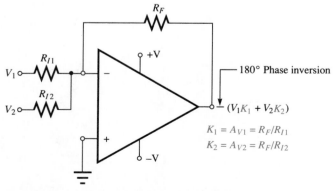

Figure 14–4 The op-amp linear mixer (adder).

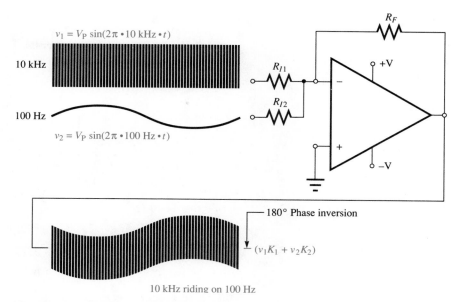

Figure 14–5   Linear sinusoidal mixing.

$$K_N = A_{V(N)} = R_F/R_{I(N)} \tag{14–3}$$

where N is the number of the input and input resistor.

Now, let's see what happens when two very different frequencies (sinusoidal waveforms) are mixed linearly, as illustrated in Figure 14–5. As you can see, each sinusoidal signal is clearly identified in the output. The 10-kHz signal is distinct from the 100-Hz signal. This is partly because the two frequencies are so far apart. In any case, the output signal is the sum of the instantaneous voltages that exist at any point in time (t). Each input voltage at any instant in time is expressed as $v = V_P \sin(\omega t)$, where $\omega = 2\pi f$. The output voltage at any instant in time (t) is the sum of the weighted instantaneous voltages, $v_{\text{out}} = -(v_1 K_1 + v_2 K_2)$. In effect, the voltage of the lower frequency displaces the higher frequency up or down in voltage (like a bias voltage that floats up and down in a sinusoidal manner). Again, the Superposition Theorem is at work. Consider Example 14–2.

$$v = V_P \sin(\omega t) \tag{14–4}$$

where $\omega = 2\pi f$.

EXAMPLE 14–2

Determine the instantaneous output voltage at $t = 2.3$ ms for Figure 14–6.

$$v_1 = V_{P(1)} \sin(\omega t) = 4 \, V_P \cdot \sin(2 \cdot \pi \cdot 20 \text{ kHz} \cdot 2.3 \text{ ms}) = -3.78 \text{ V}$$

$$v_2 = V_{P(2)} \sin(\omega t) = 2 \, V_P \cdot \sin(2 \cdot \pi \cdot 1 \text{ kHz} \cdot 2.3 \text{ ms}) = +0.5 \text{ V}$$

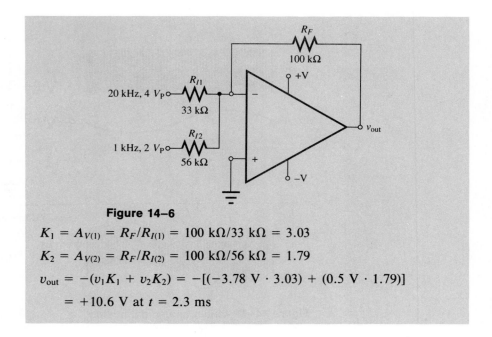

Figure 14–6

$$K_1 = A_{V(1)} = R_F/R_{I(1)} = 100 \text{ k}\Omega/33 \text{ k}\Omega = 3.03$$

$$K_2 = A_{V(2)} = R_F/R_{I(2)} = 100 \text{ k}\Omega/56 \text{ k}\Omega = 1.79$$

$$v_{out} = -(v_1 K_1 + v_2 K_2) = -[(-3.78 \text{ V} \cdot 3.03) + (0.5 \text{ V} \cdot 1.79)]$$

$$= +10.6 \text{ V at } t = 2.3 \text{ ms}$$

Design Note 14–1 will help you visualize linear mixing for a variety of frequencies at different amplitudes. The BASIC program makes use of the IBM® high-resolution graphics mode to actually plot and display linearly mixed sinusoidal signals. Line 110 of the program calculates the total instantaneous voltage at any point in time (t), where in this case $t = X \cdot 0.001$ (in other words, time is incremented in 1-ms steps). The total instantaneous voltage is calculated and plotted 600 times over a 600-ms time period (lines 100 through 140).

Linear mixers are commonly used in audio production and recording consoles. The circuit of Figure 14–7 is one channel of a multichannel audio

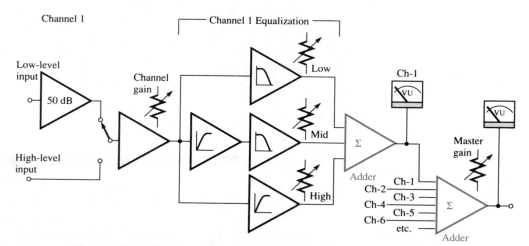

Figure 14–7   Linear mixer circuits in a recording console (multi-channel audio mixer).

DESIGN NOTE 14–1 LINEAR MIXING

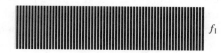

f_1

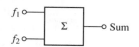

f_2

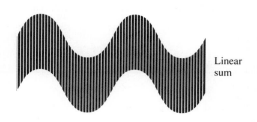

Linear sum

This program uses the high-resolution graphics mode of the IBM PC® to plot the linear sum of two sine waves.

BASIC PROGRAM

```
10 REM  * LINEAR MIXER PROGRAM *
15 SCREEN 2:KEY OFF
20 CLS
25 CLEAR
30 PRINT "LINEAR MIXER PROGRAM"
40 PRINT""
50 INPUT "ENTER FREQUENCY ONE (0 TO 100 HZ) - ";F1
60 INPUT "ENTER PEAK VOLTAGE FOR FREQUENCY ONE (100 V MAX.) - ";EP1
70 INPUT "ENTER FREQUENCY TWO (0 TO 10 HZ) - ";F2
80 INPUT "ENTER PEAK VOLTAGE FOR FREQUENCY TWO (100 V MAX.) - ";EP2
90 N = 100
95 LINE (0,100)-(600,100):LINE (600,0)-(600,200)
97 FOR X = 0 TO 200 STEP 10:PSET (599,X):PSET (601,X):NEXT X
100 FOR X = 1 TO 600
110 Y = (EP1 * SIN(6.283*F1*X*.001)) + (EP2 * SIN(6.283*F2*X*.001))
115 IF F1 = 0 THEN Y = Y + EP1
116 IF F2 = 0 THEN Y = Y + EP2
120 Y = -Y + 100
130 LINE (M,N)-(X,Y)
135 M=X:N=Y
140 NEXT X
150 INPUT "ANOTHER PLOT? (Y/N) ";A$
160 IF A$="N" THEN SCREEN 0:CLS:KEY ON:END
170 GOTO 20
```

mixer. All the remaining channels are identical. Each channel has a high-level input for the outputs of tape and compact-disc machines and a low-level input for a microphone (the microphone requires about 50 dB of voltage amplification to equal the output level of a tape machine). To compensate for variations in source quality, three-band equalization is provided. An adder (linear mixer) is used to recombine the three audio bands into one; a VU meter is used to monitor the output level of the channel; and another adder is used to sum all of the channels to one output line. A stereo mixing console would have two output adders, one for left output and one for right output. The output of all channels would have a selector switch to direct the audio to the left or right adder. Each output has a VU meter so the final output can be monitored.

Time for a short self-check.

Self-Check 14–1

1. What is a linear mixer?
2. Why is the term *linear* applied to these mixers?
3. What is a weighted input?
4. Describe how a linearly mixed 2-kHz signal and 30-Hz signal would look when viewed on an oscilloscope.
5. Name a common application for linear mixers.

14–2 NONLINEAR MIXERS

INTRODUCTION TO NONLINEAR MIXERS

Nonlinear mixers are circuits that use devices that have nonlinear output vs input characteristics. As you know, diodes, BJTs, and FETs all have nonlinear voltage vs current curves: for the diode, it's the forward voltage vs forward current relationship; for the BJT, it's the V_{BE} vs I_C relationship; and for the FET, it's the V_{GS} vs I_D relationship (transconductance curve). In each case, the graph is curved, indicating that the relationship is nonlinear.

This nonlinearity can cause severe distortion of the applied signals. This is why the BJT and FET must be biased for operation in the most linear portions of the curve, and the output voltage or current is limited to a small portion of the curve if low-distortion linear amplification is desired. While the nonlinearity of these devices is in some cases a serious problem, it is exactly what is needed for nonlinear mixing applications.

When nonlinear mixing is desired, the most nonlinear portion of the operating curve for the device is used. When two or more input signals combine in the device over this nonlinear operating region, new frequencies called products are created. Notice Figure 14–8. The block symbol for the nonlinear mixer contains a large X. This indicates that multiplication of two input signals is taking place $(\sin f_1 \cdot \sin f_2)$ which produces two products $[\cos(f_1 + f_2) - \cos(f_1 - f_2)]$. The two products that are generated are known as *sum* and *difference frequencies*. Depending on the type of nonlinear mixer, the two input frequencies may also appear at the output of the mixer with the sum and difference frequencies.

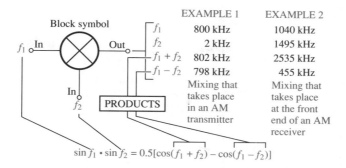

Figure 14–8 Nonlinear mixing.

Note the two examples given in Figure 14–8. When 2-kHz audio is nonlinearly mixed with an 800-kHz radio frequency, the results are 802 kHz (the sum) and 798 kHz (the difference). This is the mixing that takes place in an amplitude-modulated (AM) broadcast transmitter or CB radio (more on this later). The second example of Figure 14–6 illustrates what happens in an AM radio receiver. A station is received at 1,040 kHz and mixed with a frequency of 1,495 kHz. The two products are 2,535 kHz and 455 kHz. The 455-kHz signal is the intermediate frequency used in the receiver and contains the same information, in the form of neighboring frequency components, as does the original 1,040-kHz signal.

Nonlinear mixers are used in AM transmitters, AM and FM radios, and TV sets. Let's take a few moments to consider the purpose for the mixer in one of these receivers, the AM receiver. System operation is very similar in FM and TV receivers.

THE HETERODYNE RECEIVER

Figure 14–9 is a block diagram of a common AM radio. This block diagram is also commonly referred to as a **heterodyne receiver,** or **superheterodyne receiver.** AM, FM, and TV receivers are all heterodyne receivers. The word *heterodyne* means "to mix." The incoming station signal is mixed with an oscillator frequency. In this way, the incoming signal is converted to an intermediate frequency (the difference frequency). The combination of the mixer and oscillator is known as a **frequency converter.** In AM radios, it is desired to convert the incoming station frequency and associated side-band information (music, voice, etc.) to an intermediate frequency (IF) of 455 kHz. The IF section of the radio is a high-gain bandpass filter. It has a bandwidth of approximately 10 kHz with very steep skirts (rolloff) and a voltage gain of 60 to 90 dB. Only one station can be converted to 455 kHz and pass through the IF section.

Once the station information has passed through the IF section, it is detected. **Detection,** for amplitude-modulated signals, is a form of rectification, as shown in Figure 14–9. In this case, a diode is used to block all positive alternations of the 455-kHz signal. The negative-going pulses that pass through the diode are filtered or integrated by using a capacitor (not shown). The average voltage on the capacitor is the original audio, which is then amplified to drive a speaker.

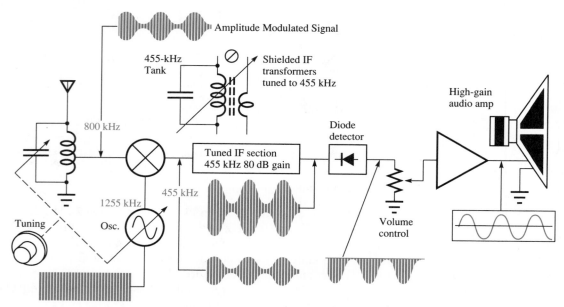

Figure 14–9 The mixer in the heterodyne receiver.

Now, let's go back to the front-end converter. As shown, an incoming station is at 800 kHz. Since it is adjusted to resonate at 800 kHz, the front-end tuning (tank circuit) provides some preselection. The 800-kHz station signal is applied to the mixer; the oscillator is simultaneously adjusted (gang-tuned) to 1255 kHz; and the 1255-kHz sine wave from the oscillator also enters the mixer. The mixer will produce the sum and difference frequencies as products. However, this mixer is tuned to resonate at 455 kHz. Thus, the 800-kHz, 1,255-kHz and 2,055-kHz (sum) signals are rejected by the resonant circuit. Only the difference frequency, 455 kHz, is passed into the 455-kHz IF section. Consider Example 14–3.

EXAMPLE 14–3

It is desired to receive an AM station at a frequency of 620 kHz. The receiver's intermediate frequency is 455 kHz. What frequency must the oscillator be to convert the 620-kHz station to a 455-kHz IF? The 455-kHz IF is the difference frequency, where $f_{osc} - f_{station} = f_{IF}$. Therefore, $f_{osc} = f_{IF} + f_{station} = 455$ kHz $+ 620$ kHz $= 1,075$ kHz

Let's look at some of the nonlinear mixer circuits that can be used in heterodyne receivers and other applications.

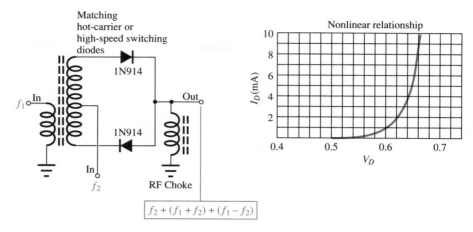

Figure 14–10 A balanced diode mixer.

EXAMPLES OF NONLINEAR MIXERS

Balanced Diode Mixer

Figure 14–10 illustrates a balanced diode mixer. The diodes provide the nonlinearity needed to create products. The input signals must forward bias the diodes and in so doing must operate on the very nonlinear characteristic curve. It is the responsibility of f_2 to alternately forward bias the diodes, so f_2 must be 5 to 10 $V_{\text{P-P}}$ in amplitude for satisfactory operation. Usually an oscillator supplies f_2. The f_1 signal cannot get to the output because the output is ground-referenced and both ends of the secondary winding are floating. The secondary is balanced above ground. Thus, f_1 is only able to mix in the diodes with f_2. The resulting sum and difference frequencies are available at the output. If only the sum or difference frequency is desired in the output, a tank circuit tuned to the desired frequency can be substituted for the RF choke.

The diode mixer is a passive mixer that has a conversion loss in the range of 5 to 10 dB, a loss that must be compensated for using amplification. The advantage of the diode mixer is its wide dynamic range (it can handle very weak and very strong f_1 signals). Hot-carrier diodes or high-speed switching diodes are used for this mixer.

BJT Mixer

Figure 14–11 illustrates a typical front-end converter for AM receivers. This converter uses a BJT mixer stage. The oscillator signal is fed into the emitter and the station signal is fed into the base. The transistor is biased for a V_B of about 1.5 V. The 1,495-kHz oscillator signal forces the transistor to operate in the nonlinear portion of the V_{BE} vs I_C curve. Thus, products are produced. However, in this case, the collector is tuned to 455 kHz. This means the 1,040-kHz, the 1,495-kHz, and the 2,535-kHz signals are greatly attenuated and only 455 kHz is passed to the IF section.

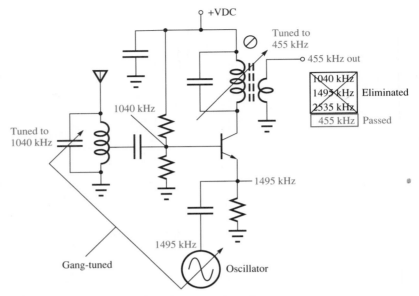

Figure 14–11 A BJT mixer for a receiver front end.

This circuit is fairly simple and has the advantage of providing conversion gain. In other words, the incoming station signal is not only frequency-converted, it is amplified. However, the transistor must be of the low-noise type and have a wide dynamic range. The transistor should be specified by the manufacturer for mixer use.

JFET Mixer

As shown in Figure 14–12, the JFET can be used as a mixer. The square-law relationship of I_D to V_{GS} provides the nonlinearity needed for the production of sum and difference frequencies. The oscillator signal should be about 2 $V_{\text{P-P}}$ to force the FET to operate over a good portion of the transconductance curve. The JFET mixer has the advantages of lower noise, good dynamic range, and conversion gain.

Note that the front-end tank circuit is tuned to resonate at 620 kHz and the oscillator is set at 1,075 kHz. The difference frequency is 455 kHz, the IF frequency. The mixer drain circuit is tuned to 455 kHz. All other frequencies are greatly attenuated.

Dual-Gate MOSFET Mixer

The dual-gate MOSFET mixer of Figure 14–13 has all the advantages of the JFET mixer plus excellent isolation of the oscillator from the mixer and antenna circuits. The separate insulated gates (two inputs) greatly hinder the oscillator signal from getting into the antenna circuit and being radiated into the air. Also, the oscillator sees a constant load as determined by the bias-voltage divider. This prevents the oscillator from being pulled off frequency with changes in load. Gate 2 (oscillator input) is usually biased at +4 V, depending on the MOSFET, and the self-bias for gate 1 is about −1 V.

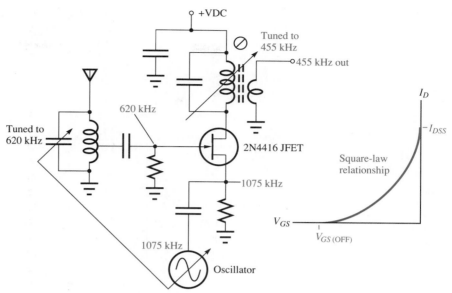

Figure 14–12   A JFET mixer.

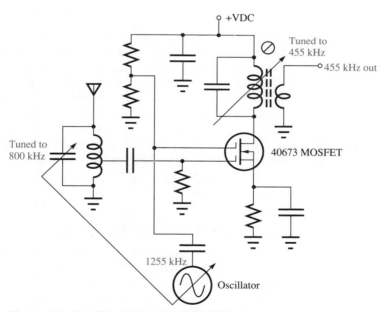

Figure 14–13   The dual-gate MOSFET mixer.

Differential Balanced Mixer

Integrated circuits (ICs) are often used in mixer circuits as well as in discrete devices. Figure 14–14 shows a balanced mixer circuit using the very popular CA3028A. Signal f_1, applied to pin 2, is amplified equally through each differential transistor to the output transformer. This means both ends of the center-tapped side of the transformer (pins 8 and 6) are electrically balanced,

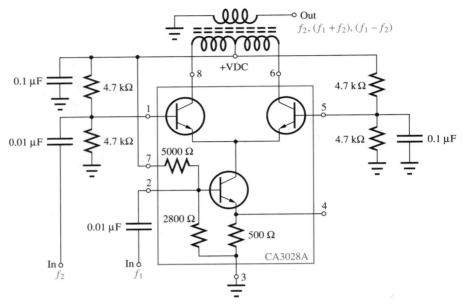

Figure 14–14 An IC balanced mixer.

(that is, both ends go high or low at the same time). Thus, f_1 is never able to produce across the primary side the difference of potential that is required to produce an output from the secondary. Therefore, f_1 is eliminated from the output. Even so, f_1 still mixes with f_2, which is applied to pin 1. As a result, f_2 and the sum and difference frequencies are present at the output. A capacitor can be added between pins 8 and 6 to resonate with the primary of the transformer at the desired product frequency (sum or difference). This mixer has the advantages of conversion gain and automatic elimination of the f_1 signal from the output. Balanced mixers such as this are used in single-sideband communications equipment, the discussion of which is beyond the purpose of this text.

INTERMODULATION DISTORTION (IMD)

We are now at a point where we can discuss intermodulation distortion (IMD) in amplifiers intended for linear amplification. IMD is a very undesirable distortion created by the nonlinearity of amplifiers. As you know, active devices have plenty of nonlinearity. Legitimate and desired signals can use this nonlinearity to create mixing products, which do not exist in the original signal and are considered a form of distortion. Thus, desired signals, such as frequencies in voice or music, intermix or intermodulate to produce a vast number of sum and difference frequencies, which is perceived as a harsh and raspy sound when IMD is severe. IMD products are kept low by operating BJTs and FETs in the most linear portion of their transfer curves and by using FETs for very-low-level signals only. Negative feedback also greatly reduces IMD.

IMD can be a problem in mixers if more frequencies than the intended one are permitted to arrive at the mixer input(s). The products that are generated can produce more products, creating a competitive noise level. At the front end of a receiver this can mean severe interference with the desired station signal.

TROUBLESHOOTING MIXERS

The mixer itself is a single stage within a system. It is a very important stage. In an AM receiver, for example, if the mixer stops functioning there will be no audio heard at the speaker and no 455-kHz signal anywhere in the IF section, since the mixer generates the 455-kHz signal. This makes it fairly easy to determine which half of the AM receiver system is inoperative.

So, if there is no 455-kHz signal coming from the mixer output, does that mean the mixer is bad? Maybe. The mixer cannot function if the oscillator is bad. The oscillator frequency is needed to mix with the incoming station signal to produce the 455-kHz product. Also, DC voltage must be present and proper bias voltage. As such, you will need to make sure the mixer is receiving all voltages, both DC and AC, for proper operation. Here is a practical checklist:

1. Use the oscilloscope to check for an output from the mixer.
2. Use the oscilloscope to check for an output from the oscillator. The oscillator output should be of the appropriate level for the type of mixer. Emitter- or source-fed mixers require about 2 V_{P-P}. Passive-diode mixers require oscillator injection voltages of about 10 V_{P-P}. Base- or gate-fed mixers of the common-emitter or common-source configuration may require very little oscillator drive, depending on the biasing of the device.
3. Use your multimeter to check DC levels: V_{CC}, V_{DD}, V_B, V_{BE}, V_{GS}.

While it is true that many things, such as broken current paths and bad capacitors, could be the cause of a malfunctioning mixer, in most cases you will find the active device itself is bad. If DC is present and the two mixing signals are present, the device is most likely bad.

Self-Check 14–2

1. How does nonlinear mixing differ from linear mixing?
2. What is a mixing product?
3. Name an example of a passive mixer and give one of its disadvantages.
4. What is the main advantage of active mixers over passive mixers?
5. How do mixer circuits eliminate all frequencies from the output except the desired product?
6. You can assume the mixer stage in a system is bad only after checking what?

14–3 MODULATION

INTRODUCTION TO AMPLITUDE MODULATION

AM

Amplitude modulation (AM) is the process in which audio frequencies are mixed nonlinearly with a radio frequency. The purpose is to convert the audio information to a much higher frequency range for transmission. In the process, sum and difference frequencies are created directly above and below the center radio frequency. The center frequency is loosely referred to as the carrier. The sum frequencies are a band of frequencies called the upper sideband (USB) and the difference frequencies are called the lower sideband (LSB). Each frequency component in the sidebands corresponds to an audio frequency. For example, a 500-Hz voice frequency is positioned 500 Hz above the carrier in the upper sideband and 500 Hz below the carrier in the lower sideband. If the carrier is 800 kHz, the resulting upper side frequency is 800.5 kHz and the lower side frequency is 799.5 kHz. Each voice frequency is mixed with the carrier in like manner, forming the USB and mirror-image LSB.

The Envelope

Figure 14–15 demonstrates amplitude modulation. For simplicity, a single audio tone, such as 1 kHz, is used to mix with the carrier frequency. The resulting waveform at the output of the mixer is an amplitude modulated signal, often referred to as an AM **envelope**. The mixer circuit does not allow the original audio tone to appear in the output. The envelope that is shown at the output is composed of three distinct frequencies: the original carrier acting as a center reference frequency (f_C), the upper side frequency (carrier + audio tone, $f_C + f_A$), and the lower side frequency (carrier − audio tone, $f_C − f_A$). The instantaneous voltage of the envelope ($v_{(t)}$) at any specified time (t) is simply the sum of the instantaneous voltages of these three frequencies. The envelope expression looks like this:

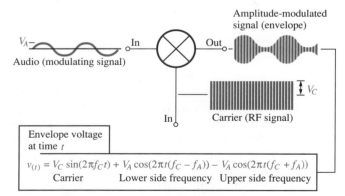

Figure 14–15 Amplitude modulation (AM).

$$v_{(t)} = V_C \sin(2\pi f_C t) + V_A \cos[2\pi t(f_C - f_A)] - V_A \cos[2\pi t(f_C + f_A)]$$

where the envelope voltage at time t is the sum of the instantaneous carrier voltage and side-frequency voltages.

It is important for you to realize that the overall shape of the envelope is the result of the sum of the instantaneous carrier and side-frequency voltages. The carrier itself never changes in amplitude as the overall envelope does. Also, assuming the audio to be of a fixed peak-to-peak amplitude, the upper and lower side frequencies are fixed in amplitude. The overall envelope is created as the side frequencies change in phase over time. The phase cycle of the side frequencies is repeated with every cycle of the applied audio tone.

When the envelope is viewed using an oscilloscope, it appears as though the carrier is changing in amplitude with the audio. We say that the audio is *modulating* the carrier. In fact, the carrier never changes in amplitude and, therefore, the carrier carries nothing. In the radio receiver, the carrier (f_c) is converted to the IF frequency along with the side frequencies, or sidebands. When the IF signal is detected to recover the audio, it is the envelope that is rectified and filtered. Also, the envelope does not exist in the air between the transmitting antenna and the receiver. The carrier and sidebands are transmitted simultaneously, yet they are distinct. It is in the receiver that they combine to form the envelope.

Program Demonstrations

Design Note 14–2 uses the high-resolution graphics mode of the IBM PC® to demonstrate amplitude modulation. You can use this program to generate AM envelopes. When the voltage of the audio tone is half the carrier's voltage, the envelope will be at 100% modulation. Radio station engineers try to keep the level of modulation as close to 100% as possible without overmodulating. Overmodulation causes strong distortion products. You will be able to experiment with this using the computer program. Line 110 of the program contains the formula that creates the envelope. The formula contains the three distinct components of the envelope: carrier, upper side frequency, and lower side frequency.

Design Note 14–3 is an amplitude modulation (AM) analysis program. This program proves that what we have discussed regarding the distinct USB, carrier, and LSB. Using this program, you will enter the carrier frequency and a lower side frequency. The program will automatically generate the corresponding upper side frequency. The carrier, upper side frequency, and lower side frequency will all be displayed and plotted at the same time along with the resulting envelope. Think of the three main signals being transmitted through the air and the envelope being generated in the receiver as the three signals combine. If you watch carefully, you will see the side frequency voltages canceling the carrier voltage at the narrow parts of the envelope and adding to the carrier at the wide parts of the envelope. This will help you understand the phase shifting between the side frequencies and carrier that creates the envelope. You should find this relatively short program very interesting to use.

DESIGN NOTE 14–2 AMPLITUDE MODULATION

CARRIER

f_1

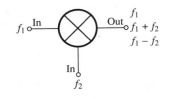
In f_1
Out f_1
$f_1 + f_2$
$f_1 - f_2$
In f_2

AUDIO

f_2

ENVELOPE
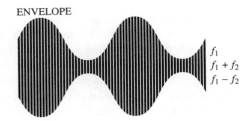
f_1
$f_1 + f_2$
$f_1 - f_2$

This program uses the high-resolution graphics mode of the IBM PC® to plot the nonlinear sum of a carrier frequency and a modulating frequency.

BASIC PROGRAM

```
10 REM  * AMPLITUDE MODULATION PROGRAM *
15 SCREEN 2:KEY OFF
20 CLS
25 CLEAR
30 PRINT "AMPLITUDE MODULATION PROGRAM"
40 PRINT ""
50 INPUT "ENTER CARRIER FREQUENCY (50 TO 300 HZ) ";F1
60 INPUT "ENTER PEAK VOLTAGE FOR CARRIER (50 V MAX.) - ";EP1
70 INPUT "ENTER MODULATING FREQUENCY (0 TO 20 HZ) ";F2
80 PRINT "ENTER PEAK VOLTAGE FOR MODULATING FREQUENCY (";EP1/2;"
V MAX) ";
85 INPUT EP2
90 N = 100
95 LINE (0,100)-(600,100):LINE (600,0)-(600,200)
97 FOR X = 0 TO 200 STEP 10:PSET (599,X):PSET (601,X):NEXT X
100 FOR X = 1 to 600
105 W1 = 6.283 * F1:W2 = 6.283 * F2:T = X * .001
110 Y = (EP1*SIN(W1*T)) + (EP2*COS(T*(W1-W2)) - (EP2*COS(T*(W1+W2))
115 IF F1 = 0 THEN Y = Y + EP1
116 IF F2 = 0 THEN Y = Y + EP2
120 Y = -Y + 100
130 LINE (M,N)-(X,Y)
135 M = X:N = Y
140 NEXT X
150 INPUT "ANOTHER PLOT? (Y/N) ";A$
160 IF A$ = "N" THEN SCREEN 0:CLS:KEY ON:END
170 GOTO 20
```

CARRIER

f_1

UPPER SIDE FREQUENCY

$f_1 + f_2$

LOWER SIDE FREQUENCY

$f_1 - f_2$

ENVELOPE

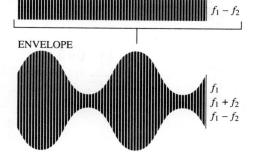

f_1
$f_1 + f_2$
$f_1 - f_2$

This program uses the high-resolution IBM®
graphics to illustrate that an AM envelope
is the combination of a fixed-amplitude
carrier and upper and lower side
frequencies. The carrier and lower side
frequency are entered and the program
generates and plots the envelope.

BASIC PROGRAM

```
10 REM  * AMPLITUDE MODULATION
ANALYSIS PROGRAM *
20 SCREEN 2:KEY OFF
30 CLS
40 CLEAR
50 PRINT "AMPLITUDE MODULATION
ANALYSIS PROGRAM"
60 PRINT ""
70 INPUT "ENTER THE CARRIER FREQUENCY
(50 HZ TO 100 HZ) ";F1
80 INPUT "ENTER PEAK VOLTAGE FOR
CARRIER (20 V MAX.) - ";EP1
90 PRINT "ENTER THE LOWER SIDE
FREQUENCY (I.E.-";F1-5;" HZ) ";
100 INPUT F2
110 PRINT "ENTER PEAK VOLTAGE FOR
LOWER SIDE FREQUENCY (";EP1/2;"
V MAX) ";
120 INPUT EP2
130 CLS
140 LINE (0,25)-(600,25):LINE
(600,0)-(600,200)
150 LINE (0,65)-(600,65):LINE
(0,95)-(600,95):LINE
(0,155)-(600,155)
160 FOR X = 0 TO 200 STEP 5:PSET
(599,X):PSET (601,X):NEXT X
170 B = 25:D = 65:I = 95:K = 155
180 FOR X = 1 TO 600
190 W1 = 6.283 * F1:W2 = 6.283 * F2:T
= X * .001
```

```
200 Y = EP1*SIN(W1*T):Y = -Y+25:LINE
(A,B)-(X,Y):A = X:B = Y
210 Y = EP2*SIN(T*(W1+(W1-W2))):Y =
-Y+65:LINE (C,D)-(X,Y):C = X:D = Y
220 Y = EP2*SIN(W2*T):Y = -Y+95:LINE
(H,I)-(X,Y):H = X:I = Y
230 Y = (EP1*SIN(W1*T))+(EP2*SIN
(W2*T))+(EP2*SIN(T*(W1+(W1-W2))))
240 Y = -Y+155:LINE (J,K)-(X,Y):J =
X:K = Y
250 NEXT X
260 M = 175
270 FOR X = 1 TO 600
280 T = X * .001
290 Y = 2*EP2*COS(T*(W1-W2))
300 Y = -Y+155-EP1
310 LINE (L,M)-(X,Y)
320 L = X:M = Y
330 NEXT X
340 LOCATE 3,18:PRINT F1;" HZ
CARRIER":LOCATE 8, 18:PRINT
F1+F1-F2;" HZ UPPER SIDE FREQUENCY"
350 LOCATE 12,18:PRINT F2;" HZ LOWER
SIDE FREQUENCY"
360 LOCATE 18,18:PRINT F1-F2;" HZ
AUDIO CONTAINED ON ENVELOPE PEAKS"
370 LOCATE 24,1
380 INPUT " ANOTHER PLOT? (Y/N) ";A$
390 IF A$ = "N" THEN SCREEN 0:CLS:KEY
ON:END
400 GOTO 30
```

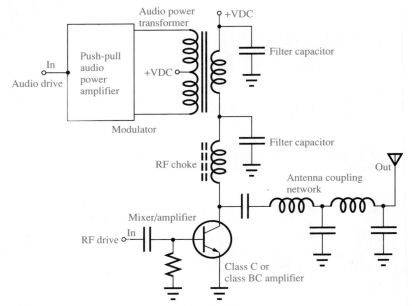

Figure 14–16   A low-power AM transmitter.

EXAMPLES OF LOW-POWER AM TRANSMITTERS

AM Transmitter Configuration

Figure 14–16 is a partial schematic of a typical low-power AM transmitter. This circuit is called the final power amplifier (PA) stage with modulator. The modulator is a class B push-pull audio power amplifier and the final PA is a class C or BC stage. An oscillator and RF amplifier (not shown) provide the RF drive to the final PA. The audio signal is superimposed on the DC to the collector of the transistor via the secondary of the audio power transformer. Sidebands are generated in the transistor. The RF choke provides a large X_L at the radio frequencies. Thus, a large RF voltage is developed across the choke, and transferred to the antenna via the lowpass-filter coupling network.

Circuits such as this are found in CB radios of all makes. High-power AM transmitter circuit diagrams look much the same but are on a much larger scale and vacuum tubes are used.

Experimental AM Transmitter

Figure 14–17 is a schematic of a simple and inexpensive AM transmitter. The audio drive is provided by a simple transistor or op-amp audio amplifier (not shown). A microphone can be used to drive the audio amplifier or a single tone from a sine wave generator (not shown). The RF drive can come from an RF signal generator or you can build an oscillator circuit to do the job. We will study oscillators in the next chapter.

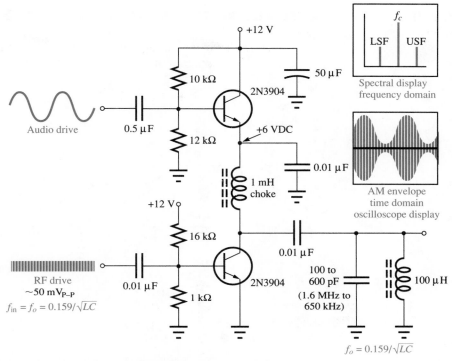

Figure 14–17 An experimental AM transmitter.

The final PA transistor (lower transistor) is biased class BC. This biases the transistor almost at threshold, so low-level RF at the base is sufficient to drive the transistor. In this case, approximately 50 mV$_{P-P}$ is all that is needed for full output. This drive level must be adjusted for optimum performance of the transmitter—the envelope at the output must look clean and undistorted. Adjust the audio drive level for different amounts of modulation. You will find that this circuit works like that in Design Note 14–2.

The audio rides on a DC reference (+6 V) at the emitter of the modulator transistor (upper transistor). This audio is passed through the 1-mH RF choke to the collector of the final PA, which acts as the mixer. Audio mixes nonlinearly with amplified RF, creating mixing products. The mixing products are the sum and difference frequencies that are close to the carrier. The tank circuit in the output removes the audio component, leaving the carrier and upper and lower side frequencies to be radiated into the air (f_C, $f_C + f_A$, $f_C - f_A$). (Connect a few feet of wire to the output as an antenna).

One final note: The frequency of the RF drive must match the resonant frequency of the output tank circuit, where the frequency of operation $f_c = 0.159/\sqrt{LC}$. You will be able to use an AM radio to pick up your transmission over a very short distance if f_o is in the AM broadcast band (540 kHz to 1610 kHz).

$$f_o = 1/(2\pi\sqrt{LC}) \cong 0.159/\sqrt{LC} \tag{14–5}$$

EXAMPLE 14–4

Determine the center operating frequency and the upper and lower side frequency components from Figure 14–18.

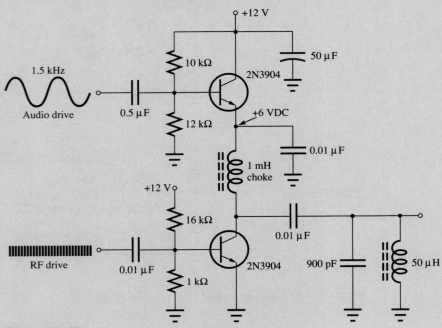

Figure 14–18

$$f_o = f_c \cong 0.159/\sqrt{LC} = 0.159/\sqrt{50\ \mu H \cdot 900\ pF}$$

$$= 0.159/(0.212 \cdot 10^{-6}) = 750\ kHz$$

$$f_A = 1.5\ kHz$$

Upper Side Frequency (USF)

$$USF = f_c + f_A = 750\ kHz + 1.5\ kHz = 751.5\ kHz$$

Lower Side Frequency (LSF)

$$LSF = f_c - f_A = 750\ kHz - 1.5\ kHz = 748.5\ kHz$$

Spectral Analysis

If a spectrum analyzer is available, you can observe the transmitted signal and actually see vertical spikes on a CRT screen that represent the individual frequency components. This is called *viewing the signal in the frequency domain*. The display is called a *spectral display* and is illustrated in Figure 14–17. If voice modulation is used, you will see a wide array of vertical spikes on each side of the center frequency, all of which change in amplitude as you talk—except the center carrier frequency, which remains at a constant amplitude with or without modulation. Time for a short self-check.

**Self-Check
14–3**

1. The carrier transmitted from an AM transmitter changes in amplitude with the audio. True or false?
2. What are the three distinct components that make up the transmitted AM signal?
3. If the modulating frequency is 2 kHz and the carrier frequency is 680 kHz, what are the upper and lower side frequencies?

SUMMARY

FORMULAS

(14–1) $K_1 = (R_2 \parallel R_L \cdots \parallel R_N)/(R_1 + (R_2 \parallel R_L \cdots \parallel R_N))$

(14–2) $V_{out} = V_1 K_1 + V_2 K_2 + \cdots + V_N K_N$

(14–3) $K_N = A_{V(N)} = R_F/R_{I(N)}$ (for inverting adder)

(14–4) $v = V_P \sin(\omega t)$ $(\omega = 2\pi f)$

(14–5) $f_o = 1/(2\pi\sqrt{LC}) \cong 0.159/\sqrt{LC}$

CONCEPTS

- Linear mixes are used to combine frequencies, or signals, without creating new frequencies (products) or distortion.
- Linear mixers are used in audio mixing consoles to combine audio sources.
- Nonlinear mixers are used to multiply signals to obtain mixing products called *sum* and *difference* frequencies.
- Nonlinear mixers are used in radio receivers (heterodyne receivers) to convert radio station signals to a lower intermediate frequency.
- Diodes, BJTs, and FETs are all nonlinear devices.
- Any nonlinearity in the operation of a linear amplifier will cause intermodulation distortion (IMD) products.
- You cannot assume the mixer to be bad until you have checked for the presence of DC levels and the two mixing signals, particularly the oscillator signal.
- Nonlinear mixing is used in AM transmitters to create the AM signal for transmission.
- In an AM signal, the upper sideband is the sum of the audio frequencies and the carrier frequency, and the lower sideband is the difference between the audio frequencies and the carrier frequency.
- The transmitted AM signal contains three distinct parts obtained through nonlinear mixing: the carrier, the upper sideband, and the lower sideband.

NEED-TO-KNOW SOLUTION

Linear and nonlinear mixers are not the same circuit nor do they function in the same way. The linear mixer simply adds the instantaneous voltages of two or more applied signals. No new frequencies are generated in the process. Nonlinear mixers multiply the applied signals and create products referred to as *sum* and *difference* frequencies. In AM systems, the sum of the audio and an RF carrier is the upper sideband and the difference between the audio and carrier frequency is the lower sideband (i.e., 910 kHz + 2 kHz = 912 kHz = USB and 910 kHz − 2 kHz = 908 kHz = LSB). Linear mixers are used for signal combining and nonlinear mixers are used for frequency conversion (i.e., a station signal at 1,420 kHz is converted to an intermediate frequency of 455 kHz in the AM receiver by mixing the 1,420 kHz with 1,875 kHz).

QUESTIONS

14–1 LINEAR MIXERS

1. What is a linear mixer?
2. What is a weighted input of a linear mixer?
3. To what does the term *linear* refer when it is used in *linear mixer*?
4. For what purpose are linear mixers used?
5. Describe the waveform that results when a 60-Hz signal is linearly mixed with an 8-kHz signal.

14–2 NONLINEAR MIXERS

6. Why are nonlinear mixers called *nonlinear*?
7. List three nonlinear devices.
8. What portion of the characteristic, or operating, curve of a device is used for nonlinear mixing?
9. Describe the block symbol for a nonlinear mixer.
10. What are mixing products?
11. List three applications for nonlinear mixers.
12. What does *heterodyne* mean?
13. What is a frequency converter?
14. Pertaining to AM receivers, what is detection?
15. What is the standard intermediate frequency for most AM receivers?
16. Name one advantage and one disadvantage of the balanced diode mixer.
17. If a nonlinear mixer produces sum and difference frequencies, why is only the difference frequency available at the output of a mixer in an AM receiver?
18. Is a diode mixer (a) active or (b) passive?
19. What is an advantage of active mixers compared to passive mixers?
20. What are three advantages of the JFET mixer?
21. What is one additional advantage of the dual-gate MOSFET mixer?
22. Briefly explain how the f_1 signal is eliminated from the output of the balanced mixer in Figure 14–14.
23. How is IMD minimized in amplifier circuits?
24. What checks should you make before you replace the active device in a supposedly malfunctioning mixer circuit?

14–3 MODULATION

25. What is the purpose for amplitude modulation?
26. What are the products of amplitude modulation called (besides *sum* and *difference* frequencies)?

27. What are the main parts, or components, of an AM signal?
28. Does the carrier in an AM signal ever change in amplitude?
29. What does the carrier actually carry?
30. The transmitted information of an AM signal is contained in
    (a) the carrier   (b) the upper sideband
    (c) the lower sideband   (d) both b and c

PROBLEMS

14–1 LINEAR MIXERS

1. Determine the output voltage for the circuit of Figure 14–19.

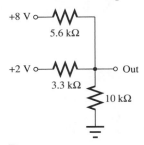

Figure 14–19

2. Determine the output voltage for the circuit of Figure 14–20.

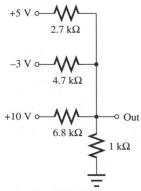

Figure 14–20

3. Determine the output voltage at $t = 5$ ms for the circuit of Figure 14–21.

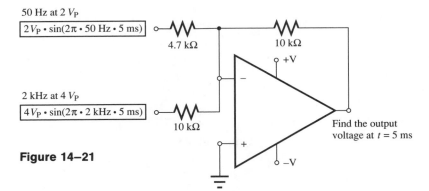

Figure 14–21

4. Determine the output voltage at $t = 9$ ms for the circuit of Figure 14–22.

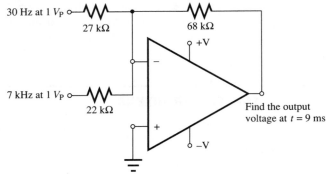

Figure 14–22

14–2 NONLINEAR MIXERS

5. Calculate the products resulting from the nonlinear mixing of 1,530 kHz and 1,985 kHz.
6. Calculate the products resulting from the nonlinear mixing of 7.15 MHz and 6 MHz.

14–3 MODULATION

7. An 860-kHz carrier is amplitude modulated with a 1,500-Hz audio tone. Calculate the upper and lower side frequencies.
8. A 14.250-MHz carrier is amplitude modulated with a 2.5-kHz audio tone. Calculate the upper and lower side frequencies.
9. A band of voice frequencies from 100 Hz to 3.5 kHz is used to modulate a 910-kHz carrier. Calculate the range of the upper and lower sidebands.
10. A band of voice frequencies from 300 Hz to 3 kHz is used to modulate a 7.11-MHz carrier. Calculate the range of the upper and lower sidebands.

ADDITIONAL PROBLEMS

11. Determine the output voltage for the circuit of Figure 14–23.

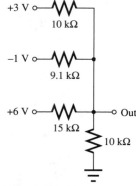

Figure 14–23

12. Determine the output voltage for the circuit of Figure 14–24.

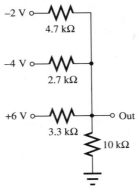

Figure 14–24

13. Determine the output voltage at $t = 0.7$ ms for the circuit of Figure 14–25.

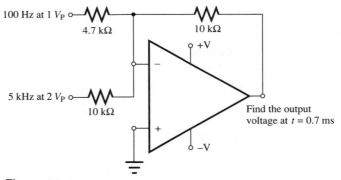

Figure 14–25

14. Determine the output voltage at $t = 1.8$ ms for the circuit of Figure 14–26.

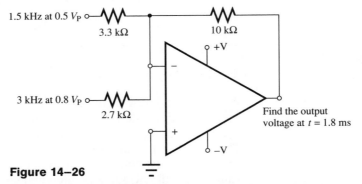

Figure 14–26

15. Calculate the products resulting from the nonlinear mixing of 1,210 kHz and 1,665 kHz.

16. Calculate the products resulting from the nonlinear mixing of 9 MHz and 12.2 MHz.

17. A 920-kHz carrier is amplitude modulated with a 2,000-Hz audio tone. Calculate the upper and lower side frequencies.

18. Determine the center operating frequency and the upper and lower side frequency components from Figure 14–27.

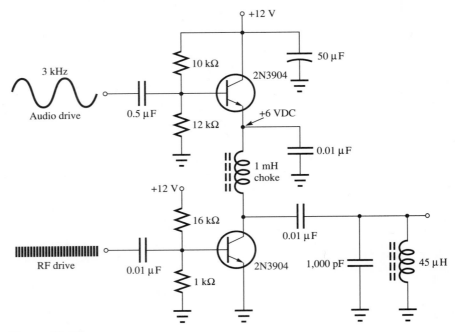

Figure 14–27

19. A band of voice frequencies from 80 Hz to 2.8 kHz is used to modulate a 14.25-MHz carrier. Calculate the range of the upper and lower sidebands.

20. A band of voice frequencies from 300 Hz to 3 kHz is used to modulate a 21.5-MHz carrier. Calculate the range of the upper and lower sidebands.

ANSWERS TO SELF-CHECKS

SELF-CHECK 14–1

1. An adder is a linear mixer. A linear mixer is any circuit in which signals are combined while the circuit is operating linearly where the graph of the output vs input is a straight line.

2. The graph of the output vs input is a straight line.

3. The output resulting from an input depends on the ratio of resistor values. It could be a loss, as in a voltage divider, or a gain, as in an op-amp circuit.

4. The 2-kHz signal would appear to ride on the 30-Hz signal. The 30-Hz signal is a floating bias for the 2-kHz signal.

5. Audio mixing consoles

SELF-CHECK 14–2

1. In nonlinear mixing, products are generated. No products are generated in linear mixing.
2. A mixing product is the result of nonlinear mixing and will be either the sum or difference of frequencies applied to the mixer.
3. An example of a passive mixer is a balanced diode mixer. It has the disadvantage of 5 to 10 dB of signal loss.
4. Conversion gain
5. A tuned circuit is used in the mixer output. The resonant circuit is tuned to the desired product frequency.
6. Check for proper DC levels and the presence of the two input signals, particularly the oscillator signal in the case of an AM receiver.

SELF-CHECK 14–3

1. False
2. Carrier, upper sideband, lower sideband
3. USF = 682 kHz, LSF = 678 kHz

SUGGESTED PROJECTS

1. Add some of the main concepts from this chapter to your Electronics Notebook.
2. Build and test the AM transmitter circuit of Figure 14–17. Vary the amplitude of the audio signal to change the amount (percent) of modulation. 100% modulation occurs when the envelope is at 0 V at its most narrow points. Adjust the RF drive voltage for optimum output (should be approximately 50 mV$_{P-P}$).
3. Use the design-note programs to reinforce what you have learned in this chapter regarding linear and nonlinear mixing.

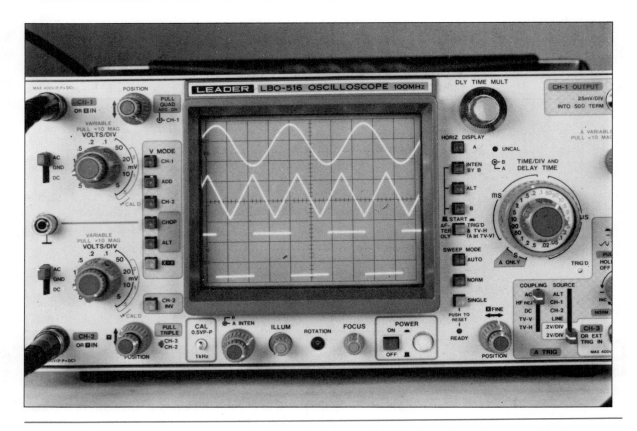

A function generator is able to produce a variety of waveforms, such as the square, triangle, and sine waves shown on this oscilloscope screen. The square wave is a step function and the triangle wave is a ramp function. (Courtesy of Leader Instruments Corp.)

15 Oscillators, Function Generators, and Timers

OBJECTIVES

After studying this chapter, you will be able to
- describe the requirements for sustained oscillation.
- describe conditions needed for oscillation to begin.
- describe and identify a large variety of *RC* and *LC* oscillators.
- design and analyze a large variety of *RC* and *LC* oscillators.
- describe the purpose and performance of a large variety of *RC* and *LC* oscillators.
- modify an oscillator for variable-frequency capability.
- identify crystal oscillators.
- compare the performance of crystal oscillators to that of *LC* oscillators.
- identify basic function generator circuits.
- design and analyze basic function generator circuits.
- use the 555 timer to design timing and waveform generator circuits.
- modify an oscillator for voltage-control capability.
- explain the theory of operation of the phase-locked loop.
- list several applications for the phase-locked loop.
- list at least four design considerations to insure a frequency-stable oscillator.

NEED TO KNOW

In the last chapter we discussed nonlinear mixers and showed how they are used in radio circuits as frequency converters. We said that the incoming station frequency is mixed with an oscillator frequency, producing the intermediate frequency (IF), which is the difference between the station and oscillator frequencies. The mixer cannot do its job without the oscillator. To receive a variety of stations, the oscillator must be variable in frequency.

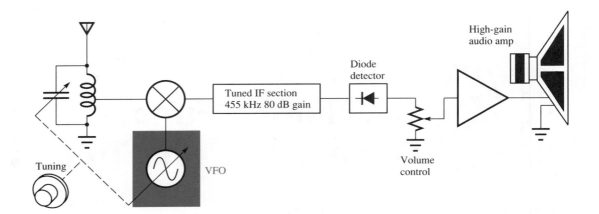

Can you name a couple of oscillator circuits that can be used as the variable-frequency oscillator in the radio receiver? Can you explain the basic theory of operation for oscillators? Can you actually design a variable-frequency oscillator circuit? Oscillators are widely used in electronic systems of all kinds—transmitters, receivers, test equipment, modems, intercoms, frequency synthesizers, and more. The oscillator is a basic building block about which you have a need to know. Enjoy your exploration into the oscillator block.

INTRODUCTION

This chapter covers a wide range of oscillators in terms of design, analysis, applications, and variety. You will begin your exploration with an introduction to oscillators and oscillator theory. From there, you will be introduced to a wide variety of resistor–capacitor (*RC*), inductor–capacitor (*LC*), and crystal-type oscillators. You will learn how to adapt oscillators for variable-frequency performance using mechanical and electronic means. The versatility of function generators and timers will also be explored with a variety of circuits. You will be introduced to several very useful and versatile integrated circuits, such as the 555 timer, the XR2206 function generator, and the XR2211 phase-locked loop. Design considerations for stable oscillator circuits will also be presented. By the time you finish this chapter, you will have gained a broad foundational knowledge of oscillators and their applications.

15–1 INTRODUCTION TO OSCILLATORS

WHAT IS AN OSCILLATOR?

An **oscillator** is an electronic circuit that is designed to continuously create, or generate, a periodic waveform at a particular frequency. The oscillator is able to convert DC into some form of pulsating DC or AC.

Figure 15–1 illustrates common block symbols for oscillators or frequency generators. Usually a waveform symbol is placed within the generator sym-

SINE WAVE OSCILLATOR/GENERATOR

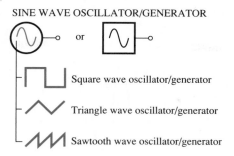

Square wave oscillator/generator

Triangle wave oscillator/generator

Sawtooth wave oscillator/generator

Figure 15–1   Oscillator/generator schematic symbols.

bol to indicate the type of waveform the generator produces. An arrow may be drawn diagonally through the oscillator symbol to indicate that the oscillator is a **variable-frequency oscillator (VFO).** Ground and DC lines may or may not be indicated with the symbol. If they are not indicated, they are assumed to exist.

As shown in Figure 15–2, every oscillator contains two fundamental parts: an amplifier and a reactive feedback network. The reactive feedback network is either an *RC* network or an *LC* network. Its purpose is to determine the frequency of oscillation (f_o), or frequency of operation. The amplifier is needed to make up for signal losses in the reactive network in order to sustain oscillations. Now, let's take a closer look at the requirements for oscillation.

REQUIREMENTS FOR OSCILLATION

Loss, Gain, and 0° Total Phase Shift

There are two basic requirements for sustained oscillation: the total loop gain must equal one (1) and the total loop phase shift must equal 0° or 360° to provide positive feedback.

1. Loop gain = $A_V B = 1$
2. Total loop phase shift = 0° = 360°

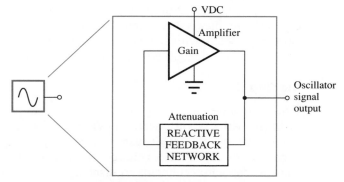

Figure 15–2   The two parts of an oscillator.

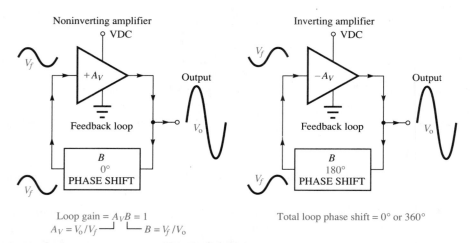

Figure 15–3   Requirements for oscillation.

Figure 15–3 illustrates these two requirements. Note that the reactive feedback network has a loss B. The feedback network acts as a voltage divider, attenuating the output signal to some level equal to the feedback voltage over the output voltage, $B = V_f/V_o$. The amplifier must have sufficient gain A_V to amplify V_f back to the output level V_o. Thus, $A_V = V_o/V_f$ and $A_V B = 1 = $ loop gain. In this way, the output voltage is maintained at some fixed level.

This AC output voltage is sustained at only one frequency. It is the frequency at which the total loop phase shift is 0°, or 360°. Note that if a noninverting amplifier is used in Figure 15–3, the reactive feedback network must provide a phase shift of 0° at the frequency of oscillation f_0. If an inverting amplifier is used, the reactive feedback network must provide a phase shift of 180° at f_o. In either case, positive feedback at one frequency is obtained.

Proper Gain

If the voltage gain of the amplifier is less than V_o/V_f at the frequency where the total loop phase shift is 0°, the oscillator will not oscillate. If the voltage gain is greater than V_o/V_f, the oscillator will begin to oscillate and rapidly increase in amplitude until severe clipping of the waveform occurs, in which case the amplifier is driven into saturation and cutoff. Maintaining the proper gain is a problem with some oscillator designs. As you will soon see, in some designs automatic gain control can be employed to solve the problem.

Starting Conditions

How can an oscillator start oscillating if the amplifier has nothing to amplify to begin with? Good question! When DC is first applied to the oscillator circuit, a surge of current rushes through the components and devices. This surge causes capacitors to charge. In the case of LC feedback networks, the charged capacitor(s) begins to discharge through the inductance. This creates a ringing effect between the inductor and capacitor(s). The ringing is immediately amplified and fed back into the *LC* network to sustain the ringing. If the initial loop gain is greater than 1 ($A_V B > 1$), the ringing actually increases in amplitude over several cycles until maximum output is reached, at which point an equilibrium is reached between amplifier gain and feedback network loss or the amplifier is simply driven into saturation and cutoff. In the case of *RC* feedback networks, the initial surge of current causes the amplifier to become unbalanced. This initial imbalance is amplified and repeated until maximum oscillation is reached. Some *RC* oscillators operate simply on the time it takes for a capacitor to charge, then discharge. This will become more clear as we explore specific oscillator circuits.

Before continuing, take time for a quick self-check.

Self-Check 15–1	1. What is an oscillator?
	2. What are the two main parts of an oscillator?
	3. What are the two requirements for sustained oscillation?
	4. If an inverting amplifier is used in an oscillator circuit, what must be the phase shift of the reactive feedback network at the frequency of oscillation?

15–2 SINE WAVE OSCILLATOR

In this section, you will explore common sine wave oscillators. The first three sine wave oscillators use an *RC* feedback network and are intended for oscillating frequencies below 1 MHz. The remaining oscillators, intended for higher oscillating frequencies, use *LC* networks or crystals in the feedback network.

WIEN-BRIDGE OSCILLATOR

General Description

The Wien-bridge oscillator is a very low-distortion sine wave oscillator designed to operate at frequencies below 1 MHz. It uses an *RC* feedback network. Distortion is as low as about 0.01%, which means that distortion products are 80 dB below signal level. That is a very clean output. Wien-bridge oscillators are used in high-quality equipment that tests the distortion characteristics of amplifiers.

Theory of Operation

The Wien-bridge oscillator is shown in Figure 15–4. As you can see, the op-amp is used to bridge between the resistive negative-feedback voltage divider and the *RC* positive-feedback network. At the frequency of oscillation (f_o), the attenuation of the *RC* feedback network is 1/3, so the ratio ($R_f + R_I$)/R_I must provide a gain of 3. Thus, $B = 1/3$, $A_V = 3$, and $A_V B = 1$. The phase shift provided by the *RC* network at f_o is 0°. This 0° phase shift occurs at a frequency where $R = X_C$, where $R_1 = R_2 = R$ and $C_1 = C_2 = C$. The formula for the frequency of oscillation is derived from the X_C formula as follows:

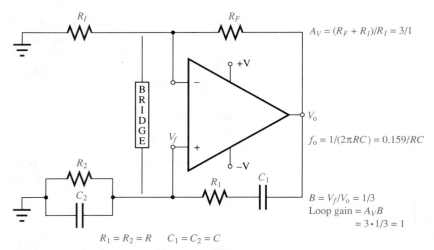

Figure 15–4 The Wien-bridge oscillator.

$X_C = 1/(2\pi f_o C)$,

$f_o = 1/(2\pi X_C C)$

Since $X_C = R$,

$f_o = 1/(2\pi RC) \cong 0.159/RC$ (15–1)

Also,

$C = 1/(2\pi R f_o) \cong 0.159/R f_o$ (15–2)

where R is given.

Proof

Let's take a moment to prove that the phase angle is $0°$ and $B = 1/3$ at the frequency of operation.

$B = V_f/V_o = (R_2 \parallel -jX_{C2})/[(R_2 \parallel -jX_{C2}) + R_1 - jX_{C1}]$

$= (1/((1/R_2) + (1/-jX_{C2})))/[(1/((1/R_2) + (1/-jX_{C2}))) + R_1 - jX_{C1}]$

To simplify the proof, we will assume $R_1 = R_2 = X_{C1} = X_{C2} = 1\ \Omega$. Therefore,

$B = [1/((1/1) + (1/-j1))]/[(1/((1/1) + (1/-j1))) + 1 - j1]$

$= [1/(1 + j1)]/[(1/(1 + j1)) + 1 - j1]$

$= (1/1.414\angle +45°)/[(1/1.414\angle +45°) + 1 - j1]$

$= (0.707\angle -45°)/[(0.707\angle -45°) + 1 - j1]$

$= (0.707\angle -45°)/[0.5 - j0.5 + 1 - j1]$

$= (0.707\angle -45°)/(1.5 - j1.5)$

$= (0.707\angle -45°)/(2.12\angle -45°)$

$= 0.707/2.12 = 1/3$ and $\angle -45° - \angle -45° = 0°$

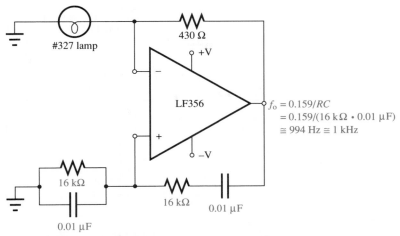

Figure 15–5   Wien-bridge with tungsten lamp.

Automatic Gain Control

As you know, the gain of the amplifier must be 3 to sustain oscillation. To satisfy this requirement, R_F might be 20 kΩ and R_I might be 10 kΩ. However, there is a problem. In all probability, this oscillator will not self-start. A much higher initial gain is needed to start the Wien bridge oscillating. Figure 15–5 shows a typical solution to the problem. A low-voltage, low-current lamp is used in the negative feedback network. The tungsten filament of the lamp has a positive temperature coefficient. As the lamp heats and begins to glow, the resistance of the filament increases. The change in resistance can be tenfold. Therefore, when DC is first applied, the lamp is cold and its resistance is low. As a result, the initial gain (A_V) of the op-amp is very high. This high gain allows the oscillator to start quickly. As oscillation builds, the lamp heats and begins to glow. Soon an equilibrium is reached as the filament resistance in the lamp increases and the oscillator stabilizes.

Figure 15–6 shows another adaptation of the Wien-bridge oscillator. In this case, an LED/CdS (light-emitting diode and cadmium disulfide photoresistor) optocoupler is used to control the gain of the op-amp. The dark resistance of the photoresistor is very high. Thus, the initial gain of the op-amp is very high. When oscillation begins, the LEDs begin to glow and the resistance of the photoresistor drops significantly. The output signal maintains the brightness of the LEDs, which control the resistance of the photo resistor, which controls the gain of the op-amp to sustain oscillation.

Note also in Figure 15–6 that this Wien-bridge is a variable-frequency oscillator (VFO). A dual 100-kΩ potentiometer is used to adjust the oscillator over a 100 : 1 range. This makes a high-quality, low-cost piece of test equipment, useful for testing filter response and distortion in amplifiers.

Study Example 15–1.

EXAMPLE 15–1 ▬▬▬▬▬▬▬▬▬▬▬▬▬▬▬▬▬▬▬

Design a Wien-bridge oscillator that can be tuned over a 1000 : 1 range—from approximately 10 Hz to 10 kHz. Use Figure 15–6 as your

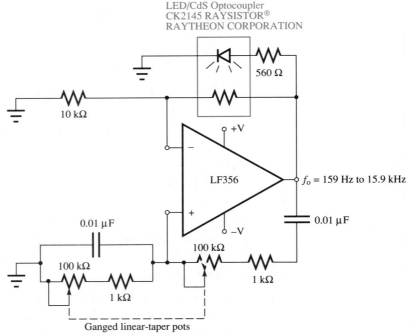

Figure 15–6 Optocoupler gain control and variable-frequency control.

model. A dual 1-MΩ potentiometer will provide the variable control. Minimum resistance will be 1 kΩ, the 1-kΩ resistors. Maximum resistance will be 1.001 MΩ = 1,001 kΩ. Calculate a value for the network capacitors (C). When the resistance is minimum, the frequency will be at its highest, 10 kHz. Thus,

$$C \cong 0.159/Rf_o = 0.159/(1 \text{ k}\Omega \cdot 10 \text{ kHz}) = 0.016 \ \mu\text{F}$$

Use a parallel combination of standard capacitor values to obtain a value as close as possible to 0.016 μF.

Use the 0.016-μF capacitor value to calculate the actual frequency range.

$$f_o \cong 0.159/RC = 0.159/(1 \text{ k}\Omega \cdot 0.016 \ \mu\text{F}) = 9{,}938 \text{ Hz} \cong 10 \text{ kHz}$$

$$f_o \cong 0.159/RC = 0.159/(1001 \text{ k}\Omega \cdot 0.016 \ \mu\text{F}) = 9.93 \text{ Hz} \cong 10 \text{ Hz}$$

TWIN-TEE OSCILLATOR

General Description

The twin-tee oscillator is shown in Figure 15–7. This oscillator is most suitable for single-frequency operation below 1 MHz, not as a VFO (due to the number of network resistors). Though not as clean as the Wien-bridge oscillator, its total waveform distortion is in the area of 1% or less, which places distortion products at less than −40 dB.

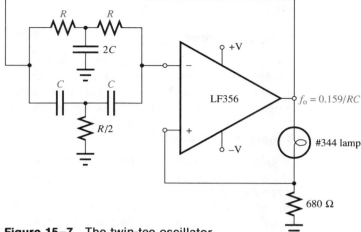

Figure 15–7 The twin-tee oscillator.

Theory of Operation

The theory of operation for this oscillator is very straightforward. The reactive network is in the negative-feedback path. This reactive network is a notch filter formed by parallel highpass and lowpass filters. The frequency of oscillation is at the notch frequency, where the negative feedback is minimal. Less negative feedback means more amplifier gain. With the help of the positive feedback network (a lamp and a 680-Ω resistor) the attenuation loss of the notch filter at f_o is easily overcome. The frequency of oscillation is the frequency at which $R = X_C$, making $f_o = 0.159/RC$, the same as for the Wien-bridge oscillator.

Automatic Gain Control

Self-starting is also a problem with this oscillator. Once again, a lamp can be used to make the initial gain of the op-amp very high. Once oscillation has begun, the lamp heats and its filament resistance increases, reducing the amount of positive feedback and amplifier gain to a level of equilibrium. An LED/CdS arrangement can also be used in place of the 680-Ω resistor, in which case a 10-kΩ resistor would replace the lamp. Consider Example 15–2.

EXAMPLE 15–2 ▮▮▮▮▮▮▮▮▮▮▮▮▮▮▮▮▮▮▮▮▮▮▮▮▮▮▮▮▮▮▮▮▮

Design a twin-tee oscillator to operate at 1 kHz. Use Figure 15–7 as your model. To start, select a standard value for C, such as 0.01 μF. The $2C$ capacitor will be a 0.02-μF capacitor or two paralleled 0.01-μF capacitors. Since $f_o \cong 0.159/RC$, $R = 0.159/Cf_o$.

$R \cong 0.159/(0.01\ \mu\text{F} \cdot 1\ \text{kHz}) = 15,900\ \Omega$

Use a 15.8-kΩ, 1% film resistor.

$f_o \cong 0.159/RC = 0.159/(15.8\ \text{k}\Omega \cdot 0.01\ \mu\text{F}) = 1,006\ \text{Hz} \cong 1\ \text{kHz}$

PHASE-SHIFT OSCILLATOR

General Description

The phase-shift oscillator, shown in Figure 15–8, is simple to make but is intended mainly for single-frequency operation below 1 MHz. However, one of the resistors can be variable to allow frequency adjustment over a narrow range. Distortion is in the area of 1% or −40 dB.

Theory of Operation

Notice that only the inverting input is used. The op-amp provides a 180° phase shift, so the reactive network must provide an additional 180°. Thus, three *RC* sections work together to provide this total phase shift of 180°. Naturally, there is only one frequency at which the total phase shift for the reactive network is 180°. In the process of creating the phase shift, the network also causes significant attenuation of the feedback signal, where $B \cong 1/30$. Therefore, the amplifier gain must be 30, where the feedback resistor is 30 times *R*. This is a critical value. If the gain is a little high, the oscillation will steadily increase in amplitude until severe clipping occurs at the output. If the gain is slightly low, the oscillator will not oscillate. As with other RC oscillators, automatic gain control is very desirable, if not absolutely necessary. The LED/CdS arrangement is a good choice as shown. The following formula is used to calculate the frequency of oscillation:

$$f_o \cong 0.065/RC \qquad (15-3)$$

and

$$R \cong 0.065/Cf_o \qquad (15-4)$$

Study Example 15–3.

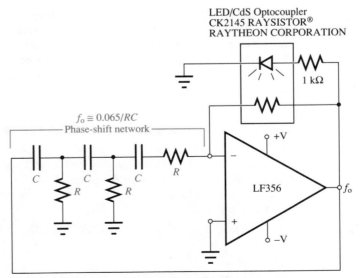

Figure 15–8 The phase-shift oscillator.

EXAMPLE 15–3 ▮▮▮▮▮

Let's design a phase-shift oscillator for an oscillating frequency of 500 Hz. We can use Figure 15–8 as our model. We'll start with a standard capacitor value of 0.1 μF for the capacitors.

$R \cong 0.065/Cf_o = 0.065/(0.1 \; \mu\text{F} \cdot 500 \; \text{Hz}) = 1,300 \; \Omega$

Use 1%, 1300-Ω resistors.

$f_o \cong 0.065/RC = 0.065/(1,300 \; \Omega \cdot 0.1 \; \mu\text{F}) = 500 \; \text{Hz}$

COLPITTS OSCILLATOR

General Description

Shown in Figure 15–9 is the Colpitts oscillator, perhaps the most commonly used oscillator of all the LC oscillators that we will explore in this section. For Colpitts and all LC oscillators, the frequency of oscillation f_o is the frequency at which the total inductive reactance is equal to the total capacitive reactance in the tuned circuit or reactive network. Thus, f_o is where $X_{Lt} = X_{Ct}$, $X_L = 2\pi fL$, and $X_C = 1/(2\pi fC)$. So,

$2\pi fL = 1/(2\pi fC)$

$(2\pi fL)(2\pi fC) = 1$

$4\pi^2 f^2 LC = 1$

$f^2 = 1/(4\pi^2 LC)$

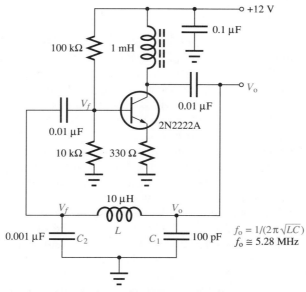

Figure 15–9   A BJT Colpitts oscillator.

$$f = 1/(2\pi\sqrt{LC})$$

$$f_o = 1/(2\pi\sqrt{LC}) \cong 0.159/\sqrt{LC} \tag{15-5}$$

LC oscillators can operate at frequencies into the hundreds of megahertz. Due to their relatively low unity-gain frequency (f_T), most op-amps cannot be used at frequencies above 1 MHz. Therefore, BJTs or FETs are normally used above 1 MHz. Stray capacitance, device capacitance, and lead inductance have a greater effect on these oscillators because of the high-frequency operation. Therefore, lead length and circuit layout are important.

The Colpitts oscillator of Figure 15–9 uses a common-emitter BJT configuration. The amplifier is biased for class A operation. The proper amount of amplifier gain is obtained through proper selection of the RF choke and by adjusting the value of the emitter resistor or bias voltage. Input and output $0.01\text{-}\mu\text{F}$ coupling capacitors are used to block DC and pass the feedback signal. The two series capacitors in the feedback network, C_1 and C_2 with center junction to ground, are an identifying characteristic of Colpitts oscillators.

Theory of Operation

Since the amplifier is the CE configuration, there is a 180° phase difference between V_o and V_f. An additional 180° is needed from the *LC* feedback network to obtain the overall 360°, or 0°, phase shift around the loop. The *LC* network provides this 180° phase shift at f_o.

Since the output voltage (V_o) is applied to C_1 and the feedback voltage is taken from across C_2, the attenuation factor *B* of the *LC* network is approximately X_{C2}/X_{C1}, where $B = V_f/V_o \cong X_{C2}/X_{C1}$.

$$B \cong X_{C2}/X_{C1} = [1/(2\pi fC_2)]/[1/(2\pi fC_1)] = 2\pi fC_1/2\pi fC_2 = C_1/C_2$$

$$B \cong C_1/C_2 \tag{15-6}$$

$$A_V > C_2/C_1 \tag{15-7}$$

The loaded amplifier gain must be greater than $1/B = C_2/C_1$ to start and maintain oscillation. For the oscillator of Figure 15-9, $B \cong C_1/C_2 = 100$ pF/0.001 μF = 1/10. This ratio is fairly common for Colpitts configurations. In order for oscillation to begin, the loaded amplifier gain must be greater than 10. In this case A_V is approximately equal to $X_{L(\text{choke})}/R_E$. If too much load is connected to the output, the oscillator will not oscillate because with R_{load} in parallel with $X_{L(\text{choke})}$, the gain of the amplifier is reduced. Thus the loaded amplifier gain must be greater than 10 for oscillation to begin. Once oscillation has begun, it quickly builds in amplitude until the transistor is driven into cutoff and saturation. Most distortion in the signal is removed by the ringing tank (*LC* network). Even so, some clipping is usually evident in the output signal, with the peak-to-peak output voltage equal to twice the applied DC voltage. The output voltage of Figure 15–9 is almost 24 $V_{\text{P-P}}$. Without an automatic gain control system, it is almost impossible to maintain the amplifier gain equal to $1/B$. As a result, the distortion products at the output of this oscillator are in the range of 1 to 3% or more.

The frequency of oscillation depends primarily on L and C_t, where C_t equals to C_1 in series with C_2.

$$C_t = (C_1 \cdot C_2)/(C_1 + C_2) \tag{15–8}$$

For the circuit of Figure 15–9:

$$C_t = (100 \text{ pF} \cdot 0.001 \ \mu\text{F})/(100 \text{ pF} + 0.001 \ \mu\text{F}) = 90.9 \text{ pF}$$

$$f_o = 1/2\pi\sqrt{LC} = 1/(2\pi\sqrt{10 \ \mu\text{H} \cdot 90.9 \text{ pF}}) \cong 5.28 \text{ MHz}$$

This does not take into consideration the effects of stray capacitance and other factors that tend to lower f_o slightly.

The Clapp Oscillator

The Clapp oscillator of Figure 15–10 is a member of the Colpitts family. It is distinguished from a conventional Colpitts by the capacitor(s) in series with the inductor. This is a variable-frequency oscillator provided by the variable capacitors. The frequency of oscillation depends on the value of L and the combined capacitance of the three paralleled capacitors, which, through the ground, are in series with C_1 and C_2. (Note the 10 : 1 relationship of C_1 to C_2). Assuming the 10-pF trimmer is set at 5 pF, the total capacitance of the paralleled capacitors ranges between 62 and 75 pF (2 pF + 5 pF + 55 pF = 62 pF and 15 pF + 5 pF + 55 pF = 75 pF). C_1 and C_2 are in series, totaling 90.9 pF. This 90.9 pF is actually in series with the paralleled capacitors, forming a resonant loop. Thus the range of total loop capacitance is 36.9 pF to 41.1 pF:

$$(62 \cdot 90.9)/(62 + 90.9) = 36.9 \text{ pF}$$

and

$$(75 \cdot 90.9)/(75 + 90.9) = 41.1 \text{ pF}$$

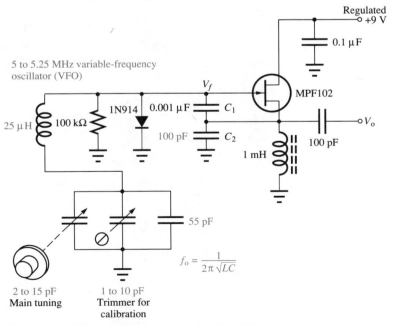

Figure 15–10 A series-tuned, variable-frequency Colpitts oscillator (Clapp oscillator).

Formula 15–5 is used to calculate the upper and lower range frequencies. In this case, the range is approximately 5 to 5.25 MHz:

$$f_o = 1/2\pi\sqrt{LC} = 1/2\pi\sqrt{25\ \mu H \cdot 41.1\ pF} = 4.97\ MHz$$

$$f_o = 1/2\pi\sqrt{LC} = 1/2\pi\sqrt{25\ \mu H \cdot 36.9\ pF} = 5.24\ MHz$$

Since this calculated range is a little lower than 5 to 5.25 MHz, the calibration trimmer should be adjusted. Should we increase its capacitance, or should we decrease its capacitance? That's right, decrease its capacitance. Perhaps you would like to pause here and take the time to determine what its value should be to insure that at least the 5 to 5.25 MHz range is covered.

As you can see, this Colpitts/Clapp oscillator uses positive feedback from the source-follower (common-drain) configuration. V_f and V_o are in phase. The X_C of C_2 is ten times that of C_1. Thus, the feedback voltage is developed across C_2 and transparently fed to the gate through C_1. Because of the source-follower configuration, the FET is never overdriven. Therefore, this oscillator produces less distortion than the Colpitts previously discussed, less than 1%. Also, the FET is automatically biased due to negative clamping action provided by the diode.

The very clean, low-distortion, operation of this configuration makes it the most popular choice in LC oscillator design. Without a capacitor in series with the inductor, it is a pure Colpitts oscillator. With a capacitor in series with the inductor it is a Clapp oscillator.

Consider Example 15–4.

EXAMPLE 15–4 ▉

A Clapp oscillator, like that of Figure 15–10, has the following component values: $L = 50\ \mu H$, $C_1 = 0.001\ \mu F$, $C_2 = 100\ pF$, and a 5-to-20-pF tuning capacitor is in parallel with a 100-pF capacitor. Determine the range of total capacitance and the frequency range of oscillation.

Paralleled capacitors:

5 pF ∥ 100 pF to 20 pF ∥ 100 pF = 105 to 120 pF

C_1 in series with C_2:

(1,000 pF · 100 pf)/(1,000 pF + 100 pF) = 90.9 pF

Paralleled capacitors in series with 90.9 pF:

$$C_{t(min)} = (105\ pF \cdot 90.9\ pF)/(105\ pF + 90.9\ pF) = 48.7\ pF$$

$$C_{t(max)} = (120\ pF \cdot 90.9\ pF)/(120\ pF + 90.9\ pF) = 51.7\ pF$$

Range of capacitance = 48.7 to 51.7 pF

Frequency range:

$$f_{o(max)} \cong 0.159/\sqrt{LC} = 0.159/\sqrt{50\ \mu H \cdot 48.7\ pF} = 3.22\ MHz$$

$$f_{o(min)} \cong 0.159/\sqrt{LC} = 0.159/\sqrt{50\ \mu H \cdot 51.7\ pF} = 3.13\ MHz$$

$$f_{o(range)} \cong 3.13\ to\ 3.22\ MHz$$

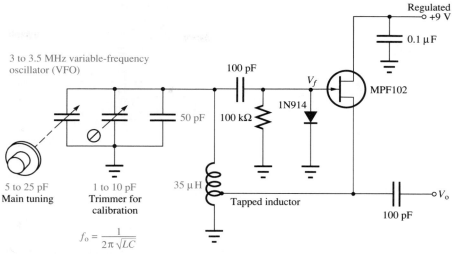

Figure 15–11 A Hartley VFO.

HARTLEY OSCILLATOR

Figure 15–11 illustrates a Hartley oscillator. This oscillator is readily identified by the tapped inductor, which provides positive feedback to start and sustain oscillation. The autotransformer action of the tapped inductor makes up for voltage loss from gate to source. Once again, this is a VFO with the paralleled capacitors forming a resonant loop with the inductor. The range of total capacitance and value of the inductor is used to determine the frequency range. As discussed earlier, the diode is essential for negative clamping, which automatically provides the correct amount of bias according to signal level (negative peak voltage being stored on the 100-pF capacitor).

EXAMPLE 15–5 ▐▬▬▬▬▬▬▬▬▬▬▬▬▬▬▬

Analysis of Figure 15–11
Range of total capacitance (assume the trimmer is set to 5 pF):

$C_{t(min)} = 5 \text{ pF} + 5 \text{ pF} + 50 \text{ pF} = 60 \text{ pF}$

$C_{t(max)} = 25 \text{ pF} + 5 \text{ pF} + 50 \text{ pF} = 80 \text{ pF}$

Frequency range:

$f_{o(max)} \cong 0.159/\sqrt{LC} = 0.159/\sqrt{35 \ \mu\text{H} \cdot 60 \text{ pF}} = 3.47 \text{ MHz}$

$f_{o(min)} \cong 0.159/\sqrt{LC} = 0.159/\sqrt{35 \ \mu\text{H} \cdot 80 \text{ pF}} = 3.00 \text{ MHz}$

$f_{o(range)} \cong 3.00 \text{ to } 3.47 \text{ MHz}$

ARMSTRONG OSCILLATOR

The Armstrong oscillator of Figure 15–12 is very straightforward. The *LC* tank circuit rings at the frequency of oscillation and is continually energized by the class A amplifier. The inductor is an RF transformer with a small

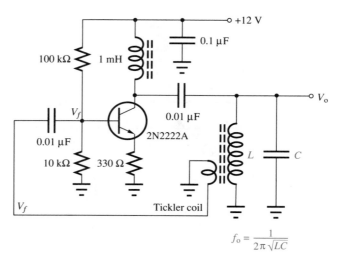

$$f_o = \frac{1}{2\pi\sqrt{LC}}$$

Figure 15–12   An Armstrong (tickler) oscillator.

secondary winding. This winding is often called the **tickler coil** because it is used to stimulate the amplifier into oscillation by providing positive feedback. The amplifier provides a 180° phase shift and the tickler coil provides another 180° phase shift to create a total loop phase shift of 360° (0°). The balance between feedback attenuation B and amplifier gain A_V is very difficult. In most cases, the transistor is driven into saturation and cutoff, leaving the tank circuit to remove distortion products like a high-Q bandpass filter. In other words, the ringing tank restores the sinusoidal waveform. Depending on the amount of loading in the output, distortion products can be greater than 1%. Because of this higher distortion and RF transformer requirement, the Armstrong is rarely used.

CRYSTAL OSCILLATORS

Crystal oscillators make use of the high-frequency resonant vibration of a crystal slice to determine the frequency of oscillation. These oscillators are more stable in terms of frequency change with temperature than are LC oscillators. The performance of these oscillators is based on the piezoelectric effect.

The Piezoelectric Effect

Figure 15–13 illustrates the piezoelectric effect very simply. A slice of crystal, when placed under mechanical stress, produces a pulse of electricity across its thickness. Conversely, if a voltage is applied to the crystal, it will warp slightly in a direction that depends on the polarity of voltage. If an AC signal is applied to the crystal, the crystal will flex rapidly and, in so doing, generate a voltage of its own. If the frequency of the applied AC is equal to the natural mechanical resonance of the crystal, the crystal will appear to be a very low resistance with crystal voltage aiding the applied AC. In other words, the crystal acts like a series resonant LC circuit with an extremely

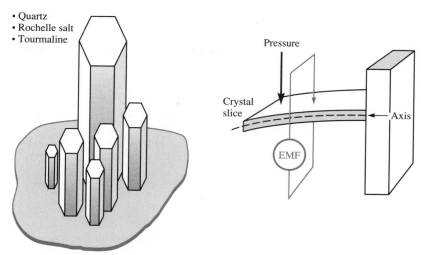

Figure 15–13 The piezoelectric effect in crystals.

high Q. That means the crystal can be used for high-Q filters or as the resonant circuit in an oscillator. Usually quartz or tourmaline is used for radio frequency crystals.

The Radio-Frequency Crystal

Figure 15–14 illustrates the schematic symbols for radio-frequency crystals. Also, the construction of a typical crystal assembly is shown with its electrical equivalent.

Mechanically, the radio-frequency crystal is a thin wafer of crystal with metal contact foils on each surface. Spring wires are soldered to the contact foils and are used to suspend the crystal within the metal case. The terminal pins allow the assembly to be plugged into a socket on the circuit board.

Electrically, the crystal wafer is a high-Q series resonant circuit. The electrically equivalent inductance of L_S is very high, ranging as high as 10,000 H for some low-frequency crystals. The series capacitance C_S is very low in fractions of picofarads. For example, a 5-MHz crystal may have an

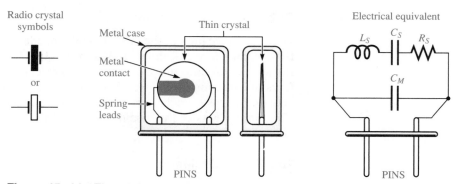

Figure 15–14 The radio-frequency crystal.

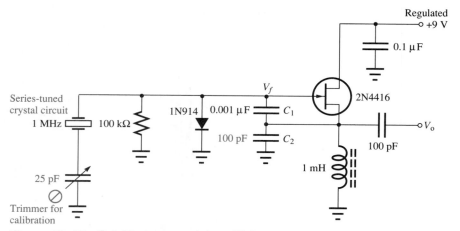

Figure 15–15   Colpitts-type crystal oscillator.

equivalent inductance of 0.1 H and a series capacitance of 0.0101 pF. If the equivalent series resistance R_S is 1 kΩ, the Q will be over 3,000:

$$X_L = 2\pi fL = 2\pi \cdot 5 \text{ MHz} \cdot 0.1 \text{ H} = 3.14 \text{ MΩ},$$

$$Q = X_L/R = 3.14 \text{ MΩ}/1 \text{ kΩ} = 3,140$$

Q's of up to 100 are barely possible with LC circuits.

Note the mounting capacitance (C_M) that is in parallel with the crystal. This mounting capacitance allows the crystal to operate in a parallel-resonant mode at a frequency slightly higher than the series-resonant frequency. In the parallel-resonant mode, C_M is in series with C_S in the overall tank loop. C_M is always much larger than C_S. Thus, the total capacitance is only slightly less than C_S itself. For example, say the mounting capacitance for the 5-MHz crystal is 4 pF. The total loop capacitance is

$$C_{\text{loop}} = (C_M \cdot C_S)/(C_M + C_S) \tag{15–9}$$

$$C_{\text{loop}} = (4 \text{ pF} \cdot 0.0101 \text{ pF})/(4 \text{ pF} + 0.0101 \text{ pF}) = 0.010075 \text{ pF}$$

This slight decrease in capacitance sets the parallel-resonant mode at about 6.5 kHz higher than the series-resonant mode. The crystal can be operated in either mode.

Colpitts Crystal Oscillator

Once again we look at the basic Colpitts oscillator, this time with a crystal in the resonant loop, as shown in Figure 15–15. Here, the crystal is operated in the series-resonant mode and the trimmer capacitor is used for fine tuning. Crystal trimming in this way is often called *netting*. The ratio C_1/C_2 can be adjusted to insure self-start and a low-distortion output approaching 0.1%. The crystal makes this oscillator very frequency stable with temperature change.

The Pierce Oscillator

Another very common crystal oscillator circuit is the Pierce oscillator shown in Figure 15–16. The Pierce oscillator is characterized by the placement of

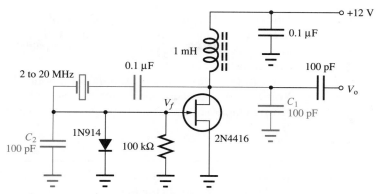

Figure 15–16   The Pierce oscillator.

the crystal in the negative-feedback path of a common-emitter or common-source configuration. Since the crystal is in the negative-feedback path, it must provide a 180° phase shift at the resonant frequency. The crystal is able to do this by oscillating just above its series-resonant frequency in the parallel-resonant mode. Even so-called weak or sluggish crystals start oscillating readily in this circuit. C_1 and C_2 are feedback capacitors that complete the resonant loop with the crystal. The size of these capacitors can be varied to provide minimum distortion and sure starts. Distortion products for these oscillators can be as low as 0.1% (equal to −60 dB).

Overtone and Harmonic Crystal Oscillators

A crystal can be cut in such a way as to vibrate, or oscillate, at a harmonic of its fundamental when placed in an amplifier circuit that is tuned to the harmonic. Overtone crystals are cut to resonate at an odd multiple of the fundamental frequency, usually 3×, 5×, or 7×. Since crystals become very thin and fragile when cut for frequencies above 10 MHz, it is best to use a crystal that is able to oscillate in overtone for higher frequencies. Figure 15–17 is an example of a third-overtone crystal oscillator. The crystal is a 7-MHz, third-overtone crystal. This means it will oscillate at three times its

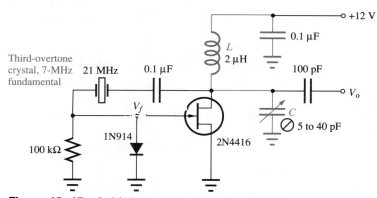

Figure 15–17   A third-overtone crystal oscillator.

fundamental frequency. The metal case of the crystal is marked as a 21-MHz overtone crystal. L and C in the drain circuit are tuned to resonate at 21 MHz. The overtone crystal provides the needed 180° phase shift to start and sustain oscillation.

We have covered a fairly significant amount of information in this section. You will find a table summarizing these oscillators in the summary at the end of this chapter. Take time to review and answer the questions in the self-check.

Self-Check 15–2

1. Of the three RC oscillators discussed in this section, which has the lowest percent distortion?
2. Why does the Wien-bridge oscillator oscillate at a frequency where $R = X_C$?
3. Describe one method of automatic gain control for RC oscillators.
4. Design a phase-shift oscillator to oscillate at 3 kHz. The capacitors shall be 0.0047 μF. Calculate the value for the resistors (R).
5. Using Figure 15–10 as a model, calculate the range of oscillation when $C_1 = 500$ pF, $C_2 = 50$ pF, $L = 5$ μH, the main tuning capacitor is 1 to 10 pF, the calibration trimmer is set at 4 pF, and the fixed paralleled capacitor is 30 pF.
6. What is the major identifying feature of the Hartley oscillator?
7. What is the main advantage of crystal oscillators compared to LC oscillators?
8. What is an overtone crystal?

15–3 FUNCTION GENERATORS

INTRODUCTION TO FUNCTION GENERATORS

Function generators are electronic circuits that perform a particular mathematical function and, in so doing, generate a continuous and periodic waveform (a waveform repeated at a certain interval and frequency). In most cases an RC integrator circuit is used to generate a triangle waveform from a square wave, since the slopes of the triangle represent the integral of the area under the square wave (recall Section 12–9). A comparator is generally used to create a square-wave signal by quickly switching between high and low output states (+ and ground, or + and −). In this section, you will explore the circuits that are used for these purposes. You will also discover multifunction generators that produce sine wave outputs as well as triangle and square-wave ones.

TRIANGLE AND SQUARE-WAVE GENERATION

A Precision Function Generator

Figure 15–18 is a fine example of a square-wave and triangle-wave function generator. The first stage (LM311 with 1-kΩ pull-up resistor R_P) is a compar-

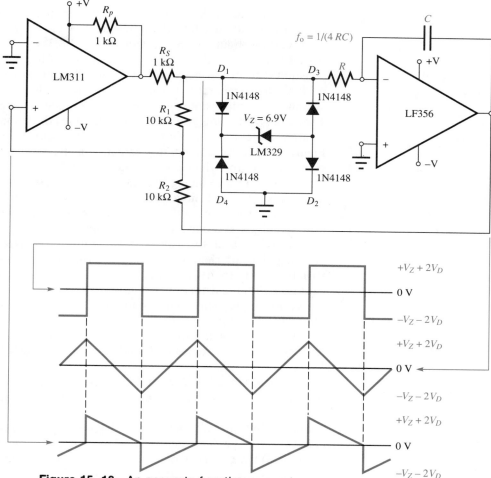

Figure 15–18 An accurate function generator.

ator. The last stage is an integrator circuit (R, C, and LF356). Between the input and output stages is a precision voltage reference formed by R_S and the diode array. The diode array uses four high-speed switching diodes to automatically switch the polarity of the zener diode. This insures equal plus and minus voltages as the output of the comparator switches between $+V$ and $-V$. When the comparator output is high ($+V$), D_1 and D_2 are forward biased and the precision zener provides $+6.9$ V plus two diode drops ($\cong +6.9$ V $+ 1.4$ V $= +8.3$ V). When the comparator output is low ($-V$), D_3 and D_4 are forward biased and the precision zener provides -6.9 V plus two diode drops ($\cong -6.9$ V $- 1.4$ V $= -8.3$ V). These plus and minus voltage references ($\cong \pm 8.3$ V) are used to determine the switching points for the comparator and maximum charge voltage for the integrator capacitor (C).

Theory of Operation

When the noninverting ($+$) input of the comparator becomes slightly positive, the output goes high ($+V$). The output stays high because the $+8.3$-V reference is fed back to the noninverting input via R_1. The only way the comparator will switch to the low state $(-V)$ is if -8.3 V is supplied to the noninverting input via R_2 to cancel the $+8.3$-V reference. Over a short period of time, this does happen. The output of the integrator is moving at a constant rate in the negative direction. This negative-going voltage is fed back to the comparator via R_2. When -8.3 V is reached, the comparator switches to the low state $(-V)$ and the reference voltage switches to -8.3 V. The output of the integrator instantly reverses direction, now heading in the positive direction. As you can see from the waveform timing diagrams of Figure 15–18, the comparator remains in the low state until the positive-going slope of the triangle wave reaches $+8.3$ V. This process is repeated at a constant rate, producing both a 50%-duty-cycle square-wave output from the comparator and diode array and a very linear triangle wave from the integrator. The slopes of the triangle wave are very linear because the capacitor is charged at a constant rate through R.

The diode is used to ensure precise timing and perfectly balanced positive and negative alternations of the waveforms regardless of supply-voltage variations. Alternatively, an LF356 can be used as a comparator, in which case no pull-up resistor is needed, and a 1-kΩ resistor can be substituted for the entire diode array. This reduces cost and you still have a very good function generator.

Whether or not the diode array is used, the frequency of oscillation is determined by the values of R and C. Consider the following derivation:

You should recall that $Q = CV$ and $\triangle Q = C \cdot \triangle V$ where $\triangle Q$ is the change in quantity of charge on the capacitor C when the total change in voltage is $\triangle V$.

Let $V_Z + 2V_D = V$. Then $\triangle V = 2(V_Z + 2V_D) = 2V =$ the total change in capacitor voltage. The capacitor takes time to charge or discharge (T_{charge}). Thus the quantity of charge and charge voltage changes over time.

$$\triangle Q / T_{\text{charge}} = C \cdot \triangle V / T_{\text{charge}} = C \cdot 2V / T_{\text{charge}}$$

Also,

$$\triangle Q / T_{\text{charge}} = I_R = V/R$$

Therefore, by substitution,

$$V/R = C \cdot 2V / T_{\text{charge}}$$

Rearranging we see that

$$T_{\text{charge}} = 2RC$$

The total cycle time is $2T_{\text{charge}} = 4RC = T$. Therefore, since $f = 1/T$, $f_o = 1/(4RC)$.

$$f_o = 1/(4RC) = 0.25/RC \qquad (15\text{–}10)$$

and

$$R = 1/(4Cf_o) = 0.25/Cf_o \qquad (15\text{–}11)$$

Consider Example 15–6.

EXAMPLE 15–6

A function generator like that of Figure 15–18 uses a 4-V zener diode in the diode array. $R = 10$ kΩ and $C = 0.003$ μF. What is the frequency of oscillation and the peak-to-peak amplitude of the triangle wave?

$f_o = 0.25/RC = 0.25/(10$ k$\Omega \cdot 0.003$ μF$) = 8,333$ Hz

$V_P \cong 4$ $V + 1.4$ $V = 5.4$ V, $V_{P-P} = 2V_P = 10.8$ V_{P-P}

The frequency of oscillation can be made variable by using a potentiometer, wired as a rheostat, in series with R. R then determines the highest frequency and the sum of R and the potentiometer resistance determines the lowest frequency. For Example 15–6, if R is 10 kΩ and a variable series resistor is 100 kΩ, the frequency range will be from 758 to 8,333 Hz since $R_{max} = 110$ kΩ and $R_{min} = 10$ kΩ.

A Simple Square-Wave Generator

Figure 15–19 shows a simple, single-op-amp square-wave generator. This circuit generates a good 50%-duty-cycle square wave but a poor triangle wave. Because the capacitor charges through R instead of a constant current source, the slopes of the triangle wave are not linear. The op-amp acts as a comparator with the switching threshold established by R_1 and R_2. When the capacitor voltage slightly exceeds the threshold voltage, the output switches states, as indicated by the waveform timing diagrams. Frequency can be increased by lowering the threshold voltage or by decreasing R and/or C. If the threshold voltage is set at 0.245 times $\pm$VDC, the frequency of oscillation is simply $1/RC$. As shown in Figure 15–19, a 220-kΩ resistor and a 71.5-

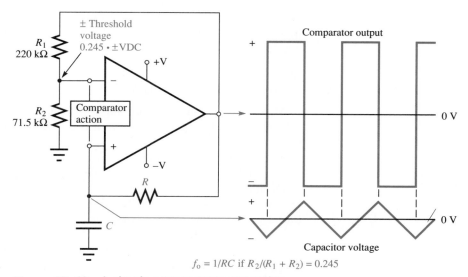

$f_0 = 1/RC$ if $R_2/(R_1 + R_2) = 0.245$

Figure 15–19   A simple square-wave generator.

$k\Omega$ resistor (1% film resistor) can be used to accomplish this. Also, a 100-$k\Omega$ and a 33-$k\Omega$ resistor can be used as a close substitute (33 $k\Omega$/(100 $k\Omega$ + 33 $k\Omega$) = 0.248).

$$f_o = 1/RC$$

where $R_1/(R_1 + R_2) = 0.245$, and   (15–12)

$$R = 1/Cf_o$$ (15–13)

Look at Example 15–7.

EXAMPLE 15–7

Design a single-stage op-amp square-wave generator like that of Figure 15–19. The frequency of oscillation shall be 100 Hz. Use a 0.047-μF capacitor.

$$R_1 = 100 \text{ k}\Omega \qquad R_2 = 32.4 \text{ k}\Omega \text{ (1% film resistor)}$$

$$R_1/(R_1 + R_2) = 0.245$$

$$R = 1/Cf_o = 1/(0.047 \ \mu\text{F} \cdot 100 \text{ Hz}) = 212.8 \text{ k}\Omega$$

MULTIFUNCTION GENERATORS

A Precision Multifunction Generator

Part of Figure 15–20 should look familiar to you. It's the precision function generator circuit of Figure 15–18 with some added features. Notice that variable-frequency capability has been added with the 1-$M\Omega$ potentiometer (wired as a rheostat). An audio-taper potentiometer is used to provide a better spread of frequencies on the high end. The frequency range for this circuit is

$$f_{o(\text{min})} = 0.25/RC = 0.25/(1.001 \text{ M}\Omega \cdot 0.01 \ \mu\text{F}) = 25 \text{ Hz}$$
$$f_{o(\text{max})} = 0.25/RC = 0.25/(1 \text{ k}\Omega \cdot 0.01 \ \mu\text{F}) = 25 \text{ kHz}$$

Also, a sine-shaper circuit has been added, along with a variable-gain amplifier. The triangle-wave output is converted to a sine wave in the transistor array (shaper circuit). This is accomplished by taking advantage of the nonlinear characteristics of the transistors near cutoff. The relationship between base-emitter voltage and collector current is logarithmic near cutoff. Thus, the triangle wave is rounded at its peaks to approximate a sine wave. The shape trim–pot is used to adjust the drive level to the shaper circuit, thereby controlling the amount of rounding on the peaks. When adjusted to the closest possible sine-wave approximation, the amount of sine-wave distortion is an amazingly low 0.5% or less. Overall performance of this function-generator circuit is very good, making it an excellent piece of test equipment for the electronics lab.

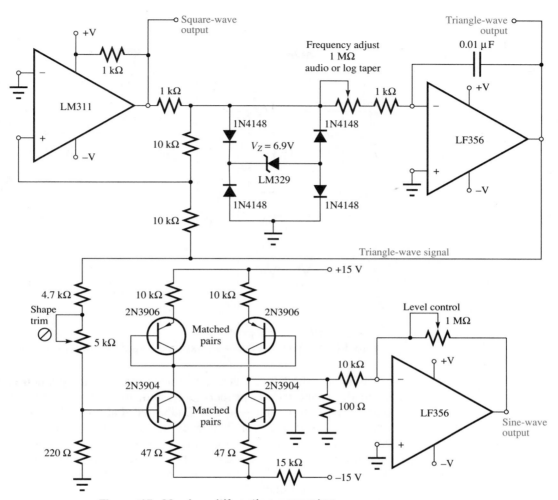

Figure 15–20 A multifunction generator.

The XR2206 Function Generator IC

Wouldn't it be nice to have the entire circuit of Figure 15–20 on a single chip? That's exactly what the XR2206 integrated circuit is. As shown in Figure 15–21, this IC generates square, triangle, and sine waveforms. External components are for timing, level control, sine/triangle selection, and sine shaping. The timing capacitor is between pins 5 and 6. The 1-MΩ and 100-kΩ potentiometers (wired as rheostats) provide variable-frequency selection over a range of approximately 90 Hz to 100 kHz. Audio-taper or logarithmic potentiometers should be used to help spread out the upper end of the frequency range. The 100-kΩ pot can be used for fine adjustment or it can be set at some position to determine the maximum upper frequency limit. If it is set at 10 kΩ, the maximum range of the 1-MΩ pot will be from about 90 Hz to 9 kHz, where the formula for frequency calculation is: $f_o = 1/RC$. Formulas 15–12 and 15–13 apply to the XR2206.

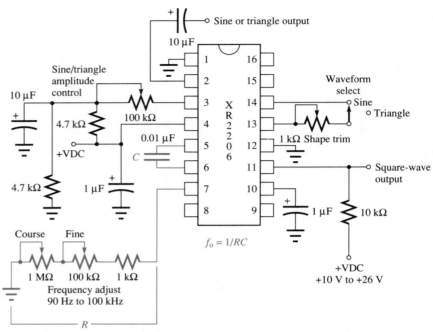

Figure 15–21   The XR2206—an extremely versatile function-generator IC.

Obviously, the XR2206 is a fine choice for a laboratory function generator. Once the shape trim is properly adjusted, distortion products will be less than 0.5%, better than −46 dB. Calibrated dials or knobs on the variable resistors can be used for frequency selection. For accuracy, a frequency counter can be used if available. In any case, the oscilloscope can be used to measure the period of a signal at the output of a circuit under test. Thus, precise calibration of the function generator dial is not always necessary.

Time for a self-check.

**Self-Check
15–3**

1. What is a function generator (in general)?
2. What type of circuit is normally used to generate a linear triangle wave?
3. What type of circuit is used to generate a square wave?
4. What is the frequency of oscillation for a circuit like Figure 15–18 if $R =$ 15 kΩ and $C = 0.001$ μF?
5. Briefly explain the operation of the simple square-wave generator of Figure 15–19.
6. What percent distortion can you expect to get from the XR2206 when the shape-trim control is properly adjusted?

15–4 THE 555 TIMER

CIRCUIT DESCRIPTION

General Description

The 555 timer integrated circuit is one of the most versatile circuits in the designer's inventory. It can be used as a timer circuit to control the duration of events, as a function generator producing square, triangle, and sawtooth waveforms, or as a control circuit for pulse width or pulse position modulation. It is manufactured by many companies in low- and medium-power versions and is also available as a pair in one package, the 556. You will want to give the 555 the same position of high regard and prominence as the op-amp. Space does not permit us to fully investigate the 555 here. However, we will explore some of its main functions and applications. Enjoy your exploration.

Circuit Description

Figure 15–22 shows the dual-in-line package (DIP) version of the 555 with pin numbers, pin description, and internal electronics. First of all, notice the resistor voltage divider between pins 8 and 1. This voltage divider establishes trip points for the two comparators. The lower trip point for comparator A is 1/3 VDC. The higher trip point supplied to comparator B is 2/3 VDC. As you can see, comparator A is normally high at its output because of the positive 1/3 VDC at its noninverting input. Also, comparator B is normally low at its output due to the positive 2/3 VDC at its inverting input. This means the flip-flop normally has a high (+VDC) at its set input (S) and a low (gnd) at its reset (R) input.

So, what's a **flip-flop**? A flip-flop is a circuit commonly used in digital systems. The flip-flop in the 555 is called an RS flip-flop. The RS stands for reset and set. The reset and set inputs are control inputs that determine the

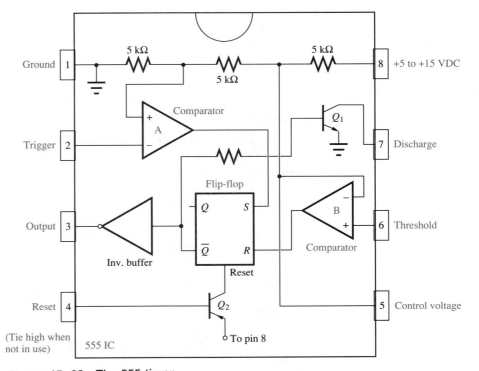

Figure 15–22   The 555 timer.

state of the two outputs (Q and $\overline{Q}$). When set goes high, Q goes high and $\overline{Q}$ goes low. The outputs remain this way until set goes low and reset goes high. When this occurs, the state of the outputs flips, $\overline{Q}$ goes high and Q goes low. There is also a master reset that can be used to freeze the present state of the flip-flop and ignore all set and reset inputs. When pin 4 of the 555 is low (gnd), the flip-flop is disabled or frozen. This function is not used in many applications. Usually, pin 4 is tied to +VDC.

As stated earlier, the output of comparator A is normally high and the output of comparator B is normally low. Thus, set (S) is high and reset (R) is low. Q is high and $\overline{Q}$ is low. The output buffer amplifier is an inverter, which makes the output at pin 3 normally high under these conditions. Now, let's see the 555 in action.

THE 555 AS A TIMER

Monostable Multivibrators

Figure 15–23 illustrates the 555 being used as a timer. When pin 2 goes low, pin 3 goes high and stays high for a predetermined length of time. Timers such as this are classified as **monostable multivibrators,** which means the circuit has one normal output condition. In this case, pin 3 is normally low, its normal monostable condition.

Theory of Operation

The length of time pin 3 stays high is determined by the time it takes for the capacitor C to charge to 2/3 VDC through resistor R. This length of time (T) is equal to:

$$T = 1.1\ RC \tag{15–14}$$

and

$$R = T/(1.1\ C) \tag{15–15}$$

where C is given.

Let's follow the operating sequence. As you can see, pin 2 is held high by the 10-kΩ pull-up resistor. For the timing operation to begin, pin 2 must momentarily go low—it must at least drop slightly below 1/3 VDC. This triggers the output of comparator A to momentarily go high. The flip-flop becomes set since the set input momentarily goes high. This causes Q to go high and $\overline{Q}$ to go low. The inverting buffer causes pin 3 to go high. Notice also that Q_1 was on when $\overline{Q}$ was high and C was shorted to ground via pin 7. Since $\overline{Q}$ went low, Q_1 turned off, allowing C to begin charging through R. When the charge voltage reaches slightly more than 2/3 VDC, comparator B's output goes high. This instantly resets the flip-flop which causes $\overline{Q}$ to go high, Q_1 to turn on, C to be discharged, and pin 3 to go low. The timer circuit is now back in its stable condition and will wait for another trigger pulse (momentary ground) at pin 2.

Example 15–8 demonstrates how simple it is to design a timer circuit with the 555.

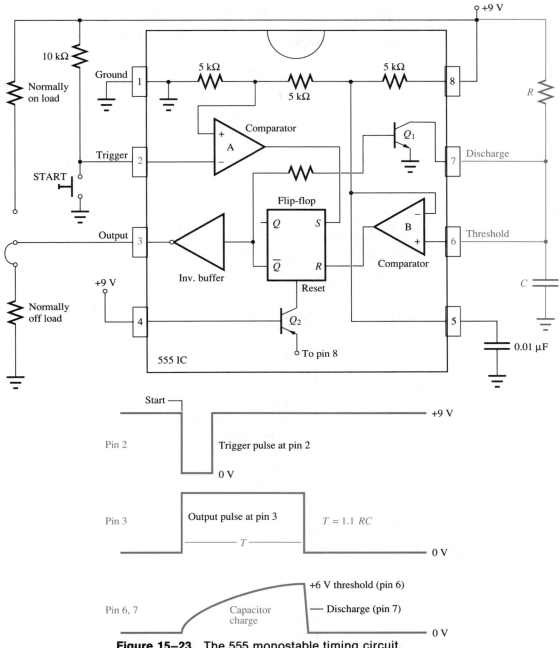

Figure 15–23   The 555 monostable timing circuit.

EXAMPLE 15–8

Use the 555 to generate a 100 ms ON pulse. Let $C = 0.1 \mu F$.

$R = T/(1.1C) = 100 \text{ ms}/(1.1 \cdot 0.1 \mu F) = 909 \text{ k}\Omega \text{ (1% film)}$

THE 555 AS A SQUARE-WAVE GENERATOR

General Description

Figure 15–24 illustrates the 555 being used as a square-wave generator, also referred to as an **astable** (meaning "not stable") **multivibrator.** Notice capacitor C must now charge through $R_1 + R_2$. When Q_1 turns on and pin 7 goes low, capacitor C discharges through R_2. The resulting triangle waveform across the capacitor, along with the pin 3 output, is also shown in Figure 15–24.

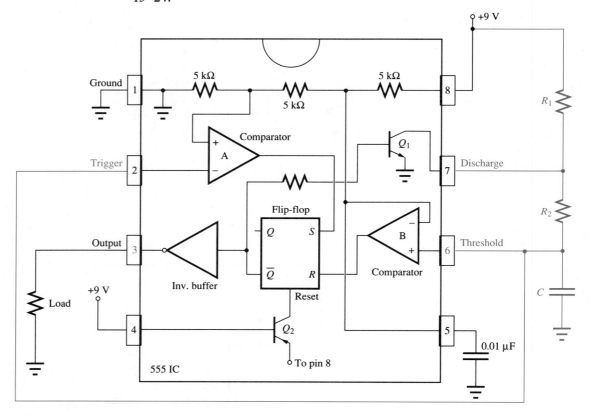

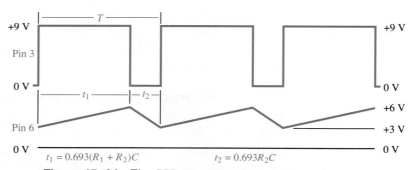

$$t_1 = 0.693(R_1 + R_2)C \qquad t_2 = 0.693R_2C$$

Figure 15–24 The 555 as a square-wave generator.

Theory of Operation

When power is first applied, pin 2 is low, comparator A output is high, the flip-flop is set, $\overline{Q}$ is low, Q_1 is off, C begins to charge through $R_1 + R_2$, and pin 3 is high. When the capacitor's charge voltage reaches 2/3 VDC, comparator B's output goes high, the flip-flop is reset, $\overline{Q}$ goes high, Q_1 turns on, C begins to discharge through R_2, and the pin 3 output goes low. When the capacitor's charge voltage drops slightly below 1/3 VDC, the output of comparator A once again goes high, the flip-flop is set, $\overline{Q}$ goes low, Q_1 turns off, C begins to charge through $R_1 + R_2$, and pin 3 goes high. This process is repeated over and over again as the capacitor voltage rises and falls betweens 1/3 and 2/3 VDC, triggering the two comparators.

Percent Duty Cycle, Time, and Frequency

Notice in Figure 15–24 that the duty cycle of the square wave is greater than 50%. In other words, the ON time t_1 compared to the total cycle time T is greater than 0.5 or 50%.

$$\% \text{ Duty Cycle} = (t_{ON}/T) \cdot 100\% \tag{15-16}$$

Since C must charge through $R_1 + R_2$ and discharge only through R_2, it is impossible for this circuit to attain a duty cycle of 50% or less. The times for charge (t_1) and discharge (t_2) are given as

$$t_1 = 0.693 \cdot (R_1 + R_2) \cdot C \tag{15-17}$$

$$t_2 = 0.693 \cdot R_2 \cdot C \tag{15-18}$$

The total cycle time T is:

$$T = t_1 + t_2 = 0.693 \cdot C \cdot (R_1 + 2R_2) \tag{15-19}$$

The frequency (f_o) of oscillation is:

$$f_o = 1/T \tag{15-20}$$

Example 15–9 demonstrates how the duty cycle can be set at very close to 50%.

EXAMPLE 15–9 ▬▬▬▬▬▬▬▬▬▬▬▬▬▬▬▬▬▬▬▬▬

An astable multivibrator like that of Figure 15–24 has the following component values: $R_1 = 1 \text{ k}\Omega$, $R_2 = 100 \text{ k}\Omega$, and $C = 0.1 \text{ } \mu\text{F}$. Calculate the pin 3 ON time, OFF time, total cycle time, frequency of oscillation, and percent duty cycle.

$$t_1 = \text{ON time} = 0.693 \cdot (R_1 + R_2) \cdot C$$

$$= 0.693 \cdot (1 \text{ k}\Omega + 100 \text{ k}\Omega) \cdot 0.1 \text{ } \mu\text{F} = 6.999 \text{ ms}$$

$$t_2 = \text{OFF time} = 0.693 \cdot R_2 \cdot C$$

$$= 0.693 \cdot 100 \text{ k}\Omega \cdot 0.1 \text{ } \mu\text{F} = 6.93 \text{ ms}$$

$$T = t_1 + t_2 = 6.999 \text{ ms} + 6.93 \text{ ms} = 13.929 \text{ ms}$$

$$f_o = 1/T = 1/13.929 \text{ ms} = 71.8 \text{ Hz}$$

$$\% \text{ Duty Cycle} = (t_1/T) \cdot 100\%$$

$$= (6.999 \text{ ms}/13.929 \text{ ms}) \cdot 100\% = 50.25\%$$

Obtaining Less Than 50% Duty Cycle

Adding a diode to the 555 square-wave oscillator as shown in Figure 15–25 makes possible duty cycles of any percent, even less than 50%. As you can see, the capacitor C charges through R_1 and D, as D is forward biased. Diode D bypasses R_2. The capacitor discharges through R_2 as before. The diode simply removes R_2 from Formula 15–17. Thus, $t_1 = 0.693 \cdot R_1 \cdot C$.

THE 555 AS A SAWTOOTH GENERATOR

General Description

The 555 circuit of Figure 15–26 is a linear sawtooth generator. An external BJT constant-current source is used to charge the capacitor. The charge

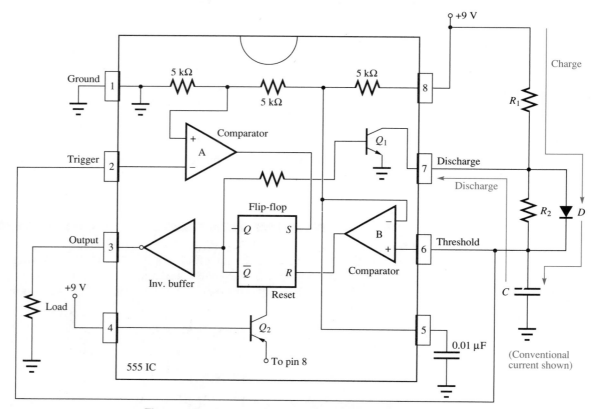

Figure 15–25 The shunt diode makes 50% or less duty cycles possible.

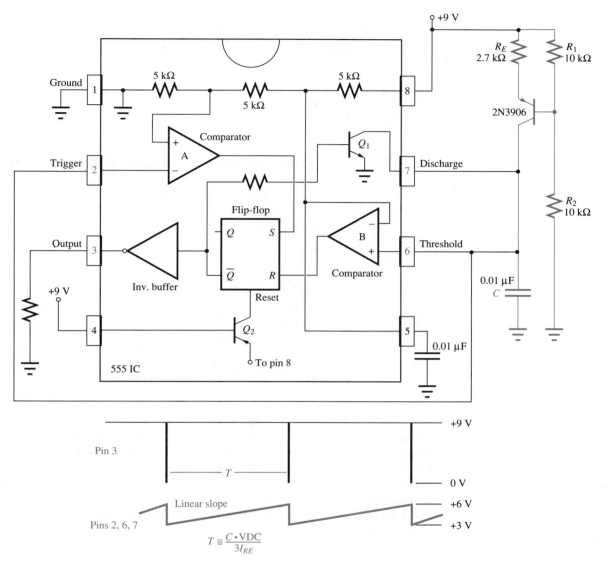

Figure 15–26 A linear ramp generator.

current is the same as the emitter current of the transistor, which is constant because V_B is constant as established by R_1 and R_2. The constant current causes the capacitor voltage to rise at a constant linear rate.

Theory of Operation

Recall from circuit analysis theory that the quantity of charge on a capacitor is equal to the product of capacitance and charge voltage, $Q = CV$. Also, a quantity of charge accumulating over time produces a current, $Q/T = I$. Therefore, since $Q = CV$, $I = CV/T$ and $T = CV/I$. In this case, V is the change in voltage, which is a little more than 1/3 VDC. This is because the capacitor voltage rises and falls between less than 1/3 VDC and 2/3 VDC.

The sawtooth ramp begins when the capacitor is quickly discharged to a voltage less than 1/3 VDC and ends when the capacitor voltage reaches approximately 2/3 VDC. Thus, the time T for one cycle is: $T \cong C \cdot 1/3 \text{ VDC}/I_{RE}$.

$$T \cong C \cdot \text{VDC}/3I_{RE} \tag{15-21}$$

We can use Figure 15–26 for Example 15–10.

EXAMPLE 15–10 ▮▮▮▮▮▮▮▮▮▮▮▮▮▮▮▮▮▮▮▮▮▮▮▮▮▮▮▮▮▮

Calculate time and frequency for the circuit of Figure 15–26.

$\text{VDC} = +9 \text{ V},$

$V_B = 4.5 \text{ V},$

$V_{RE} \cong 4.5 \text{ V} - 0.7 \text{ V} = 3.8 \text{ V},$

$I_{RE} = 3.8 \text{ V}/2.7 \text{ k}\Omega = 1.41 \text{ mA}$

$T \cong 0.01 \ \mu\text{F} \cdot 9 \text{ V}/(3 \cdot 1.41 \text{ mA}) = 0.09 \ \mu\text{F}/4.23 \text{ mA}$

$\qquad = 21.3 \ \mu\text{s}$

$f \cong 1/T = 46.9 \text{ kHz}$

In practice, I have found the frequency to be less than the theoretical calculated value. This is due to the ambiguity of the minimum sawtooth voltage, which may vary and which depends on how much Q_1 is able to discharge the capacitor. The formula assumes that the ramp rises from 1/3 VDC to 2/3 VDC. In practice, I have found the ramp to rise from a minimum of approximately 1/5 VDC to 2/3 VDC ($\frac{2}{3}$ VDC $- \frac{1}{5}$ VDC $= \frac{7}{15}$ VDC $= 0.467$ VDC). In any case, the value of R_E can be adjusted to tailor the frequency to what you want.

Take time to review this section before answering the questions of Self-Check 15–4.

Self-Check 15–4

1. Explain the series of events that take place when pin 2 of the 555 timer circuit, Figure 15–23, is momentarily contacted to ground.
2. Calculate the value of resistor R that is needed for a 10-ms ON time if a 0.02-μF capacitor is used in the timer circuit of Figure 15–23.
3. Why is the duty cycle greater than 50% for the square-wave generator of Figure 15–24?
4. Given the following values for the circuit of Figure 15–24, calculate ON time, OFF time, total cycle time, frequency, and percent duty cycle: $R_1 = 47 \text{ k}\Omega$, $R_2 = 10 \text{ k}\Omega$, $C = 0.003 \ \mu\text{F}$.
5. How does the diode in the circuit of Figure 15–25 permit duty cycles less than 50%?

6. Given the following values for the sawtooth generator of Figure 15–26, calculate the approximate frequency of oscillation: VDC = 12 V, R_1 = 4.7 kΩ, R_2 = 10 kΩ, R_E = 1 kΩ, C = 0.047 μF. Assume a 0.7-V base–emitter voltage drop and assume the sawtooth voltage rises from 1/3 VDC to 2/3 VDC.

15–5 VOLTAGE-CONTROLLED OSCILLATORS

INTRODUCTION TO VOLTAGE-CONTROLLED OSCILLATORS

Voltage-controlled oscillators (VCOs) are oscillator circuits whose frequency can be varied with an applied DC or low-frequency AC voltage. The DC voltage control of the frequency makes it possible for the oscillator to be tuned remotely through a long DC cable without the problems associated with stray capacitance and inductance. Also, voltage control makes it possible to use a computer to control the frequency of the oscillator. The computer generates a large range of very small step voltages that are used to change the oscillator's frequency in small steps. Thus, the computer becomes interfaced to the oscillator. This is used in scanner radios and special circuits called *frequency synthesizers,* which you will learn about in another course.

A low-frequency AC, such as audio, can be applied to the voltage control input to frequency-modulate the oscillator. The changing voltage of the audio causes the frequency to change at the same rate. In this way, the audio information is stored in the rapidly shifting radio frequency. Any of the following circuits can be used as a simple FM transmitter.

CLAPP VOLTAGE-CONTROLLED OSCILLATOR (VCO)

Figure 15–27 illustrates a practical voltage-controlled oscillator. The circuit is a varactor-tuned Clapp oscillator. The theory of operation is very simple. The 10-turn potentiometer supplies a +4.5-to-+9-V range of voltage to the reverse-biased varactor diode (recall varactors from Section 2–6). As voltage is increased, the varactor capacitance decreases with the spreading of its junction (barrier). This capacitance is in parallel with a trimmer and a fixed capacitor. A resonant loop is formed in the usual way for Clapp oscillators, with the paralleled capacitors in series with the feedback capacitors and the inductor. The 0.1-μF coupling capacitor and the 0.001-μF coupling capacitor are considered transparent. The 0.1-μF coupling capacitor is necessary to block the DC control voltage from getting to the gate of the FET.

The graph included in Figure 15–27 shows the relationship between control voltage and capacitance. As you can see, the MV1404 has a much greater range of capacitance than is being used for this application. Also, the change in capacitance with voltage is fairly linear, which makes dial calibration a little easier.

Here are some things to remember when designing a circuit like this:

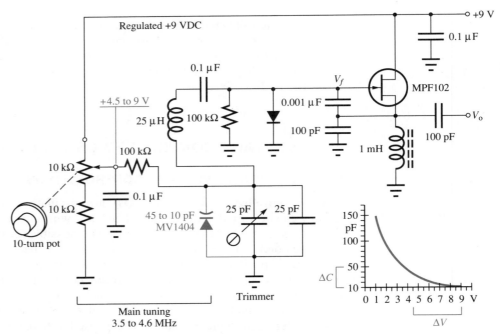

Figure 15–27 A varactor-tuned VCO.

VCO Design Considerations

1. Determine the range of DC voltage from the range of capacitance that is needed for the application.
2. Make sure the varactor is reverse biased by the control voltage.
3. Use an *RC* filter between the potentiometer's wiper arm and the varactor as shown in Figure 15–27. The filter should be as close to the varactor as possible. The wire from the filter capacitor to the wiper can be as long as needed. This electrically separates the potentiometer from the oscillator.
4. Use regulated DC for the oscillator and potentiometer. Any variations in the DC will cause frequency shifting of the oscillator.
5. Use a DC-blocking capacitor between the inductor and the FET. Otherwise, the DC control voltage will saturate the FET.

VOLTAGE-CONTROLLED CRYSTAL OSCILLATOR (VCXO)

Crystal oscillators can also be voltage-controlled. A **voltage-controlled crystal oscillator (VCXO)** is illustrated in Figure 15–28. The series-tuned crystal can be pulled off frequency by as much as 4 or 5 kHz and still maintain excellent frequency stability. This type of circuit is used in certain radio receiver circuits to provide a kind of fine tuning or clarification. Also, a fixed voltage divider can be used instead of the potentiometer, and audio can be applied to the center of the divider. The audio AC superimposed on the DC control voltage causes the varactor to frequency modulate the oscillator. This makes a simple FM transmitter.

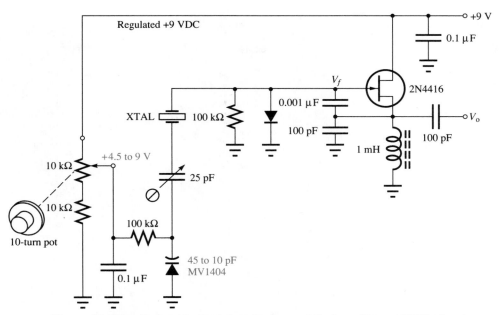

Figure 15–28   A varactor-tuned crystal-controlled oscillator VCXO circuit.

VOLTAGE-CONTROLLED FUNCTION GENERATOR

This is a good time to go back to the versatile XR2206 function-generator IC. This IC makes an excellent, low-frequency (<1 MHz) FM transmitter as shown in Figure 15–29. As you can see, the operating frequency is now voltage controlled with the 5-kΩ linear potentiometer. The formula for f_o includes the wiper-arm control voltage V_C, R_C, R, and C.

$$f_o = \frac{1 + [(R/R_C) \cdot (1 - (V_C/3))]}{RC} \qquad (15\text{–}22)$$

For the center frequency of oscillation, the wiper arm of the potentiometer should be set midway. Thus, V_C is half of the regulated supply voltage. Let's use Figure 15–29 in Example 15–11 and calculate the center frequency of oscillation.

EXAMPLE 15–11 ▮▮▮▮▮▮▮▮▮▮▮▮▮▮▮▮▮▮▮▮▮▮

Calculate the center frequency of oscillation for the circuit of Figure 15–29. Assume +VDC = +12 V and V_C = +6 V.

$$f_o = \frac{1 + [(R/R_C) \cdot (1 - (V_C/3))]}{RC}$$

$$= \frac{1 + [(2.2\ k\Omega/10\ k\Omega) \cdot (1 - (6\ V/3))]}{2.2\ k\Omega \cdot 0.0022\ \mu F}$$

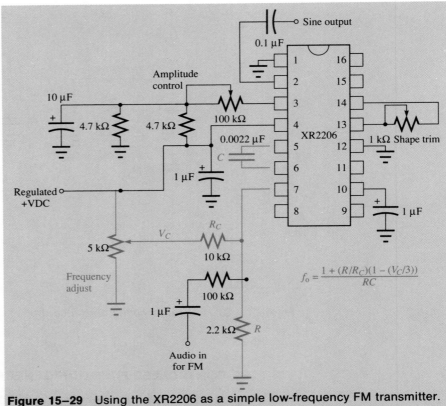

Figure 15–29   Using the XR2206 as a simple low-frequency FM transmitter.

$$= \frac{1 + (0.22 \cdot -1)}{4.84 \, E - 6} = \frac{0.78}{4.84 \, E - 6} = 161.2 \text{ kHz}$$

The 5-kΩ potentiometer can be adjusted to change this frequency.

When audio is applied to the audio input to pin 7 as shown in Figure 15–29, it is superimposed on the DC control voltage that is present across R. The voltage variations of the audio cause the frequency to shift above and below the center carrier frequency of 161.2 kHz. The amplitude of the audio will determine the amount of frequency shifting or deviation. Thus audio amplitude changes are converted to frequency deviation. The audio frequencies are contained in the rate of frequency deviation. For example, a 1-kHz audio signal will cause the frequency to deviate at the rate of 1 kHz. Thus, the audio information is contained in a 161.2-kHz FM signal.

This circuit is useful in carrier-current intercom systems. These systems use the 115-V wiring in the house or building to transfer intercom signals from one room to another. Usually, these intercoms operate in the range of 165 to 185 kHz. This signal is superimposed on the 60-Hz AC through passive highpass filters. The frequency-modulated signal passes through the filter to the AC line without the 60-Hz power passing back through the filter to the intercom circuit. In this way, the power lines in the building serve a dual purpose.

THE PHASE-LOCKED LOOP (PLL)

Introduction to Phase-Locked Loops (PLLs)

The subjects of VCOs and FM brings us to the phase-locked loop (PLL). The phase-locked loop is used for many applications, perhaps the most common being FM demodulation (recovering audio from a frequency-modulated carrier). Phase-locked loops are also used in frequency synthesizers contained in transmitters and scanning radio receivers. These interesting circuits have the ability to lock onto a frequency and follow any changes in that frequency. The PLL converts any frequency change to a change in voltage. In other words, the PLL is a VCO in reverse. Whereas the VCO converts control-voltage changes to frequency changes, the PLL converts frequency changes to voltage changes.

The PLL Block Diagram

Figure 15–30 is the block diagram of the basic PLL. As you can see, there are three main blocks to the PLL system: (1) a phase detector, (2) a lowpass filter, and (3) a voltage-controlled oscillator. The VCO you are already familiar with. A DC control voltage is used to set the frequency of the VCO. The lowpass filter is a simple passive RC lowpass filter, which is referred to as the *loop filter*. You are also familiar with the phase detector. The phase detector is a nonlinear mixer. Recall that mixers generate products that are sum and difference frequencies. It is the difference frequency that interests us here. The difference frequency between f_{in} and f_o is either very-low-frequency AC riding on a DC level or pure DC.

Theory of Operation

The basic operation of the PLL is very simple. When f_{in} is initially applied, it is mixed with f_o producing a difference frequency. If f_{in} is within the range of the VCO and the difference frequency ($f_o - f_{in}$ or $f_{in} - f_o$) is low enough to pass through the lowpass loop filter, the VCO will be forced to change its frequency. The change in the VCO frequency brings it closer and closer to

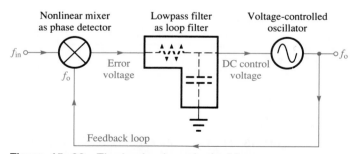

Figure 15–30 The basic phase-locked loop.

the input frequency until $f_o = f_{in}$ and $f_o - f_{in} = 0$ Hz. This happens very quickly. When $f_o = f_{in}$, the loop is said to be locked. Once locked, the voltage at the output of the mixer and loop filter is a pure DC level representing simply a phase difference between f_o and f_{in}. It is the amount of DC control voltage that is needed to make $f_o = f_{in}$.

Capture Range

Figure 15–31 illustrates the importance of the loop filter. The frequency response of the loop filter determines the capture range of the PLL. The **capture range** is the range of frequencies above and below the free-running frequency of the VCO that the PLL will respond to and lock onto. The free-running frequency is simply the natural frequency of oscillation of the VCO when f_{in} is not applied.

The cutoff frequency of the lowpass filter is the maximum difference in frequency that can exist between f_{in} and f_o for the loop to lock. Thus, the maximum upper capture frequency is $f_{in} - f_o = f_{co(\text{loop filter})}$ above $f_{o(\text{free-running})}$. The minimum lower capture frequency is $f_o - f_{in} = f_{co(\text{loop filter})}$ below $f_{o(\text{free-running})}$.

$$f_{\text{upper capture}} \cong f_o + f_{co(\text{loop filter})} \tag{15–23}$$

$$f_{\text{lower capture}} \cong f_o - f_{co(\text{loop filter})} \tag{15–24}$$

Consider Example 15–12.

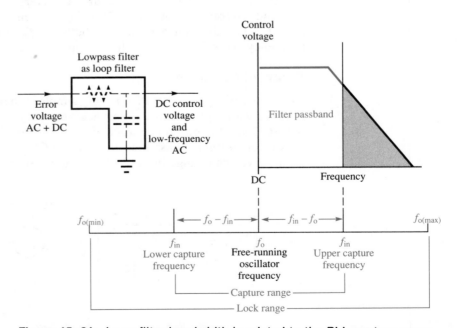

Figure 15–31 Loop filter bandwidth is related to the PLL capture range.

EXAMPLE 15-12 ▮▮

In a PLL system the VCO has a free-running frequency of 175 kHz. The loop filter is made up of a 330-Ω resistor and a 0.1-μF capacitor. What is the approximate capture range of the PLL?

$$f_{co} = 1/(2\pi RC) = 1/(2 \cdot \pi \cdot 330 \ \Omega \cdot 0.1 \ \mu F) = 4823 \ Hz \cong 5 \ kHz$$

$$f_{\text{upper capture}} \cong f_o + f_{co(\text{loop filter})} = 175 \ kHz + 5 \ kHz = 180 \ kHz$$

$$f_{\text{lower capture}} \cong f_o - f_{co(\text{loop filter})} = 175 \ kHz - 5 \ kHz = 170 \ kHz$$

The capture range is from 170 kHz to 180 kHz.

Lock Range

Once the PLL locks on to an input frequency, how far can it track or follow the frequency before it loses lock? The answer to that question determines the **lock range** which is also called the **tracking range.** The lock range is equal to the range of the VCO. This is the range over which the DC control voltage can change the frequency of the VCO. That, of course, depends on oscillator design.

The PLL as an FM Demodulator

As stated earlier, the PLL is commonly used as an FM demodulator, converting the frequency deviations of an FM signal back to the original audio. The incoming FM signal causes a variation in the DC voltage at the output of the phase detector and loop filter. This variation in the DC level at the output of the loop filter is a copy of the original audio and is caused by phase variations between f_{in} and f_o. Even though the VCO is forced to follow the frequency deviation of the input signal so that f_o always equals f_{in}, there is a wide variation in phase difference between the two. Thus, the DC control voltage will vary up and down with the phase changes that correspond with frequency deviation. The VCO stays locked on the rapidly deviating FM signal by the rapidly varying DC control voltage, which is a copy of the original audio. The audio is taken from the output of the loop filter and amplified for use.

The circuit of Figure 15-32 is one example of a PLL used as an FM demodulator. The XR2211 is a sister chip to the XR2206. The XR2206 is used as the transmitter and the XR2211 is used as the receiver. Notice the circuitry inside the XR2211. Phase detector 1 and the VCO are used as the primary PLL for FM demodulation. The loop filter is formed by R_F and C_F, chosen for a cutoff frequency of about 5 kHz, giving a capture range of ± 5 kHz. The free-running frequency of the VCO is determined by R and C.

$$f_o = 1/RC \tag{15-25}$$

In this case, f_o is approximately $1/(15 \ k\Omega \cdot 400 \ pF) = 167 \ kHz$, assuming the variable resistor is set to 5 kΩ.

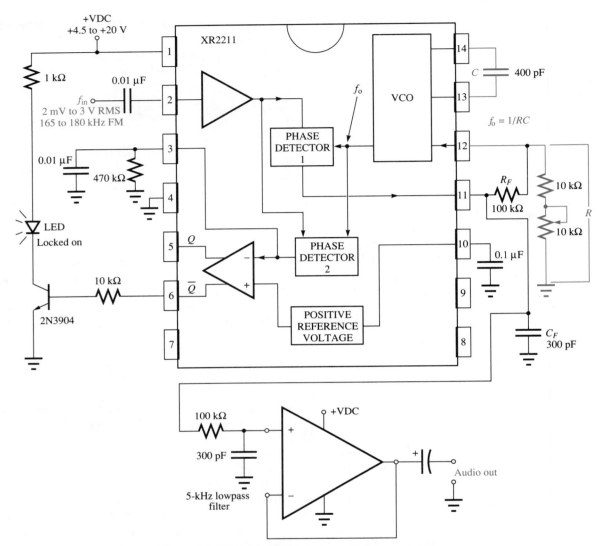

Figure 15–32 The XR2211 as an FM demodulator.

The frequency-modulated signal is applied to pin 2 and the audio is recovered at pin 11, across C_F. A second 5-kHz lowpass filter is added along with a buffer amplifier to remove noise and provide a low-impedance output. Further amplification is added as needed.

Notice that the XR2211 has a second phase detector, phase detector 2. Its output filter is at pin 3. The purpose of this phase detector and filter is to provide a steady high or low output at pin 5 or 6. In this case, pin 6 is used to drive a transistor in the class D switching mode. When a signal is present at pin 2 and the loop is locked, pin 6 is high and the LED is on. This is similar to the FM stereo light on many home stereo receivers.

TABLE 15–1

IC	Type	$f_{o(max)}$	Application
LM565	PLL	500 kHz	FM demodulation, tone decoding, modems
LM566	VCO	1 MHz	FM, function generator, tone generator
LM567	PLL	500 kHz	Touch-tone decoding, ultrasonic control, carrier current remote control
MC2833	VCO	60 MHz	Low-power FM transmitter
NE564	PLL	65 MHz	High-speed modems, frequency synthesizers, signal generators
XR2211	PLL	300 kHz	FM demodulator, tone decoder
XR2206	VCO	1MHz	FM, function generator

Other PLLs and VCOs

A wide range of PLL and VCO ICs are available for many applications. Table 15–1 is a sampling of some of them.

In addition to the many integrated-circuit PLLs, you can assemble a PLL using a separate phase detector, VCO, and loop filter. Sometimes this is necessary depending on the application and frequency range. In any case, the theory of operation is the same.

Take a few moments to review this section and answer the questions of Self-Check 15–5.

Self-Check 15–5

1. In a general sense, what is a VCO?
2. Name and describe the device that makes voltage control of a Clapp oscillator possible.
3. Explain the basic idea behind frequency modulation.
4. Using Figure 15–29 as a model, determine f_o if $V_C = +4$ V, $R_C = 15$ kΩ, $R = 3.3$ kΩ, and $C = 0.001$ μF.
5. Describe the purpose for the loop filter in a PLL system.
6. What is the difference between capture range and lock range for a PLL?

15–6 INSURING OSCILLATOR FREQUENCY STABILITY

FILTERING THE DC LINE

In an electronic system that has many functional blocks, there are many branching DC supply lines to these blocks from the main bus. As, such, the main bus can be an illegitimate means of transferring signals between blocks. Signals on the DC line are referred to as noise. This noise cannot be permitted to reach the oscillator circuit. If it does, the oscillator will be modulated in amplitude and/or frequency. Because the oscillator is used as a signal source for mixing, it must be as clean and stable as possible. Therefore, it is essential that a simple RC or LC lowpass filter be used between the oscillator circuit and the main DC bus line. Usually a 100-Ω resistor in series and a 0.1-

μF capacitor in parallel is sufficient to block line noise from getting to the oscillator.

THE VOLTAGE REGULATOR

Just as important as filtering is voltage regulation. Other circuits on the DC line may load the line and cause the line voltage to dip periodically. No variation in DC line voltage can be permitted at the oscillator, because this will cause frequency and amplitude shifting. Figure 15–33 illustrates how regulation and filtering can be accomplished. The zener diode is the simplest of all regulators.

TEMPERATURE-STABLE COMPONENTS

For an oscillator to be frequency stable, the reactive components must be temperature stable. Inductors and capacitors must not change their value with reasonable changes in temperature. Most modern inductors are fairly stable, especially coils that are wound on toroidal ferrite cores. Care must be taken in the selection of capacitor types. For *RC*, low-frequency oscillators or function generators, polyester (Mylar®) or polyethylene film capacitors should be used. NPO ceramic capacitors may also be used (NPO = negative positive zero temperature coefficient). For *LC* and crystal oscillators, polystyrene, mica, or silver mica capacitors should be used. These capacitors are all very temperature stable. Bypass, filtering, and coupling capacitors can be generic ceramic-disc capacitors or film capacitors.

THE BUFFER AMPLIFIER

When an oscillator is connected to the stage it is intended to drive, its frequency of oscillation is often influenced by the capacitive and resistive

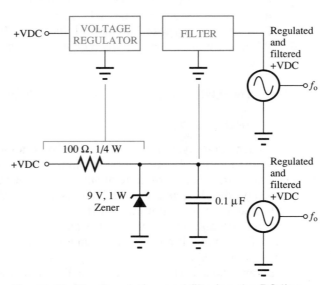

Figure 15–33   Regulating and filtering the DC line.

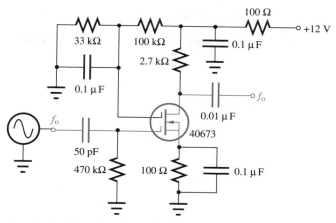

Figure 15–34   A buffer amplifier stage.

loading effects of the receiving stage. Also, power demanded by the receiving stage causes slow heating in the oscillator, which causes frequency drift. Naturally this is not desirable. The common solution to this problem is the use of the buffer amplifier. Figure 15–34 illustrates a good buffer amplifier using the dual-gate MOSFET. The input resistance is very high and the input capacitance is very low. Thus, this buffer will not load the oscillator to any significant degree. Notice the *RC* filter in the DC supply line to the buffer. You don't want noise getting into the buffer either. Other buffer amplifier designs use cascoded FETs and BJTs.

CRYSTAL FREQUENCY STABILITY

Crystal oscillators are far more frequency stable than *LC* oscillators over a given temperature range. Standard commercial crystals are rated by percent frequency change over a given temperature range, usually −30 to +60°C. The percent frequency change is usually rated somewhere around 0.003%, equal to 30 Hz for every 1 MHz. For example, if a 2-MHz crystal has a temperature rating of 0.003%, the frequency may drift by 60 Hz over a −30 to +60°C range in temperature. A 0.001% rating indicates the frequency drift is only 10 Hz per million. A 2-MHz, 0.001% crystal may drift 20 Hz over a −30 to +60°C temperature range. Compare that to *LC* oscillators, which can drift thousands, even tens of thousands, of hertz over the same temperature range.

For extreme frequency stability, special crystals can be placed in small ovens. The oven is a small insulated can in which the crystal is placed along with a heating element (Nichrome® wire) and a temperature sensor (thermistor, or bimetal strip switch). The temperature in the oven is maintained at around 60°C. Since the temperature is fixed, the frequency of the crystal remains stable. Some ovens are made larger to include the entire oscillator circuit. Thus, all components are maintained at the same constant temperature. Ovens are used in broadcast transmitters, frequency counters, and other critical applications where accuracy and stability are important. With the oven, stability of 0.0001% or better is possible (1 Hz for every 1 MHz).

Time for review and self-check.

Self-Check 15–6

1. List three design considerations to insure the stability and purity of an *LC* oscillator.
2. What is the purpose for the buffer amplifier?
3. Which has the best frequency stability (a) an *LC* oscillator, or (b) a crystal oscillator?
4. What is the purpose for a crystal oven?
5. What does it mean if a crystal has a temperature rating of 0.001%?

SUMMARY

FORMULAS

Wien-Bridge and Twin-Tee Oscillators

(15–1) $f_o = 1/(2\pi RC) \cong 0.159/RC$

(15–2) $C = 1/(2\pi R f_o) \cong 0.159/R f_o$

Phase-Shift Oscillator

(15–3) $f_o \cong 0.065/RC$

(15–4) $R \cong 0.065/C f_o$

LC Oscillators

(15–5) $f_o = 1/(2\pi\sqrt{LC}) \cong 0.159/\sqrt{LC}$

Colpitts Oscillator

(15–6) $B \cong C_1/C_2$

(15–7) $A_V > C_2/C_1$

(15–8) $C_t = (C_1 \cdot C_2)/(C_1 + C_2)$

Crystal

(15–9) $C_{\text{loop}} = (C_M \cdot C_S)/(C_M + C_S)$

Two-Op-Amp Function Generator

(15–10) $f_o = 1/(4RC) = 0.25/RC$

(15–11) $R = 1/(4C f_o) = 0.25/C f_o$

Single Op-Amp Square-Wave Generator and XR2206 Function Generator

(15–12) $f_o = 1/RC$

(15–13) $R = 1/C f_o$

555 Timer

(15–14) $T = 1.1\,RC$

(15–15) $R = T/(1.1\,C)$

555 Square-Wave Generator

(15–16)   % Duty Cycle $= (t_{\text{ON}}/T) \cdot 100\%$

(15–17) $t_1 = 0.693 \cdot (R_1 + R_2) \cdot C$

(15–18) $t_2 = 0.693 \cdot R_2 \cdot C$

(15–19) $T = t_1 + t_2 = 0.693 \cdot C \cdot (R_1 + 2R_2)$

(15–20) $f_o = 1/T$

555 Sawtooth Generator

(15–21) $T \cong C \cdot \text{VDC}/3I_{RE}$

Voltage-Controlled XR2206 Function Generator

(15–22) $f_o = \dfrac{1 + [(R/R_C) \cdot (1 - (V_C/3))]}{RC}$

Phase-Locked Loop

(15–23) $f_{\text{upper capture}} \cong f_o + f_{co(\text{loop filter})}$

(15–24) $f_{\text{lower capture}} \cong f_o - f_{co(\text{loop filter})}$

XR2211 PLL

(15–25) $f_o = 1/RC$

CONCEPTS

■ For oscillation to take place, the total loop gain of the amplifier must be no less than 1 and the total loop phase shift must be 0° at the desired frequency of oscillation.

■ A loop gain greater than 1 causes overdriving of the amplifier and clipping of the signal.

■ For most oscillators, the initial loop gain must be greater than 1 for oscillation to begin.

■ Some form of automatic gain control is desirable in some oscillator designs to provide high initial loop gain and automatically reduce gain as oscillation begins.

■ The Wien-bridge oscillator has the least distortion of the *RC*-type oscillators.

■ The Colpitts oscillator, or variations of it, is the most popular *LC*-type oscillator.

- Generally speaking, *RC* oscillators are intended for use below 1 MHz and *LC* oscillators for use above 1 MHz.
- The Colpitts oscillator is identified by the capacitor voltage divider in the resonant loop.
- The Clapp variation of the Colpitts has a capacitor(s) in series with the inductor in the resonant loop.
- The Hartley oscillator is identified by the tapped inductor.
- The Armstrong oscillator is identified by the tuned transformer.
- Crystal oscillators are far more stable than *LC* oscillators are.
- A monostable multivibrator is a timer circuit.
- An astable multivibrator is a square-wave generator.
- A varactor diode can be used to convert any *LC* or crystal oscillator into a voltage-controlled oscillator.
- The phase-locked loop (PLL) is used to recover audio information from a frequency-modulated signal. It is also used in frequency synthesizers for transmitters and scanning receivers, as tone detectors, and in modems to recover digital data from an analog signal.
- The PLL includes a phase comparator, a loop filter, and a VCO.
- The PLL loop filter determines the capture range.
- The frequency range capability of the VCO determines the lock range of the PLL.
- The DC line to the oscillator should be filtered and regulated.
- For frequency stability, temperature-stable components must be used in oscillator design.
- A buffer amplifier should be used to prevent the receiving stage from loading the oscillator.
- An oven can be used to provide a very-frequency-stable crystal oscillator circuit by maintaining a constant temperature.

Sine Wave Oscillator Summary

Type	Frequency Range	Distortion	Description
Wien-bridge	<1 MHz	0.01%	Used in high-quality test instruments, requires a dual potentiometer for tuning, needs automatic gain control
Twin-tee Phase-shift	<1 MHz	1 to 3%	Intended for single-frequency operation, needs automatic gain control
Colpitts Clapp Hartley Armstrong	up to 100 MHz and higher	0.5 to 3%	Intended for high-frequency applications, VFO capability with variable inductor or variable capacitor, used in transmitters and radio receivers, ~0.1% frequency stability

Type	Frequency Range	Distortion	Description
Crystal	30 kHz to 200 MHz	0.1%	Intended mainly for single-frequency operation, netting with a trimmer cap is possible, frequency modulating with a varactor is possible over a narrow range, good frequency stability (0.001% or better)
Sine function generator	<1 MHz	<0.5%	Variable over a large range, used as a test instrument, used as low-frequency FM transmitter, good frequency stability

NEED-TO-KNOW SOLUTION

Colpitts or Hartley oscillators are normally used for variable-frequency oscillators in radio receivers. These oscillators are described in Section 15–2. The oscillator is a class A amplifier that has a tuned feedback loop. The frequency of oscillation is the frequency at which the total loop phase shift is 0°. For sustained oscillation, the total loop gain must be at least 1 where $A_V B = 1$ and B is the attenuation factor of the feedback loop.

The following variable-frequency oscillator can be used as the oscillator block in the AM radio system diagram.

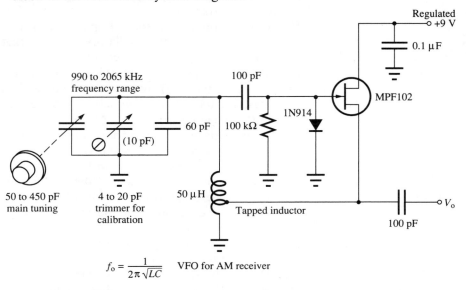

$$f_0 = \frac{1}{2\pi\sqrt{LC}}$$ VFO for AM receiver

QUESTIONS

15–1 INTRODUCTION TO OSCILLATORS

1. What is an oscillator?
2. What is a VFO?

3. What are the two fundamental parts of an oscillator?
4. What are the two basic requirements for sustained oscillation?
5. Describe the oscillator's activity if the loop gain is less than 1.
6. Describe the oscillator's activity if the loop gain is greater than 1.
7. If the reactive feedback network is connected between the output and the inverting input of an op-amp, what is the amount of phase shift the feedback network must provide at the frequency of oscillation?

15–2 SINE-WAVE OSCILLATORS

8. Generally speaking, RC-type oscillators are intended for operation in what frequency range?
9. Describe how the design of the Wien-bridge oscillator satisfies the requirements for oscillation.
10. What is the approximate attenuation factor B for the reactive feedback network of the Wien-bridge oscillator?
11. If the initial voltage gain of the op-amp in a Wien-bridge oscillator is 28, will the circuit oscillate? Explain.
12. What is the phase angle of the feedback voltage from the reactive feedback network at f_o for the Wien-bridge oscillator?
13. Why is automatic gain control needed in the Wien-bridge, twin-tee, and phase-shift oscillators?
14. Briefly explain why the twin-tee oscillator oscillates at its notch frequency.
15. Is the twin-tee intended for (a) single-, or (b) variable-frequency applications? Explain.
16. Explain the basic theory of operation for the phase-shift oscillator.
17. Of these three RC oscillators, which creates the least distortion? (a) Wien-bridge (b) twin-tee (c) phase-shift
18. What is the primary identifying feature of the Colpitts oscillator?
19. In a Colpitts oscillator, what determines the attenuation factor B?
20. Describe the relationship between inductive and capacitive reactance in the tuned network of an LC oscillator at f_o.
21. Why are discrete devices normally used for high-frequency LC oscillator circuits instead of op-amps?
22. Explain why an oscillator, with a common-emitter or common-source amplifier, may not oscillate if the load is too great.
23. How is the Clapp oscillator identified?
24. What is the purpose for the diode from gate to ground in an FET oscillator circuit?
25. Why is the Clapp oscillator of Figure 15–10 more desirable for use than the Colpitts of Figure 15–9?
26. How is the Hartley oscillator identified?
27. How is the Armstrong oscillator identified?
28. Explain how the Armstrong circuit provides the proper phase shift in the feedback network.
29. Briefly explain the piezoelectric effect.
30. Which is more frequency stable with temperature change, (a) an LC oscillator, or (b) a crystal oscillator?

31. How can a mounted crystal have both a series and parallel resonant mode?
32. Which is higher, (a) a crystal's series-resonant frequency, or (b) its parallel-resonant frequency? Why?
33. Why does a crystal have such a high Q compared to LC circuits?
34. How is the Pierce crystal oscillator identified?
35. In a Pierce oscillator, the crystal must provide how much phase shift at f_o?
36. What is an overtone crystal?
37. Why are overtone crystals needed? Why not just make the crystal thinner to oscillate at the higher frequency?

15-3 FUNCTION GENERATORS

38. What is a function generator?
39. What circuit is normally used to create a square-wave signal?
40. What is the purpose for the zener diode in the function generator of Figure 15–18?
41. Why are the slopes of the triangle wave so straight (linear) in the function generator of Figure 15–18?
42. What factors determine the frequency of oscillation for the function generator of Figure 15–18?
43. What determines the peak-to-peak amplitude of the triangle wave in the circuit of Figure 15–18?
44. Explain how f_o can be made variable for the circuit of Figure 15–18.
45. Why is the simple circuit of Figure 15–19 considered a good square-wave generator but not a good triangle-wave generator?
46. Briefly explain the operation of Figure 15–19.
47. Briefly explain how the sine-shaper circuit in Figure 15–20 converts the triangle wave to a sine wave approximation.
48. What is the XR2206?

15-4 THE 555 TIMER

49. What is the 555 integrated circuit?
50. Describe the sequence of events for the circuit of Figure 15–23 starting from pin 2 momentarily going low.
51. What is the condition of the two Q outputs from the flip-flop in the 555 if R momentarily goes high?
52. What is the purpose for Q_1 inside the 555 chip?
53. What is the purpose for pin 4 of the 555?
54. The charge voltage on capacitor C in 555 circuits never gets higher than what value?
55. What is the difference between a monostable multivibrator and an astable multivibrator?
56. Explain what factors determine the percent duty cycle for the square-wave output of the 555 astable multivibrator.
57. Explain how the diode in the 555 circuit of Figure 15–25 enables the circuit to generate duty cycles above or below 50%.
58. Briefly explain the theory of operation of the sawtooth generator of Figure 15–26.

15–5 VOLTAGE-CONTROLLED OSCILLATORS

59. What device makes voltage control possible for LC and crystal oscillators?
60. Are varactor diodes operated in (a) forward bias, or (b) reverse bias? Explain.
61. Explain how an oscillator can be frequency modulated.
62. List at least three VCO design considerations.
63. What is a VCXO?
64. Relate audio amplitude and frequency to frequency deviation in an FM system.
65. What are the three main blocks of a PLL?
66. Where are PLLs used?
67. How is the PLL opposite of the VCO?
68. If the cutoff frequency of the loop filter is 10 kHz and the VCO of the PLL is free-running at 180 kHz, will the PLL lock onto a 160-kHz input signal? Explain.
69. Describe the output of the loop filter when $f_o = f_{in}$ of the PLL.
70. What is the difference between capture range and lock range?
71. Briefly explain how the PLL recovers the original audio from a frequency-modulated input signal.

15–6 INSURING OSCILLATOR FREQUENCY STABILITY

72. Why is it important to filter the DC line voltage that is supplied to an oscillator?
73. Why is it important to regulate the DC line voltage that is supplied to an oscillator?
74. What type of capacitors should you use for LC and crystal oscillator circuits?
75. Why should you use a buffer amplifier following an LC or crystal oscillator circuit?
76. What does it mean if a crystal's temperature rating is 0.003%?
77. What is the purpose for a crystal oven?

PROBLEMS

15–1 INTRODUCTION TO OSCILLATORS

1. If the attenuation factor B of the reactive feedback, network in an oscillator is 0.15 at f_o, what must the amplifier's voltage gain A_V be to sustain oscillation?
2. If $A_V = 10$ and $B = 0.08$, will the oscillator oscillate? Demonstrate mathematically.

15–2 SINE-WAVE OSCILLATORS

3. Identify Figure 15–35 and calculate f_o.
4. If the capacitors of Figure 15–35 are changed to 0.0022 μF, what will f_o be?

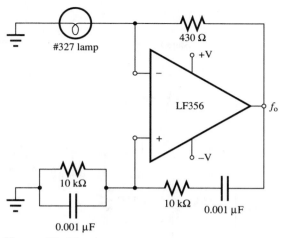

Figure 15–35

5. For Figure 15–35, calculate the value of capacitance C needed for an f_o of 400 Hz.
6. Identify Figure 15–36 and calculate f_o.

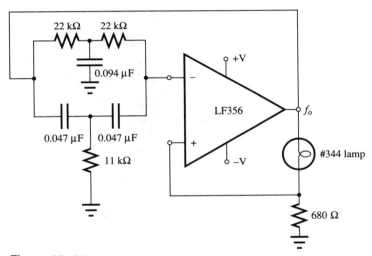

Figure 15–36

7. For Figure 15–36, what values should the resistors be for an f_o of 2 kHz?
8. Identify Figure 15–37 and calculate f_o.
9. For Figure 15–37, what values should the resistors be for an f_o of 10 kHz?
10. Identify Figure 15–38 and calculate f_o.
11. For Figure 15–38, what value should the inductor be for an f_o of 7.5 MHz?
12. For the oscillator of Figure 15–38 to oscillate, the amplifier gain A_V must be greater than what value?

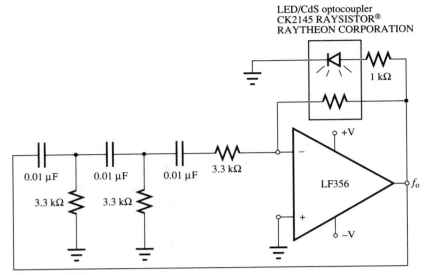

Figure 15–37

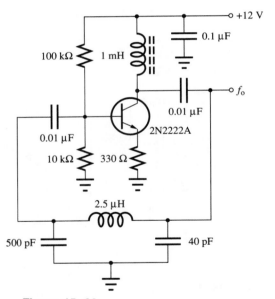

Figure 15–38

13. Identify Figure 15–39 and calculate the range of f_o.
14. Identify Figure 15–40 and calculate the range of f_o.
15. A crystal has an equivalent inductance of 1 H, a series capacitance of 0.02 pF, a series resistance of 2 kΩ, and a mounting capacitance of 5 pF. Calculate the crystal's series and parallel resonant frequencies.
16. A crystal has an equivalent inductance of 5.5 H, a series capacitance of 0.008 pF, a series resistance of 1.5 kΩ, and a mounting capacitance of 3.5 pF. Calculate the crystal's series and parallel resonant frequencies.

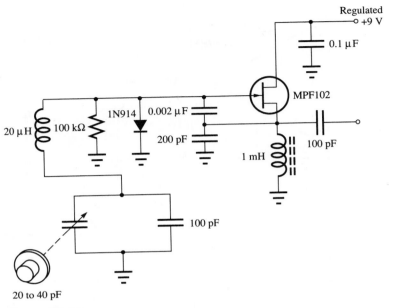

Figure 15–39

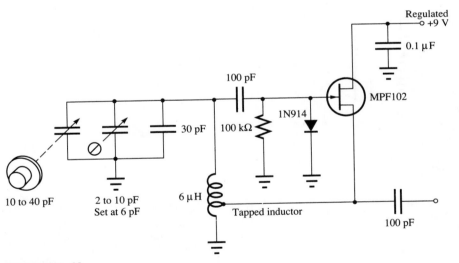

Figure 15–40

15–3 FUNCTION GENERATORS

17. Calculate f_o and V_{P-P} for the circuit of Figure 15–41.
18. Consider f_o for the circuit of Figure 15–42.
19. Calculate the range of f_o for the circuit of Figure 15–43.

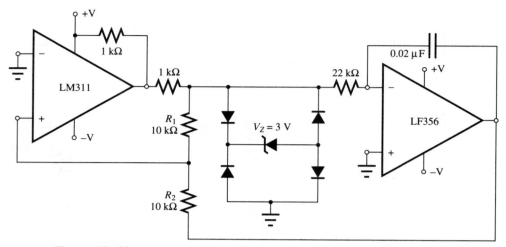

Figure 15–41

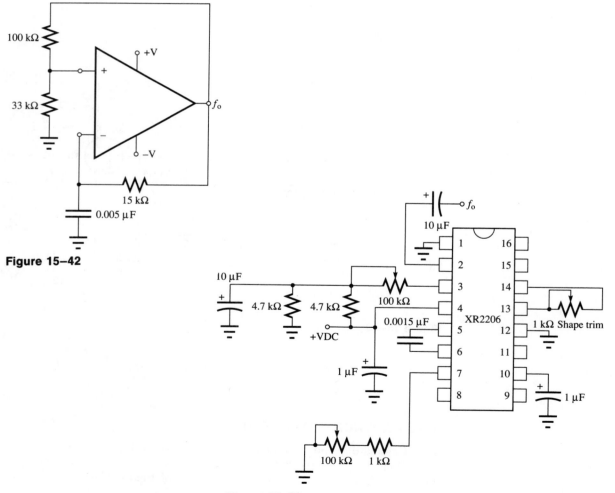

Figure 15–42

Figure 15–43

15–4 THE 555 TIMER

20. Identify the circuit of Figure 15–44 and calculate T.
21. Identify the circuit of Figure 15–45 and calculate f_o and percent duty cycle.
22. Identify the circuit of Figure 15–46 and calculate f_o.

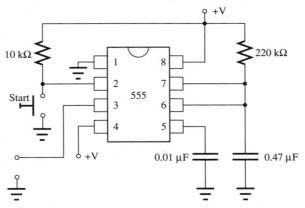

Figure 15–44

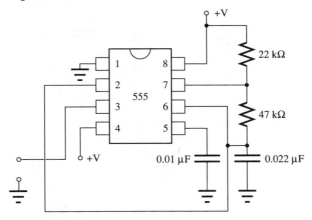

Figure 15–45

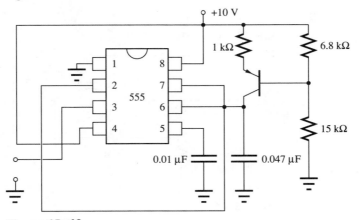

Figure 15–46

15–5 VOLTAGE-CONTROLLED OSCILLATORS

23. Calculate the range of f_o for the circuit of Figure 15–47.
24. Calculate f_o for the circuit of Figure 15–48.
25. Calculate the capture range for the PLL of Figure 15–49.
26. Calculate the capture range for the PLL of Figure 15–50.

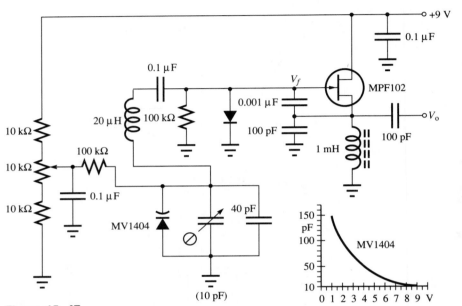

Figure 15–47

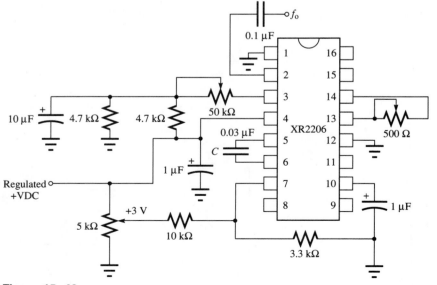

Figure 15–48

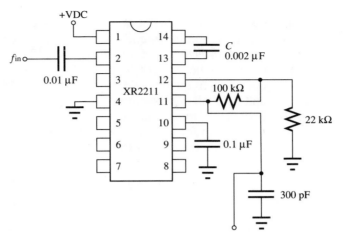

Figure 15–49

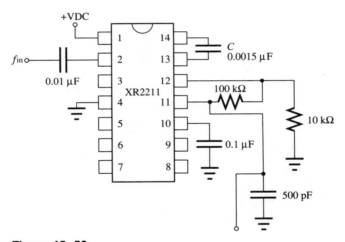

Figure 15–50

15–6 INSURING OSCILLATOR FREQUENCY STABILITY

27. If a 6.25-MHz crystal has a temperature rating of 0.001%, what is the maximum change in frequency over the specified temperature range?
28. If a 9.2-MHz crystal has a temperature rating of 0.0005%, what is the maximum change in frequency over the specified temperature range?

ADDITIONAL PROBLEMS

29. Calculate the value of R needed to design a Wein-bridge oscillator for an operating frequency of 5 kHz. Let $C = 0.005 \ \mu F$. Draw your circuit and label all components.

30. Calculate the value of R and $R/2$ needed to design a twin-tee oscillator for an operating frequency of 8 kHz. Let $C = 0.01$ μF. Draw your circuit and label all components.
31. Calculate the value of R needed to design a phase-shift oscillator for an operating frequency of 10 kHz. Let $C = 0.0022$ μF. Draw your circuit and label all components.
32. For the Colpitts oscillator of Figure 15–9, what value should L be changed to for an f_o of 7 MHz?
33. Determine the range of oscillation for Figure 15–51.

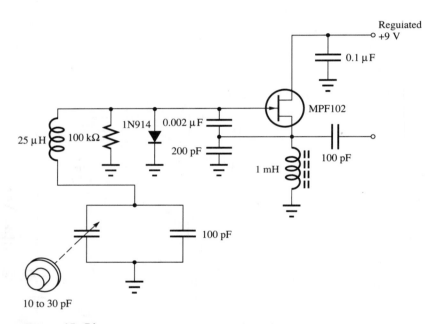

Figure 15–51

34. For the circuit of Figure 15–18, if C is 0.01 μF, what must be the value of R for an f_o of 40 kHz?
35. Determine the value for C if R is 10 kΩ and the desired operating frequency is 400 Hz in Figure 15–19.
36. Suggest values for R and C to cause an XR2206 to oscillate at 10 kHz.
37. Suggest values for R and C to cause a 555 timer to output a 100-ms pulse. Let $R \geq 1$ kΩ.
38. Determine the center operating frequency and the approximate capture range for the PLL of Figure 15–52.

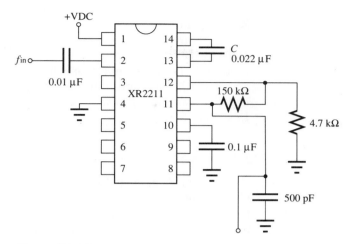

Figure 15–52

ANSWERS TO SELF-CHECKS

SELF-CHECK 15–1

1. An oscillator is an electronic circuit that is designed to generate a continuous and periodic waveform at a particular frequency, converting DC to AC.
2. Amplifier, reactive feedback network
3. Total loop gain equal to 1, total loop phase shift equal to 0°
4. 180°

SELF-CHECK 15–2

1. Wien-bridge oscillator
2. At the frequency where $R = X_C$ the total phase shift is 0°.
3. Use a small, low-current tungsten lamp, which has a positive temperature coefficient, in the voltage-gain feedback loop.
4. The resistors need to be exactly 4,610 Ω for 3 kHz operation.
5. Range of parallel capacitance is 35 to 44 pF. Range of total capacitance is 20.6 to 23.4 pF. Range of frequency is 14.714 to 15.682 MHz.
6. Tapped inductor
7. Greater frequency stability
8. A crystal cut to oscillate at an odd harmonic of the crystal's fundamental frequency

SELF-CHECK 15–3

1. An electronic circuit that performs one or more mathematical functions and, in so doing, generates continuous and periodic waveforms

2. An integrator
3. A comparator
4. 16.667 kHz
5. Figure 15–19 is a comparator whose output switches between $+$VDC and $-$VDC. The capacitor charges through R, reaching a positive or negative switching threshold established by R_1 and R_2.
6. Less than 0.5%

SELF-CHECK 15–4

1. Comparator A momentarily goes high. The flip-flop is set. Pin 3 goes high. Q_1 turns off, allowing the capacitor to charge through R. Comparator B goes high when the capacitor voltage reaches 2/3 VDC. The flip-flop is reset. Pin 3 goes low. The timing cycle is finished.
2. 454.5 kΩ
3. Because the ON time is determined by $R_1 + R_2$ and the OFF time is determined only by R_2
4. ON time $= t_1 = 118,5\ \mu$s, OFF time $= t_2 = 20.8\ \mu$s,
   Total cycle time $= T = 139.3\ \mu$s, $f = 7,179$ Hz, % duty cycle $= 85\%$
5. The capacitor charges only through the diode and R_1. Therefore, the ON time is determined only by R_1, which can be lower in value than R_2.
6. $\cong 16.7$ kHz

SELF-CHECK 15–5

1. An oscillator whose frequency can be changed by changing a DC control voltage
2. The varactor diode—increasing the reverse bias voltage decreases junction capacitance
3. An audio signal is used to rapidly vary the frequency of the oscillator. The changing voltage of the audio causes the frequency to change above and below the center frequency.
4. 280.8 kHz
5. The loop filter determines the capture range for the PLL. It also makes sure that only the difference frequency $(f_o - f_{in})$ reaches the VCO.
6. The capture range is the narrow range of frequency over which the PLL will lock onto a signal. The lock range is the full frequency range of the VCO and is the range over which the VCO will track a signal it is locked onto.

SELF-CHECK 15–6

1. Lowpass filter on the DC line, regulated DC line voltage, temperature-stable capacitors
2. To prevent the oscillator from being loaded down by the next stage thus being pulled off frequency
3. (b)

4. To provide a stable environmental temperature to frequency stabilize the crystal
5. 0.001% = 10 Hz per 1 MHz of frequency variation over a specified temperature range.

SUGGESTED PROJECTS

1. Add some of the main concepts, formulas, and procedures from this chapter to your Electronics Notebook.
2. Build and test some of the oscillator circuits in this chapter.
3. Build one of the multifunction generator circuits on a PC board and use it as a test instrument. You will want to mount it in a project box. You can use two 9-V batteries to power it or build a power supply (AC to DC converter, Sections 2–4 through 2–6).
4. Build a frequency modulator using the XR2206 (Figure 15–29). Apply a 2-Hz sine wave to the audio input and use an oscilloscope to observe the frequency deviation (pin 2). Adjust the amplitude of the 2-Hz sine wave and observe the amount of frequency deviation. Increase the frequency slowly from 2 Hz to 5 Hz and observe the increased rate of deviation.

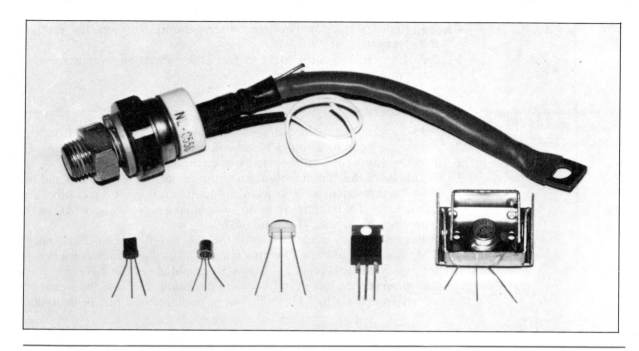

Thyristors are switching devices. Shown here is a sampling of the wide variety of thyristors available. The thyristors shown are silicon controlled rectifiers (SCRs) and TRIACs in a range of voltage and current ratings.

16 Switching Devices

OBJECTIVES

After studying this chapter, you will be able to

■ identify the schematic symbol for SUSs, SCRs, GCSs, DIACs, SBSs, TRIACs, UJTs, and PUTs.
■ describe the construction and operation of SUSs, SCRs, GCSs, DIACs, SBSs, TRIACs, UJTs, and PUTs.
■ describe general uses or applications for SUSs, SCRs, GCSs, DIACs, SBSs, TRIACs, UJTs, and PUTs.
■ explain important concepts that apply to switching devices such as delay angle and conduction angle.

NEED TO KNOW

OK. Let's take a little quiz. Match the devices with applications from the following two lists.

Applications	Devices
1. Full-wave AC power control	GTO
2. Pulse-width motor speed control	TRIAC
3. Half-wave AC power control	UJT
4. Pulsating DC power control	SCR
5. Relaxation oscillator	PUT
6. Programmable trigger level circuit	DIAC
7. Overvoltage protection	SBS

At this point, you may not even know what these applications are, not to mention the devices. However, from the list of applications you can probably sense the importance of the listed devices. Once you learn about these devices, you will find many interesting applications of your own. I know you will find this chapter interesting because these devices are very unique in design and performance.

INTRODUCTION

This chapter covers a broad range of switching devices that are referred to as *electronic switches* or *latches*. The basic characteristic of these devices is that they are off and nonconducting until a voltage threshold is reached. When the threshold is reached, the device turns on and stays on until certain turnoff conditions are met. Thus, these devices are either ON or OFF with no in-between state, transferring nearly all or no power to a load.

Many of these devices are known as thyristors. Thyristors are semiconductor switches made of four or five alternating layers of *P* and *N* material. Some thyristors have a control gate and others do not. Among the thyristors you will explore in this chapter are silicon unilateral switches (SUSs), silicon controlled rectifiers (SCRs), DIACS, TRIACS, and programmable unijunction transistors (PUTs). You will also explore the unijunction transistor (UJT), which is a switching device that is not a thyristor.

The Need to Know section lists some common applications for these devices. They are used in all types of power control circuits because of their high efficiency (low power dissipation compared to load power) and ruggedness. Enjoy your exploration.

16–1 SILICON UNILATERAL SWITCHES (SUSs)

OVERVIEW

The **silicon unilateral switch (SUS),** also known as the **Shockley diode,** is a four-layer diode that has forward current blocking characteristics up to a certain voltage threshold. Once the voltage threshold is reached, the SUS quickly switches on and conducts forward current. This device is described as *unilateral* because it conducts current only in one direction. It can be used in any application in which a voltage threshold is monitored.

The schematic symbol, layer diagrams, and functional analogy for the SUS are shown in Figure 16–1. Like a normal diode, the SUS has a positive terminal called the anode (*A*) and a negative terminal called the cathode (*K*).

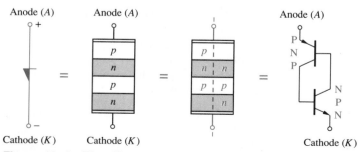

Figure 16–1   The silicon unilateral switch (SUS).

Forward conventional current (hole flow) is from anode to cathode. As you can see, the SUS is four layers of silicon. This is functionally equivalent to paralleled PNP and NPN transistors as shown.

THEORY OF OPERATION

Latching Action

From the overview, you are aware that the SUS switches on, in the forward-conducting mode, when a certain forward bias threshold voltage is reached from anode to cathode. Consider the circuit of Figure 16–2. Notice that the base current of Q_1 is the collector current of Q_2 and the base current of Q_2 is the collector current of Q_1. In this way, a positive-feedback current loop is formed between the two transistors. If the total current gain in this current loop is equal to or greater than one (1), the transistors will drive each other on and keep each other in conduction until the external voltage is removed or the anode and cathode current is reduced to a low level by external means. When forward conducting, the device is said to be *latched on.* Thus, switching devices such as this are also referred to as **latches.**

Alpha and SUS Operation

Now, let's use Figure 16–2 to look at this a little more closely. Recall that alpha (α) is the ratio of collector to emitter current, or the current gain from emitter to collector, where $\alpha = I_C/I_E$ and is always less than one (1). Each of the two transistors, Q_1 and Q_2, has an alpha value that increases with emitter current and temperature. When a small forward voltage is applied to the SUS, a very small forward current flows through the SUS even before threshold is reached. If the applied voltage is increased slowly, the forward current, I_A and I_K, also increases slowly. This causes the alpha of each transistor to increase. When the breakover threshold voltage (V_{BO}) is reached, the total alpha of the two transistors will have reached one (1). In other words, the total loop current gain of the two transistors is 1, which means the positive feedback loop is now able to sustain itself and the two

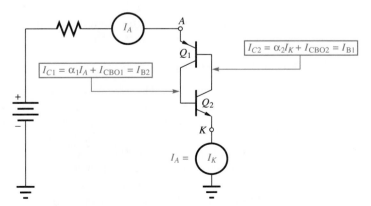

Figure 16–2 SUS current analysis.

transistors latch up, conducting heavily. Doesn't this remind you of the requirements for oscillation—positive feedback with a loop gain of 1 or greater?

Mathematical Proof

Let's see if we can demonstrate this mathematically. For Q_1, $\alpha_1 = I_{C1}/I_A$ and $I_{C1} = \alpha_1 I_A$; for Q_2, $\alpha_2 = I_{C2}/I_K$ and $I_{C2} = \alpha_2 I_K$.

There is also a small leakage current between the collector and base that is usually ignored, I_{CBO}. In this case, the leakage current is significant and cannot be ignored. Therefore, $I_{C1} = \alpha_1 I_A + I_{CBO1}$ and $I_{C2} = \alpha_2 I_K + I_{CBO2}$.

As you can see in Figure 16–2, $I_{C1} = I_{B2}$ and $I_{B2} = I_K - I_{C2}$. Thus, $\alpha_1 I_A + I_{CBO1} = I_K - I_{C2}$. Since $I_{C2} = \alpha_2 I_K + I_{CBO2}$,

$$\alpha_1 I_A + I_{CBO1} = I_K - (\alpha_2 I_K + I_{CBO2})$$

$$\alpha_1 I_A + I_{CBO1} = I_K - \alpha_2 I_K - I_{CBO2})$$

Again, from Figure 16–2, you can see that $I_A = I_K$. Therefore,

$$\alpha_1 I_K + I_{CBO1} = I_K - \alpha_2 I_K - I_{CBO2}$$

Solving for I_K,

$$\alpha_1 I_K + I_{CBO1} = I_K(1 - \alpha_2) - I_{CBO2}$$

$$\alpha_1 I_K = I_K(1 - \alpha_2) - I_{CBO2} - I_{CBO1}$$

$$\alpha_1 I_K - I_K(1 - \alpha_2) = -I_{CBO2} - I_{CBO1}$$

$$I_K \cdot [\alpha_1 - (1 - \alpha_2)] = -I_{CBO2} - I_{CBO1}$$

$$I_K \cdot [-1 + \alpha_1 + \alpha_2] = -I_{CBO2} - I_{CBO1}$$

$$I_K = I_A = \frac{I_{CBO2} + I_{CBO1}}{1 - (\alpha_1 + \alpha_2)} \tag{16-1}$$

As you can see from Formula 16–1, the anode and cathode current is very dependent on leakage current and alphas. As the applied forward voltage is increased, the leakage current and alphas both increase. As the alphas increase, the denominator of the formula approaches zero. As the denominator approaches zero, the anode and cathode current must become very large. Thus, when $(\alpha_1 + \alpha_2) = 1$, the device's forward current is very high, limited by bulk resistance and external components.

The SUS Characteristic Curve

Figure 16–3 reinforces what we have discussed with a test circuit and the resulting characteristic curve. As the voltage (V_A) is increased, V_{AK} increases. As V_{AK} increases, the manufacturer's ratings of V_{DRM} and I_{DRM} are eventually exceeded. V_{DRM} is the maximum repetitive peak device voltage that can be applied without the device switching on (latching). I_{DRM} is the maximum repetitive peak device current that can flow without the device switching on. Soon after V_{AK} is further increased above V_{DRM}, the threshold voltage or *forward breakover voltage* (V_{BO}) is reached. The low-level current at this point is called the *switching current* (I_S). The region from 0 V to V_{BO} is

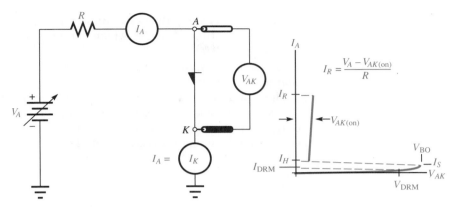

Figure 16-3 SUS theory of operation.

known as the *forward blocking region*, where a large amount of forward current is blocked until V_{BO} is reached. At V_{BO}, the device very quickly latches into a saturated state, where V_{AK} is very low ($V_{AK(on)} \cong 1$ V) and the cathode current is high, limited by an external resistor. In order for the SUS to remain latched, the external resistor must be small enough to allow the anode current to be greater than the holding current (I_H). If the anode current drops below the holding current, the SUS will unlatch and return to the forward blocking condition.

APPLICATION

The Relaxation Oscillator

Figure 16-4 illustrates an application for the SUS device. This circuit is a sawtooth generator of the relaxation-oscillator family. Relaxation oscillators use switching devices or latches to automatically discharge a capacitor every time it charges to a threshold voltage or breakover voltage. The constant-

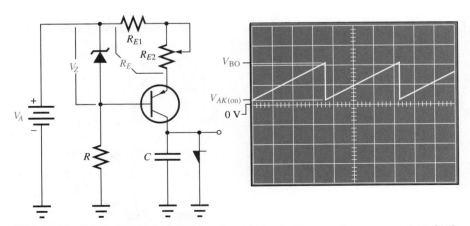

Figure 16-4 Sawtooth generator using a constant-current source and an SUS.

current source causes the capacitor to charge linearly. The capacitor charge current is determined by I_E, which can be varied by changing the value of R_{E2} as shown [$I_E \cong (V_Z - 0.7 \text{ V})/R_E$]. However, I_E must be less than the holding-current value or the SUS will not reset and allow the capacitor to charge once again.

The charge current determines the rate of charge, which determines the frequency of oscillation. Recall from Chapter 12 that $T = C \cdot \triangle V/I$ where T is the time for charge, C is the capacitance, V is the change in charge voltage, and I is the charge current. Thus,

$$T = C(V_{\text{BO}} - V_{AK(\text{on})})/I_E \qquad (16-2)$$

and

$$f_o \cong 1/T = I_E/C(V_{\text{BO}} - V_{AK(\text{on})}) \qquad (16-3)$$

where $I_E = (V_Z - 0.7 \text{ V})/R_E$, V_{BO} is the breakover voltage for the SUS device, and $V_{AK(\text{on})}$ is the anode to cathode saturation voltage.

Formula 16–3 is an approximation, since the discharge time is not taken into consideration. In practice, the frequency of oscillation will be slightly lower than the calculated value. Also, because it is a relatively slow device, the SUS is intended for use at frequencies in the audio range. Consider Examples 16–1 and 16–2.

EXAMPLE 16–1 ■■■■■■■■■■■■■■■■■■■■■■■■■■■■■■■■■■■■

For a relaxation oscillator like that of Figure 16–4, determine the approximate frequency of oscillation if $V_A = 20$ V, $V_Z = 5.1$ V, $R_E = 33$ kΩ, $C = 0.1$ μF, $V_{\text{BO}} = 10$ V, $V_{AK(\text{on})} = 1$ V.

$I_E = (V_Z - 0.7 \text{ V})/R_E = (5.1 \text{ V} - 0.7 \text{ V})/33 \text{ k}\Omega = 133 \text{ } \mu\text{A}$

$f_o \cong I_E/C(V_{\text{BO}} - V_{AK(\text{on})}) = 133 \text{ } \mu\text{A}/[0.1 \text{ } \mu\text{F} \cdot (10 \text{ V} - 1 \text{ V})]$
$\quad = 148 \text{ Hz}$

EXAMPLE 16–2 ■■■■■■■■■■■■■■■■■■■■■■■■■■■■■■■■■■■■

A relaxation oscillator like that of Figure 16–4 has the following values: $V_A = 18$ V, $V_Z = 6.2$ V, $R_E = 68$ kΩ, $C = 0.5$ μF, $V_{\text{BO}} = 8$ V, $V_{AK(\text{on})} = 1$ V, and $I_H = 65$ μA.

First, C must be able to charge to the breakover voltage, which in this case is 8 V. This is possible because $V_A - V_Z$ is greater than $V_{\text{BO}} = 8$ V. Second, $I_C \cong I_E$ must be lower than I_H for the SUS. Otherwise, the SUS will latch ON and never turn OFF.

$I_E = (V_Z - 0.7 \text{ V})/R_E = (6.2 \text{ V} - 0.7 \text{ V})/68 \text{ k}\Omega = 80.9 \text{ } \mu\text{A}$

I_H is specified as 65 μA. That means the SUS will not turn off and the circuit will not oscillate. R_E must be higher in value to reduce I_E below I_H. Also, V_Z could be reduced.

Take time now to review this section and answer the self-check questions.

1. What basic condition must be met within the SUS before it will latch? What causes this condition to occur?
2. What condition must be met for the SUS to remain latched?
3. Which is higher, (a) I_{DRM} or (b) I_H? Explain.
4. While operating in the forward blocking region, the SUS conducts no current at all. True or false?
5. For a relaxation oscillator like that of Figure 16–4, determine the approximate frequency of oscillation if $V_A = 24$ V, $V_Z = 3$ V, $R_E = 10$ kΩ, $C = 0.22$ μF, $V_{BO} = 12$ V, $V_{AK(on)} = 1$V.

16–2 SILICON CONTROLLED RECTIFIERS (SCRs)

OVERVIEW

The **silicon controlled rectifier (SCR)** is another unilateral four-layer device. Like the SUS, the SCR is a diode that has a breakover voltage that must be reached before any significant forward conduction begins. The difference between the SUS and the SCR is that the SCR can be controlled. That is, the breakover voltage can be lowered by applying a voltage and current to a control terminal called the *gate*. Since the SCR has this capability, it can be used as an adjustable rectifier, forward conducting at any predetermined point in the applied AC or pulsating DC waveform. More on this later.

Figure 16–5 shows the schematic symbol, the layer diagram, and the functional analogy for the SCR. The layer structure is modified to accommodate the gate terminal, which is the base of the NPN transistor. Like any diode, current is unilateral (in one direction) from anode to cathode (conventional current).

THEORY OF OPERATION

Gate-Current Triggering

Figure 16–6 illustrates the basic operation of the SCR. Until the normally open push-button switch is closed, the SCR will remain off in the forward blocking region. When the button is pressed, gate current is injected into the

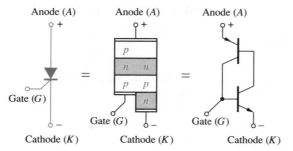

Figure 16–5 The silicon controlled rectifier (SCR).

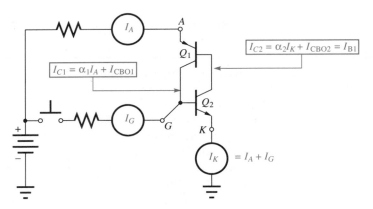

Figure 16–6   SCR current analysis.

feedback loop via the base of Q_2. If the injected gate current is high enough, the SCR will fire (trigger) and conduct heavily. However, the gate current does not have to be very high to cause the SCR to trigger. The gate current is much less than the switching current, holding current, or saturation current. Only a small amount of gate current is needed to increase I_K and α_2 (alpha of Q_2). The increase in alpha and gate current causes I_{C2} and I_{B1} to increase, which causes α_1 and I_{C1} to increase. This brings us back around the loop to the gate/base of Q_2. Once the total alpha is raised to 1, the SCR will latch on. Thus, the latching process in an SCR is motivated by gate current instead of only anode to cathode voltage, as in the SUS.

No-Gate-Current Operation

Let's take another look at the operation of the SCR, using test circuits and characteristic curves. Figure 16–7 shows an SCR test circuit and resulting characteristic curve. Notice there is no gate voltage or current. The SCR is now functioning as an SUS. As V_A is increased, the SCR conducts very little current until V_{BO} and I_S is reached. Once V_{BO} is reached, the SCR latches on and stays on as long as the anode current is greater than the holding current. However, SCRs are not usually operated in this manner. Manufacturers advise against using the breakover voltage to obtain latching in SCRs, since the sudden conduction at the high voltage level can cause a very high instantaneous power dissipation that can cause the SCR to fail. For normal operation, the gate should be used to trigger the SCR.

Gate Current and Breakover Voltage

Figure 16–8 illustrates the effect the gate current has on the trigger point for the SCR. As gate current is increased, by increasing V_G, the voltage breakover point decreases. In other words, the SCR will trigger at lower and lower anode to cathode voltages as the gate current is increased. Also, the holding current is lowered as gate current is increased. However, if gate current is removed after the SCR is latched, the required holding current increases to the normal level (I_{HO}). From the characteristic curves, you should conclude that the SCR will latch on at lower values of V_{AK} as I_G is increased.

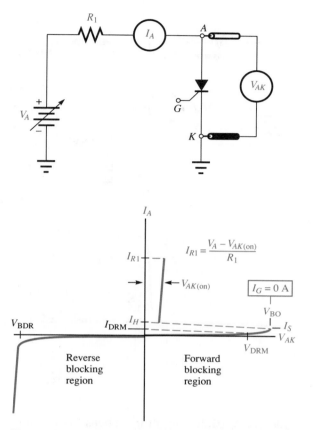

Figure 16–7 SCR test circuit and characteristic curve.

Gate Pulse Triggering

In many applications, the SCR is triggered on using a gate pulse. This is illustrated in Figure 16–9. However, if a gate pulse is to be used, the pulse must remain on long enough for the SCR to go into full conduction. Notice the timing diagrams of Figure 16–9. It takes time for the anode current to rise and for the anode to cathode voltage to drop. The manufacturer defines the gate turn-on time (t_{gt}) as the time starting from the 50% point on the rising edge of the gate pulse to the 90% point on the rising anode current, corresponding to the 10% point on the falling anode to cathode voltage. The point here is to make sure the width of the gate pulse is longer in time than the t_{gt} specification for the SCR.

Resetting the SCR

As you are probably aware, the SCR *cannot* be turned off by simply removing the gate current. The only way to turn off an SCR is to reduce the anode current below the holding-current value. Once the SCR is latched there are two ways this can be done, (1) interrupt the anode current, or (2) use forced commutation. As you can see in Figure 16–10, the SCR can be reset by

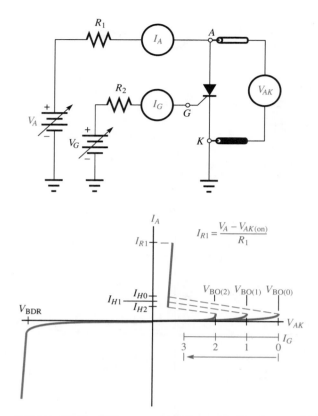

Figure 16–8 Gate current influences the forward breakover voltage and the holding current.

opening the series pushbutton or by closing the shunting pushbutton. In either case, the anode current is forced to drop below the holding-current level and the SCR shuts off. **Forced commutation** accomplishes the same thing in a different way. Instead of the anode current being interrupted by an open or a bypass, a voltage of reverse polarity is momentarily applied across the SCR as a CEMF to oppose the anode current, thereby reducing it below the holding value.

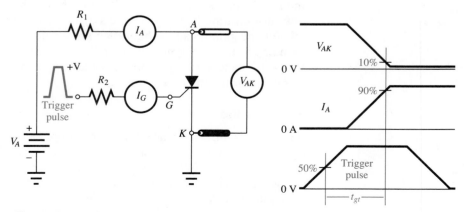

Figure 16–9 Pulse-triggering the SCR.

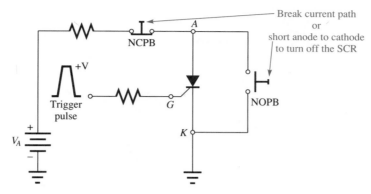

Figure 16–10   Resetting the SCR.

False Triggering of the SCR

False triggering is triggering that occurs when it is not wanted. There are three main sources of false triggering:

1. A high rate of rise in anode voltage can cause false triggering. In other words, if the change in voltage (dv) over a change in time (dt) is too great, charge currents can be caused to flow between layers of the SCR that will trigger it on. This means that SCRs are relatively low-frequency devices and the rate of rise of anode voltage (dv/dt) must be kept below the manufacturer's rating for the SCR. Many SCRs are rated for a maximum rate of change in anode voltage of 50 V/μs. In some applications, a resistor in series with a capacitor is placed from anode to cathode to absorb or slow down rapidly rising voltages. This simple circuit is called a **snubber** and will be discussed again later.

2. Transient voltages arriving at the anode can cause the SCR to trigger if the transient plus normal anode voltage is greater than the breakover voltage. Metal-oxide varistors (MOVs) and zeners can be used to clip the transients at the anode and prevent false triggering.

3. Spurious gate signals caused by stray capacitance, mutual inductance, or line noise can cause the SCR to trigger if the spurious signals are long enough in duration and high enough in amplitude. Gate circuitry should be kept close to the gate whenever possible or a shielded cable to the gate should be used. Also, a 0.01- to 0.1-μF capacitor can be placed between the gate and cathode to short spurious signals.

APPLICATIONS

Full-Wave DC Power Control

Figure 16–11 shows the SCR at work as a DC power control device. The DC source is an unfiltered source supplying pulsating DC to the load resistor and SCR. With each DC pulse at the anode, the SCR has an opportunity to turn on. The SCR is automatically reset as each DC pulse returns to the zero level (0 V). As the anode voltage rises, the SCR could be triggered on at any point, depending on the amount of gate current. The gate current is controlled by

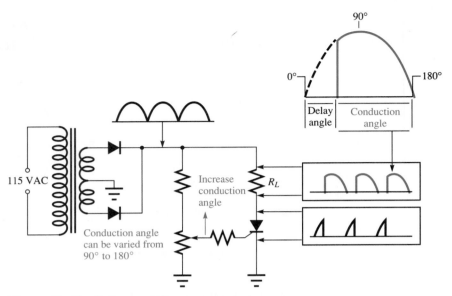

Figure 16–11   Full-wave DC power control.

the potentiometer. If the wiper arm is high, the gate voltage will be high and the gate current will be relatively high. This causes the SCR to trigger early on the rising anode voltage. If the wiper arm is low, the gate voltage will be low and the gate current will be relatively low. This causes the SCR to trigger later on the rising anode voltage. Thus, the trigger point on the rising side of each pulse can be delayed depending on the amount of gate current. This is known as the **delay angle** and ranges from near 0° to near 90°. The **conduction angle** is the portion of the DC pulse, in degrees, during which the SCR is on and the load is receiving current and voltage (power). If the wiper arm on the potentiometer is high, the delay angle is short and the conduction angle is long. If the wiper is all the way down, the SCR may not fire at all and the load receives no power. When the SCR does trigger, it always triggers on the rising side of the DC pulse between 0° and 90°. Thus, the conduction angle will range between 90° and 180°. The load responds to the average DC voltage that appears across its terminals.

Overvoltage Warning Circuit

Figure 16–12 illustrates an overvoltage warning circuit that makes use of the latching characteristic of the SCR. Once triggered, the SCR stays on until the anode current is interrupted. The reset button is used to interrupt the cathode current (in this case, to reset the SCR). The SCR circuit is connected to a bridge rectifier, which charges the capacitor. With 115 VAC applied, the capacitor charges to approximately 160 V, the peak AC voltage. The potentiometer branch monitors this voltage, having been set just below the gate triggering threshold. If the line voltage increases above 115 V, the capacitor charge voltage increases and the gate voltage increases, causing the SCR to trigger, and latch on. This causes the warning lamp to light. The light will stay on until the SCR is manually reset.

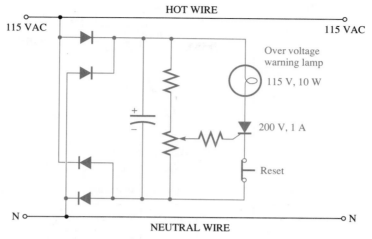

Figure 16–12 Using the SCR in an overvoltage warning circuit.

SCR TYPES AND RATINGS

The selection chart of Figure 16–13 shows a small sampling of SCRs available from Motorola Semiconductor, Inc. This will give you some idea of the package styles and ratings. Even though the SCRs of this chart range up to only 8 A, SCRs rated up to 1,000 A or more are also available. We can use this selection chart to identify important SCR ratings as follows:

$I_{T(RMS)}$ the maximum continuous RMS current the SCR can conduct—the ON RMS current.

V_{DRM} the maximum peak repetitive forward blocking voltage that may be applied without the SCR triggering on.

V_{RRM} the maximum peak repetitive reverse blocking voltage that may be applied without the SCR breaking down in the reverse direction.

I_{TSM} the maximum nonrepetitive surge current the SCR can withstand for a specified time.

I_{GT} the maximum value of gate trigger current that should trigger the SCR on. (For latching applications, the gate current should be greater than this value for reliable operation. **Sensitive-gate** SCRs have I_{GT} ratings 100 times less than regular SCRs—i.e., 0.2 mA as compared to 20 mA.)

V_{GT} the amount of gate voltage needed to produce the specified value of I_{GT}.

T_J the junction temperature.

Other Important Ratings Found on Data Sheets

I_{GM} forward peak gate current. This rating is usually 1000 times greater than I_{GT}.

I_{DRM} and I_{RRM} the maximum peak repetitive blocking current corresponding with V_{DRM} and V_{RRM}. This current is approximately a million times smaller than $I_{T(RMS)}$, in the microamps.

		On-State (RMS) Current						
		1.6 AMPS		**4 AMPS**				
		$T_C = 85°C$	$T_C = 65°C$	$T_C = 93°C$	$T_C = 30°C$			
		Case 79-04 TO-205AD (TO-39) Style 3		Case 77-06 TO-225AA (TO-126) Style 2			Case 369-03 Style 4	Case 369A-04 Style 4
V_{DRM}	50 V	2N2323	2N4213	MCR1906-2	MCR106-2 2N6237	C106F		
	100 V	2N2324	2N4214	MCR1906-3	MCR106-3 2N6238	C106A	MCR703-1	MCR703[1]
	200 V	2N2326	2N4216	MCR1906-4	MCR106-4 2N6239	C106B	MCR704-1	MCR704[1]
V_{RRM}	400 V	2N2329	2N4219	MCR1906-6	MCR106-6 2N6240	C106D	MCR706-1	MCR706[1]
	600 V			MCR1906-8	MCR106-8 2N6241	C106M	MCR708-1	MCR708[1]
	800 V							
MAXIMUM ELECTRICAL CHARACTERISTICS	I_{TSM} (Amps) 60 Hz	15			25	20	25	
	I_{GT} (mA)	0.2	0.1	1	0.2		0.075	
	V_{GT} (V)	0.8		1	0.8		1	
	T_J Operating Range (°C)	−65 to +125		−65 to +110	−40 to +110			

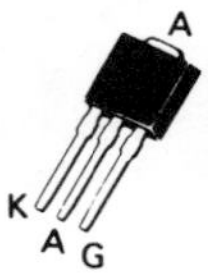

(1) For tape and reel, add suffix "RL."

Figure 16–13   SCR selection chart. (Copyright by Motorola, Inc. Used by permission.)

I_H the holding current—the minimum amount of anode current needed to keep the SCR latched.

dv/dt the critical rise of OFF-state voltage—the minimum rise in OFF-state voltage that will cause the SCR to switch on.

GATE-CONTROLLED SWITCHES (GCSs)

The GCS/GTO

In many applications it would be an advantage to be able to use the gate to turn the SCR off as well as on, as is done with BJTs. The problem is, regular SCRs cannot be turned off using the gate. However, there is a small family of SCRs called **gate-controlled switches (GCSs)** that do have this capability.

On-State (RMS) Current						
6 AMPS	8 AMPS					
$T_C = 30°C$	$T_C = 70°C$	$T_C = 75°C$		$T_C = 83°C$		
 Sensitive Gate				Sensitive Gate		
Case 77-06 TO-225AA (TO-126) Style 2	Case 221C-02 Style 2	Case 221A-04 TO-220AB Style 3				
MCR506-2	MCR218-2FP	MCR218-2	C122F1	MCR72-2	50 V	
MCR506-3		MCR218-3	C122A1	MCR72-3	100 V	V_{DRM}
MCR506-4	MCR218-4FP	MCR218-4	C122B1	MCR72-4	200 V	
MCR506-6	MCR218-6FP	MCR218-6	C122D1	MCR72-6	400 V	V_{RRM}
MCR506-8	MCR218-8FP	MCR218-8	C122M1	MCR72-8	600 V	
	MCR218-10FP	MCR218-10	C122N1	MCR72-10	800 V	
40	80		90	100	I_{TSM} (Amps) 60 Hz	MAXIMUM ELECTRICAL CHARACTERISTICS
0.2	30	25	C122( )1 25	0.2	I_{GT} (mA)	
1	2.5	1.5			V_{GT} (V)	
−40 to +110	−40 to +125		−40 to +100		T_J Operating Range (°C)	

Figure 16–13 (*continued*)

For these devices, the gate is used to turn the device both on and off. Because of the gate turn-off capability, these devices are also called **gate turn-off devices (GTOs).** The GTO is illustrated in Figure 16–14. For Figure 16–14a, the GTO turns on when the gate pulse goes high. When the gate pulse goes low, the GTO turns off because of the reverse bias provided by the load voltage on the cathode. As shown in Figure 16–14b, the load is connected to the anode instead of the cathode and a capacitor is placed in series with the gate to provide a negative impulse to the gate for turn-off.

Applications

GTOs are used in applications such as high-speed switching power supplies and for pulse-width motor speed control circuits. A pulse-width control circuit is illustrated in Figure 16–15. The GTO is turned on and off by a pulse train that can be varied in duty cycle. The GTO supplies a pulsating current to the DC motor that corresponds to the control pulse train. The motor

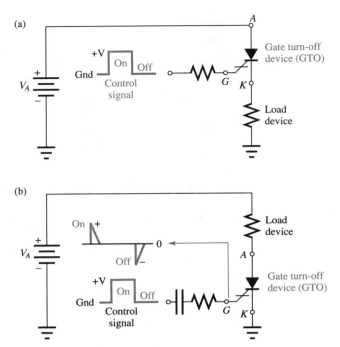

Figure 16–14 The gate turn-off SCR (GTO).

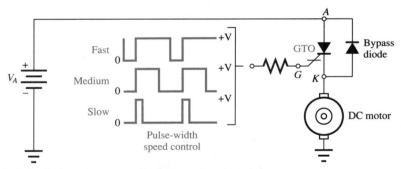

Figure 16–15 Using the GTO in a pulse-width speed control circuit for a DC motor.

responds to the average current in its armature. When the average level is high, the motor runs fast and when the average is low the motor runs slow. Why not use a rheostat? The rheostat would use a tremendous amount of power—power that is wasted. The GTO uses very little power since it acts as a switch. When it is on, the current is high but the voltage across the GTO is very low. Thus GTO power dissipation is low. When the GTO is off, the current is nil and the power dissipation is nil. Therefore, very little power is wasted. Electric vehicles use control circuits like this.

Time for a self-check.

**Self-Check
16–2**

1. List two similarities between the SUS and the SCR.
2. What is one important difference between the SUS and SCR?

3. Explain how the amount of gate current effects V_{BO} and I_H for an SCR.
4. List two ways an SCR can be turned off (reset).
5. Explain the relationship between gate current and conduction angle for the circuit of Figure 16–11.
6. Describe the difference between an SCR and a GTO.

16–3 DIACs AND SBSs

DIACs

Overview

Up to this point we have been exploring unilateral switching devices, devices that trigger and conduct only in one direction. With this section, we begin to explore bilateral switches, devices that conduct in both directions. The first of these is the DIAC. The **DIAC** is a dual-electrode AC trigger device. That is, it can be triggered on the positive or negative alternation of an AC signal.

The schematic symbol, layer diagram, and functional analogy for the DIAC is shown in Figure 16–16. The terms *anode* and *cathode* no longer have any meaning, since the device is bidirectional. Therefore, it is customary to label the terminals simply as main terminal 1 (MT 1) and main terminal 2 (MT 2). As you can see, the DIAC is two paralleled and antipolarized SUSs.

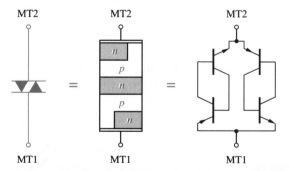

Figure 16–16 The DIAC, a two-terminal AC trigger device.

Theory of Operation

As you might expect, the DIAC exhibits the characteristics of two paralleled and antipolarized SUSs. This is illustrated in Figure 16–17. The DIAC has a breakover voltage threshold for each polarity and each alternation of the applied AC. The waveform shown in Figure 16–17 is the voltage waveform that appears across the DIAC. The DIAC is off starting at zero-crossing for each alternation. As the voltage across the DIAC rises in either direction, a breakover voltage is reached and the DIAC switches on, dropping the output voltage to near ground. When the DIAC is on there is a small MT 2 to MT 1 voltage drop of approximately 1 V or so. The characteristic curve shows the

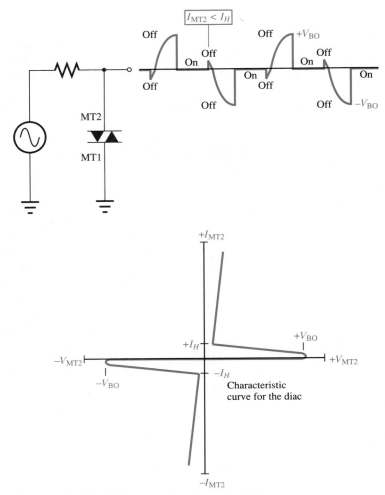

Figure 16–17 DIAC operating characteristics.

holding current required to maintain conduction in either direction. The series resistor in any DIAC circuit must be low enough in value that the on current is greater than the required holding current. Naturally, the DIAC resets, or turns off, as each applied AC alternation approaches zero-crossing or at any point in the alternation where the device current drops below the holding value.

Applications

DIACs are used in overvoltage protection circuits to trigger on when excessive voltage spikes are present on an AC line and as trigger devices for the gate of SCRs and TRIACs (to be covered in the next section). DIACs are generally medium- and high-power devices.

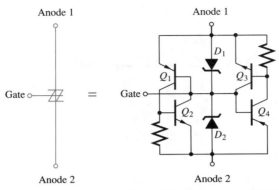

Figure 16–18   The silicon bilateral switch (SBS).

SILICON BILATERAL SWITCHES (SBSs)

Overview

The silicon bilateral switch (SBS) is similar to the DIAC, yet different. The DIAC and SBS are both bilateral or bidirectional devices. However, the SBS is faster, made for low breakover voltages, has a gate that may or may not be used, and is an integrated circuit (IC) instead of a single four-layer device.

Figure 16–18 shows the schematic symbol and functional diagram for the SBS. Strange as it may seem, this device has two anodes. The reason for this strange labeling is the internal zener diodes. The anode of a zener is connected to each main terminal and the device will function in the ON state when a positive potential is applied to the terminal. For example, when a positive potential greater than $V_Z + 0.7$ V is applied to anode 1, D_1 and D_2 conduct, providing a -0.7-V bias voltage for the base of Q_1 with respect to anode 1. This causes Q_1 to conduct, which triggers Q_2 and latch-up occurs. Q_3 and Q_4 are off. When anode 2 is positive, Q_4 and Q_3 turn on while Q_1 and Q_2 are off. The trigger voltage in either direction is $\pm(V_Z + 0.7$ V$)$. Breakover voltages usually range between 6 and 10 V with the gate open (not connected). The Motorola MBS4991, MBS4992, and MBS4993 are a few of the SBS devices available.

Operating Characteristics

Figure 16–19 illustrates the operating characteristics of the SBS. The output waveform and the characteristics curve look the same as for the DIAC. The difference is the SBS triggers at a lower voltage and handles much less power than the DIAC. While DIACs are designed for two- and three-digit breakover voltages, SBSs are designed for one- and two-digit breakover voltages. The resistors shown connected to the gate of the SBS in Figure 16–19 are optional. When used, they cause base current to flow which causes the device to trigger at lower anode voltages. The resistors can be the same value for symmetrical triggering or different values for asymmetrical triggering. Resistors in the range of 10 kΩ to 100 kΩ are used.

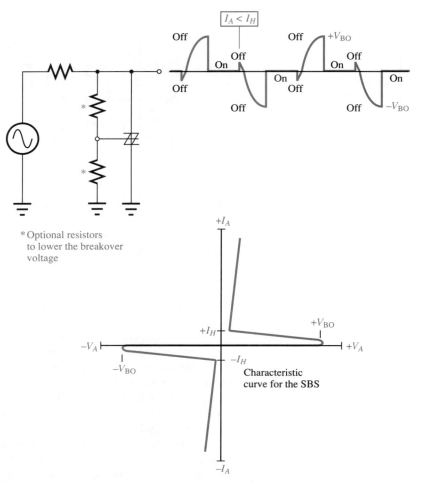

Figure 16–19   SBS operating characteristics.

Application

Figure 16–20 shows one application for which the SBS may be used. This is a very simple relaxation oscillator. The theory of operation is easy to understand. The capacitor charges until the breakover voltage is reached. At that point, the SBS switches on and discharges the capacitor to the point where capacitor-discharge current and resistor current is less than the required holding current. The resistor value must be large enough such that the current through it when the SBS is on is less than the holding current. When I_A drops below I_H, the SBS turns off and the capacitor charges again. A constant-current source can be used to provide a linear charge ramp voltage (sawtooth waveform).

We will look at another common application for the SBS a little later. For now, take time to test your understanding by answering the questions of Self-Check 16–3.

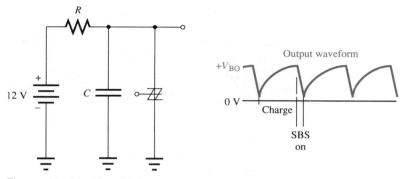

Figure 16–20 The SBS relaxation oscillator.

**Self-Check
16–3**

1. Briefly describe the operating characteristics of the DIAC.
2. List three differences between the DIAC and SBS.

16–4 TRIACs

OVERVIEW

The next logical step in device development beyond the DIAC is the TRIAC. The TRIAC is a three-terminal AC switch, one of the terminals being a gate that is used to determine the breakover voltage. The operation of the TRIAC is like that of the SCR. However, the TRIAC is able to function bilaterally, or bidirectionally as far as current and voltage is concerned. Because of charge accumulation within the TRIAC, it is not able to switch rapidly from one polarity to another. Thus, the TRIAC is a very-low-frequency device intended for 50-Hz and 60-Hz operation.

The schematic symbol, layer diagram, and functional analogy for the TRIAC is shown in Figure 16–21. As you can see, the TRIAC is a five-layer thyristor that is functionally equivalent to two paralleled and antipolarized SCRs. As with the DIAC, since it is an AC device, the main terminals of the

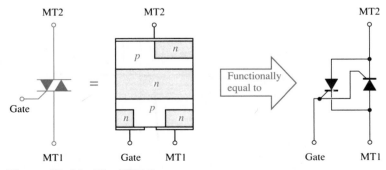

Figure 16–21 The TRIAC.

TRIAC are not labeled as anode or cathode. The gate terminal is connected to an *np* and a *pn* diode junction between the gate and MT 1. Forward biasing either gate diode will inject current into the device which will cause it to trigger. Normally, when MT 2 is positive, a positive pulse is applied to the gate to trigger the TRIAC on and when MT 2 is negative, a negative pulse is applied to the gate to trigger the TRIAC on (all polarities referenced to MT 1).

THEORY OF OPERATION

Characteristic Curves

Figure 16–22 illustrates the operation of the TRIAC with a test circuit and a set of characteristic curves. Since it is similar to the SCR characteristics, this should look familiar to you. Unlike the SCR, the TRIAC offers bilateral operation, as indicated by the characteristic curves. As the potentiometer is set higher, the gate current increases and the TRIAC fires sooner on the rising edge of each alternation, both positive and negative. Notice also the influence gate current has on the holding current. This may be obvious to you, but notice that the polarity of the gate voltage and current automatically changes with the polarity of MT2 with each alternation of the applied AC.

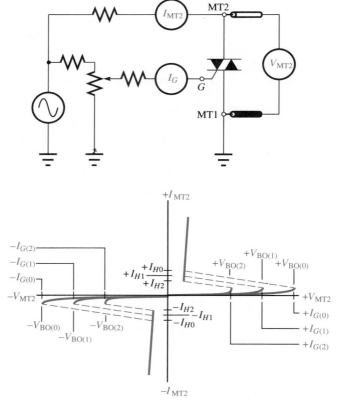

Figure 16–22 Gate current's influence on holding current and breakover voltage.

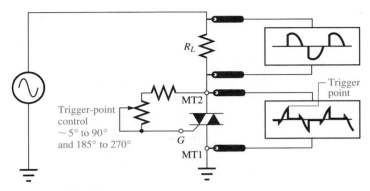

Figure 16–23 Simple full-wave power control using the TRIAC.

Varying the Conduction Angle for Power Control

The operation of the TRIAC is illustrated further in Figure 16–23. This is a simple full-wave power control circuit (an SCR would provide half-wave control). The amount of gate current determines the trigger point, the point in the applied AC waveform at which the TRIAC turns on. By adjusting the rheostat, the gate current is changed and so is the trigger point. In this way, the delay angle and conduction angle of the TRIAC can be controlled. This circuit provides control from approximately 5° to almost 90° and from approximately 185° to near 270°. The minimum power point is when the delay angle is almost 90°, when the TRIAC is off for the rising side of each alternation. Under these conditions, the RMS voltage and current to the load is cut in half, since half of each alternation is blocked, and the power dissipated by the load is 1/4 of maximum ($0.5\ E \cdot 0.5\ I = 0.25\ P$).

APPLICATIONS

Phase Control

A broader range of power control can be obtained using phase delay. This very common approach to TRIAC control is shown in Figure 16–24. Notice the TRIAC is triggered by an SBS that has a threshold of approximately ±8 V. The 0.1-μF capacitor charges to ±8 V and triggers the SBS, which triggers the TRIAC. There are two delay networks, (1) the 27-kΩ resistor and the 0.1-μF capacitor, and (2) the 100-kΩ rheostat plus 1-kΩ resistor and the 0.2-μF capacitor. The combined charge delay of these two networks determines when and if the SBS and TRIAC trigger. When the 100-kΩ rheostat is set for maximum resistance, the delay is very long, so long that the capacitors never charge high enough during any alternation to trigger the SBS. When the rheostat is at minimum resistance, the capacitors charge quickly, causing the SBS to fire early in the alternation.

The Snubber Network

Figure 16–25 shows the snubber network that is needed when inductive loads are to be controlled. Inductive loads present a special problem to the TRIAC. The problem is that inductor voltage and current are 90° out of

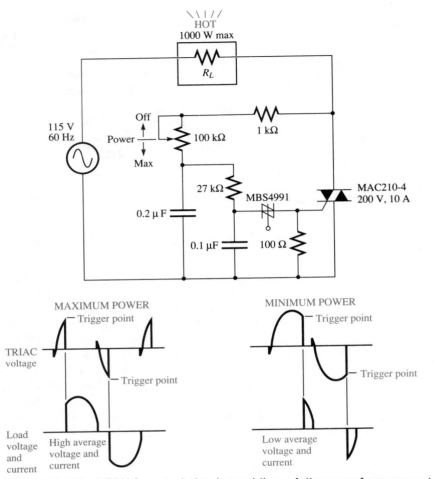

Figure 16–24   A TRIAC control circuit providing a full range of power control.

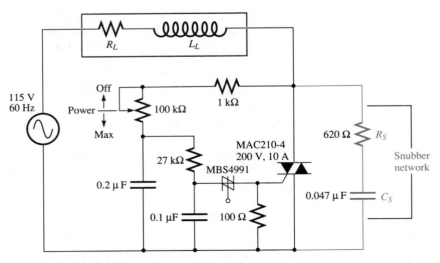

Figure 16–25   The snubber network insures control for inductive loads.

phase. When the load current drops below the holding-current level of the TRIAC, the inductive load provides a high reverse voltage to the TRIAC. This sudden reverse voltage false triggers the TRIAC back on again. Like SCRs, the TRIAC can be false-triggered by a rapidly rising terminal voltage (dv/dt). The snubber network compensates for the inductive load and absorbs the sudden jump in reverse voltage. When the TRIAC is on, the snubber capacitor is discharged. When the TRIAC attempts to turn off, the capacitor aids it by shorting the sudden inductor voltage. Thus, the TRIAC stays off until triggered on by the gate circuit and full control over both alternations is maintained. Values for R_S and C_S are approximate and may have to be changed somewhat, depending on the load.

TRIAC TYPES AND RATINGS

TRIAC parameters and ratings are much the same as for SCRs. Figure 16–26 is a selection chart showing a sampling of TRIACs of different power ratings and case styles. As an example, the T2500M is in a TO-220 case having a maximum RMS current rating ($I_{T(RMS)}$) of 6 A, a maximum peak repetitive forward blocking voltage rating (V_{DRM}) of 600 V_p (424 V_{RMS}), a maximum nonrepetitive surge-current rating (I_{TSM}) of 60 A, a maximum trigger-current rating (I_{GT}) of 60 mA at 25°C, and a maximum gate trigger-voltage rating (V_{GT}) of 2.5 V at 25°C.

Amazingly, this small TRIAC is able to handle up to 2,544-W loads ($V_{RMS} \cdot I_{RMS} = P = 424$ V $\cdot$ 6 A $= 2,544$ W). Though not shown in the chart, the maximum peak *on* terminal voltage (V_{TM}) for this device is 2 V. That means the *maximum* peak power dissipation of the device itself is a mere 17 W_p (2 $V_P \cdot 8.5 A_P = 17 W_P$) while it is on. The average power dissipation is much less. In practice, the average power dissipation of the device would only be approximately 5 to 10 W, depending on conduction angle, with a 2,544-W load. This is a power efficiency greater than 99.3% (100% $\cdot$ 2,544 W/2,561 W = 99.3%). Not bad, huh?

Take time to review this section and answer the questions of self-check 16–4.

Self-Check 16–4

1. List three similarities between the TRIAC and SCR.
2. Is the TRIAC a high-speed or a low-speed device?
3. Explain how the conduction angle of the TRIAC can be increased by changing the gate current.
4. What is the purpose of phase control for TRIACs?
5. What is a snubber network and what does it do?

16–5 UNIJUNCTION TRANSISTORS (UJTs)

In this section, we will explore the unijunction transistor (UJT) and the programmable unijunction transistor (PUT). You will be surprised to see the similarities between the two and even more surprised to see the differences. UJTs and PUTs are interesting semiconductor devices that are used as triggers. We will consider their theory of operation and an application for each.

		On-State (RMS) Current			
		0.6 AMPS		2.5 AMPS		4 AMPS
		$T_C = 50°C$ 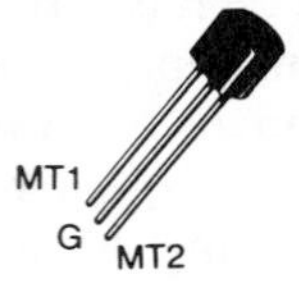		$T_C = 70°C$ 		$T_C = 85°C$
				Sensitive Gate		
		Case 29-04 TO-226AA (TO-92) Style 12		Case 77-06 TO-225AA (TO-126) Style 5		
V_{DRM}	200 V	MAC97-4	MAC97A4	T2322B	T2323B	2N6071
	400 V	MAC97-6	MAC97A6	T2322D	T2323D	2N6073
	600 V	MAC97-8	MAC97A8	T2322M	T2323M	2N6075
	800 V					
MAXIMUM ELECTRICAL CHARACTERISTICS	I_{TSM} (Amps)	8		25		30
	I_{GT} @ 25°C (mA) MT2(+)G(+) MT2(+)G(−) MT2(−)G(−) MT2(−)G(+)	10 10 10 10	5 5 5 7	10 10 10 10	25 40 25 40	30 — 30 —
	V_{GT} @ 25°C (V) MT2(+)G(+) MT2(+)G(−) MT2(−)G(−) MT2(−)G(+)	2 2 2 2.5		2.2 2.2 2.2 2.2		@ −40°C 2.5 — 2.5 —
	T_J Operating Range (°C)			−40 to +110		

Figure 16–26 TRIAC selection chart. (Copyright by Motorola, Inc. Used by permission.)

THE UJT

Introduction to the UJT

The schematic symbol and layer diagram for the unijunction transistor (UJT) is shown in Figure 16–27. Immediately you notice the similarity between the UJT symbol and the symbol for an FET. But be careful here. The UJT is not

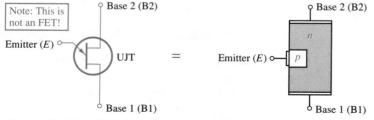

Figure 16–27 The unijunction transistor (UJT).

On-State (RMS) Current						
4 AMPS		**6 AMPS**				
$T_C = 85°C$		$T_C = 80°C$				
 G MT2 MT1 **Sensitive Gate**		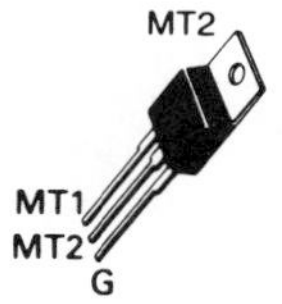 MT2 MT1 MT2 G		 MT1 MT2 G		
Case 77-06 TO-225AA (TO-126) Style 5		Case 221A-04 TO-220AB Style 4		Case 221C-02 Style 3		
2N6071A	2N6071B	T2500B	T2801B	T2500BFP	200 V	
2N6073A	2N6073B	T2500D	T2801D	T2500DFP	400 V	V_{DRM}
2N6075A	2N6075B	T2500M	T2801M	T2500MFP	600 V	
		T2500N	T2801N	T2500NFP	800 V	
30		60		80	I_{TSM} (Amps)	
					I_{GT} @ 25°C (mA)	
5	3	25		80	MT2(+)G(+)	
5	3	60		80	MT2(+)G(−)	
5	3	25		80	MT2(−)G(−)	
10	5	60		80	MT2(−)G(+)	
					V_{GT} @ 25°C (V)	
@ −40°C		2.5		4	MT2(+)G(+)	
2.5		2.5		4	MT2(+)G(−)	
2.5		2.5		4	MT2(−)G(−)	
2.5		2.5		4	MT2(−)G(+)	
−40 to +110					T_J Operating Range (°C)	

Text running down right side: MAXIMUM ELECTRICAL CHARACTERISTICS

Figure 16–26   (*continued*)

an FET! The junction in an FET is operated reverse bias. The junction in the UJT is operated forward bias. Notice the unusual labeling of the UJT terminals. There are two bases and an emitter in the middle. As you will soon see, the primary terminals are the emitter and base 1.

As you can see from the layer diagram, there are no layers to the UJT. The UJT is basically a single n-material chip with a small p region imbedded in one side. A single junction is formed between the p and n materials.

Theory of Operation

As stated earlier, the UJT is a trigger device. Figure 16–28 illustrates what that means. The triggering takes place between the emitter and base 1. The basic operation is simple. As V_E is increased with the potentiometer, a peak-point voltage (V_P) is reached at which the EB1 junction becomes forward biased and current is injected into the base 1 region. As the current flows from emitter to base 1, the resistance of the base-1 area decreases. This allows more current to flow and the base-1 bulk resistance decreases further.

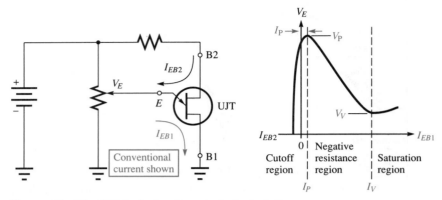

Figure 16–28 UJT test circuit and characteristic curve.

This process is called **conductivity modulation.** Finally, the base-1 bulk resistance reaches its minimum resistance value at the valley point (V_V and I_V) on the characteristic curve. The region on the curve between V_P and V_V is the **negative-resistance region**—the operating region in which the base-1 bulk resistance decreases during conductivity modulation. Any further increase in emitter current beyond the valley point is a linear increase due to an increase in V_E. In this region, the base-1 bulk resistance does not decrease any further and the device is said to be *in saturation.*

Current I_{EB2} is a small reverse leakage current that exists between base 2 and the emitter. This current is insignificant and ceases when V_E approaches the peak point voltage. Be careful when interpreting the characteristic curve. I_V is much greater than I_P. I_V is usually in milliamps and I_P is in microamps.

The Intrinsic Standoff Ratio (η)

Let's take a closer look now at the inside of the UJT to see how the peak-point voltage (the trigger voltage) is established. Again, the concept here is simple. As shown in Figure 16–29, the emitter to base 1 junction is a silicon diode junction. Approximately 0.4 to 0.7 V (V_D) is needed to forward bias the diode junction. However, 0.7 V is not enough to trigger the device. Notice the *n*-material is divided into two bulk-resistance regions, r_{B2} and r_{B1}. (The r_{B1} bulk resistance is the bulk resistance that decreases after V_P is reached.) The two bulk resistances are obviously in series and form a voltage

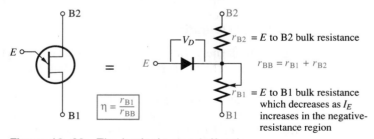

Figure 16–29 The intrinsic standoff ratio.

divider. The voltage drop across r_{B1} acts as a reverse bias on the emitter–base 1 junction. Therefore, before the diode junction can become forward biased V_E must be equal to 0.7 V + V_{rB1}, where $V_P \cong$ 0.7 V + V_{rB1}.

As you can see, the voltage drop across r_{B1} plays a major role in determining the trigger voltage V_P. V_{rB1} is intrinsic to this device by design and serves to standoff or oppose the emitter bias voltage V_E. Thus, the voltage divider ratio of $r_{B1}/(r_{B1} + r_{B2})$ is called the **intrinsic standoff ratio,** symbolized with the lowercase Greek letter eta (η).

$$\eta = r_{B1}/(r_{B1} + r_{B2}) = r_{B1}/r_{BB} \qquad (16\text{–}4)$$

where r_{BB} is the total bulk resistance $r_{B1} + r_{B2}$.

For most UJTs, the value for η is in the range of 0.5 to 0.85. Values for r_{BB} usually range between 3 and 10 kΩ unmodulated (no emitter current or voltage). When the UJT is modulated ($V_E > V_P$ and $I_{EB1} > I_P$), r_{B1} drops from approximately 5 kΩ down to the area of 100 to 200 Ω.

The actual peak-point voltage (trigger voltage) will depend on the intrinsic standoff ratio and the voltage applied to the device from B2 to B1 (V_{B2B1}).

$$V_P \cong 0.7 + \eta V_{B2B1} \qquad (16\text{–}5)$$

Formula 16–5 is an approximation because the diode forward voltage may be anywhere between 0.4 V and 0.7 V depending on device and temperature. Consider Examples 16–3 and 16–4.

EXAMPLE 16–3 ▐▬▬▬▬▬▬▬▬▬▬▬▬▬▬▬▬▬▬▬▬▬▬▬▬▬▬▬▬▬▬▬▬

A 2N4870 UJT has an intrinsic standoff ratio (η) of 0.63 and 24 V is applied from $B2$ to $B1$. What is the approximate trigger voltage V_P?

$V_P \cong 0.7 + \eta V_{B2B1} = 0.7$ V + (0.63 · 24 V) = 15.8 V

EXAMPLE 16–4 ▐▬▬▬▬▬▬▬▬▬▬▬▬▬▬▬▬▬▬▬▬▬▬▬▬▬▬▬▬▬▬▬▬

A 2N4870 UJT has an intrinsic standoff ratio (η) of 0.68 and 12 V is applied from $B2$ to $B1$. What is the approximate trigger voltage V_P?

$V_P \cong 0.7 + \eta V_{B2B1} = 0.7$ V + (0.68 · 12 V) = 8.86 V

Application

Figure 16–30 illustrates a common application for the UJT, the relaxation oscillator. A deeper understanding of the UJT can be obtained by considering the operation of this circuit. You probably already know basically how this circuit functions. The capacitor charges until V_C reaches V_P at the emitter of the UJT. Once V_P is reached, the emitter junction becomes forward biased and the base-1 bulk resistance quickly modulates to a very low value. This allows the capacitor to quickly discharge through the emitter junction.

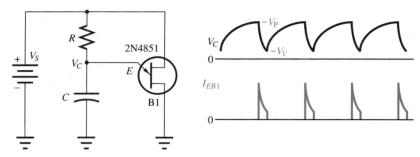

Figure 16–30   The UJT relaxation oscillator.

The capacitor voltage drops to the valley voltage level, which is usually near 2.5 V. At this valley voltage, the I_{EB1} current is less than I_V. This allows the UJT to reset (turn off) and the capacitor charges again.

Now, let's take a closer look. When the capacitor charges to V_P, the emitter current I_{EB1} must be greater than I_P for the UJT to trigger. This means that R must not be so large in value that it limits the emitter current to less than I_P. Therefore:

$$R < (V_S - V_P)/I_P \tag{16–6}$$

Also, R must not be so small in value that the emitter current when the capacitor is discharged at V_V is greater than I_V. If I_{EB1} is greater than I_V, the UJT will remain on in saturation and the oscillator will be latched up (will not oscillate). Therefore:

$$R > (V_S - V_V)/I_V \tag{16–7}$$

Consider Examples 16–5 and 16–6.

EXAMPLE 16–5 ▮▮▮▮▮▮▮▮▮▮▮▮▮▮▮▮▮▮▮▮▮▮▮▮▮▮

A 2N4870 UJT has an intrinsic standoff ratio (η) of 0.6 and is used as the trigger in a relaxation oscillator like that of Figure 16–30. $V_S = 30$ V, $V_V = 2.5$ V, $I_V = 5$ mA, and $I_P = 1$ μA. Calculate the minimum and maximum values for R.

$V_P \cong 0.7 + \eta V_{B2B1} = 0.7$ V $+ (0.6 \cdot 30$ V$) = 18.7$ V

$R_{minimum} = (V_S - V_V)/I_V = (30$ V $- 2.5$ V$)/5$ mA $= 5{,}500$ Ω

$R_{maximum} = (V_S - V_P)/I_P = (30$ V $- 18.7$ V$)/1$ μA $= 11.3$ MΩ

$5{,}500$ $\Omega < R < 11.3$ MΩ

EXAMPLE 16–6 ▮▮▮▮▮▮▮▮▮▮▮▮▮▮▮▮▮▮▮▮▮▮▮▮▮▮

A UJT has an intrinsic standoff ratio (η) of 0.63 and is used as the trigger in a relaxation oscillator like that of Figure 16–30.

$V_S = 24$ V, $V_V = 2.3$ V, $I_V = 4$ mA, and $I_P = 4$ μA

R is 3.3 kΩ. Will this circuit oscillate?

$V_P \cong 0.7 + \eta V_{B2B1} = 0.7$ V $+ (0.63 \cdot 24$ V$) = 15.8$ V

$R_{minimum} = (V_S - V_V)/I_V = (24$ V $- 2.3$ V$)/4$ mA $= 5,425$ Ω

$R_{maximum} = (V_S - V_P)/I_P = (24$ V $- 15.8$ V$)/4$ μA $= 2.05$ MΩ

$5,425$ $\Omega < R < 2.05$ MΩ

Since R is less than 5,425 Ω, the circuit will not oscillate. It will latch up in saturation.

As you can see from Example 16–5 and 16–6, R can be any value over a very wide range. Values for R and C are chosen for the desired frequency of oscillation.

THE PUT

Introduction to the PUT

The **programmable unijunction transistor (PUT)** is not a unijunction transistor at all. It is a thyristor, a four-layer device much like an SUS. In fact, it is an SUS that can be programmed (biased) to trigger over a wide range of voltage. So why is it called a unijunction transistor if it isn't one? Functionally, the PUT can replace the UJT in a circuit because it has very similar operating characteristics. You'll see this very soon. PUTs have the advantage of being faster, more sensitive, less costly, and programmable.

Figure 16–31 shows the schematic symbol, the layer diagram, and the functional analogy for the PUT. Yes, the PUT looks very similar to the SCR. But be careful. Notice where the gate is in the different diagrams of Figure 16–31. The gate is close to the anode instead of the cathode. The position of the gate in a PUT allows you to place a voltage divider at the gate to reverse bias the anode and keep it turned off. The anode voltage must be approximately 0.7 V higher than the gate voltage before the device can turn on. Thus, the device's trigger voltage is programmed according to the gate potential.

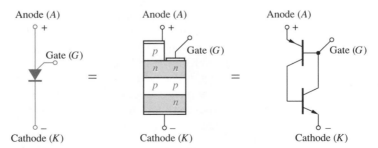

Figure 16–31   The programmable unijunction transistor (PUT).

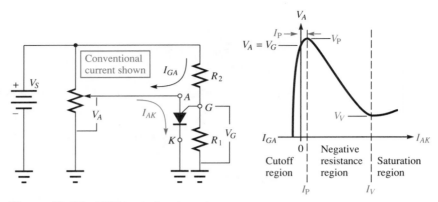

Figure 16–32 PUT test circuit and characteristic curve.

Theory of Operation

Figure 16–32 demonstrates a test circuit and shows the characteristic curve for the PUT. Notice the characteristic curve is the same as for the UJT. The standoff ratio is now provided by the external voltage divider, R_1 and R_2. This means the standoff ratio is not fixed and can be changed as desired. In the test circuit, the anode voltage (V_A) is increased slowly by adjusting the potentiometer. When V_A reaches V_G, the leakage current (I_{GA}) from gate to anode ceases. When V_A reaches V_P, the device triggers and V_A drops to V_V. As long as I_{AK} is greater than I_V, the device will stay latched on.

The peak-point voltage is calculated much the same way as it was for UJTs. In this case, $R_1/(R_1 + R_2)$ is the standoff ratio.

$$V_P \cong 0.7 \text{ V} + V_S \cdot R_1/(R_1 + R_2) \tag{16–8}$$

Application

Figure 16–33 illustrates an interesting application for the PUT. The 2N6027 PUT is used in a battery charging circuit to trigger the SCR on. Pulsating DC is applied to the SCR, which conducts for some portion of each pulsation. The actual control circuit operates from the battery that is being charged. The 0.1-μF capacitor charges to the peak-point voltage through the 10-kΩ resistor. Once V_P is reached, the PUT triggers on and discharges the capacitor through the transformer winding. This current surge sends a pulse to the secondary winding, which is connected to the gate of the SCR. The SCR turns on and stays on until its anode voltage drops down to the battery voltage. As the battery charges, the battery voltage increases. As the battery voltage increases, the gate voltage of the PUT also increases because the voltage divider voltage increases. This causes the capacitor to charge to a higher voltage before the PUT can trigger. That means it takes longer for the PUT to trigger and the SCR to trigger. Thus, the SCR triggers later on the DC pulsations, which reduces the SCR's conduction angle. So, as the battery charges, the conduction angle of the SCR becomes less and less, until the SCR no longer triggers on (depending on the setting of the potentiometer).

The 10-V zener diode is used to limit the capacitor-charge voltage to 10 V. When the voltage at the gate of the PUT reaches approximately 9.3 V or so,

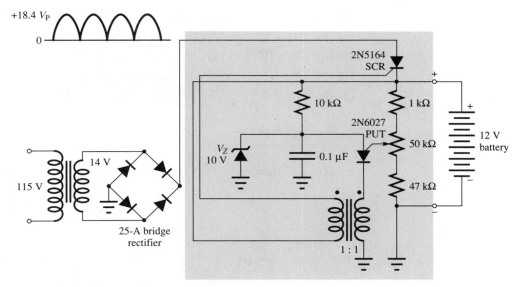

Figure 16–33 The PUT as a control device in a battery-charging circuit.

the PUT will no longer trigger on and neither will the SCR. If the wiper arm on the potentiometer is all the way down, the PUT gate voltage will be 6 to 7 V and the PUT and SCR will continue to trigger on with every pulsation of the DC and never stop. This brings the battery up to maximum charge and keeps it on trickle charge. When the wiper arm on the potentiometer is all the way up, the PUT gate voltage will be 12 V or so and the PUT and SCR will never trigger on, since the PUT anode voltage is limited to 10 V. Thus the circuit is off when the wiper is in the up position.

Take time to review this section to clearly understand the differences and similarities between UJTs and PUTs. Make sure you can answer the self-check questions before continuing.

Self-Check 16–5

1. How does the UJT get its name?
2. What is the intrinsic standoff ratio and what does it have to do with the operation of the UJT?
3. A 2N2646 UJT has an intrinsic standoff ratio (η) of 0.7 and is used as the trigger in a relaxation oscillator like that of Figure 16–30. $V_S = 20$ V, $V_V = 3$ V, $I_V = 6$ mA, and $I_P = 1$ μA. Calculate the minimum and maximum values for R.
4. Why is the PUT not really a UJT?
5. What determines the standoff ratio for a PUT?

SUMMARY

FORMULAS

(16–1) $I_K = I_A = \dfrac{I_{CBO2} + I_{CBO1}}{1 - (a_1 + a_2)}$ (SUS current)

(16–2) $T = C(V_{BO} - V_{AK(on)})I_E$ (SUS relaxation oscillator)

(16–3) $f_o \cong 1/T = I_E/C(V_{BO} - V_{AK(on)})$ (SUS relaxation oscillator)

(16–4) $\quad \eta = r_{B1}/(r_{B1} + r_{B2}) = r_{B1}/r_{BB}$ $\quad$ (UJT standoff ratio)

(16–5) $\quad V_P \cong 0.7 + \eta V_{B2B1}$ $\quad$ (UJT peak-point voltage)

(16–6) $\quad R < (V_S - V_P)/I_P$ $\quad$ (Maximum UJT emitter resistor)

(16–7) $\quad R > (V_S - V_V)/I_V$ $\quad$ (Minimum UJT emitter resistor)

(16–8) $\quad V_P \cong 0.7 \text{ V} + V_S \cdot R_1/(R_1 + R_2)$ $\quad$ (PUT peak-point voltage)

DEVICE SUMMARY

Device	Symbol	General Description	Applications
SUS		Thyristor, unilateral switch, no gate	DC overvoltage protection, relaxation oscillator, to trigger an SCR
SCR		Thyristor, unilateral switch, gate turn-on, low- to high-power capability	Unidirectional power control, full-wave DC power control, half-wave AC power control
GCS/GTO		Thyristor, unilateral switch, gate turn-on and -off, low- and medium-power capability	Pulse-width DC control, DC switching
DIAC		Thyristor, bilateral switch, no gate, medium- and high-power capability	AC overvoltage protection, trigger device for TRIACs
SBS		Integrated circuit, bilateral switch, gate used to modify turn-on voltage, low voltage, low power	Relaxation oscillator, trigger device for SCRs and TRIACs
TRIAC		Thyristor, bilateral switch, gate turn-on, medium- to high-power capability, 50- or 60-Hz operation	Full-wave AC power control
UJT		Unilateral switch, low voltage, low power, no gate, single *pn* junction	Relaxation oscillator, SCR trigger device
PUT		Thyristor, unilateral switch, gate programmed threshold voltage, low voltage, low power	Relaxation oscillator, SCR trigger device

PARAMETER SUMMARY

Thyristor Parameters

V_{BO}	breakover voltage
$V_{AK(on)}$	forward voltage with device conducting
$I_{T(RMS)}$	maximum continuous RMS current
V_{DRM}	maximum peak repetitive forward blocking voltage without the device triggering on
I_{TSM}	maximum nonrepetitive surge current
I_{GT}	maximum value of gate trigger current
V_{GT}	gate voltage needed to produce the specified value of I_{GT}
T_J	the junction temperature
I_{GM}	forward peak gate current
I_{DRM}	maximum peak repetitive blocking current corresponding with V_{DRM}
I_H	the holding current
dv/dt	the critical rise of OFF-state voltage

UJT/PUT Parameters

I_{EB2}	OFF-state leakage current
I_{EB1}	ON-state forward current
I_P	peak-point current, trigger current
I_V	valley-point current
V_P	peak-point voltage, trigger voltage
V_V	valley-point voltage, on voltage
η	intrinsic standoff ratio for UJT, r_{B1}/r_{BB}

NEED-TO-KNOW SOLUTION

1. TRIAC
2. GTO
3. SCR
4. SCR
5. UJT, PUT, SBS
6. PUT
7. DIAC, TRIAC, SCR

QUESTIONS

16–1 SILICON UNILATERAL SWITCHES (SUSs)

1. What is another name for the SUS?
2. Select the symbol for the SUS from Figure 16–34.
3. The SUS is a unilateral device. What does that mean?
4. Describe the construction of the SUS.
5. What is a latch?
6. What causes the SUS to latch or latch on?

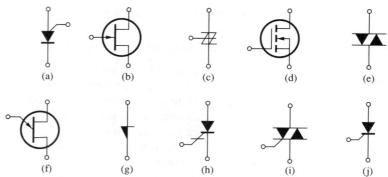

Figure 16–34

7. What does the alpha of the transistors in the SUS have to do with latch-up?
8. What is the main condition or requirement for latch-up in a thyristor such as the SUS?
9. What does Formula 16–1 tell you about the SUS?
10. What does it mean to say the SUS is operating in the forward blocking region or mode?
11. What is the relationship between V_{DRM}, V_{BO}, and $V_{AK(on)}$ for an SUS?
12. Explain how the SUS is turned off.
13. Briefly, explain the operation of Figure 16–35.

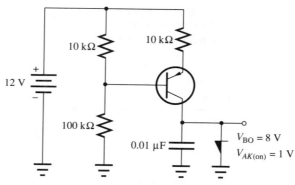

Figure 16–35

16–2 SILICON CONTROLLED RECTIFIERS (SCRs)

14. How is the SCR similar to an SUS?
15. Select the symbol for the SCR from Figure 16–34.
16. Is the SCR (a) a unilateral device, or (b) a bilateral device?
17. Explain the effect gate current has on V_{BO} for the SCR.
18. Explain why SCRs should be gate-triggered instead of anode-triggered like SUSs.
19. What does the duration of the gate pulse have to do with SCR turn-on?
20. List two ways the SCR can be turned off.

21. Briefly explain forced commutation.
22. List three sources of false triggering for SCR circuits.
23. Explain how the conduction angle is controlled for an SCR in a pulsating DC power-control circuit.
24. Which of the waveforms of Figure 16–36 would you observe on an oscilloscope across the load?

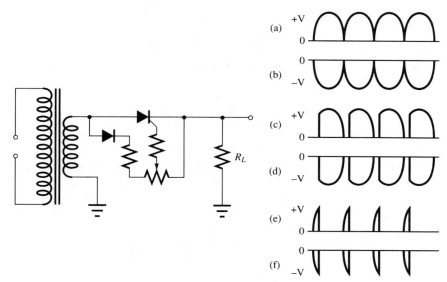

Figure 16–36

25. What is a sensitive-gate SCR?
26. Which is greater?   (a) I_H (b) $I_{T(RMS)}$ (c) I_{DRM}
27. What is a GCS and how is it different than an SCR?
28. For what are GTOs used?
29. Select the symbol for the GTO from Figure 16–34.

16–3 DIACs AND SBSs

30. What is a DIAC?
31. Select the symbol for the DIAC from Figure 16–34.
32. Why are the DIAC terminals not labeled anode and cathode?
33. Is the DIAC (a) an AC device, or (b) a DC device?
34. Describe the basic operating characteristics of the DIAC.
35. For what are DIACs used?
36. What is an SBS?
37. List two ways the SBS is different than the DIAC.
38. Select the symbol for the SBS from Figure 16–34.
39. Is the SBS (a) low-power, or (b) a high-power device?
40. Is is necessary to use the gate of the SBS?
41. How do the operating characteristics of the SBS compare to the DIAC?
42. Explain the operation of the circuit in Figure 16–37.

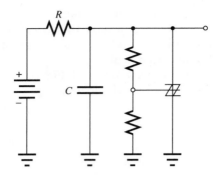

Figure 16–37

16–4 TRIACs

43. What is a TRIAC?
44. How does the TRIAC differ from a DIAC?
45. Is a TRIAC intended mainly for (a) AC, or (b) DC power control?
46. Select the symbol for the TRIAC from Figure 16–34.
47. How does the amount of gate current affect the breakover voltage of the TRIAC?
48. How is a TRIAC turned off?
49. If the gate current to the TRIAC is high, will the delay angle be (a) large, or (b) small?
50. If the gate current to the TRIAC is high, will the conduction angle be (a) large, or (b) small?
51. What is phase control as it pertains to TRIACs?
52. If a capacitor connected to the trigger device in a phase control circuit takes a relatively long time to charge, will the conduction angle of the TRIAC be (a) large, or (b) small?
53. What is a snubber, or snubber network? What is its purpose?
54. Would you say a TRIAC is (a) a highly-efficient, or (b) an inefficient AC power control device? Explain.

16–5 UNIJUNCTION TRANSISTORS (UJTs)

55. Why is a UJT so named?
56. Select the symbol for the UJT from Figure 16–34.
57. What is the significance of I_P and V_P on the characteristic curve for a UJT?
58. What is conductivity modulation?
59. Is the UJT a high-power device?
60. What exactly is the intrinsic standoff ratio and what does it have to do with V_P?
61. What is the circuit of Figure 16–38? Explain its operation.
62. Explain why the value of R must be within certain limits for proper operation of the circuit in Figure 16–38.

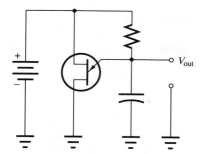

Figure 16–38

63. What is a PUT?
64. Select the symbol for the PUT from Figure 16–34.
65. How does the PUT differ from the UJT?
66. How is the PUT similar to the UJT?
67. What advantages does the PUT have over the UJT?
68. What determines the standoff ratio for the PUT?

PROBLEMS

16–1 SILICON UNILATERAL SWITCHES (SUSs)

1. Calculate the approximate frequency of oscillation for the circuit of Figure 16–35.
2. If the 100-kΩ resistor in Figure 16–35 is changed to 130 kΩ, what is the frequency of oscillation?
3. If I_H for the SUS of Problem 1 is 25 μA, will the circuit oscillate?

16–5 UNIJUNCTION TRANSISTORS (UJTs)

4. A 2N4870 UJT has an intrinsic standoff ratio (η) of 0.65 and 12 V is applied from $B2$ to $B1$. What is the approximate trigger voltage V_P?
5. A 2N4871 UJT has an intrinsic standoff ratio (η) of 0.75 and 18 V is applied from $B2$ to $B1$. What is the approximate trigger voltage V_P?
6. An MU4891 UJT has an intrinsic standoff ratio (η) of 0.7 and is used as the trigger in a relaxation oscillator like that of Figure 16–30. $V_S = 12$ V, $V_V = 2$ V, $I_V = 4$ mA, and $I_P = 0.6$ μA. Calculate the minimum and maximum values for R.
7. An MU10 UJT has an intrinsic standoff ratio (η) of 0.6 and is used as the trigger in a relaxation oscillator like that of Figure 16–30. $V_S = 15$ V, $V_V = 1.7$ V, $I_V = 2$ mA, and $I_P = 2$ μA. Calculate the minimum and maximum values for R.
8. An MU10 UJT has an intrinsic standoff ratio (η) of 0.6 and is used as the trigger in a relaxation oscillator like that of Figure 16–30. $V_S = 18$ V, $V_V = 1.9$ V, $I_V = 1.5$ mA, and $I_P = 3$ μA. R is 5.6 kΩ. Will this circuit oscillate?

9. Calculate the approximate trigger voltage (V_P) for the circuit of Figure 16–39.

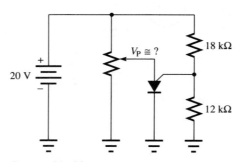

Figure 16–39

10. If the 12-kΩ resistor of Figure 16–39 is changed to 8.2 kΩ, what is the trigger voltage?

ADDITIONAL PROBLEMS

11. Calculate the approximate frequency of oscillation for the circuit of Figure 16–40.

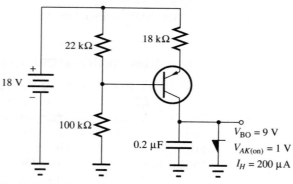

Figure 16–40

12. If the 18-kΩ resistor in Figure 16–40 is changed to 22 kΩ, what is the frequency of oscillation?
13. If the 18-kΩ resistor in Figure 16–40 is changed to 10 kΩ, will the circuit oscillate?
14. A UJT has an intrinsic standoff ratio (η) of 0.7 and 18 V is applied from $B2$ to $B1$. What is the approximate trigger voltage V_P?

15. A UJT has an intrinsic standoff ratio (η) of 0.73 and 9 V is applied from $B2$ to $B1$. What is the approximate trigger voltage V_P?

16. A UJT has an intrinsic standoff ratio (η) of 0.68 and is used as the trigger in a relaxation oscillator like that of Figure 16–30. $V_S = 14$ V, $V_V = 2.2$ V, $I_V = 5$ mA, and $I_P = 2$ μA. Calculate the minimum and maximum values for R.

17. A UJT has an intrinsic standoff ratio (η) of 0.65 and is used as the trigger in a relaxation oscillator like that of Figure 16–30. $V_S = 16$ V, $V_V = 1.8$ V, $I_V = 3.4$ mA, and $I_P = 1.8$ μA. Calculate the minimum and maximum values for R.

18. A UJT has an intrinsic standoff ratio (η) of 0.7 and is used as the trigger in a relaxation oscillator like that of Figure 16–30. $V_S = 24$ V, $V_V = 2.1$ V, $I_V = 3$ mA, and $I_P = 1.6$ μA. R is 2.7 kΩ. Will this circuit oscillate?

19. Calculate the approximate trigger voltage (V_P) for the circuit of Figure 16–41.

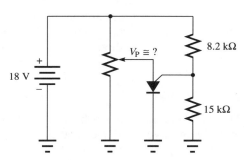

Figure 16–41

20. If the 8.2-kΩ resistor of Figure 16–41 is changed to 22 kΩ, what is the trigger voltage?

ANSWERS TO SELF-CHECKS

SELF-CHECK 16–1

1. For latch-up to take place, the total loop current gain within the SUS must be equal to 1. Increasing the anode voltage increases leakage current, which increases base current and increases the alpha of each transistor.

2. The anode current must be greater than the holding current.

3. I_H is greater. I_{DRM} is a leakage current before the device triggers on.

4. False

5. $I_E = 230$ μA, $f_o \cong 95$ Hz

SELF-CHECK 16–2

1. Both the SUS and SCR are four-layer thyristors and they both have a threshold voltage that must be reached before the device switches to the ON state.
2. The SCR has a control gate used to trigger the SCR at lower breakover voltages.
3. Increasing gate current decreases V_{BO} and I_H.
4. (1) Decrease anode current below the holding level.
   (2) Use forced commutation.
5. As gate current is increased by raising the wiper arm, the SCR fires earlier, making the conduction angle greater.
6. The GTO has a gate that is used for both turn-on and turn-off.

SELF-CHECK 16–3

1. The DIAC is bidirectional (bilateral) and can be used in AC circuits. It is like two paralleled and antipolarized SUSs.
2. The SBS is faster, has a gate, and is an integrated circuit instead of a single, four-layered device.

SELF-CHECK 16–4

1. The TRIAC and SCR are both three-terminal devices. They are thyristors. They have similar operating characteristics except the TRIAC is bilateral.
2. Low-speed device
3. Like the SCR, the conduction angle of the TRIAC can be increased by increasing the gate current or applying an on pulse earlier in the AC alternation.
4. The purpose for phase control is to delay the turn-on voltage or pulse to the gate of the TRIAC. Thus, the conduction angle for each alternation is varied.
5. A snubber network is a resistor in series with a capacitor. The network is placed in parallel with the TRIAC, or SCR, to absorb any rapid change in voltage caused by inductive loads. Without the snubber, the thyristor may not turn off and control is lost.

SELF-CHECK 16–5

1. The UJT has a single *pn* junction.
2. The intrinsic standoff ratio is the voltage divider ratio within the UJT which includes the bulk resistance from the emitter to base 1 and base 2 to the emitter. The voltage drop across the base-1 bulk resistance reverse biases the *pn* junction and prevents turn-on until the emitter voltage exceeds this voltage by approximately 0.7 V.

3. $V_P \cong 14.7$ V, $2,833\ \Omega < R < 5.3$ MΩ
4. The PUT is a four-layer thyristor. The UJT is a single junction device.
5. The standoff ratio for a PUT is determined by an external voltage divider.

SUGGESTED PROJECTS

1. Add some of the main concepts and formulas from this chapter to your Electronics Notebook.
2. Build and test some of the circuits in this chapter, such as Figures 16–4, 16–11, 16–15, 16–24, and 16–30.

This MAP130 switching power supply by *POWER-ONE* is only 8.5″ long, 4.5″ wide and 2″ deep, yet it can supply +5 V at 20 A, +12 V at 5-A peak, −12 V at 1 A, and −5 V at 1 A. All output voltages are held within 0.2% for line voltage variation from 90 VAC to 132 VAC. Output voltages are held within 1% for load variation from 20% to 100% (i.e., less than 1% decrease from +5 V when the load varies from 4 A to 20 A). (Photograph courtesy of *POWER-ONE, INC.,* Camarillo, CA)

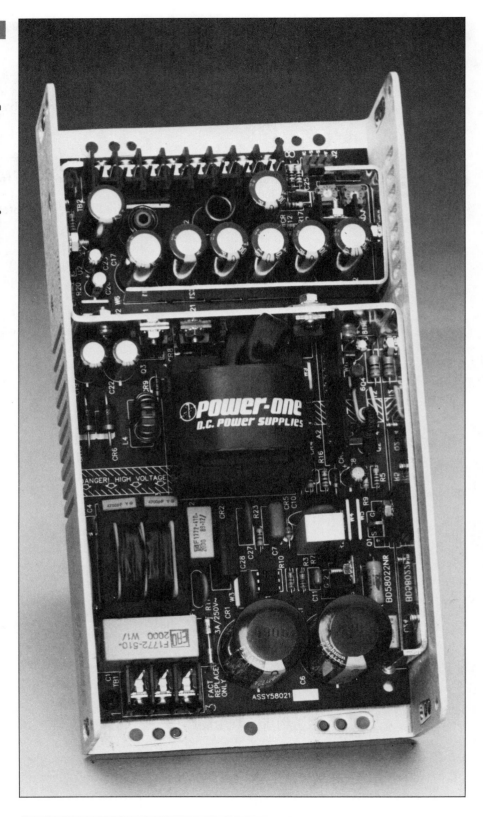

17

Linear and Nonlinear Power Supplies

OBJECTIVES

After studying this chapter, you will be able to

- explain the purpose for each functional block of a regulated DC power supply or DC to DC converter.
- analyze, design, and build a variety of linear and nonlinear voltage regulators.
- explain the difference between linear and nonlinear voltage regulators.
- explain the operation of pulse-width-modulated switching voltage regulators.
- explain the difference between inverters and converters.
- describe various types of inverters and converters.

NEED TO KNOW

The company where you work decides to modernize their electronics laboratory. A long power panel is to be installed along the back of a long workbench against a wall. This power panel will have both AC and DC outlets (AC electrical outlets and banana-jack pairs for DC) spaced every three feet down the bench. A high-efficiency variable DC power supply must be built and installed under the bench to supply power to the DC jacks. The output voltage of the supply must be adjustable over a range of 5 to 24 V. It must be designed for a maximum load current of 10 A. Design the supply.

Can you do it? No? OK. The good news is that you will be able to design this supply by the time you finish this chapter. A good knowledge of power supplies and voltage regulators is power in the hands of the technician or engineer. Don't forget, a solution to this problem is provided at the end of the chapter. Try not to look until you feel you know how to do it.

INTRODUCTION

You are going to find this chapter extremely practical and useful. Here, you will be introduced to a wide variety of linear and nonlinear power supplies and regulators. Circuit theory that you have gained from previous chapters will be applied as you explore first discrete, then integrated voltage regulators and related circuits. The importance of this material cannot be overemphasized, because power supplies are at the heart of every conceivable electronic system, and the troubleshooting skills that you have already acquired can only be applied to circuits and systems that you can understand. The overall purpose for this chapter is to help you understand the analysis, design, and operation of a wide variety of power supplies. Enjoy your exploration!

17–1 INTRODUCTION TO VOLTAGE REGULATORS

OVERVIEW OF POWER SUPPLIES

Power Supplies

Power supplies are electronic circuits, or minor systems, that are designed to produce a specified AC or DC voltage at a specified maximum current from an existing AC or DC source. A power supply may produce a DC voltage from an AC source, a DC voltage from a DC source, an AC voltage from an AC source, or an AC voltage from a DC source. The voltage may be stepped up to a voltage higher than the source or stepped down.

Linear and Nonlinear Power Supplies

Among other descriptions, a power supply may be described as being linear or nonlinear. A **linear power supply** uses a linear voltage regulator to drop a DC source down to a desired level and regulate it at that level. The linear voltage regulator uses power devices that are operated in the region between saturation and cutoff, along the linear region. Characteristically, the linear regulator dissipates a considerable amount of power because of this midrange operation. **Nonlinear power supplies** operate power devices in saturation or cutoff, alternating rapidly between the two. Since the device is either fully on or off, it dissipates very little power. Because of the switched ON–OFF operation of these nonlinear supplies, they are called **switching supplies, switching regulators, switchers,** or **choppers.**

Linear and nonlinear supplies are designed using discrete components, integrated circuits, or a combination of both. Often, discrete power transistors, op-amps, and comparators are used to complete the circuit. Some manufacturers offer **hybrid** integrated circuits that have discrete and integrated circuits together in one package.

THE REGULATED DC POWER SUPPLY

AC to DC Converters

Figure 17–1 is a general block diagram for a regulated DC power supply. Typically, a step-up or step-down transformer is used to bring the voltage

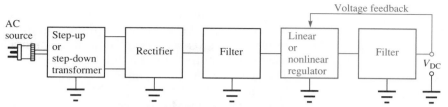

Figure 17–1 General block diagram for regulated DC power supplies.

into the desired range. The secondary voltage is then rectified and filtered. You should recall this from Chapter 2. A linear or nonlinear voltage regulator follows the filter. In some cases, additional filtering after the regulator is necessary or desirable. A good regulator uses voltage feedback to monitor the output voltage and automatically make adjustments to accommodate different loads. A heavier load tends to drop the output voltage down and the voltage feedback is used to increase the conduction, or conduction time, of the controlling devices to compensate for the drop. Both linear and nonlinear power supplies of this type are loosely referred to as **AC to DC converters.**

Filtering and Regulation

Perhaps this is the best place to make sure you understand the difference between filtering and regulation. **Filtering** is the means by which pulsating DC is converted to a relatively smooth DC. A lowpass filter, acting as an integrator, is used for this purpose. This could be a single filter capacitor or an inductor and capacitor combination (Section 2–5). **Regulation** is the means by which the DC output voltage from the supply is held at a constant, or near constant, level regardless of variations in load, line voltage, or temperature. A good regulator will compensate for variations in any of these. The zener regulators of Section 3–1 are not good regulators by themselves. However, as you will soon see, they do play an important role in linear and nonlinear regulator circuits.

Ripple and Regulation

You should recall that **ripple** is rapid variations in the DC that are caused by incomplete filtering of the pulsating DC. Using large-value capacitors, it is possible to reduce the peak-to-peak ripple voltage to a very low amount. A ripple of 50 mV$_{\text{P-P}}$ is considered very good for a DC source of 6 V or higher and is fairly easy to achieve depending on the quality of the filter and load.

Regulation is measured, or rated, in two ways. First, from Chapter 3, you learned about percent regulation. Recall, $\% \text{ Reg} = 100\% \cdot (V_{NL} - V_{FL})/V_{FL}$, where V_{NL} is the no-load voltage and V_{FL} is the full-load voltage at the output of the regulator. There is another way regulators are rated besides percent. Manufacturers usually specify a drop in voltage for a certain increase in load (current). For example, the LM309, 5-V IC regulator will maintain the output voltage within 15 mV of 5 V over a 5-mA to 1.5-A load range.

Regulation can improve ripple in many cases. For example, let's say a poorly filtered 10-V DC source has a ripple of 5 $V_{\text{P-P}}$. That means the voltage periodically dips down to 7.5 V and peaks out at 12.5 V. As long as the regulated output voltage is about 5 V or less, the regulator will be able to cut off the ripple. This is known as **ripple rejection** and is specified in dB. For example, an LM109 is specified to have a minimum of 50 dB ripple rejection, meaning the output ripple is at least 50 dB below the level of the input ripple. This assumes the input ripple never dips below the minimum input voltage level needed by the regulator. The regulator itself usually needs a voltage source that is at least 2 to 3 volts higher than the regulated voltage because of internal voltage drops. This is known as the **input–output voltage differential.** The absolute minimum input–output voltage differential is called the **dropout voltage.** Many linear regulators require a minimum differential of 2 to 3 V. For example, a well-filtered 8-V DC source is ideal for a 5-V regulator.

Load and Line Regulation

The regulator is able to compensate for load variations and line variations. As we have already discussed, **load regulation** is expressed as a change in output voltage of so many millivolts over a certain range of change in *load* (current). **Line regulation** is rated as a change in output voltage of so many millivolts over a certain range of change in *input voltage*. For example, the line regulation rating for the LM309 regulator IC is a change in output voltage of only 4 mV over an input-voltage range of 7.1 to 25 V. Not bad!

INVERTERS AND CONVERTERS

We will also explore inverters and converters in this chapter. An **inverter** is a DC to AC converter. Figure 17–2 shows a typical block diagram of a DC to DC converter that includes an inverter. The inverter chops the DC source into a pulsating DC square wave. The pulsating DC is then applied to a transformer, which steps the voltage up. The stepped-up square-wave voltage is then rectified and filtered to obtain a pure DC at a higher voltage than the original DC source. It is generally assumed that a DC to DC converter is a step-up converter, since only a regulator is needed for step-down applications. Thus, unless otherwise defined in context, a **DC to DC converter** is a step-up power supply and an **AC to DC converter** is either step-up or step-down.

Inverters are also used alone to convert a DC source to a desired AC voltage. For example, some inverters convert 12.6 V DC to 120 V AC. Thus, electric lights and some motors and appliances can be powered from a car battery. High-power inverters are used to convert DC from a large bank of batteries and photovoltaic array to AC to power homes.

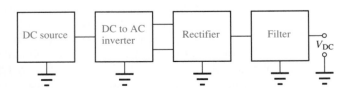

Figure 17–2 General block diagram for a DC to DC converter.

In the following sections, you will first explore linear voltage regulators, then nonlinear regulators, and finally inverters and converters. Pause now to test your understanding by answering the questions of self-check 17–1.

1. What is the basic difference between linear power supplies and nonlinear power supplies?
2. What is the purpose of an AC to DC converter?
3. What is the difference between line regulation and load regulation?
4. What is a DC to DC converter?
5. What is an inverter?

17–2 DISCRETE LINEAR VOLTAGE REGULATORS

DEVELOPMENT OF THE BASIC LINEAR VOLTAGE REGULATOR

Introduction to Discrete Linear Voltage Regulators

To begin our study of linear regulators, we will explore the design of the basic voltage regulator using discrete components. Once you understand the design and operation of the discrete regulator, you will understand the inner workings of the integrated-circuit linear regulator. From the start you should realize that the IC regulators are less expensive, take up less space, and are usually of a higher quality than what you can make using discrete components. However, knowledge of discrete linear regulators is essential to implementing them when IC regulators are not readily available or are not able to handle the load requirements. Also, some manufacturers of power supplies still use discrete-component design in high-power supplies.

The Simple Zener-Diode Voltage Regulator

Let's begin with the heart of the linear regulator, the **zener diode.** Figure 17–3 illustrates the most basic of all linear regulators. This is a shunt regulator using the zener diode. The zener diode is used to shunt some of the total current around the load device. You should recall from Section 3–2 that the

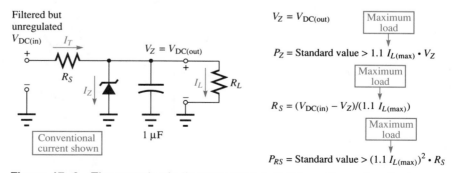

Figure 17–3 The most basic linear voltage regulator—the zener diode.

total current through the series resistor is constant and is shared by the load and zener. If the load increases, the zener current decreases and vice versa. The design formulas are from Section 3–2 and are listed again here for use in this section.

Component Ratings

$$V_Z = V_{DC(out)} \tag{17-1}$$

$$P_Z = \text{Standard Value} > 1.1 \, I_{L(max)} \cdot V_Z \tag{17-2}$$

$$R_S = (V_{DC(in)} - V_Z)/(1.1 \, I_{L(max)}) \tag{17-3}$$

$$P_{RS} = \text{Standard Value} > (1.1 \, I_{L(max)})^2 \cdot R_S \tag{17-4}$$

The 1-μF capacitor in parallel with the zener in Figure 17–3 is included to filter noise generated by the zener itself. The capacitor also lowers the AC impedance of the zener, reducing the likelihood of positive feedback on the regulated DC line. Such feedback can cause severe instability in some circuits. Often, much larger values of capacitance are needed for circuit stability.

As you know from previous study, the zener regulator is very inefficient, since much power is dissipated in the zener and series resistor. Also, because wide variations in zener current and temperature are possible, the regulation could be improved with further design.

The Series-Pass Voltage Regulator

Now we begin to greatly improve the efficiency and power-handling capability of the linear regulator by adding a series-pass transistor, which is illustrated in Figure 17–4. Most of the power is handled and dissipated by the series transistor, since it is in series with the load. The theory of circuit operation is very basic here, for this is really a DC emitter-follower current amplifier. The base current controls the emitter current and the emitter

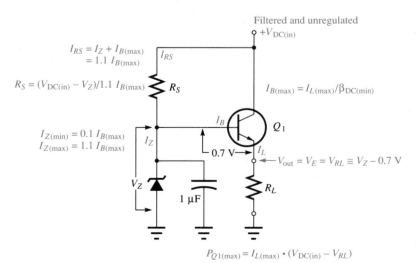

Figure 17–4 The basic series-pass regulator.

voltage is 0.7 V less than the base voltage. Thus, the load voltage is approximately 0.7 V less than the zener voltage. Note that I_{RS} is the sum of the base current and the zener current. Also, I_{RS} is a constant value over the range of load (emitter current). When the load increases, the base current increases and the zener current decreases. The zener gives up some of its current to drive the base.

The worst-case condition for the zener occurs when there is no load (load resistor removed). With no load, there is no base current and the zener current is maximum. Thus, zener power dissipation is maximum with no load.

From these observations and your prior circuit analysis experience, the following formulas are established for the purpose of circuit analysis:

$$V_E = V_{RL} \cong V_Z - 0.7 \text{ V} \tag{17–5}$$

$$I_L = V_E/R_L \tag{17–6}$$

$$I_B = I_L/\beta_{DC} \tag{17–7}$$

$$V_{RS} = V_{DC(in)} - V_Z \tag{17–8}$$

$$I_{RS} = V_{RS}/R_S \tag{17–9}$$

$$I_Z = I_{RS} - I_B \tag{17–10}$$

$$P_Z = I_Z \cdot V_Z \tag{17–11}$$

$$P_{RS} = I_{RS} \cdot V_{RS} \tag{17–12}$$

$$P_L = I_L \cdot V_E \tag{17–13}$$

$$P_{Q1} = I_L \cdot V_{CE} = I_L \cdot (V_{DC(in)} - V_E) \tag{17–14}$$

Percent power efficiency = $100\% \cdot P_{out}/P_{in}$. In this case,

$$\% \text{ Eff} \cong 100\% \cdot P_L/(P_L + P_{Q1}) \tag{17–15}$$

Consider Example 17–1 as we apply these formulas in the analysis of Figure 17–5.

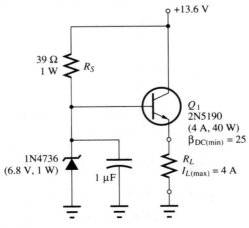

Figure 17–5

EXAMPLE 17–1 ▮▮▮▮▮▮▮

Here, we will do a thorough analysis of the circuit of Figure 17–5 using our analysis formulas.

$$V_E = V_{RL} \cong V_Z - 0.7 \text{ V} = 6.8 \text{ V} - 0.7 \text{ V} = 6.1 \text{ V}$$

$$I_L = 4 \text{ A maximum}$$

$$I_B = I_L/\beta_{DC} = 4 \text{ A}/25 = 160 \text{ mA}$$

$$V_{RS} = V_{DC(in)} - V_Z = 13.6 \text{ V} - 6.8 \text{ V} = 6.8 \text{ V}$$

$$I_{RS} = V_{RS}/R_S = 6.8 \text{ V}/39 \text{ } \Omega = 174 \text{ mA}$$

$$I_Z = I_{RS} - I_B = 174 \text{ mA} - 160 \text{ mA} = 14 \text{ mA}$$

$$P_Z = I_Z \cdot V_Z = 14 \text{ mA} \cdot 6.8 \text{ V} = 95.2 \text{ mW}$$

$$P_{Z(max)} = I_{Z(max)} \cdot V_Z = 174 \text{ mA} \cdot 6.8 \text{ V} = 1.18 \text{ W}$$

Note: The power rating of the zener is too low to handle the no-load condition when I_Z is maximum.

$$P_{RS} = I_{RS} \cdot V_{RS} = 174 \text{ mA} \cdot 6.8 \text{ V} = 1.18 \text{ W}$$

Note: The series resistor is underrated. At least a 2-W resistor must be used.

$$P_L = I_L \cdot V_E = 4 \text{ A} \cdot 6.1 \text{ V} = 24.4 \text{ W}$$

$$P_{Q1} = I_L \cdot V_{CE} = I_L \cdot (V_{DC(in)} - V_E) = 4 \text{ A} \cdot 7.5 \text{ V} = 30 \text{ W}$$

$$\text{\% Eff} \cong 100\% \cdot P_L/(P_L + P_{Q1})$$
$$\cong 100\% \cdot 24.4 \text{ W}/54.4 \text{ W} = 44.9 \text{ \%}$$

Note: The efficiency is actually less than 44.9% because of the power dissipated by the zener and R_S.

The Darlington-Pair Series-Pass Voltage Regulator

As you probably noticed, the zener and R_S in Example 17–1 dissipated a relatively large amount of power, requiring at least a 2-W resistor and a 2-W zener to meet worst-case conditions (no load). This problem can be greatly reduced by increasing the current gain of the circuit. To accomplish this, a power Darlington transistor or a Darlington pair can be used. The Darlington (illustrated in Figure 17–6) has a very high β_{DC}, which means the base current is low and the zener power rating will be low. Now the difference between V_E and V_Z is approximately 1.4 V instead of 0.7 V because of the two base–emitter junctions. This must be taken into consideration when designing the Darlington series regulator.

Designing the Darlington Series-Pass Voltage Regulator

Let's make a list of the parameters that you will have to know or calculate in order to design a Darlington series-pass voltage regulator. The design formulas are included in the list.

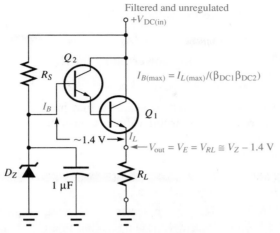

Figure 17–6 Series-pass Darlington pair.

1. You must know the highest DC input voltage ($V_{DC(in)}$) and the desired regulated output voltage (V_E or V_{RL}).
2. You must know the maximum load ($I_{L(max)}$).
3. You must calculate the power dissipation of Q_1 to determine the power rating ($P_{Q1(max)} = I_{L(max)} \cdot V_{CE}$), which must be greater than the actual worst-case power dissipation. A heat sink of proper size must be used to transfer heat away from the transistor case to keep the case temperature down.
4. The lower-power piggybacked transistor (Q_2) must have a collector current rating greater than the maximum base current of Q_1.

$$I_{B(Q1,max)} = I_{L(max)}/\beta_{DC1(min)} \tag{17–16}$$

   where $\beta_{DC1(min)}$ is the minimum h_{FE} from the data sheet.
5. Calculate the power dissipation of Q_2 to determine the power rating. Power rating must be greater than the actual worst-case power dissipation. $V_E = V_{RL}$.

$$P_{Q2(max)} = I_{B(Q1,max)} \cdot (V_{DC(in)} - 0.7\ \text{V} - V_E) \tag{17–17}$$

6. Next, you will need to determine the maximum Q_2 base current (I_B).

$$I_{B(max)} = I_{B(Q2,max)} = I_{B(Q1,max)}/\beta_{DC2(min)} \tag{17–18}$$

$$I_{B(max)} = I_{L(max)}/(\beta_{DC1(min)} \cdot \beta_{DC2(min)}) \tag{17–19}$$

7. Now determine the voltage rating for the zener.

$$V_Z \cong V_{RL} + 1.4\ \text{V} \tag{17–20}$$

8. When I_B is maximum, as calculated in step 6, the zener current will be minimum and should be equal to at least $0.1\ I_B$.

$$I_{Z(min)} = 0.1\ I_{B(max)} \tag{17–21}$$

$$I_{Z(max)} = 1.1\ I_{B(max)} \qquad \text{(no load)} \tag{17–22}$$

9. Determine a safe power rating for the zener.

$$P_{Z(rating)} > I_{Z(max)} \cdot V_Z \tag{17–23}$$

10. Calculate the value for the series resistor (R_S).

$$R_S = (V_{DC(in)} - V_Z)/I_{Z(max)} \qquad (17\text{--}24)$$

11. Determine the power rating for R_S.

$$P_{RS(Rating)} > I_{Z(max)} \cdot (V_{DC(in)} - V_Z) \qquad (17\text{--}25)$$

Components must be selected that have current, voltage, and power ratings greater than circuit values. Consider Example 17–2.

EXAMPLE 17–2 ▮▮▮▮▮▮▮▮▮

Design a Darlington series-pass voltage regulator, like that of Figure 17–6, from the following requirements: $V_{DC(in)} = 18$ V, $V_{DC(out)} = V_E = 12$ V, $I_{L(max)} = 2$ A.

$$P_{Q1(max)} = I_{L(max)} \cdot V_{CE} = 2 \text{ A} \cdot 6 \text{ V} = 12 \text{ W}$$

Use at least a 20-W transistor on a large heat sink. The current rating for the transistor must be at least 2 A. Let's assume the minimum β_{DC} (h_{FE}) for such a transistor is 40.

$$I_{B(Q1,max)} = I_{L(max)}/\beta_{DC1(min)} = 2 \text{ A}/40 = 50 \text{ mA}$$

$$\begin{aligned}
P_{Q2(max)} &= I_{B(Q1,max)} \cdot (V_{DC(in)} - 0.7 \text{ V} - V_E) \\
&= 50 \text{ mA} \cdot (18 \text{ V} - 0.7 \text{ V} - 12 \text{ V}) \\
&= 50 \text{ mA} \cdot 5.3 \text{ V} = 265 \text{ mW}
\end{aligned}$$

Use at least a 0.5-W transistor with a current rating of at least 50 mA (100-mA rating is better).
Let's assume the minimum β (h_{FE}) for such a transistor is 100.

$$I_{B(max)} = I_{B(Q2,max)} = I_{B(Q1,max)}/\beta_{DC2(min)} = 50 \text{ mA}/100 = 500 \text{ μA}$$

$$V_Z \cong V_{RL} + 1.4 \text{ V} = 12 \text{ V} + 1.4 \text{ V} = 13.4 \text{ V}$$

Use a 13-V zener.

$$I_{Z(min)} = 0.1 \, I_{B(max)} = 0.1 \cdot 500 \text{ μA} = 50 \text{ μA}$$

$$I_{Z(max)} = 1.1 \, I_{B(max)} = 1.1 \cdot 500 \text{ μA} = 550 \text{ μA}$$

$$P_{Z(Rating)} > I_{Z(max)} \cdot V_Z = 550 \text{ μA} \cdot 13 \text{ V} = 7.15 \text{ mW}$$

Use a 13-V, 250-mW zener (1N4700).

$$\begin{aligned}
R_S = (V_{DC(in)} - V_Z)/I_{Z(max)} &= (18 \text{ V} - 13 \text{ V})/550 \text{ μA} \\
&= 9{,}091 \text{ Ω}
\end{aligned}$$

$$\begin{aligned}
P_{RS(Rating)} > I_{Z(max)} \cdot (V_{DC(in)} - V_Z) &= 550 \text{ μA} \cdot (18 \text{ V} - 13 \text{ V}) \\
&= 2.75 \text{ mW}
\end{aligned}$$

Use a 9.1-kΩ, 1/8-W resistor.

CURRENT LIMITING

The Need for Current Limiting

What do you think might happen if the load device is suddenly shorted? Grim thought, huh? Well, we don't want the series-pass power transistor to be blown. We might assume that a fuse appears somewhere in the DC source. If so, the fuse may save the transistor if the fuse blows fast enough and the instantaneous surge current is not greater than the surge rating for the transistor. Instead of keeping our fingers crossed and replacing fuses, we can design the circuit with built-in current limiting. This is a good circuit to have in shop power supplies that are frequently accidently shorted.

A Simple Current-Limiting Circuit

As shown in Figure 17–7, the limiter circuit is composed of only two components, a series current-limit resistor R_{Limit} and a current-sensing transistor Q_2. Basic theory is used to reveal how this works. When the load current is high enough to cause a 0.7-V drop across R_{Limit}, the base–emitter junction of Q_2 becomes forward biased and Q_2 conducts from collector to emitter. This bypasses Q_1 base current around Q_1, causing Q_1 to conduct much less. Also, the 0.7 V needed from base to emitter of Q_1 is reduced. Thus, when $I_{L(\text{max})}$ is reached, Q_2 comes on and reduces the conduction of Q_1, which maintains the load current at the limit. Q_2 takes control away from the zener. As you can see in Figure 17–7, the maximum load current is 1.4 A, because that's the amount of current needed to produce a 0.7-V drop across R_{Limit}.

$$R_{\text{Limit}} \cong 0.7\text{V}/I_{L(\text{max})} \tag{17–26}$$

$$I_{L(\text{max})} \cong 0.7 \text{ V}/R_{\text{Limit}} \tag{17–27}$$

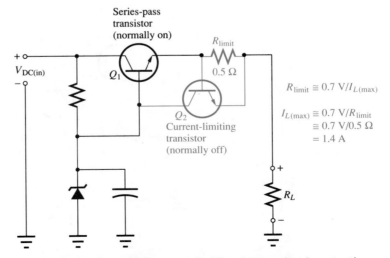

Figure 17–7 Constant-current limiting for overload protection.

When the Limiter Takes Over

Maximum load current is caused by a reduction in load resistance or a dead short. In either case, regulation is lost, the output voltage decreases, and the series-pass transistor's power dissipation is very high. The power rating of the pass transistor must be higher than this maximum dissipation and the transistor must be mounted on a large heat sink. A temperature-sensing switch mounted on the heat sink is a good idea. This is an encapsulated bimetal switch that breaks the main current path when a temperature threshold is reached. In any case, the circuit must be designed to withstand a dead short for extended periods of time.

OVERVOLTAGE PROTECTION

Thus far, we have discussed voltage regulation and current limiting. Including overvoltage protection in the design of a voltage regulator is also wise. If the series-pass transistor(s) short for some reason, the entire source voltage will be applied to the load device. Obviously that's not desirable. The load device may be destroyed due to voltage breakdown and overdissipation. Therefore, a circuit is needed that will monitor the output voltage and take quick action to remove power. One such circuit is illustrated in Figure 17–8. The circuit consists of the zener and resistor at the output and an SCR after the fuse. When the output voltage exceeds the zener voltage, the zener conducts and triggers the SCR. The SCR latches on and blows the fuse. This circuit is called a **crowbar** because, when the SCR fires, it is like throwing an iron crowbar across the DC line to ground.

The zener voltage rating at the output must be slightly higher than the regulated output voltage. For the circuit of Figure 17–8, the output voltage is approximately 6.1 V. Therefore, the same 6.8-V zener in the output provides an adequate margin for protection.

It is important that the fuse's current rating be higher than the maximum current limit of the current-limiter circuit. Otherwise, when the output of the

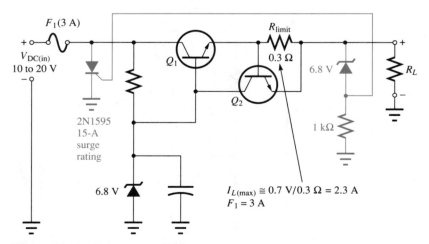

Figure 17–8 Using a "crowbar" for overvoltage protection.

regulator is overloaded, the fuse would blow before the limiter circuit could take control. As you can see in Figure 17–8, the current is limited to approximately 2.3 A. Thus, a 3-A fuse is adequate. The surge rating of the SCR must be much higher than the fuse current rating, so the SCR is not sacrificed along with the fuse.

PROBLEMS WITH THE SERIES-PASS VOLTAGE REGULATOR

The linear voltage regulators that we have just discussed have several serious problems which add up to one major one: relatively poor voltage regulation over a wide range of loads. (That doesn't mean the regulators discussed thus far are not useable. They do regulate and offer protection to the load device.) Some of the problems can easily be corrected. Study Figure 17–8.

First, zener voltage changes with zener current. In other words, as the load changes, the base current changes, which causes the zener current to change. As base current increases, due to increased load, zener voltage decreases. The resulting decrease in zener voltage causes the load voltage to decrease. The change may be as much as 0.5 V over a large change in load. Second, the voltage drop in the emitter region of the series-pass transistor increases as the load increases. This causes the output voltage to drop slightly. Third, a voltage drop exists across the current-limit resistor (R_{Limit}). As you know, this can be as high as 0.7 V. Altogether, these problems add up to as much as a 1.5-V drop in output voltage over a wide range of load. That's not at all desirable. However, these problems can be solved. Read on.

VOLTAGE-FEEDBACK CONTROL

Feedback Action

The solution to the problems previously discussed is voltage-feedback control. The idea is simple. The output voltage is monitored by an amplifier, such as an op-amp. The monitored voltage is compared to the zener reference voltage and the very slight difference between the two is amplified and used to control the series-pass transistor(s). Take a look at Figure 17–9. The zener reference voltage is fairly constant in this circuit because the zener current is not affected by load variations. The output voltage is monitored with a voltage divider and sent back to the inverting input of the op-amp. The op-amp amplifies the slight difference between V_{Ref} and V_F. If the load is increased, the output voltage will drop very slightly. This very slight drop in output voltage is greatly amplified by the op-amp acting as a difference amplifier with maximum gain. Since V_F is slightly lower than V_{Ref}, the output of the op-amp becomes more positive, which increases the conduction of Q_2 and Q_1. This keeps the output voltage within millivolts of the no-load output voltage. In fact, the feedback loop also takes care of would-be voltage drops caused by the emitter of the power transistor(s) and the limit resistor.

The Feedback Ratio (K)

Notice in Figure 17–9 that if $V_F \cong V_{Ref}$ the regulated output voltage must be greater than V_{Ref} because of the voltage divider. Consider this: If R_2 is

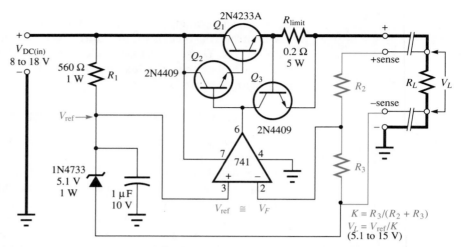

Figure 17–9 A linear voltage regulator with voltage feedback and remote sense.

shorted with a wire, the full output voltage appears at the inverting input of the op-amp. This immediately makes the output of the op-amp less positive and reduces the conduction of Q_2 and Q_1. Thus, the output voltage instantly drops to equal the zener voltage, in this case approximately 5.1 V. Therefore, the minimum output voltage for this circuit is equal to the zener reference voltage. Now, when the wire across R_2 is removed, the voltage at pin 2 of the op-amp is much less than the reference voltage at pin 3 for a very brief instant. This causes the voltage at pin 6 to increase, which causes the transistors to conduct more, causing the output voltage to increase until $V_{R3} \cong V_{Ref}$—all within microseconds. The amount of load voltage (V_L) will depend on the voltage-divider ratio $K = R_3/(R_2 + R_3)$. From this we derive the following mathematical relationships: $V_{Ref} \cong V_F = V_{R3} = V_L \cdot R_3/(R_2 + R_3) = V_L \cdot K$

$$K = R_3/(R_2 + R_3) \tag{17–28}$$

$$1/K = (R_2 + R_3)/R_3 = 1 + R_2/R_3$$

$$(1/K) - 1 = R_2/R_3$$

$$R_2 = [(1/K) - 1] \cdot R_3 \tag{17–29}$$

$$V_L = V_F/K \cong V_{Ref}/K \tag{17–30}$$

$$K = V_F/V_L \cong V_{Ref}/V_L \tag{17–31}$$

Consider Example 17–3.

EXAMPLE 17–3

For a voltage-feedback linear regulator circuit, the reference voltage is 5.1 V and the desired output voltage is 9 V. If R_3 is 1 kΩ, what is the value of R_2?

$V_L = 9$ V, $V_{\text{Ref}} = 5.1$ V

$K \cong V_{\text{Ref}}/V_L = 5.1$ V/9 V $= 0.567$

$R_2 = [(1/K) - 1] \cdot R_3 = [(1/0.567) - 1] \cdot 1$ kΩ

$\quad = [1.764 - 1] \cdot 1$ k$\Omega = 0.764 \cdot 1$ k$\Omega = 764$ Ω

Use a 765-Ω, 1% film resistor.
A potentiometer wired as a rheostat would provide variable control.

Remote Sense

Look again at Figure 17–9. Notice the plus and minus sense lines. These lines are relatively light-gauge wires that extend from the power supply to a remote load device. Heavier-gauge wire is used to carry power to the load device. If the distance between the load device (R_L) and the power supply is significant compared to the size wire and amount of current, there will be some voltage drop across the main-load wires. This voltage drop along the main lines undermines the regulation. To compensate for this line drop, remote sense lines are used. Using the remote sense lines, the difference amplifier is able to monitor the load voltage right at the load device. Thus, regardless of the line drops, the voltage across the load is held constant. Notice that the bottom of the zener and the bottom of R_3 is connected to the negative sense line. In this way, any voltage drop on the heavy ground-return line from the load device is added to the zener voltage and the feedback voltage where it is canceled at the inputs to the op-amp. You will see remote-sense terminals on all commercial heavy-duty DC regulated power supplies.

Input–Output Voltage Differential

Recall that the minimum input–output voltage differential is the minimum difference in voltage between the output and input of the regulator that allows the regulator to continue to regulate. It is very common for the linear regulators to require a differential of 2 to 3 V (closer to 3 V). This is reflected in the voltage range specification on the schematic of Figure 17–9. Notice that $V_{\text{DC(in)}}$ is specified as 8 to 18 V. If the desired output voltage is 5.1 V, the minimum input voltage must be 8 V to maintain regulation. If the desired output is 15 V, the input voltage must be at least 18 V. If R_2 is made variable, with an input voltage of 18 V, the output voltage can be varied over a range of 5.1 to 15 V.

Too Much Differential

It is possible to have too great a voltage differential. If the differential is excessive, the voltage drop across the power transistor(s) will be high, the power dissipation in the series-pass transistor(s) will be very high, and the efficiency of the linear voltage regulator will be very low. For fixed regulators, where R_2 or R_3 is not variable, the differential should be no more than 3 to 5 V. This is especially true for high-current supplies.

Linear Regulation Design Note

Take time to carefully study Design Note 17–1. You will find this design note to be a very useful tool in designing linear, Darlington-pair, voltage-feedback regulators. A 3-V zener diode is used as a reference voltage, permitting an output voltage range from 3 V to approximately 3 V less than the DC input voltage. Another zener voltage can be used for the reference if desired, as long as the new reference voltage is used in the program formulas. Note that the 3-V zener is rated as such with 250 μA of forward test current. Thus, R_1 is always calculated to provide 250 μA of zener current. If you select a different zener diode, make sure the manufacturer's test current is used. Keep in mind also that a single Darlington transistor can be selected to replace the Darlington pair. Don't forget that a medium- to large-finned heat sink is required for Q_1. Also, remember to keep the input-output voltage differential low to reduce Q_1 power dissipation and increase regulator efficiency.

A Dual-Polarity, Tracking Voltage Regulator

Figure 17–10 illustrates a dual-polarity regulator circuit. This is also a **tracking voltage regulator.** Notice that the reference voltage for the negative

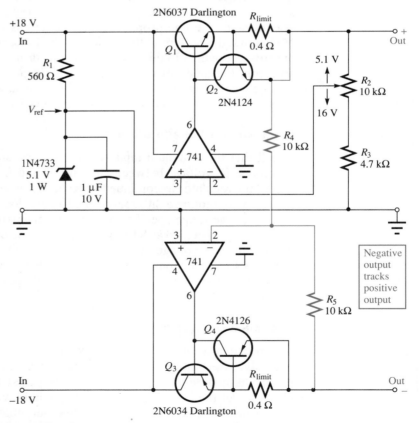

Figure 17–10 A dual-polarity, tracking voltage regulator with current limiting.

DESIGN NOTE 17–1 A LINEAR VOLTAGE REGULATOR

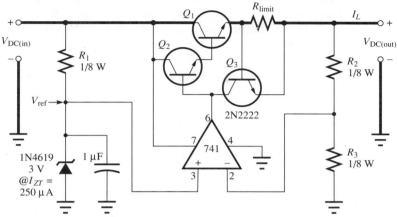

DESIGN FORMULAS

$$V_{DC(in)} \geq V_{DC(out)} + \underline{3\text{ V}}$$

$$\boxed{\begin{array}{c}\text{Minimum Input-Output}\\\text{Voltage Differential}\end{array}}$$

$$V_{DC(out)} = V_L$$

$$K = V_{Ref}/V_L = 3\text{ V}/V_L$$

$$R_2 = [(1/K) - 1] \cdot R_3$$
$$= [(V_L/3\text{ V}) - 1] \cdot R_3$$

$$R_1 = (V_{DC(in)}) - V_Z)/I_{ZT}$$
$$= (V_{DC(in)} - 3\text{ V})/250\ \mu A$$

$$R_{Limit} \cong 0.7\text{ V}/I_{L(max)}$$

$$P_{RLimit(Rating)} \geq 0.7\text{ V} \cdot I_{L(max)}$$

$$P_{Q1(Rating)} \geq 2(V_{DC(in)} - V_L) \cdot I_{L(max)}$$

$$P_{Q2(Rating)} \geq 2(V_{DC(in)} - V_L - 0.7\text{ V}) \cdot \underline{(I_{L(max)}/\beta_{Q1})}$$

$$\beta_{Q1}\beta_{Q2} \geq I_{L(max)}/\underline{20\text{ mA}} \qquad \boxed{I_{BQ1} = I_{EQ2}}$$

$$\boxed{\begin{array}{c}\text{Maximum Op-Amp}\\\text{Output Current}\end{array}}$$

BASIC PROGRAM

```
10 REM  * LINEAR VOLTAGE REGULATOR
PROGRAM *
20 CLS
30 PRINT "LINEAR VOLTAGE REGULATOR
PROGRAM"
40 PRINT""
50 REM  INPUT SECTION
60 INPUT "ENTER DESIRED OUTPUT VOLTAGE -
";VOUT
70 INPUT "ENTER MAXIMUM LOAD (CURRENT) -
";IMAX
80 PRINT "DC INPUT VOLTAGE MUST BE AT
LEAST 3 V HIGHER THAN THE DC OUTPUT
VOLTAGE."
90 INPUT "ENTER DC INPUT VOLTAGE - ";VIN
100 INPUT "ENTER DESIRED VALUE FOR R3 -
";R3
110 REM  CALCULATION SECTION
120 K = 3/VOUT
130 R2 = ((1/K) - 1)  *  R3
140 R1 = (VIN - 3)/.00025
150 RLIMIT = .7/IMAX
160 PRLIMIT = .7 * IMAX
170 PQ1 = (VIN - VOUT)  * IMAX
180 PRINT "THE MINIMUM TOTAL DC BETA MUST
BE ";IMAX/.02
190 INPUT "ENTER THE MINIMUM DC BETA FOR
Q1 (USUALLY 15 TO 30) - ";BQ1
200 PQ2 = (VIN - VOUT - .7)  *  (IMAX/BQ1)
210 PRINT "THE MINIMUM DC BETA FOR Q2 MUST
BE ";(IMAX/.02)/BQ1
220 EFF = 100  *  VOUT/VIN
230 REM  OUTPUT SECTION
240 PRINT""
250 PRINT "R1 IS A STANDARD VALUE CLOSE TO
";R1;" OHMS."
260 PRINT "R2 IS A STANDARD VALUE CLOSE TO
";R2;" OHMS."
270 PRINT "THE CURRENT-LIMIT RESISTOR
SHOULD BE A STANDARD VALUE CLOSE TO
";RLIMIT;" OHMS."
280 PRINT "Q1 SHOULD HAVE A POWER RATING
EQUAL TO OR GREATER THAN ";2*PQ1;" WATTS."
290 PRINT "Q1 MUST BE ABLE TO HANDLE A
CONTINUOUS CURRENT EQUAL TO ";IMAX;"
AMPS."
300 PRINT "THE VOLTAGE RATING FOR Q1 MUST
BE GREATER THAN ";VIN;" VOLTS."
310 PRINT "Q2 SHOULD HAVE A POWER RATING
EQUAL TO OR GREATER THAN ";2*PQ2;" WATTS."
320 PRINT "Q2 MUST BE ABLE TO HANDLE A
CONTINUOUS CURRENT EQUAL TO ";IMAX/BQ1;"
AMPS."
330 PRINT "THE VOLTAGE RATING FOR Q2 MUST
BE GREATER THAN ";VIN;" VOLTS."
340 PRINT "THE OVERALL POWER EFFICIENCY AT
MAXIMUM LOAD IS ";EFF;"%."
350 INPUT "ANOTHER PROBLEM? (Y/N) - ";A$
360 IF A$ = "Y"  THEN GOTO 10
370 CLS:END
```

supply is the regulated positive output voltage. The negative regulator circuit, composed of the lower 741 and Q_3 is actually a high-power unity-gain amplifier. Therefore, when R_2 is adjusted, both outputs change voltage at the same time. R_4 or R_5 could be made variable to allow for calibration of the two outputs to cause the negative voltage to be exactly equal and opposite to the positive voltage. Notice that current limiting is provided for each polarity. In this case, the current is limited to approximately 0.7 V/0.4 Ω = 1.75 A.

THE SHUNT REGULATOR

A Super Zener Regulator

Figure 17–11 illustrates the not-so-common shunt regulator. This circuit is actually a super zener-diode shunt regulator. The op-amp and the Darlington power transistor amplify the zener's current-handling capability. Now, Q_1 acts as a high-power zener. Since voltage feedback is used and the actual zener diode operates at a fixed current, the regulation is very good.

Theory of Operation

You probably already have the circuit of Figure 17–11 figured out. Let's discuss it anyway. We'll assume that R_3 is set so the output voltage is 12 V. The R_3, R_4 divider drops the 12 V down to 5.1 V, so V_F (pin 3) $\cong$ V_{Ref} (pin 2). Pin 6 of the op-amp (error amplifier) drives the base of Q_1 enough to cause a 12-V drop from collector to emitter. Since 18 V is applied, a 6-V drop exists across R_2. Regardless of load, R_2 will always have a 6-V drop as long as the 18-V source is constant. (It won't be, but for the sake of discussion we will assume it is.) This means the current through R_2 is always approximately 6 V/10 Ω = 0.6 A. Therefore, the 0.6 A of current must be shared by Q_1 and the load, where $I_{R2} = I_{Q1} + I_L$. Now, if the load increases ($\uparrow I_L$), the Darlington current must decrease ($\downarrow I_{Q1}$) to maintain I_{R2} at approximately 0.6 A ($\leftrightarrow I_{R2} = \downarrow I_{Q1} + \uparrow I_L$) and V_{R2} at about 6 V. So how does Q_1 know to reduce its current? When the load increases, the output voltage drops very slightly. This very slight drop is amplified by the error amplifier. Pin 3 be-

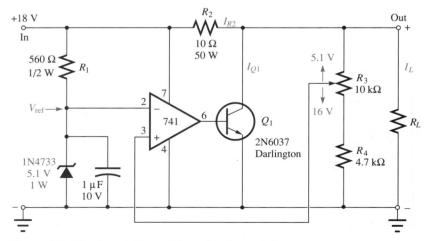

Figure 17–11   A variable-voltage shunt regulator.

comes slightly less positive and the base drive at pin 6 is reduced. This makes Q_1 conduct less, transferring needed current to the load.

Shunt Regulator Efficiency

The voltage regulation of the shunt regulator is very good but its power-handling efficiency can be very poor. For the circuit of Figure 17–11, let's say the load is 0.1 A at 12 V. I_{R2} is 0.6 A, so I_{Q1} must be 0.5 A. The load dissipates 0.1 A · 12 V = 1.2 W. The series resistor R_2 dissipates 0.6 A · 6 V = 3.6 W. The Darlington transistor dissipates 0.5 A · 12 V = 6 W. The percent efficiency is (100% · P_{out}/P_{in}):

$$\% \text{ Eff} = 100\% \cdot P_L/(P_{R2} + P_{Q1} + P_L) \tag{17–32}$$

In this case, the % Eff = 100% · 1.2 W/(3.6 W + 6 W + 1.2 W) = 11.1%. That's not very good at all. It could be even worse if the output voltage is set lower. Let's say the output is set to 6 V. That means there is 12 V across R_2 and the current through R_2 is 1.2 A. Therefore, P_{R2} = 1.2 A · 12 V = 14.4 W. If the load current is only 0.1 A, Q_1 must take the remaining 1.1 A. So, P_{Q1} = 1.1 A · 6 V = 6.6 W and P_L = 0.1 A · 6 V = 0.6 W. The % Eff is now 100% · 0.6 W/(14.4 W + 6.6 W + 0.6 W) = 2.78%. Not good!

The efficiency of the shunt regulator is always highest when V_{R2} is kept low and most of the total current is sent to the load. For example, let's say the output voltage is set at 16 V and the load is 150 mA. V_{R2} will be 2 V and I_{R2} will be 200 mA. In this case I_{Q1} is only 50 mA. P_L = 150 mA · 16 V = 2.4 W. P_{R2} = 200 mA · 2 V = 0.4 W and P_{Q1} = 50 mA · 16 V = 0.8 W. The percent efficiency is now 100% · 2.4 W/(0.4 W + 0.8 W + 2.4 W) = 66.7%. That's much better! So remember, when designing a shunt regulator make sure that the voltage differential across R_2 is small and that most of the current goes to the load. Ideally, $V_{DC(in)}$ should be about 2 to 3 V higher than V_L and you should select R_2 so I_{R2} is 10 to 30% higher than I_L. Pretend that Q_1 is a high-power zener and use the design formulas discussed at the beginning of this section and Section 3–2. Consider Example 17–4.

EXAMPLE 17–4 ▮▮▮▮▮▮▮▮▮▮▮▮▮▮▮▮▮▮▮▮▮▮▮▮▮▮▮▮

A shunt regulator regulates a 3-A load at 5 V. The DC input voltage is 13.6 V and the series resistor is 2.5 Ω (I_{R2}). Calculate the power delivered to the load device, the power dissipated in the shunt transistor, and the power dissipated in the series resistor. Also, calculate the regulator's efficiency.

I_{R2} = (13.6 V − 5 V)/2.5 Ω = 3.44 A

P_{R2} = 3.44 A · (13.6 V − 5 V) = 29.6 W

P_{Q1} = (3.44 A − 3 A) · 5 V = 2.2 W

P_L = 3 A · 5 V = 15 W

% Eff = 100% · $P_L/(P_{R2} + P_{Q1} + P_L)$
    = 100% · 15 W/(29.6 W + 2.2 W + 15 W) = 32.1%

Well it's about time for a self-check. Take time to review this section and test your understanding by answering the questions of self-check 17–2.

---

1. What are some disadvantages of the simple zener-diode voltage regulator?
2. A basic series-pass voltage regulator has the following values: $V_{DC(in)} = 12$ V, $R_S = 1.2$ kΩ, $V_Z = 5.6$ V, $P_{Z(Rating)} = 250$ mW, $R_L = 25$ Ω, transistor $\beta_{DC(min)} = 80$. Calculate V_L, I_L, I_B, I_Z, P_{RS}, P_Z, P_{Q1}, P_L, and % Eff. Is the power rating of the zener sufficient for this circuit?
3. Design a Darlington series-pass voltage regulator like that of Figure 17–6. $V_{DC(in)} = 8$ V. $V_E = V_{RL} = V_{DC(out)} = 5$ V. $I_{L(max)} = 6$ A. $\beta_{Q1(min)} = 40$. $\beta_{Q2(min)} = 90$. Describe the required components in terms of voltage, current, and power rating. Specify the resistance and minimum power rating for R_S.
4. List three problems of the basic series-pass voltage regulator.
5. For a voltage-feedback linear regulator circuit like that of Figure 17–9, the reference voltage is 3.3 V and the desired output voltage is 12 V. If R_3 is 2.2 kΩ, what is the value of R_2?
6. Under what operating conditions is the shunt regulator efficiency the highest?

17–3 IC LINEAR VOLTAGE REGULATORS

FIXED, THREE-TERMINAL, IC VOLTAGE REGULATORS

For medium- and low-power applications, manufacturers have provided us with a wide range of integrated-circuit voltage regulators. These IC regulators include precision voltage references, temperature compensation, and overload and short-circuit protection. All of the discrete devices and op-amps that you explored in Section 17–2 are contained in one integrated circuit. We will begin our exploration of IC voltage regulators with a discussion of fixed, three-terminal voltage regulators.

IC Regulator Implementation

Figure 17–12 illustrates the use of the three-terminal regulator. What could be simpler! A fixed-voltage three-terminal regulator is selected according to

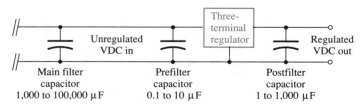

Figure 17–12 Three-terminal voltage regulators.

desired output voltage and maximum load current for the application. The DC source is filtered with a relatively large-value capacitor to reduce DC ripple to a level that will not violate the minimum input–output voltage differential. Recall that linear regulators generally require that the minimum DC input voltage be several volts higher than the regulated output voltage, which includes the negative peak of any DC ripple. The prefilter capacitor is recommended by the manufacturer if the regulator is more than six inches (lead length) from the main filter capacitor(s). To improve transient response (regulator response to load impulses), a postfilter is also recommended. This filter also reduces the AC impedance at the regulator to minimize the possibility of positive feedback problems on the DC line. (Positive feedback can cause unwanted oscillations throughout a circuit.)

Common Case Styles

Figure 17–13 illustrates the case styles commonly used for three-terminal regulators. The TO-3 case is used for higher-power applications in which the load requires 1 A or more of current. Naturally, a proper heat sink is required, but remember, the power dissipated by the regulator can be greatly limited by keeping the input–output voltage differential low. The popular TO-220 case is used for 0.1-A to 3-A voltage regulators. Again, a proper heat sink is required. The TO-39 and TO-92 case-style regulators are ideal for low-power circuits such as preamplifiers and oscillators. These generally require no heat sink although a clip-on heat sink can be used with the TO-39 case and should be used if the load current is high and the voltage differential is high.

The terminal designations, or descriptions, shown in Figure 17–13 are true for most fixed regulators but not all. Make sure you refer to the manufacturer's data sheet to determine the actual terminal designation for the regulator you intend to use.

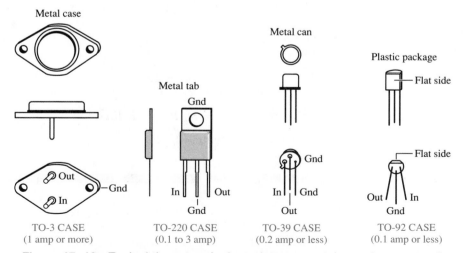

Figure 17–13 Typical three-terminal regulator case styles and current ratings.

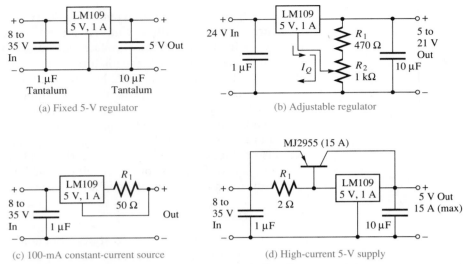

(a) Fixed 5-V regulator   (b) Adjustable regulator

(c) 100-mA constant-current source   (d) High-current 5-V supply

Figure 17–14   The versatility of three-terminal voltage regulators.

Fixed- and Variable-Voltage Applications

As illustrated in Figure 17–14, three-terminal regulators are more versatile than you might think. We'll use the 5-V, 1-A LM109 as an example. Figure 17–14a shows the LM109 in its common fixed-voltage application. However, as shown in Figure 17–14b, the fixed regulator may also be used to obtain higher regulated output voltages. Here, the output voltage is adjustable or variable depending on the value of R_2. Notice that R_1 is between the output terminal and the common terminal. That means the voltage across R_1 must be 5 V. Therefore, the total output voltage will be the sum of V_{R1} and V_{R2}—in this case, 5 V + V_{R2}. The voltage across R_2 is determined by two currents, I_{R1} and I_Q (the quiescent current of the regulator specified on the data sheet). Therefore, the formula for total output voltage is derived like this:

$$\begin{aligned}
V_{\text{out}} &= V_{\text{Reg}} + V_{R2} \\
&= V_{\text{Reg}} + R_2 \cdot (I_{R1} + I_Q) \\
&= V_{\text{Reg}} + R_2 \cdot ((V_{\text{Reg}}/R_1) + I_Q) \\
&= V_{\text{Reg}} + (R_2 V_{\text{Reg}}/R_1) + (R_2 I_Q) \\
&= V_{\text{Reg}} \cdot (1 + R_2/R_1) + (R_2 I_Q)
\end{aligned}$$

$$V_{\text{out}} = V_{\text{Reg}} \cdot (1 + R_2/R_1) + (R_2 I_Q) \qquad (17\text{–}33)$$

Consider Example 17–5.

EXAMPLE 17–5

A 5-V fixed regulator is used to create a higher regulated output voltage. R_1 is 270 Ω and R_2 is 330 Ω. The common-terminal quiescent current is 5.2 mA. Calculate the output voltage.

$$V_{out} = V_{Reg} \cdot (1 + (R_2/R_1) + (R_2 I_Q)$$
$$= 5 \text{ V} \cdot (1 + 330 \text{ }\Omega/270 \text{ }\Omega) + (330 \text{ }\Omega \cdot 5.2 \text{ mA})$$
$$= 5 \text{ V} \cdot 2.22 + 1.72 \text{ V}$$
$$= 11.1 \text{ V} + 1.72 \text{ V} = 12.82 \text{ V}$$

Fixed Regulators as Constant-Current Sources

Figure 17–14c shows the LM109 used as a constant-current source. Since the voltage between the regulator's output terminal and its common terminal is 5 V, the voltage across R_1 is 5 V, making the current through R_1 constant. In this case, the current is a constant 5 V/50 Ω = 100 mA.

Power-Boosting the Fixed Regulator

Finally, Figure 17–14d is a very interesting example of how to increase the current-handling capability of the fixed regulator. The theory here is simple. The external power transistor comes on and begins to bypass current around the regulator when the voltage drop across R_1 becomes 0.6 to 0.7 V. In other words, if the load increases so the current through R_1 is large enough to cause a 0.7-V drop, the external transistor comes on and bypasses any further increases in current around the regulator. In this case, the maximum current the LM109 must handle is approximately 0.7 V/2 Ω = 350 mA. Any current greater than 350 mA passes through the external transistor. The output voltage is still regulated at 5 V. Figures 17–14b and 14d can be combined if desired.

Common Three-Terminal Regulators

Table 17–1 is a listing of common three-terminal linear voltage regulators with primary specifications. The minimum input voltage for each regulator

TABLE 17–1   COMMON THREE-TERMINAL LINEAR REGULATORS

Type	V_{in} min/max (V)	V_{out} (V)	I_{max} (A)	I_Q (mA)	Line Reg (mV)	Load Reg (mV)
					Maximum Values Given	
MC78L05AC	+6.7/+30	+5	0.1	6	150 (+7 to +20 V)	60 (1 to 100 mA)
MC79L05AC	−6.7/−30	−5	0.1	6	200 (−7 to −20 V)	60 (1 to 100 mA)
LM109H	+6.7/+35	+5	0.2	10	50 (+7 to +25 V)	50 (5 to 500 mA)
LM109K	+7.2/+35	+5	1	10	50 (7.1 to 25 V)	100 (5 mA to 1.5 A)
LM340K-5.0	+7/+35	+5	1	6.5	10 (7.5 to 20 V)	25 (5 mA to 1.5 A)
LM340K-12	+14/+35	+12	1	6.5	18 (14.8 to 27 V)	32 (5 mA to 1.5 A)
LM340K-15	+17/+35	+15	1	6.5	22 (17.9 to 30 V)	35 (5 mA to 1.5 A)
LM320K-5.0	−7/−25	−5	1.5	2	40 (−7 to −25 V)	100 (5 mA to 1.5 A)
LM320K-12	−14/−35	−12	1	4	20 (−14 to −35 V)	80 (5 mA to 1 A)
LM320K-15	−17/−40	−15	1	4	20 (−17 to −40 V)	80 (5 mA to 1 A)
MC1468	±17/±30	±15	0.1	N/A	20 (18 to 30 V)	30 (0 to 50 mA)

reflects the minimum input–output voltage differential, also known as the *dropout voltage*. For example, the MC78L05AC has a minimum input voltage requirement of 6.7 V. Since it has a 5-V output, the minimum differential, or dropout, voltage is 1.7 V. The input–output voltage differential must be kept higher than 1.7 V. The maximum current values assume the power dissipation of the device is not exceeded and that proper heat sinking is provided (keep the voltage differential low). Line regulation is a maximum change in output voltage for the specified change in input voltage. Load regulation is a maximum change in output voltage for the specified change in load current.

ADJUSTABLE IC VOLTAGE REGULATORS

The LM117

Some three-terminal voltage regulators are designed specifically for variable or adjustable operation. An example of this is the very popular LM117K (the K indicates the TO-3 case style) shown in Figure 17–15. The maximum input voltage for this IC is 40 V. The maximum load current the LM117K can handle is 1.5 A. The minimum regulated output voltage for the LM117 is 1.25 V. The LM117 allows a wider range of output voltages than does an LM109.

The output voltage is determined using Formula 17–33, $V_{out} = V_{Reg} \cdot (1 + R_2/R_1) + (R_2 I_Q)$, where $I_{Adj} = I_Q$. For adjustable regulators, the data sheets refer to the common-terminal current as *adjustment pin current* (I_{Adj}), not quiescent current (I_Q). R_1 is usually between 200 Ω and 300 Ω.

A question you may now have is: How can I determine the value of R_2 to get a specific output voltage? Formula 17–33 must be rearranged as follows:

$$V_{out} = V_{Reg} \cdot (1 + R_2/R_1) + (R_2 I_{Adj})$$

$$V_{out} = V_{Reg} + V_{Reg} R_2/R_1 + R_2 I_{Adj}$$

$$V_{out} = V_{Reg} + R_2 \cdot (V_{Reg}/R_1 + I_{Adj})$$

$$R_2 \cdot (V_{Reg}/R_1 + I_{Adj}) = V_{out} - V_{Reg}$$

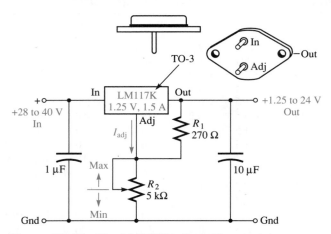

Figure 17–15 The LM117K adjustable regulator.

$$R_2 = \frac{V_{out} - V_{Reg}}{(V_{Reg}/R_1) + I_{Adj}}$$

(17–34)

Look at Example 17–6.

EXAMPLE 17–6 ▮

An LM117 is used to create a 12-V regulator. R_1 is chosen to be 270 Ω. I_{Adj} is specified as 50 μA. What is the proper value for R_2?

$$R_2 = \frac{V_{out} - V_{Reg}}{(V_{Reg}/R_1) + I_{Adj}}$$

$R_2 = (12 \text{ V} - 1.25 \text{ V})/((1.25 \text{ V}/270 \text{ Ω}) + 50 \text{ μA})$
$\quad = 10.75 \text{ V}/4.68 \text{ mA} = 2.3 \text{ kΩ}$

Use a 2.2-kΩ resistor and a 100-Ω resistor in series.

A Dual-Polarity DC Supply—The LM117 and LM137 Pair

Figure 17–16 shows the LM117 and LM137 as a complementary pair in a dual-polarity adjustable supply. The LM137 is the same as the LM117 except

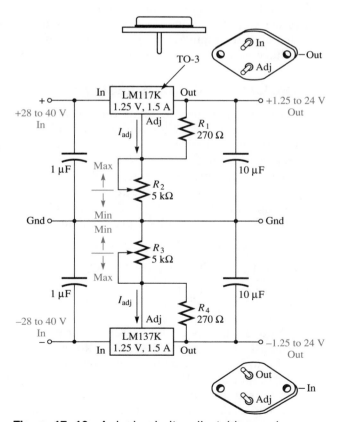

Figure 17–16 A dual-polarity adjustable supply.

TABLE 17–2   COMMON ADJUSTABLE LINEAR REGULATORS

| Type | V_{diff}
$V_{in} - V_{out}$
(V) | V_{out}
(V) | Maximum Values Given | | | |
			I_{max} (A)	I_{Adj} (μA)	Line Reg (%/V)	Load Reg (%)
LM723	3 to 38	+2 to +37	0.15	N/A	0.3	0.6
LM117K	3 to 40	+1.2 to +37	2.2	100	0.02	0.3
LM137K	3 to 40	−1.2 to −37	2.2	100	0.02	0.5
LM150K	3 to 35	+1.2 to +33	3	100	0.05	1
LM133K	3 to 35	−1.2 to −32	3	100	0.05	1
LM196K	3 to 20	+1.25 to +15	10	100	0.05	0.1

it is designed for negative-voltage operation. With ±40 V applied, ±1.25 to ±37 V is available at the outputs. Both regulators offer excellent *line regulation* of 0.02% change in output voltage per 1-V change in input voltage. That means that if the output is set for 10 V, the output will only change by 2 mV for a 1-V change in input voltage. The *load regulation* is 0.3% or better. That means the output voltage will only change by 0.3% over the full range of load current (from 10 mA to 1.5 A). If the output is set at 10 V, the maximum change due to load variations is 10 · 0.003 = 30 mV. Not bad!

Table 17–2 is a listing of common adjustable linear voltage regulators with primary specifications. V_{Diff} is the input–output voltage differential. Notice that all listed regulators require a minimum differential of 3 V. If the output voltage is to be 2 V, the input must be 5 V, and so on.

THE LM723 IC VOLTAGE REGULATOR

Let's take the time to focus on a very popular and versatile adjustable regulator, the LM723. As you can see in Figure 17–17, the LM723 is a 14-pin DIP IC. It is capable of delivering 150 mA to a load device with an output voltage range of 2 to 37 V. Notice the IC contains a precision voltage reference (D_1), a constant-current source, and A_2. The reference voltage at pin 6 is a very stable 7.15 V. The IC also contains an error amplifier (A_1) and a current-limit transistor (Q_2). The regulator circuit of Figure 17–17 is configured for an output voltage greater than 7.15 V where:

$$V_{out} = V_{Ref} \cdot (R_1 + R_2)/R_2 \qquad (17\text{–}35)$$

where $V_{Ref} = 7.15\ V$ for the 723 IC.

$$R_1 = \frac{R_2(V_{out} - V_{Ref})}{V_{Ref}} \qquad (17\text{–}36)$$

Notice that this circuit has only four external components: R_1 and R_2 to establish the output voltage, R_{Limit} to establish the current-limit threshold, and a low-value capacitor to compensate and stabilize the error amplifier. The output of the IC is pin 10, which is wired over to the limit resistor and the current-sensing transistor at pins 2 and 3. As in our discrete linear regulators, the final output is after the current-limit resistor. Figure 17–17 is configured for output voltage regulation in the 7- to 37-V range. Now, take a minute to study Example 17–7.

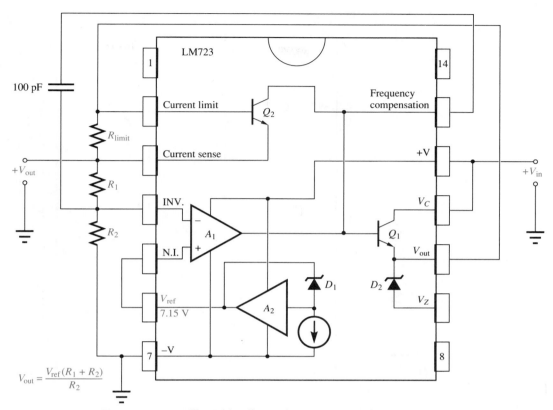

Figure 17–17 The 723 adjustable voltage regulator.

$$V_{out} = \frac{V_{ref}(R_1 + R_2)}{R_2}$$

EXAMPLE 17–7

Design a regulator circuit using the 723 IC. The output voltage shall be 12 V and current shall be limited to approximately 100 mA. Assume a 0.7-V threshold for the current-limit circuit. Let $R_2 = 2.2$ kΩ.

$R_{Limit} = 0.7$ V/100 mA $= 7$ Ω

Use a 6.8-Ω resistor. $\frac{1}{8}$ W is fine.

$R_1 = [2.2$ kΩ $\cdot$ (12 V $-$ 7.15 V)]/7.15 V $= 1{,}492$ Ω

Use a 1.5-kΩ resistor.

The DC source voltage must be at least 3 V higher than the 12-V output. If 15 V is used, it must be well filtered.

Using the 723 as a Low-Voltage Regulator

Figure 17–18 illustrates how to configure the 723 for low-voltage regulation in the range of 2 to 7 V. Notice that the reference voltage at pin 6 is divided down by R_1 and R_2. The output voltage is compared to this reduced reference. Therefore, the output voltage must be less than 7.15 V. Analysis and

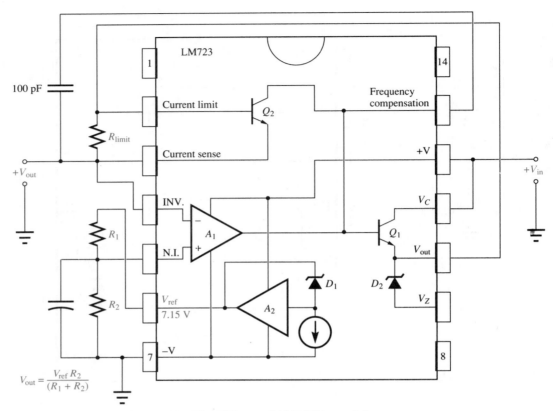

Figure 17–18   The 723 as a 2-V to 7-V regulator.

design formulas are straightforward. We'll use Formulas 17–37 and 17–38 in Example 17–8.

$$V_{out} = V_{Ref}R_2/(R_1 + R_2) \qquad\qquad (17\text{–}37)$$

$$R_1 = R_2(V_{Ref} - V_{out})/V_{out} \qquad\qquad (17\text{–}38)$$

EXAMPLE 17–8

Design a regulator circuit using the 723 IC. The output voltage shall be 5 V and current shall be limited to approximately 50 mA. Assume a 0.7-V threshold for the current-limit circuit. Let R_2 be 2.74 kΩ, 2%.

$R_{Limit} = 0.7\ \text{V}/50\ \text{mA} = 14\ \Omega$

Use a 13-Ω resistor. $\frac{1}{8}$ W is fine.

$R_1 = R_2(V_{Ref} - V_{out})/V_{out} = 2.74\ \text{kΩ} \cdot (7.15\ \text{V} - 5\ \text{V})/5\ \text{V}$
    $= 1{,}178\ \Omega$

Use a 1.18-kΩ, 1% resistor.

Check:

$$V_{out} = V_{Ref}R_2/(R_1 + R_2)$$
$$= 7.15 \text{ V} \cdot 2.74 \text{ k}\Omega/(1.18 \text{ k}\Omega + 2.74 \text{ k}\Omega) = 4.998 \text{ V}$$

The DC source voltage must be at least 3 V higher than the pin 6, 7.15-V reference. If 10 V is used, it must be well filtered.

Power-Boosting the 723

Figure 17–19 shows the addition of a power transistor at pin 10 of the 723. The circuit is configured for regulation in the 7 to 37-V range. The addition of the power transistor is a simple and effective improvement. A Darlington need not be used here for most applications, since the 723 is able to deliver as much as 150 mA of base-drive current. At this drive level, load current in the range of 4 to 6 A is possible with a single power transistor. Darlingtons should be used for higher load current demands. Proper heat sinking is essential. The input–output voltage differential should be no less than 4 V. Also, the differential should not be too high, since it increases power dissipation in the power transistor and 723 IC.

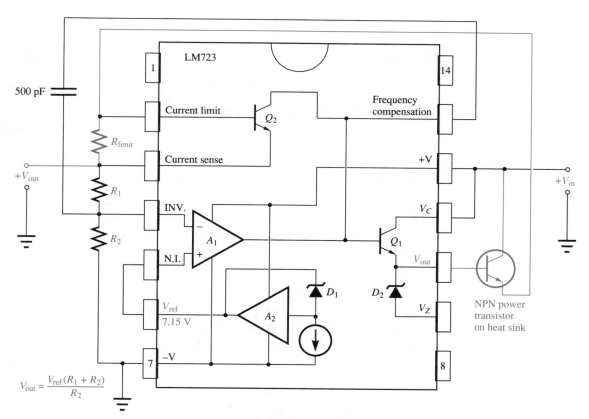

Figure 17–19   The 723 with power-boosted output.

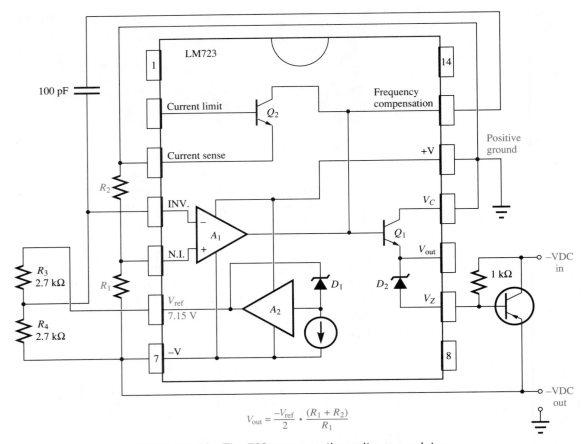

$$V_{\text{out}} = \frac{-V_{\text{ref}}}{2} \cdot \frac{(R_1 + R_2)}{R_1}$$

Figure 17–20   The 723 as a negative voltage regulator.

The 723 as a Negative Voltage Regulator

The versatility of the 723 is again demonstrated in Figure 17–20. The entire circuit is operated at a negative potential and the positive ground is shifted to pins 11 and 12. The output power transistor is an emitter-follower with Q_1 and D_2 providing its base drive voltage. The voltage drop across R_1, pin 5, is compared to half of the reference voltage (7.15 V/2) at pin 4. If the output voltage drops slightly due to an increase in load, the voltage across R_1 will decrease. This makes the output of A_1 become more negative, which decreases the conduction of Q_1 and increases the base drive voltage to the power transistor. Thus, the would-be drop in output voltage is limited to a few millivolts. The analysis and design formulas are as follows:

$$V_{\text{out}} = -V_{\text{Ref}} \cdot (R_1 + R_2)/2R_1 \tag{17–39}$$

$$R_1 = -V_{\text{Ref}}R_2/(2V_{\text{out}} + V_{\text{Ref}}) \tag{17–40}$$

Consider Example 17–9.

EXAMPLE 17–9 ▮▮▮▮▮▮▮

Design a negative regulator circuit using the 723 IC. The output voltage shall be -15 V. Let $R_2 = 2.74$ kΩ, 2%.

$R_1 = -V_{\text{Ref}}R_2/(2V_{\text{out}} + V_{\text{Ref}})$
$\quad = -7.15$ V $\cdot$ 2.74 k$\Omega/(-30$ V $+ 7.15$ V)
$\quad = -19{,}591/-22.85 = 857$ Ω

Use an 866-Ω, 2% resistor.

Check:

$V_{\text{out}} = -V_{\text{Ref}} \cdot (R_1 + R_2)/2R_1$
$\quad\quad = -7.15$ V $\cdot$ 3,606 $\Omega/1{,}732$ $\Omega = -14.89$ V

The DC source voltage must be at least -18 V.

Note: R_1 could be made variable to get exactly -15 V.

You will see the 723 regulator again later as we explore switching regulators. For now, take time to review and answer the questions of Self-Check 17–3.

Self-Check 17–3

1. List three applications for which the three-terminal regulator may be used.
2. Explain *dropout voltage* in terms of linear voltage regulators.
3. An LM117 is used to create a 9-V regulator like that of Figure 17–15. R_1 is selected to be 220 Ω. I_{Adj} is specified to be 50 μA. What is the proper value for R_2?
4. Design a +15-V regulator using the 723 IC. Current shall be limited to approximately 80 mA and R_2 shall be 3.01 kΩ. Calculate R_{Limit}, R_1, and specify the minimum DC input voltage.
5. Design a -18-V regulator using the 723 IC. Let $R_2 = 3.16$ kΩ. Calculate R_1 and specify the minimum DC input voltage.

17–4 SWITCHING DC POWER SUPPLIES

INTRODUCTION TO SWITCHING POWER SUPPLIES

Advantages and Disadvantages

In this section, you will explore a very different type of power supply and regulator, the switching supply. This type of supply has become very popular for some very significant reasons. Nonlinear switching regulators operate at efficiencies of 80 to 95% while linear regulators operate in the range of 10 to 80%. As a direct result, switching regulators dissipate less power, which means less heat is generated and smaller heat sinks are justified. Because of

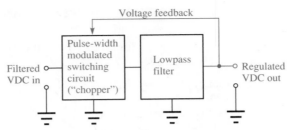

Figure 17-21 Block diagram of the switching voltage regulator.

the smaller heat sinks, there is less weight and occupied space. Some possible disadvantages of the switching regulator are that the circuits are slightly more complicated and they require an inductor (which adds significant cost) and the switching action generates radio-frequency energy that can be radiated into the air if care is not taken. In most cases, you will find that these disadvantages are outweighed by the tremendous advantages of higher efficiency, smaller size, and less weight.

The Basic Switching Circuit

Figure 17-21 is the basic block diagram of a switching regulator. Filtered DC is applied to a pulse-width-modulated switching circuit. The switching circuit chops the DC into a high-frequency square wave whose duty cycle can be varied. Consequently, these circuits are often loosely referred to as *choppers*. Following the chopper is a lowpass filter composed of a series inductor and a parallel capacitor. The cutoff frequency of the filter is several decades below the switching, or chopping, frequency. In reality, this lowpass filter is an integrator that is able to average-out the DC square-wave pulses and provide a smooth DC to the load. We'll explore this more later.

Figure 17-22 is a look inside the blocks of the switching regulator. The duty cycle of the chopped square wave determines the final DC output voltage. Notice that when the duty cycle is high, the output voltage is high; when the duty cycle is low, the output voltage is low. The DC output voltage is sampled by a voltage divider and a feedback voltage is used to control the duty cycle. If the load increases in the output, the output voltage tends to drop, but only slightly. The feedback voltage also drops slightly and signals the switching circuit to increase the duty cycle slightly. This feedback action maintains the output voltage within millivolts of the no-load voltage over a wide range of loads.

THE PULSE-WIDTH-MODULATION CIRCUIT

A Common Pulse-Width Modulator

So how does the chopper circuit work? I knew you would ask that. Look at Figure 17-23. The comparator is at the heart of the chopper circuit, or pulse-width modulator. First, consider Figure 17-23a. A ramp voltage, sawtooth or triangle, is applied to the noninverting input and a DC level is applied to

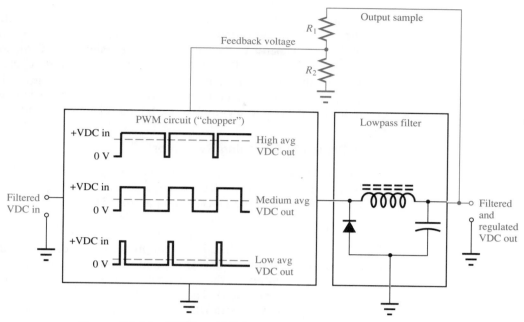

Figure 17–22 PWM and VDC out.

the inverting input of the comparator. The ramp voltage is fixed at some peak value less than +V. The positive ramp voltage is compared to the DC level with every cycle. When the ramp voltage is slightly greater than the DC level, the output of the comparator switches high (ON). When the ramp voltage falls slightly below the DC level, on the falling edge of the ramp waveform, the output of the comparator switches low (OFF). Thus a square wave is produced.

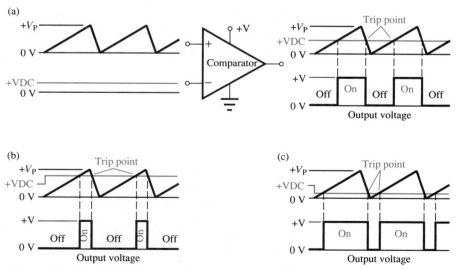

Figure 17–23 The comparator pulse-width modulator.

Figures 17–23b and 17–23c illustrate what happens when the DC level at the inverting input of the comparator is changed. In 17–23b, the DC level is increased. This raises the trip points on the ramp waveform so the comparator output is high for less time. In other words, the duty cycle is reduced. In 17–23c, the duty cycle is increased by lowering the DC level. Notice that the trip points are lower on the ramp waveform. Now let's see how this comparator circuit fits into a complete switching regulator circuit.

A Complete Switching Regulator

Figure 17–24 is a complete 50-kHz switching regulator. Let's break it down into parts. The two LF356 op-amps generate the ramp voltage waveform that is supplied to the LM111 comparator. The error amplifier amplifies the slight difference in voltage between the feedback voltage (V_F) and the reference voltage (V_{Ref}), where V_F is slightly higher than 1.235 V. The output of the error amplifier is a DC level that provides the reference for the comparator, which determines the trip points and square-wave duty cycle. The square-wave output of the comparator drives the output transistors on and off (nonlinear operation). The square-wave collector voltage of the 2N6191 is converted to a smooth DC by the output filter (integrator).

Paralleled Capacitors

Note that there are three paralleled 100-μF filter capacitors in the output. Why not just one 300-μF capacitor? There are two reasons. First, paralleling the capacitors reduces lead and internal inductance that would act to increase ripple and transients in the output. Second, each capacitor has what is called an **equivalent series resistance (ESR).** The ESR of the capacitor creates a voltage drop that varies with changes in charge current that correspond with rising and falling inductor current and square-wave pulses. This varying voltage drop of the ESR adds to the output ripple voltage. The total output ripple voltage is $\Delta V_C + V_{ESR}$. By paralleling output capacitors, the V_{ESR} component is reduced. The 0.1-μF capacitor in the output is used to cancel filter-capacitor inductance and cancel sharp transients.

A Closer Look

Let's take a closer look at the regulation process in Figure 17–24. If the load increases (more current demand) the output voltage drops down slightly. This slight drop is instantly amplified by the error amplifier and the DC level at the output of the error amplifier and pin 3 of the comparator drops slightly. Now, what happens at pin 7 of the comparator? Recall from Figure 17–23 that the duty cycle increases because the lower DC at pin 3 lowers the trip points. The increased duty cycle causes the output transistors to conduct longer for each cycle, which prevents the output voltage from dropping further. The actual change in output voltage over a wide range of load change is usually only 10 to 100 mV. Output ripple voltage is usually only 5 to 50 mV$_{P-P}$.

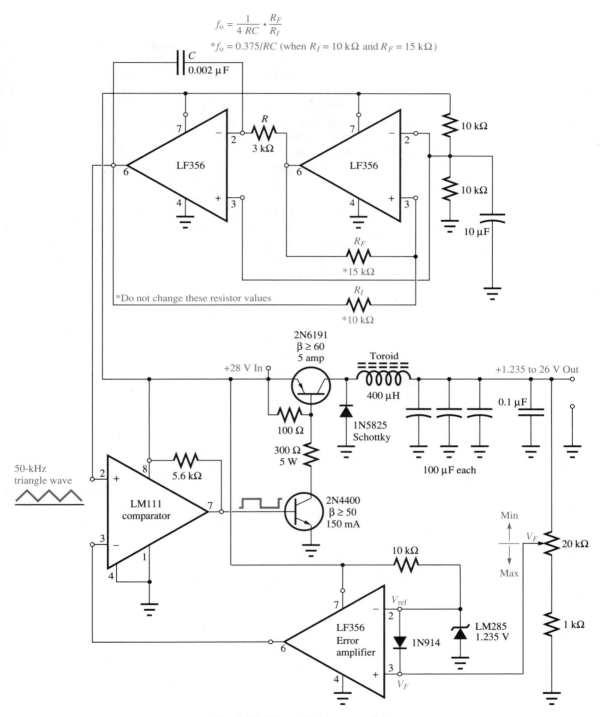

$$f_o = \frac{1}{4\,RC} \cdot \frac{R_F}{R_I}$$

$*f_o = 0.375/RC$ (when $R_I = 10\ \text{k}\Omega$ and $R_F = 15\ \text{k}\Omega$)

Figure 17–24   A 50-kHz switching regulator.

The 723 as a Switching Regulator

You are probably surprised to see the 723 voltage regulator used as a nonlinear switching regulator in Figure 17–25. Again we see the 723's great versatility. The 723 drives a Darlington pair, which is switched on and off. The output filter network converts the pulsating DC to a slightly rippled DC output. The output is sampled and a feedback voltage is applied to the inverting input of amplifier A_1 acting as a comparator. This feedback voltage is compared to a reference, which in this case is less than 7.15 V, because of the voltage divider ratio $R_2/(R_1 + R_2)$. If the feedback voltage is slightly less than the reference voltage, the output of A_1 goes high, causing Q_1 and the Darlington pair to conduct. The conduction of the Darlington pair corrects the drop in output voltage.

But wait a minute. Where is the ramp waveform oscillator? Good question. This circuit operates without one. The entire circuit is an oscillator, a relaxation oscillator. The output capacitor discharges through the load device and its charge voltage drops. The output of the comparator (A_1) goes high and the Darlington pair turns on. Current is supplied to the load and

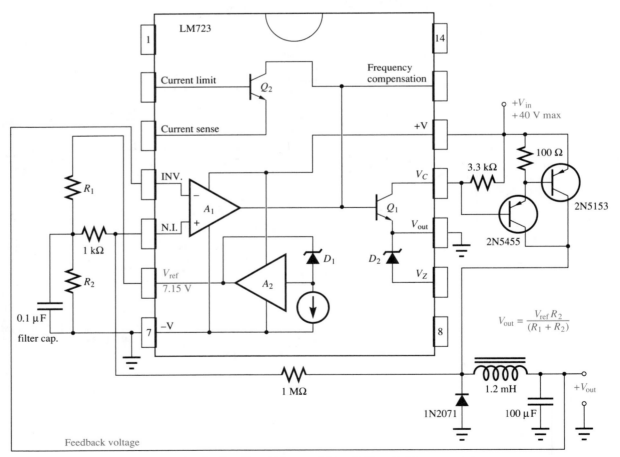

Figure 17–25 The 723 as a 2-V to 7-V switching regulator.

TABLE 17–3

Type	$f_{osc(max)}$ (kHz)	V_{in}(V)	$I_{L(max)}$
LM1578	100	2 to 40	750 mA
HS7107	200	10 to 100	7 A
MC34060A	200	7 to 40	200 mA
MC34063A	42	3 to 40	1.5 A
XR-1524	300	8 to 40	100 mA
XR-1525A	500	8 to 35	500 mA
SGS L296	200	8 to 50	4 A

output voltage returns to a level slightly higher than the reference voltage at pin 5. Then, the output of A_1 goes low, the Darlington pair turns off, and the output capacitor begins to discharge again. This discharge/charge cycling is continuous. The frequency of the cycling is largely determined by the effect the load has on the LC integrator. In any case, the regulation is remarkably good and the ripple is very low, both below 100 mV over a full load range.

One more thing: what is the purpose for the 1-kΩ resistor and the 1-MΩ resistor? These resistors add a small amount of hysteresis to the comparator so it does not switch radically or randomly. In other words, the reference voltage at pin 5 varies slightly above and below the reference established by R_1 and R_2 as the Darlington pair switches on and off.

Popular IC Switching Regulators

Table 17–3 is a list of many popular IC switching regulators. Using an integrated circuit offers the same flexibility as discrete devices with the advantage of fewer components and usually lower cost.

THE STEP-DOWN CONFIGURATION

Let's take a closer look at the lowpass filter—which is actually an integrator, since a pulsating DC square wave is applied to it. The filter configuration shown in Figures 17–24, 17–25, and 17–26 is known as the **step-down** or **buck configuration.** That means the output voltage is lower than the peak pulse amplitude of the driving DC square wave.

I know you've been wondering about the diode in the filter network. The diode is often referred to as the **recirculation diode.** In this discussion, you will see why. Study Figure 17–26. Waveform timing diagrams are shown so you can see how the components work together to provide a low-ripple load current and voltage. While Q_1 and Q_2 are on, the Q_2 collector current increases as the inductor current and the inductor's magnetic field increases. During this time, the change in inductor current is in the positive, or increasing, direction ($+\Delta I_L$). This increasing inductor current is replacing charge on

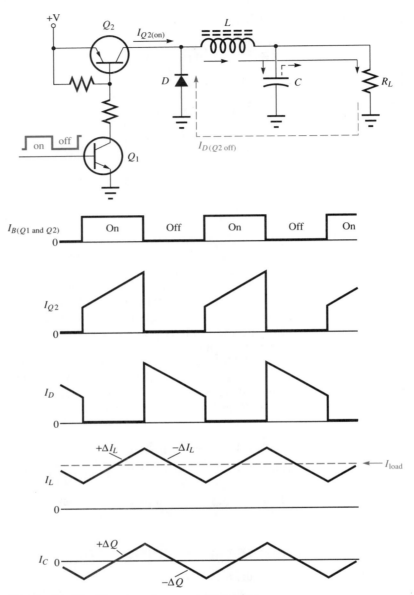

Figure 17–26 The step-down configuration.

the capacitor $(+\Delta Q)$ and supplying current to the load. While Q_1 and Q_2 are off, the Q_2 collector current is zero and the magnetic field around the inductor collapses. The collapsing magnetic field keeps current flowing out to the capacitor and load. However, as the field collapses, the inductor current weakens and the capacitor takes over for a short time, supplying the load. During this off time, when the magnetic field collapses, the inductor current path is completed by the diode, which forward conducts. This diode current I_D decreases with $-\Delta I_L$ and flows only during the off time. The diode should be a high-speed, low-voltage-drop diode such as a Schottky diode and should be rated for full load current.

THE STEP-UP CONFIGURATION

Flyback and Step-Up Action

Figure 17–27 illustrates how the output circuit can be modified to create a regulated DC output voltage higher than the DC input voltage. This is known as the **step-up** or **boost configuration** and is accomplished by taking advan-

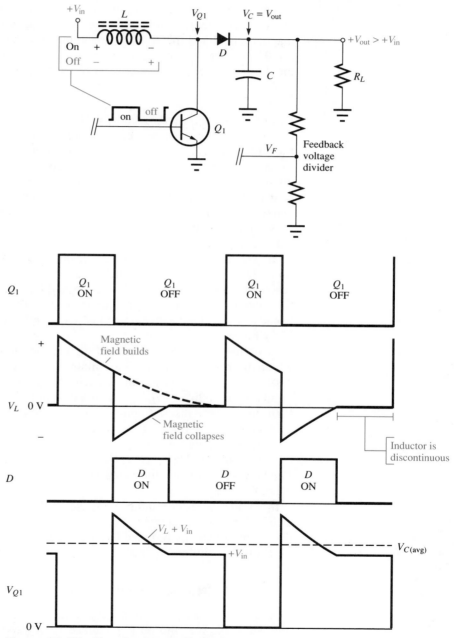

Figure 17–27   The step-up configuration.

tage of the **flyback** or collapsing magnetic field action of the inductor. When Q_1 is on, the current through the inductor and the field around the inductor increase as the voltage across the inductor decreases. While Q_1 is off, the magnetic field collapses, inducing a voltage across the inductor that forward biases the diode and feeds the output capacitor and load. At the instant the magnetic field begins to collapse, a large voltage that adds to the DC input voltage is induced across the inductor, much like placing batteries in series-aiding. Thus, the output capacitor is able to reach a charge voltage higher than the DC input voltage. The longer Q_1 is on, the greater the magnetic field and the greater the induced voltage will be when Q_1 is turned off. Thus, if more voltage or charge current is needed to service the load, Q_1 must conduct for a longer portion of each square-wave cycle.

Discontinuity

Notice the waveform diagrams for V_L and V_{Q1} of Figure 17–27. These waveforms indicate that the inductor's magnetic field has totally collapsed before the end of the Q_1 off time. That means the inductor voltage and current drops to zero, leaving just the capacitor to supply load current during the remaining portion of the off time. This is known as **discontinuity** and the inductor is said to be **discontinuous** or operating in the **discontinuous mode.** This is usually undesirable, since the output ripple voltage increases.

What causes discontinuity? Two factors: First, the inductor is too small in value compared to the applied pulse frequency, and second, the load is *too light*. What is needed here is a $5L/R$ decay time that is greater than the off time. This is obtained by using a reasonably large inductor and a low load resistance. I know this sounds strange, but the higher the load (more current) the longer it takes for the magnetic field to fully decay (collapse). This is because more load current means a lower load resistance, which makes $5L/R$ longer.

Switching regulator filters are designed for a minimum load current below which discontinuity begins. This minimum load current is a percentage of the maximum load current. Many switching regulators are designed for discontinuity at 10 or 20% of $I_{L(max)}$. A 10% discontinuity requires a larger inductor than does a 20% discontinuity, and so on. As the inductor becomes larger, cost and size increase. Low discontinuity current and low output ripple voltage is obtained by using a high-frequency square-wave drive circuit in the range of 50 kHz to 200 kHz. For example, the discontinuity shown in Figure 17–27 can be eliminated simply by doubling or tripling the square-wave frequency.

In summary, discontinuity increases output ripple. Discontinuity occurs at low load-current levels. The minimum load current rating and percent discontinuity can be reduced by increasing L and/or frequency. Discontinuity occurs in any configuration of the lowpass filter.

THE INVERTING CONFIGURATION

Figure 17–28 shows how to configure the output for output-voltage polarity inversion. Notice, the output voltage is negative and the input voltage is positive. The flyback action of the inductor is once again used. While Q_1 is on, the inductor's field builds up. When Q_1 is off, the field collapses and the

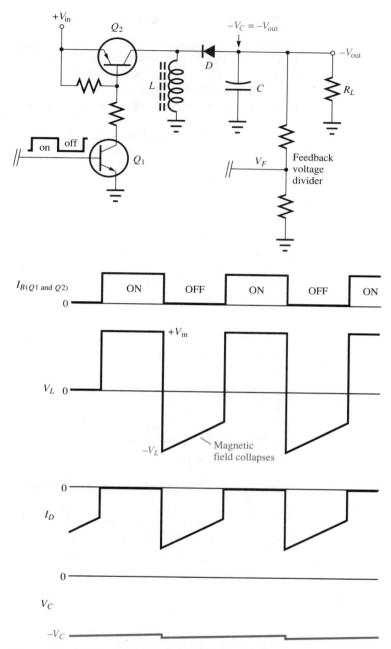

Figure 17–28 The inverting configuration.

polarity of the inductor reverses. Thus, while Q_1 is off, the top of L is negative, the diode becomes forward biased, and C charges to a negative potential. As always, feedback voltage is used to control the duty cycle of the DC square wave. If the output voltage drops slightly, the on time is increased storing more energy in the inductor. At the instant Q_1 turns off, the stronger magnetic field begins to collapse, inducing a higher voltage across the inductor, which compensates for the slight drop in output voltage.

INDUCTOR AND CAPACITOR VALUES

The following formulas should be used to calculate the minimum values for L and C in the three configurations previously discussed. Notice in each inductor formula, $\Delta I_L = 2I_{L(max)} \cdot$ discontinuity factor, where a discontinuity factor of 0.1 equals 10% discontinuity. For example, if the maximum load current is 4 A and 10% discontinuity is acceptable, $\Delta I_L = 2I_{L(max)} \cdot 0.1 = 2 \cdot 4$ A $\cdot$ $0.1 = 0.8$ A.

For the step-down configuration,

$$L > \frac{V_{out} \cdot (V_{in} - V_{out})}{\Delta I_L \cdot V_{in} \cdot f_{osc}} \tag{17-41}$$

$$C > \frac{V_{out} \cdot (V_{in} - V_{out})}{8 \cdot L \cdot V_{in} \cdot f_{osc}^2 \cdot V_{Rip}} \tag{17-42}$$

where V_{Rip} is the maximum desired peak-to-peak ripple voltage in the output. For the step-up configuration,

$$L > \frac{V_{in}^2 \cdot (V_{out} - V_{in})}{\Delta I_L \cdot V_{out}^2 \cdot f_{osc}} \tag{17-43}$$

$$C > \frac{I_{L(max)} \cdot (V_{out} - V_{in})}{V_{out} \cdot f_{osc} \cdot V_{Rip}} \tag{17-44}$$

For the inverting configuration,

$$L > \frac{V_{in}^2 \cdot |V_{out}|}{\Delta I_L \cdot (V_{in} + |V_{out}|)^2 \cdot f_{osc}} \tag{17-45}$$

$$C > \frac{I_{L(max)} \cdot |V_{out}|}{(|V_{out}| + V_{in}) \cdot f_{osc} \cdot V_{Rip}} \tag{17-46}$$

Consider Examples 17–10, 17–11, and 17–12.

EXAMPLE 17–10

Calculate the minimum values for L and C in a step-down switching regulator configuration. $f_{osc} = 100$ kHz, $V_{in} = 15$ V, $V_{out} = 5$ V, $I_{L(max)} = 3$ A, $V_{Rip(max)} = 50$ mV$_{P-P}$, 10% discontinuity.

$\Delta I_L = 2I_{L(max)} \cdot 0.1 = 2 \cdot 3$ A $\cdot 0.1 = 0.6$ A

$$L > \frac{V_{out} \cdot (V_{in} - V_{out})}{\Delta I_L \cdot V_{in} \cdot f_{osc}} = \frac{5 \text{ V} \cdot (15 \text{ V} - 5 \text{ V})}{0.6 \text{ A} \cdot 15 \text{ V} \cdot 100 \text{ kHz}} = 55.6 \ \mu H$$

$$C > \frac{V_{out} \cdot (V_{in} - V_{out})}{8 \cdot L \cdot V_{in} \cdot f_{osc}^2 \cdot V_{Rip}}$$

$$= \frac{5 \text{ V} \cdot (15 \text{ V} - 5 \text{ V})}{8 \cdot 55.6 \ \mu H \cdot 15 \text{ V} \cdot (100 \text{ kHz})^2 \cdot 50 \text{ mV}}$$

$$= 15 \ \mu F$$

55.6 μH and 15 μF are the minimum values for L and C. Usually, 100 to 500 μH of inductance and 100 to 500 μF of capacitance is used for frequencies between 50 kHz and 200 kHz.

EXAMPLE 17–11 ▄▄▄▄▄▄▄▄▄▄

Calculate the minimum values for L and C in a step-up switching regulator configuration. $f_{osc} = 100$ kHz, $V_{in} = 5$ V, $V_{out} = 15$ V, $I_{L(max)} = 300$ mA, $V_{Rip(max)} = 10$ mV$_{P-P}$, 20% discontinuity.

$$\Delta I_L = 2I_{L(max)} \cdot 0.2 = 2 \cdot 0.3 \text{ A} \cdot 0.2 = 0.12 \text{ A}$$

$$L > \frac{V_{in}^2 \cdot (V_{out} - V_{in})}{\Delta I_L \cdot V_{out}^2 \cdot f_{osc}} = \frac{(5 \text{ V})^2 \cdot (15 \text{ V} - 5 \text{ V})}{0.12 \text{ A} \cdot (15 \text{ V})^2 \cdot 100 \text{ kHz}} = 92.6 \ \mu\text{H}$$

$$C > \frac{I_{L(max)} \cdot (V_{out} - V_{in})}{V_{out} \cdot f_{osc} \cdot V_{Rip}} = \frac{300 \text{ mA} \cdot (15 \text{ V} - 5 \text{ V})}{15 \text{ V} \cdot 100 \text{ kHz} \cdot 10 \text{ mV}} = 200 \ \mu\text{F}$$

92.6 μH and 200 μF are the minimum values for L and C.

EXAMPLE 17–12 ▄▄▄▄▄▄▄▄▄▄

Calculate the minimum values for L and C in an inverting switching regulator configuration. $f_{osc} = 150$ kHz, $V_{in} = 10$ V, $V_{out} = -15$ V, $I_{L(max)} = 200$ mA, $V_{Rip(max)} = 10$ mV$_{P-P}$, 30% discontinuity.

$$\Delta I_L = 2I_{L(max)} \cdot 0.3 = 2 \cdot 0.2 \text{ A} \cdot 0.3 = 0.12 \text{ A}$$

$$L > \frac{V_{in}^2 \cdot |V_{out}|}{\Delta I_L \cdot (V_{in} + |V_{out}|)^2 \cdot f_{osc}} = \frac{(10 \text{ V})^2 \cdot 15 \text{ V}}{0.12 \text{ A} \cdot (10 \text{ V} + 15 \text{ V})^2 \cdot 150 \text{ kHz}}$$
$$= 133 \ \mu\text{H}$$

$$C > \frac{I_{L(max)} \cdot |V_{out}|}{(|V_{out}| + V_{in}) \cdot f_{osc} \cdot V_{Rip}} = \frac{200 \text{ mA} \cdot 15 \text{ V}}{(15 \text{ V} + 10 \text{ V}) \cdot 150 \text{ kHz} \cdot 10 \text{ mV}}$$
$$= 80 \ \mu\text{F}$$

133 μH and 80 μF are the minimum values for L and C.

About the Inductor

The inductor should be of the toroidal type. These are self-shielding, which greatly reduces the amount of electromagnetic interference (EMI) that is radiated into the air. Usually 20 to 50 turns of enamel- or varnish-coated solid copper wire are wound on low-frequency toroidal cores with outer diameters of 1.5 to 2 in. For load currents of 1 to 10 A, AWG #22 to AWG #18 wire should be used. Inductors and cores for switching regulator circuits are available from manufacturers such as:

- Pulse Engineering of San Diego, CA
- A. I. E. Magnetics of Nashville, TN
- Amidon Associates of North Hollywood, CA
- Ferroxcube of Saugerties, NY
- Arnold Engineering Co. of Marengo, IL

$\Delta I_L = 2I_{L(\text{max})} \cdot$ Discontinuity Factor (Usually 0.05 to 0.3)

$$L > \frac{V_{\text{out}} \cdot (V_{\text{in}} - V_{\text{out}})}{\Delta I_L \cdot V_{\text{in}} \cdot f_{\text{osc}}}$$

$$C > \frac{V_{\text{out}} \cdot (V_{\text{in}} - V_{\text{out}})}{8 \cdot L \cdot V_{\text{in}} \cdot f_{\text{osc}}^2 \cdot V_{\text{Rip}}}$$

Diode current rating greater than the maximum load current. Reverse voltage rating greater than the DC input voltage.

Step-down configuration

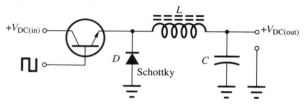

Step-up configuration

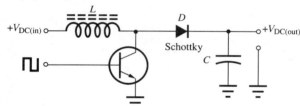

$$L > \frac{V_{\text{in}}^2 \cdot (V_{\text{out}} - V_{\text{in}})}{\Delta I_L \cdot V_{\text{out}}^2 \cdot f_{\text{osc}}}$$

$$C > \frac{I_{L(\text{max})} \cdot (V_{\text{out}} - V_{\text{in}})}{V_{\text{out}} \cdot f_{\text{osc}} \cdot V_{\text{Rip}}}$$

Diode current rating of at least twice the maximum load current. Reverse voltage rating greater than the DC output voltage

$$L > \frac{V_{\text{in}}^2 \cdot |V_{\text{out}}|}{\Delta I_L \cdot (V_{\text{in}} + |V_{\text{out}}|)^2 \cdot f_{\text{osc}}}$$

$$C > \frac{I_{L(\text{max})} \cdot |V_{\text{out}}|}{(|V_{\text{out}}| + V_{\text{in}}) \cdot f_{\text{osc}} \cdot V_{\text{Rip}}}$$

Diode current rating of at least twice the maximum load current. Reverse voltage rating greater than twice the DC output voltage.

Inverting configuration

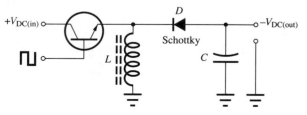

BASIC PROGRAM

```
10 REM  * SWITCHING REGULATOR OUTPUT NETWORKS *
20 CLS
30 PRINT "SWITCHING REGULATOR OUTPUT NETWORKS"
40 PRINT ""
50 PRINT "(1) STEP-DOWN CONFIGURATION"
60 PRINT "(2) STEP-UP CONFIGURATION"
70 PRINT "(3) INVERTING CONFIGURATION"
80 INPUT "SELECT DESIRED CONFIGURATION BY NUMBER. - ";N
90 PRINT ""
100 INPUT "ENTER THE MAXIMUM LOAD CURRENT - ";IMAX
110 INPUT "ENTER THE DESIRED DISCONTINUITY FACTOR - ";DISFACT
120 INPUT "ENTER THE DC OUTPUT VOLTAGE - ";VOUT
130 INPUT "ENTER THE DC INPUT VOLTAGE - ";VIN
140 INPUT "ENTER THE OSCILLATOR FREQUENCY - ";FOSC
150 INPUT "ENTER THE MAXIMUM DESIRED PEAK-TO-PEAK RIPPLE VOLTAGE -
";VRIP
160 IL = 2 * IMAX * DISFACT
170 IF N = 1 THEN ID = IMAX:VD = VIN:L = (VOUT * (VIN - VOUT))/(IL *
VIN * FOSC)
180 IF N = 1 THEN C = (VOUT * (VIN - VOUT))/(8 * L * VIN * FOSC^2 *
VRIP)
190 IF N = 2 THEN ID = 2 * IMAX:VD = 2 * VOUT:L = (VIN^2 *
(VOUT - VIN))/(IL * VOUT^2 * FOSC)
200 IF N = 2 THEN C = (IMAX * (VOUT - VIN))/(VOUT * FOSC *
VRIP)
210 IF N = 3 THEN ID = 2 * IMAX:VD = 2 * VOUT:L = (VIN^2 *
ABS(VOUT))/(IL * (VIN + ABS(VOUT))^2 * FOSC)
220 IF N = 3 THEN C = (IMAX * ABS(VOUT))/((ABS(VOUT) + VIN) *
FOSC * VRIP)
230 REM OUTPUT SECTION
240 PRINT ""
250 PRINT "THE MINIMUM CONTINUOUS CURRENT RATING FOR THE
DIODE MUST BE ";ID;" AMPS."
260 PRINT "THE MINIMUM VOLTAGE RATING FOR THE DIODE MUST BE
";ABS(VD);" VOLTS."
270 PRINT "THE MINIMUM INDUCTOR VALUE MUST BE ";L;" H."
280 PRINT "THE MINIMUM CAPACITOR VALUE MUST BE ";C;" F."
290 PRINT "USE TWO OR THREE PARALLELED CAPACITORS FOR C."
300 PRINT ""
310 INPUT "ANOTHER PROBLEM? (Y/N) ":A$
320 IF A$ = "Y" THEN GOTO 10
330 CLS:END
```

Design Note 17–2

Design Note 17–2 puts it all together for you. Study it carefully and notice the comments regarding the recirculation diode (Schottky diode). The computer program makes switching network design easy. Follow the program lines to see how the formulas are applied. Running the program will provide you with an infinite number of examples, since you will be able to specify quantities.

Well, we have covered quite a bit of information about switching regulators in this section. You will see them frequently throughout your career. Take time now to go back and review this section.

Self-Check 17–4	

Self-Check 17–4

1. List three advantages of the switching regulator.
2. Briefly explain how a ramp voltage, a DC level, and a comparator can produce a pulse-width-modulated square wave.
3. Why is the lowpass filter an integrator?
4. If the output voltage drops slightly because of increased load, what happens to the duty cycle of the square wave in a switching circuit?
5. Calculate the minimum values for L and C in a step-up switching regulator configuration. $f_{osc} = 75$ kHz, $V_{in} = 12$ V, $V_{out} = 18$ V, $I_{L(max)} = 2$ A, $V_{Rip(max)} = 50$ mV$_{P-P}$, 5% discontinuity.

17–5 INVERTERS AND CONVERTERS

DC TO AC INVERTERS

Inverter?

The terms *inverter* and *converter* are frequently used to describe different things. There are some guidelines, but often the meaning of the terms must be clarified in context. In the last section, we used the term *inverter* to describe the conversion from a positive DC voltage to a negative DC voltage. The inverting configuration of the lowpass filter circuit inverts the DC polarity. In this section, we use the term *inverter* to describe a large family of circuits that are used to convert DC to AC. Thus, a DC to AC converter is conventionally referred to as an **inverter.**

Oscillator-Driven Inverter

There are two general groups of inverters. Figure 17–29 is one example of the first group—oscillator-driven inverters. The comparator relaxation oscillator drives the transistors on and off. Power transistors Q_1 and Q_2 (high-speed switching transistors) conduct alternately. In so doing, each half of the primary winding is taken to ground and voltage of alternating polarity is induced in the secondary. The output voltage from the secondary is generally stepped up. The peak to peak amplitude of the secondary is determined by the transformer's primary to secondary turns ratio. Since the output voltage is a square wave, the peak voltage of the square wave should equal

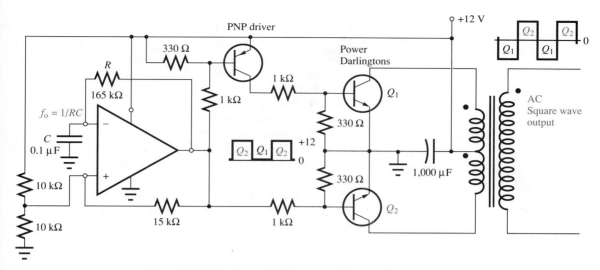

Figure 17–29 An oscillator-driven inverter.

the desired RMS value. For example, if the inverter is used to power a 120-V electric drill, the peak amplitude of the square wave should be 120 V. With 12 VDC applied, the half-primary to secondary turns ratio should be 1 : 10 (such as 200-turn center-tapped primary and a 1,000-turn secondary). Naturally, the frequency of the square wave is determined by the RC relaxation oscillator. The oscillator in Figure 17–29 is set for approximately 60 Hz.

Self-Excited Inverter

Figure 17–30 is an example of the second general group of inverters, the self-excited inverters. In this particular circuit two transformers are used. The

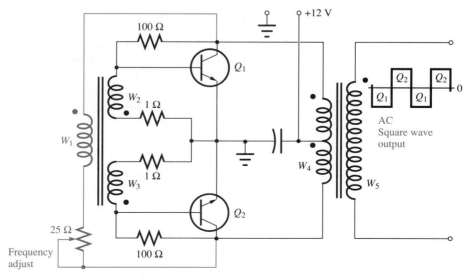

Figure 17–30 A dual-transformer self-excited inverter.

input transformer is used to drive the power transistors one after the other. When DC is first applied, one of the transistors will saturate. Let's say Q_1 turns on first. That makes the collector of Q_1 near ground and the collector of Q_2 at +24 V. Note that the primary winding of the output transformer (W_4) is center tapped. As current flows in one half, an equal voltage is induced across the other half, making the total primary voltage equal to 24 V.

Now, with the collector of Q_2 high and the collector of Q_1 low, current flows through the 25-Ω rheostat and the primary of the input transformer (W_1). This induces voltage across the two secondary windings as the W_1 magnetic field expands. The sense dots on the windings indicate that the polarity of W_2 is such that Q_1 is held on with a positive base-emitter voltage. The polarity of W_3 holds Q_2 off. Q_1 stays on until the magnetic field of W_1 fully expands and stops. The time this takes is determined by the $5L/R$ time constant between the rheostat and W_1. Thus, the rheostat is adjusted to set the time for magnetic field expansion which determines the switching frequency.

Once the magnetic field stops expanding, Q_1 turns off and the field quickly collapses, inducing voltage of opposite polarity in W_2 and W_3. This causes Q_2 to come on. The collector of Q_2 goes low and the collector of Q_1 is high. Thus, current flows through W_1 and the rheostat, inducing a voltage across W_2 and W_3 that keeps Q_1 off and Q_2 on. Q_2 stays on until the magnetic field of W_1 is fully expanded. With no further field expansion, no more voltage is induced across W_3 and Q_2 turns off. The magnetic field rapidly collapses causing Q_1 to turn on and we are back where we started.

Some self-excited inverters use only one transformer. Such a transformer has two additional low-voltage secondary windings that are used to drive the bases of the two power transistors alternately.

DC TO DC CONVERTERS

Converter?

The term *converter* is as loosely used as the term *inverter*. A plug-in-the-wall AC to DC power supply is called a **converter,** as is a circuit that converts a DC voltage to a higher DC voltage. In our discussion here, we refer to the converter as the DC-to-higher-DC type. One thing you should notice in the following two converter circuits is that each converter is a rectified and filtered inverter. Think about it.

Push-Pull Converters

Figure 17–31 is a good example of a modern DC to DC converter. The XR-1524 IC is designed to drive a push-pull power transistor arrangement. The duty cycle, or on time, of Q_1 and Q_2 is controlled by voltage feedback and pulse-width modulation circuitry, just like the switching regulators previously discussed. The on time of the power Darlingtons determines the amount of energy in the magnetic field of the output transformer, which determines the duration of the secondary pulses and the output voltage. The secondary voltage is an AC square wave that is rectified and filtered. The

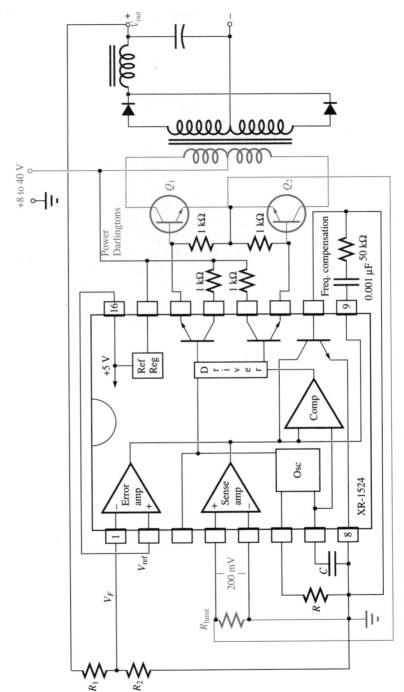

Figure 17–31 The XR-1524 DC to DC converter.

actual DC output voltage, as determined by the transformer turns ratio and the feedback voltage divider (R_1 and R_2), can be any amount.

Notice that this circuit not only has output voltage regulation, it also has current limiting of the power Darlingtons. The emitter of each Darlington finds ground through a current-sense circuit (R_{Limit} and the sense amplifier). The sense voltage is 200 mV. For example, if it is desired to limit the current to 5 A, R_{Limit} must be 200 mV/5 A = 0.04 Ω. A more detailed description of the XR-1524 and other similar ICs can be obtained from the EXAR Corporation's data book.

Flyback Converter

Figure 17–32 illustrates a pulse-width-modulated flyback converter. The circuit is a basic switching regulator as discussed in the previous section. Output voltage is regulated within tens of millivolts by controlling the on time of the MOSFET. This is called a **flyback converter** because the magnetic field of the primary collapses into the secondary when the MOSFET is off. The collapsing magnetic field induces one polarity across the secondary and, when the MOSFET is on, the expanding magnetic field induces the opposite polarity. Thus, the magnetic field flying back into the windings induces half of the total cycle. Again, the secondary voltage is an AC square wave that is rectified and filtered.

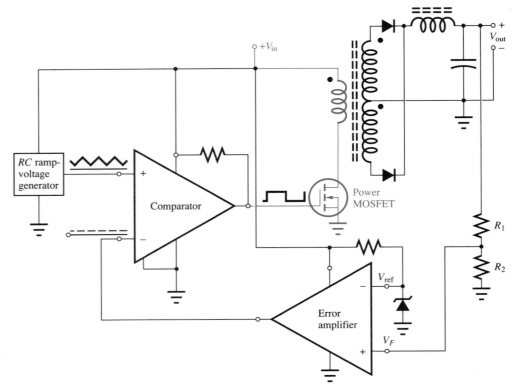

Figure 17–32 A regulated flyback DC to DC converter.

MANUFACTURERS

The following is a list of manufacturers that offer a wide range of linear and nonlinear voltage regulator ICs for AC to DC converters, DC to DC converters, and DC to AC inverters. These ICs are found in their linear circuits data books.

Motorola Semiconductor, Inc.
P. O. Box 20912
Phoenix, AZ 85036

National Semiconductor Corporation
2900 Semiconductor Drive
P. O. Box 58090
Santa Clara, CA 95052-8090

EXAR Corporation
2222 Qume Drive
San Jose, CA 95131

Harris Semiconductor
P. O. Box 2021
Cathedral Station
Boston, MA 02118

Signetics Corporation
811 E. Arques Avenue
P. O. Box 3409
Sunnyvale, CA 94088-3409

SGS Semiconductor Corporation
1000 East Bell Road
Phoenix, AZ 85022

Time once again for a self-check.

Self-Check 17–5

1. What is a DC to AC inverter?
2. What is the difference between an oscillator-driven inverter and a self-excited inverter?
3. What is the basic function of a DC to DC converter?
4. What is a flyback converter?
5. What circuit is the exact opposite of an AC to DC converter?

SUMMARY

FORMULAS

Component Ratings for the Zener Regulator

(17–1) $V_Z = V_{DC(out)}$

(17–2) $P_Z = \text{Standard Value} > 1.1\, I_{L(max)} \cdot V_Z$

(17–3) $R_S = (V_{DC(in)} - V_Z)/(1.1\, I_{L(max)})$

(17–4) $P_{RS} = \text{Standard Value} > (1.1\, I_{L(max)})^2 \cdot R_S$

Analysis of Basic Series-Pass Regulator (Figure 17–4)

(17–5) $V_E = V_{RL} \cong V_Z - 0.7\text{ V}$

(17–6) $I_L = V_E/R_L$

(17–7) $I_B = I_L/\beta_{DC}$

(17–8) $V_{RS} = V_{DC(in)} - V_Z$

(17–9) $I_{RS} = V_{RS}/R_S$

(17–10) $I_Z = I_{RS} - I_B$

(17–11) $P_Z = I_Z \cdot V_Z$

(17–12) $P_{RS} = I_{RS} \cdot V_{RS}$

(17–13) $P_L = I_L \cdot V_E$

(17–14) $P_{Q1} = I_L \cdot V_{CE} = I_L \cdot (V_{DC(in)} - V_E)$

(17–15) $\%\text{ Eff} \cong 100\% \cdot P_L/(P_L + P_{Q1})$

Darlington Pair Series-Pass Design (Figure 17–6)

(17–16) $I_{B(Q1,max)} = I_{L(max)}/\beta_{DC1(min)}$

(17–17) $P_{Q2(max)} = I_{B(Q1,max)} \cdot (V_{DC(in)} - 0.7\text{ V} - V_E)$

(17–18) $I_{B(max)} = I_{B(Q2,max)} = I_{B(Q1,max)}/\beta_{DC2(min)}$

(17–19) $I_{B(max)} = I_{L(max)}/\beta_{DC1(min)} \cdot \beta_{DC2(min)})$

(17–20) $V_Z \cong V_{RL} + 1.4\text{ V}$

(17–21) $I_{Z(min)} = 0.1\, I_{B(max)}$

(17–22) $I_{Z(max)} = 1.1\, I_{B(max)}$ (no load)

(17–23) $P_{Z(Rating)} > I_{Z(max)} \cdot V_Z$

(17–24) $R_S = (V_{DC(in)} - V_Z)/I_{Z(max)}$

(17–25) $P_{RS(Rating)} > I_{Z(max)} \cdot (V_{DC(in)} - V_Z)$

Current Limiting (Figure 17–7)

(17–26) $R_{Limit} \cong 0.7\text{ V}/I_{L(max)}$

(17–27) $I_{L(max)} \cong 0.7\text{ V}/R_{Limit}$

Voltage-Feedback Regulation (Figure 17–9)

(17–28) $K = R_3/(R_2 + R_3)$

(17–29) $R_2 = [(1/K) - 1] \cdot R_3$

(17–30) $V_L = V_F/K \cong V_{Ref}/K$

(17–31) $K = V_F/V_L \cong V_{Ref}/V_L$

Shunt Regulator Efficiency (Figure 17–11)

(17–32) $\%\text{ Eff} = 100\% \cdot P_L/(P_{R2} + P_{Q1} + P_L)$

Three-Terminal Regulator (Figure 17–14b)

$$(17\text{–}33) \quad V_{\text{out}} = V_{\text{Reg}} \cdot (1 + R_2/R_1) + (R_2 I_Q)$$

LM117 Adjustable Regulator (Figure 17–15)

$$(17\text{–}34) \quad R_2 = \frac{V_{\text{out}} - V_{\text{Reg}}}{(V_{\text{Reg}}/R_1) + I_{\text{Adj}}}$$

LM723 Voltage Regulator (Figure 17–17)

$$(17\text{–}35) \quad V_{\text{out}} = V_{\text{Ref}} \cdot (R_1 + R_2)/R_2$$

$$(17\text{–}36) \quad R_1 = \frac{R_2(V_{\text{out}} - V_{\text{Ref}})}{V_{\text{Ref}}}$$

LM723 Low-Voltage Regulator (Figure 17–18)

$$(17\text{–}37) \quad V_{\text{out}} = V_{\text{Ref}} R_2/(R_1 + R_2)$$

$$(17\text{–}38) \quad R_1 = R_2(V_{\text{Ref}} - V_{\text{out}})/V_{\text{out}}$$

LM723 Negative-Voltage Regulator (Figure 17–20)

$$(17\text{–}39) \quad V_{\text{out}} = -V_{\text{Ref}} \cdot (R_1 + R_2)/2R_1$$

$$(17\text{–}40) \quad R_1 = -V_{\text{Ref}} R_2/(2V_{\text{out}} + V_{\text{ref}})$$

Switching Regulator Configurations (Figures 17–26, 27, 28)

$$[\Delta I_L = 2I_{L(\text{max})} \cdot \text{Discontinuity Factor}]$$

For the step-down configuration,

$$(17\text{–}41) \quad L > \frac{V_{\text{out}} \cdot (V_{\text{in}} - V_{\text{out}})}{\Delta I_L \cdot V_{\text{in}} \cdot f_{\text{osc}}}$$

$$(17\text{–}42) \quad C > \frac{V_{\text{out}} \cdot (V_{\text{in}} - V_{\text{out}})}{8 \cdot L \cdot V_{\text{in}} \cdot f_{\text{osc}}^2 \cdot V_{\text{Rip}}}$$

For the step-up configuration,

$$(17\text{–}43) \quad L > \frac{V_{\text{in}}^2 \cdot (V_{\text{out}} - V_{\text{in}})}{\Delta I_L \cdot V_{\text{out}}^2 \cdot f_{\text{osc}}}$$

$$(17\text{–}44) \quad C > \frac{I_{L(\text{max})} \cdot (V_{\text{out}} - V_{\text{in}})}{V_{\text{out}} \cdot f_{\text{osc}} \cdot V_{\text{Rip}}}$$

For the inverting configuration,

$$(17\text{–}45) \quad L > \frac{V_{\text{in}}^2 \cdot |V_{\text{out}}|}{\Delta I_L \cdot (V_{\text{in}} + |V_{\text{out}}|)^2 \cdot f_{\text{osc}}}$$

$$(17\text{--}46) \quad C > \frac{I_{L(\text{max})} \cdot |V_{\text{out}}|}{(|V_{\text{out}}| + V_{\text{in}}) \cdot f_{\text{osc}} \cdot V_{\text{Rip}}}$$

CONCEPTS

- Linear voltage regulators are far less efficient than nonlinear regulators.
- Filtering removes ripple, while regulation maintains the output voltage nearly constant over a wide range of load.
- Regulators require a minimum input–output voltage differential called the dropout voltage.
- Voltage regulators are able to compensate for both line-voltage variations and load variations.
- An inverter is a DC to AC converter.
- DC to DC converters are generally thought of as being step-up DC supplies.
- The simple zener-shunt voltage regulator is very inefficient and regulation is not real good.
- It is wise to include current limiting in regulator design, since this protects the regulator from overload and short-circuit conditions.
- It is wise to include a crowbar circuit in regulator design, since this protects the load from damage caused by overvoltage if a series-pass transistor shorts.
- The series-pass voltage regulator is not a good regulator without voltage feedback.
- Voltage feedback holds the output voltage within tens of millivolts over a wide variation in load.
- Remote-sense lines are used when large amounts of power must be transferred over long lines to a load device. The sense lines enable the power supply to regulate right at the load device, thus compensating for line voltage drops.
- Shunt regulator efficiency is very poor if the input–output voltage differential is high and the shunt transistor conducts more current than the load.
- Three-terminal linear regulators are very good choices for regulator applications because of low cost and ease of use. However, the input–output voltage differential must be kept low to operate at a reasonable efficiency.
- The LM117 and LM723 are very versatile and popular linear voltage regulator ICs.
- Nonlinear switching power supplies, or regulators, are far more efficient than linear regulators and require smaller heat sinks, weigh less, and occupy less space.
- The switching regulator is composed of a feedback-controlled pulse-width modulator and a lowpass filter acting as an integrator.
- Discontinuity occurs when the inductor's magnetic field fully collapses before the on pulse is reapplied. This usually occurs for low-load conditions (low current).
- Switching regulators usually oscillate in the 50-kHz to 200-kHz range allowing the filter components to be relatively small.

■ Flyback converters operate from collapsing magnetic flux over half of the cycle while the power switching device is off.

PROCEDURES

Darlington Pair Series-Pass Regulator Design (Figure 17–6)

1. You must know the highest DC input voltage ($V_{DC(in)}$) and the desired regulated output voltage (V_E or V_{RL}).
2. You must know the maximum load ($I_{L(max)}$).
3. You must calculate the power dissipation of Q_1 to determine the power rating ($P_{Q1} = I_{L(max)} \cdot V_{CE}$). The power rating must be greater than the actual worst-case power dissipation.
4. The lower-power piggybacked transistor (Q_2) must have a collector current rating greater than the maximum base current of Q_1.
5. Calculate the power dissipation of Q_2 to determine the power rating. The power rating must be greater than the actual worst-case power dissipation.
6. Determine the maximum Q_2 base current (I_B).
7. Determine the voltage rating for the zener.
8. When I_B is maximum, as calculated in step 5, the zener current will be minimum and should be equal to at least $0.1\, I_B$.
9. Determine a safe power rating for the zener.
10. Calculate the value for the series resistor (R_S).
11. Determine the power rating for R_S.

NEED-TO-KNOW SOLUTION

The circuit shown here should meet the requirements very nicely. You'll find this type of regulator discussed in Section 17–4. A few additional comments are needed here. The triangle-wave oscillator frequency is determined using the formula $f_o = 0.3/RC$ and is accurate only if 15-kΩ and 10-kΩ feedback resistors are used (or other values (such as 30 kΩ and 20 kΩ) in the same ratio). Notice that the reference voltage is 3.1 V and comes from a voltage divider across a 6.2-V temperature-compensated zener. It is important to use switching transistors, since their junction capacitance is low and their ON and OFF switching times are much faster than those of transistors designed for linear operation. A fuse or circuit breaker is a must! You could use a 15-A button breaker. The toroidal inductor will be 2 to 2.5 in. in outer diameter and must be wrapped with at least #16 enamel-coated solid copper wire. Fully wrap the toroid with one tight layer of wire. This should provide more than enough inductance.

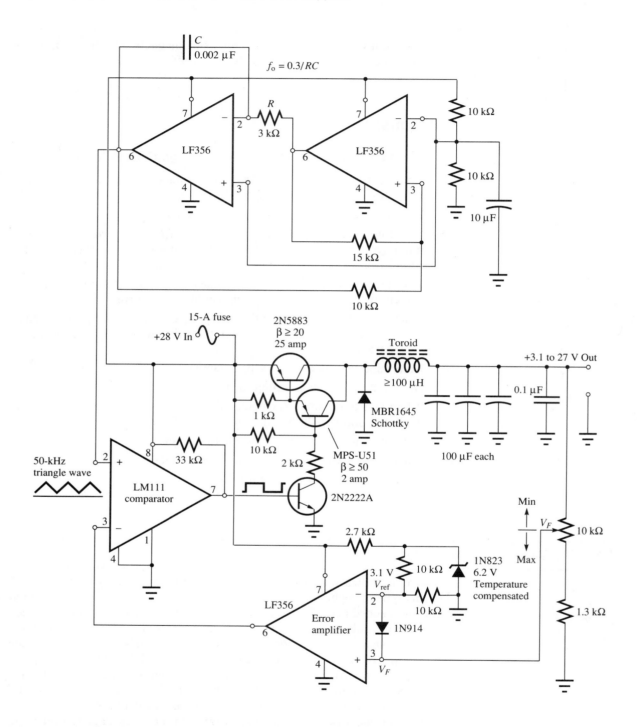

QUESTIONS

17–1 INTRODUCTION TO VOLTAGE REGULATORS

1. What is a linear power supply?
2. What is a nonlinear power supply?
3. What are three other names given to switching power supplies?

4. What are the main blocks of an AC to DC converter?
5. Explain the difference between filtering and regulation.
6. What is ripple?
7. Describe two ways regulation is measured or specified.
8. Explain how regulation greatly reduces ripple in many cases.
9. What is dropout voltage?
10. How does line regulation differ from load regulation?
11. How does an inverter differ from a converter?

17–2 DISCRETE LINEAR VOLTAGE REGULATORS

12. What is the main disadvantage of the simple zener-diode shunt regulator?
13. Is the simple zener regulator intended for (a) low-power, or (b) high-power applications?
14. Under what conditions does the zener-diode dissipate the most power?
15. Explain how the power dissipated by the zener and series resistor is greatly reduced using a series-pass Darlington pair.
16. Why is current limiting a good idea in regulator design?
17. Briefly explain how the limit resistor (R_{Limit}) and limit transistor work together to limit the maximum load.
18. What circuit is called a *crowbar* and what purpose does it serve?
19. What are the problems that make the basic series-pass regulator a relatively poor regulator?
20. Explain how voltage feedback to an error amplifier greatly improves regulation.
21. What is the purpose of remote sensing for regulated DC supplies?
22. Explain why it is not desirable to have too much input–output voltage differential.
23. What is a dual-polarity tracking regulator?
24. Explain why the transistor shunt regulator is like a super zener regulator.
25. Explain why the shunt regulator's efficiency is very poor when the load is light (high-resistance load device).

17–3 IC LINEAR VOLTAGE REGULATORS

26. How can the power dissipation of a three-terminal voltage regulator be kept to a minimum?
27. Three-terminal regulators can only be used as fixed-voltage regulators as determined by the manufacturer. True or false?
28. From Table 17–2, select an adjustable regulator IC suitable for an output voltage range of +3 to +15 V at 4 A.
29. List three applications for the 723 voltage regulator.
30. What is the maximum load the 723 itself can supply?

17–4 SWITCHING DC POWER SUPPLIES

31. What are the advantages and possible disadvantages of switching regulators as compared to linear regulators?

32. What are the two main blocks to a switching regulator?
33. Explain how a comparator can be used as a pulse-width modulator.
34. What is the purpose for the lowpass filter at the output of a switching regulator?
35. What happens to the duty cycle of the square-wave drive if the load increases?
36. In the lowpass filter, why should two or more paralleled filter capacitors be used instead of just one larger capacitor?
37. What is ESR and what effect does it have?
38. Explain why the 723 switching regulator of Figure 17–25 switches on and off even though it has no ramp-voltage oscillator.
39. What is the purpose for the recirculation diode in the lowpass filter network?
40. Explain how the inductor is used to step up the DC output voltage in Figure 17–27.
41. What is flyback action?
42. What is discontinuity and why does it occur?
43. How can the percent discontinuity be reduced?
44. Explain what flyback action has to do with the negative output voltage of the DC to DC inverter in Figure 17–28.

17–5 INVERTERS AND CONVERTERS

45. What is a DC to AC inverter?
46. What are two general types of inverters?
47. What determines the peak-to-peak output voltage for the inverter of Figure 17–29?
48. Explain how the rheostat in Figure 17–30 can change the frequency of oscillation.
49. Explain, in general terms, the conversion process that takes place in a DC to DC step-up converter.
50. How does a flyback converter differ from a push-pull DC to DC converter?

PROBLEMS

17–2 DISCRETE LINEAR VOLTAGE REGULATORS

1. Determine the following parameters from Figure 17–33.

   V_{RL}, I_L, I_B, V_{RS}, I_{RS}, I_Z, P_Z, P_{RS}, P_L, P_{Q1}, and % efficiency

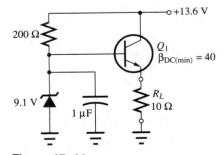

Figure 17–33

2. Determine the following parameters from Figure 17–34.

    V_{RL}, I_L, I_B, V_{RS}, I_{RS}, I_Z, P_Z, P_{RS}, P_L, P_{Q1}, and % efficiency

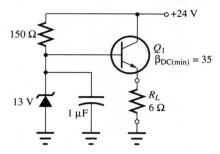

Figure 17–34

·3. Design a Darlington series-pass voltage regulator from information given in Figure 17–35. Suggest values and minimum ratings for all components based on calculations. Possible zener ratings are 250 mW, 500 mW, 1 W, 1.5 W, 5 W, and 10 W.

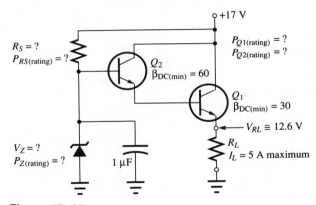

Figure 17–35

4. Design a Darlington series-pass voltage regulator from information given in Figure 17–36. Based on calculations, suggest values and minimum ratings for all components.

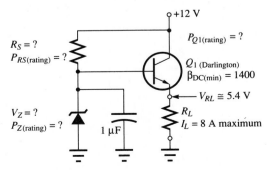

Figure 17–36

5. Calculate I_{Limit} and V_Z for Figure 17–37.
6. What value should R_{Limit} be in Figure 17–37 if current is to be limited to approximately 5 A?

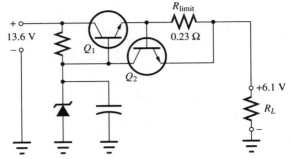

Figure 17–37

7. Suggest a reasonable value for the fuse current rating and the crowbar-circuit zener-diode voltage in Figure 17–38.

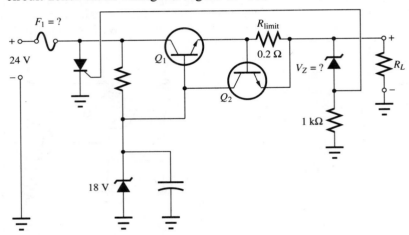

Figure 17–38

8. Determine the value for R_2 in Figure 17–39.

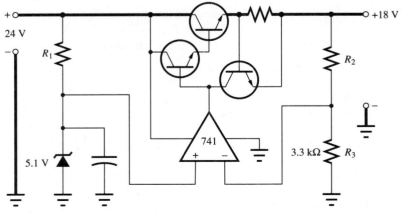

Figure 17–39

9. Determine the output voltage for Figure 17–40.
10. Calculate the input–output voltage differential for Figure 17–40.

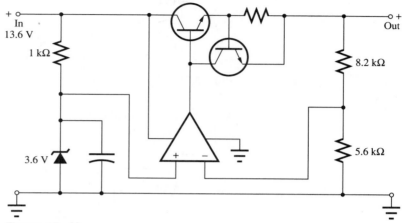

Figure 17–40

11. Calculate the output voltage and power efficiency for Figure 17–41.
12. Calculate the maximum short-circuit current for Figure 17–41.

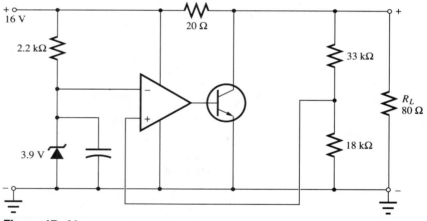

Figure 17–41

17–3 IC LINEAR VOLTAGE REGULATORS

13. Determine the output voltage for Figure 17–42.

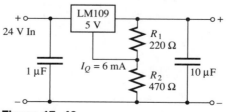

Figure 17–42

14.   Determine the output current and load voltage for Figure 17–43.

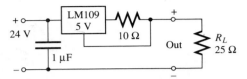

Figure 17–43

15.   At what value of load (current) does the bypass transistor of Figure 17–44 begin to conduct?

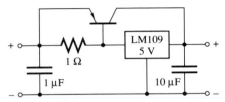

Figure 17–44

16.   Determine the range of output voltage for Figure 17–45.

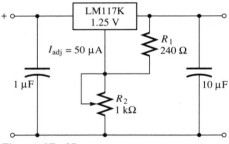

Figure 17–45

17.   For Figure 17–45, what should be the value of R_2 for a 12-V output?
18.   Calculate the output voltage and approximate current limit for Figure 17–46.

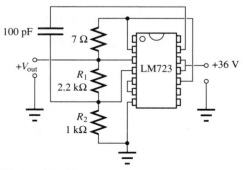

Figure 17–46

19. Calculate the output voltage and approximate current limit for Figure 17–47.

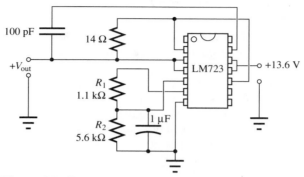

Figure 17–47

20. Design a circuit like Figure 17–47 for 5 V at 100 mA maximum load current.
21. Determine the value of R_1 in Figure 17–48 for −10 V output.

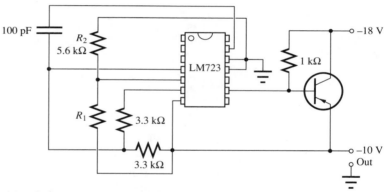

Figure 17–48

17–4 SWITCHING DC POWER SUPPLIES

22. Calculate the minimum values for L and C in a step-down switching regulator configuration with the following specifications: $f_{osc} = 80$ kHz, $V_{in} = 20$ V, $V_{out} = 13.5$ V, $I_{L(max)} = 2$ A, $V_{Rip(max)} = 100$ mV$_{P-P}$, 20% discontinuity.
23. Calculate the minimum values for L and C in a step-down switching regulator configuration with the following specifications: $f_{osc} = 40$ kHz, $V_{in} = 14$ V, $V_{out} = 9$ V, $I_{L(max)} = 5$ A, $V_{Rip(max)} = 50$ mV$_{P-P}$, 10% discontinuity.
24. Calculate the minimum values for L and C in a step-up switching regulator configuration with the following specifications: $f_{osc} = 150$ kHz, $V_{in} = 12$ V, $V_{out} = 18$ V, $I_{L(max)} = 1$ A, $V_{Rip(max)} = 75$ mV$_{P-P}$, 30% discontinuity.

25. Calculate the minimum values for L and C in a step-up switching regulator configuration with the following specifications: $f_{osc} = 200$ kHz, $V_{in} = 5$ V, $V_{out} = 9$ V, $I_{L(max)} = 1.5$ A, $V_{Rip(max)} = 50$ mV$_{P-P}$, 10% discontinuity.

26. Calculate the minimum values for L and C in an inverting switching regulator configuration with the following specifications: $f_{osc} = 100$ kHz, $V_{in} = +12$ V, $V_{out} = -18$ V, $I_{L(max)} = 200$ mA, $V_{Rip(max)} = 25$ mV$_{P-P}$, 40% discontinuity.

27. Calculate the minimum values for L and C in an inverting switching regulator configuration with the following specifications: $f_{osc} = 75$ kHz, $V_{in} = +14$ V, $V_{out} = -24$ V, $I_{L(max)} = 2$ A, $V_{Rip(max)} = 50$ mV$_{P-P}$, 20% discontinuity.

ADDITIONAL PROBLEMS

28. Determine the following parameters from Figure 17–49.

    V_{RL}, I_L, I_B, V_{RS}, I_{RS}, I_Z, P_Z, P_{RS}, P_L, P_{Q1}, and % efficiency

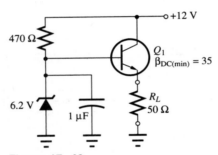

Figure 17–49

29. Design a Darlington series-pass voltage regulator from information given in Figure 17–50. Suggest values and minimum ratings for all components based on calculations. Possible zener ratings are 250 mW, 500 mW, 1 W, 1.5 W, 5 W, and 10 W.

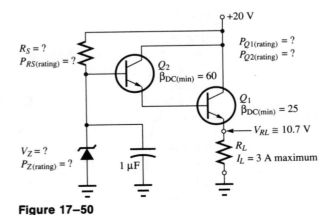

Figure 17–50

30. Design a Darlington series-pass voltage regulator from information given in Figure 17–51. Suggest values and minimum ratings based on calculations for all components.

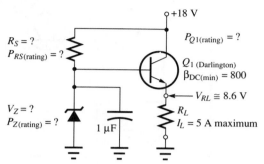

$R_S = ?$
$P_{RS(rating)} = ?$

$+18$ V

$P_{Q1(rating)} = ?$

Q_1 (Darlington)
$\beta_{DC(min)} = 800$

$V_{RL} \cong 8.6$ V

$V_Z = ?$
$P_{Z(rating)} = ?$

1 µF

R_L
$I_L = 5$ A maximum

Figure 17–51

31. Calculate I_{Limit} and V_Z for Figure 17–52.

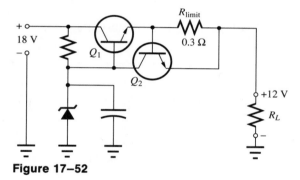

$+$
18 V
$-$

Q_1

Q_2

R_{limit}
0.3 Ω

$+12$ V

R_L

$-$

Figure 17–52

32. Suggest a reasonable value for the fuse current rating and the crowbar-circuit zener-diode voltage in Figure 17–53.

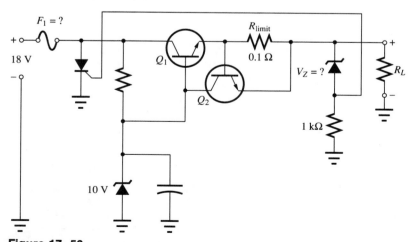

$F_1 = ?$

$+$
18 V
$-$

Q_1

Q_2

R_{limit}
0.1 Ω

$V_Z = ?$

R_L

$+$

$-$

1 kΩ

10 V

Figure 17–53

33. Determine the value for R_2 in Figure 17–54.

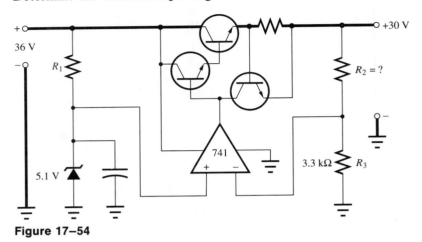

Figure 17–54

34. Determine the output voltage for Figure 17–55.

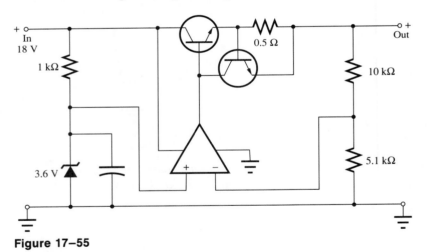

Figure 17–55

35. Determine the output voltage for Figure 17–56.

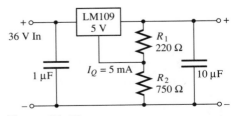

Figure 17–56

36. Calculate the output voltage and approximate current limit for Figure 17–57.

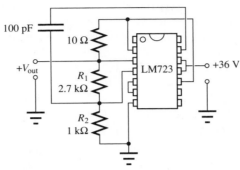

Figure 17–57

37. Calculate the minimum values for L and C in a step-down switching regulator configuration with the following specifications: $f_{osc} = 60$ kHz, $V_{in} = 24$ V, $V_{out} = 14$ V, $I_{L(max)} = 3$ A, $V_{Rip(max)} = 75$ mV$_{P-P}$, 20% discontinuity.

ANSWERS TO SELF-CHECKS

SELF-CHECK 17–1

1. Linear power supplies operate power devices in the middle of their linear operating region between cutoff and saturation. Nonlinear supplies operate the power devices in a switching mode alternating between cutoff and saturation.
2. The AC to DC converter converts an AC source to a higher or lower DC voltage that is usually regulated using a linear or nonlinear regulator circuit.
3. Line regulation is output voltage regulation that compensates for variations in line voltage (DC input voltage). Load regulation is output voltage regulation that compensates for changes in load.
4. A DC to DC converter is usually understood to be a voltage step-up converter.
5. An inverter is usually understood to be a DC to AC converter.

SELF-CHECK 17–2

1. Zener-regulator power efficiency is often very low and regulation is not very good.
2. $V_L = 4.9$ V, $I_L = 196$ mA, $I_B = 2.45$ mA, $I_Z = 2.88$ mA, $P_{RS} = 34.1$ mW, $P_Z = 16.1$ mW, $P_{Q1} = 1.39$ W, $P_L = 0.96$ W, % Eff = 40.9%. The power rating of the zener is more than sufficient.
3. Q_1: $P_{Q1(max)} = 6$ A $\cdot$ V $= 18$ W
   Use a 25- to 40-W transistor with a continuous-current rating of at least 6 A.
   Q_2: $P_{Q2(max)} = (6$ A$/40) \cdot (8$ V $- 0.7$ V $- 5$ V$) = 0.345$ W.
   Zener: $V_Z = 5 + 1.4$ V $= 6.4$ V

Use a 6.2-V or 6.8-V, 250-mW, zener.

R_S: $R_S = (8\ V - 6.2\ V)/(0.15\ A/90) = 1.8\ V/1.67\ mA = 1,078\ \Omega$

Use a 1-kΩ, 1/8-W resistor.

4. (1) The zener voltage changes with changes in load.
   (2) Increased emitter-region voltage drop with increase in load.
   (3) Voltage drop across R_{Limit} changes with load.

5. $K = 3.3\ V/12\ V = 0.275$, $R_2 = [(1/0.275) - 1] \cdot 2.2\ k\Omega = 5.8\ k\Omega$
   Use a 5.76-kΩ, 1% film resistor or a 5.6-kΩ resistor in series with a 200-Ω resistor.

6. Efficiency is highest when the voltage across the series resistor is low and most of the total current goes to the load.

SELF-CHECK 17–3

1. (1) fixed-voltage operation, (2) adjustable higher-voltage operation, (3) as a constant-current source

2. Dropout voltage is the minimum input–output voltage differential at which the regulator begins to lose its regulating capability. The input–output voltage differential must be higher than the dropout voltage.

3. $R_2 = (9\ V - 1.25\ V)/(5.68\ mA + 50\ \mu A)$
   $= 7.75\ V/5.73\ mA = 1353\ \Omega$
   Use a 13.3-kΩ, 2% resistor.

4. $V_{DC(in)} \geq +18\ V$, $R_{Limit} \cong 0.7\ V/80\ mA = 8.75\ \Omega$
   Use an 8.66-Ω, 2% resistor.
   $R_1 = 3.01\ k\Omega \cdot (15\ V - 7.15\ V)/7.15\ V = 3,304\ \Omega$
   Use a 3.3-kΩ resistor.

5. $V_{DC(in)} \geq -21\ V$
   $R_1 = -7.15\ V \cdot 3.16\ k\Omega/(2 \cdot -18\ V + 7.15\ V) = 783\ \Omega$
   Use a 787-Ω, 2% resistor.

SELF-CHECK 17–4

1. (1) higher efficiency, (2) switching device dissipates less power, (3) less weight and space

2. The DC level (voltage) determines the trip voltage for the comparator. The ramp voltage sets the output of the comparator high when the ramp voltage exceeds the DC level. The output of the comparator drops low when the ramp voltage drops down below the DC level. If the DC level is raised, the comparator will not trip high until the ramp voltage exceeds the higher DC level. Thus, the width of the output pulse is narrower when the comparator trips higher on the ramp waveform and wider when the comparator trips lower on the ramp waveform.

3. Simply because a DC square wave is applied to it. The lowpass filter integrates the DC square wave.

4. The duty cycle of the square wave increases with increased load.

5. $L > 178\ \mu H$, $C > 178\ \mu F$

SELF-CHECK 17–5

1. A DC to AC inverter is a DC to AC converter that usually includes an oscillator-driven or self-excited push-pull amplifier and a step-up transformer.
2. An oscillator-driven inverter uses an *RC* oscillator to drive the push-pull output transistors and a self-excited inverter uses transformer windings for positive feedback to sustain oscillation.
3. The basic function of a DC to DC converter is to step up DC voltage.
4. A flyback converter is a DC to DC converter that energizes the primary of a transformer for half a cycle; the collapsing magnetic field induces current and voltage for the other half cycle.
5. A DC to AC inverter

SUGGESTED PROJECTS

1. Add some of the main concepts and formulas from this chapter to your Electronics Notebook.
2. Build and test the linear regulator of Figure 17–9. Use a DC source that is in the range of 8 to 12 V with at least 4-A capacity. Make sure you mount Q_1 on a heat sink (4 × 6″ with cooling fins). For our purpose here, eliminate R_2 and R_3 and tie pin 2 of the op-amp to the output (+). The output voltage will be regulated at the zener voltage. Don't use the sense lines. Simply connect the anode of the zener to ground. Vary the load over a range of 100 mA to 1 A and measure the output voltage for each load. Use load resistors between 5 Ω, 5 W and 50 Ω, 0.5 W. Make a graph that shows the relationship between load and output voltage.

   Now remove the op-amp from the circuit and jumper the cathode of the zener to the base of Q_2. You should now have a series-pass Darlington-pair regulator with no voltage feedback, similar to Figure 17–6. Vary the load as before and graph the results. Compare the performance of the two circuits by comparing the graphs you made. Which is better?
3. Obtain a 723 IC voltage regulator and build and test some of the regulator circuits shown in this chapter.
4. Build and test the switching circuits of Figures 17–24 and 17–25.

High-power industrial lasers are used for precision fabrication in computer-aided manufacturing systems. Shown in this photo, a powerful light beam is used to cut through a steel plate. Lasers are on the high-power end of opto-electronic devices. (Michael Rizza, STOCK/Boston.)

18 Optoelectronic Devices

OBJECTIVES

After studying this chapter, you will be able to

- characterize visible and invisible light in terms of frequency, wavelength, and intensity.
- convert various photometric units of illuminance to corresponding radiometric units of irradiance.
- identify and describe differences in common structures of light-emitting diodes.
- identify significant LED operating parameters from charts and graphs provided on data sheets.
- explain the operation of and purpose for multiplexed LED displays.
- explain the construction and operation of electroluminescent panels.
- explain the construction and operation of nematic liquid crystal displays (LCDs).
- identify and explain the operation of a variety of photodetectors—including photoresistors, photodiodes, phototransistors, photothyristors, and photologic.
- identify and explain the uses for a variety of optocouplers and optointerrupters.
- explain laser theory and the general operation of injection lasers, gas lasers, and solid-crystal lasers.
- explain how optoelectronic devices are used in a basic fiber-optic communication link.
- explain the use and operation of the semiconductor optical amplifier.

NEED TO KNOW

Sometime in the not-too-distant future, your boss may approach you and ask you to devise some way to safely interface a computer to several electronic circuits. It is intended that the computer will be able to control 115-V AC ceiling lights in five rooms, a 240-V AC electric hot water heater, a 24-V burglar alarm system, and a 115-V AC night security light system. All these circuits can cause serious computer damage if the interface circuits are not designed properly.

Describe the components or devices that you would use to insure a safe interface between the computer and the external circuits. Any ideas? By the time you finish this chapter, you will have plenty of ideas. This kind of assignment will be no problem for you. Press forward and enjoy!

INTRODUCTION

This chapter is an introduction to the world of optoelectronics. Optoelectronics is that area of electronics in which light and electronics are brought together—light is used to control electronic devices and electronic devices are used to create visible or invisible light. Naturally, we do not have the room here to cover optoelectronics topics extensively. Yet, you will be introduced to a wide variety of optoelectronic devices in a very practical way: Devices will be explained and applications will be shown.

Optoelectronic devices can be divided into two general categories: photoemitters and photodetectors. Photoemitters generate light and photodetectors respond to light. Here you will explore these two categories along with an introduction to electronic display devices, lasers, and fiber-optic devices. The material in this chapter is useful in itself. However, I am sure you will want to study some of these topics further from topic-specific sources. Enjoy your exploration.

18–1 THE LIGHT SPECTRUM

WAVELENGTH (λ) AND FREQUENCY (f)

In previous chapters, we have discussed the frequency response of many devices in terms of bandwidth measured in hertz (Hz). In this chapter, you will explore optoelectronic devices whose bandwidth and performance is measured in wavelength (λ, lambda). This practice has been established by convention, because wavelength is more closely related to the actual dimensional construction of many devices. The wavelength of a radio-wave or light-wave frequency is the physical distance between wavefronts or pulse peaks as the energy travels through free space. In free space, radio and light waves travel at a velocity of $300 \cdot 10^6$ m/s. This velocity is symbolized with the lowercase c. The wavelength in free space is expressed in meters per cycle (m/cyc), since the frequency in cycles per second is traveling at $300 \cdot 10^6$ meters per second. Thus, wavelength λ = velocity c/frequency f = (m/s)/(cyc/s) = m/cyc

$\lambda = c/f = (300 \cdot 10^6 \text{ m/s})/f$ (in free space)   (18–1)

Consider Examples 18–1 and 18–2.

EXAMPLE 18–1

What is the wavelength of a 20.5-MHz ratio frequency?

$\lambda = c/f = (300 \cdot 10^6 \text{ m/s})/(20.5 \cdot 10^6 \text{ Hz}) = 14.63 \text{ m}$

EXAMPLE 18–2

What is the wavelength of a 540-THz (terahertz) light frequency?

$\lambda = c/f = (300 \cdot 10^6 \text{ m/s})/(540 \cdot 10^{12} \text{Hz})$

$= 555 \cdot 10^{-9} \text{ m} = 555 \text{ nm}$

Note: Wavelength is expressed simply in meters. It is understood that the length is per cycle.

Figure 18–1 illustrates the portion of the frequency spectrum that pertains to the devices in this chapter. Take time to carefully study this figure until you understand the relationship between frequency and wavelength. Usually, a spectrum graph such as this is not labeled in frequency, only in wavelength. Scientists and engineers refer to specific light frequencies in terms of wavelength using any of three common units: micrometers (1 μm = $1 \cdot 10^{-6}$ m), nanometers (1 nm = $1 \cdot 10^{-9}$ m), or angstroms (1 Å = $1 \cdot 10^{-10}$ m). As an example, 0.5 μm = 500 nm = 5,000 Å. Most manufacturers specify the spectral response of their devices in terms of nonometers (nm). However, you should be able to mentally convert to μm or Å if necessary.

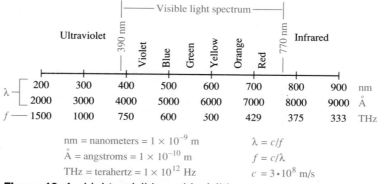

Figure 18–1 Light—visible and invisible.

Something else you should notice about Figure 18–1 is that frequency decreases from left to right. This is because wavelength is increasing from left to right and $f = c/\lambda$.

$$f = c/\lambda = (300 \cdot 10^6 \text{ m/s})/\lambda \quad \text{(in free space)} \tag{18–2}$$

EXAMPLE 18–3

What is the approximate wavelength and frequency for blue visible light? Express the wavelength in μm, nm, and Å.

From Figure 18–1, the wavelength is approximately 480 nm = 0.48 μm = 4,800 Å. The approximate frequency is:

$$f = c/\lambda = 300 \cdot 10^6/480 \cdot 10^{-9} \text{ m} = 625 \cdot 10^{12} \text{ Hz} = 625 \text{ THz}$$

QUANTIFYING LIGHT

In addition to frequency and wavelength, how do we quantify light in terms of brightness or intensity? This is important in determining the responsivity and sensitivity of light-emitting and light-detecting devices. The amount of light produced by a light source is known as its **luminous intensity** and is measured in **candelas** or **candles (cd).** The light energy contains **luminous flux,** much like an electric or magnetic field. The unit of luminous flux is the **lumen (lm).** The luminous flux from a point light source is spread out uniformly and spherically in all directions. As shown in Figure 18–2, one candle of light intensity produces one lumen of flux per steradian. A **steradian (sr)** is a conically shaped angle that encloses a spherical surface area equal to the square of the radius of the sphere. Thus, 1 cd = 1 lm/sr.

The amount of light that actually falls on the surface of an object or device is referred to as **illuminance** or **illumination.** Illumination is measured in foot-

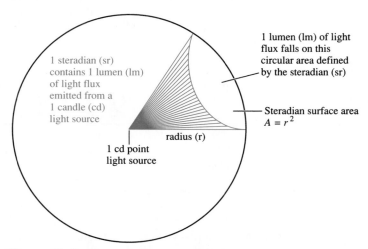

Figure 18–2 One candle, one steradian, one lumen.

TABLE 18–1

Multiply	By	To Get
cd	1	lm/sr
lm	1	cd · sr
lux	1	lm/m^2
lux	0.0929	fc
fc	1	lm/ft^2
fc	10.764	lm/m^2
W (radiative power)	680*	lm
lm	1.4706*	mW
fc	1.4706*	mW/ft^2
fc	15.83*	mW/m^2
fc	1.583*	μW/cm^2
mW/m^2	0.0632*	fc
mW/m^2	0.0632*	lm/ft^2
mW/ft^2	0.68*	fc
mW/ft^2	7.32*	lm/m^2

* At 555 nm.

candles or lumens per square meter. A **foot candle (ft-cd** or **fc)** is simply one lumen of light falling on a surface area of one square foot (1 fc = 1 lm/ft^2). For example, if the radius of the sphere shown in Figure 18–2 is 1 ft, one lumen of light from the one-candle source falls on a surface area of 1 ft^2 which is 1 fc of illumination. Since there are 10.764 square feet per meter, 1 fc = 10.764 lm/m^2. One **lux** is equal to 1 lm/m^2 and 1 fc = 10.764 lux. As a point of reference, the human eye functions best in a 0.01- to 100-fc range of illumination.

All of the units discussed thus far are referred to as *photometric units*. **Photometric units** are units that are used to quantify visible light. The entire frequency spectrum, including visible and invisible light, is quantified in **radiometric units** using the watt as its basic unit. For example, one candle is equal to one lumen per steradian and is equal to 1.4706 mW/sr at a wavelength of 555 nm, which is greenish-yellow light in the middle of the visible light spectrum. In radiometric units, illuminance, or illumination, is referred to as **irradiance.** Table 18–1 is provided as an aid to converting between units.

Study Examples 18–4 and 18–5.

EXAMPLE 18–4

What is the radiometric equivalent of 15.4 fc of illuminance at a wavelength of 555 nm? Express your answer in mW/m^2.

1 fc = 15.83 mW/m^2

therefore,

15.4 fc = 15.4 · 15.83 mW/m^2 = 243.8 mW/m^2

EXAMPLE 18–5

What is the photometric equivalent of 25 mW/ft^2 of irradiance at a wavelength of 555 nm? Express your answer in lm/m^2.

1 mW/ft^2 = 0.68 fc

25 mW/ft^2 = 25 · 0.68 fc = 17 fc

1 fc = 10.764 lm/m^2

17 fc = 17 · 10.764 lm/m^2 = 183 lm/m^2

1 mW/ft^2 = 7.32 lm/m^2

25 mW/ft^2 = 25 · 7.32 lm/m^2 = 183 lm/m^2

Review this section by answering the questions and solving the problems of Self-Check 18–1.

Self-Check 18–1

1. Calculate the wavelength of orange light at a frequency of 470 THz. Express your answer in μm, nm, and Å.
2. Calculate the frequency of green light at 525 nm.
3. What is illuminance?
4. What is the difference between photometric units and radiometric units?
5. What is the photometric equivalent of 100 mW/m^2 of irradiance at a wavelength of 555 nm? Express your answer in fc.

18–2 OPTOELECTRONIC EMITTERS AND DISPLAYS

INTRODUCTION

In this section, we will explore a variety of common optoelectronic light emitters and displays. In so doing, we will take a closer look at light-emitting diodes (LEDs) and ways in which they are used. Also, we will introduce the electroluminescent panel that is commonly used today for control-panel lighting and backlighting for liquid-crystal displays (LCDs). This section is meant to be introductory in nature since these topics can be expanded well beyond the space permitted in this text. Nevertheless, you will gain a practical understanding of how these devices are made and how they operate.

LIGHT-EMITTING DIODES AND DISPLAYS

General LED Characteristics

Figure 18–3 is a photograph of a small sampling of the many shapes and sizes of light-emitting diodes and displays. Their shape and size varies widely and is determined almost totally by application. The color of emission from the

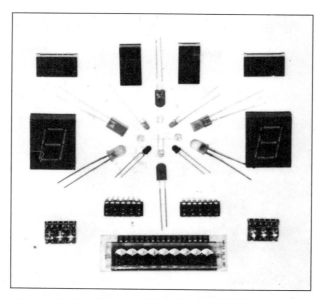

Figure 18–3   Light-emitting diodes (LEDs) and displays.

LED is determined by the mix of semiconductor materials used. Gallium arsenide (GaAs) and aluminum–gallium arsenide (AlGaAs) are the base semiconductor materials; they are doped with impurities such as silicon (Si), zinc (Zn), tellurium (Te), indium (In), and phosphorus (P). The LED can be tailored to emit light anywhere in a range of approximately 550 nm to 950 nm. Operating lifetimes for LEDs is extremely long—in most cases, 100,000 to 1,000,000 hours. That's between 11.4 and 114 years, assuming conservative operating conditions.

As you know from previous study, the LED is operated in the forward-biased mode. Forward voltage drops range between 1.5 and 2.5 V with forward currents ranging between a few milliamps to over 100 ma, depending on LED type and application.

When forward biased, electrons in the n material are excited to a higher energy level and are able to cross the narrowed depletion region to the p material. As electrons cross the barrier, they drop into holes in the p material and release energy. For gallium arsenide diodes, most of the energy is released in the form of visible or invisible light (infrared).

Epitaxially-Grown Surface LEDs

Figure 18–4 illustrates the construction of a very simple LED structure known as the epitaxially grown surface LED. **Epitaxy** is the controlled growth of a layer of semiconductor material on the surface of an existing semiconductor substrate. The growth is accomplished as high-temperature vaporized material condenses and accumulates on the surface of the substrate. In the process, the grown or deposited material copies the crystalline structure of the substrate. Also, impurities added to the deposited material form layers of n-type and p-type material.

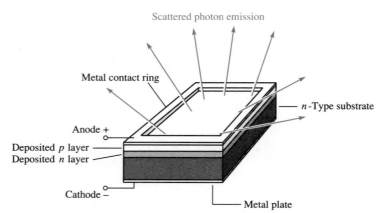

Figure 18–4   Epitaxially grown surface LED.

The top p layer is extremely thin and is the active layer. It is in this top layer that recombination takes place. As the electrons fall into the holes, energy is given up in the form of light–photon emission. Light is emitted from the entire surface and edges of the p layer.

Planar Diffused Surface LEDs

Figure 18–5 illustrates the planar diffused surface LED. A thin p layer is formed in the top surface of the n substrate by diffusing impurities into the surface at high temperatures. In the process, a junction and depletion region is formed. When the device is forward biased, photons are emitted from the entire surface p layer.

Etched-Well LEDs

Figure 18–6 illustrates the etched-well LED. The reason for the name should be obvious to you from the diagram. A small opening called the *well* is etched into a top n layer. The very thin n-type window layer is an AlGaAs layer that supplies electrons to the active p layer. Because the lower metal contact is directly under the base of the well, recombination is confined to this region. Thus, photons are emitted through the window and the small

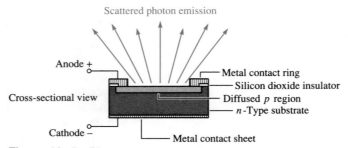

Figure 18–5   Planar diffused surface LED.

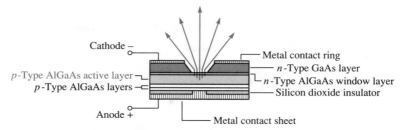

Figure 18–6 Etched-well LED.

well opening. The emission is far more concentrated than the surface LEDs previously discussed, making this type of LED ideal for launching light into the end of a very small optical fiber for data transmission. We will discuss fiber optics more later.

Edge-Emitting LEDs

An even more concentrated photon beam is obtained from the edge-emitting diode shown in Figure 18–7. As you can see, this LED is completely enclosed top and bottom. The only place for light to escape is from the edge of the active p layer. The configuration of the upper metal contact causes emissions to be concentrated over a small section of the active layer. Thus, emission from this LED is a concentrated elliptical beam, making it ideal for launching light into very thin optical fibers. The edge-emitting LED is a close cousin to the laser diode, which we will explore later.

LED Data Sheet Information

The data sheets for the MLED76 will serve to illustrate important packaged LED characteristics. Let's consider some of the more important data. First, notice that this is a visible red LED emitting red light at a wavelength of 660 nm. If the LED is to be modulated for data transmission, a photodetector device that is most sensitive at or near 660 nm should be selected for the receiving end.

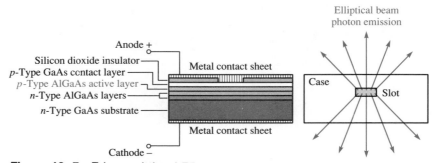

Figure 18–7 Edge-emitting LED.

MOTOROLA
■ **SEMICONDUCTOR** ■
TECHNICAL DATA

Visible Red LED

This device is designed for a wide variety of applications where visible light emission is desirable, and can be used in conjunction with any MRD700 series detector. The MLED76 features high power output, using gallium aluminum arsenide technology.

- Low Cost
- Popular Case 349 Package
- Uses Stable Long-Life LED Technology
- Clear Epoxy Package

MLED76

**VISIBLE RED
LED
660 nm**

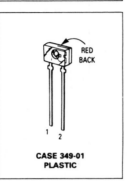

**CASE 349-01
PLASTIC**

MAXIMUM RATINGS

Rating	Symbol	Value	Unit
Reverse Voltage	V_R	5	Volts
Forward Current — Continuous	I_F	60	mA
Forward Current — Peak Pulse	I_F	1	A
Total Power Dissipation @ T_A = 25°C (Note 1) Derate above 35°C	P_D	132 2	mW mW/°C
Ambient Operating Temperature Range	T_A	−40 to +100	°C
Storage Temperature	T_{stg}	−40 to +100	°C
Lead Soldering Temperature (Note 2)	—	260	°C

ELECTRICAL CHARACTERISTICS (T_A = 25°C unless otherwise noted)

Characteristic	Symbol	Min	Typ	Max	Unit
Reverse Leakage Current (V_R = 3 V)	I_R	—	100	—	nA
Reverse Leakage Current (V_R = 5 V)	I_R	—	10	100	μA
Forward Voltage (I_F = 60 mA)	V_F	—	1.8	2.2	V
Temperature Coefficient of Forward Voltage	ΔV_F	—	−2.2	—	mV/K
Capacitance (f = 1 MHz)	C	—	50	—	pF

OPTICAL CHARACTERISTICS (T_A = 25°C unless otherwise noted)

Characteristic	Symbol	Min	Typ	Max	Unit
Peak Wavelength (I_F = 60 mA)	λp	—	660	—	nm
Spectral Half-Power Bandwidth	$\Delta\lambda$	—	20	—	nm
Continuous Power Output (I_F = 60 mA) (Note 3)	P_O	—	2.2	—	mW
Instantaneous Power Output (I_F = 100 mA)	P_O	—	4	—	mW
Instantaneous Axial Intensity (I_F = 100 mA) (Note 4)	I_O	0.8	1.3	—	mW/sr
Power Half-Angle	ϑ	—	±30	—	°
Optical Turn-On Time	t_{on}	—	200	—	ns
Optical Turn-Off Time	t_{off}	—	150	—	ns
Half-Power Electrical Bandwidth (Note 5)	BWe	—	6	—	MHz

Notes: 1. Measured with device soldered into a typical printed circuit board.
2. 5 seconds max; 1/16 inch from case. Heat sink should be applied during soldering, to prevent case temperature from exceeding 100°C.
3. Measured using a Photodyne 88xLA with a #350 integrating sphere.
4. On-axis, with cone angle of ±13°.
5. I_F = 100 mA pk-pk, 100% modulation.

MLED76

TYPICAL CHARACTERISTICS

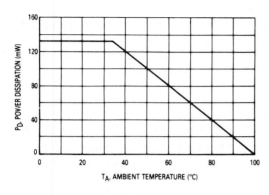

Figure 1. Power Dissipation

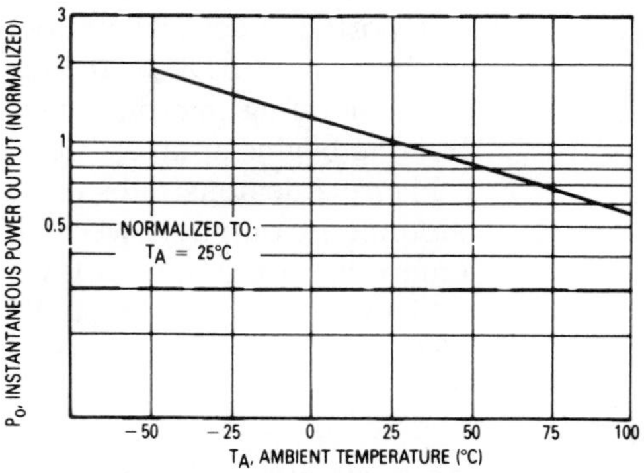

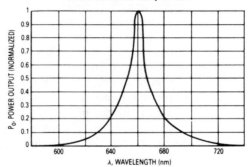

**Figure 2. Instantaneous Power Output
versus Ambient Temperature**

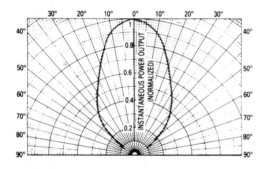

Figure 3. Spatial Radiation Pattern

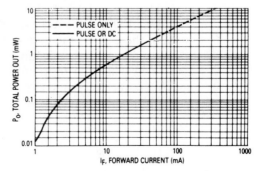

Figure 4. Relative Spectral Emission

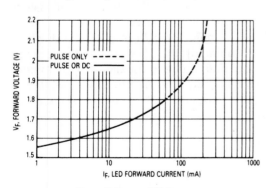

**Figure 5. Forward Voltage
versus Forward Current**

**Figure 6. Instantaneous Power Output
versus Forward Current**

The maximum ratings should never be exceeded for reliable operation. Most important, the circuit in which the MLED76 is used should not apply a reverse voltage greater than 5 V and should not apply a continuous forward current greater than 60 mA.

Important electrical and optical characteristics are illustrated graphically on the second page of the data sheets. Figure 1 graphically illustrates the power derating that must take place as temperature increases. Notice that derating begins at an ambient (surrounding) temperature of 35°C.

Figure 2 demonstrates the relationship between ambient temperature and photometric output power. Note that the LED is more efficient and provides a more intense output at lower operating temperatures.

Figure 3 is a polar graph illustrating the spatial radiation pattern from the LED. This graph shows the relationship between the power radiated directly from the center of the LED to power radiated at all angles up to ±90°. The half-power angle is usually specified in the optical characteristics table and can be determined from the polar graph. In this case, the 0.5 power points are at approximately ±32°. The LED structure and the type of case/lens will determine the spatial pattern.

Figure 4 clearly demonstrates the spectral emission of the LED. As specified, the graph indicates predominant emissions at 660 nm. The half-power emissions bandwidth is approximately ±10 nm (equal to a $\Delta\lambda$ half-power bandwidth of 20 nm).

Figures 5 and 6 graphically show the forward current, voltage, and output power characteristics. The solid portions of the curves indicate continuous forward current up to 60 mA and the dashed portions indicate pulsed current. Notice the relationship between forward current and output power in Figure 6. For this LED, the relationship is not fully linear. However, it is fairly linear for a forward current of between approximately 6 to 60 mA. If the LED is biased at 30 mA, it can be intensity modulated from an audio amplifier to transmit your voice on a light beam with a minimum of distortion. Usually an infrared LED is used for this purpose.

If the LED is to be used simply as an indicator light or part of a display, most of the data on the data sheets is unimportant. However, if the LED is to be used in a communications application, much of the data will be important. You will need to know voltage and current parameters, spatial and spectral parameters, and ON/OFF time parameters. As you have seen, all of that information is readily available from the data sheets.

LED DISPLAYS

Multiplexed Seven-Segment Displays

Much earlier in this text you were introduced to LEDs and seven-segment LED displays. Recall that these display digits are wired internally as either common anode or common cathode. In most digital readout systems today, seven-segment displays are wired such that all corresponding segments of many displays are wired together. Common anodes or common cathodes of

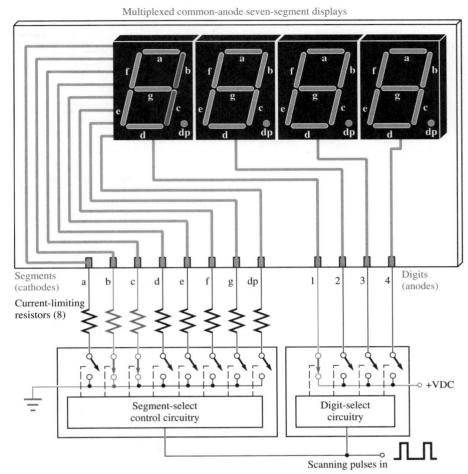

Figure 18–8   Multiplexed seven-segment displays.

each display remain separate. This is illustrated in Figures 18–8 and 18–9 with a four-digit, multiplexed common-anode display. A multiplexed display requires only one driver circuit. The driver circuit provides, in this case, a ground for each of the seven segments. Another circuit selects the individual digit by providing a positive voltage to the common-anode terminal for that digit. The digits are energized rapidly one after the other. At the moment a digit is energized, the segment driver circuit provides a ground connection for the segments that must be illuminated. For example, if the first digit is a 1, terminals b and c are taken to ground through current-limit resistors while terminal 1 receives a positive voltage. If the second digit is a 3, terminals a, b, g, c, and d are taken to ground through current-limit resistors when terminal 2 receives a positive voltage. In this way, all digits are scanned at a frequency that is high enough so your eye cannot detect any flicker (greater than 20 times per second per digit). The clock rate for a four-digit multiplexed display should be at least 80 Hz, so each digit will be energized at least 20 times per second.

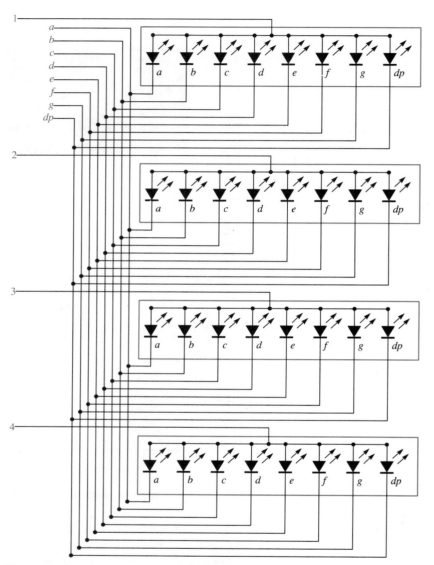

Figure 18–9 Multiplex wiring of seven-segment common-anode LED displays.

Multiplexed 5 × 7 Alphanumeric Displays

Figure 18–10 illustrates a display device that can be used to display numbers or letters. This is described as an alphanumeric display. It is made of seven rows and five columns of dot LEDs. This display is a 5 × 7 dot matrix in which the dot LEDs are multiplexed. Each alphanumeric display requires a 5 × 7 multiplex driver that energizes individual dot LEDs the same way digits and segments are selected in multiplexed seven-segment displays. For example, the third dot LED in the second row is energized by making row-terminal 2 positive and column-terminal 3 negative.

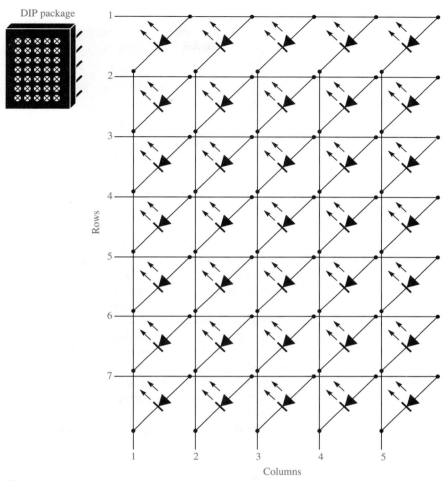

Figure 18–10 5 × 7 alphanumeric LED display.

ELECTROLUMINESCENT PANELS

Electroluminescent panels are thin panels that radiate light evenly from their entire surface. They are used as backlighting on control panels and as backlighting for liquid-crystal displays, and are called *electroluminescent panels* because they become **luminescent** (emit light) when the thin phosphor inner layer is excited by an alternating difference of potential on the two surfaces. Luminescence in the presence of the excitation voltage is known as **fluorescence** and luminescence that continues after the excitation is removed is called **phosphorescence.**

Figure 18–11 shows the construction of a typical electroluminescent panel. A thin layer of phosphor is sandwiched between two panels. At least one of the panels is transparent; it may be flexible plastic or glass. The inside surface of each outer panel is coated with a transparent conductive coating such as indium tin oxide. A terminal is affixed in contact with the coating.

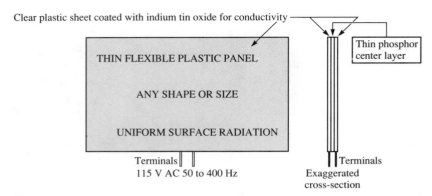

Figure 18–11 Electroluminescent panels.

The sandwich construction forms a capacitor, the phosphor being the dielectric and the indium tin oxide the plates.

AC must be applied for continuous luminescence. With each alternation, electrons in the phosphor are excited to a higher energy level. As the electrons fall back to their normal static state, the material fluoresces and energy is released as light. A fresh supply of excited electrons is generated with each alternation.

The frequency of the applied AC is normally in the range of 50 Hz to 400 Hz, with the brightest luminescence at 400 Hz. The frequency not only affects brightness, but color of light as well (wavelength).

Even though the panel requires a relatively high voltage (100 to 150 V), because the panel is a capacitor operating at a low frequency, the power dissipated by the panel is very low. The capacitive reactance is very high and the leakage current is very low. Operating current is usually in the neighborhood of only 0.7 mA per square inch. A 5-in. by 10-in. panel would draw only about 35 mA at 115 V AC. That's only 4 W of power dissipated over a large surface.

Electroluminescent panels can be made in a great variety of shapes as well as size and color of emission, which makes them useful for a multitude of applications—from exit signs to backlighting computer displays. Electroluminescent panels make a significant contribution to the readability of liquid-crystal displays (coming up next).

LIQUID-CRYSTAL DISPLAYS (LCDs)

LCD Advantages and Disadvantages

Liquid-crystal displays (LCDs) have replaced LED displays in virtually all portable equipment, especially calculators and hand-held test equipment. There are two significant reasons for this: First, LCDs consume only a fraction of the power consumed by LED displays. They operate in the approximate range of 2 to 8 V AC at 20 to 60 Hz and draw only microamps of current. (DC is not used to energize the LCD because internal electrolysis would take place, deteriorating the display.) Second, LCDs can be configured for graphics and special symbols far more easily than LEDs can be employed. The biggest disadvantage of the LCD is slow recovery time (usually in the range of 100 to 200 ms) when an activating voltage is removed.

Basic LCD Construction

Figure 18–12 illustrates the construction of a seven-segment twisted nematic liquid-crystal display. The front panel is a polarized glass panel that has nearly invisible metal-oxide segments deposited on the inside surface. Very thin metal oxide traces connect the segments to external terminals. The next layer is the very thin nematic liquid-crystal layer, which is contained with a perimeter seal. The third layer is a second polarized glass panel that has the same segment patterns deposited on its inside surface. This time, all of the segments are electrically tied together and connect to a common terminal. The back of this glass panel can be silvered to create a mirror to reflect light back out through the display or the glass can be left clear and an electroluminescent panel can be used for backlighting.

Twisted Nematic LCD Theory of Operation

So how does the LCD work? If you have an LCD calculator and a pair of polarized sunglasses, or a polarizing filter for your camera, you can demonstrate to yourself how the LCD works. Look at your calculator's LCD display through your polarized sunglasses (calculator off). As you do so, rotate your sunglasses. What happens? At some point in rotation, the entire LCD screen becomes very dark. Why? The front glass panel of the display is polarized. When the polarization of your glasses and the display are crossed at a right angle, nearly all light is blocked from passing. This is because light reflected from the display is polarized in one direction and can only pass through a filter of the same polarization. Now let's apply this to two common types of LCDs—transmissive and reflective.

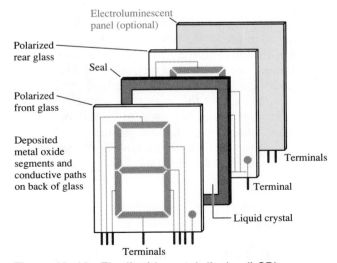

Figure 18–12   The liquid-crystal display (LCD).

Transmissive Twisted Nematic LCDs

Transmissive LCDs are backlighted displays. The front glass and the rear glass of the display are polarized the same direction—we'll say horizontally. Light emitted from the rear electroluminescent panel becomes horizontally polarized as it passes through the rear glass. The pinlike crystals in the liquid-crystal medium are naturally structured in a spiral fashion. The light follows these spirals and changes polarization by 90° before it reaches the front glass. By the time the light reaches the horizontally polarized front glass, it has become vertically polarized and cannot pass through. Therefore, the entire display is darkened and light is blocked.

When a small difference of potential is applied to corresponding front and back metal-oxide segments of the display, the tiny pinlike crystals of the liquid-crystal medium break from their spiral structure and align with the electric field. That means the light in the area of the segments is *not* rotated by 90°. The polarization remains horizontal from rear to front and light passes through the front glass. Thus, the energized segments appear illuminated and the surrounding area is dark. This is the kind of liquid-crystal display used on some portable computers.

Reflective Twisted Nematic LCDs

Reflective LCDs have a mirror coating on the back of the rear glass and the rear lighting is not used. Also, the polarization of the front glass is opposite that of the rear glass. Say the front glass is horizontally polarized and the inside surface of the rear glass is vertically polarized. With no segments energized, light enters the front glass and becomes horizontally polarized. Light then travels through the spiraled crystals and becomes vertically polarized. This matches the rear-glass polarization, so the light passes through the rear glass and reflects off of the mirror coating. The light comes back through the spiraled crystals and rotates to again match the horizontal polarization of the front glass. The light exits the front glass making the entire display appear light in color.

When a small difference of potential is applied to corresponding segments on the inside of the front and rear glass, the spiral pattern of the crystals is broken and entering light, being horizontally polarized, is not able to get through the vertical polarization of the rear glass. That means the light cannot get to the rear mirror surface to be reflected back to the front. Thus, the area behind the energized segment appears dark. This is the kind of liquid-crystal display used in calculators, watches, hand-held test equipment, and some portable computers.

Time for a pause and review. Go back and review this section and answer the questions of Self-Check 18–2.

Self-Check 18–2

1. Compare the emission characteristics of the planar-diffused-surface LED to the etched-well LED.
2. What causes an LED to emit light?
3. Which LED structure emits the most concentrated beam?

4. Using Figure 18–8, describe how the *g* segment of the third digit is energized.

5. What is the difference between reflective and transmissive liquid-crystal displays?

18–3 LIGHT-ACTIVATED DEVICES

INTRODUCTION TO PHOTODETECTORS

In this section, you will explore the complement of photoemitters, photodetectors. Photodetectors are light-activated, or light-controlled, devices. You will discover that there are many different types of photodetectors and that they are suitable for many different applications. In terms of wavelength of light response or **spectral response,** some photodetectors are broadbanded while others are narrowbanded. Nearly every semiconductor device covered in earlier chapters has been adapted by manufacturers for light activation or photodetection. You will explore the more common ones here.

PHOTORESISTORS

Introduction

A photoresistor, also known as a *photoconductive cell,* is a simple flat-surface device whose between-terminal resistance varies with impinging light intensity. Figure 18–13 shows a common encased photoresistor. The zigzag pattern seen on the substrate is a photosensitive material—usually cadmium sulphide (CdS) or cadmium selenide (CdSe). The metal case and glass cover provide for environmental protection and ease of mounting. Photoresistors are available in a variety of cases and even without cases.

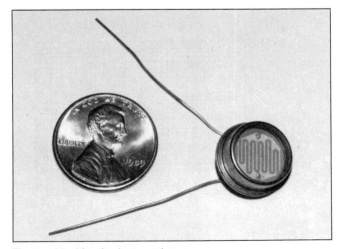

Figure 18–13 A photoresistor.

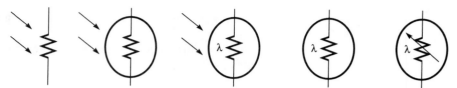

Figure 18–14 Common photoresistor symbols.

Schematic Symbols

Like many devices, there is a wide variation in commonly used schematic symbols. Figure 18–14 illustrates these common variations. The lambda symbol (λ) next to the resistor is for wavelength, which implies that the resistor is wavelength sensitive. The arrows, of course, indicate light rays or incoming radiation. On occasion, you will see these arrows drawn squiggly instead of straight.

Light vs Resistance

Figure 18–15 graphically shows the relationship between impinging light intensity and resistance. Notice that resistance is the inverse of light intensity. As you can see, the light intensity is in units of lm/m^2 which is lux. Recall that 1 lux = 0.0929 fc, 100 lux = 100 lm/m^2 = 9.29 fc, and so on. You should be aware of these conversions (Table 18–1) because different manufacturers may use different units and you may have to do a conversion to compare the performance of devices. At an impinging intensity of 1 lux, this particular photoresistor has a resistance of approximately 12 kΩ. In total darkness, the resistance, often specified as the **dark resistance** for the photoresistor, would be even higher. From the graph (Figure 18–15) the resistance can be approximated for any level of impinging light. Consider Example 18–6.

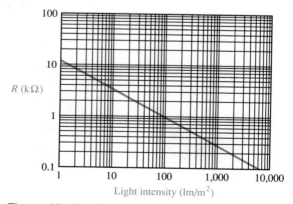

Figure 18–15 Resistance vs light intensity.

EXAMPLE 18–6

Determine the meter current for the light-meter circuit of Figure 18–16.

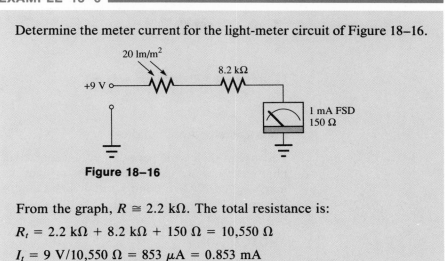

Figure 18–16

From the graph, $R \cong 2.2$ kΩ. The total resistance is:

$R_t = 2.2$ kΩ + 8.2 kΩ + 150 Ω = 10,550 Ω

$I_t = 9$ V/10,550 Ω = 853 μA = 0.853 mA

Photoresistor Spectral Response

Figure 18–17 graphically illustrates the spectral response for cadmium sulfide and cadmium selenide photoresistors. As you can see, the CdS cell is most sensitive at 570 nm and the CdSe cell is most sensitive to 700-nm visible light. Both cells respond well to variations in white light, since all wavelengths of visible light are contained in white light.

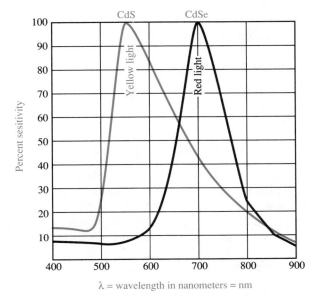

Figure 18–17 Spectral response for CdS and CdSe photoresistors.

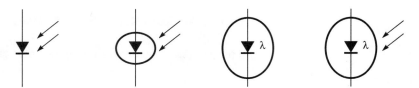

Figure 18–18   Photodiode symbols.

Photoresistor Applications

Because of their wide variation in resistance with changes in light intensity, photoresistors are useful as sensors in light meters, burglar alarms, automatic light ON/OFF control circuits and autoexposure control circuits for cameras.

PHOTODIODES

Introduction

Photodiodes are diodes whose junctions are exposed to light, usually through a small glass window or lens. They are operated in reverse bias making use of the reverse-bias leakage current. Recall that this reverse-bias leakage current in regular diodes is mostly a function of temperature—as temperature increases, leakage current increases. The same is also true for photodiodes. However, in addition to thermal effects, photodiode leakage current is excited by impinging light, or photon bombardment.

The photodiode is a very fast device, turning on and off very quickly with light impulses. By contrast, the photoresistor is very slow. Photodiode response time is in the nanoseconds compared to tens, even hundreds, of milliseconds for photoresistors.

Schematic Symbols

As shown in Figure 18–18, we once again see a variety of symbols used to represent a device. Again, the arrows and/or lambda symbol indicate the diode is light sensitive or light activated.

Photodiode Structure and Operation

Figure 18–19 shows the layer structure of the typical photodiode. As you can see, the diode is reverse biased. Leakage current is encouraged by the impinging light as the light imparts energy to the atomic structure of the top p layer. Electrons migrate from the p layer through the junction to the n layer and exit at the cathode terminal. Current is in the microamps.

Photodiode Case Styles

Case styles vary widely for photodiodes, as for other devices. Figure 18–20 illustrates a few of the common case styles available today. Case styles are created by the manufacturer to match particular applications. For example,

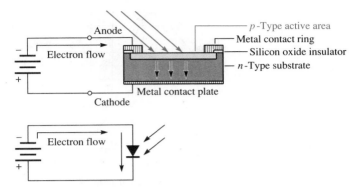

Figure 18–19 Photodiode structure and operation.

Figure 18–20 Common photodiode case styles.

case 209 is used for open-air applications in which light is received through the air, while cases 210 and 349 are most often used for interfacing with fiber-optic systems.

Reverse Current vs Light Intensity

Figure 18–21 illustrates the light response of a typical photodiode, the MRD500. This set of characteristic curves demonstrates the reverse conduc-

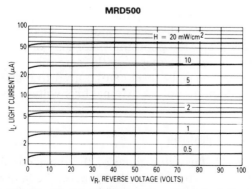

Figure 18–21 Photodiode characteristic curves. (Copyright by Motorola, Inc. Used by permission.)

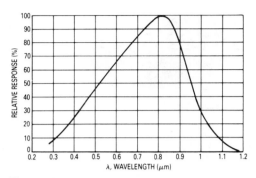

Figure 18–22 MRD500 spectral response. (Copyright by Motorola, Inc. Used by permission.)

tivity of the diode at different levels of impinging light. The units used for light intensity are mW/cm². These are radiometric units and are used because this diode is most sensitive at an invisible infrared wavelength. As shown in Figure 18–22, the MRD500 is most sensitive at approximately 810 nm. Notice also, from Figure 18–21, that the reverse voltage capability is very high, a maximum of 100 V for the MRD500. Also, the amount of reverse voltage has very little to do with the amount of reverse leakage current. At an intensity of 2 mW/cm², the reverse current, also called **light current (I_L),** is almost constant at 6 μA for any amount of reverse voltage from 10 to 100 V. It is mainly light intensity that determines the bias condition of the diode, not to exclude some temperature sensitivity as well.

Photodiode Applications

Photodiodes are used as detectors in the receivers of infrared remote-control systems and as detectors at the receiving end of fiber-optic systems.

PHOTOTRANSISTORS

Introduction

Phototransistors are transistors that have their collector–base junction exposed to light through a glass window or lens. Case styles are the same as for photodiodes, and the phototransistor may or may not have a base terminal. Collector current increases with increasing impinging light intensity. A steady quiescent light level can be used to bias the transistor at a specific operating point and/or an external bias voltage via the base terminal can be used.

Schematic Symbols

Figure 18–23 illustrates some of the most common phototransistor schematic symbols. Though not shown here, the lambda symbol (λ) may also be used. Phototransistors are available as Darlingtons as well as single transistors.

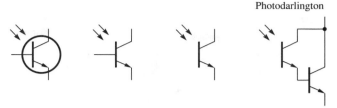

Figure 18–23 Phototransistor symbols.

Phototransistor Structure and Operation

Figure 18–24 shows the layer diagram for the phototransistor. Notice the similarity to the photodiode. However, in this case, external voltage (V_{CE}) is applied, just as for a regular transistor. The base region is very thin and its conductivity increases with light, causing a base current to flow. Naturally, this light-stimulated base current causes an amplified increase in collector current. The output is taken from the collector in the common-emitter configuration just as it would be for a regular transistor.

Due to current amplification, the phototransistor is more sensitive to light than the photodiode. However, the phototransistor is generally slower in response to impulse light than a photodiode is, because the base region is very thin, which makes collector to emitter capacitance relatively high. Response times for phototransistors are in the tens of microseconds compared to a few nanoseconds for photodiodes. For this reason, most high-speed fiber-optic data systems use photodiode detectors followed by conventional high-speed amplifiers.

Figure 18–25 illustrates the phototransistor's response to varying levels of light intensity. Figure 18–25b looks very similar to the characteristic curves for a conventional transistor. Instead of showing collector curves at various base current levels, this graph shows collector curves at different levels of light intensity. Like regular transistors, load lines can be drawn and the quiescent bias point can be determined to suit the application. The light intensity sets the Q point. Standard collector curves are also provided on data sheets for three-terminal phototransistors, so the Q-point can be set using a conventional bias scheme.

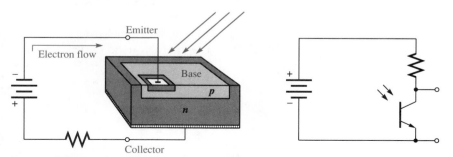

Figure 18–24 Phototransistor structure and operation.

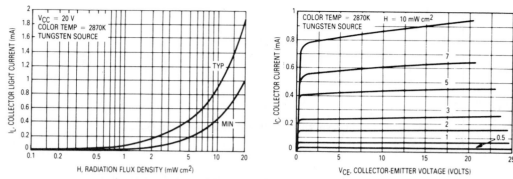

Figure 18–25 MRD150 characteristic curves. (Copyright by Motorola, Inc. Used by permission.)

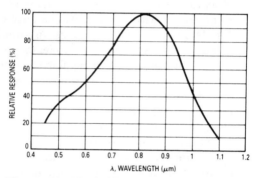

Figure 18–26 MRD150 spectral response. (Copyright by Motorola, Inc. Used by permission.)

Figure 18–26 shows the spectral response for the MRD150 phototransistor. The response is very broad, accommodating half of the visible light spectrum and peaking at 820 nm in the infrared area. This spectral response is typical of many phototransistors.

Let's look at Examples 18–7 and 18–8, which make use of the MRD150 and its characteristic curves.

EXAMPLE 18–7

Determine the output voltage for the optoamplifier circuit of Figure 18–27. Use the characteristic curves for the MRD150.

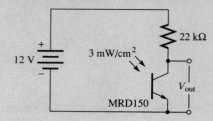

Figure 18–27

At an impinging intensity of 3 mW/cm^2, the collector current is approximately 0.25 mA. The voltage drop across the collector resistor is 0.25 mA · 22 kΩ = 5.5 V. Therefore, the collector–emitter voltage must be 12 V − 5.5 V = 6.5 V.

EXAMPLE 18–8

Determine the light intensity necessary to securely energize the relay in Figure 18–28.

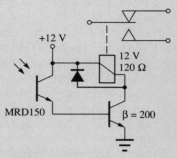

Figure 18–28

The relay requires 12 V/120 Ω = 100 mA of current. The driver transistor has a $\beta_{DC} = 200$. For the driver to supply 100 mA to the relay, the base current must be 100 mA/200 = 0.5 mA. In other words, 0.5 mA of base current is needed to saturate the driver transistor. The MRD150 must supply this base current. According to the characteristic curves, the impinging light intensity must be at least 6 mW/cm^2 for an MRD150 collector–emitter current of 0.5 mA.

LIGHT-ACTIVATED SCHMITT TRIGGERS

General Description

Figure 18–29 shows the case style for the MRD750 and its corresponding schematic symbol (excluding the resistor). This optoelectronic device is a Schmitt trigger, also referred to as a *logic output device*. The external resis-

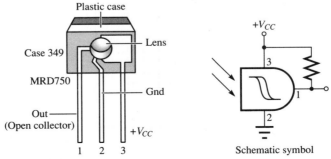

Figure 18–29 MRD750 light-activated Schmitt trigger.

tor from pin 1 to 3 is necessary for the MRD750, since it is an open-collector device. When light of a high enough intensity impinges on the lens, the circuit triggers and the output (pin 1) goes low (near ground). Pin 1 will not return high until the impinging light drops below a certain level, a level that is lower than the initial trigger level. This optohysteresis is graphically represented in Figure 18–30.

Normalized Transfer Characteristics

Figure 18–30 is a normalized graph. That means the gradations are factors representing a percentage of a specified value. In this case, the data sheet for the MRD750 indicates that the light required to trigger the device on is typically 0.5 mW/cm². Therefore, the 1 on the horizontal axis represents 0.5 mW/cm². The MRD750 turns off when the light drops to approximately 75% of the normal. Thus, when the incident light drops below 0.75 · 0.5 mW/cm² = 0.375 mW/cm², the device turns off and the output goes high. The vertical scale of the graph is normalized to whatever the DC supply voltage is. If the supply voltage is +5 V, the 1 represents +5 V, 0.8 represents +4 V, 0.5 represents +2.5 V, and so on.

Light-Activated Schmitt Trigger Applications

Light-activated Schmitt triggers are used in noisy optoelectronic environments where incoming light is noisy in the form of sporadic intensity variations. As long as the intensity variations are small, the Schmitt trigger will make stable logic choices (choices between a high or low output). A practical use for the light-activated Schmitt trigger would be to activate a control circuit that turns on street lights at dusk. This would provide some immunity to false triggering from ambient light reflections and cloud/sun shadowing at sunset.

LIGHT-ACTIVATED THYRISTORS

General Description

SCRs and TRIACs have also been adapted as photodetectors. Light-activated SCRs (**LASCR**s) and light-activated TRIACs (**LATRIAC**s) are illus-

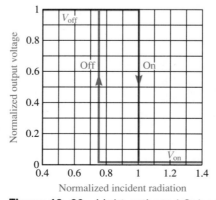

Figure 18–30   Light-activated Schmitt trigger transfer characteristics.

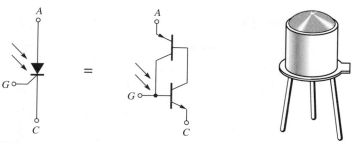

Figure 18–31   Light-activated SCR (LASCR).

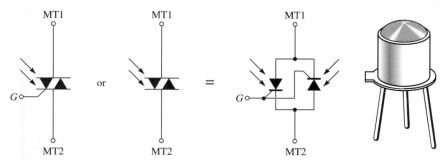

Figure 18–32   Light-activated TRIAC (LATRIAC).

trated in Figures 18–31 and 18–32. In each case, the gate terminal may or may not be present in the schematic symbol or on the actual device. These devices are also available in many different case styles. The principles of operation are the same as for other photodetectors and standard thyristors. A light threshold is reached that increases the internal loop gain of the thyristor to one (1). At that point, the thyristor latches on. The thyristor remains on until anode or main-terminal current drops below the holding value.

Photothyristor Applications

Photothyristors are low-power devices designed for medium and high-voltage applications at very low current levels. Their main purpose is to trigger larger, conventional heavy-duty thyristors in AC circuits. Figure 18–33 is an

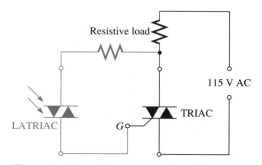

Figure 18–33   LATRIAC application.

example. The LATRIAC supplies gate current to the TRIAC to trigger it on when the incident light is at threshold or higher. As long as the impinging light is intense enough, the LATRIAC triggers with every AC cycle and so does the TRIAC. The LATRIAC/TRIAC combination serves as a light-activated relay for AC load control.

We'll look at more photothyristor applications in the next section as we discuss optocouplers. For now, review this section and answer the questions of Self-Check 18–3.

Self-Check 18–3

1. Which of these has the fastest response time to a light pulse?
   (a) photoresistor   (b) photodiode   (c) phototransistor
2. Which color LED would be the best light source for a CdS photo-resistor?
   (a) green LED   (b) yellow LED   (c) red LED
3. List two applications for photodiodes.
4. Are photodiodes operated in (a) forward bias, or (b) reverse bias?
5. At a V_{CE} of 10 V, what amount of light intensity does an MRD150 need to produce 600 μA of collector current?
6. Explain optohysteresis for a light-activated Schmitt trigger.
7. What is the intended purpose for photothyristors?

18–4 OPTOCOUPLERS AND OPTOINTERRUPTERS

INTRODUCTION TO OPTOISOLATORS

An **optoisolator** is a hybrid integrated circuit that includes an LED on one side and a photodetector on the other. The entire IC is hermetically sealed and lighttight. It is called an *optoisolator* because it is used to electrically isolate a low-voltage circuit from a high-voltage circuit or one low-voltage circuit from another. A low-voltage control circuit is used to energize the LED. Light from the LED is then optically coupled to the detector, which is used to control a secondary circuit. For this reason, optoisolators are also called **optocouplers** or optical coupling devices.

Optoisolators isolate sensitive circuits, such as computer chips, from the hazards associated with controlling high-voltage and high-power circuits. They offer the advantages of separating high-voltage circuits from low-voltage circuits, blocking power circuit voltage spikes from returning to the control circuit, and preventing ground loop problems in data and control systems. They are capable of safely isolating 5-V computer circuits from hundreds of volts in the output circuit. Optoisolators are also relatively inexpensive, take up little space, and greatly simplify control circuitry.

Figure 18–34 illustrates the most popular optoisolator package, the six-pin DIP. Also shown is a sampling of the many optoisolator LED to detector combinations. You are already familiar with these photodetectors as discrete devices. Table 18–2 is a listing of some common optoisolators. Now, let's take a closer look at some of these optoisolators with some applications.

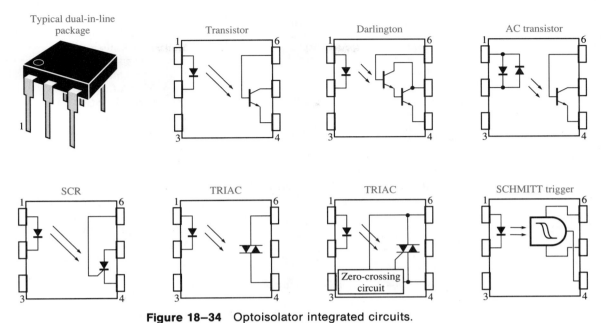

Figure 18–34   Optoisolator integrated circuits.

TABLE 18–2   OPTOISOLATORS

Type	Description	Significant Ratings
4N38	Transistor Output	$I_{F(max)}$ = 80 mA (LED) I_C/I_F typically 0.5 to 0.9 7,500 V peak isolation V_{CEO} = 80 V, $I_{C(max)}$ = 100 mA $P_{D(max)}$ = 150 mW (transistor)
H11D1	Transistor Output	$I_{F(max)}$ = 60 mA (LED) I_C/I_F typically 0.3 to 0.7 7,500 V peak isolation V_{CEO} = 300 V, $I_{C(max)}$ = 100 mA $P_{D(max)}$ = 150 mW (transistor)
H11B1	Darlington Output	$I_{F(max)}$ = 60 mA (LED) I_C/I_F typically 10 to 15 7,500 V peak isolation V_{CEO} = 25 V, $I_{C(max)}$ = 100 mA $P_{D(max)}$ = 150 mW (transistor)
MOC119	Darlington Output	$I_{F(max)}$ = 60 mA (LED) I_C/I_F typically 8 to 12 7,500 V peak isolation V_{CEO} = 30 V, $I_{C(max)}$ = 150 mA $P_{D(max)}$ = 150 mW (transistor)

(Table continues)

TABLE 18–2   *(continued)*

Type	Description	Significant Ratings
4N40	SCR Output	$I_{F(max)} = 60$ mA (LED) $I_{FT} = 30$ mA (max LED current to trigger the SCR) 7,500 V peak isolation $V_{DM(max)} = 200$ V peak (SCR) $I_{T(RMS)} = 300$ mA (SCR) $P_{D(max)} = 400$ mW (SCR)
MOC3009	TRIAC Output	$I_{F(max)} = 60$ mA (LED) $I_{FT} = $ typically 15 mA (LED current to trigger the TRIAC) 7,500 V peak isolation $V_{DRM(max)} = 250$ V peak (TRIAC) $P_{D(max)} = 300$ mW (TRIAC)
MOC3041	TRIAC Output	$I_{F(max)} = 60$ mA (LED) $I_{FT} = 15$ mA (max LED current to trigger the TRIAC) 7,500 V peak isolation $V_{DRM(max)} = 400$ V peak (TRIAC) $P_{D(max)} = 150$ mW (TRIAC)
MOC5007	Logic–Schmitt Trigger	$I_{F(max)} = 60$ mA (LED) $I_{F(on)}$ typically 1 mA (output low) $I_{F(off)}$ typically 0.75 mA (output high) 7,500 V peak isolation Supply Voltage = 3 to 16 V Output Current = 50 mA (max) $P_{D(max)} = 150$ mW (Schmitt)

TRANSISTOR-OUTPUT OPTOISOLATORS

Current Transfer Ratio

Transistor-output optoisolators are available in a wide range of output transistor parameters both in single and Darlington configurations. The transistor can be biased in one or both of two ways: make use of the base terminal and/or apply a forward current to the LED. Data sheets for these optoisolators provide collector curve graphs for both I_C/I_F and I_C/I_B relationships. However, the primary intention for these devices is that forward LED current (input) controls the transistor collector current (output). The equivalent of β_{DC} for these devices is the DC **current transfer ratio** (β_{CTR}) which is I_C/I_F. As you can see from Table 18–2, this ratio can be anything from 0.3 to 15. Single-transistor devices usually have a current transfer ratio in the range of 0.2 to 1 and Darlingtons are usually in the range of 5 to 20. The transfer ratio is often expressed as a percent (0.7 = 70% and 5 = 500%, and so on).

$$\beta_{CTR} = I_C/I_F \tag{18–3}$$

$$I_F = I_C/\beta_{CTR} \tag{18–4}$$

Characteristic Curves

Figure 18–35 shows two transfer graphs that are normally available on data sheets. Notice that these graphs clearly demonstrate the relationship between forward LED current (I_F) and resulting collector current (I_C). From the graphs, you can see that the transfer ratio is not constant for all values of I_F. Also, the transfer ratio varies somewhat from one device to the other. The graphs provided are intended as a guide demonstrating typical characteristics.

Transistor Optoisolator Applications

Transistor optoisolators can be operated as switching devices or as linear devices, in which case an audio signal riding on a DC bias is applied to the LED and optically transferred to the output transistor. This would be used in a situation where circuit isolation or extreme input–output buffering is necessary.

Example 18–9 is a typical application for the transistor optoisolator. This is an application in which the output transistor is operated as a switch to activate the relay. Notice the 5-V computer circuit is easily interfaced to the 24-V relay circuit. LED current must be high enough to saturate the transistor. What value should R be?

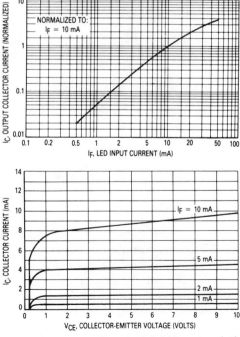

Figure 18–35 4N38 transfer characteristics. (Copyright by Motorola, Inc. Used by permission.)

EXAMPLE 18–9 ▬▬▬▬▬▬▬

If the current transfer ratio for the 4N38 of Figure 18–36 is 0.6, what is the maximum value for R?

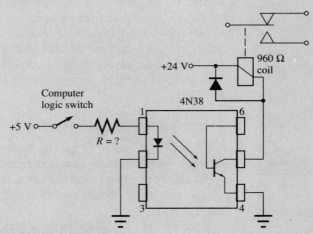

Figure 18–36

First, determine the relay coil current:

$I_{coil} = I_C = 24$ V/960 Ω = 25 mA

With a transfer ratio of 0.6, the LED current must be:

$I_F = I_C/0.6 = 25$ mA/0.6 = 41.7 mA   (25 mA/41.7 mA = 0.6)

Assume the LED forward voltage drop to be 1.5 V. Then,

$R = (5$ V $- 1.5$ V)/41.7 mA = 84 Ω

Use an 82-Ω resistor making $I_F = (5$ V $- 1.5$ V)/82 Ω = 42.7 mA.

THYRISTOR-OUTPUT OPTOISOLATORS

General Description

As you know, thyristor-output optoisolators are those that have an LASCR or LATRIAC for an output device. These devices make it very easy to interface sensitive low-voltage computer circuits to noisy, spike-ridden, high-voltage AC control circuits. In addition to the obvious design considerations regarding output device voltage, current, and power dissipation, a primary design consideration is the amount of LED current needed to insure reliable triggering. This is specified as I_{FT}, forward LED trigger current. Consider Example 18–10.

EXAMPLE 18–10

Determine the maximum value of R that will insure reliable triggering of the 4N40 in Figure 18–37. I_{FT} is specified as a maximum required value of 30 mA.

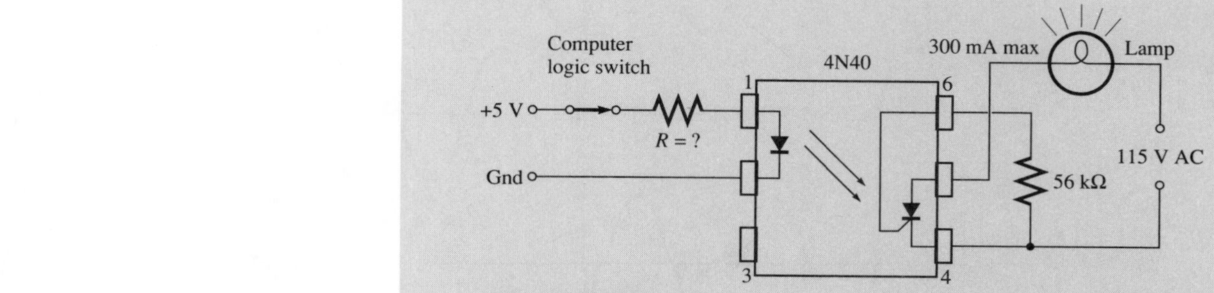

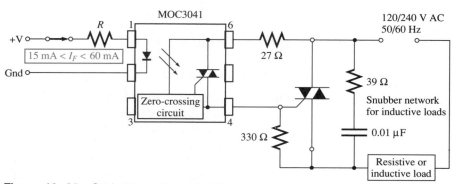

Figure 18–37

Assume a 1.5-V forward voltage drop for the LED.

$R = (5 \text{ V} - 1.5 \text{ V})/30 \text{ mA} = 117 \text{ }\Omega$

Use 110 Ω, making $I_{FT} = (5 \text{ V} - 1.5 \text{ V})/110 \text{ }\Omega = 31.8 \text{ mA}$

Figure 18–38 shows a very simple computer to high-voltage DC to AC interface. Again, the value of R must be chosen to insure reliable triggering of the LATRIAC. For the MOC3041, the LATRIAC is guaranteed to trigger if the LED current is 15 mA or higher. As before, R is calculated using Ohm's law. In most cases, it is safe to assume the LED will drop approximately 1.5 V. Circuit values and configurations such as this are specified and recommended by the manufacturers in their data sheets and application notes.

Figure 18–38   Optically isolated TRIAC circuit.

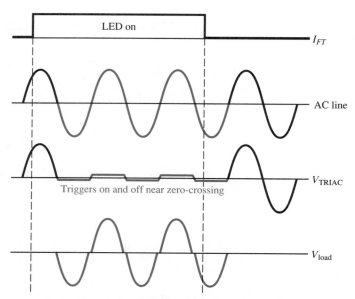

Figure 18–39 Main TRIAC triggers near zero-crossing with the MOC3041 driver.

Zero-Crossing Triggering

The MOC3041 is an example of TRIAC optoisolators that include zero-crossing circuits. This circuit insures that the LATRIAC and the external TRIAC do not trigger when the AC supply voltage is on a peak. Triggering only takes place near zero-crossing. This eliminates surge currents and switching spikes that otherwise would occur.

Figure 18–39 is a timing diagram illustrating the operation of this type of optoisolator. Examine this figure carefully. See how the TRIACs do not trigger on until the LED is on *and* the AC line voltage is near zero. Naturally, the TRIACs remain off after the LED is turned off and the AC line voltage nears zero-crossing, reducing the holding current to zero. Also, realize that the TRIACs trigger on and off with every alternation of the AC line voltage near zero-crossing as long as the LED is on.

OPTOINTERRUPTERS

General Description

Optointerrupters are special kinds of optocouplers. They are designed to permit mechanical interference between the LED and the optodetector. Figure 18–40 shows a variety of common case styles for these devices. In each case, the LED is separated from the optodetector by an air gap or channel.

Figure 18–41 illustrates optointerrupter design more clearly. Usually, the detectors are limited to phototransistors or light-activated Schmitt triggers so ON/OFF output conditions are controlled by a mechanical device that interrupts the light beam between emitter and detector.

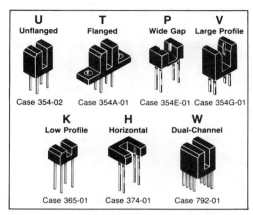

Figure 18–40   Optointerrupters. (Copyright by Motorola, Inc. Used by permission.)

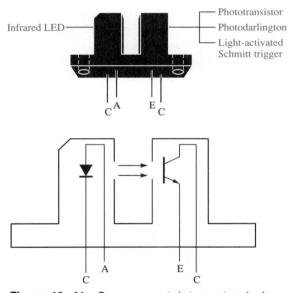

Figure 18–41   Common optointerrupter design.

Optointerrupter Applications

The basic purpose for the optointerrupter is to provide an electromechanical connection or interface. Figure 18–42 is an example of how the optointerrupter might be used. A constant current is applied to the LED, producing a constant light beam from LED to detector. The chopper wheel rapidly interrupts the light beam as it rotates. The output device chops the DC creating a square-wave pulse train. Digital circuitry is then used to count the pulses to determine speed of rotation or to determine the relative position of the wheel.

This is often applied in robotics to determine the distance traveled by the robot as its wheels turn. The robot's computer simply counts the interrup-

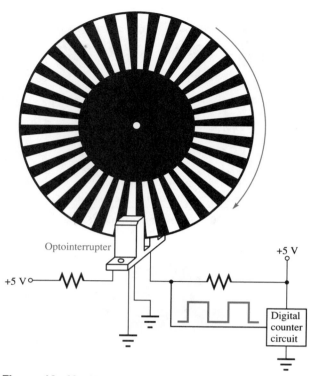

Figure 18–42 Using the optointerrupter to determine speed or position of a rotating shaft.

tions as the wheels turn. In this way, a programmed path of travel is simply a series of numbers the robot's computer uses to compare to the interruption count as each wheel rotates. Power to the drive motor for the wheel is removed when the interruption count matches the number stored in the robot's computer memory.

Optointerrupters are widely used in industry to monitor manufacturing processes. A mechanical blade is used to interrupt the light beam to signify that a specific process has begun or has ended. In this way, the control computer is able to monitor and command the necessary sequence of events.

Self-Check 18–4

1. Explain current transfer ratio as it applies to transistor optoisolators.
2. Discuss a primary design consideration when using optothyristors to interface a computer circuit to an AC power circuit.
3. Why would you want to use an optoisolator to interface a computer to the "outside world"?
4. What type of optoisolator should you use to interface a computer with a 115-V AC light control circuit?
5. What is the general purpose or use for optointerrupters?

18–5 LASERs

INTRODUCTION TO LASERs

L-A-S-E-R

A **laser** is a device that produces **l**ight **a**mplification by **s**timulated **e**mission of **r**adiation. In this section, you will discover what that means and how it is accomplished in three different types of lasers: the semiconductor injection laser, the gas laser, and the solid-crystal laser. Before we consider each of these, it is best that you gain a general understanding of lasers and laser theory.

A Bit of History

In the late 1910s, Albert Einstein was the first to postulate laser concepts. He reasoned that light could be characterized as being made up of particles called **photons.** Further, he theorized that these particles could be collected and concentrated to form powerful pulses of light energy at a specific wavelength. Einstein believed that if a photon collided with an atom that was excited to a higher energy state, the atom would release energy in the form of a photon that was an identical twin to the invading photon. Thus, the quantity of photons would increase, increasing light intensity. His concept of stimulated emission is the basis of modern laser theory.

In the late 1950s and early 1960s, the laser finally came into existence. American scientists Arthur L. Schawlow and Charles H. Townes fully developed practical laser theory in a paper published in 1958. By 1960, Theodore H. Maiman had created the first operational laser. It was a pulsed ruby laser. Ali Javan built and operated the first continuous-wave (CW) helium–neon laser in 1961. Gallium arsenide was used in the first semiconductor injection lasers by several American companies by 1962.

Laser Light Characteristics

Lasers emit intense beams of light. Unlike heat-type light sources such as tungsten lamps, the laser emits a concentrated beam that has very little divergence (spread angle). This means the light rays (paths of travel) are nearly parallel to each other. Parallel light rays are known as **collimated** rays. Laser light is **monochromatic,** meaning the light is all of the same color and wavelength. It is also coherent. **Coherent** light is light that is formed of a large number of light waves that are in phase with each other. Thus, all wavefronts are together and aid each other. These characteristics working together enable the light beam to be very intense and travel a great distance.

Basic Laser Theory

What causes the laser beam to be monochromatic, collimated, and coherent? To answer this question, let's look at the three diagrams of Figure 18–43. In Figure 18–43a, we see that the laser is made of three main parts: the laser

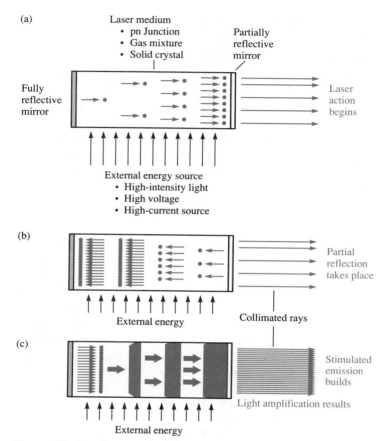

Figure 18–43 Laser principles.

medium, an external source of energy, and reflective end mirrors. The three common laser mediums that we will explore in this section are the *pn* semiconductor junction, a gaseous mixture, and solid crystal. The electrons surrounding the atoms of the medium are excited to a higher energy level by an external energy source. The external energy source is usually high-intensity light, high voltage, or relatively high current. The energy source excites the electrons to higher energy levels. When an electron falls to its original state, energy is released in the form of light (photon emission). This type of light emission is known as **spontaneous emission.** Spontaneous emission is the normal type of light emission that takes place in neon, fluorescent, and incandescent lamps. Spontaneous emission is characterized as being random, scattered, incoherent, and polychromatic—covering a wide portion of the light spectrum.

In a laser, spontaneous emission starts a chain reaction in which emitted photons collide with excited atoms, causing them to release energy in the form of light. In such a case, the atom's electrons are *stimulated* to release their excess energy by the collision. Photons that are released through stimulation collide with other atoms and the chain reaction continues. This process is known as the **stimulated emission of radiation.** When emission is stimulated, each collision produces an additional photon that moves in the same direction as the invading photon. Also, the emitted energy is of the same wavelength.

Stimulated emission is directed through the use of end mirrors. On one end of the laser medium is a fully reflective mirror. On the other end is a partially reflective mirror. The partially reflective mirror reflects 30 to 40% of the light that hits its surface. The area in the medium between the mirrors is a cavity in which photons resonate. This cavity area is known as the **Fabry-Perot resonator.**

As shown in Figure 18–43a, stimulated emission begins by the reflection of a photon or photons from the fully reflective mirror. This reflection is perfectly perpendicular to the mirror surface, sending the photon(s) down the medium toward the partially reflective mirror. Along the way, collisions take place that release more photons in the same direction. The wavefront builds in strength until it exits through the partially reflective mirror. At the partially reflective mirror, some of the photons are reflected back down the medium toward the fully reflective mirror, as shown in Figure 18–43b. Along the way, the wavefront builds, due to stimulated emission. At the fully reflective mirror all photons are reflected in phase and are sent back toward the partially reflective mirror. Because all photons are traveling together in a parallel manner, light intensity is amplified through the repeated process of stimulated emission, as shown in Figure 18–43c. This process takes place in an instant as the lasing action reaches an upper limit determined by the amount of externally applied energy and/or the physical constraints of the medium (such as power dissipation in the form of heat).

THE SEMICONDUCTOR INJECTION LASER

Injection Laser Construction

The semiconductor injection laser, or diode laser, is shown in Figure 18–44, which shows several views of a simplified layer diagram. Gallium arsenide (GaAs) and aluminum gallium arsenide (AlGaAs) are common semiconductor materials used to form the n and p layers of the structure. As you can see, a thin, narrow channel is formed in the depletion region between n and p layers and between two insulating layers forming a light-wave guide. The lower diagram is an internal cross-sectional view that has been greatly exaggerated for clarity. The active region is in the depletion region and is very thin compared to the entire structure. It is in this active region that lasing action through stimulated emissions takes place. On each end of the active region are the mirrors (reflective coatings) necessary to perpetuate the lasing action, forming the Fabry-Perot resonator.

Injection Laser Theory of Operation

With forward bias applied, electrons are injected through the n layer and cross the junction. As the electrons fall into holes in the p material, energy is released as heat and light. This light is spontaneous and incoherent at low-current levels. As forward current is increased, a point is reached at which there are enough excited electrons in the active region for lasing action to

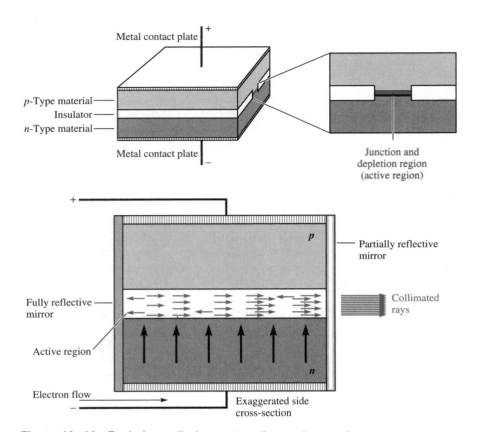

Figure 18–44   Basic laser diode construction and operation.

begin. Photons bounce off the fully reflective mirror and collide with excited electrons, causing stimulated emission of more photons, all heading in the same direction. Amplified light exits the partially reflective end and 30 to 40 percent is reflected back down the channel to continue the lasing action. The emitted light (visible) or radiation (invisible) is coherent and fairly well collimated, though not as well collimated as other types of lasers.

The intensity of the laser beam can be varied by controlling the amount of forward current above the lasing threshold value. In this way, the beam can be intensity modulated to transmit audio, video, and computer data.

Injection Laser Applications

Injection lasers are used in a wide variety of applications. They are at the heart of compact disc (CD) players, supplying a narrow beam that is further concentrated by a lens system. The concentrated beam is bounced off the compact disc's surface, carrying intensity fluctuations that are sensed by a photodetector. The fluctuations of the reflected beam contain digital information that is converted to the original audio or video material using a digital to analog converter. Injection lasers are also used in long-distance fiber-optic communication systems. The laser is used to launch an intensity modulated digital signal down the center of a thin glass fiber that is tens of kilometers long. A photodetector on the receiving end converts the modulated light back to electrical impulses.

THE GAS LASER

Gas Laser Construction

Gas lasers are gas-filled glass or quartz tubes as shown in Figure 18–45. The laser tube consists of a cylindrical outer glass envelope and an inner glass capillary. On one end of the tube is a metal terminal called the anode (+) and on the other end is the cathode terminal (−). At one end is a fully reflective mirror, at the other a partially reflective mirror (usually 35% reflective). The partially reflective mirror, which is the output, may be on either end of the tube, cathode or anode. The tube is evacuated, purged of residual oxygen, and filled with the desired gas mixture. The gas mixture determines the wavelength of the light beam and the output power level. Gases commonly used in laser tubes are helium (He), neon (Ne), carbon dioxide (CO_2), carbon monoxide (CO), argon (Ar), krypton (Kr), and Xenon (Xe).

When the laser tube is enclosed in a protective aluminum cylinder with insulated electrode caps and high-voltage leads, it is referred to as a **laser head.** The laser head may also include a special safety shutter at the output end of the tube. This shutter must be opened for operation and helps prevent accidental eye damage. When the laser tube is mounted in an elongated aluminum box that also contains the laser's power supply, it is referred to as a *self-contained laser system.*

Gas Laser Theory of Operation

A high voltage is applied to the anode and cathode of the tube, usually in the range of 5,000 to 10,000 V. This high voltage ionizes the gas in the tube as in a neon lamp. The gas begins to emit light spontaneously and reflections between the two mirrors begin. Instantly, the tube shifts to the stimulated-emission mode in the bore of the tube within the capillary between the two mirrors. Photons collide with excited electrons, releasing more photons in the same direction. Light intensity builds as amplification through stimulated emission takes place. The majority of the beam (65%) exits the tube via the partially reflective mirror, while 35% is reflected back down the capillary to compound and amplify the light intensity with greatly multiplied stimulated

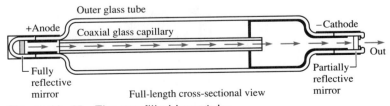

Figure 18–45 The gas-filled laser tube.

emissions. The lasing action almost instantly reaches a maximum intensity and a highly collimated and continuous beam escapes the output port.

Once the lasing action has begun, the operating voltage is reduced to as little as one tenth of the starting voltage. Usually, the operating voltage is in the range of 700 to 3,000 V for the common helium–neon (HeNe) lasers. Operating current is usually only a few milliamps to tens of milliamps for HeNe lasers. The gas laser beam is less divergent than the diode laser beam and can be at a much higher power level, depending on gas mix and construction. Output power levels range up to 75 mW continuous wave (CW) for HeNe lasers to thousands of watts continuous wave for CO_2 lasers.

Gas Laser Applications

Gas lasers are used in laser radar systems, missile guidance systems, targeting systems, fiber-optic systems, point-to-point communication systems (such as satellite to submarine), medical diagnostics and surgery, road grading and ground leveling, light shows for entertainment, and many many more applications.

THE SOLID CRYSTAL LASER

Crystal Laser Construction

Figure 18–46 illustrates the basic construction of a crystal laser, in this case a ruby-rod crystal laser. The construction is simple. A ruby rod is encased by a coiled high-power flash tube. A mounting block holds the coiled flash tube and ruby rod in position. The ruby rod has a silver coating at the mounting end and a partial coating at the output end.

Crystal Laser Theory of Operation

Ruby is a fluorescent crystal of aluminum oxide (Al_2O_3) doped with chromium (Cr). It emits light when the chromium atoms are excited by high-intensity light pulses. High-voltage pulses are used to repeatedly fire the flash tube. When the flash tube fires, chromium atoms in the ruby rod become excited. Electrons falling back to their normal state spontaneously emit photons. Some of the photons are emitted parallel to the length of the

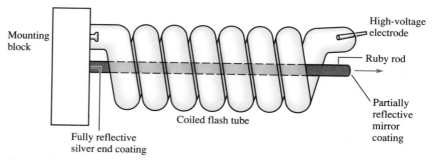

Figure 18–46 Solid-crystal ruby-rod laser.

rod. This sets the stage for stimulated emissions. Within an instant, photons are reflected from each end of the rod and stimulated emissions build to a powerful pulse that exits the partially reflective end. Each flash of the flash tube produces a powerful deep red laser pulse from the ruby rod ($\lambda = 694.3$ nm). This is known as **optical pumping.**

Some solid-crystal lasers are designed to operate in the continuous-wave (CW) mode using a continuous high-intensity light source. Light sources used for continuous operation are tungsten-halogen lamps and mercury, krypton, or xenon arc lamps.

Crystal Laser Applications

Crystal lasers are among the most powerful of all lasers. With a concentrating lens system, they can be used to cut through thick steel plates and diamond. Pinpoint areas at temperatures in excess of 5,500°C are possible. Crystal lasers are used for precision welding and cutting of metals. They also have potential in missile-defense weapons.

Scratching the Surface

Be aware that we have only covered a small portion of the world of lasers in this section. There are many variations to what we have covered here. There are many types of laser diodes including arrays and stacks of laser diodes for high-power performance. Also, there are many design variations in gas and solid lasers—and we have not even mentioned liquid lasers, glass lasers, chemical lasers, and dynamic gas lasers. For now, it is sufficient for you to have a basic understanding of laser technology as presented here. Take time to review this section and answer the questions of Self-Check 18–5.

Self-Check 18–5

1. LASER is an acronym for what?
2. What is the difference between spontaneous emission and stimulated emission?
3. What is the purpose for the partially reflective mirror in a laser?
4. What is coherent light?
5. What is collimated light?
6. Which laser type is used for fiber-optic communications?

18–6 OPTOELECTRONIC DEVICES FOR FIBER OPTICS

INTRODUCTION TO FIBER OPTICS

The purpose for this section is not to cover the subject of fiber optics, but to consider fiber optics as a predominant application for devices we have already discussed. The very broad topic of fiber optics will be covered in great detail in a later course and text. Here, I simply want to introduce you to the basic fiber-optic system so you will have a better understanding of how many optoelectronic devices are used. I will also introduce you to a recent innovation in fiber-optic devices, the semiconductor optical amplifier. This section is meant to be very incomplete.

A BASIC FIBER-OPTIC LINK

Basic Link Description

Figure 18–47 illustrates a very practical, low-cost, short-distance, one-way (simplex), fiber-optic data link. The overall link consists of three main parts: a photoemitter on the transmitting end (left), a photodetector on the receiving end (right), and a fiber-optic cable linking the two.

Notice on the far left a data processor, such as a computer, feeds ON/OFF (high/low) digital data to a modulator circuit. The modulator is simply the transistor that drives the photoemitter, which is the modulated device. The photoemitter rapidly turns on and off as the data is fed to it via the modulator. Light pulses, representing digital data, are launched from the emitter's lens into the end of the relatively thin optical fiber.

In this case, the optical fiber, at the center of the optical cable, is not so thin. 1,000 microns (μm) is considered to be thick for an optical fiber but is typical for low-speed, short-distance systems. High-speed systems use glass fibers less than 100 microns in diameter.

The light pulses are guided down the inside of the fiber to the receiving end. At the receiving end, the light is coupled to the lens of the detector and is concentrated on the surface of the detector chip. The photodetector, acting as a demodulator, converts the light pulses back to electrical voltage pulses, which are amplified to the correct level and fed into the signal processor (receiving computer or terminal).

Fiber-Optic Low-Cost System Link (FLCS)

The link shown in Figure 18–47 is a standard link offered by Motorola Semiconductor, Inc. It is a low-cost link intended for low data rates (200,000 pulses per second or less) and short distances (less than 180 m). Actual data rates are greatly affected by the length of the cable—the longer the cable, the lower the data rate. Thick fibers, such as the 1,000-micron fiber in this link, tend to attentuate and widen the light pulses. At high data rates, a thick fiber will actually blur the light pulses together, causing them to overlap and become inseparable. The longer the cable, the greater the problem. Therefore, the data rate must be set to match the length and type of cable.

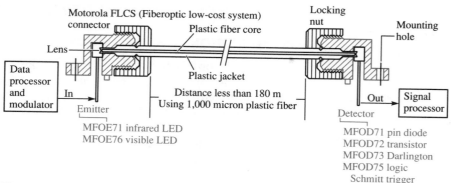

Figure 18–47 A low-cost, short-distance fiber-optic communication system.

Notice that either the visible red LED (MFOE76) or the infrared LED (MFOE71) may be used as the emitter. The amount of drive current needed for these emitters is determined by the length of the optic cable—the longer the cable, the higher must the forward current be. Higher current means more light energy launched into the cable. Graphs are available on the data sheets to help you determine the needed forward current for your application. These devices also have rise and fall response times (electrical to light conversion rise and fall times) that determine the maximum data rate for the device. However, in most cases, the size and length of the optical fiber is still the most significant limitation to data rate.

On the receive end, notice the wide variety of photodetectors available for this system. Of all of these detectors, the photodarlington detector is the most sensitive and should be used for long cable lengths (up to 180 m) to compensate for fiber light attenuation. If high data rate is desired, the PIN photodiode should be used, since it is the fastest device (has the shortest rise and fall times). However, this is a low-speed system, so high data rate is not a consideration. The Schmitt trigger is the least sensitive of all the photodetectors and is intended for short links (less than 60 m). Information regarding these devices and system configuration is presented in their data sheets.

Analog Transmission?

The link of Figure 18–47 can also be used to transmit voice instead of digital data. In such a case, the photoemitter must be biased near the middle of its forward current operating range. This will automatically bias on the photodetector on the receive end. An audio amplifier is used to bias and intensity modulate the photoemitter. An audio amplifier is also used on the receive end to amplify the detected audio. Bias level on the emitter end may have to be adjusted for minimum distortion. The phototransistor or photodarlington should be used on the receive end. The logic output detector cannot be used, since its output is high or low with no in-between.

THE SEMICONDUCTOR OPTICAL AMPLIFIER

The SOA

In high-speed, long-distance, fiber-optic data links, modulated injection lasers are used as emitters and the fibers are very thin (less than 100 μm). The high intensity of the diode laser permits long-distance transmission and the thin fiber prevents widening of the light pulses. Transmission over distances of tens of kilometers is possible in these systems. However, at some point in the optical line, the light signal must be amplified and rebuilt to maintain system integrity. This is now being accomplished quite economically with a relatively new device called the **semiconductor optical amplifier (SOA).**

Single-Pass Small-Signal Gain (g_0)

Figure 18–48 shows a diagram of the SOA. This device is actually an injection laser that has no reflective coatings at its ends. Light enters the active region (channel) on the left and is amplified by repeated stimulated emissions as the photons make their way down the channel. By the time the light exits

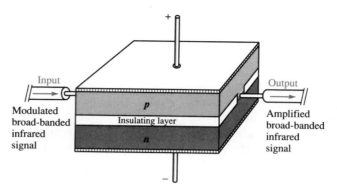

Figure 18–48   The semiconductor optical amplifier.

the SOA on the right, it is 10 to 40 dB stronger than it was coming in. The light amplification is known as the **single-pass small-signal gain** g_0. The amount of amplification is a function of physical channel length and injection current—the more current and the longer the channel, the greater the single-pass gain.

The input and output fibers must be carefully interfaced to the ends to minimize loss and reflections. A special antireflection coating is used at the output end to minimize reflections back down the channel. Such reflections encourage lasing action independent of the incoming signal, and this creates noise and signal distortion.

SOA Applications

SOAs are very inexpensive amplifiers that can be used as signal repeaters (amplifiers) in **wavelength division multiplexed** systems **(WDMs)**. These systems are very broadbanded systems in which the fiber carries many light signals of different wavelengths all at the same time. Figure 18–49 illustrates such a system. The large upper diagram is the conventional WDM system. As you can see, it is very complicated and very expensive. The light wavelength demultiplexer must separate all wavelengths of incoming light and route each wavelength to its own detection and amplification strip. Once each wavelength is amplified, it is recombined (multiplexed) in the light wavelength multiplexer and launched into the fiber. The SOA replaces all of this with a typical small-signal bandwidth of 4,000 GHz = 4 THz = $4 \cdot 10^{12}$ Hz.

Time for a self-check.

**Self-Check
18–6**

1. List the three main parts of the fiber-optic link.
2. What is the most significant limitation to a link's data rate?
3. Which type of photodetector is the most sensitive, permitting longer fiber links?
4. How is an SOA similar to an injection laser?
5. Describe an application for the SOA.

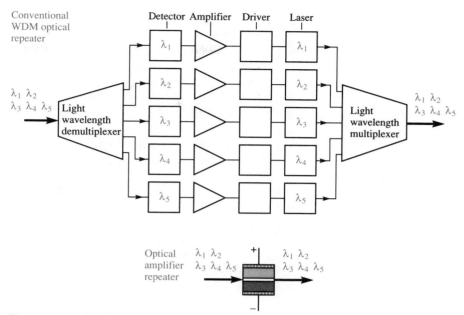

Figure 18–49 The semiconductor optical amplifier replaces expensive and complicated repeaters.

SUMMARY

FORMULAS

(18–1) $\lambda = c/f = (300 \cdot 10^6 \text{ m/s})/f$ (in free space)

(18–2) $f = c/\lambda = (300 \cdot 10^6 \text{ m/s})/\lambda$ (in free space)

(18–3) $\beta_{\text{CTR}} = I_C/I_F$

(18–4) $I_F = I_C/\beta_{\text{CTR}}$

CONCEPTS

- As frequency increases, wavelength decreases.
- 1 μm (micrometer) = 1,000 nm (nanometer) = 10,000 Å (angstroms)
- One candela (candle, cd) of light produces one lumen (lm) of light flux per steradian (sr).
- A foot-candle (fc) is one lumen of light flux falling on a one-square-foot surface area, 1 fc = 1 lm/ft^2.
- One lux is one lumen of flux per square meter, 1 lux = 1 lm/m^2.
- Photometric units of illuminance correspond with radiometric units of irradiance.
- Photoemitters generate light and photodetectors respond to light.
- A device's spectral response indicates the wavelength(s) at which the device is most sensitive.
- Multiplexing LEDs reduces control circuitry and power consumption. LEDs are selected one at a time in rapid succession.
- The phosphor in an electroluminescent panel fluoresces when its atoms are excited by an AC voltage.

- LCDs can be transmissive (use backlighting) or reflective (with a mirror back panel).
- Crystals in the nematic LCD cause the light to change polarization when passing through if no voltage is applied. With an applied voltage, there is no change in polarization.
- The application of light increases the conductivity of photodetectors.
- The photodiode is the fastest of all photodetectors discussed in this chapter.
- Optoisolators (optocouplers) provide excellent isolation between high-voltage circuits and sensitive low-voltage control circuits.
- Optointerrupters provide a means of interfacing mechanical functions with electronic monitoring and control circuits.
- Laser light is monochromatic (one wavelength), coherent (all in phase), and collimated (parallel rays with very little divergence).
- Lasing action takes place in a Fabry-Perot resonator in which stimulated photon emissions of the same direction and wavelength build in numbers and intensity as they are reflected from end to end in the lazing medium.
- Distance of transmission through an optical fiber is mostly limited by the size of the fiber, input power, and type of detector.
- The rate of data transmission in optical fibers is mainly limited by the optical fiber itself—its thickness and length. The optical fiber causes pulses to widen and overlap, becoming indistinct.
- The semiconductor optical amplifier uses one-pass lasing action (stimulated emissions) to increase the intensity of the light signal.

NEED-TO-KNOW SOLUTION

Optoisolators that have light-activated TRIAC outputs can be used to interface the computer to the five room ceiling lights, the hot water heater, and the night security light system. Since the LATRIAC is a low-power device in the optoisolator, it must be used to trigger a much more powerful TRIAC. See Figure 18–38. The 24-V burglar alarm system can be controlled using a phototransistor or photodarlington-type optoisolator. See Figure 18–36.

QUESTIONS

18–1 THE LIGHT SPECTRUM

1. What is the approximate frequency range of visible light?
2. What is wavelength?
3. What is the value of the speed of light in free space?
4. How is wavelength related to frequency?
5. Define luminous intensity.
6. What is the relationship between a candle, a lumen, and a steradian?
7. What is illuminance?
8. What is the radiometric equivalent of illuminance?
9. What is one lux?
10. What is the difference between photometric and radiometric units?

18–2 OPTOELECTRONIC EMITTERS AND DISPLAYS

11.   Which of the schematic symbols of Figure 18–50 is an LED?
12.   What determines the color, or wavelength of radiation, of an LED?
13.   What is the life expectancy for an LED that is conservatively operated?
14.   What causes light emission from an LED?
15.   What is epitaxy?
16.   How does the etched-well LED differ from the planar surface-emitting LED?
17.   What is the main advantage of the edge-emitting LED?
18.   How can you obtain important information regarding the characteristics and ratings for a particular LED?
19.   What does the spatial radiation pattern for an LED tell you?
20.   What does the spectral emission graph for an LED tell you?
21.   Briefly explain what it means to multiplex seven-segment LED display digits.
22.   Why is digit multiplexing preferred over a direct, continuous, and separate drive for each digit?
23.   What is the minimum scan frequency per digit for a multiplexed display so the eye does not detect flicker?

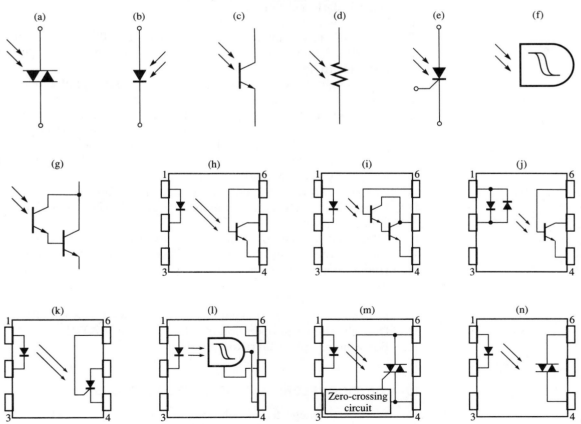

Figure 18–50

24. What is the difference between fluorescence and phosphorescence?
25. What causes the phosphor layer of an electroluminescent panel to luminesce?
26. What are some applications for electroluminescent panels?
27. Compare LCDs to LEDs in terms of power consumption and ON/OFF speed.
28. Describe the basic operating phenomenon that makes twisted nematic LCDs work.
29. Why is polarized glass needed in twisted nematic LCD displays?
30. What is the difference between transmissive and reflective twisted nematic LCDs?

18–3 LIGHT-ACTIVATED DEVICES

31. Which of the schematic symbols of Figure 18–50 is a photoresistor?
32. Compare the spectral response of CdS and CdSe photoresistors.
33. What is the relationship between light intensity and device resistance for photoresistors?
34. Compare the light/dark reaction speed of the photoresistor to the photodiode.
35. What is dark resistance?
36. List two applications for photoresistors.
37. Which of the schematic symbols of Figure 18–50 is a photodiode?
38. Describe the operation of a photodiode in terms of biasing and why it responds to light.
39. How is light current related to light intensity for a photodiode?
40. List two common applications for photodiodes.
41. Which of the schematic symbols of Figure 18–50 is a phototransistor?
42. Compare the performance of the phototransistor and photodarlington to the photodiode in terms of sensitivity and response time.
43. Is the spectral response for a phototransistor typically very broad or is it typically very narrow?
44. Describe two ways the phototransistor can be biased.
45. Which of the schematic symbols of Figure 18–50 is a light-activated Schmitt trigger?
46. What does it mean to say a graph is normalized to a specific value?
47. Describe the optohysteresis of a light-activated Schmitt trigger.
48. Under what circumstances should a light-activated Schmitt trigger be used?
49. What is a LASCR?
50. Which of the schematic symbols of Figure 18–50 is a LATRIAC?
51. Describe the basic operation of a LASCR or a LATRIAC.
52. For what are photothyristors used?

18–4 OPTOCOUPLERS AND OPTOINTERRUPTERS

53. What is an integrated-circuit optoisolator?
54. What is being isolated and what is being coupled regarding optoisolators?

55. Which of the schematic symbols of Figure 18–50 is a photodarlington optoisolator?
56. Explain current transfer ratio.
57. Is a β_{CTR} of 6 relatively high or low?
58. Would a β_{CTR} of 10 be for a phototransistor optoisolator or would it be for a photodarlington optoisolator?
59. List two possible applications for phototransistor optoisolators.
60. What is a primary design consideration when using a thyristor-output optoisolator?
61. Which of the schematic symbols of Figure 18–50 is an LASCR optoisolator?
62. Explain the purpose for the zero-crossing triggering circuit in an LATRIAC optoisolator.
63. What is the primary function or purpose for optointerrupters?
64. List two possible applications for optointerrupters.

18–5 LASERS

65. Who is credited with being first to postulate laser concepts?
66. List the three characteristics of laser light and describe each.
67. What is spontaneous emission?
68. What is stimulated emission?
69. What does stimulated emission have to do with light amplification?
70. What is a Fabry-Perot resonator?
71. What is the general range of reflectivity, in percent, for partially reflective mirrors used in lasers?
72. Describe the basic construction of the injection laser.
73. Describe the basic operation of the injection laser.
74. List two common applications for the injection laser.
75. In regard to gas lasers, what is a laser head?
76. List four gases used in gas lasers.
77. Briefly describe lasing action in gas laser tubes.
78. List three common applications for gas lasers.
79. Explain optical pumping in regard to solid-crystal lasers.
80. List two applications for solid-crystal lasers.

18–6 OPTOELECTRONIC DEVICES FOR FIBER OPTICS

81. List the three main parts of a one-way fiber-optic link.
82. What is the most significant factor that limits the data rate in a fiber-optic link?
83. Of all the receive-end photodetectors, which has the fastest response to light pulses?
84. Briefly explain what type of photodetector should be used for an analog (voice modulated) fiber-optic link and explain how it is biased to a low-distortion Q point.
85. Compare and contrast the SOA to the injection laser.
86. What is single-pass small-signal gain in regard to SOAs?
87. Describe a very significant application for SOAs.
88. What is WDM? Describe WDM.

PROBLEMS

18–1 THE LIGHT SPECTRUM

1. What is the wavelength of a 146.8-MHz radio frequency?
2. What is the wavelength of a 550-kHz radio frequency?
3. What is the wavelength of a 950-THz frequency?
4. What is the wavelength of a 550-THz frequency?
5. What is the frequency of a 500-nm wavelength?
6. What is the frequency of an 8500-Å wavelength?
7. What is the frequency of a 0.420-μm wavelength?
8. What is the frequency of a 25-mm wavelength?
9. Express 0.005 fc in units of mW/m^2.
10. Express 3.3 lux in units of lm/m^2.
11. Express 8 fc in units of μW/cm^2.
12. Express 7 mW/ft^2 in units of fc.
13. Express 1000 lm in units of watts.
14. Express 50 lux in units of fc.

18–3 LIGHT-ACTIVATED DEVICES

15. Determine the current in the circuit of Figure 18–51.

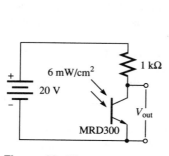
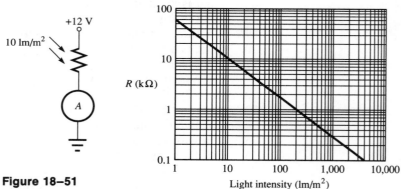

Figure 18–51

16. From the graph of Figure 18–51, what is the approximate light intensity needed to set the photoresistor's resistance at 2 kΩ?
17. Determine the output voltage (V_{CE}) for the circuit of Figure 18–52.

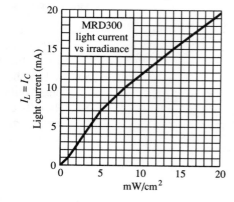

Figure 18–52

18. Determine the output voltage in Figure 18–52 if the impinging light intensity is increased to 10 mW/cm².
19. Determine the minimum light intensity necessary to securely energize the relay in Figure 18–53. Use the graph of Figure 18–52.

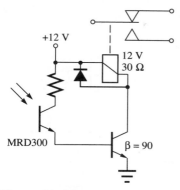

Figure 18–53

18–4 OPTOCOUPLERS AND OPTOINTERRUPTERS

20. Determine the maximum value for R in Figure 18–54 to ensure the relay is securely energized. Assume a β_{CTR} of 4.

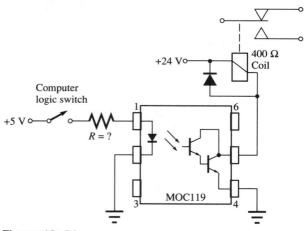

Figure 18–54

21. Determine the maximum value for R in Figure 18–55 to ensure the relay is securely energized. Assume a β_{CTR} of 0.7.
22. Determine the maximum value of R in Figure 18–56 that will ensure reliable triggering of the LATRIAC optoisolator. The maximum required forward trigger current for this device is 30 mA.

ADDITIONAL PROBLEMS

23. Determine the current in the circuit of Figure 18–57.
24. Using the graph of Figure 18–57, what is the approximate light intensity needed to set the output voltage at approximately 12 V?

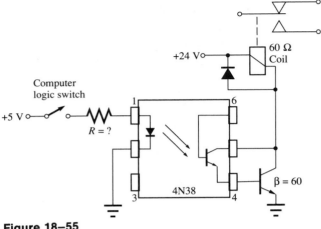

Figure 18–55

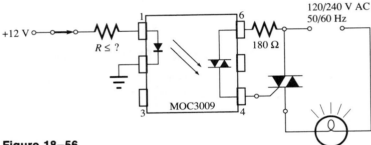

Figure 18–56

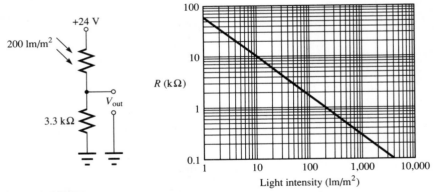

Figure 18–57

25. Determine the output voltage (V_{CE}) for the circuit of Figure 18–58.
26. Determine the minimum amount of impinging light intensity needed to insure total saturation of the transistor in Figure 18–58.
27. Determine the light intensity necessary to set the output collector voltage to +6 V in Figure 18–59. Use the graph of Figure 18–58 for the MRD300.
28. Determine the output voltage for the circuit of Figure 18–59 if the irradiance is 15 mW/cm².
29. Determine the output voltage for the circuit of Figure 18–59 if the irradiance is 2 mW/cm².

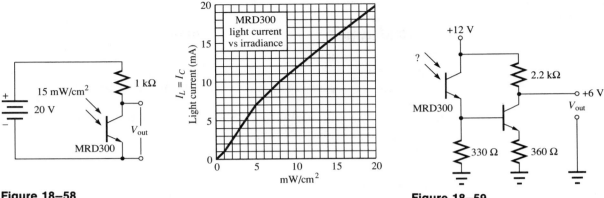

Figure 18–58

Figure 18–59

30. Determine the maximum value for R in Figure 18–60 to insure the relay is securely energized. Assume a β_{CTR} of 5.

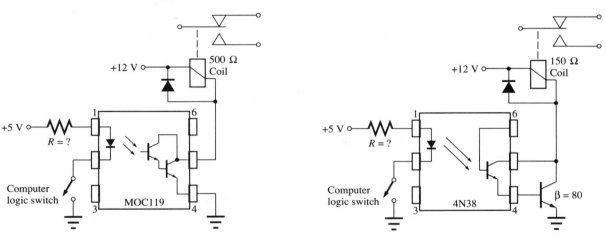

Figure 18–60

Figure 18–61

31. Determine the maximum value for R in Figure 18–61 to insure the relay is securely energized. Assume a β_{CTR} of 0.8.

32. Determine the maximum value of R in Figure 18–62 that will insure reliable triggering of the LATRIAC optoisolator. The maximum required forward trigger current for this device is 20 mA.

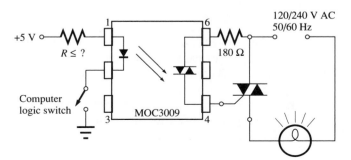

Figure 18–62

ANSWERS TO SELF-CHECKS

SELF-CHECK 18–1

1. $0.638\ \mu m = 638\ nm = 6{,}380\ \text{Å}$
2. 571.4 THz
3. Illuminance is the amount of light that falls on the surface of an object or device.
4. Photometric units apply to visible light and radiometric units apply to invisible radiation.
6. 6.32 fc

SELF-CHECK 18–2

1. Emission from the etched-well LED is more concentrated (less scattered) than that from the planar LED.
2. In gallium arsenide materials, energy is released partially as light in the form of photon emission as a recombination takes place (excited electron falling into a hole).
3. The edge-emitting LED emits the most concentrated beam.
4. Terminal 3 must receive a positive potential and terminal g must be taken to ground through a current-limiting resistor.
5. Reflective LCDs have a mirrored back, transmissive LCDs are back-lighted.

SELF-CHECK 18–3

1. (b)
2. (b)
3. (1) detector in a remote control system (2) detector in a fiber-optic system
4. (b)
5. $7\ mW/cm^2$
6. For a Schmitt trigger, the impinging trigger light intensity is greater than the light intensity at which the Schmitt trigger turns off. Thus, the Schmitt trigger does not turn on and off at the same light intensity threshold.
7. The purpose for photothyristors is to trigger larger heavy-duty thyristors in AC circuits since they themselves are low-power devices.

SELF-CHECK 18–4

1. The current transfer ratio is simply the ratio of output collector current to input forward LED current.
2. The LED control current must be high enough to ensure reliable triggering of the optothyristor.
3. The optoisolator is used to prevent high voltages and voltage transients from getting back to, and destroying, the computer circuits.
4. A LASCR or a LATRIAC output optoisolator can be used to interface a computer to a 115-V AC light circuit.

5. The basic purpose for the optointerrupter is to provide an electrome-chanical interface.

SELF-CHECK 18–5

1. *Light Amplification* through *Stimulated Emission* of *Radiation*
2. Spontaneous emission is emission that occurs when an excited electron released energy as light when it falls back to its normal energy state. Stimulated emission is emission that takes place when a photon collides with an excited electron. The electron gives up its energy in the form of photon emission.
3. The partially reflective mirror reflects 30 to 40 percent of the photons back into the lasing medium to sustain continuous lasing action.
4. Coherent light is light whose wavefronts are all in phase, aiding each other.
5. Collimated light is light that travels in parallel lines with little or no divergence.
6. Injection lasers and gas lasers

SELF-CHECK 18–6

1. Photoemitter, optical fiber, photodetector
2. Thickness and length of the optical fiber, or cable
3. Photodarlington
4. The SOA is similar to an injection laser in construction and in light amplification. Light amplification is accomplished through single-pass lasing action caused by repeated occurrences of stimulated emission from input to output.
5. The SOA is used as a broadbanded amplifier or repeater in a long fiber-optic system.

SUGGESTED PROJECTS

1. Add some of the main concepts from this chapter to your Electronics Notebook.
2. Design and build a 115-V light control circuit using an MOC3041 (or equivalent) optoisolator IC and an external power TRIAC. See Figure 18–38.
3. Obtain an infrared LED and an infrared photodetector and experiment with remote-control circuits.
4. Obtain a simple fiber-optic link kit from an electronic supplier. These are available with tutorial information for $15 to $50. This will increase your understanding of fiber-optic links and you may find a practical use for it. Possible suppliers are

   • Jameco Electronics, 1355 Shoreway Road, Belmont, CA 94002
   • DC Electronics, P. O. Box 3202, Scottsdale, AZ 85271-3203
   • Edmund Scientific, 101 E. Gloucester Pike, Barrington, NJ 08007

High-power vacuum tubes used in powerful broadcast transmitters. These devices cannot be replaced by transistors because of the high power levels. (Courtesy of Varian, Eimac Associates, Inc.)

19 High-Power Vacuum Devices in a Solid-State World

OBJECTIVES

After studying this chapter, you should be able to

- identify the schematic symbol for a variety of vacuum tubes—such as vacuum diodes, triodes, tetrodes, pentodes, beam power tubes, and cathode ray tubes.
- explain thermionic emission and vacuum-diode operation.
- explain the purpose for the control grid, the screen grid, and the suppressor grid.
- explain vacuum-tube phenomena such as space charge and secondary emissions.
- describe the order in which the power supplies for high-power tetrodes must be turned on.
- describe basic protection circuitry for high-power tubes.
- describe methods of cooling high-power tubes.

NEED TO KNOW

Imagine yourself entering the electronic communications field in the not-too-distant future after having completed your initial electronics training. You had been led to believe that vacuum tubes were obsolete so you gave them little thought and were given little opportunity to study them. Now you discover that vacuum tubes are alive and well in many areas of communications—such as AM, FM, shortwave, and television broadcasting, along with microwave ground-to-ground and air-to-ground communications. Suddenly you feel a bit insecure, because you were never really introduced to these high-power devices. You have discovered that you really do have a need to know.

An example of what you will undoubtedly run into is a statement like this: "The screen current on the final high-power tetrode is too high." Now what does that mean? What is a tetrode and what is the screen? By the time you finish this chapter, you will know the answer to these questions.

INTRODUCTION

In this chapter, you will be introduced to basic vacuum-tube principles because vacuum tubes still play a vital role in the world of electronic communications and broadcasting, especially in the areas of high-power broadcasting and microwave applications. According to a leading tube manufacturer, sales of vacuum tubes in the United States are well over $150 million per year. That may be small compared to total semiconductor sales but it represents the lion's share of sales of devices for high-power applications. Since the high-power industry is still dominated by vacuum-tube devices, it is an area that cannot be ignored.

Many textbooks today have deleted the topic of vacuum tubes for several reasons: low-power vacuum tubes are obsolete, the topic can easily demand a large portion of a book, and the semiconductor field has expanded greatly, demanding more textbook pages. In effect, vacuum tubes have been squeezed out. For the same reasons, it is not practical to include an extensive coverage of vacuum tubes in this text. However, the attempt has been made here to provide you with a thorough understanding of vacuum-tube theory with very limited calculations. Also, practical information relating to high-power applications is included.

The purpose of this chapter is not to make you an expert in vacuum tubes. Entire books have been dedicated to that topic. Admittedly, much has been left out of this chapter, including an in-depth study of classes of operation, circuit configurations, and many applications. The coverage of microwave vacuum-tube devices is intentionally omitted, since these devices are usually covered in later courses and texts.

The intended purpose for this chapter is to introduce you to the species, so to speak, to give you a feel for the physics that makes vacuum tubes operate and to give you an idea of how they are constructed. You will also be introduced to how they must be "handled" in a circuit. The information here is basic, practical, and relevant. Enjoy!

19–1 INTRODUCTION TO VACUUM TUBES

WHAT IS A VACUUM TUBE?

A **vacuum tube** is an electronic device, of great variety, that conducts electron flow in one direction from a heated cathode to a collector known as the *plate* or **anode**. Electrons travel through a vacuum or an ionized gas in a small chamber surrounded by a glass, ceramic, or metal and ceramic envelope (enclosure). They are characterized as being much larger than semiconductor devices but are essential for many applications in the fields of high-power AM and FM broadcasting, microwave communications and radar, and television transmissions.

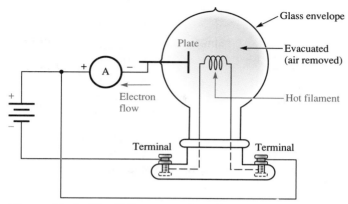

Figure 19–1 The Edison experiment.

EARLY BEGINNINGS

The vacuum tube was developed by many late-19th-century electronics pioneers. Among them were Heinrich Geissler of Germany, Sir William Crookes of Great Britain, and Thomas Edison of the United States. Edison inserted a small metal plate inside one of his light bulbs and discovered that a small current flowed from the hot filament to the plate. His experiment is shown in Figure 19–1. This phenomenon became known as the **Edison effect.** Edison failed to pursue his basic discovery further. However, what he had discovered was significant and led the way for the electronics revolution of the 20th century.

THERMIONIC EMISSION

What Edison had discovered was **thermionic emission,** which takes place when certain conductor materials are heated to high temperatures. At these high temperatures, valence electrons become highly excited (elevated in energy level). In this excited state, many valence electrons break away from their atoms and are able to actually leap into the surrounding air or vacuum, as is illustrated in Figure 19–2. These emitted electrons quickly return to the conductor because of the positive charge they leave behind. However, there are so many of them temporarily escaping on a regular basis that an electron cloud, known as a **space charge,** is formed around the conductor.

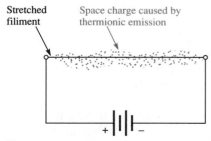

Figure 19–2 Thermionic emission from the hot filament.

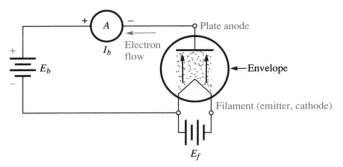

Figure 19-3   Fleming's valve—the vacuum diode.

FLEMING'S VALVE

In 1904, a British scientist by the name of John A. Fleming applied the Edison effect to the first recognized vacuum diode. Shown schematically in Figure 19–3, the Fleming valve was an improvement over Edison's experiment. Fleming intended to create an electronic device that would conduct electron flow in only one direction, much like a fluid check valve. In his device, a filament is heated by an electrical current. At a high temperature, thermionic emission takes place at the surface region of the filament. A positive potential applied to the plate (anode) attracts the electrons away from the heated filament. Emitted electrons are restored to the filament by the source. The filament in Fleming's valve acts as the emitter and the plate acts as the collector. Since the plate is not heated and has a very low thermionic emission activity, current will not flow from plate to filament if the polarity of the external voltage is reversed.

FILAMENT AND CATHODE

Figure 19–4 shows the filament and cathode structures for modern vacuum tubes. The cathode of the vacuum tube is the emitter. It can be heated directly by an applied current or indirectly, using a separate heater filament and cathode surface. The **directly heated cathode** is a heater filament made of thoriated tungsten. When the tungsten wire is manufactured, a small amount of thorium is added to the mix. The thorium atoms increase the thermionic activity and emissions by nearly a thousand times. The proper amount of voltage and current is applied to the filament to keep its temperature in the area of 1600°C. The **indirectly heated cathode** is usually a nickel cylinder coated with barium or strontium oxide. The cathode is heated to 700 to 800°C by a tungsten filament. Indirectly heated cathodes require less heater power than directly heated cathodes and emit more electrons. However, the oxide coating of indirectly heated cathodes deteriorates over time, evaporating and redepositing on other electrodes in the tube, and thus shortening the life of the tube.

The electrical power needed to heat the directly or indirectly heated cathode is one of the greatest disadvantages of the low-power vacuum tubes.

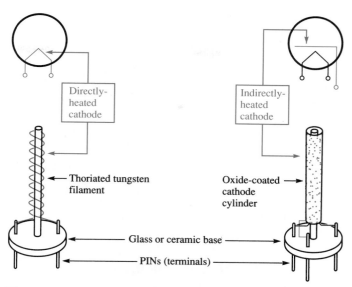

Figure 19-4 Directly and indirectly heated cathodes in vacuum tubes.

This cathode power expenditure is necessary, but greatly reduces the overall power efficiency of low-power tubes (vacuum amplifiers). Low-power tubes that have a maximum plate dissipation (device power dissipation) of 2 W may require 1 W or so of filament power. High-power vacuum tubes used in transmitters require anywhere between 1,000 and 4,000 W of filament power. However, this does not detract markedly from overall power efficiency, because plate dissipation capability is very high. For example, a 35,000-W vacuum tube may require a filament voltage of 10 V at 300 A of current (3,000 W). The power demanded by the filament in this case is relatively insignificant compared to the plate dissipation and potential output power. Nevertheless, a hefty and somewhat costly filament supply circuit is required to heat the tube. At present, this requirement is unavoidable since solid-state devices have not yet replaced high-power transmitting tubes for HF, VHF, UHF and microwave applications.

Before continuing to a more detailed exploration of vacuum diodes and other vacuum tubes, take time to review and answer the questions of Self-Check 19-1.

Self-Check 19-1

1. Who is credited with the discovery of thermionic emission?
2. What is thermionic emission?
3. What is the Fleming valve?
4. Explain space charge.
5. What is the physical difference between directly and indirectly heated cathodes?

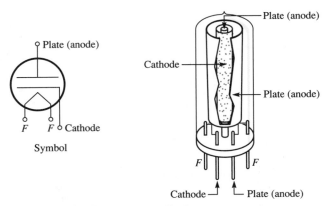

Figure 19–5 The vacuum diode.

19–2 VACUUM DIODES

VACUUM-DIODE CHARACTERISTICS

Introduction to Vacuum Diodes

The vacuum diode consists of a directly or indirectly heated cathode, which emits electrons when heated, an anode plate that collects the electrons, and an evacuated glass envelope. The schematic symbol of an indirectly heated vacuum diode and a pictorial of a low-power vacuum diode are shown in Figure 19–5. Notice the cylindrical and concentric arrangement of the filament, cathode, and plate. This is typical of most vacuum tubes. However, realize that vacuum diodes come in a great variety of sizes and pin configurations. The data sheet for the particular vacuum diode will demonstrate pin arrangement and assignment as well as normal values of filament voltage and current and maximum values of plate current (I_p), plate voltage (plate to cathode voltage, E_p), and plate power dissipation ($I_p \cdot E_p$).

Vacuum-Diode Characteristics

Figure 19–6 illustrates a test circuit and the resulting characteristic graph. The graph is determined for a specific filament voltage. If the specified filament voltage is used, it is assumed that the cathode will be heated to the proper temperature for operation. In many cases, the filament voltage can be AC or DC—for example, 6.3 VDC or 6.3 VAC (RMS). AC filament voltage is nearly always used for indirectly heated cathodes. A DC filament voltage is shown in Figure 19–6 for simplicity. The DPDT switch permits forward and reverse biasing of the tube. The plate supply is variable. Notice first of all that there is absolutely no current in the reverse direction. A vacuum diode cannot conduct from plate to cathode (electron flow). With forward bias, the vacuum diode increases its forward conduction in relation to the amount of plate voltage. How does that compare to a semiconductor diode? That's right. The semiconductor diode has a nearly vertical characteristic

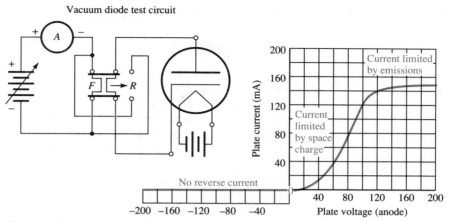

Figure 19–6 Vacuum-diode characteristics.

curve past the barrier potential point (~0.6 to 0.7 V). So, why does a vacuum diode have a sloped curve?

Space-Charge Effect

The vacuum diode has a sloped characteristic curve in the forward-conduction mode because of the space charge that exists around the cathode. An electron cloud forms that has a repelling effect on other electrons on the cathode. As the plate voltage is increased, more and more electrons are able to penetrate the space charge and journey to the plate. Finally, the plate voltage reaches a saturation point, at which no further increase in electron flow is possible. The cathode can only produce so many free electrons at a given temperature. If the cathode temperature is increased by increasing filament voltage, the emissions will increase. This is not wise to do to a new tube, since it will most certainly shorten the tube's life. If a tube has been in service a long time there is little to lose.

Gas-Filled Diodes

Some tube-type diodes are gas- or vapor-filled. Usually, high-power diodes are filled with helium, argon, neon, or mercury vapor. The schematic symbol for a gas-filled tube includes a black dot within the envelope (within the circle) to indicate the tube is gas-filled. **Mercury-vapor diodes** are quite common for high-voltage rectifier applications. A small amount of mercury that is near the filament is heated when the cathode is heated. Soon the tube fills with a mercury vapor. When a plate voltage is applied and rises in amplitude, the vapor reaches a firing point—a voltage level at which the vapor ionizes, releasing a large quantity of electrons and creating positive ions. The ionized gas acts as the medium for transfer of large amounts of electrons from the cathode to the plate. As a result, the space charge effect is greatly reduced and the forward conduction more closely resembles that of the semiconductor diode.

VACUUM-DIODE APPLICATIONS

The High-Voltage DC Supply

Figure 19–7 illustrates a typical application for tube-type diodes. In this case, mercury-vapor tubes are used. Notice the similarity of this circuit to the solid-state full-wave rectifier circuits you have already studied. However, there are significant differences. The mercury-vapor tubes must be heated long enough to raise the cathode to operating temperature and create mercury vapor. When AC is applied to the primary side of the transformer, a low-voltage secondary winding supplies voltage and current to the filaments of the two tubes. A time-delay relay (normally open) is used to give the tube the time it needs to heat before the plate circuit is completed. The time delay is usually 30 to 60 seconds.

Safety

The bleeder resistor is used to discharge the high-voltage filter capacitors when AC is removed. This is for safety purposes, to render the capacitor harmless in a short time. *However, never trust bleeder resistors to do their job.* There always is, or should be, a grounding stick nearby. This should be used to insure total discharge of the high-voltage capacitors. The grounding stick has an insulated handle, a metal rod with a hook, and a braided grounding strap connected to ground. While working on the high-voltage equipment, always leave the grounding stick hooked on the high-voltage capacitor terminal. When the stick is returned to its hanger, a small switch (an interlock) that allows the high-voltage supply to be turned on is closed.

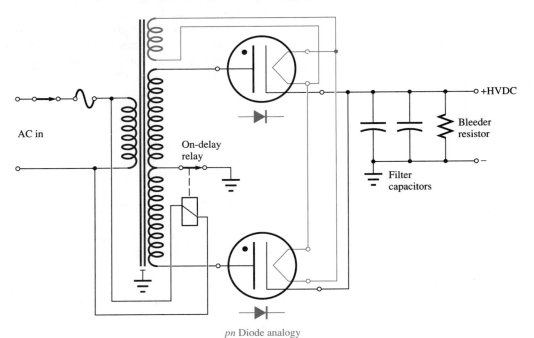

pn Diode analogy

Figure 19–7 A high-voltage supply using vacuum-diode tubes.

Solid-State Stacks vs Tube Rectifiers

In many high-voltage applications today, solid-state diode stacks are used to replace tube rectifiers. These stacks consist of a series chain of usually 1,000-V diodes, each paralleled by high-value resistors and small capacitors. The resistors and capacitors help balance the high voltage evenly across all series diodes. Solid-state diode stacks are not fail-safe. They do fail with one, then another, then another diode in the string shorting. They are less forgiving to high-voltage transients than tube-type diodes. Therefore, you will still find the older mercury-vapor diodes used in some high-voltage equipment.

Thyratrons

More often, you will see the close cousin to the mercury-vapor diode, the gas-filled **thyratron,** which is equivalent in operation to the SCR. It is a rectifier tube that has a control grid used to control the firing point (firing voltage) for each pulsating alternation. Like the SCR, the conduction angle can be controlled, and, therefore, so can the DC output voltage from the supply.

Time for a self-check.

Self-Check 19–2

1. Why is the characteristic conduction curve for a vacuum diode moderately sloped instead of nearly vertical, as is the case for solid-state diodes?
2. Why does the characteristic conduction curve level out horizontally above some value of plate voltage?
3. Identify two conditions that must be met before a tube diode can conduct.
4. Why must a mercury-vapor diode be heated for some time before plate voltage is applied?
5. What is a grounding stick and what is its purpose?

19–3 VACUUM TRIODES

VACUUM-TRIODE CHARACTERISTICS

Introduction to Vacuum Triodes

The vacuum triode was first patented by the American inventor Lee de Forest in 1907. Originally, it was called the *audion*. De Forest discovered that a metal grid, placed in the electric field between the cathode and plate of a vacuum diode, could be used to control the amount of cathode emissions. In other words, this metal grid could be used to control the plate current, which determined the voltage drop across a series resistor. This turned the vacuum diode into an amplifier, since a small signal on the metal grid was able to produce large current and voltage variations at the plate. Because this new device had three terminals instead of just two, it became known as a **vacuum triode.**

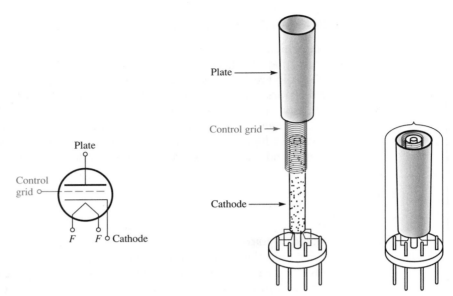

Figure 19–8   The vacuum triode tube.

Figure 19–8 shows the schematic symbol and a pictorial representation of the vacuum triode. Like vacuum diodes, vacuum triodes are manufactured in many different shapes, styles, pin-outs, and power ratings. They are even manufactured as multiple devices in the same glass envelope in combinations with different tube types.

From Figure 19–8, you can see the metal grid, known as the **control grid,** that is placed between the cathode and the plate. All migrating electrons must pass through the control grid to the plate. A negative potential applied to the control grid is used to repel electrons back to the cathode. Actually, an electric field is established between the control grid and the cathode that opposes electrons from leaving the cathode in the first place. The magnitude of the negative control-grid voltage determines the amount of cathode to plate current.

Characteristic Curves

Figure 19–9 illustrates a test circuit and the resulting characteristic curves. The curves are determined for a specific filament voltage (E_f). As stated earlier, AC filament voltage is nearly always used for indirectly heated cathodes and some directly heated cathodes, depending on tube type and application. A DC filament voltage is shown in Figure 19–9 for simplicity.

The control-grid voltage is set to a specific bias voltage and the plate voltage is increased from zero volts to maximum. Each curve on the chart is created in this way. Each vacuum triode has its own set of characteristic curves as provided by the manufacturer. These curves indicate the operating range for plate voltage, plate current, and control-grid voltage. For class A biasing, the tube of Figure 19–9 would have a bias of −1 to −2 V. A bias voltage of −6 V or greater would cut the tube off. A bias voltage of 0 V would cause the tube to forward conduct heavily like a vacuum diode.

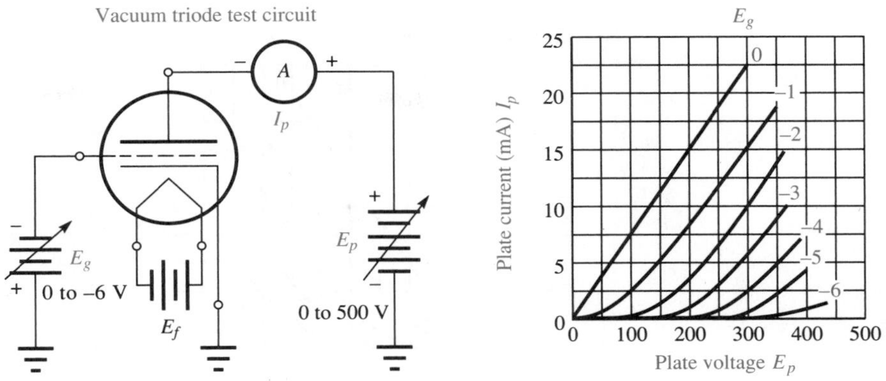

Figure 19–9 Vacuum triode characteristics.

Transconductance (g_m)

There are many important characteristics or ratings for vacuum-tube amplifiers. One of them is the vacuum-amplifier's transconductance (g_m). You may recall this from your study of FETs. For vacuum amplifiers, it is the ratio of a change in plate current (ΔI_p) resulting from a change in control-grid voltage (ΔE_g).

$$g_m = \Delta I_p / \Delta E_g \qquad (19\text{–}1)$$

Figure 19–10a demonstrates the static transconductance for a vacuum triode. It is static because the plate voltage is held constant, making the value of transconductance somewhat idealized. In the case shown, the plate voltage is held constant at +200 V.

EXAMPLE 19–1

Determine the static transconductance for Figure 19–10a. The change in plate current is approximately 5 mA for a 1-V change in control-grid voltage, from −1 V to −2 V.

$g_m = \Delta I_p / \Delta E_g = 5\text{ mA}/1\text{ V} = 5{,}000\ \mu\text{S}$

(Microsiemens is equal to the older unit of micromhos.)

AC Plate Resistance (r_p)

The AC plate resistance of the vacuum-amplifier tube is another important parameter. The AC plate resistance (r_p) is the equivalent AC resistance of the tube. It is the ratio of a change in plate voltage (ΔE_p) resulting from a change in plate current (ΔI_p).

$$r_p = \Delta E_p / \Delta I_p \qquad (19\text{–}2)$$

Shown in Figure 19–10b is the static AC plate resistance for a triode amplifier. In this case, the ratio is established as the control voltage is held constant at −2 V.

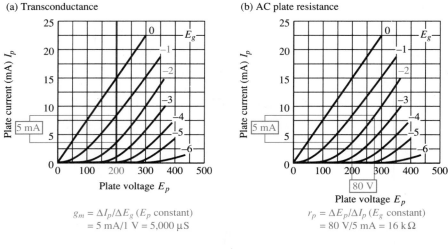

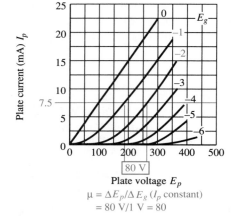

(a) Transconductance

$g_m = \Delta I_p / \Delta E_g \ (E_p \text{ constant})$
$= 5 \text{ mA}/1 \text{ V} = 5{,}000 \ \mu\text{S}$

(b) AC plate resistance

$r_p = \Delta E_p / \Delta I_p \ (E_g \text{ constant})$
$= 80 \text{ V}/5 \text{ mA} = 16 \text{ k}\Omega$

(c) Amplification factor

$\mu = \Delta E_p / \Delta E_g \ (I_p \text{ constant})$
$= 80 \text{ V}/1 \text{ V} = 80$

$g_m \cdot r_p = \mu$
$5{,}000 \ \mu\text{S} \cdot 16 \text{ k}\Omega = 80$

Figure 19–10 Transconductance, plate resistance, and the amplification factor.

EXAMPLE 19–2

Determine the static AC plate resistance for Figure 19–10b. For the same 5-mA change in current, the plate voltage varies by approximately 80 V.

$$r_p = \Delta E_p / \Delta I_p = 80 \text{ V}/5 \text{ mA} = 16 \text{ k}\Omega$$

The AC plate resistance of the tube is important and must be considered in cases where maximum power transfer is desired. Recall that the impedance of the load must match the impedance of the source for maximum power transfer from the source to the load. For vacuum tube amplifiers, this is usually accomplished using an impedance-matching transformer or an *LC* impedance-matching network. More on this later.

Amplification Factor (μ)

The static amplification factor (μ = mu) for a tube is the ratio of the change in plate voltage (ΔE_p) to a change in control-grid voltage (ΔE_g) while the plate current is held constant. The static amplification factor is the highest voltage gain you can expect to get from the tube and is idealized. In practice you cannot obtain a dynamic mu as high as the static mu because the plate load reduces the mu. More on this later.

$$\mu = \Delta E_p / \Delta E_g \tag{19–3}$$

EXAMPLE 19–3

Determine the static mu (μ) for Figure 19–10c. The plate current is held constant at 7.5 mA. The plate voltage changes by 80 V, while the grid voltage changes by only 1 V.

$$\mu = \Delta E_p / \Delta E_g = 80 \text{ V} / 1 \text{ V} = 80 \text{ (no units)}$$

From the curves of Figure 19–10c, you should be able to see that the mu varies depending on the range of control voltage used. In this case, the range is from -1 to -2 V. The mu is significantly less in the control-voltage range from -2 to -3 V. However, the manufacturer specifies the static parameters for the most likely area of class A operation on the characteristic curves.

The static amplification factor for the tube is also the product of static transconductance and AC plate resistance. Notice in Figure 19–10 that the static transconductance is 5,000 μS and the static AC plate resistance is 16 kΩ. The product of the two is 5,000 μS $\cdot$ 16 kΩ = 80 (no units).

$$\mu = g_m \cdot r_p \tag{19–4}$$

Again, the static mu is the highest possible voltage gain for the tube. This value is idealized and is only approached when the load is much greater than the AC plate resistance of the tube.

LOAD LINES AND BIASING FOR TRIODES

Load Line and Stage Gain

Figure 19–11 illustrates a triode amplifier and the tube's characteristic curves. Notice that the tube has a fixed DC bias of -1.5 V. The input impedance to the tube is very high and is equal to 470 kΩ. In normal operation, the grid conducts little or no current since it has a negative potential and is actually repelling electrons. Therefore, the grid appears open and the total input impedance is equal to the value of the grid resistor, in this case 470 kΩ. The filament voltage is set at the manufacturer's recommended voltage.

The characteristic curves are only valid at the manufacturer's specified filament voltage.

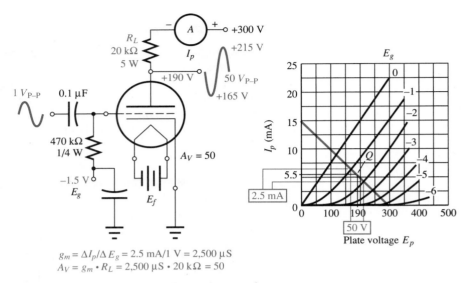

$$g_m = \Delta I_p / \Delta E_g = 2.5 \text{ mA}/1 \text{ V} = 2,500 \text{ }\mu\text{S}$$
$$A_V = g_m \cdot R_L = 2,500 \text{ }\mu\text{S} \cdot 20 \text{ k}\Omega = 50$$

Figure 19–11 Triode amplifier voltage gain.

The DC load line is drawn according to the extreme conditions of cutoff and total saturation. The method used to determine the DC load line is the same as that used for BJTs and FETs. For this circuit, the maximum plate current when the plate voltage is near zero (saturated) is 300 V/20 kΩ = 15 mA. The maximum plate voltage when the tube is cut off and plate current is near zero is the full 300-V supply voltage. Since the control-grid bias is −1.5 V, the Q point (quiescent operating point) is at approximately $I_{p(Q)} = 5.5$ mA and $E_{p(Q)} = 190$ V.

The applied input signal is 1 $V_{\text{P-P}}$. That means the grid bias varies between −1 and −2 V. From the load line, you can see that this 1-V change in E_g causes an approximate 50-V change in plate voltage and 2.5-mA change in plate current. The amplifier's output/input voltage gain is 50 $V_{\text{P-P}}$/1 $V_{\text{P-P}}$ = 50. The characteristic curves of Figure 19–11 are the same as those in Figure 19–10. The static mu, or amplification factor, for this tube is 80. The actual dynamic amplification factor (A_V) for this tube circuit is 50. If the load resistance is increased, the amplification factor will also increase, heading toward a maximum value of 80. However, increasing the load resistance reduces plate current and causes the tube to operate in the more nonlinear areas of the characteristic curves. Therefore, for a circuit to be practical, we must accept dynamic amplification factors that are much less than the static mu of the tube itself.

The dynamic transconductance of this tube operating with the 20-kΩ load is found to be 2,500 μS ($g_m = \Delta I_p / \Delta E_g = 2.5$ mA/1 V = 2,500 μS). The amplifier's gain is the product of dynamic transconductance and load resistance (R_L). In this case, 2,500 μS · 20 kΩ = 50 = A_V.

$$A_V = g_m \cdot R_L \tag{19-5}$$

where the gain or amplification factor A_V of the amplifier is the product of the dynamic transconductance and the total load resistance.

Fixed Bias

Just as there are many ways to bias BJTs or FETs, there are several ways to bias vacuum triodes. Thus far, we have illustrated fixed bias as once again shown in Figure 19–12a. As the name implies, the bias point or Q point is fixed. The incoming signal (drive) rides on the bias voltage. This is a very solid form of control grid bias but it requires a separate bias supply. Even so, this is the method most often used in high-power amplifier applications.

Grid-Leak Bias

Grid-leak bias, also known as signal bias, is shown in Figure 19–12b. This is a form of self-bias in which the input signal causes grid current to flow during the positive alternations. With each positive alternation of the input signal,

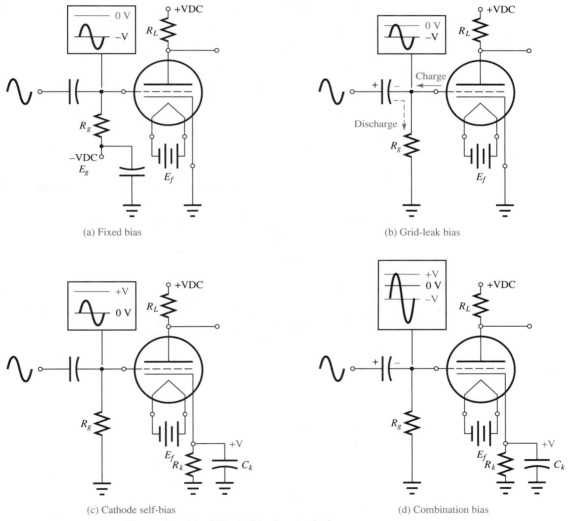

(a) Fixed bias

(b) Grid-leak bias

(c) Cathode self-bias

(d) Combination bias

Figure 19–12 Triode biasing techniques.

the coupling capacitor's charge is restored to peak value. During negative alternations, a small portion of the capacitor's charge leaks off through the grid-leak resistor (R_g). This creates a negative potential at the top of the grid-leak resistor and clamps the input signal to a negative reference as shown. This method of biasing has the advantage of being automatic and dynamic. In other words, the bias point is adjusted more negative for stronger signals and prevents the tube from being overdriven. However, there are two serious disadvantages. First, the bias point floats around with drive level (input level), which means the amplifier's gain is changing with drive level. Second, and more important, is what happens if drive is removed. If drive is lost (no input signal) the bias leaks off (capacitor discharges) and the tube conducts very heavily, insuring self-destruction. That's not good.

Cathode Self-Bias

A solution to the self-destruction problem is cathode self-bias as shown in Figure 19–12c. Cathode, or plate, current establishes a voltage drop across the cathode resistor R_k. This voltage drop is positive from cathode to ground and makes the cathode more positive than the control grid. In other words, the control grid looks negative with respect to the cathode. You've seen this before with n-channel FETs. A relatively large-value bypass capacitor (C_k) is needed to stabilize the bias voltage. The desired quiescent plate current and control-grid voltage determine the needed value of R_k.

$$R_k = |E_g|/I_{p(Q)} \tag{19–6}$$

EXAMPLE 19–4 ▮▮▮▮▮▮▮▮▮▮▮▮▮▮▮▮▮▮▮

Determine the value of cathode resistor needed to cathode-self-bias the amplifier circuit of Figure 19–11.

$I_{p(Q)} = 5.5$ mA, $E_{g(Q)} = -1.5$ V

$R_k = |E_g|/I_{p(Q)} = 1.5$ V/5.5 mA $= 273\ \Omega$

Bypass R_k with a capacitor that is large compared to the operating frequency range. For example, 10 μF to 100 μF for an audio amplifier and 0.01 μF to 0.1 μF for a radio-frequency amplifier.

Combination Bias

Figure 19–12d becomes a combination bias scheme when the peak input signal is larger than the bias voltage. Clamping action at the control grid takes place when the positive peak drive voltage is greater than the positive cathode voltage. This enables the tube to handle strong drive signals without threat to the tube. Also, if the drive is removed, the cathode self-bias insures that the tube will not lapse into full forward conduction and burn itself up.

AC Load Line and Circuit Calculations

Example 19–5 illustrates the steps necessary to analyze a loaded triode amplifier. Notice the two load lines, DC and AC. Recall from previous study of BJT and FET amplifier circuits that the AC load line is different (steeper) than the DC load line mainly because of AC coupling to a load (capacitor coupling in this case). The AC load line is defined by the same basic formulas as was used in solid-state amplifier circuits. In each formula, Z_L is the total AC load impedance at the plate.

AC Load Line Formulas

$$i_{p(sat)} = I_{p(Q)} + (E_{p(Q)}/Z_L) \qquad\qquad (19\text{--}7)$$

$$e_{p(cutoff)} = E_{p(Q)} + (I_{p(Q)} \cdot Z_L) \qquad\qquad (19\text{--}8)$$

EXAMPLE 19–5

Determine the DC load line, the Q point, the AC load line, and the voltage gain for the circuit of Figure 19–13. Cathode voltage is given as +6 V.

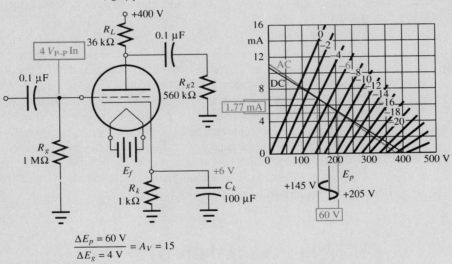

$$\frac{\Delta E_p = 60\text{ V}}{\Delta E_g = 4\text{ V}} = A_V = 15$$

Figure 19–13

1. $I_{p(Q)} = V_k/R_k = 6\text{ V}/1\text{ k}\Omega = 6\text{ mA}$
2. $E_{p(Q)} = V_{supply} - V_{RL} - V_k = V_{supply} - (I_{p(Q)} \cdot R_L) - V_k$
    $= 400\text{ V} - (6\text{ mA} \cdot 36\text{ k}\Omega) - 6\text{ V} = 178\text{ V}$
3. DC Load Line: $I_{(sat)} = V_{supply}/(R_L + R_k)$
    $\qquad\qquad\qquad\quad = 400\text{ V}/(36\text{ k}\Omega + 1\text{ k}\Omega)$
    $\qquad\qquad\qquad\quad = 10.8\text{ mA}$
    $\qquad E_{p(cutoff)} = V_{supply} = 400\text{ V}$
4. $Z_L = R_L \parallel R_{g2} = 36\text{ k}\Omega \parallel 560\text{ k}\Omega = 33.8\text{ k}\Omega$

5. AC Load Line: $i_{p(sat)} = I_{p(Q)} + E_{p(Q)}/Z_L$
$$= 6 \text{ mA} + 178 \text{ V}/33.8 \text{ k}\Omega$$
$$= 6 \text{ mA} + 5.27 \text{ mA} = 11.27 \text{ mA}$$
$$e_{p(cutoff)} = E_{p(Q)} + (I_{p(Q)} \cdot Z_L)$$
$$= 178 \text{ V} + (6 \text{ mA} \cdot 33.8 \text{ k}\Omega)$$
$$= 178 \text{ V} + 203 \text{ V} = 381 \text{ V}$$

6. With 4 V_{P-P} applied, the grid voltage swings between -4 and -8 V. Using the AC load line, the plate voltage swing is approximately $+145$ V to $+205$ V $= 60 \ V_{P-P}$.

$$A_V = v_{out}/v_{in} = 60 \ V_{P-P}/4 \ V_{P-P} = 15$$

Also, $A_V = g_m \cdot Z_L = 443 \ \mu S \cdot 33.8 \text{ k}\Omega = 15$,
where $g_m = \Delta I_p/\Delta E_g \cong 1.77 \text{ mA}/4 \text{ V} = 443 \ \mu S$.

Notice the AC load line of Example 19–5 is very close to the DC load line. The reason, of course, is the very light load (R_{g2}), which is the input impedance of the next stage. If R_{g2} were 56 kΩ instead of 560 kΩ, the AC load line would be very steep and the voltage gain would be much less than 15.

Take time to review this section and answer the questions of Self-Check 19–3.

Self-Check 19–3

1. Is the control grid of a triode used to reduce the plate current or is it used to increase the plate current? Explain.
2. What is static transconductance and how is it calculated?
3. How does the static mu (μ) of a tube compare to the actual voltage gain (A_V) of the amplifier circuit?
4. Explain the advantages of cathode self-bias over grid-leak bias.
5. A triode amplifier has a total AC load of 25.6 kΩ. A 3-V change in grid voltage causes a 3-mA change in plate current. What is the voltage gain of the circuit?

19–4 VACUUM TETRODES

INTRODUCTION TO VACUUM TETRODES

Tetrode Construction

A vacuum tetrode tube is a tube that has four main electrodes: the cathode, the plate, the control grid, and a screen grid. The cathode may be heated directly or indirectly. Figure 19–14 illustrates the schematic symbol and representative construction of a tetrode. As you can see, the tetrode has an additional grid called the **screen grid.** The screen grid is placed between the control grid and the plate (anode). It is physically a wire mesh or bar arrangement through which electrons must pass on their way to the plate. As with

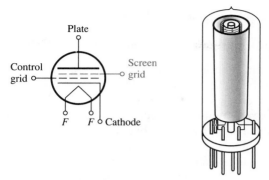

Figure 19–14 The vacuum tetrode tube.

all tubes, the tetrode is manufactured in many variations that include size, shape, design, and power-handling capability.

Triode Limitations

So why do we need a screen grid? The screen grid was added to overcome some of the limitations of the triode. The triode has considerable capacitance between its plate and control grid. This is an example of **interelectrode capacitance.** Electrostatic lines of force extend from the plate to the control grid, just as electrostatic lines of force extend from the positive plate to the relatively negative plate in any capacitor. This interelectrode capacitance severely limits the high-frequency response of the tube, since it is in the negative-feedback path from plate to control grid for the common-cathode configuration. Recall from your study of transistor-amplifier frequency response how this capacitance in the negative feedback path is amplified and appears as a large Miller input capacitance shunting the input impedance of the amplifier.

This interelectrode capacitance not only affects high-end frequency response, it is also the major cause of amplifier instability. At some frequency, the amplifier may be able to satisfy the requirements for oscillation (loop gain equal or greater than 1 and in-phase feedback). To prevent this, external capacitance must be added so as to cancel the effects of the plate to control grid interelectrode capacitance. This technique is known as **neutralization,** the pursuit of which is beyond the intended purpose of this chapter.

Screen Grid Reduces Interelectrode Capacitance

The screen grid acts as a shield between the plate and the control grid. A positive potential, less than the plate potential, is applied to the screen grid. Most electrostatic lines of force now extend from the screen to the control grid. Lines of force also extend from the plate to the screen but very few lines of flux extend from plate to control grid. Thus, the capacitance from plate to control grid is greatly reduced. As a result, the tetrode has a higher frequency response than the triode and can operate with higher gain without fear of oscillations. While triodes have amplification factors (μ) ranging from 5 to 200, tetrodes range from 300 to 700. Voltage and power gains are also higher for tetrodes than for triodes.

VACUUM-TETRODE CHARACTERISTICS

Test Circuit and Characteristics

Operating characteristics for the tetrode are very different than those for the triode because the screen grid plays a dominant role in determining plate characteristics. Let's see how and why. Figure 19–15 illustrates a test circuit and corresponding characteristic curves for a tetrode. First, notice the test circuit. The control-grid bias is variable and will be set in 2-V increments from 0 V to −8 V. The screen bias is fixed at +90 V. The screen voltage is always suggested by the manufacturer and any set of characteristic curves is for a specific filament voltage and screen voltage. The plate supply voltage is variable from 0 V to +500 V.

Characteristic curves for tetrodes are only valid for a specific filament voltage and screen voltage as specified by the manufacturer.

Now, let's consider the characteristic curves of Figure 19–15. All curves are for a fixed value of filament and screen voltage. In this case, the screen voltage is fixed at +90 V. Each curve shown is the graph of plate current that results from plate voltage changing from 0 V to +500 V while the control-grid bias is set at a specific value. Notice that these curves are very strange. Plate current first increases, then decreases in the negative-resistance region, then increases rapidly to a maximum value that is nearly constant over a wide range of plate voltage. These curves are very different than for triodes and the reason is the screen. Let's see why.

The Negative-Resistance Region

Why does the plate current initially increase, then almost immediately decrease as plate voltage begins to increase from 0 V? The physics that takes place here is very interesting. The screen voltage (+90 V in this case) attracts the negatively charged electrons that are emitted from the cathode. These electrons are accelerated from cathode to screen by the positive

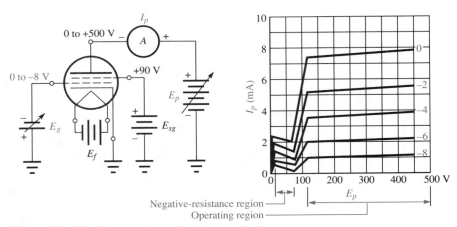

Figure 19–15 Vacuum tetrode characteristics.

screen potential. As the plate voltage is increased slightly above 0 V, some of the electrons pass through the screen with high velocity and are then slowed by the same screen potential that once accelerated them. Some of the electrons that have passed through the screen then see the slightly positive plate and continue to the plate. Most electrons are attracted back to the screen. Thus, the plate shows a marginal initial current.

As the plate voltage is increased further, in the range of say +10 to +90 V, more of the electrons that pass through the screen hit the plate. However, these electrons are accelerated further by the increased plate voltage and hit the plate with great impact. The impact on the plate causes a relatively large quantity of electrons on the plate to be emitted into the area between the plate and the screen, forming a space charge. These electrons are known as **secondary emissions.** In the plate-voltage range of +10 to +90 V most of the secondary emissions are captured by the screen, since it is at a higher positive potential than the plate. This means that more electrons are emitted secondarily from the plate and captured by the screen than initially hit the plate. The result is a drop in plate current in the approximate plate-voltage range of +10 to +90 V. Plate current drops because the plate gives up more electrons than it receives, even though plate voltage is increasing. A decrease in current with an increase in voltage is known as **negative resistance.**

This negative-resistance phenomenon is even more interesting at a plate voltage of +60 V as compared to +10 V. The difference of potential between the screen and plate when the plate is at +60 V is only 30 V, yet secondary emissions increase further and plate current decreases further. This is because the plate voltage accelerates the incoming electrons further, causing more secondary emissions from the collisions. The resulting space charge is greater, making more electrons available for the screen to capture.

The Constant-Current or Operating Region

As long as the plate voltage is less than the screen voltage, the screen current is very high. This is because the screen is capturing cathode-emitted electrons and secondarily emitted electrons from the plate. This is not the way you want to operate a tetrode. The screen grid is not designed to handle a large amount of current and dissipate a large amount of power. In normal operation, the plate voltage is much higher than the screen voltage, so most of the cathode emissions arrive at the plate and no secondary emissions are attracted to the screen.

Look again at the characteristic curves of Figure 19–15. Let's resume our discussion as the plate voltage is increased above the screen voltage. As the plate voltage is increased above +90 V, no secondary emissions from the plate are attracted to the screen. Also, more and more of the electrons emitted from the cathode are accelerated through the screen to the plate. At a plate potential of approximately +110 V, the plate current reaches a near-maximum value. As plate voltage is increased further between +110 V and +500 V, there is very little further increase in plate current. In other words, the tetrode becomes a constant-current device.

Why does plate current reach a maximum value once the plate voltage is slightly higher than the screen voltage? Because the screen grid determines the quantity of electrons emitted from the cathode, along with filament voltage and control-grid bias. It is the screen potential that attracts and accelerates the electrons from the cathode. As the electrons approach the screen grid, they are being accelerated through a uniform electrostatic field. Most of these electrons rush through the screen and are captured by the positive plate as long as the plate potential is higher than the screen potential. Since the screen acts as a shield, the plate potential is not seen by the cathode. For the most part, the plate can only influence electrons that are accelerated into the region between the screen and itself. Thus, electrons arriving at the plate were originally pulled away from the cathode by the fixed positive screen potential, not the plate potential.

Operating Limitations

The tetrode has some operating limitations that must be considered. First, it should never be operated with zero, or low, plate voltage. If the screen voltage is present and there is no plate voltage, the screen will receive all the emitted cathode current and will burn up (assuming no overcurrent sensing circuit is present in the screen supply). Second, with a drive signal applied to the control grid, the plate voltage can never be allowed to drop below the value of the screen voltage. If this occurs during the positive peaks of the drive signal, the tube will be temporarily forced into the negative-resistance region, causing output signal distortion and possible overdissipation of the screen. Thus, the input drive must be kept low so the minimum plate voltage is always greater than the screen voltage.

Load Lines and Q Point

We will not take the time to demonstrate it here, but the load lines for tetrodes are developed on the characteristic curves the same way as for triodes. For the case shown in Figure 19–15, a quiescent operating point of $I_{p(Q)} = 4$ mA, $E_{p(Q)} = 300$ V, and $E_g \cong -3.7$ V on a load line from $E_{p(\text{cutoff})} = 500$ V to $I_{p(\text{sat})} = 10$ mA would be most likely for class A operation.

Time for another self-check. Take the time to review this section.

**Self-Check
19–4**

1. What is the screen grid and where is it placed in the tetrode?
2. What improvements are made by adding a screen grid?
3. What is the negative-resistance region on the characteristic curves for tetrodes?
4. Why does the screen current increase and the plate current decrease in the negative resistance region?
5. Why should the plate voltage always be higher than the screen voltage?

19–5 PENTODES AND BEAM POWER TUBES

VACUUM PENTODES

Pentode Construction

Figure 19–16 shows the schematic symbol and representative cross-sectional diagram of the vacuum pentode tube. The pentode is so named because it has five electrodes: the cathode, the control grid, the screen grid, the sup-

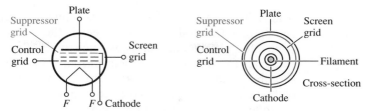

Figure 19–16 The vacuum pentode tube.

pressor grid, and the plate. The suppressor grid, a metal mesh or bar arrangement that is placed between the screen grid and the plate, is how the pentode differs from the tetrode. Furthermore, the suppressor grid is usually (not always) internally connected to the cathode as shown.

The Suppressor Grid

So what does the suppressor grid suppress? Recall the discussion of secondary emissions from the plate and the way the screen was able to collect these space-charge electrons at low levels of plate voltage. The suppressor grid reduces secondary emissions and repels secondarily emitted electrons back to the plate. In other words, the space charge is greatly reduced at the plate. This is made possible because the suppressor grid is at a negative potential compared to the plate and screen (suppressor connected to cathode in most cases). Thus, electrons that are accelerated through the screen grid actually decelerate through the suppressor grid, reducing secondary emissions. Any secondary emissions that do occur are returned to the plate by the repulsive negative potential of the suppressor grid. In summary, the suppressor grid reduces secondary emissions, prevents secondary emissions from reaching the screen, and eliminates the negative-resistance region on the characteristic curves. We'll look more closely at pentode characteristics in a moment.

THE BEAM POWER TUBE

Figure 19–17 illustrates the beam power tube. It is a power tube that has internal metal plates that form the cathode-emitted electrons into fan-shaped

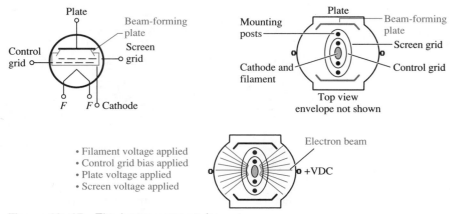

• Filament voltage applied
• Control grid bias applied
• Plate voltage applied
• Screen voltage applied

Figure 19–17 The beam power tube.

beams. The beam-forming plates are shown on each end of the elliptical grids and flattened cathode. As can be seen in the schematic symbol, the plates are connected to the cathode. Thus, they are at a negative potential, as are the electrons in the beam. The electrons have no choice but to avoid the beam-forming plates on their journey to the pentode plate. The beam-forming plates also act as suppressors to suppress secondary emissions from the pentode plate. Because of the beam forming and concentration of electrons, the beam power tube has a very high power gain compared to triodes, tetrodes, and other pentodes.

PENTODE AND BEAM POWER TUBE CHARACTERISTICS

Figure 19–18 shows a test circuit and set of characteristic curves for a beam power tube. The shapes of the characteristic curves are also the same for pentodes. The curves indicate that the negative resistance region has been eliminated for both the pentode and beam power tube. You may also recognize these curves as being very similar to those for n-channel JFETs, and so they are.

As before, each set of characteristic curves for a tube is determined for a specific filament voltage and screen voltage. In this case, the screen voltage is set at +300 V. The control-grid voltage is set at 5-V increments from −30 to 0 V. For each setting of the control-grid bias, the plate voltage is increased from 0 V to +500 V. Notice the plate current increases rapidly reaching a nearly constant level as plate voltage is increased. Thus, the pentode and beam power tubes are constant-current devices like the tetrode but without the negative-resistance region.

The cathode current is the sum of the screen current and the plate current for all values of plate voltage. Also, the total cathode current is fairly constant for all values of plate voltage. That means the screen current must decrease as the plate current increases, since screen current shifts to plate current as the plate voltage is increased. The screen current does not reach a minimum value until the plate current reaches maximum for each negative bias voltage. Therefore, according to the characteristic curves of Figure 19–18, when plate voltage is below approximately 50 V the screen current can

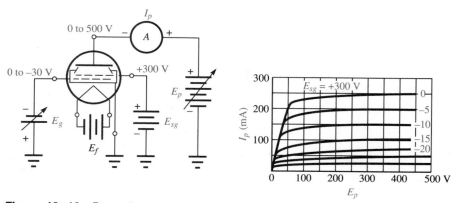

Figure 19–18   Pentode and beam power tube characteristics.

be quite high. As you can see, the plate voltage should be kept high enough so the tube is operating in the constant-current portion of the curves, thus preventing excessive screen current.

BEAM POWER TUBE APPLICATION

Figure 19–19 illustrates a classic application for beam power tubes and other power pentodes. As you can see, the circuit is a transformer-coupled push-pull amplifier, with each tube handling one alternation of any input cycle. Notice that a voltage divider is used to provide proper (specified) screen bias from the plate supply. A fixed supply is used to provide the -25 V of bias to the control grids via the input transformer's secondary. This places the quiescent operating point at $I_{p(Q)} \cong 50$ mA and $E_{p(Q)} \cong 400$ V.

Each half of the primary side of the output transformer has an impedance of approximately 2 kΩ, reflected from the 8-Ω load in accordance with the square of the turns ratio. Since the transformer is the load to the tubes, the DC load line is a nearly vertical line at 400 v. This is because the DC

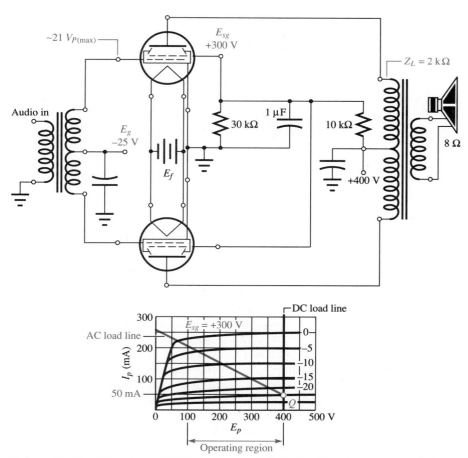

Figure 19–19 Class B push-pull audio amplifier using two beam power tubes.

resistance of the windings is very low. The AC load line is a diagonal running from the Q point to $i_{p(sat)} \cong 250$ mA where $i_{p(sat)} = I_{p(Q)} + E_{p(Q)}/Z_L = 50$ mA + (400 V/2 kΩ) = 250 mA (Formula 19–7). The safe, and low-distortion, operating region for each tube is from 50 to 200 mA of plate current and 100 to 400 V of plate voltage. The maximum positive peak voltage that can appear at the control grid of each tube is approximately 21 V. The maximum peak-to-peak input voltage level is determined by the input transformer's turns ratio and the 21-V peak limitation.

The overall theory of operation for this tube-type push-pull amplifier is the same as for transistor types. The difference here, of course, is the need for a filament supply, a control-grid supply, a screen supply or voltage-divider network, and a high-voltage plate supply. The tube's cathode must be heated for some time before screen and plate voltage and drive are applied.

So, why bother with all of this when you can simply use transistors? When it comes to 10,000-W and greater amplifiers, tubes are still the best choice as far as circuit simplicity and cost are concerned. High-power audio amplifier circuits like Figure 19–19 are common in broadcast transmitters. Instead of the speaker load, the amplifier is used to modulate the high-voltage plate or screen supply of the final radio-frequency power amplifier in the transmitter. You will learn more about this later in another textbook and course.

Take a few minutes to review and answer the questions of Self-Check 19–5.

Self-Check 19–5

1. What is a pentode?
2. What is the purpose for the suppressor grid?
3. How does a beam power tube differ from a standard pentode?
4. Compared to the cathode potential, what is the potential of the suppressor grid in most cases?
5. The characteristic curves for pentodes are similar to what semiconductor device's curves?

19–6 THE CATHODE RAY TUBE (CRT)

INTRODUCTION TO CATHODE RAY TUBES (CRTs)

Cathode ray tubes (CRTs) are special vacuum tubes used as display devices for televisions, computer displays, and oscilloscopes. The CRT can be divided into three main sections: (1) the electron gun assembly, (2) the deflection system, and (3) the phosphor-coated screen. The electron gun assembly creates a narrow beam of electrons that stream down the inside neck of the tube. Within the gun assembly are focus and acceleration anodes used to concentrate the beam and focus it to a small spot on the face of the CRT. The deflection system is used to bend the beam to cause it to move horizontally and vertically on the back of the phosphor-coated screen.

Oscilloscopes use electrostatic deflection systems in which the electron beam must travel between two sets of metal plates, a horizontal set and a vertical set. The difference of potential on pairs of plates determines the direction in which the beam is influenced to bend. Televisions use electro-magnetic deflection and focus systems. In these systems, an electromagnetic field is generated by a multiple-coil assembly, called a *yoke,* on the outside neck of the CRT. The magnetic field invades the CRT and influences the displacement of the beam. For our discussion here, we will explore only the electrostatic CRT.

THE ELECTROSTATIC CRT

The Base and Terminal Pins

A typical electrostatic CRT is shown in Figure 19–20. The pictorial is of a simplified CRT with the envelope removed. The base of the CRT is an arrangement of terminal pins and a keyway used to assist in proper connection of a socket with interconnect wires. Two of these base pins are used to supply filament voltage and current. Other pins are used for connection to the cathode, control grid, anodes, and deflection plates.

The Electron Gun

The indirectly heated barium-oxide-coated cathode is enclosed by a cylindrical control grid. The control grid has a small surface hole through which emitted electrons may pass and form a beam. The electron beam must then go through a set of acceleration and focusing anodes. A high positive potential is placed on the acceleration anodes and a lower positive potential is

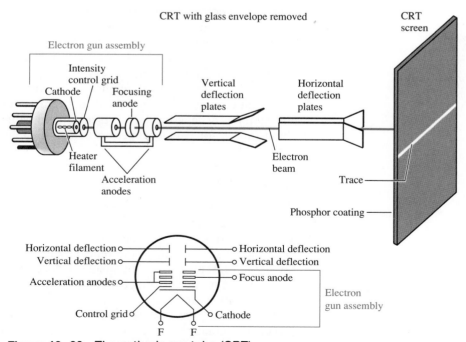

Figure 19–20   The cathode-ray tube (CRT).

applied to the focus anode. As a result, electrostatic lines of force extend from the acceleration anodes to the control grid and from the acceleration anodes to the focus anode. The acceleration anodes both accelerate the electrons and work with the focus anode to form an electronic lens that creates a pinpoint beam on the phosphor screen. The potential (voltage) on the focus anode is adjusted to set the focal point right at the phosphor surface.

Deflection

When the electron beam is centered on the screen, the potential on each deflection plate in a pair is the same. For example, each plate may have +200 V applied. An amplifier with a differential output is used to drive each set or pair of deflection plates. For horizontal deflection, the left plate, as you face the screen, of the two horizontal-deflection plates, starts out more positive than the right plate. This starts the beam on the left side of the screen, since a more positive potential on the left plate attracts the beam. A ramp voltage is used to drive the horizontal deflection amplifier, so the left plate becomes less positive and the right plate becomes more positive, which attracts the beam across the screen horizontally. A vertical-deflection amplifier with a differential output is used to drive the vertical-deflection plates in much the same way. When the top plate is more positive than the lower plate, the beam is pulled upward on the screen. When the lower plate is more positive than the upper plate, the beam is pulled downward on the screen.

Screen Characteristics

When the electron beam strikes the phosphor coating on the inside face of the screen, atoms in the phosphor coating become excited and release light. Valence electrons rise and fall in energy levels releasing light energy. This is known as **fluorescence.** As the beam moves on, the phosphor coating continues to glow for a short period of time. This is known as **phosphorescence.** The length of time the coating phosphoresces is known as its **persistence.** It is the time from when the electron beam is removed to when the light emission has decayed to 1% of its maximum value. Persistence ranges from about 0.03 s for oscilloscopes to 0.06 s for televisions and 3 s for radar screens.

The Return Path

How do the electrons that bombard the screen return to the cathode to complete the circuit? The electrons that hit the screen must go somewhere. They can't simply accumulate on the screen. If they did, a charge would build on the screen that would repel any further electrons (repel the beam). So where do they go? On the inside surface of the surrounding glass envelope is a conductive coating called the **aquadag,** which is colloidal graphite. A high positive potential is applied to the aquadag. When the electron beam strikes the phosphor coating, a very large number of electrons bounce off the screen as secondary emissions. These electrons are free of the inside surface of the screen and are rapidly attracted to the aquadag. They are drained off

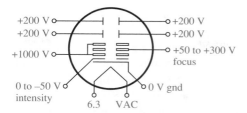

Figure 19–21   Generalized voltages for CRTs.

by the aquadag and returned to the ground to which the cathode is connected. Often, the aquadag and the acceleration anodes are connected together at the same high positive potential.

CRT Voltages

Figure 19–21 illustrates typical voltages that are applied to the electrodes of the electrostatic CRT. Naturally, these voltages vary depending on the actual CRT. In Figure 19–21, the cathode is at ground potential and all voltages are referenced to it. Notice the +1000 V applied to the acceleration anodes and the range of voltage on the focus anode. Also, notice the +200-V quiescent voltage applied to the deflection plates for a centered-beam condition. The negative control-grid voltage is used to vary the intensity of the beam and the brightness on the screen.

All voltages shown in Figure 19–21 are representative of the relative potentials that exist on the different electrodes. In a particular application, the cathode may be at −500 V, the control grid at −525 V, the acceleration anodes at +500 V, the aquadag at +500 V, and the focus anode at −400 V. The deflection plates may be at any potential between +100 V and +400 V. Also, many CRTs use anode and aquadag voltages as high as 12,000 V or so. In any case, these voltages are lethal, and great care must be taken to safely discharge high-voltage capacitors and the aquadag before repairs are attempted.

**Self-Check
19–6**

1. What are the three main parts of a CRT?
2. What is the difference between an electromagnetic and an electrostatic CRT?
3. Describe the parts of an electron gun assembly in an electrostatic CRT.
4. How is the electron beam focused onto the phosphor screen?
5. Briefly explain how the electron beam is electrostatically deflected across the screen horizontally.

19–7 HIGH-POWER VACUUM TUBES

INTRODUCTION TO HIGH-POWER VACUUM TUBES

In this section, your exploration will be limited to a few areas of importance that are usually omitted by many texts. You will consider the handling of high-power vacuum tubes in terms of supply voltages, protection circuitry, and cooling systems. You will be made aware of many operating considerations that do not exist for semiconductors and, for the most part, the obsolete low-power vacuum tubes. The vacuum-tube theory presented earlier applies directly to high-power vacuum tubes.

This section cannot and does not even begin to cover all there is to know about these powerful devices. However, the purpose here is to give you a general understanding of the circuit and cooling requirements for high-power vacuum tubes. You can further your knowledge as desired or needed by visiting a good technical library and obtaining information from manufacturers such as Varian EIMAC and General Electric.

CONTROL AND PROTECTION CIRCUITS

Figure 19–22 is a partial schematic diagram of the final power amplifier in a high-power AM transmitter. The schematic diagram shows most of the circuitry that is needed to support power-amplifier tubes. Through the examination of this representative circuit you will gain a basic understanding of how power tubes must be controlled and protected. Vacuum tubes such as these are very costly and can be destroyed in operation if electronic safeguards are not provided.

Control Circuitry

Voltages are applied to the power tube in timed stages. First, the filament voltage must be applied to allow the cathode/filament to heat to operating temperature. Next, the control-grid bias must be applied to ensure control over the tube before screen and plate voltage is applied. Recall that without negative control-grid bias the tube will conduct very heavily when plate and screen voltage are applied. After the negative bias is applied, the plate and screen voltage can be applied. The screen voltage is *never* applied without the plate voltage. If it were, the screen would collect all cathode-emitted electrons and dissipate a damaging amount of power.

Filament Control Circuitry

Let's begin our examination of Figure 19–22 by considering the filament circuit. Basically, a filament transformer is used to convert 240 VAC to 10 VAC at a very high current level, in this case 300 A (300 A and more of filament current is normal for high-power tubes in the range of 30 to 100 kW). Though only one power tube is shown here, a high-power transmitter typically has four high-power tubes (two audio, two RF). Each tube requires its own heavy-duty transformer (similar to a welding machine) to supply current and voltage to its filaments. As shown here, the filament voltage and current is usually applied in a step-start fashion. Let's see how.

First, the filament's ON button is pressed. This energizes the self-holding contactor (CC1) that supplies AC to the filament transformer's primary. When this contactor pulls in, power is applied to the filament transformer's primary and to a time-delay contactor on the secondary side. The time-delay contactor (CC2) is normally open and delays closing for a few seconds or so.

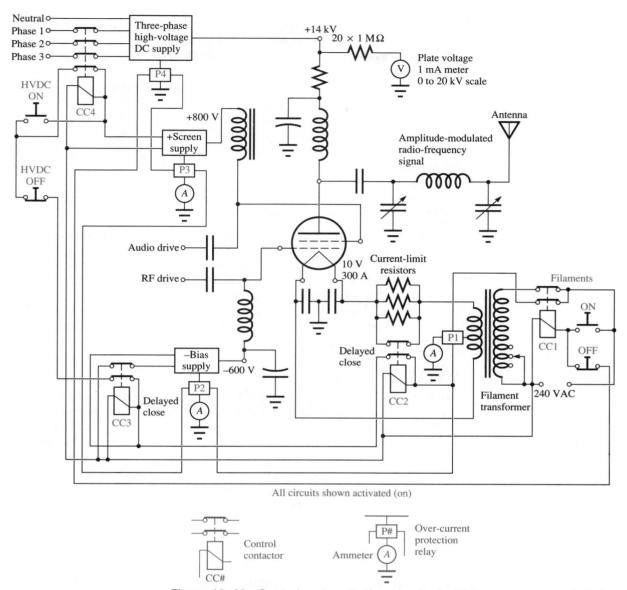

Figure 19–22 Control and protection circuits for high-power vacuum tubes.

Until the time-delay contactor closes, therefore, current is supplied to the filaments through a parallel arrangement of heavy-duty resistors. This is desirable because it prevents a very large initial surge of current through the filaments. When the filaments are cold, their resistance is low, which encourages a large inrush of current. As the filaments heat, their resistance increases (positive temperature coefficient). A very large initial inrush of current can permanently damage the filaments and destroy the tube. The surge resistors stay in-line for a few seconds until the time-delay contactor (CC2) pulls in and bypasses the resistors.

Notice the taps on the primary side of the filament transformer. These taps are usually available and permit some adjustment of the filament voltage to compensate for differences in line voltage and tube aging. Many engineers start a new tube at a lower-than-specified filament voltage to increase the life of the tube. When the tube is new, the cathode/filament does not need to be as hot to provide the required emissions. For the tube shown, an engineer may set the initial filament voltage in the range of 9.5 to 9.8 V and increase it as the tube ages. As time goes on, the filament voltage is increased to maintain cathode emissions high enough for full-power output. Useful life for most power tubes is in the range of 5,000 to 15,000 hours, depending on tube type and type of service.

Negative Bias Control Circuitry

Notice the filament time-delay contactor (CC2) has a set of auxiliary contacts that supply power to the negative bias supply and its time-delay contactor (CC3). Once the filament time-delay contactor pulls in, say five seconds after the filament's ON button is pushed, the negative bias delay relay begins to time out. The delay of this contactor may be set for from thirty seconds to three minutes, depending on manufacturer's recommendations, to allow the cathode to reach operating temperature. Once CC3 pulls in, the negative bias voltage is applied to the control grid.

High Voltage Plate Supply and Screen Supply

Auxiliary contacts on the negative bias contactor (CC3) pass control voltage along to the high-voltage supply contactor. The high-voltage supply contactor (CC4) is a three-phase contactor that is self-holding once the HVDC ON button is pressed. Therefore, once the negative bias time delay has ended, the high-voltage supply can be energized by manually pressing the HVDC ON button. In this circuit, screen voltage (+800 V) and plate voltage (+14,000 V) are applied at the same time. The circuit is wired in such a way that screen voltage cannot be applied without plate voltage. The HVDC ON button could be bypassed, so the screen and plate voltages would be applied automatically. However, most high-power transmitter circuits are designed as they are to permit the operator to make sure negative bias is present before high voltage is applied. Some modern transmitters are totally computer controlled. In these the computer monitors all voltages and controls the entire turn-on process. Once all time delays have finished, all voltages have been applied, and the tube(s) appear to be stable, the RF drive signal and the audio drive signal may be applied.

Protection Circuitry

If the tube becomes jeopardized due to an output loading problem or a loss of one of the supplies, a circuit must be in place that will automatically shut the system down. Shutdown must occur quickly. There is no time to wait for the human operator to shut power down. Among other sensor devices are overcurrent protection relays. These relays are designated as P1, P2, P3, and P4 in Figure 19–22 and are usually in the ground-return path for each supply as shown. All of these relays have normally closed contacts through which control voltage is passed to the various supply contactors. Each protection relay is preset to energize at a specific current threshold. The ground-return current for the particular supply flows through the coil of the protection relay. If the current threshold for the protection relay is reached, its contacts pull open and control voltage is interrupted. When the control-voltage circuit is interrupted, all power supply contactors release, and power is immediately removed. Though not shown, temperature, air flow, water level, and other normally-closed-contact sensors are also in series with the protection-relay contacts in the control-voltage loop. An ammeter is also present in the ground-return path for most supplies. All ammeters and voltmeters are mounted on the front panel, so the operator can easily check all circuits at regular intervals.

Flags

Each protection relay, and all other sensors—such as temperature sensors, airflow sensors, and water-level sensors for water-cooled systems—have a flag that is set when a fault occurs. For example, if the screen current increases to the threshold (trip level), the protection relay for the screen supply energizes and breaks the control-voltage path (loop). At the same time, another self-holding relay (not shown) pulls in and lights a front-panel light that is labeled "Screen Supply." The operator sees the light, which serves as a flag to inform the operator that the system was shut down due to too much screen current. A master reset button is used to reset all flags before the system is brought up again.

As you can see, high-power vacuum tubes require a significant amount of circuitry to control the application of operating voltages and to protect the tube(s). In addition to all of this, special consideration must be given to proper cooling of the tube. In most cases, power tubes are either forced-air cooled or water cooled, as we will now investigate.

COOLING SYSTEMS

Forced-Air Cooling

Figure 19–23 illustrates how high-power tubes are forced-air cooled. A blower motor is used to force air into an enclosure. The only air escape from the enclosure is through the pin or contact base and through the cooling fins of the power tube as directed by the cowling. Since it bridges the plate (cooling fins) and the chassis, which is usually at ground potential, the cowling is made of an insulative material, such as Teflon. The air flow in CFM (cubic feet per minute) must be at or above that which is specified by the tube manufacturer for the particular tube, its power dissipation, and operating environment. Not shown in the diagram is a small microswitch located in the mouth of the blower. This microswitch is connected to an air vane that causes the switch to close as long as the air is flowing at the specified rate. If the blower slows or air flow becomes restricted, the microswitch opens and the control-voltage loop is interrupted, power shuts down, and an air-flow flag is set.

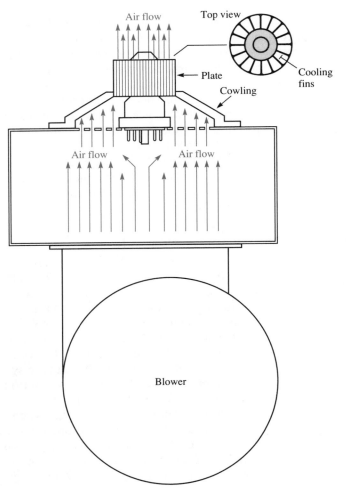

Figure 19–23 Air cooling of power tubes.

Figure 19–24 is an example of an air-cooled power tube. It is the EIMAC 3CX800A7 800-W power triode. Notice the plate-contact strap mounted on top of the cowling. The cowling surrounds the tube and the strap is latched to make tight contact with the plate, which is the large metal cooling-fin portion of the tube. Air is forced up around the mounting socket and through the cowling and cooling fins.

Vapor-Phase Cooling

Figure 19–25 illustrates a vapor-phase cooling system for high-power tubes. This type of cooling system is normally used for transmitters at and above 50 kW. If you look closely at the diagram, you will notice that this cooling system is not like the water-cooling system for your car. In an automobile system, the water is not permitted to boil but is circulated in liquid form throughout the system. However, in a vapor-phase system, the water is permitted to turn into steam at the plate of the tube(s). When the water is

Figure 19–24   The 3CX800A7 power tube. (Courtesy of Varian, Eimac Associates, Inc.)

converted from liquid to vapor, large quantities of heat are removed from the large copper plate of the tube. To convert 1 gram of water to vapor at 100°C requires 540 calories of heat. Compare that to only about 30 calories of heat needed to raise the temperature of 1 gram of water from 40 to 70°C. This means that 18 times more heat is removed from the tube for a given quantity of water when the water is converted to steam at the plate instead of simply being heated from 40 to 70°C as is done in water-cooled systems.

Let's take an overall look at the vapor-phase system. The water level is maintained at the proper level in the boiler by an automatic gravity-feed system. Water from the control box seeks its own level in the boiler. Sensors in the control box indicate when water must be added to the system due to evaporative loss or leak. Water may be added automatically from a reservoir through a solenoid-controlled valve or manually. If the water gets too low, a second sensor in the control box causes the system control voltage to be interrupted and a low-water flag to be set.

As water is converted to steam in the boiler, steam escapes from the boiler through a large glass tube. The steam is routed to the heat exchanger, or condenser, which is mounted above the transmitter either inside or outside the building. High-volume fans are used to cool the condenser. Condensed and cooled water is gravity fed back down the water return line to the boiler. The pressure equalization line is needed to insure that steam pressure does not back the water out of the boiler. It would take only a matter of seconds for the power tube to self-destruct without water.

Since the plate of the tube is bolted to the boiler, the boiler is at a high voltage. Therefore, the entire boiler must be insulated from the chassis. The boiler sits on ceramic insulators and glass and/or synthetic tubing is used to transfer water and steam in and out of the boiler. All terminal connections are available on top of the tube, since it is inverted.

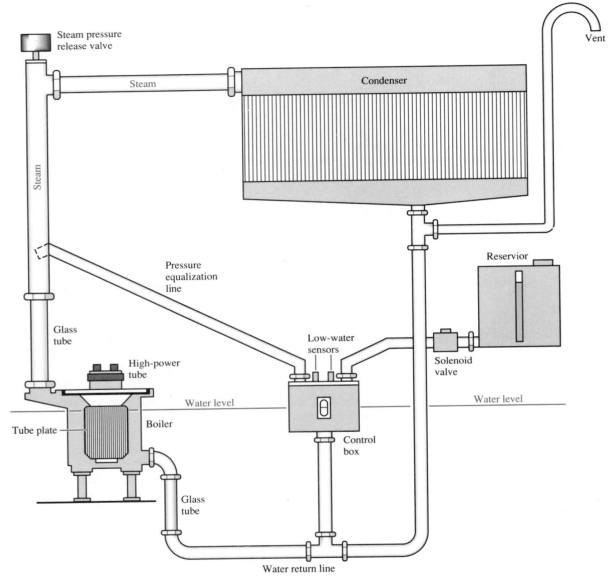

Figure 19–25 Vapor-phase cooling system.

The 4CV250,000C Vapor-Cooled Power Tube

Figure 19–26 is a photograph of a very-high-power vacuum tetrode. This tube is vapor cooled and is mounted with the plate (cooling vanes) down into the boiler. The 4CV250,000C is rated for a maximum plate dissipation of 250,000 W, producing nearly 500,000 W of output power. The tube itself weighs 180 lbs (81.8 kg), is 26.9 in. high (68.3 cm) and 15.1 in. in diameter (38.3 cm). Its thoriated tungsten filament is rated at 12 V, drawing 650 A of current. Internal filament supports are water cooled. Typical operating pa-

Figure 19–26 The 4CV250,000C power tube. (Courtesy of Varian, Eimac Associates, Inc.)

rameters for Class C continuous-wave transmission (as in FM transmission) are as follows:

Typical Class C Operation for the 4CV250,000C	
Plate voltage	19.0 kV
Screen voltage	800 VDC
Grid voltage	−800 VDC
Plate current	32.5 A
Screen current	≅3.5 A
Grid current	≅2.5 A
Driving power	≅3 kW
Plate output power	460 kW
Plate dissipation	155 kW
RF load impedance	275 Ω

As you have seen from this section, high-power vacuum tubes require a lot of special control and protection circuitry to insure reliable and long-lived operation. Power must be applied to the tube in this order: filament voltage, control-grid bias, plate and screen voltage. The tube(s) must be monitored carefully for overcurrent conditions and power must be removed instantly when an overload is detected. High-power tubes also require special cooling systems that are interconnected with the control and protection system via special flow and level sensors. Take time now to review this section and answer the questions of Self-Check 19–7.

Self-Check 19–7

1. What is a step-start filament circuit?
2. Which of these should be applied first to a high-power tetrode?
   (a) plate voltage   (b) screen voltage
   (c) control-grid bias   (d) filament voltage
3. Which of the choices in question two should be applied second?
4. Describe the operation of an overcurrent protection relay.
5. Why is vapor-phase cooling of high-power tubes more efficient than water cooling?

SUMMARY

FORMULAS

(19–1) $g_m = \Delta I_p / \Delta E_g$ (transconductance)

(19–2) $r_p = \Delta E_p / \Delta I_p$ (AC plate resistance)

(19–3) $\mu = \Delta E_p / \Delta E_g$ (amplification factor)

(19–4) $\mu = g_m \cdot r_p$ (amplification factor)

(19–5) $A_V = g_m \cdot R_L$ (voltage gain)

(19–6) $R_k = |E_b| / I_{p(Q)}$ (cathode self-bias resistor)

(19–7) $i_{p(\text{sat})} = I_{p(Q)} + (E_{p(Q)} / Z_L)$ (AC load line)

(19–8) $e_{p(\text{cutoff})} = E_{p(Q)} + (I_{p(Q)} \cdot Z_L)$ (AC load line)

CONCEPTS

- The cathode of a vacuum tube releases electrons when sufficiently heated—a process called *thermionic emission.*
- Thermionically emitted electrons are attracted to the positively charged plate (anode).
- A mesh or barlike structure called a *control grid* is placed between the cathode and plate in a triode to control electron flow. The control grid is negatively biased.
- The screen grid in a tetrode is used to reduce interelectrode capacitance, thereby increasing tube frequency response and frequency stability.
- The positive potential on the screen grid in a tetrode or pentode determines the maximum amount of plate current. The plate potential has little effect on plate current.
- Secondary emissions from the plate when plate potential is less than screen potential are captured by the screen in a tetrode. This causes plate resistance to decrease as plate voltage is increased until it equals the screen potential. This is known as negative resistance, since plate current decreases as plate voltage increases.

- The negative resistance effect is eliminated in pentodes because the suppressor grid reduces secondary emissions and prevents secondary emissions from being collected by the screen.
- Pentodes and beam power tubes have characteristic curves similar to those of *n*-channel JFETs.
- In a CRT, the purpose for the electron gun is to form and focus the electron beam.
- In an electrostatic CRT, the electron beam is deflected vertically and horizontally by applying an imbalanced positive potential to plate pairs. The electron beam is attracted toward the more positive plate.
- In an electromagnetic CRT, the electron beam is deflected vertically and horizontally by the magnetic fields of two coils on the neck of the CRT.
- The phosphor coating on the screen of a CRT fluoresces when bombarded by electrons and phosphoresces for a short time once the beam is removed. This is known as persistence.
- Heavy-duty contactors are used to control power turn-on to a high-power tube in proper sequence: filaments first, then negative control-grid bias, then plate and screen voltage.
- Overcurrent protection relays are used to interrupt the control-voltage circuit when current to a tube electrode is too high.
- A flag is usually a light that lights when a protection relay or other protection device is tripped. Flags must be reset before the system is restarted.
- Forced-air cooling requires that a certain rate of flow of air be produced through the finned plate of the high-power tube.
- Vapor-phase cooling takes advantage of the fact that much more heat is removed from the tube when the plate of the tube converts the water to steam than if the plate merely increases the temperature of the water in a range below the boiling point.

PROCEDURES

Applying Power to a High-Power Tetrode

1. Apply filament voltage in a step-start fashion.
2. Apply control-grid bias.
3. Apply plate and screen voltage or plate then screen voltage. Never apply screen voltage before plate voltage.
4. Apply audio- or radio-frequency drive.

NEED-TO-KNOW SOLUTION

As you know by now, a tetrode is a vacuum tube that has a cathode, control grid, screen grid, and plate. The screen grid is very important since it reduces interelectrode capacitance and, depending on the positive bias applied to it, determines the maximum plate current. The screen grid will draw some current in normal operation but it must not draw too much or it will dissipate too much power and melt and/or warp, shorting against the control grid and/or plate. Destruction of the screen means the destruction of the tube. That's why overcurrent protection circuits are so important in high-power tube circuits.

QUESTIONS

19–1 INTRODUCTION TO VACUUM TUBES

1. What is a vacuum tube?
2. What is the Edison effect?
3. Explain thermionic emission.
4. What is the space charge and how is it formed?
5. Describe Fleming's valve.
6. What is the common name for the anode of a vacuum tube?
7. Describe the directly heated cathode.
8. Describe the indirectly heated cathode.
9. What is the coating on an indirectly heated cathode?
10. Filaments do not take very much power. True or false?

19–2 VACUUM DIODES

11. Which of the schematic symbols in Figure 19–27 is that of the vacuum
    Fig. 19–27 diode?

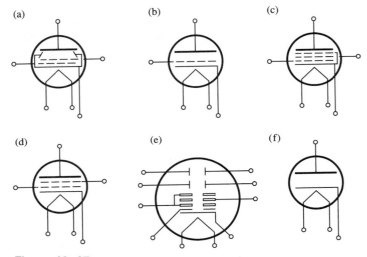

(a)   (b)   (c)   (d)   (e)   (f)

Figure 19–27

12. Describe the construction of a typical vacuum diode.
13. What kind of information can you get from the data sheet for a vacuum diode?
14. Which is usually used to heat an indirectly heated cathode, (a) AC or (b) DC?
15. What does cathode space charge have to do with forward conduction characteristics of the vacuum diode?
16. Explain how the vapor is formed in a mercury-vapor diode.
17. How does the gas in a gas-filled diode improve forward-conduction characteristics?
18. Where might mercury-vapor diodes be used?
19. What is the purpose for a bleeder resistor in a high-voltage DC supply?
20. What is a thyratron?

19–3 VACUUM TRIODES

21. Which of the schematic symbols in Figure 19–27 is that of the vacuum triode?
22. Describe the construction of a basic vacuum triode.
23. Who is credited with the first vacuum triode?
24. With respect to the cathode, is the control-grid voltage (a) negative or (b) positive?
25. Does proper biasing of the control grid have the effect of (a) increasing plate current or (b) decreasing plate current?
26. Will making the control grid more negative as compared to the cathode (a) increase plate current or (b) decrease plate current?
27. Why are the characteristic curves for a particular tube dependent on, or based on, a specific filament voltage?
28. What happens to plate current and plate power dissipation when control-grid bias is removed, where $E_g = 0$ V?
29. What is static transconductance?
30. What is the static AC plate resistance for a vacuum tube?
31. Why is it important to know the AC plate resistance for a tube?
32. Describe the static amplification factor for a vacuum tube.
33. How does the static mu for a tube compare to a vacuum-tube amplifier's actual circuit voltage gain?
34. How is dynamic transconductance different from static transconductance?
35. What is fixed bias in regard to vacuum tubes?
36. Describe grid-leak bias.
37. Describe the advantages and disadvantages of grid-leak bias.
38. Describe cathode self-bias.
39. What is the advantage of combination bias?
40. What factors determine the slope of the AC load line?

19–4 VACUUM TETRODES

41. Which of the schematic symbols in Figure 19–27 is that of the vacuum tetrode?
42. How is the tetrode physically different than the triode?
43. What is interelectrode capacitance?
44. What are two major limitations of the vacuum triode?
45. How does the screen grid reduce plate-to-control-grid internal capacitance?
46. Characteristic curves for a tetrode are based on a specific filament voltage and what else?
47. Describe the negative-resistance characteristic of a tetrode.
48. What causes the negative-resistance phenomenon in tetrodes?
49. Why does the plate current of a tetrode reach a maximum value when plate voltage is slightly higher than screen voltage?
50. Why should the tetrode never be operated with a plate voltage lower than the screen voltage?

19–5 PENTODES AND BEAM POWER TUBES

51. Which of the schematic symbols in Figure 19–27 is that of the vacuum pentode?
52. What purpose does the suppressor grid serve in a pentode?
53. What is the usual potential on the suppressor grid compared to the cathode potential?
54. How is the beam power tube physically different than the regular pentode?
55. List two purposes for the beam-forming plates in a beam power tube.
56. Why is there no negative-resistance region in the characteristic curves for a pentode or beam power tube?
57. How are the characteristic curves for a pentode similar to the characteristic curves for an *n*-channel JFET?

19–6 THE CATHODE RAY TUBE (CRT)

58. What are the three main sections of a cathode ray tube?
59. What are the two basic types of CRTs?
60. List the parts of the electron gun assembly in a CRT.
61. Explain in simple terms how the electron beam is focused on the CRT screen.
62. Describe how the electron beam is deflected vertically in an electrostatic CRT.
63. What is the difference between fluorescence and phosphorescence?
64. In regard to the phosphor coating on the CRT screen, what is persistence?
65. Explain how the overall circuit in a CRT is completed. In other words, where do the electrons go once they hit the screen of the CRT?

19–7 HIGH-POWER VACUUM TUBES

66. What is the overall purpose for the control circuitry in a high-power tube circuit?
67. Why is it important to turn on a high-power tetrode a step at a time?
68. Why is a step-start filament circuit a good idea for high-power tube circuits?
69. Can the filament voltage of a new tube be set slightly lower than the value specified by the manufacturer when it is first installed? Why?
70. Why is it important that the screen voltage not come on before the plate voltage in a high-power tetrode circuit?
71. What is the purpose for protection circuitry in a high-power tube system?
72. Describe the operation of an overcurrent protection relay.
73. Besides the protection relays what other protection devices might there be in the control-voltage loop?
74. If a failure occurs in a high-power transmitter system, how will you know where the failure occurred?
75. Briefly describe forced-air cooling.

76. How do you know how much forced air is needed in order to cool a high-power tube?
77. Briefly describe vapor-phase cooling.
78. Why is vapor-phase cooling more efficient than a simple water-cooling system?
79. Why is the boiler in a vapor-phase cooling system insulated from chassis ground?
80. How will you know if water is getting low in the vapor-phase cooling system?

PROBLEMS

19-3 VACUUM TRIODES

1. Use the characteristic curves of Figure 19–28 to determine the static transconductance with the plate voltage held constant at 4,000 V while the control-grid voltage changes between −400 and −600 V. (Use Figure 19–10 as an example.)

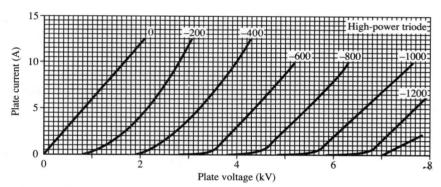

Figure 19–28

2. Use the characteristic curves of Figure 19–28 to determine the static AC plate resistance with the control-grid voltage held constant at −600 V while the plate current changes between 5 and 7.5 A. (Use Figure 19–10 as an example.)
3. Use the characteristic curves of Figure 19–28 to determine the static mu (μ) with the plate current held constant at 6.25 A while the control-grid voltage changes between −400 and −600 V. (Use Figure 19–10 as an example.)
4. Use the characteristic curves of Figure 19–29 to determine the static transconductance with the plate voltage held constant at 150 V while the control-grid voltage changes between −20 and −30 V. (Use Figure 19–10 as an example.)
5. Use the characteristic curves of Figure 19–29 to determine the static AC plate resistance with the control-grid voltage held constant at −20 V while the plate current changes between 25 and 50 mA. (Use Figure 19–10 as an example.)
6. Use the characteristic curves of Figure 19–29 to determine the static mu (μ) with the plate current held constant at 25 mA while the control-

grid voltage changes between −20 and −30 V. (Use Figure 19–10 as an example.)

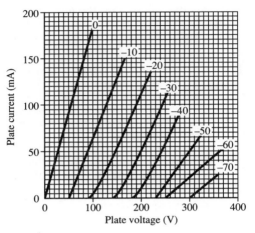

Figure 19–29

7. Draw the DC load line and plot the Q point for the circuit of Figure 19–30. (Use Figure 19–11 as an example.)
8. For Figure 19–30, determine the voltage gain (A_V) with a 20-V peak-to-peak input signal.

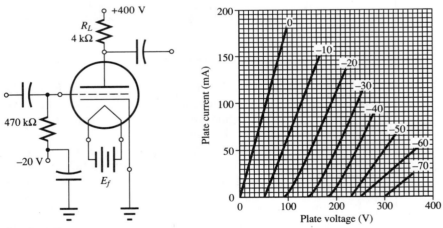

Figure 19–30

9. For Figure 19–30, determine the dynamic transconductance of the tube as the control-grid voltage varies between −10 and −30 V.
10. If cathode self-bias was used in Figure 19–30 instead of fixed bias, what value would R_k be?

11. If the circuit of Figure 19–30 is capacitor-coupled to a 10-kΩ resistor, what are the values of $i_{p(\text{sat})}$ and $e_{p(\text{cutoff})}$ that define the AC load line?

12. Draw the AC load line defined in Problem 11 on the chart of Figure 19–30. Use the AC load line to determine the voltage gain with the 20-V peak-to-peak input signal. (Use Figure 19–13 as an example.)

13. Draw the DC load line and plot the Q point for the circuit of Figure 19–31. (Use Figure 19–13 as an example.)

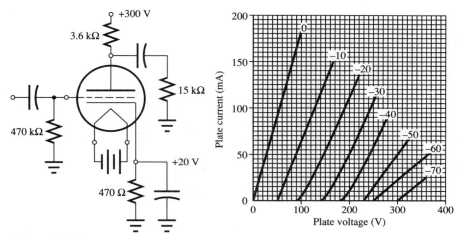

Figure 19–31

14. For Figure 19–31, determine and draw the AC load line.

15. For Figure 19–31, determine the dynamic transconductance of the tube as the control-grid voltage varies between -10 and -30 V.

16. Use the dynamic transconductance calculated in Problem 15 and the total AC load on the plate (Z_L) to calculate the voltage gain (A_V).

17. Use the AC load line of Figure 19–31 to determine the voltage gain with a 20-V peak-to-peak input signal. (Use Figure 19–13 as an example.)

ADDITIONAL PROBLEMS

18. Determine the screen voltage for Figure 19–32.

19. Define the DC load line for the circuit of Figure 19–32. (Find $I_{p(\text{sat})}$ and $E_{p(\text{cutoff})}$.)

20. Determine the Q point for the circuit of Figure 19–32. (Find $I_{p(Q)}$ and $E_{p(Q)}$.)

21. Define the AC load line for the circuit of Figure 19–32. (Find $i_{p(\text{sat})}$ and $e_{p(\text{cutoff})}$.)

22. Use the curves of Figure 19–32 to determine the dynamic transconductance ($\Delta I_p / \Delta E_g$) with an input signal of 10 $V_{\text{P-P}}$

23. Calculate the voltage amplification factor for the circuit of Figure 19–32.
24. Calculate the peak-to-peak output voltage for the circuit of Figure 19–32.
25. Calculate the plate power dissipation for the circuit of Figure 19–32.

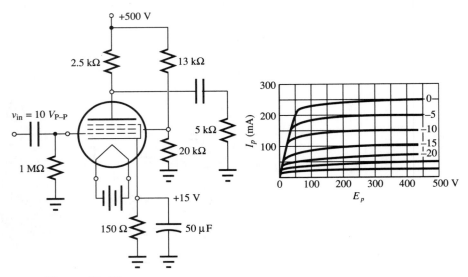

Figure 19–32

26. Calculate the power dissipated in the 5-kΩ load resistor with a 10 V_{P-P} sine wave applied to the circuit of Figure 19–32.
27. Calculate the total power delivered to the amplifier from the 500-V supply and calculate the amplifier's power efficiency. (% Eff = 100% · $P_{out}/P_{in(total)}$).

ANSWERS TO SELF-CHECKS

SELF-CHECK 19–1

1. Thomas A. Edison
2. Thermionic emission occurs when electrons escape the bonds of a conductor at high temperatures.
3. Fleming's valve was the first practical vacuum-tube diode.
4. Space charge is the cloud of electrons that exists around a conductor due to continual thermionic emissions (or secondary emissions, as you will see later).
5. The directly heated cathode is the filament itself (thoriated tungsten). An indirectly heated cathode has a separate tungsten filament serving as the heater.

SELF-CHECK 19–2

1. The cathode develops a space charge that works against the positive plate potential. The space charge has a repelling effect on other electrons on the cathode.
2. The cathode is only able to emit a certain number of electrons at a given temperature. Thus, a further increase in plate voltage has no effect on plate current.
3. First, the cathode must be heated. Second, the plate must be positive compared to the cathode.
4. A vapor must form inside the tube. The vapor ionizes and conducts electrons from cathode to plate.
5. The grounding stick is a conductive rod and hook with a long strap to ground. It has an insulated handle and is used to ensure that all circuits are discharged while repairs are made.

SELF-CHECK 19–3

1. The control grid is used to reduce current. A negative bias is applied to the control grid to act as a repelling force to electrons on the cathode.
2. Static transconductance is the ratio of the change in plate current for a given change in control-grid bias while plate voltage is held constant, $g_m = \Delta I_p / \Delta E_g$.
3. The static mu (μ) of the tube is always higher than the actual amplification (A_V) realized in a circuit.
4. Grid-leak bias varies with drive level. With no drive, grid-leak bias leaks off and the tube conducts heavily. Cathode self-bias is stable with or without a drive signal.
5. The dynamic transconductance is 3 mA/3 V = 1,000 μS. The amplifier's voltage gain into a 25.6-kΩ AC load is 1,000 μS · 25.6 kΩ = 25.6.

SELF-CHECK 19–4

1. The screen grid is a mesh or barlike grid that is placed between the control grid and the plate.
2. The screen grid reduces interelectrode capacitance and increases the tube's frequency response and stability.
3. The negative-resistance region is that part on the plate-current curve at which the plate current decreases as the plate voltage increases.
4. Secondary emissions from the plate are captured by the screen, which decreases plate current and increases screen current.
5. The plate voltage should be higher than the screen voltage to insure that secondary emissions from the plate are attracted back to the plate.

SELF-CHECK 19–5

1. A pentode is a vacuum tube that has a cathode, control grid, screen grid, suppressor grid, and plate.

2. The suppressor grid reduces secondary emissions from the plate and prevents secondarily emitted electrons from being attracted to the screen, thus eliminating the negative-resistance characteristic.
3. The beam power tube has a shield that directs the electrons to the plate and reduces secondary emissions.
4. In most cases, the suppressor grid is at the same potential as the cathode.
5. An *n*-channel JFET

SELF-CHECK 19–6

1. (1) the electron gun assembly, (2) the deflection system, (3) the phosphor-coated screen
2. The electromagnetic CRT uses a set of coils on the neck of the CRT to create a magnetic field used to deflect the electron beam. The electrostatic CRT uses two sets of internal deflection plates to deflect the beam by electrostatic attraction and repulsion.
3. The electron gun assembly consists of a filament to heat the cathode, a solid control grid with a small center hole, and acceleration and focusing anodes.
4. The electrons in the beam are influenced by the electrostatic lines of force that exist between the acceleration anode(s) and the focusing anode. The electrostatic field causes the beam to converge on the phosphor coating.
5. When the beam is at center screen, the potential on both horizontal-deflection plates is equal. An amplifier with a differential output is used to shift the potential on the plate pairs. The electron beam is pulled toward the more positive plate.

SELF-CHECK 19–7

1. A step-start filament circuit is one that has heavy-duty resistors in series with the filament for a short time when filament voltage is applied. This reduces the surge in initial filament current.
2. (d)
3. (c)
4. The overcurrent protection relay has normally closed contacts that are part of the control voltage loop that feeds voltage to the power supply contactors. The coil of the protection relay is powered by the supply current. If the supply current is too high, reaching a set threshold, the protection relay energizes and opens its contacts to break the control-voltage circuit.
5. Much more heat is removed from the tube when water is converted to steam.

**SUGGESTED
PROJECTS**

1. Add some of the main concepts from this chapter to your Electronics Notebook.
2. Visit a local radio or television station to see how high-power vacuum tubes are used in their transmitters.

APPENDIX A
Data Sheets

CONTRIBUTORS

MOTOROLA, INC. DATA SHEETS

Motorola data sheets are the copyright of Motorola, Inc and are reproduced by written permission.

NATIONAL SEMICONDUCTOR CORPORATION DATA SHEETS

National Semiconductor data sheets are reprinted with written permission of National Semiconductor Corporation. National holds no responsibility for any circuitry described. National reserves the right at any time to change without notice said circuitry.

> **Life Support Policy**
>
> National's products are not authorized for use as critical components in life support devices or systems without the express written approval of the president of National Semiconductor Corporation. As used herein:
>
> 1. Life support devices or systems are devices or systems which, (a) are intended for surgical implant into the body, or (b) support or sustain life and whose failure to perform, when properly used in accordance with instructions for use provided in the labeling, can be reasonably expected to result in a significant injury to the user.
>
> 2. A critical component is any component of a life support device or system whose failure to perform can be reasonably expected to cause the failure of the life support device or system, or to affect its safety or effectiveness.

EXAR CORPORATION DATA SHEETS

EXAR data sheets are the copyright of EXAR Corporation and are reproduced with express written authorization.

APPENDIX A   TABLE OF CONTENTS

MOTOROLA DATA SHEETS

NATIONAL SEMICONDUCTOR DATA SHEETS

EXAR DATA SHEETS

MAXIMUM RATINGS

Rating	Symbol	Value	Unit
Collector-Emitter Voltage	V_{CEO}	40	Vdc
Collector-Base Voltge	V_{CBO}	60	Vdc
Emitter-Base Voltage	V_{EBO}	6.0	Vdc
Collector Current — Continuous	I_C	200	mAdc
Total Device Dissipation @ T_A = 25°C Derate above 25°C	P_D	625 5.0	mW mW/°C
*Total Device Dissipation @ T_C = 25°C Derate above 25°C	P_D	1.5 12	Watts mW/°C
Operating and Storage Junction Temperature Range	T_J, T_{stg}	− 55 to + 150	°C

*THERMAL CHARACTERISTICS

Characteristic	Symbol	Max	Unit
Thermal Resistance, Junction to Case	$R_{\theta JC}$	83.3	°C/W
Thermal Resistance, Junction to Ambient	$R_{\theta JA}$	200	°C/W

*Indicates Data in addition to JEDEC Requirements.

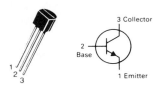

2N3903
2N3904

CASE 29-04, STYLE 1
TO-92 (TO-226AA)

3 Collector

2 Base

1 Emitter

GENERAL PURPOSE
TRANSISTOR

NPN SILICON

ELECTRICAL CHARACTERISTICS (T_A = 25°C unless otherwise noted.)

Characteristic		Symbol	Min	Max	Unit
OFF CHARACTERISTICS					
Collector-Emitter Breakdown Voltage(1) (I_C = 1.0 mAdc, I_B = 0)		$V_{(BR)CEO}$	40	—	Vdc
Collector-Base Breakdown Voltage (I_C = 10 μAdc, I_E = 0)		$V_{(BR)CBO}$	60	—	Vdc
Emitter-Base Breakdown Voltage (I_E = 10 μAdc, I_C = 0)		$V_{(BR)EBO}$	6.0	—	Vdc
Base Cutoff Current (V_{CE} = 30 Vdc, V_{EB} = 3.0 Vdc)		I_{BL}	—	50	nAdc
Collector Cutoff Current (V_{CE} = 30 Vdc, V_{EB} = 3.0 Vdc)		I_{CEX}	—	50	nAdc
ON CHARACTERISTICS					
DC Current Gain(1)		h_{FE}			—
(I_C = 0.1 mAdc, V_{CE} = 1.0 Vdc)	2N3903 2N3904		20 40	— —	
(I_C = 1.0 mAdc, V_{CE} = 1.0 Vdc)	2N3903 2N3904		35 70	— —	
(I_C = 10 mAdc, V_{CE} = 1.0 Vdc)	2N3903 2N3904		50 100	150 300	
(I_C = 50 mAdc, V_{CE} = 1.0 Vdc)	2N3903 2N3904		30 60	— —	
(I_C = 100 mAdc, V_{CE} = 1.0 Vdc)	2N3903 2N3904		15 30	— —	
Collector-Emitter Saturation Voltage(1) (I_C = 10 mAdc, I_B = 1.0 mAdc) (I_C = 50 mAdc, I_B = 5.0 mAdc)		$V_{CE(sat)}$	— —	0.2 0.3	Vdc
Base-Emitter Saturation Voltage(1) (I_C = 10 mAdc, I_B = 1.0 mAdc) (I_C = 50 mAdc, I_B = 5.0 mAdc)		$V_{BE(sat)}$	0.65 —	0.85 0.95	Vdc
SMALL-SIGNAL CHARACTERISTICS					
Current-Gain — Bandwidth Product (I_C = 10 mAdc, V_{CE} = 20 Vdc, f = 100 MHz)	2N3903 2N3904	f_T	250 300	— —	MHz

2N3903, 2N3904

ELECTRICAL CHARACTERISTICS (continued) (T_A = 25°C unless otherwise noted.)

Characteristic		Symbol	Min	Max	Unit
Output Capacitance (V_{CB} = 5.0 Vdc, I_E = 0, f = 1.0 MHz)		C_{obo}	—	4.0	pF
Input Capacitance (V_{BE} = 0.5 Vdc, I_C = 0, f = 1.0 MHz)		C_{ibo}	—	8.0	pF
Input Impedance (I_C = 1.0 mAdc, V_{CE} = 10 Vdc, f = 1.0 kHz)	2N3903 2N3904	h_{ie}	1.0 1.0	8.0 10	k ohms
Voltage Feedback Ratio (I_C = 1.0 mAdc, V_{CE} = 10 Vdc, f = 1.0 kHz)	2N3903 2N3904	h_{re}	0.1 0.5	5.0 8.0	X 10^{-4}
Small-Signal Current Gain (I_C = 1.0 mAdc, V_{CE} = 10 Vdc, f = 1.0 kHz)	2N3903 2N3904	h_{fe}	50 100	200 400	—
Output Admittance (I_C = 1.0 mAdc, V_{CE} = 10 Vdc, f = 1.0 kHz)		h_{oe}	1.0	40	μmhos
Noise Figure (I_C = 100 μAdc, V_{CE} = 5.0 Vdc, R_S = 1.0 k ohms, f = 10 Hz to 15.7 kHz)	2N3903 2N3904	NF	— —	6.0 5.0	dB

SWITCHING CHARACTERISTICS

Delay Time	(V_{CC} = 3.0 Vdc, V_{BE} = 0.5 Vdc,		t_d	—	35	ns
Rise Time	I_C = 10 mAdc, I_{B1} = 1.0 mAdc)		t_r	—	35	ns
Storage Time	(V_{CC} = 3.0 Vdc, I_C = 10 mAdc,	2N3903 2N3904	t_s	— —	175 200	ns
Fall Time	I_{B1} = I_{B2} = 1.0 mAdc)		t_f	—	50	ns

(1) Pulse Test: Pulse Width ≤ 300 μs, Duty Cycle ≤ 2.0%.

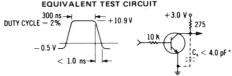

FIGURE 1 – DELAY AND RISE TIME EQUIVALENT TEST CIRCUIT

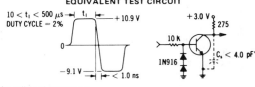

FIGURE 2 – STORAGE AND FALL TIME EQUIVALENT TEST CIRCUIT

*Total shunt capacitance of test jig and connectors

TYPICAL TRANSIENT CHARACTERISTICS
— T_J = 25°C --- T_J = 125°C

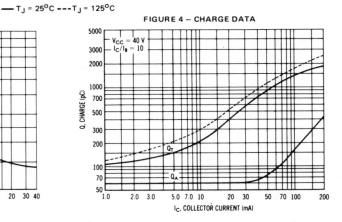

FIGURE 3 – CAPACITANCE

FIGURE 4 – CHARGE DATA

MAXIMUM RATINGS

Rating	Symbol	Value	Unit
Collector-Emitter Voltage	V_{CEO}	40	Vdc
Collector-Base Voltage	V_{CBO}	40	Vdc
Emitter-Base Voltage	V_{EBO}	5.0	Vdc
Collector Current — Continuous	I_C	200	mAdc
Total Device Dissipation @ $T_A = 25°C$ Derate above 25°C	P_D	625 5.0	mW mW/°C
Total Power Dissipation @ $T_A = 60°C$	P_D	250	mW
Total Device Dissipation @ $T_C = 25°C$ Derate above 25°C	P_D	1.5 12	Watts mW/°C
Operating and Storage Junction Temperature Range	T_J, T_{stg}	−55 to +150	°C

*THERMAL CHARACTERISTICS

Characteristic	Symbol	Max	Unit
Thermal Resistance, Junction to Case	$R_{\theta JC}$	83.3	°C/W
Thermal Resistance, Junction to Ambient	$R_{\theta JA}$	200	°C/W

2N3905
2N3906

CASE 29-04, STYLE 1
TO-92 (TO-226AA)

3 Collector

2 Base

1 Emitter

1
2
3

GENERAL PURPOSE TRANSISTOR

PNP SILICON

ELECTRICAL CHARACTERISTICS ($T_A = 25°C$ unless otherwise noted.)

Characteristic		Symbol	Min	Max	Unit
OFF CHARACTERISTICS					
Collector-Emitter Breakdown Voltage(1) ($I_C = 1.0$ mAdc, $I_B = 0$)		$V_{(BR)CEO}$	40	—	Vdc
Collector-Base Breakdown Voltage ($I_C = 10$ μAdc, $I_E = 0$)		$V_{(BR)CBO}$	40	—	Vdc
Emitter-Base Breakdown Voltage ($I_E = 10$ μAdc, $I_C = 0$)		$V_{(BR)EBO}$	5.0	—	Vdc
Base Cutoff Current ($V_{CE} = 30$ Vdc, $V_{BE} = 3.0$ Vdc)		I_{BL}	—	50	nAdc
Collector Cutoff Current ($V_{CE} = 30$ Vdc, $V_{BE} = 3.0$ Vdc)		I_{CEX}	—	50	nAdc
ON CHARACTERISTICS(1)					
DC Current Gain ($I_C = 0.1$ mAdc, $V_{CE} = 1.0$ Vdc)	2N3905 2N3906	h_{FE}	30 60	— —	—
($I_C = 1.0$ mAdc, $V_{CE} = 1.0$ Vdc)	2N3905 2N3906		40 80	— —	
($I_C = 10$ mAdc, $V_{CE} = 1.0$ Vdc)	2N3905 2N3906		50 100	150 300	
($I_C = 50$ mAdc, $V_{CE} = 1.0$ Vdc)	2N3905 2N3906		30 60	— —	
($I_C = 100$ mAdc, $V_{CE} = 1.0$ Vdc)	2N3905 2N3906		15 30	— —	
Collector-Emitter Saturation Voltage ($I_C = 10$ mAdc, $I_B = 1.0$ mAdc) ($I_C = 50$ mAdc, $I_B = 5.0$ mAdc)		$V_{CE(sat)}$	— —	0.25 0.4	Vdc
Base-Emitter Saturation Voltage ($I_C = 10$ mAdc, $I_B = 1.0$ mAdc) ($I_C = 50$ mAdc, $I_B = 5.0$ mAdc)		$V_{BE(sat)}$	0.65 —	0.85 0.95	Vdc
SMALL-SIGNAL CHARACTERISTICS					
Current-Gain — Bandwidth Product ($I_C = 10$ mAdc, $V_{CE} = 20$ Vdc, $f = 100$ MHz)	2N3905 2N3906	f_T	200 250	— —	MHz
Output Capacitance ($V_{CB} = 5.0$ Vdc, $I_E = 0$, $f = 100$ kHz)		C_{obo}	—	4.5	pF

MOTOROLA SMALL-SIGNAL SEMICONDUCTORS

2N3905, 2N3906

ELECTRICAL CHARACTERISTICS (continued) (T_A = 25°C unless otherwise noted.)

Characteristic		Symbol	Min	Max	Unit
Input Capacitance (V_{BE} = 0.5 Vdc, I_C = 0, f = 100 kHz)		C_{ibo}	—	10.0	pF
Input Impedance (I_C = 1.0 mAdc, V_{CE} = 10 Vdc, f = 1.0 kHz)	2N3905	h_{ie}	0.5	8.0	k ohms
	2N3906		2.0	12	
Voltage Feedback Ratio (I_C = 1.0 mAdc, V_{CE} = 10 Vdc, f = 1.0 kHz)	2N3905	h_{re}	0.1	5.0	X 10⁻⁴
	2N3906		0.1	10	
Small-Signal Current Gain (I_C = 1.0 mAdc, V_{CE} = 10 Vdc, f = 1.0 kHz)	2N3905	h_{fe}	50	200	—
	2N3906		100	400	
Output Admittance (I_C = 1.0 mAdc, V_{CE} = 10 Vdc, f = 1.0 kHz)	2N3905	h_{oe}	1.0	40	μmhos
	2N3906		3.0	60	
Noise Figure (I_C = 100 μAdc, V_{CE} = 5.0 Vdc, R_S = 1.0 k ohm, f = 10 Hz to 15.7 kHz)	2N3905	NF	—	5.0	dB
	2N3906		—	4.0	

SWITCHING CHARACTERISTICS

			Symbol	Min	Max	Unit
Delay Time	(V_{CC} = 3.0 Vdc, V_{BE} = 0.5 Vdc		t_d	—	35	ns
Rise Time	I_C = 10 mAdc, I_{B1} = 1.0 mAdc)		t_r	—	35	ns
Storage Time		2N3905	t_s	—	200	ns
	(V_{CC} = 3.0 Vdc, I_C = 10 mAdc,	2N3906		—	225	
Fall Time	I_{B1} = I_{B2} = 1.0 mAdc)	2N3905	t_f	—	60	ns
		2N3906		—	75	

(1) Pulse Width ≤ 300 μs, Duty Cycle ≤ 2.0%.

FIGURE 1 – DELAY AND RISE TIME EQUIVALENT TEST CIRCUIT

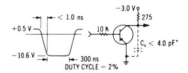

FIGURE 2 – STORAGE AND FALL TIME EQUIVALENT TEST CIRCUIT

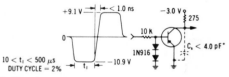

*Total shunt capacitance of test jig and connectors

TRANSIENT CHARACTERISTICS
—— T_J = 25°C --- T_J = 125°C

FIGURE 3 – CAPACITANCE

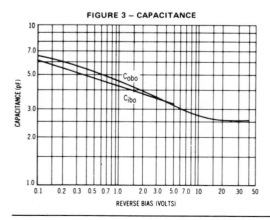

FIGURE 4 – CHARGE DATA

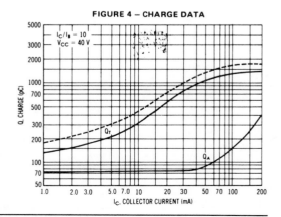

MOTOROLA SMALL-SIGNAL SEMICONDUCTORS

MAXIMUM RATINGS

Rating	Symbol	2N2218 2N2219 2N2221 2N2222	2N2218A 2N2219A 2N2221A 2N2222A	2N5581 2N5582	Unit
Collector-Emitter Voltage	V_{CEO}	30	40	40	Vdc
Collector-Base Voltage	V_{CBO}	60	75	75	Vdc
Emitter-Base Voltage	V_{EBO}	5.0	6.0	6.0	Vdc
Collector Current — Continuous	I_C	800	800	800	mAdc
		2N2218,A 2N2219,A	2N2221,A 2N2222,A	2N5581 2N5582	
Total Device Dissipation @ T_A = 25°C Derate above 25°C	P_D	0.8 4.57	0.5 2.28	0.6 3.33	Watt mW/°C
Total Device Dissipation @ T_C = 25°C Derate above 25°C	P_D	3.0 17.1	1.2 6.85	2.0 11.43	Watts mW/°C
Operating and Storage Junction Temperature Range	T_J, T_{stg}		−65 to +200		°C

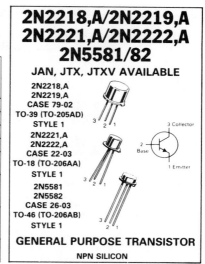

**2N2218,A/2N2219,A
2N2221,A/2N2222,A
2N5581/82**

JAN, JTX, JTXV AVAILABLE

2N2218,A
2N2219,A
CASE 79-02
TO-39 (TO-205AD)
STYLE 1

2N2221,A
2N2222,A
CASE 22-03
TO-18 (TO-206AA)
STYLE 1

2N5581
2N5582
CASE 26-03
TO-46 (TO-206AB)
STYLE 1

3 Collector
2 Base
1 Emitter

GENERAL PURPOSE TRANSISTOR

NPN SILICON

ELECTRICAL CHARACTERISTICS (T_A = 25°C unless otherwise noted.)

Characteristic		Symbol	Min	Max	Unit
OFF CHARACTERISTICS					
Collector-Emitter Breakdown Voltage (I_C = 10 mAdc, I_B = 0) Non-A Suffix A-Suffix, 2N5581, 2N5582		$V_{(BR)CEO}$	30 40	— —	Vdc
Collector-Base Breakdown Voltage (I_C = 10 μAdc, I_E = 0) Non-A Suffix A-Suffix, 2N5581, 2N5582		$V_{(BR)CBO}$	60 75	— —	Vdc
Emitter-Base Breakdown Voltage (I_E = 10 μAdc, I_C = 0) Non-A Suffix A-Suffix, 2N5581, 2N5582		$V_{(BR)EBO}$	5.0 6.0	— —	Vdc
Collector Cutoff Current (V_{CE} = 60 Vdc, $V_{EB(off)}$ = 3.0 Vdc) A-Suffix, 2N5581, 2N5582		I_{CEX}	—	10	nAdc
Collector Cutoff Current (V_{CB} = 50 Vdc, I_E = 0) Non-A Suffix (V_{CB} = 60 Vdc, I_E = 0) A-Suffix, 2N5581, 2N5582 (V_{CB} = 50 Vdc, I_E = 0, T_A = 150°C) Non-A Suffix (V_{CB} = 60 Vdc, I_E = 0, T_A = 150°C) A-Suffix, 2N5581, 2N5582		I_{CBO}	— — — —	0.01 0.01 10 10	μAdc
Emitter Cutoff Current (V_{EB} = 3.0 Vdc, I_C = 0) A-Suffix, 2N5581, 2N5582		I_{EBO}	—	10	nAdc
Base Cutoff Current (V_{CE} = 60 Vdc, $V_{EB(off)}$ = 3.0 Vdc) A-Suffix		I_{BL}	—	20	nAdc
ON CHARACTERISTICS					
DC Current Gain (I_C = 0.1 mAdc, V_{CE} = 10 Vdc) 2N2218,A, 2N2221,A, 2N5581(1) 2N2219,A, 2N2222,A, 2N5582(1)		h_{FE}	20 35	— —	—
(I_C = 1.0 mAdc, V_{CE} = 10 Vdc) 2N2218,A, 2N2221,A, 2N5581 2N2219,A, 2N2222,A, 2N5582			25 50	— —	
(I_C = 10 mAdc, V_{CE} = 10 Vdc) 2N2218,A, 2N2221,A, 2N5581(1) 2N2219,A, 2N2222,A, 2N5582(1)			35 75	— —	
(I_C = 10 mAdc, V_{CE} = 10 Vdc, T_A = −55°C) 2N2218A, 2N2221A, 2N5581 2N2219A, 2N2222A, 2N5582			15 35	— —	
(I_C = 150 mAdc, V_{CE} = 10 Vdc)(1) 2N2218,A, 2N2221,A, 2N5581 2N2219,A, 2N2222,A, 2N5582			40 100	120 300	

2N2218/19/21/22, A SERIES, 2N5581/82

ELECTRICAL CHARACTERISTICS (continued) (T_A = 25°C unless otherwise noted.)

Characteristic		Symbol	Min	Max	Unit
(I_C = 150 mAdc, V_{CE} = 1.0 Vdc)(1)	2N2218,A, 2N2221,A, 2N5581		20	—	
	2N2219,A, 2N2222,A, 2N5582		50	—	
(I_C = 500 mAdc, V_{CE} = 10 Vdc)(1)	2N2218, 2N2221		20	—	
	2N2219, 2N2222		30	—	
	2N2218A, 2N2221A, 2N5581		25	—	
	2N2219A, 2N2222A, 2N5582		40	—	
Collector-Emitter Saturation Voltage(1)		$V_{CE(sat)}$			Vdc
(I_C = 150 mAdc, I_B = 15 mAdc)	Non-A Suffix		—	0.4	
	A-Suffix, 2N5581, 2N5582		—	0.3	
(I_C = 500 mAdc, I_B = 50 mAdc)	Non-A Suffix		—	1.6	
	A-Suffix, 2N5581, 2N5582		—	1.0	
Base-Emitter Saturation Voltage(1)		$V_{BE(sat)}$			Vdc
(I_C = 150 mAdc, I_B = 15 mAdc)	Non-A Suffix		0.6	1.3	
	A-Suffix, 2N5581, 2N5582		0.6	1.2	
(I_C = 500 mAdc, I_B = 50 mAdc)	Non-A Suffix		—	2.6	
	A-Suffix, 2N5581, 2N5582		—	2.0	

SMALL-SIGNAL CHARACTERISTICS

Characteristic		Symbol	Min	Max	Unit
Current-Gain — Bandwidth Product(2)		f_T			MHz
(I_C = 20 mAdc, V_{CE} = 20 Vdc, f = 100 MHz)	All Types, Except		250	—	
	2N2219A, 2N2222A, 2N5582		300	—	
Output Capacitance(3)		C_{obo}	—	8.0	pF
(V_{CB} = 10 Vdc, I_E = 0, f = 100 kHz)					
Input Capacitance(3)		C_{ibo}			pF
(V_{EB} = 0.5 Vdc, I_C = 0, f = 100 kHz)	Non-A Suffix		—	30	
	A-Suffix, 2N5581, 2N5582		—	25	
Input Impedance		h_{ie}			kohms
(I_C = 1.0 mAdc, V_{CE} = 10 Vdc, f = 1.0 kHz)	2N2218A, 2N2221A		1.0	3.5	
	2N2219A, 2N2222A		2.0	8.0	
(I_C = 10 mAdc, V_{CE} = 10 Vdc, f = 1.0 kHz)	2N2218A, 2N2221A		0.2	1.0	
	2N2219A, 2N2222A		0.25	1.25	
Voltage Feedback Ratio		h_{re}			X 10^{-4}
(I_C = 1.0 mAdc, V_{CE} = 10 Vdc, f = 1.0 kHz)	2N2218A, 2N2221A		—	5.0	
	2N2219A, 2N2222A		—	8.0	
(I_C = 10 mAdc, V_{CE} = 10 Vdc, f = 1.0 kHz)	2N2218A, 2N2221A		—	2.5	
	2N2219A, 2N2222A		—	4.0	
Small-Signal Current Gain		h_{fe}			—
(I_C = 1.0 mAdc, V_{CE} = 10 Vdc, f = 1.0 kHz)	2N2218A, 2N2221A		30	150	
	2N2219A, 2N2222A		50	300	
(I_C = 10 mAdc, V_{CE} = 10 Vdc, f = 1.0 kHz)	2N2218A, 2N2221A		50	300	
	2N2219A, 2N2222A		75	375	
Output Admittance		h_{oe}			μmhos
(I_C = 1.0 mAdc, V_{CE} = 10 Vdc, f = 1.0 kHz)	2N2218A, 2N2221A		3.0	15	
	2N2219A, 2N2222A		5.0	35	
(I_C = 10 mAdc, V_{CE} = 10 Vdc, f = 1.0 kHz)	2N2218A, 2N2221A		10	100	
	2N2219A, 2N2222A		25	200	
Collector Base Time Constant		$r_b'C_c$	—	150	ps
(I_E = 20 mAdc, V_{CB} = 20 Vdc, f = 31.8 MHz)	A-Suffix				
Noise Figure		NF	—	4.0	dB
(I_C = 100 μAdc, V_{CE} = 10 Vdc, R_S = 1.0 kohm, f = 1.0 kHz)	2N2222A				
Real Part of Common-Emitter High Frequency Input Impedance		Re(h_{ie})	—	60	Ohms
(I_C = 20 mAdc, V_{CE} = 20 Vdc, f = 300 MHz)	2N2218A, 2N2219A				
	2N2221A, 2N2222A				

(1) Pulse Test: Pulse Width ≤ 300 μs, Duty Cycle ≤ 2.0%.
(2) f_T is defined as the frequency at which $|h_{fe}|$ extrapolates to unity.
(3) 2N5581 and 2N5582 are Listed C_{cb} and C_{eb} for these conditions and values.

MOTOROLA SMALL-SIGNAL SEMICONDUCTORS

MAXIMUM RATINGS

Rating	Symbol	2N3053	2N3053A	Unit
Collector-Emitter Voltage(1)	V_{CEO}	40	60	Vdc
Collector-Base Voltage	V_{CBO}	60	80	Vdc
Emitter-Base Voltage	V_{EBO}	5.0		Vdc
Collector Current — Continuous	I_C	700		mAdc
Total Device Dissipation @ T_C = 25°C Derate above 25°C	P_D	5.0 28.6		Watts mW/°C
Operating and Storage Junction Temperature Range	T_J, T_{stg}	−65 to +200		°C
Lead Temperature 1/16″, ±1/32″ From Case for 10 s	T_L	+235		°C

THERMAL CHARACTERISTICS

Characteristic	Symbol	Max	Unit
Thermal Resistance, Junction to Case	$R_{\theta JC}$	35	°C/W

(1) Applicable 0 to 100 mA (Pulsed):
 Pulse Width ≤ 300 μsec., Duty Cycle ≤ 2.0%.
 0 to 700 mA; Pulse Width ≤ 10 μsec., Duty Cycle ≤ 2.0%.

2N3053,A

**CASE 79-02, STYLE 1
TO-39 (TO-205AD)**

GENERAL PURPOSE TRANSISTOR

NPN SILICON

Refer to 2N3019 for graphs.

ELECTRICAL CHARACTERISTICS (T_A = 25°C unless otherwise noted.)

Characteristic		Symbol	Min	Max	Unit
OFF CHARACTERISTICS					
Collector-Emitter Breakdown Voltage(2) (I_C = 100 μAdc, I_B = 0) 2N3053 2N3053A		$V_{(BR)CEO}$	40 60	— —	Vdc
Collector-Emitter Breakdown Voltage(2) (I_C = 100 mAdc, R_{BE} = 10 ohms) 2N3053 2N3053A		$V_{(BR)CER}$	50 70	— —	Vdc
Collector-Base Breakdown Voltage (I_C = 100 μAdc, I_E = 0) 2N3053 2N3053A		$V_{(BR)CBO}$	60 80	— —	Vdc
Emitter-Base Breakdown Voltage (I_E = 100 μAdc, I_C = 0)		$V_{(BR)EBO}$	5.0	—	Vdc
Collector Cutoff Current (V_{CE} = 30 Vdc, $V_{BE(off)}$ = 1.5 Vdc) 2N3053 (V_{CE} = 60 Vdc, $V_{BE(off)}$ = 1.5 Vdc) 2N3053A		I_{CEX}	—	0.25	μAdc
Emitter Cutoff Current (V_{BE} = 4.0 Vdc, I_C = 0) 2N3053		I_{EBO}	—	0.25	μAdc
Base Cutoff Current (V_{CE} = 60 Vdc, $V_{BE(off)}$ = 1.5 Vdc) 2N3053A		I_{BL}	—	0.25	μAdc
ON CHARACTERISTICS(1)					
DC Current Gain (I_C = 150 mAdc, V_{CE} = 2.5 Vdc) (I_C = 150 mAdc, V_{CE} = 10 Vdc)		h_{FE}	25 50	— 250	—
Collector-Emitter Saturation Voltage (I_C = 150 mAdc, I_B = 15 mAdc) 2N3053 2N3053A		$V_{CE(sat)}$	— —	1.4 0.3	Vdc
Base-Emitter Saturation Voltage (I_C = 150 mAdc, I_B = 15 mAdc) 2N3053 2N3053A		$V_{BE(sat)}$	— 0.6	1.7 1.0	Vdc
Base-Emitter On Voltage (I_C = 150 mAdc, V_{CE} = 2.5 Vdc) 2N3053 2N3053A		$V_{BE(on)}$	— —	1.7 1.0	Vdc
SMALL-SIGNAL CHARACTERISTICS					
Current-Gain — Bandwidth Product (I_C = 50 mAdc, V_{CE} = 10 Vdc, f = 20 MHz)		f_T	100	—	MHz
Output Capacitance (V_{CB} = 10 Vdc, I_E = 0, f = 140 kHz)		C_{obo}	—	15	pF
Input Capacitance (V_{BE} = 0.5 Vdc, I_C = 0, f = 140 kHz)		C_{ibo}	—	80	pF

(2) Pulse Test: Pulse Width ≤ 300 μs, Duty Cycle ≤ 2.0%.

MOTOROLA SMALL-SIGNAL SEMICONDUCTORS

MOTOROLA
■ SEMICONDUCTOR ■
TECHNICAL DATA

PNP
2N5879, 2N5880
NPN
2N5881, 2N5882

COMPLEMENTARY SILICON
HIGH-POWER TRANSISTORS

. . . designed for general-purpose power amplifier and switching applications.

- Collector-Emitter Sustaining Voltage —
  $V_{CEO(sus)}$ = 60 Vdc (Min) — 2N5879, 2N5881
  = 80 Vdc (Min) — 2N5880, 2N5882
- DC Current Gain —
  h_{FE} = 20 (Min) @ I_C = 6.0 Adc
- Low Collector — Emitter Saturation Voltage —
  $V_{CE(sat)}$ = 1.0 Vdc (Max) @ I_C = 7.0 Adc
- High Current — Gain-Bandwidth Product —
  f_T = 4.0 MHz (Min) @ I_C = 1.0 Adc
- Recommended for New Circuit Designs

15 AMPERE
COMPLEMENTARY SILICON
POWER TRANSISTORS

60–80 VOLTS
160 WATTS

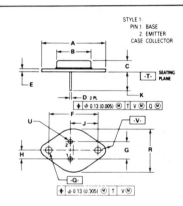

*MAXIMUM RATINGS

Rating	Symbol	2N5879 2N5881	2N5880 2N5882	Unit
Collector-Emitter Voltage	V_{CEO}	60	80	Vdc
Collector-Base Voltage	V_{CB}	60	80	Vdc
Emitter-Base Voltage	V_{EB}	5.0		Vdc
Collector Current — Continuous Peak	I_C	15 30		Adc
Base Current	I_B	5.0		Adc
Total Device Dissipation @ T_C = 25°C Derate above 25°C	P_D	160 0.915		Watts W/°C
Operating and Storage Junction Temperature Range	T_J, T_{stg}	−65 to +200		°C

THERMAL CHARACTERISTICS

Characteristic	Symbol	Max	Unit
Thermal Resistance, Junction to Case	θ_{JC}	1.1	°C/W

*Indicates JEDEC registered data. Limits and conditions differ on some parameters and re-registration reflecting these changes has been requested. All above values meet or exceed present JEDEC registered data.

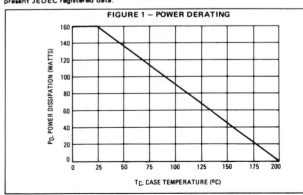

FIGURE 1 — POWER DERATING

NOTES:
1. DIMENSIONING AND TOLERANCING PER ANSI Y14.5M, 1982.
2. CONTROLLING DIMENSION: INCH.
3. ALL RULES AND NOTES ASSOCIATED WITH REFERENCED TO-204AA OUTLINE SHALL APPLY.

	MILLIMETERS		INCHES	
DIM	MIN	MAX	MIN	MAX
A	—	39.37	—	1.550
B	—	21.08	—	0.830
C	6.35	8.25	0.250	0.325
D	0.97	1.09	0.038	0.043
E	1.40	1.77	0.055	0.070
F	30.15 BSC		1.187 BSC	
G	10.92 BSC		0.430 BSC	
H	5.46 BSC		0.215 BSC	
J	16.89 BSC		0.665 BSC	
K	11.18	12.19	0.440	0.480
Q	3.84	4.19	0.151	0.165
R	—	26.67	—	1.050
U	4.83	5.33	0.190	0.210
V	3.84	4.19	0.151	0.165

CASE 1-06
TO-204AA
(TO-3)

2N5879, 2N5880 PNP, 2N5881, 2N5882 NPN

*ELECTRICAL CHARACTERISTICS (T_C = 25°C unless otherwise noted)

Characteristic		Symbol	Min	Max	Unit
OFF CHARACTERISTICS					
Collector-Emitter Sustaining Voltage (1)		$V_{CEO(sus)}$			Vdc
(I_C = 200 mAdc, I_B = 0) 2N5879, 2N5881			60	–	
2N5880, 2N5882			80	–	
Collector Cutoff Current		I_{CEO}			mAdc
(V_{CE} = 30 Vdc, I_B = 0) 2N5879, 2N5881			–	1.0	
(V_{CE} = 40 Vdc, I_B = 0) 2N5880, 2N5882			–	1.0	
Collector Cutoff Current		I_{CEX}			mAdc
(V_{CE} = 60 Vdc, $V_{BE(off)}$ = 1.5 Vdc) 2N5879, 2N5881			–	0.5	
(V_{CE} = 80 Vdc, $V_{BE(off)}$ = 1.5 Vdc) 2N5880, 2N5882			–	0.5	
(V_{CE} = 60 Vdc, $V_{BE(off)}$ = 1.5 Vdc, T_C = 150°C) 2N5879, 2N5881			–	5.0	
(V_{CE} = 80 Vdc, $V_{BE(off)}$ = 1.5 Vdc, T_C = 150°C) 2N5880, 2N5882			–	5.0	
Collector Cutoff Current		I_{CBO}			mAdc
(V_{CB} = 60 Vdc, I_E = 0) 2N5879, 2N5881			–	0.5	
(V_{CB} = 80 Vdc, I_E = 0) 2N5880, 2N5882			–	0.5	
Emitter Cutoff Current		I_{EBO}	–	1.0	mAdc
(V_{EB} = 5.0 Vdc, I_C = 0)					
ON CHARACTERISTICS					
DC Current Gain (1)		h_{FE}			–
(I_C = 2.0 Adc, V_{CE} = 4.0 Vdc)			35	–	
(I_C = 6.0 Adc, V_{CE} = 4.0 Vdc)			20	100	
(I_C = 15 Adc, V_{CE} = 4.0 Vdc)			4.0	–	
Collector-Emitter Saturation Voltage (1)		$V_{CE(sat)}$			Vdc
(I_C = 7.0 Adc, I_B = 0.7 Adc)			–	1.0	
(I_C = 15 Adc, I_B = 3.75 Adc)				4.0	
Base-Emitter Saturation Voltage (1)		$V_{BE(sat)}$	–	2.5	Vdc
(I_C = 15 Adc, I_B = 3.75 Adc)					
Base-Emitter On Voltage (1)		$V_{BE(on)}$	–	1.5	Vdc
(I_C = 6.0 Adc, V_{CE} = 4.0 Vdc)					
DYNAMIC CHARACTERISTICS					
Current-Gain–Bandwidth Product (2)		f_T	4.0	–	MHz
(I_C = 1.0 Adc, V_{CE} = 10 Vdc, f_{test} = 1.0 MHz)					
Output Capacitance		C_{ob}			pF
(V_{CB} = 10 Vdc, I_E = 0, f = 100 kHz) 2N5879, 2N5880			–	600	
2N5881, 2N5882			–	400	
Small-Signal Current Gain		h_{fe}	20	–	–
(I_C = 2.0 Adc, V_{CE} = 4.0 Vdc, f = 1.0 kHz)					
SWITCHING CHARACTERISTICS					
Rise Time	(V_{CC} = 30 Vdc, I_C = 6.0 Adc, I_{B1} = I_{B2} = 0.6 Adc See Figure 2)	t_r	–	0.7	µs
Storage Time		t_s	–	1.0	µs
Fall Time		t_f	–	0.8	µs

*Indicates JEDEC Registered Data.
(1) Pulse Test: Pulse Width ≤ 300 µs, Duty Cycle ≤ 2.0%
(2) $f_T = |h_{fe}| \bullet f_{test}$

FIGURE 2 – SWITCHING TIMES TEST CIRCUIT

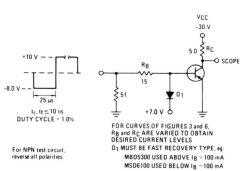

+10 V
-8.0 V
25 µs
t_r, t_f ≤ 10 ns
DUTY CYCLE = 1.0%

VCC -30 V
R_C 5.0
SCOPE
R_B 15
51
D_1
+7.0 V

FOR CURVES OF FIGURES 3 and 6,
R_B and R_C ARE VARIED TO OBTAIN
DESIRED CURRENT LEVELS
D_1 MUST BE FAST RECOVERY TYPE, eg:
MBD5300 USED ABOVE I_B ~100 mA
MSD6100 USED BELOW I_B ~100 mA

For NPN test circuit, reverse all polarities.

FIGURE 3 – TURN-ON TIME

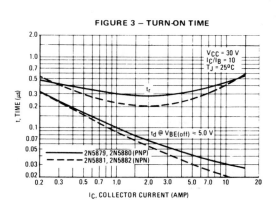

V_{CC} = 30 V
I_C/I_B = 10
T_J = 25°C

t_r

t_d @ $V_{BE(off)}$ ≈ 5.0 V

—— 2N5879, 2N5880 (PNP)
– – – 2N5881, 2N5882 (NPN)

t, TIME (µs)
I_C, COLLECTOR CURRENT (AMP)

MOTOROLA
■ **SEMICONDUCTOR** ■
TECHNICAL DATA

BD676, BD676A
BD678, BD678A
BD680, BD680A
BD682

PLASTIC MEDIUM-POWER SILICON PNP DARLINGTONS

. . . for use as output devices in complementary general-purpose amplifier applications.

- High DC Current Gain —
  h_{FE} = 750 (Min) @ I_C = 1.5 and 2.0 Adc

- Monolithic Construction

- BD676, 676A, 678, 678A, 680, 680A, 682 are complementary with BD675, 675A, 677, 677A, 679, 679A, 681

- BD 678, 678A, 680, 680A are equivalent to MJE 700, 701, 702, 703

**4.0 AMPERE
DARLINGTON
POWER TRANSISTORS
PNP SILICON**

**45, 60, 80, 100 VOLTS
40 WATTS**

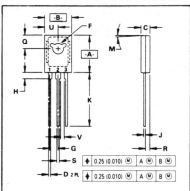

MAXIMUM RATING

Rating	Symbol	BD676 BD676A	BD678 BD678A	BD680 BD680A	BD682	Unit
Collector-Emitter Voltage	V_{CEO}	45	60	80	100	Vdc
Collector-Base Voltage	V_{CB}	45	60	80	100	Vdc
Emitter-Base Voltage	V_{EB}		5.0			Vdc
Collector Current	I_C		4.0			Adc
Base Current	I_B		0.1			Adc
Total Device Dissipation @ T_C = 25 °C Derate above 25 °C	P_D		40 0.32			Watts W/°C
Operating and Storage Junction Tempering Range	T_J, T_{stg}		−55 to +150			°C

THERMAL CHARACTERISTICS

Characteristic	Symbol	Max.	Unit
Thermal Resistance, Junction to Case	θ_{JC}	3.13	°C/W

FIGURE 1 – POWER TEMPERATURE DERATING

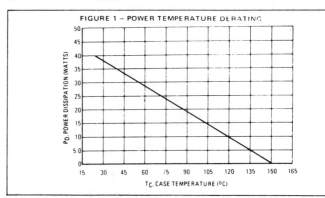

NOTES:
1. DIMENSIONING AND TOLERANCING PER ANSI Y14.5M, 1982.
2. CONTROLLING DIMENSION: INCH.

DIM	MILLIMETERS		INCHES	
	MIN	MAX	MIN	MAX
A	10.80	11.04	0.425	0.435
B	7.50	7.74	0.295	0.305
C	2.42	2.66	0.095	0.105
D	0.51	0.66	0.020	0.026
F	2.93	3.17	0.115	0.125
G	2.39 BSC		0.094 BSC	
H	1.27	2.41	0.050	0.095
J	0.39	0.63	0.015	0.025
K	14.61	16.63	0.575	0.655
M	3° TYP		3° TYP	
Q	3.76	4.01	0.148	0.158
R	1.15	1.39	0.045	0.055
S	0.64	0.88	0.025	0.035
U	3.69	3.93	0.145	0.155
V	1.02	—	0.040	—

STYLE 1:
PIN 1. EMITTER
2. COLLECTOR
3. BASE

**CASE 77-06
TO-225AA TYPE**

BD676, 676A, BD678, 678A, BD680, 680A, BD682

ELECTRICAL CHARACTERISTICS (T_C - 25°C unless otherwise noted)

Characteristic		Symbol	Min	Max	Unit
OFF CHARACTERISTICS					
Collector-Emitter Breakdown Voltage(1) (I_C = 50 mAdc, I_B = 0)	BD676, 676A BD678, 678A BD680, 680A BD682	BV_{CEO}	45 60 80 100	– – – –	Vdc
Collector Cutoff Current (V_{CE} = Half Rated V_{CEO}, I_B = 0)		I_{CEO}	. –	500	µAdc
Collector Cutoff Current (V_{CB} = Rated BV_{CEO}, I_E = 0) (V_{CB} = Rated BV_{CEO}, I_E = 0, T_C = 100°C)		I_{CBO}	– –	0 2 2 0	mAdc
Emitter Cutoff Current (V_{BE} = 5 0 Vdc, I_C = 0)		I_{EBO}	–	2 0	mAdc
ON CHARACTERISTICS					
DC Current Gain(1) (I_C = 1.5 Adc, V_{CE} = 3.0 Vdc) (I_C = 2.0 Adc, V_{CE} = 3.0 Vdc)	BD676, 678, 680, 682 BD 676A, 678A, 680A	h_{FE}	750 750	– ..	–
Collector-Emitter Saturation Voltage(1) (I_C = 1.5 Adc, I_B = 30 mAdc) (I_C = 2.0 Adc, I_B = 40 mAdc)	BD 678, 680, 682 BD 676A, 678A, 680A	$V_{CE(sat)}$		2 5 2 8	Vdc
Base-Emitter On Voltage(1) (I_C = 1.5 Adc, V_{CE} = 3.0 Vdc) (I_C = 2.0 Adc, V_{CE} = 3.0 Vdc)	BD 678, 680, 682 BD 676A, 678A, 680A	$V_{BE(on)}$	– –	2 5 2 5	Vdc
DYNAMIC CHARACTERISTICS					
Small-Signal Current Gain (I_C = 1.5 Adc, V_{CE} = 3.0 Vdc, f = 1.0 MHz)		h_{fe}	1 0	–	–

(1)Pulse Test Pulse Width ≤ 300 µs, Duty Cycle ≤ 2 0%

FIGURE 2   DC SAFE OPERATING AREA

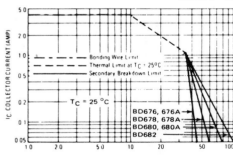

There are two limitations on the power handling ability of a transistor average junction temperature and secondary breakdown Safe operating area curves indicate I_C V_{CE} limits of the transistor that must be observed for reliable operation, e.g., the transistor must not be subjected to greater dissipation than the curves indicate.

At high case temperatures. thermal limitations will reduce the power that can be handled to values less than the limitations imposed by secondary breakdown (See AN-415)

FIGURE 3   DARLINGTON CIRCUIT SCHEMATIC

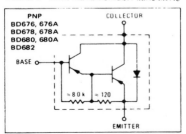

MOTOROLA
SEMICONDUCTOR
TECHNICAL DATA

IRF510
IRF511
IRF512
IRF513

N-CHANNEL ENHANCEMENT-MODE SILICON GATE TMOS POWER FIELD EFFECT TRANSISTOR

These TMOS Power FETs are designed for low voltage, high speed power switching applications such as switching regulators, converters, solenoid and relay drivers.

- Silicon Gate for Fast Switching Speeds
- Rugged — SOA is Power Dissipation Limited
- Source-to-Drain Diode Characterized for Use With Inductive Loads

Part Number	VDS	rDS(on)	ID
IRF510	100 V	0.6 Ω	4.0 A
IRF511	60 V	0.6 Ω	4.0 A
IRF512	100 V	0.8 Ω	3.5 A
IRF513	60 V	0.8 Ω	3.5 A

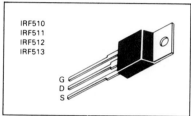

IRF510
IRF511
IRF512
IRF513

G
D
S

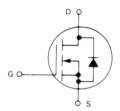

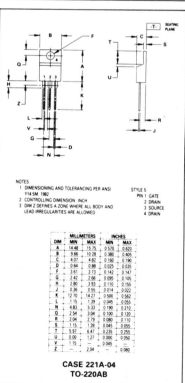

MAXIMUM RATINGS

Rating	Symbol	IRF 510	511	512	513	Unit
Drain-Source Voltage	V_DSS	100	60	100	60	Vdc
Drain-Gate Voltage (R_GS = 1.0 MΩ)	V_DGR	100	60	100	60	Vdc
Gate-Source Voltage	V_GS	± 20				Vdc
Continuous Drain Current T_C = 25°C	I_D	4.0	4.0	3.5	3.5	Adc
Continuous Drain Current T_C = 100°C	I_D	2.5	2.5	2.0	2.0	Adc
Drain Current Pulsed	I_DM	16	16	14	14	Adc
Total Power Dissipation @ T_C = 25°C Derate above 25°C	P_D	20 0.16				Watts W/°C
Operating and Storage Temperature Range	T_J, T_stg	− 55 to 150				°C

THERMAL CHARACTERISTICS

Thermal Resistance			°C/W
Junction to Case	R_θJC	6.4	
Junction to Ambient	R_θJA	62.5	
Maximum Lead Temp. for Soldering Purposes, 1/8" from case for 5 seconds	T_L	300	°C

See the MTP6N10 Designer's Data Sheet for a complete set of design curves for this product.

NOTES
1. DIMENSIONING AND TOLERANCING PER ANSI
   Y14.5M, 1982
2. CONTROLLING DIMENSION: INCH
3. DIM Z DEFINES A ZONE WHERE ALL BODY AND
   LEAD IRREGULARITIES ARE ALLOWED

STYLE 5
PIN 1. GATE
     2. DRAIN
     3. SOURCE
     4. DRAIN

DIM	MILLIMETERS MIN	MAX	INCHES MIN	MAX
A	14.48	15.75	0.570	0.620
B	9.66	10.28	0.380	0.405
C	4.07	4.82	0.160	0.190
D	0.64	0.88	0.025	0.035
F	3.61	3.73	0.142	0.147
G	2.42	2.66	0.095	0.105
H	2.80	3.93	0.110	0.155
J	0.36	0.55	0.014	0.022
K	12.70	14.27	0.500	0.562
L	1.15	1.39	0.045	0.055
N	4.83	5.33	0.190	0.210
Q	2.54	3.04	0.100	0.120
R	2.04	2.79	0.080	0.110
S	1.15	1.39	0.045	0.055
T	5.97	6.47	0.235	0.255
U	0.00	1.27	0.000	0.050
V	1.15	—	0.045	—
Z	—	2.04	—	0.080

CASE 221A-04
TO-220AB

IRF510-513

ELECTRICAL CHARACTERISTICS (T_C = 25°C unless otherwise noted)

Characteristic		Symbol	Min	Typ	Max	Unit
OFF CHARACTERISTICS						
Drain-Source Breakdown Voltage (V_{GS} = 0, I_D = 250 μA) IRF510,512		$V_{(BR)DSS}$	100	—	—	Vdc
IRF511,513			60	—	—	
Zero Gate Voltage Drain Current (V_{GS} = 0 V, V_{DS} = Rated V_{DSS})		I_{DSS}	—	—	0.25	mAdc
(V_{GS} = 0 V, V_{DS} = 0.8 Rated V_{DSS}, T_C = 125°C)			—	—	1.0	
Forward Gate-Body Leakage Current (V_{GS} = 20 V, V_{DS} = 0)		I_{GSSF}	—	—	100	nAdc
Reverse Gate-Body Leakage Current (V_{GS} = −20 V, V_{DS} = 0)		I_{GSSR}	—	—	−100	nAdc
ON CHARACTERISTICS*						
Gate Threshold Voltage (V_{DS} = V_{GS}, I_D = 250 μA)		$V_{GS(th)}$	2.0	—	4.0	Vdc
On-State Drain Current (V_{DS} = 25 V, V_{GS} = 10 V) IRF510,511		$I_{D(on)}$	4.0	—	—	Adc
IRF512,513			3.5	—	—	
Static Drain-Source On-Resistance (V_{GS} = 10 V, I_D = 2.0 A) IRF510,511		$r_{DS(on)}$	—	—	0.6	Ohms
IRF512,513			—	—	0.8	
Forward Transconductance (V_{DS} = 15 V, I_D = 2.0 A)		g_{FS}	1.0	—	—	mhos
DYNAMIC CHARACTERISTICS						
Input Capacitance		C_{iss}	—	—	150	pF
Output Capacitance	(V_{DS} = 25 V, V_{GS} = 0, f = 1.0 MHz)	C_{oss}	—	—	100	
Reverse Transfer Capacitance		C_{rss}	—	—	25	
SWITCHING CHARACTERISTICS* (T_J = 100°C)						
Turn-On Delay Time		$t_{d(on)}$	—	—	20	ns
Rise Time	$V_{DD} \approx$ 0.5 V_{DSS}, I_D = 2.0 A	t_r	—	—	25	
Turn-Off Delay Time	Z_0 = 50 Ω	$t_{d(off)}$	—	—	25	
Fall Time		t_f	—	—	20	

SOURCE DRAIN DIODE CHARACTERISTICS*

Characteristic		Symbol	Typ	Unit
Forward On-Voltage		V_{SD}	2.0	Vdc
Forward Turn-On Time	(I_S = Rated I_D, V_{GS} = 0)	t_{on}	Limited by stray inductance	
Reverse Recovery Time		t_{rr}	230	ns

INTERNAL PACKAGE INDUCTANCE (TO-220)

	Symbol	Min	Typ	Max	Unit
Internal Drain Inductance (Measured from the contact screw on tab to center of die)	L_d	—	3.5	—	nH
(Measured from the drain lead 0.25″ from package to center of die)		—	4.5	—	
Internal Source Inductance (Measured from the source lead 0.25″ from package to source bond pad.)	L_s	—	7.5	—	

*Pulse Test: Pulse Width ≤ 300 μs, Duty Cycle ≤ 2.0 %.

RESISTIVE SWITCHING

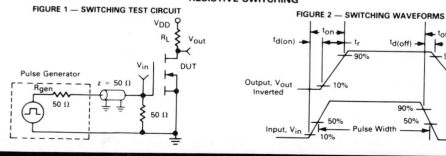

FIGURE 1 — SWITCHING TEST CIRCUIT

FIGURE 2 — SWITCHING WAVEFORMS

MOTOROLA
■ **SEMICONDUCTOR** ■
TECHNICAL DATA

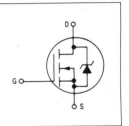

MTH35N06E
MTM35N06E

Designer's Data Sheet

TMOS IV
Power Field Effect Transistors
N-Channel Enhancement-Mode Silicon Gate

TMOS POWER FETs
35 AMPERES
$r_{DS(on)} = 0.055$ OHM
60 VOLTS

This advanced "E" series of TMOS power MOSFETs is designed to withstand high energy in the avalanche and commutation modes. These new energy efficient devices also offer drain-to-source diodes with fast recovery times. Designed for low voltage, high speed switching applications in power supplies, converters and PWM motor controls, these devices are particularly well suited for bridge circuits where diode speed and commutating safe operating area are critical, and offer additional safety margin against unexpected voltage transients.

- Internal Source-to-Drain Diode Designed to Replace External Zener Transient Suppressor — Absorbs High Energy in the Avalanche Mode — Unclamped Inductive Switching (UIS) Energy Capability Specified at 100°C.
- Commutating Safe Operating Area (CSOA) Specified for Use in Half and Full Bridge Circuits
- Source-to-Drain Diode Recovery Time Comparable to a Discrete Fast Recovery Diode
- Diode is Characterized for Use in Bridge Circuits

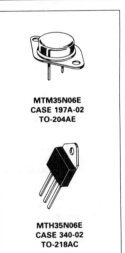

MTM35N06E
CASE 197A-02
TO-204AE

MTH35N06E
CASE 340-02
TO-218AC

MAXIMUM RATINGS (T_J = 25°C unless otherwise noted)

Rating	Symbol	Value	Unit
Drain-Source Voltage	V_{DSS}	60	Vdc
Drain-Gate Voltage (R_{GS} = 1 MΩ)	V_{DGR}	60	Vdc
Gate-Source Voltage — Continuous — Non-repetitive ($t_p \leq 50 \mu s$)	V_{GS} V_{GSM}	±20 ±40	Vdc Vpk
Drain Current — Continuous (T_C = 25°C) — Pulsed	I_D I_{DM}	35 120	Adc
Total Power Dissipation @ T_C = 25°C Derate above 25°C	P_D	150 1.2	Watts W/°C
Operating and Storage Temperature Range	T_J, T_{stg}	−65 to 150	°C

THERMAL CHARACTERISTICS

Thermal Resistance Junction to Case Junction to Ambient	$R_{\theta JC}$ $R_{\theta JA}$	0.83 30	°C/W
Maximum Lead Temperature for Soldering Purposes, 1/8″ from case for 5 seconds	T_L	275	°C

Designer's Data for "Worst Case" Conditions — The Designer's Data Sheet permits the design of most circuits entirely from the information presented. SOA Limit curves — representing boundaries on device characteristics — are given to facilitate "worst case" design.

MTH/MTM35N06E

ELECTRICAL CHARACTERISTICS (T_C = 25°C unless otherwise noted)

Characteristic	Symbol	Min	Max	Unit
OFF CHARACTERISTICS				
Drain-Source Breakdown Voltage (V_{GS} = 0, I_D = 0.25 mA)	$V_{(BR)DSS}$	60	—	Vdc
Zero Gate Voltage Drain Current (V_{DS} = Rated V_{DSS}, V_{GS} = 0) (V_{DS} = Rated V_{DSS}, V_{GS} = 0, T_J = 125°C)	I_{DSS}	— —	10 100	μA
Gate-Body Leakage Current, Forward (V_{GSF} = 20 Vdc, V_{DS} = 0)	I_{GSSF}	—	100	nAdc
Gate-Body Leakage Current, Reverse (V_{GSR} = 20 Vdc, V_{DS} = 0)	I_{GSSR}	—	100	nAdc
ON CHARACTERISTICS*				
Gate Threshold Voltage (V_{DS} = V_{GS}, I_D = 1 mA) T_J = 100°C	$V_{GS(th)}$	2 1.5	4.5 4	Vdc
Static Drain-Source On-Resistance (V_{GS} = 10 Vdc, I_D = 17.5 Adc)	$r_{DS(on)}$	—	0.055	Ohm
Drain-Source On-Voltage (V_{GS} = 10 V) (I_D = 35 Adc) (I_D = 17.5 Adc, T_J = 100°C)	$V_{DS(on)}$	— —	2.3 1.9	Vdc
Forward Transconductance (V_{DS} = 15 V, I_D = 17.5 A)	g_{FS}	14	—	mhos
DRAIN-TO-SOURCE AVALANCHE CHARACTERISTICS				
Unclamped Inductive Switching Energy See Figures 14 and 15 (I_D = 120 A, V_{DD} = 25 V, T_C = 25°C, Single Pulse, Non-repetitive) (I_D = 35 A, V_{DD} = 25 V, T_C = 25°C, P.W. ≤ 200 μs, Duty Cycle ≤ 1%) (I_D = 14 A, V_{DD} = 25 V, T_C = 100°C, P.W. ≤ 200 μs, Duty Cycle ≤ 1%)	W_{DSR}	— — —	200 500 180	mJ
DYNAMIC CHARACTERISTICS				
Input Capacitance	C_{iss}	—	3000	pF
Output Capacitance	C_{oss}	—	1500	
Reverse Transfer Capacitance	C_{rss}	—	500	
SWITCHING CHARACTERISTICS* (T_J = 100°C)				
Turn-On Delay Time	$t_{d(on)}$	—	60	ns
Rise Time	t_r	—	450	
Turn-Off Delay Time	$t_{d(off)}$	—	150	
Fall Time	t_f	—	300	
Total Gate Charge	Q_g	60 (Typ)	90	nC
Gate-Source Charge	Q_{gs}	33 (Typ)	—	
Gate-Drain Charge	Q_{gd}	35 (Typ)	—	
SOURCE DRAIN DIODE CHARACTERISTICS*				
Forward On-Voltage	V_{SD}	1.7 (Typ)	2.5	Vdc
Forward Turn-On Time	t_{on}	Limited by stray inductance		
Reverse Recovery Time	t_{rr}	200 (Typ)	—	ns
INTERNAL PACKAGE INDUCTANCE (TO-204)				
Internal Drain Inductance (Measured from the contact screw on the header closer to the source pin and the center of the die)	L_d	5 (Typ)	—	nH
Internal Source Inductance (Measured from the source pin, 0.25" from the package to the source bond pad)	L_s	12.5 (Typ)	—	
INTERNAL PACKAGE INDUCTANCE (TO-218)				
Internal Drain Inductance (Measured from the contact screw on tab to center of die) (Measured from the drain lead 0.25" from package to center of die)	L_d	4 (Typ) 5 (Typ)	— —	nH
Internal Source Inductance (Measured from the source lead 0.25" from package to source bond pad.)	L_s	10 (Typ)	—	

Dynamic Characteristics conditions: (V_{DS} = 25 V, V_{GS} = 0, f = 1 MHz) See Figure 16

Switching Characteristics conditions: (V_{DD} = 25 V, I_D = 0.5 Rated I_D, R_{gen} = 50 ohms) See Figure 9

Gate Charge conditions: (V_{DS} = 0.8 Rated V_{DSS}, I_D = Rated I_D, V_{GS} = 10 V) See Figures 17 and 18

Source Drain Diode conditions: (I_S = 35 A, V_{GS} = 0) dI_S/dt = 100 A/μs

*Pulse Test: Pulse Width ≤ 300 μs, Duty Cycle ≤ 2%.

MTH/MTM35N06E

TYPICAL ELECTRICAL CHARACTERISTICS

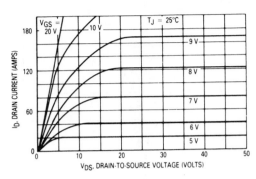

Figure 1. On-Region Characteristics

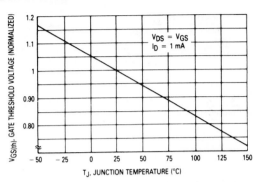

**Figure 2. Gate-Threshold Voltage Variation
With Temperature**

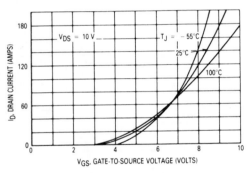

Figure 3. Transfer Characteristics

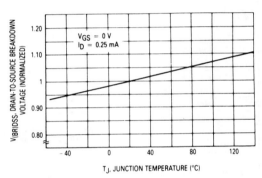

**Figure 4. Breakdown Voltage Variation
With Temperature**

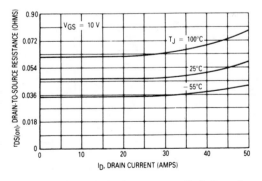

Figure 5. On-Resistance versus Drain Current

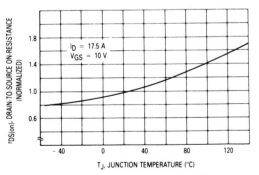

**Figure 6. On-Resistance Variation
With Temperature**

National Semiconductor Corporation

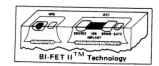

BI-FET II™ Technology

LF155/LF156/LF157 Series Monolithic JFET Input Operational Amplifiers

LF155, LF155A, LF255, LF355, LF355A, LF355B Low Supply Current

LF156, LF156A, LF256, LF356, LF356A, LF356B Wide Band

LF157, LF157A, LF257, LF357, LF357A, LF357B Wide Band Decompensated ($A_{VMIN} = 5$)

General Description

These are the first monolithic JFET input amplifiers to incorporate well matched, high voltage JFETs on the same chip with standard bipolar transistors (BI-FET™ Technology). These amplifiers feature low input bias and offset currents, low offset voltage and offset voltage drift, coupled with offset adjust which does not degrade drift or common-mode rejection. The devices are also designed for high slew rate, wide bandwidth, extremely fast settling time, low voltage and current noise and a low 1/f noise corner.

Advantages

- Replace expensive hybrid and module FET op amps
- Rugged JFETs allow blow-out free handling compared with MOSFET input devices
- Excellent for low noise applications using either high or low source impedance—very low 1/f corner
- Offset adjust does not degrade drift or common-mode rejection as in most monolithic amplifiers
- New output stage allows use of large capacitive loads (10,000 pF) without stability problems
- Internal compensation and large differential input voltage capability

Applications

- Precision high speed integrators
- Fast D/A and A/D converters
- High impedance buffers
- Wideband, low noise, low drift amplifiers
- Logarithmic amplifiers
- Photocell amplifiers
- Sample and Hold circuits

Common Features

(LF155A, LF156A, LF157A)

■ Low input bias current	30 pA
■ Low Input Offset Current	3 pA
■ High input impedance	$10^{12}\Omega$
■ Low input offset voltage	1 mV
■ Low input offset voltage temp. drift	3 $\mu V/°C$
■ Low input noise current	0.01 pA/$\sqrt{Hz}$
■ High common-mode rejection ratio	100 dB
■ Large dc voltage gain	106 dB

Uncommon Features

	LF155A	LF156A	LF157A ($A_V = 5$)	Units
■ Extremely fast settling time to 0.01%	4	1.5	1.5	μs
■ Fast slew rate	5	12	50	V/μs
■ Wide gain bandwidth	2.5	5	20	MHz
■ Low input noise voltage	20	12	12	nV/$\sqrt{Hz}$

Simplified Schematic

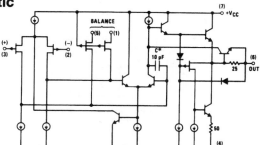

BALANCE

C* 10 pF

*3 pF in LF157 series.

TL/H/5646–1

LF155/155A/LF255/LF355/355A/355B/LF156/156A/LF256/LF356/356A/356B/LF157/157A/LF257/LF357/357A/357B

Side text (vertical): LF155/155A/LF255/LF355/355A/355B/LF156/156A/LF256/LF356/356A/356B/LF157/157A/LF257/LF357/357A/357B

Absolute Maximum Ratings

If Military/Aerospace specified devices are required, contact the National Semiconductor Sales Office/Distributors for availability and specifications.
(Note 8)

	LF155A/6A/7A	LF155/6/7	LF355B/6B/7B LF255/6/7	LF355/6/7 LF355A/6A/7A
Supply Voltage	±22V	±22V	±22V	±18V
Differential Input Voltage	±40V	±40V	±40V	±30V
Input Voltage Range (Note 2)	±20V	±20V	±20V	±16V
Output Short Circuit Duration	Continuous	Continuous	Continuous	Continuous
T_{jMAX}				
H-Package	150°C	150°C	115°C	115°C
N-Package			100°C	100°C
J-Package		150°C	115°C	115°C
M-Package			100°C	100°C
Power Dissipation at $T_A = 25°C$ (Notes 1 and 9)				
H-Package (Still Air)	560 mW	560 mW	400 mW	400 mW
H-Package (400 LF/Min Air Flow)	1200 mW	1200 mW	1000 mW	1000 mW
N-Package			670 mW	670 mW
J-Package		1260 mW	900 mW	900 mW
M-Package			380 mW	380 mW
Thermal Resistance (Typical) θ_{JA}				
H-Package (Still Air)	225°C/W	225°C/W	225°C/W	225°C/W
H-Package (400 LF/Min Air Flow)	90°C/W	90°C/W	90°C/W	90°C/W
N-Package			130°C/W	130°C/W
J-Package		100°C/W	100°C/W	100°C/W
M-Package			195°C/W	195°C/W
(Typical) θ_{JC}				
H-Package (Still Air)	23°C/W	23°C/W	23°C/W	23°C/W
H-Package (400 LF/Min Air Flow)	10°C/W	10°C/W	10°C/W	10°C/W
Storage Temperature Range	−65°C to +150°C	−65°C to +150°C	−65°C to +150°C	−65°C to +150°C
Lead Temp. (Soldering, 10 sec.) Metal Can	300°C	300°C	300°C	300°C
Lead Temp. (Soldering, 10 sec.) Plastic Dip	260°C	260°C	260°C	260°C
Soldering Information				
Dual-In-Line Package				
Soldering (10 sec.)	260°C			
Small Outline Package				
Vapor Phase (60 sec.)	215°C			
Infrared (15 sec.)	220°C			

See AN-450 "Surface Mounting Methods and Their Effect on Product Reliability" for other methods of soldering surface mount devices.
ESD rating to be determined.

DC Electrical Characteristics (Note 3) $T_A = T_j = 25°C$

Symbol	Parameter	Conditions	LF155A/6A/7A			LF355A/6A/7A			Units
			Min	Typ	Max	Min	Typ	Max	
V_{OS}	Input Offset Voltage	$R_S = 50Ω$, $T_A = 25°C$		1	2		1	2	mV
		Over Temperature			2.5			2.3	mV
$\Delta V_{OS}/\Delta T$	Average TC of Input Offset Voltage	$R_S = 50Ω$		3	5		3	5	$\mu V/°C$
$\Delta TC/\Delta V_{OS}$	Change in Average TC with V_{OS} Adjust	$R_S = 50Ω$, (Note 4)		0.5			0.5		$\mu V/°C$ per mV
I_{OS}	Input Offset Current	$T_j = 25°C$, (Notes 3, 5)		3	10		3	10	pA
		$T_j \leq T_{HIGH}$			10			1	nA
I_B	Input Bias Current	$T_j = 25°C$, (Notes 3, 5)		30	50		30	50	pA
		$T_j \leq T_{HIGH}$			25			5	nA
R_{IN}	Input Resistance	$T_j = 25°C$		10^{12}			10^{12}		Ω
A_{VOL}	Large Signal Voltage Gain	$V_S = ±15V$, $T_A = 25°C$	50	200		50	200		V/mV
		$V_O = ±10V$, $R_L = 2k$ Over Temperature	25			25			V/mV
V_O	Output Voltage Swing	$V_S = ±15V$, $R_L = 10k$	±12	±13		±12	±13		V
		$V_S = ±15V$, $R_L = 2k$	±10	±12		±10	±12		V

DC Electrical Characteristics (Note 3) $T_A = T_j = 25°C$ (Continued)

Symbol	Parameter	Conditions	LF155A/6A/7A			LF355A/6A/7A			Units
			Min	Typ	Max	Min	Typ	Max	
V_{CM}	Input Common-Mode Voltage Range	$V_S = \pm 15V$	± 11	$+15.1$ -12		± 11	$+15.1$ -12		V V
CMRR	Common-Mode Rejection Ratio		85	100		85	100		dB
PSRR	Supply Voltage Rejection Ratio	(Note 6)	85	100		85	100		dB

AC Electrical Characteristics $T_A = T_j = 25°C$, $V_S = \pm 15V$

Symbol	Parameter	Conditions	LF155A/355A			LF156A/356A			LF157A/357A			Units
			Min	Typ	Max	Min	Typ	Max	Min	Typ	Max	
SR	Slew Rate	LF155A/6A; $A_V = 1$, LF157A; $A_V = 5$	3	5		10	12		40	50		V/μs V/μs
GBW	Gain Bandwidth Product			2.5		4	4.5		15	20		MHz
t_s	Settling Time to 0.01%	(Note 7)		4			1.5			1.5		μs
e_n	Equivalent Input Noise Voltage	$R_S = 100\Omega$ $f = 100$ Hz $f = 1000$ Hz		25 25			15 12			15 12		nV/$\sqrt{Hz}$ nV/$\sqrt{Hz}$
i_n	Equivalent Input Noise Current	$f = 100$ Hz $f = 1000$ Hz		0.01 0.01			0.01 0.01			0.01 0.01		pA/$\sqrt{Hz}$ pA/$\sqrt{Hz}$
C_{IN}	Input Capacitance			3			3			3		pF

DC Electrical Characteristics (Note 3)

Symbol	Parameter	Conditions	LF155/6/7			LF255/6/7 LF355B/6B/7B			LF355/6/7			Units
			Min	Typ	Max	Min	Typ	Max	Min	Typ	Max	
V_{OS}	Input Offset Voltage	$R_S = 50\Omega$, $T_A = 25°C$ Over Temperature		3	5 7		3	5 6.5		3	10 13	mV mV
$\Delta V_{OS}/\Delta T$	Average TC of Input Offset Voltage	$R_S = 50\Omega$		5			5			5		μV/°C
$\Delta TC/\Delta V_{OS}$	Change in Average TC with V_{OS} Adjust	$R_S = 50\Omega$, (Note 4)		0.5			0.5			0.5		μV/°C per mV
I_{OS}	Input Offset Current	$T_j = 25°C$, (Notes 3, 5) $T_j \leq T_{HIGH}$		3	20 20		3	20 1		3	50 2	pA nA
I_B	Input Bias Current	$T_j = 25°C$, (Notes 3, 5) $T_j \leq T_{HIGH}$		30	100 50		30	100 5		30	200 8	pA nA
R_{IN}	Input Resistance	$T_j = 25°C$		10^{12}			10^{12}			10^{12}		Ω
A_{VOL}	Large Signal Voltage Gain	$V_S = \pm 15V$, $T_A = 25°C$ $V_O = \pm 10V$, $R_L = 2k$ Over Temperature	50 25	200		50 25	200		25 15	200		V/mV V/mV
V_O	Output Voltage Swing	$V_S = \pm 15V$, $R_L = 10k$ $V_S = \pm 15V$, $R_L = 2k$	± 12 ± 10	± 13 ± 12		± 12 ± 10	± 13 ± 12		± 12 ± 10	± 13 ± 12		V V
V_{CM}	Input Common-Mode Voltage Range	$V_S = \pm 15V$	± 11	$+15.1$ -12		± 11	± 15.1 -12		$+10$	$+15.1$ -12		V V
CMRR	Common-Mode Rejection Ratio		85	100		85	100		80	100		dB
PSRR	Supply Voltage Rejection Ratio	(Note 6)	85	100		85	100		80	100		dB

LF155/155A/LF255/LF355/355A/355B/LF156/156A/LF256/LF356/356A/356B/LF157/157A/LF257/LF357/357A/357B

LF155/155A/LF255/LF355/355A/355B/LF156/156A/LF256/LF356/LF356A/356B/LF157/157A/LF257/LF357/357A/357B *(vertical side label)*

DC Electrical Characteristics $T_A = T_j = 25°C$, $V_S = \pm 15V$

Parameter	LF155A/155, LF255, LF355A/355B		LF355		LF156A/156, LF256/356B		LF356A/356		LF157A/157 LF257/357B		LF357A/357		Units
	Typ	Max	Typ	Max	Typ	Max	Typ	Max	Typ	Max	Typ	Max	
Supply Current	2	4	2	4	5	7	5	10	5	7	5	10	mA

AC Electrical Characteristics $T_A = T_j = 25°C$, $V_S = \pm 15V$

Symbol	Parameter	Conditions	LF155/255/ 355/355B	LF156/256, LF356B	LF156/256/ 356/356B	LF157/257, LF357B	LF157/257/ 357/357B	Units
			Typ	Min	Typ	Min	Typ	
SR	Slew Rate	LF155/6: $A_V = 1$, LF157: $A_V = 5$	5	7.5	12	30	50	$V/\mu s$ $V/\mu s$
GBW	Gain Bandwidth Product		2.5		5		20	MHz
t_s	Settling Time to 0.01%	(Note 7)	4		1.5		1.5	μs
e_n	Equivalent Input Noise Voltage	$R_S = 100\Omega$ $f = 100$ Hz $f = 1000$ Hz	25 20		15 12		15 12	$nV/\sqrt{Hz}$ $nV/\sqrt{Hz}$
i_n	Equivalent Input Current Noise	$f = 100$ Hz $f = 1000$ Hz	0.01 0.01		0.01 0.01		0.01 0.01	$pA/\sqrt{Hz}$ $pA/\sqrt{Hz}$
C_{IN}	Input Capacitance		3		3		3	pF

Notes for Electrical Characteristics

Note 1: The maximum power dissipation for these devices must be derated at elevated temperatures and is dictated by T_{jMAX}, θ_{jA}, and the ambient temperature, T_A. The maximum available power dissipation at any temperature is $P_d = (T_{jMAX} - T_A)/\theta_{jA}$ or the 25°C P_{dMAX}, whichever is less.

Note 2: Unless otherwise specified the absolute maximum negative input voltage is equal to the negative power supply voltage.

Note 3: Unless otherwise stated, these test conditions apply:

	LF155A/6A/7A LF155//6/7	LF255//6/7	LF355A/6A/7A	LF355B/6B/7B	LF355//6/7
Supply Voltage, V_S	$\pm 15V \leq V_S \leq \pm 20V$	$\pm 15V \leq V_S \leq \pm 20V$	$\pm 15V \leq V_S \leq \pm 18V$	$\pm 15V \leq V_S \pm 20V$	$V_S = \pm 15V$
T_A	$-55°C \leq T_A \leq +125°C$	$-25°C \leq T_A \leq +85°C$	$0°C \leq T_A \leq +70°C$	$0°C \leq T_A \leq +70°C$	$0°C \leq T_A \leq +70°C$
T_{HIGH}	$+125°C$	$+85°C$	$+70°C$	$+70°C$	$+70°C$

and V_{OS}, I_B and I_{OS} are measured at $V_{CM} = 0$.

Note 4: The Temperature Coefficient of the adjusted input offset voltage changes only a small amount (0.5μV/°C typically) for each mV of adjustment from its original unadjusted value. Common-mode rejection and open loop voltage gain are also unaffected by offset adjustment.

Note 5: The input bias currents are junction leakage currents which approximately double for every 10°C increase in the junction temperature, T_J. Due to limited production test time, the input bias currents measured are correlated to junction temperature. In normal operation the junction temperature rises above the ambient temperature as a result of internal power dissipation, Pd. $T_j = T_A + \theta_{jA}$ Pd where θ_{jA} is the thermal resistance from junction to ambient. Use of a heat sink is recommended if input bias current is to be kept to a minimum.

Note 6: Supply Voltage Rejection is measured for both supply magnitudes increasing or decreasing simultaneously, in accordance with common practice.

Note 7: Settling time is defined here, for a unity gain inverter connection using 2 kΩ resistors for the LF155/6. It is the time required for the error voltage (the voltage at the inverting input pin on the amplifier) to settle to within 0.01% of its final value from the time a 10V step input is applied to the inverter. For the LF157, $A_V = -5$, the feedback resistor from output to input is 2 kΩ and the output step is 10V (See Settling Time Test Circuit).

Note 8: Refer to RETS155AX for LF155A, RETS155X for LF155, RETSF156AX for LF156A, RETS156X for LF156, RETS157A for LF157A and RETS157X for LF157 military specifications.

Note 9: Max. Power Dissipation is defined by the package characteristics. Operating the part near the Max. Power Dissipation may cause the part to operate outside guaranteed limits.

Typical AC Performance Characteristics (Continued)

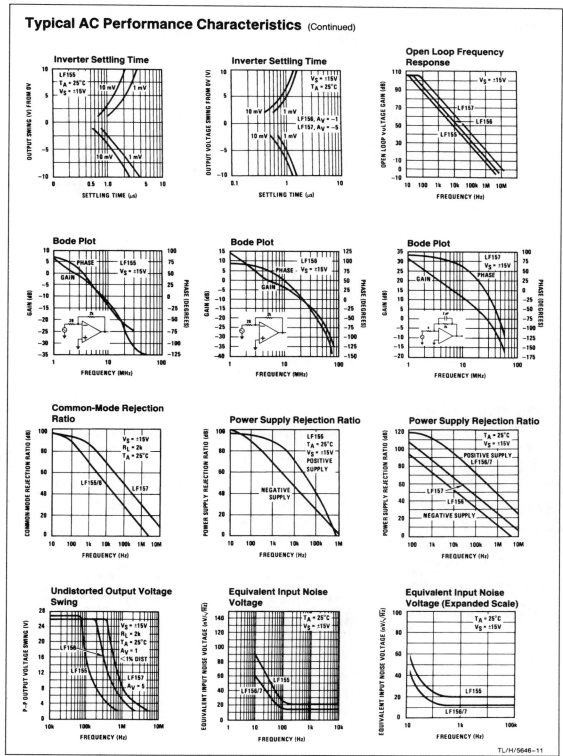

TL/H/5646–11

Sidebar (left margin): LF155/155A/LF255/LF355/355A/355B/LF156/156A/LF256/LF356/356A/356B/LF157/157A/LF257/LF357/357A/357B

Detailed Schematic

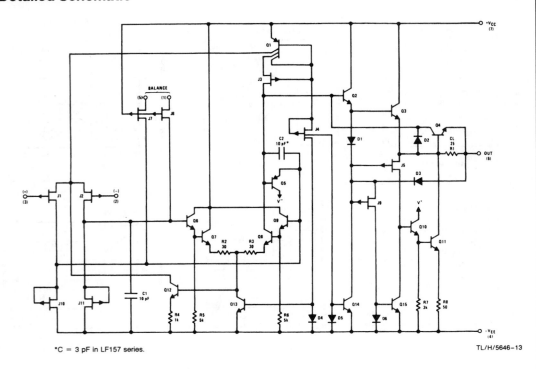

*C = 3 pF in LF157 series.

TL/H/5646–13

Connection Diagrams (Top Views)

Metal Can Package (H)

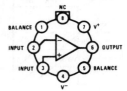

TL/H/5646–14

Order Number
LF155AH, LF156AH, LF157AH,
LF155H, LF156H, LF157H,
LF255H, LF256H, LF257H,
LF355AH, LF356AH, LF357AH,
LF355BH, LF356BH, LF357BH,
LF355H, LF356H or LF357H
See NS Package Number H08C

Dual-In-Line Package (J)

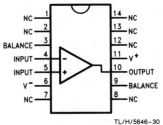

TL/H/5646–30

Order Number
LF155J, LF156J, LF157J,
LF355J, LF356J, LF357J,
LF355BJ, LF356BJ or LF357BJ
See NS Package Number J14A

Dual-In-Line Package (M and N)

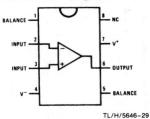

TL/H/5646–29

Order Number
LF355M, LF356M, LF357M,
LF356BM, LF355BN, LF356BN,
LF357BN, LF355N, LF356N or
LF357N
See NS Package Number
M08A or N08E

LF353

National
Semiconductor
Corporation

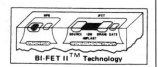

BI-FET II™ Technology

LF353 Wide Bandwidth Dual JFET Input Operational Amplifier

General Description

These devices are low cost, high speed, dual JFET input operational amplifiers with an internally trimmed input offset voltage (BI-FET II™ technology). They require low supply current yet maintain a large gain bandwidth product and fast slew rate. In addition, well matched high voltage JFET input devices provide very low input bias and offset currents. The LF353 is pin compatible with the standard LM1558 allowing designers to immediately upgrade the overall performance of existing LM1558 and LM358 designs.

These amplifiers may be used in applications such as high speed integrators, fast D/A converters, sample and hold circuits and many other circuits requiring low input offset voltage, low input bias current, high input impedance, high slew rate and wide bandwidth. The devices also exhibit low noise and offset voltage drift.

Features

- Internally trimmed offset voltage — 10 mV
- Low input bias current — 50pA
- Low input noise voltage — $16\ nV/\sqrt{Hz}$
- Low input noise current — $0.01\ pA/\sqrt{Hz}$
- Wide gain bandwidth — 4 MHz
- High slew rate — $13\ V/\mu s$
- Low supply current — 3.6 mA
- High input impedance — $10^{12}\Omega$
- Low total harmonic distortion $A_V = 10$, $RL = 10k$, $V_O = 20Vp-p$, $BW = 20\ Hz-20\ kHz$ — $<0.02\%$
- Low 1/f noise corner — 50 Hz
- Fast settling time to 0.01% — $2\ \mu s$

Typical Connection

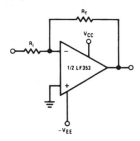

Simplified Schematic

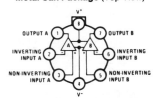

Connection Diagrams

Metal Can Package (Top View)

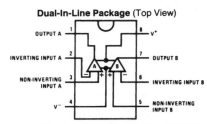

Order Number LF353H
See NS Package Number H08C

Dual-In-Line Package (Top View)

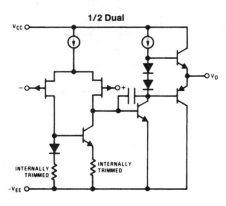

Order Number LF353J, LF353M or LF353N
See NS Package Number J08A, M08A or N08E

TL/H/5649–1

LF353

Absolute Maximum Ratings

If Military/Aerospace specified devices are required, contact the National Semiconductor Sales Office/Distributors for availability and specifications.

Supply Voltage	± 18V
Power Dissipation	(Note 1)
Operating Temperature Range	0°C to +70°C
T_j(MAX)	150°C
Differential Input Voltage	± 30V
Input Voltage Range (Note 2)	± 15V
Output Short Circuit Duration	Continuous

Storage Temperature Range	-65°C to $+150$°C
Lead Temp. (Soldering, 10 sec.)	260°C
Soldering Information	
Dual-In-Line Package	
Soldering (10 sec.)	260°C
Small Outline Package	
Vapor Phase (60 sec.)	215°C
Infrared (15 sec.)	220°C

See AN-450 "Surface Mounting Methods and Their Effect on Product Reliability" for other methods of soldering surface mount devices.

ESD rating to be determined.

DC Electrical Characteristics (Note 4)

Symbol	Parameter	Conditions	LF353			Units
			Min	Typ	Max	
V_{OS}	Input Offset Voltage	$R_S = 10$kΩ, $T_A = 25$°C		5	10	mV
		Over Temperature			13	mV
$\Delta V_{OS}/\Delta T$	Average TC of Input Offset Voltage	$R_S = 10$ kΩ		10		μV/°C
I_{OS}	Input Offset Current	$T_j = 25$°C, (Notes 4, 5)		25	100	pA
		$T_j \le 70$°C			4	nA
I_B	Input Bias Current	$T_j = 25$°C, (Notes 4, 5)		50	200	pA
		$T_j \le 70$°C			8	nA
R_{IN}	Input Resistance	$T_j = 25$°C		10^{12}		Ω
A_{VOL}	Large Signal Voltage Gain	$V_S = \pm 15$V, $T_A = 25$°C $V_O = \pm 10$V, $R_L = 2$ kΩ	25	100		V/mV
		Over Temperature	15			V/mV
V_O	Output Voltage Swing	$V_S = \pm 15$V, $R_L = 10$kΩ	± 12	± 13.5		V
V_{CM}	Input Common-Mode Voltage Range	$V_S = \pm 15$V	± 11	$+15$ -12		V V
CMRR	Common-Mode Rejection Ratio	$R_S \le 10$kΩ	70	100		dB
PSRR	Supply Voltage Rejection Ratio	(Note 6)	70	100		dB
I_S	Supply Current			3.6	6.5	mA

AC Electrical Characteristics (Note 4)

Symbol	Parameter	Conditions	LF353			Units
			Min	Typ	Max	
	Amplifier to Amplifier Coupling	$T_A = 25$°C, $f = 1$ Hz $- 20$ kHz (Input Referred)		-120		dB
SR	Slew Rate	$V_S = \pm 15$V, $T_A = 25$°C	8.0	13		V/μs
GBW	Gain Bandwidth Product	$V_S = \pm 15$V, $T_A = 25$°C	2.7	4		MHz
e_n	Equivalent Input Noise Voltage	$T_A = 25$°C, $R_S = 100\Omega$, $f = 1000$ Hz		25		nV/$\sqrt{\text{Hz}}$
i_n	Equivalent Input Noise Current	$T_j = 25$°C, $f = 1000$ Hz		0.01		pA/$\sqrt{\text{Hz}}$

Note 1: For operating at elevated temperatures, the device must be derated based on a thermal resistance of 115°C/W typ junction to ambient for the N package, and 195°C/W typ junction to ambient for the H package.

Note 2: Unless otherwise specified the absolute maximum negative input voltage is equal to the negative power supply voltage.

Note 3: The power dissipation limit, however, cannot be exceeded.

Note 4: These specifications apply for $V_S = \pm 15$V and 0°C$\le T_A \le +70$°C. V_{OS}, I_B and I_{OS} are measured at $V_{CM} = 0$.

Note 5: The input bias currents are junction leakage currents which approximately double for every 10°C increase in the junction temperature, T_j. Due to the limited production test time, the input bias currents measured are correlated to junction temperature. In normal operation the junction temperature rises above the ambient temperature as a result of internal power dissipation, P_D. $T_j = T_A + \theta_{jA} P_D$ where θ_{jA} is the thermal resistance from junction to ambient. Use of a heat sink is recommended if input bias current is to be kept to a minimum.

Note 6: Supply voltage rejection ratio is measured for both supply magnitudes increasing or decreasing simultaneously in accordance with common practice. $V_S = \pm 6$V to ± 15V.

LF353

Typical Applications

Three-Band Active Tone Control

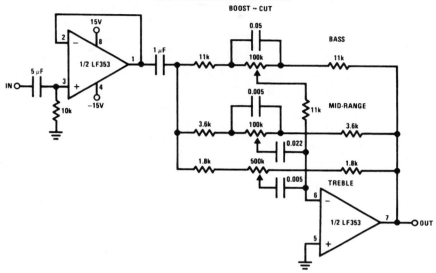

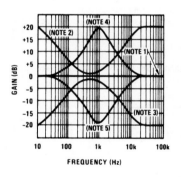

TL/H/5649–10

Note 1: All controls flat.
Note 2: Bass and treble boost, mid flat.
Note 3: Bass and treble cut, mid flat.
Note 4: Mid boost, bass and treble flat.
Note 5: Mid cut, bass and treble flat.

- All potentiometers are linear taper
- Use the LF347 Quad for stereo applications

Typical Applications (Continued)

Improved CMRR Instrumentation Amplifier

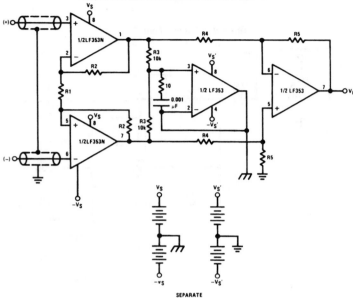

SEPARATE

$$A_V = \left(\frac{2R2}{R1} + 1\right) \frac{R5}{R4}$$

⊥⊥⊥ and ⏚ are separate isolated grounds
Matching of R2's, R4's and R5's control CMRR
With $A_{V_T} = 1400$, resistor matching = 0.01%: CMRR = 136 dB

- Very high input impedance
- Super high CMRR

Fourth Order Low Pass Butterworth Filter

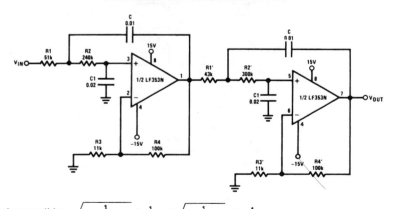

- Corner frequency $(f_c) = \sqrt{\dfrac{1}{R1R2CC1}} \cdot \dfrac{1}{2\pi} = \sqrt{\dfrac{1}{R1'R2'CC1}} \cdot \dfrac{1}{2\pi}$

- Passband gain $(H_O) = (1 + R4/R3)(1 + R4'/R3')$
- First stage Q = 1.31
- Second stage Q = 0.541
- Circuit shown uses nearest 5% tolerance resistor values for a filter with a corner frequency of 100 Hz and a passband gain of 100
- Offset nulling necessary for accurate DC performance

TL/H/5649–11

LF353

Typical Applications (Continued)

Fourth Order High Pass Butterworth Filter

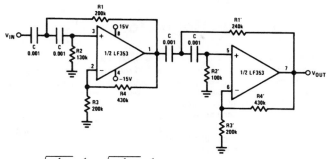

- Corner frequency $(f_C) = \sqrt{\dfrac{1}{R1R2C^2}} \cdot \dfrac{1}{2\pi} = \sqrt{\dfrac{1}{R1'R2'C^2}} \cdot \dfrac{1}{2\pi}$
- Passband gain $(H_O = (1 + R4/R3) (1 + R4'/R3')$
- First stage Q = 1.31
- Second stage Q = 0.541
- Circuit shown uses closest 5% tolerance resistor values for a filter with a corner frequency of 1 kHz and a passband gain of 10.

Ohms to Volts Converter

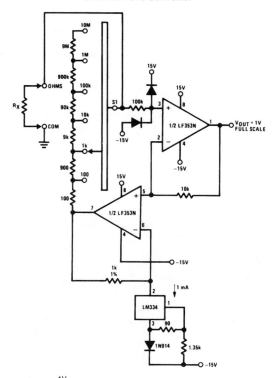

TL/H/5649–13

$$V_O = \frac{1V}{R_{LADDER}} \times R_X$$

Where R_{LADDER} is the resistance from switch S1 pole to pin 7 of the LF353.

National
Semiconductor
Corporation

LM723/LM723C Voltage Regulator

General Description

The LM723/LM723C is a voltage regulator designed primarily for series regulator applications. By itself, it will supply output currents up to 150 mA; but external transistors can be added to provide any desired load current. The circuit features extremely low standby current drain, and provision is made for either linear or foldback current limiting.

The LM723/LM723C is also useful in a wide range of other applications such as a shunt regulator, a current regulator or a temperature controller.

The LM723C is identical to the LM723 except that the LM723C has its performance guaranteed over a 0°C to +70°C temperature range, instead of −55°C to +125°C.

Features

- 150 mA output current without external pass transistor
- Output currents in excess of 10A possible by adding external transistors
- Input voltage 40V max
- Output voltage adjustable from 2V to 37V
- Can be used as either a linear or a switching regulator

Connection Diagrams

Dual-In-Line Package

```
        NC  ─┤ 1      14 ├─ NC
CURRENT LIMIT ─┤ 2      13 ├─ FREQUENCY
                             COMPENSATIONS
CURRENT SENSE ─┤ 3      12 ├─ V⁺
INVERTING INPUT ─┤ 4      11 ├─ V_C
NON−INVERTING
         INPUT ─┤ 5      10 ├─ V_OUT
        V_REF ─┤ 6       9 ├─ V_Z
          V⁻ ─┤ 7       8 ├─ NC
```

TL/H/8563−2

Top View

Order Number LM723J, LM723CJ,
LM723CM or LM723CN
See NS Package J14A, M14A or N14A

Metal Can Package

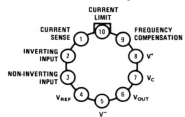

TL/H/8563−3

Note: Pin 5 connected to case.
Top View

Order Number LM723H or LM723CH
See NS Package H10C

Equivalent Circuit*

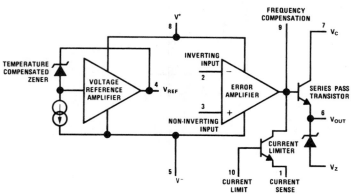

TL/H/8563−4

*Pin numbers refer to metal can package.

LM723/LM723C

Absolute Maximum Ratings

If Military/Aerospace specified devices are required, contact the National Semiconductor Sales Office/ Distributors for availability and specifications. (Note 9)

Pulse Voltage from V^+ to V^- (50 ms)	50V
Continuous Voltage from V^+ to V^-	40V
Input-Output Voltage Differential	40V
Maximum Amplifier Input Voltage (Either Input)	8.5V
Maximum Amplifier Input Voltage (Differential)	5V
Current from V_Z	25 mA
Current from V_{REF}	15 mA

Internal Power Dissipation Metal Can (Note 1)		800 mW
Cavity DIP (Note 1)		900 mW
Molded DIP (Note 1)		660 mW
Operating Temperature Range LM723		$-55°C$ to $+150°C$
LM723C		$0°C$ to $+70°C$
Storage Temperature Range Metal Can		$-65°C$ to $+150°C$
Molded DIP		$-55°C$ to $+150°C$
Lead Temperature (Soldering, 4 sec. max.)		
Hermetic Package		300°C
Plastic Package		260°C

Electrical Characteristics (Note 2)

Parameter	Conditions	LM723 Min	LM723 Typ	LM723 Max	LM723C Min	LM723C Typ	LM723C Max	Units
Line Regulation	$V_{IN} = 12V$ to $V_{IN} = 15V$		0.01	0.1		0.01	0.1	% V_{OUT}
	$-55°C \leq T_A \leq +125°C$			0.3				% V_{OUT}
	$0°C \leq T_A \leq +70°C$						0.3	% V_{OUT}
	$V_{IN} = 12V$ to $V_{IN} = 40V$		0.02	0.2		0.1	0.5	% V_{OUT}
Load Regulation	$I_L = 1$ mA to $I_L = 50$ mA		0.03	0.15		0.03	0.2	% V_{OUT}
	$-55°C \leq T_A \leq +125°C$			0.6				% V_{OUT}
	$0°C \leq T_A \leq +70°C$						0.6	% V_{OUT}
Ripple Rejection	f = 50 Hz to 10 kHz, $C_{REF} = 0$		74			74		dB
	f = 50 Hz to 10 kHz, $C_{REF} = 5$ μF		86			86		dB
Average Temperature Coefficient of Output Voltage (Note 8)	$-55°C \leq T_A \leq +125°C$		0.002	0.015				%/°C
	$0°C \leq T_A \leq +70°C$					0.003	0.015	%/°C
Short Circuit Current Limit	$R_{SC} = 10Ω$, $V_{OUT} = 0$		65			65		mA
Reference Voltage		6.95	7.15	7.35	6.80	7.15	7.50	V
Output Noise Voltage	BW = 100 Hz to 10 kHz, $C_{REF} = 0$		86			86		μVrms
	BW = 100 Hz to 10 kHz, $C_{REF} = 5$ μF		2.5			2.5		μVrms
Long Term Stability			0.05			0.05		%/1000 hrs
Standby Current Drain	$I_L = 0$, $V_{IN} = 30V$		1.7	3.5		1.7	4.0	mA
Input Voltage Range		9.5		40	9.5		40	V
Output Voltage Range		2.0		37	2.0		37	V
Input-Output Voltage Differential		3.0		38	3.0		38	V
θ_{JA}	Molded DIP		105			105		°C/W
θ_{JA}	Cavity DIP		150			150		°C/W
θ_{JA}	TO-5 Board Mount in Still Air		225			225		°C/W
θ_{JA}	TO-5 Board Mount in 400 LF/Min Air Flow		90			90		°C/W
θ_{JA}	SO					125		°C/W
θ_{JC}			25			25		°C/W

Note 1: See derating curves for maximum power rating above 25°C.

Note 2: Unless otherwise specified, $T_A = 25°C$, $V_{IN} = V^+ = V_C = 12V$, $V^- = 0$, $V_{OUT} = 5V$, $I_L = 1$ mA, $R_{SC} = 0$, $C_1 = 100$ pF, $C_{REF} = 0$ and divider impedance as seen by error amplifier ≤ 10 kΩ connected as shown in *Figure 1*. Line and load regulation specifications are given for the condition of constant chip temperature. Temperature drifts must be taken into account separately for high dissipation conditions.

Note 3: L_1 is 40 turns of No. 20 enameled copper wire wound on Ferroxcube P36/22-3B7 pot core or equivalent with 0.009 in. air gap.

Note 4: Figures in parentheses may be used if R1/R2 divider is placed on opposite input of error amp.

Note 5: Replace R1/R2 in figures with divider shown in *Figure 13*.

Note 6: V^+ must be connected to a +3V or greater supply.

Note 7: For metal can applications where V_Z is required, an external 6.2V zener diode should be connected in series with V_{OUT}.

Note 8: Guaranteed by correlation to other tests.

Note 9: Refer to RETS723X military specifications for the LM723.

TABLE I. Resistor Values (kΩ) for Standard Output Voltage

Positive Output Voltage	Applicable Figures (Note 4)	Fixed Output ±5%		Output Adjustable ±10% (Note 5)			Negative Output Voltage	Applicable Figures	Fixed Output ±5%		5% Output Adjustable ±10%		
		R1	R2	R1	P1	R2			R1	R2	R1	P1	R2
+3.0	1, 5, 6, 9, 12 (4)	4.12	3.01	1.8	0.5	1.2	+100	7	3.57	102	2.2	10	91
+3.6	1, 5, 6, 9, 12 (4)	3.57	3.65	1.5	0.5	1.5	+250	7	3.57	255	2.2	10	240
+5.0	1, 5, 6, 9, 12 (4)	2.15	4.99	0.75	0.5	2.2	−6 (Note 6)	3, (10)	3.57	2.43	1.2	0.5	0.75
+6.0	1, 5, 6, 9, 12 (4)	1.15	6.04	0.5	0.5	2.7	−9	3, 10	3.48	5.36	1.2	0.5	2.0
+9.0	2, 4, (5, 6, 9, 12)	1.87	7.15	0.75	1.0	2.7	−12	3, 10	3.57	8.45	1.2	0.5	3.3
+12	2, 4, (5, 6, 9, 12)	4.87	7.15	2.0	1.0	3.0	−15	3, 10	3.65	11.5	1.2	0.5	4.3
+15	2, 4, (5, 6, 9, 12)	7.87	7.15	3.3	1.0	3.0	−28	3, 10	3.57	24.3	1.2	0.5	10
+28	2, 4, (5, 6, 9, 12)	21.0	7.15	5.6	1.0	2.0	−45	8	3.57	41.2	2.2	10	33
+45	7	3.57	48.7	2.2	10	39	−100	8	3.57	97.6	2.2	10	91
+75	7	3.57	78.7	2.2	10	68	−250	8	3.57	249	2.2	10	240

TABLE II. Formulae for Intermediate Output Voltages

Outputs from +2 to +7 volts (Figures 1, 5, 6, 9, 12, [4]) $$V_{OUT} = \left(V_{REF} \times \frac{R2}{R1 + R2} \right)$$	Outputs from +4 to +250 volts (Figure 7) $$V_{OUT} = \left(\frac{V_{REF}}{2} \times \frac{R2 - R1}{R1} \right); R3 = R4$$	Current Limiting $$I_{LIMIT} = \frac{V_{SENSE}}{R_{SC}}$$
Outputs from +7 to +37 volts (Figures 2, 4, [5, 6, 9, 12]) $$V_{OUT} = \left(V_{REF} \times \frac{R1 + R2}{R2} \right)$$	Outputs from −6 to −250 volts (Figures 3, 8, 10) $$V_{OUT} = \left(\frac{V_{REF}}{2} \times \frac{R1 + R2}{R1} \right); R3 = R4$$	Foldback Current Limiting $$I_{KNEE} = \left(\frac{V_{OUT} R3}{R_{SC} R4} + \frac{V_{SENSE} (R3 + R4)}{R_{SC} R4} \right)$$ $$I_{SHORT\ CKT} = \left(\frac{V_{SENSE}}{R_{SC}} \times \frac{R3 + R4}{R4} \right)$$

Typical Applications

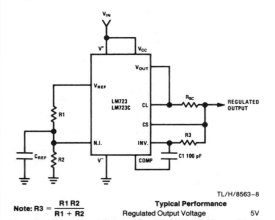

TL/H/8563–8

Note: $R3 = \dfrac{R1\ R2}{R1 + R2}$ for minimum temperature drift.

Typical Performance

Regulated Output Voltage	5V
Line Regulation (ΔV$_{IN}$ = 3V)	0.5 mV
Load Regulation (ΔI$_L$ = 50 mA)	1.5 mV

FIGURE 1. Basic Low Voltage Regulator
(V$_{OUT}$ = 2 to 7 Volts)

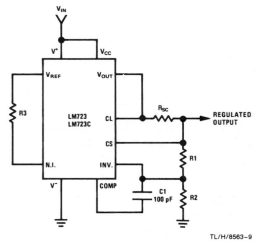

TL/H/8563–9

Note: $R3 = \dfrac{R1\ R2}{R1 + R2}$ for minimum temperature drift. R3 may be eliminated for minimum component count.

Typical Performance

Regulated Output Voltage	15V
Line Regulation (ΔV$_{IN}$ = 3V)	1.5 mV
Load Regulation (ΔI$_L$ = 50 mA)	4.5 mV

FIGURE 2. Basic High Voltage Regulator
(V$_{OUT}$ = 7 to 37 Volts)

LM723/LM723C

Typical Applications (Continued)

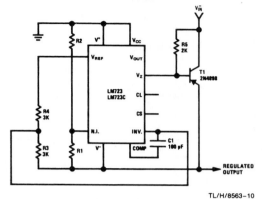

TL/H/8563–10

Typical Performance
Regulated Output Voltage   − 15V
Line Regulation (ΔV$_{IN}$ = 3V)   1 mV
Load Regulation (ΔI$_L$ = 100 mA)   2 mV

FIGURE 3. Negative Voltage Regulator

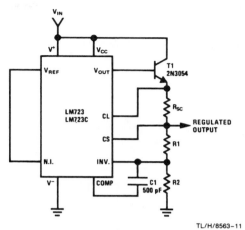

TL/H/8563–11

Typical Performance
Regulated Output Voltage   + 15V
Line Regulation (ΔV$_{IN}$ = 3V)   1.5 mV
Load Regulation (ΔI$_L$ = 1A)   15 mV

FIGURE 4. Positive Voltage Regulator
(External NPN Pass Transistor)

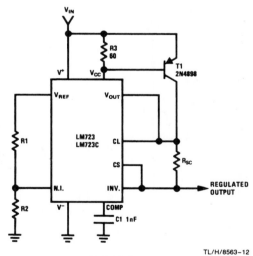

TL/H/8563–12

Typical Performance
Regulated Output Voltage   + 5V
Line Regulation (ΔV$_{IN}$ = 3V)   0.5 mV
Load Regulation (ΔI$_L$ = 1A)   5 mV

FIGURE 5. Positive Voltage Regulator
(External PNP Pass Transistor)

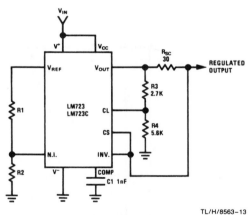

TL/H/8563–13

Typical Performance
Regulated Output Voltage   + 5V
Line Regulation (ΔV$_{IN}$ = 3V)   0.5 mV
Load Regulation (ΔI$_L$ = 10 mA)   1 mV
Short Circuit Current   20 mA

FIGURE 6. Foldback Current Limiting

Typical Applications (Continued)

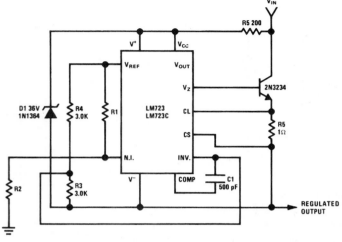

TL/H/8563–14

Typical Performance

Regulated Output Voltage	+50V
Line Regulation (ΔV_{IN} = 20V)	15 mV
Load Regulation (ΔI_L = 50 mA)	20 mV

FIGURE 7. Positive Floating Regulator

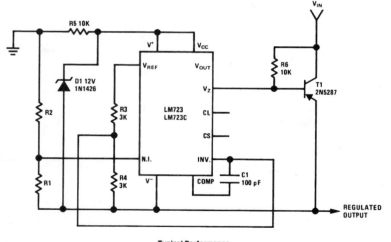

TL/H/8563–15

Typical Performance

Regulated Output Voltage	−100V
Line Regulation (ΔV_{IN} = 20V)	30 mV
Load Regulation (ΔI_L = 100 mA)	20 mV

FIGURE 8. Negative Floating Regulator

LM723/LM723C

Typical Applications (Continued)

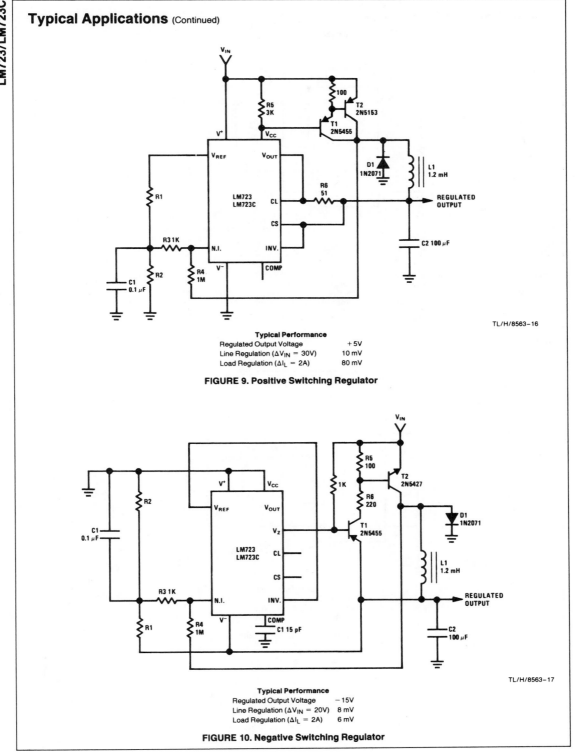

TL/H/8563–16

Typical Performance

Regulated Output Voltage	+ 5V
Line Regulation (ΔV_{IN} = 30V)	10 mV
Load Regulation (ΔI_L = 2A)	80 mV

FIGURE 9. Positive Switching Regulator

TL/H/8563–17

Typical Performance

Regulated Output Voltage	− 15V
Line Regulation (ΔV_{IN} = 20V)	8 mV
Load Regulation (ΔI_L = 2A)	6 mV

FIGURE 10. Negative Switching Regulator

A-36   Appendix A

LM723/LM723C

Typical Applications (Continued)

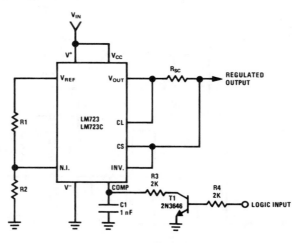

Note: Current limit transistor may be used for shutdown if current limiting is not required.

Typical Performance

Regulated Output Voltage	+5V
Line Regulation (ΔV_{IN} = 3V)	0.5 mV
Load Regulation (ΔI_L = 50 mA)	1.5 mV

TL/H/8563–18

FIGURE 11. Remote Shutdown Regulator with Current Limiting

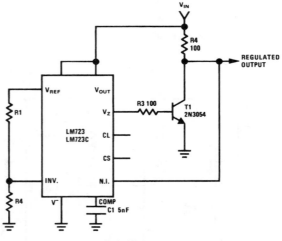

TL/H/8563–19

Typical Performance

Regulated Output Voltage	+5V
Line Regulation (ΔV_{IN} = 10V)	0.5 mV
Load Regulation (ΔI_L = 100 mA)	1.5 mV

FIGURE 12. Shunt Regulator

Typical Applications (Continued)

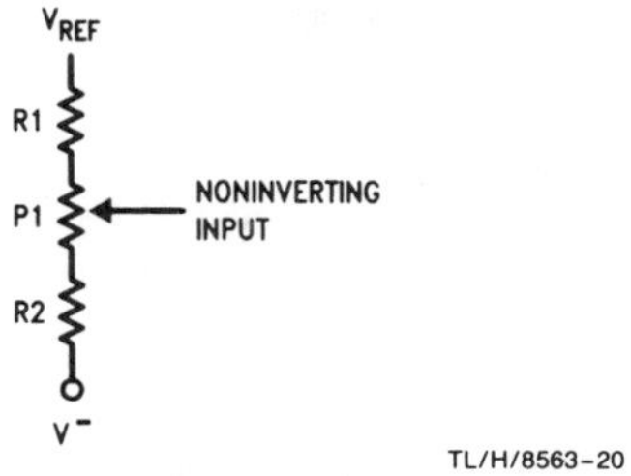

TL/H/8563–20

FIGURE 13. Output Voltage Adjust
(See Note 5)

Schematic Diagram

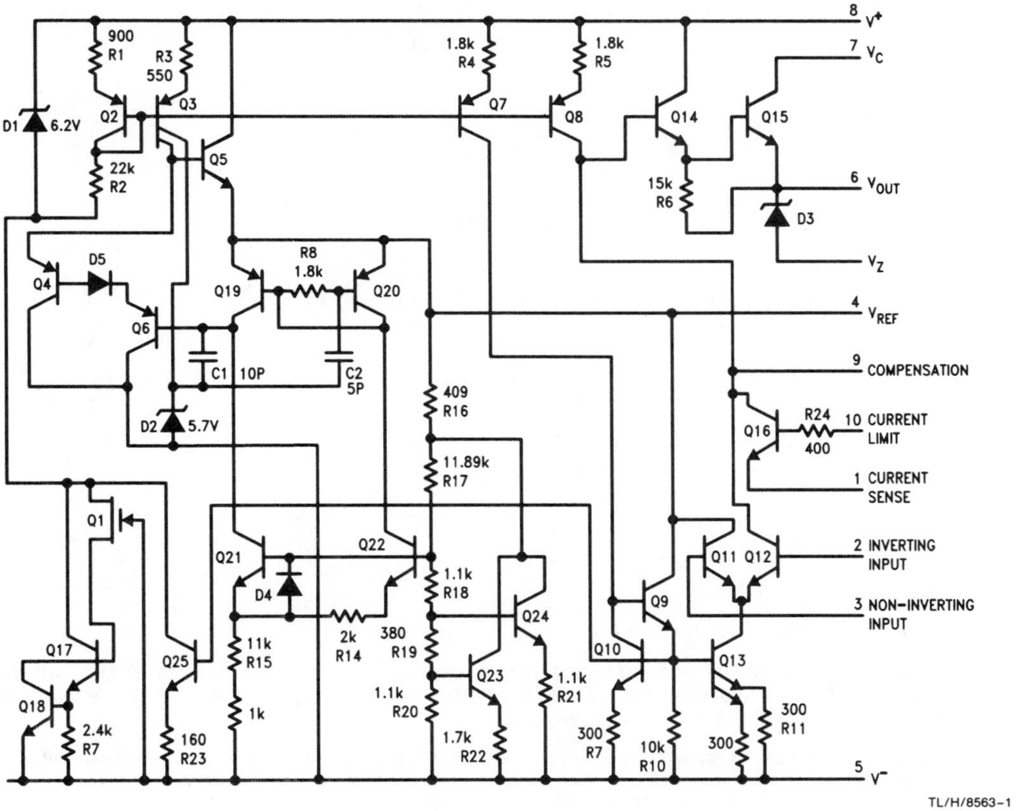

TL/H/8563–1

LIFE SUPPORT POLICY

NATIONAL'S PRODUCTS ARE NOT AUTHORIZED FOR USE AS CRITICAL COMPONENTS IN LIFE SUPPORT DEVICES OR SYSTEMS WITHOUT THE EXPRESS WRITTEN APPROVAL OF THE PRESIDENT OF NATIONAL SEMICONDUCTOR CORPORATION. As used herein:

1. Life support devices or systems are devices or systems which, (a) are intended for surgical implant into the body, or (b) support or sustain life, and whose failure to perform, when properly used in accordance with instructions for use provided in the labeling, can be reasonably expected to result in a significant injury to the user.

2. A critical component is any component of a life support device or system whose failure to perform can be reasonably expected to cause the failure of the life support device or system, or to affect its safety or effectiveness.

EXAR

XR-2206

Monolithic Function Generator

GENERAL DESCRIPTION

The XR-2206 is a monolithic function generator integrated circuit capable of producing high quality sine, square, triangle, ramp, and pulse waveforms of high-stability and accuracy. The output waveforms can be both amplitude and frequency modulated by an external voltage. Frequency of operation can be selected externally over a range of 0.01 Hz to more than 1 MHz.

The circuit is ideally suited for communications, instrumentation, and function generator applications requiring sinusoidal tone, AM, FM, or FSK generation. It has a typical drift specification of 20 ppm/°C. The oscillator frequency can be linearly swept over a 2000:1 frequency range, with an external control voltage, having a very small affect on distortion.

FEATURES

Low-Sine Wave Distortion	.5%, Typical
Excellent Temperature Stability	20 ppm/°C, Typical
Wide Sweep Range	2000:1, Typical
Low-Supply Sensitivity	0.01%V, Typical
Linear Amplitude Modulation	
TTL Compatible FSK Controls	
Wide Supply Range	10V to 26V
Adjustable Duty Cycle	1% to 99%

APPLICATIONS

Waveform Generation
Sweep Generation
AM/FM Generation
V/F Conversion
FSK Generation
Phase-Locked Loops (VCO)

ABSOLUTE MAXIMUM RATINGS

Power Supply	26V
Power Dissipation	750 mW
Derate Above 25°C	5 mW/°C
Total Timing Current	6 mA
Storage Temperature	−65°C to +150°C

FUNCTIONAL BLOCK DIAGRAM

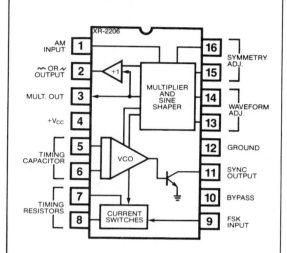

ORDERING INFORMATION

Part Number	Package	Operating Temperature
XR-2206M	Ceramic	−55°C to +125°C
XR-2206N	Ceramic	0°C to +70°C
XR-2206P	Plastic	0°C to +70°C
XR-2206CN	Ceramic	0°C to +70°C
XR-2206CP	Plastic	0°C to +70°C

SYSTEM DESCRIPTION

The XR-2206 is comprised of four functional blocks; a voltage-controlled oscillator (VCO), an analog multiplier and sine-shaper; a unity gain buffer amplifier; and a set of current switches.

The VCO actually produces an output frequency proportional to an input current, which is produced by a resistor from the timing terminals to ground. The current switches route one of the timing pins current to the VCO controlled by an FSK input pin, to produce an output frequency. With two timing pins, two discrete output frequencies can be independently produced for FSK Generation Applications.

EXAR Integrated Systems, Inc., 750 Palomar Avenue, Sunnyvale, CA 94086 * (408) 732-7970 * TWX 910-339-9233

XR-2206

ELECTRICAL CHARACTERISTICS

Test Conditions: Test Circuit of Figure 1, $V^+ = 12V$, $T_A = 25°$, $C = 0.01 \mu F$, $R_1 = 100 k\Omega$, $R_2 = 10 k\Omega$, $R_3 = 25 k\Omega$ unless otherwise specified. S_1 open for triangle, closed for sine wave.

PARAMETER	XR-2206M MIN.	XR-2206M TYP.	XR-2206M MAX.	XR-2206C MIN.	XR-2206C TYP.	XR-2206C MAX.	UNIT	CONDITIONS
GENERAL CHARACTERISTCS								
Single Supply Voltage	10		26	10		26	V	
Split-Supply Voltage	±5		±13	±5		±13	V	
Supply Current		12	17		14	20	mA	$R_1 \geqslant 10 k\Omega$
OSCILLATOR SECTION								
Max. Operating Frequency	0.5	1		0.5	1		MHz	$C = 1000 pF$, $R_1 = 1 k\Omega$
Lowest Practical Frequency		0.01			0.01		Hz	$C = 50 \mu F$, $R_1 = 2 M\Omega$
Frequency Accuracy		±1	±4		±2		% of f_O	$f_O = 1/R_1 C$
Temperature Stability		±10	±50		±20		ppm/°C	$0°C \leqslant T_A \leqslant 75°C$, $R_1 = R_2 = 20 k\Omega$
Supply Sensitivity		0.01	0.1		0.01		%/V	$V_{LOW} = 10V$, $V_{HIGH} = 20V$, $R_1 = R_2 = 20 k\Omega$
Sweep Range	1000:1	2000:1			2000:1		$f_H = f_L$	f_H @ $R_1 = 1 k\Omega$ f_L @ $R_1 = 2 M\Omega$
Sweep Linearity								
10:1 Sweep		2			2		%	$f_L = 1 kHz$, $f_H = 10 kHz$
1000:1 Sweep		8			8		%	$f_L = 100 Hz$, $f_H = 100 kHz$
FM Distortion		0.1			0.1		%	±10% Deviation
Recommended Timing Components								
Timing Capacitor: C	0.001		100	0.001		100	μF	See Figure 4.
Timing Resistors: R_1 & R_2	1		2000	1		2000	$k\Omega$	
Triangle Sine Wave Output								See Note 1, Figure 2.
Triangle Amplitude		160			160		mV/kΩ	Figure 1, S_1 Open
Sine Wave Amplitude	40	60	80		60		mV/kΩ	Figure 1, S_1 Closed
Max. Output Swing		6			6		V p-p	
Output Impedance		600			600		Ω	
Triangle Linearity		1			1		%	
Amplitude Stability		0.5			0.5		dB	For 1000:1 Sweep
Sine Wave Amplitude Stability		4800			4800		ppm/°C	See Note 2.
Sine Wave Distortion								
Without Adjustment		2.5			2.5		%	$R_1 = 30 k\Omega$
With Adjustment		0.4	1.0		0.5	1.5	%	See Figures 6 and 7.
Amplitude Modulation								
Input Impedance	50	100		50	100		$k\Omega$	
Modulation Range		100			100		%	
Carrier Suppression		55			55		dB	
Linearity		2			2		%	For 95% modulation
Square-Wave Output								
Amplitude		12			12		V p-p	Measured at Pin 11.
Rise Time		250			250		nsec	$C_L = 10 pF$
Fall Time		50			50		nsec	$C_L = 10 pF$
Saturation Voltage		0.2	0.4		0.2	0.6	V	$I_L = 2 mA$
Leakage Current		0.1	20		0.1	100	μA	$V_{11} = 26V$
FSK Keying Level (Pin 9)	0.8	1.4	2.4	0.8	1.4	2.4	V	See section on circuit controls
Reference Bypass Voltage	2.9	3.1	3.3	2.5	3	3.5	V	Measured at Pin 10.

Note 1: Output amplitude is directly proportional to the resistance, R_3, on Pin 3. See Figure 2.
Note 2: For maximum amplitude stability, R_3 should be a positive temperature coefficient resistor.

XR-2206

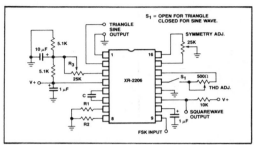

Figure 1:   Basic Test Circuit.

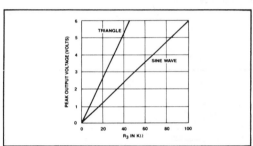

Figure 2:   Output Amplitude as a Function of the Resistor, R_3, at Pin 3.

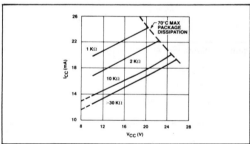

Figure 3:   Supply Current versus Supply Voltage, Timing, R.

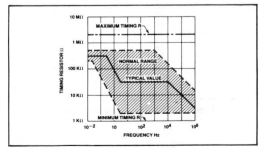

Figure 4:   R versus Oscillation Frequency.

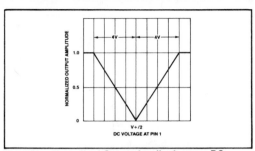

Figure 5:   Normalized Output Amplitude versus DC Bias at AM Input (Pin 1).

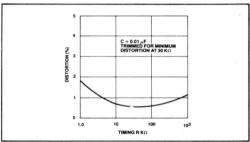

Figure 6:   Trimmed Distortion versus Timing Resistor.

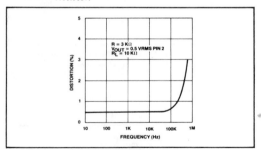

Figure 7:   Sine Wave Distortion versus Operating Frequency with Timing Capacitors Varied.

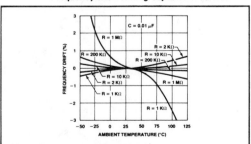

Figure 8:   Frequency Drift versus Temperature.

XR-2206

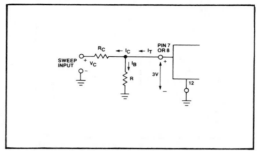

Figure 9: Circuit Connection for Frequency Sweep.

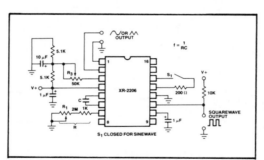

Figure 10: Circuit for Sine Wave Generation without
External Adjustment. (See Figure 2 for
Choice of R_3.)

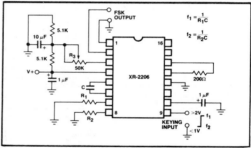

Figure 12: Sinusoidal FSK Generator.

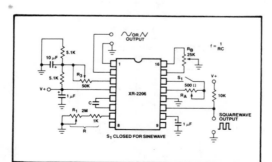

Figure 11: Circuit for Sine Wave Generation with
Minimum Harmonic Distortion. (R_3
Determines Output Swing — See Figure 2.)

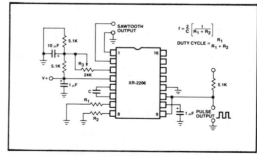

Figure 13: Circuit for Pulse and Ramp Generation.

XR-2206

Frequency-Shift Keying:

The XR-2206 can be operated with two separate timing resistors, R_1 and R_2, connected to the timing Pin 7 and 8, respectively, as shown in Figure 12. Depending on the polarity of the logic signal at Pin 9, either one or the other of these timing resistors is activated. If Pin 9 is open-circuited or connected to a bias voltage $\geq 2V$, only R_1 is activated. Similarly, if the voltage level at Pin 9 is $\leq 1V$, only R_2 is activated. Thus, the output frequency can be keyed between two levels, f_1 and f_2, as:

$$f_1 = 1/R_1C \text{ and } f_2 = 1/R_2C$$

For split-supply operation, the keying voltage at Pin 9 is referenced to V^-.

Output DC Level Control:

The dc level at the output (Pin 2) is approximately the same as the dc bias at Pin 3. In Figures 10, 11 and 12, Pin 3 is biased midway between V^+ and ground, to give an output dc level of $\approx V^+/2$.

APPLICATIONS INFORMATION

Sine Wave Generation

Without External Adjustment:

Figure 10 shows the circuit connection for generating a sinusoidal output from the XR-2206. The potentiometer, R_1 at Pin 7, provides the desired frequency tuning. The maximum output swing is greater than $V^+/2$, and the typical distortion (THD) is $<2.5\%$. If lower sine wave distortion is desired, additional adjustments can be provided as described in the following section.

The circuit of Figure 10 can be converted to split-supply operation, simply by replacing all ground connections with V^-. For split-supply operation, R_3 can be directly connected to ground.

With External Adjustment:

The harmonic content of sinusoidal output can be reduced to $\approx 0.5\%$ by additional adjustments as shown in Figure 11. The potentiometer, R_A, adjusts the sine-shaping resistor, and R_B provides the fine adjustment for the waveform symmetry. The adjustment procedure is as follows:

1. Set R_B at midpoint, and adjust R_A for minimum distortion.

2. With R_A set as above, adjust R_B to further reduce distortion.

Triangle Wave Generation

The circuits of Figures 10 and 11 can be converted to triangle wave generation, by simply open-circuiting Pin 13 and 14 (i.e., S_1 open). Amplitude of the triangle is approximately twice the sine wave output.

FSK Generation

Figure 12 shows the circuit connection for sinusoidal FSK signal operation. Mark and space frequencies can be independently adjusted, by the choice of timing resistors, R_1 and R_2; the output is phase-continuous during transitions. The keying signal is applied to Pin 9. The circuit can be converted to split-supply operation by simply replacing ground with V^-.

Pulse and Ramp Generation

Figure 13 shows the circuit for pulse and ramp waveform generation. In this mode of operation, the FSK keying terminal (Pin 9) is shorted to the square-wave output (Pin 11), and the circuit automatically frequency-shift keys itself between two separate frequencies during the positive-going and negative-going output waveforms. The pulse width and duty cycle can be adjusted from 1% to 99%, by the choice of R_1 and R_2. The values of R_1 and R_2 should be in the range of 1 kΩ to 2 MΩ.

XR-2206

PRINCIPLES OF OPERATION

Description of Controls

Frequency of Operation:

The frequency of oscillation, f_O, is determined by the external timing capacitor, C, across Pin 5 and 6, and by the timing resistor, R, connected to either Pin 7 or 8. The frequency is given as:

$$f_O = \frac{1}{RC} \ Hz$$

and can be adjusted by varying either R or C. The recommended values of R, for a given frequency range, are shown in Figure 4. Temperature stability is optimum for $4 \ k\Omega < R < 200 \ k\Omega$. Recommended values of C are from 1000 pF to 100 μF.

Frequency Sweep and Modulation:

Frequency of oscillation is proportional to the total timing current, I_T, drawn from Pin 7 or 8:

$$f = \frac{320 I_T \ (mA)}{C \ (\mu F)} \ Hz$$

Timing terminals (Pin 7 or 8) are low-impedance points, and are internally biased at +3V, with respect to Pin 12. Frequency varies linearly with I_T, over a wide range of current values, from 1 μA to 3 mA. The frequency can be controlled by applying a control voltage, V_C, to the activated timing pin as shown in Figure 9. The frequency of oscillation is related to V_C as:

$$f = \frac{1}{RC} \left[1 + \frac{R}{R_C}\left(1 - \frac{V_C}{3}\right) \right] \ Hz$$

where V_C is in volts. The voltage-to-frequency conversion gain, K, is given as:

$$K = \partial f / \partial V_C = - \frac{0.32}{R_C C} \ Hz/V$$

CAUTION: For safe operation of the circuit, I_T should be limited to $\leqslant 3$ mA.

Output Amplitude:

Maximum output amplitude is inversely proportional to the external resistor, R_3, connected to Pin 3 (see Figure 2). For sine wave output, amplitude is approximately 60 mV peak per $k\Omega$ of R_3; for triangle, the peak amplitude is approximately 160 mV peak per $k\Omega$ of R_3. Thus, for example, $R_3 = 50 \ k\Omega$ would produce approximately $\pm 3V$ sinusoidal output amplitude.

Amplitude Modulation:

Output amplitude can be modulated by applying a dc bias and a modulating signal to Pin 1. The internal impedance at Pin 1 is approximately 100 $k\Omega$. Output amplitude varies linearly with the applied voltage at Pin 1, for values of dc bias at this pin, within ± 4 volts of $V^+/2$ as shown in Figure 5. As this bias level approaches $V^+/2$, the phase of the output signal is reversed, and the amplitude goes through zero. This property is suitable for phase-shift keying and suppressed-carrier AM generation. Total dynamic range of amplitude modulation is approximately 55 dB.

CAUTION: AM control must be used in conjunction with a well-regulated supply, since the output amplitude now becomes a function of V^+.

EQUIVALENT SCHEMATIC DIAGRAM

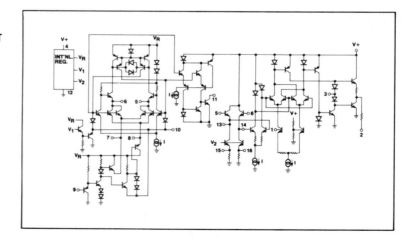

XR-2211

FSK Demodulator / Tone Decoder

GENERAL DESCRIPTION

The XR-2211 is a monolithic phase-locked loop (PLL) system especially designed for data communications. It is particularly well suited for FSK modem applications. It operates over a wide supply voltage range of 4.5 to 20 V and a wide frequency range of 0.01 Hz to 300 kHz. It can accommodate analog signals between 2 mV and 3 V, and can interface with conventional DTL, TTL, and ECL logic families. The circuit consists of a basic PLL for tracking an input signal within the pass band, a quadrature phase detector which provides carrier detection, and an FSK voltage comparator which provides FSK demodulation. External components are used to independently set center frequency, bandwidth, and output delay. An internal voltage reference proportional to the power supply provides ratio metric operation for low system performance variations with power supply changes.

The XR-2211 is available in 14 pin DTL ceramic or plastic packages specified for commercial or military temperature ranges.

FEATURES

Wide Frequency Range   0.01 Hz to 300 kHz
Wide Supply Voltage Range   4.5 V to 20 V
DTL/TTL/ECL Logic Compatibility
FSK Demodulation, with Carrier Detection
Wide Dynamic Range   2 mV to 3 V rms
Adjustable Tracking Range   (±1% to ±80%)
Excellent Temp. Stability   20 ppm/$^\circ$C, typ.

APPLICATIONS

FSK Demodulation
Data Synchronization
Tone Decoding
FM Detection
Carrier Detection

ABSOLUTE MAXIMUM RATINGS

Power Supply	20 V
Input Signal Level	3 V rms
Power Dissipation	
Ceramic Package	750 mW
Derate above T_A = +25°C	6 mV/$^\circ$C
Plastic Package	625 mW
Derate above T_A = +25°C	5.0 mW/$^\circ$C

FUNCTIONAL BLOCK DIAGRAM

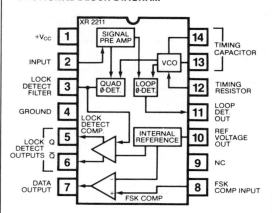

ORDERING INFORMATION

Part Number	Package	Operating Temperature
XR-2211M	Ceramic	–55°C to +125°C
XR-2211CN	Ceramic	0°C to + 75°C
XR-2211CP	Plastic	0°C to + 75°C
XR-2211N	Ceramic	–40°C to + 85°C
XR-2211P	Plastic	–40°C to + 85°C

SYSTEM DESCRIPTION

The main PLL within the XR-2211 is constructed from an input preamplifier, analog multiplier used as a phase detector, and a precision voltage controlled oscillator (VCO). The preamplifier is used as a limiter such that input signals above typically 2MV RMS are amplified to a constant high level signal. The multipling-type phase detector acts as a digital exclusive or gate. Its output (unfiltered) produces sum and difference frequencies of the input and the VCO output, f input + f input (2 f input) and f input - f input (0 Hz) when the phase detector output to remove the "sum" frequency component while passing the difference (DC) component to drive the VCO. The VCO is actually a current controlled oscillator with its nominal input current (f_0) set by a resistor (R_0) to ground and its driving current with a resistor (R_1) from the phase detector.

The other sections of the XR-2211 act to: determine if the VCO is driven above or below the center frequency (FSK comparator); produced both active high and active low outputs to indicate when the main PLL is in lock (quadrature phase detector and lock detector comparator).

EXAR Integrated Systems, Inc., 750 Palomar Avenue, Sunnyvale, CA 94086 * (408) 732-7970 * TWX 910-339-9233

XR-2211

ELECTRICAL CHARACTERISTICS

Test Conditions: Test Circuit of Figure 1, $V^+ = V^- = 6V$, $T_A = +25°C$, C = 5000 pF, $R_1 = R_2 = R_3 = R_4 = 20$ KΩ, $R_L = 4.7$ KΩ. Binary Inputs grounded, S_1 and S_2 closed unless otherwise specified.

PARAMETERS	XR-2211/2211M			XR-2211C			UNITS	CONDITIONS
	MIN.	TYP.	MAX.	MIN.	TYP.	MAX.		
GENERAL								
Supply Voltage	4.5		20	4.5		20	V	
Supply Current		4	7		5	9	mA	$R_0 \geq 10$ KΩ See Fig. 4
OSCILLATOR SECTION								
Frequency Accuracy		±1	±3		±1		%	Deviation from $f_0 = 1/R_0 C_0$
Frequency Stability								$R_1 = ½$
Temperature		±20	±50		±20		ppm/°C	See Fig. 8.
Power Supply		0.05	0.5		0.05		%/V	$V^+ = 12 \pm 1$ V. See Fig. 7.
		0.2			0.2		%/V	$V^+ = 5 \pm 0.5$ V. See Fig. 7.
Upper Frequency Limit	100	300			300		kHz	$R_0 = 8.2$ KΩ, $C_0 = 400$ pF
Lowest Practical								
Operating Frequency		0.01			0.01		Hz	$R_0 = 2$ MΩ, $C_0 = 50$ μF
Timing Resistor, R_0								See Fig. 5.
Operating Range	5		2000	5		2000	KΩ	
Recommended Range	15		100	15		100	KΩ	See Fig. 7 and 8.
LOOP PHASE DETECTOR SECTION								
Peak Output Current	±150	±200	±300	±100	±200	±300	μA	Measured at Pin 11.
Output Offset Current		±1			±2		μA	
Output Impedance		1			1		MΩ	
Maximum Swing	±4	±5		±4	±5		V	Referenced to Pin 10.
QUADRATURE PHASE DETECTOR								Measured at Pin 3.
Peak Output Current	100	150			150		μA	
Output Impedance		1			1		MΩ	
Maximum Swing		11			11		V pp	
INPUT PREAMP SECTION								Measured at Pin 2.
Input Impedance		20			20		KΩ	
Input Signal								
Voltage Required to								
Cause Limiting		2	10		2		mV rms	
VOLTAGE COMPARATOR SECTIONS								
Input Impedance		2			2		MΩ	Measured at Pins 3 and 8.
Input Bias Current		100			100		nA	
Voltage Gain	55	70		55	70		dB	$R_L = 5.1$ KΩ
Output Voltage Low		300			300		mV	$I_C = 3$ mA
Output Leakage Current		0.01			0.01		μA	$V_O = 12$ V
INTERNAL REFERENCE								
Voltage Level	4.9	5.3	5.7	4.75	5.3	5.85	V	Measured at Pin 10.
Output Impedance		100			100		Ω	

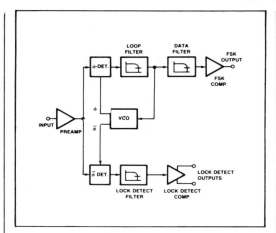

Figure 1: Functional Block Diagram of a Tone and FSK Decoding System Using XR-2211

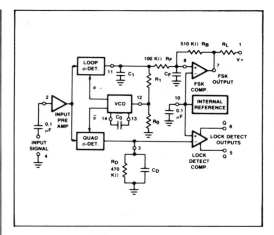

Figure 2: Generalized Circuit Connection for FSK and Tone Detection

Reference Voltage, V_R (Pin 10): This pin is internally biased at the reference voltage level, V_R: V_R = V+/2 - 650 mV. The dc voltage level at this pin forms an internal reference for the voltage levels at Pins 5, 8, 11 and 12. Pin 10 *must* be bypassed to ground with a 0.1 μF capacitor for proper operation of the circuit.

Loop Phase Detector Output (Pin 11): This terminal provides a high impedance output for the loop phase detector. The PLL loop filter is formed by R_1 and C_1 connected to Pin 11 (see Figure 2). With no input signal, or with no phase error within the PLL, the dc level at Pin 11 is very nearly equal to V_R. The peak voltage swing available at the phase detector output is equal to $\pm V_R$.

VCO Control Input (Pin 12): VCO free-running frequency is determined by external timing resistor, R_0, connected from this terminal to ground. The VCO free-running frequency, f_0, is:

$$f_0 = \frac{1}{R_0 C_0} \ \text{Hz}$$

where C_0 is the timing capacitor across Pins 13 and 14. For optimum temperature stability, R_0 must be in the range of 10 KΩ to 100 KΩ see Figure 8).

This terminal is a low impedance point, and is internally biased at a dc level equal to V_R. The maximum timing current drawn from Pin 12 must be limited to ⩽3 mA for proper operation of the circuit.

VCO Timing Capacitor (Pins 13 and 14): VCO frequency is inversely proportional to the external timing capacitor, C_0, connected across these terminals (see Figure 5). C_0 must be nonpolar, and in the range of 200 pF to 10 μF.

VCO Frequency Adjustment: VCO can be fine-tuned by connecting a potentiometer, R_X, in series with R_0 at Pin 12 (see Figure 9).

VCO Free-Running Frequency, f_0: XR-2211 does not have a separate VCO output terminal. Instead, the VCO outputs are internally connected to the phase detector sections of the circuit. However, for set-up or adjustment purposes, VCO free-running frequency can be measured at Pin 3 (with C_D disconnected), with no input and with Pin 2 shorted to Pin 10.

DESIGN EQUATIONS

(See Figure 2 for definition of components.)

1. VCO Center Frequency, f_0:

    $f_0 = 1/R_0 C_0$ Hz

2. Internal Reference Voltage, V_R (measured at Pin 10):

    V_R = V+/2 − 650 mV

3. Loop Low-Pass Filter Time Constant, τ:

    $\tau = R_1 C_1$

XR-2211

4. Loop Damping, ζ:

$$\zeta = 1/4 \sqrt{\frac{C_0}{C_1}}$$

5. Loop Tracking Bandwidth, $\pm\Delta f/f_0$:

$\Delta f/f_0 = R_0/R_1$

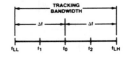

6. FSK Data Filter Time Constant, τF:

$\tau F = R_F C_F$

7. Loop Phase Detector Conversion Gain, $K\phi$: ($K\phi$ is the differential dc voltage across Pins 10 and 11, per unit of phase error at phase detector input):

$K\phi = -2V_R/\pi$ volts/radian

8. VCO Conversion Gain, K_0: (K_0 is the amount of change in VCO frequency, per unit of dc voltage change at Pin 11):

$K_0 = -1/V_R C_0 R_1$ Hz/volt

9. Total Loop Gain, K_T:

$K_T = 2\pi K\phi K_0 = 4/C_0 R_1$ rad/sec/volt

10. Peak Phase Detector Current I_A:

$I_A = V_R$ (volts)/25 mA

APPLICATIONS INFORMATION

FSK DECODING:

Figure 9 shows the basic circuit connection for FSK decoding. With reference to Figures 2 and 9, the functions of external components are defined as follows: R_0 and C_0 set the PLL center frequency, R_1 sets the system bandwidth, and C_1 sets the loop filter time constant and the loop damping factor. C_F and R_F form a one-pole post-detection filter for the FSK data output. The resistor R_B (= 510 KΩ) from Pin 7 to Pin 8 introduces positive feedback across the FSK comparator to facilitate rapid transition between output logic states.

Recommended component values for some of the most commonly used FSK bands are given in Table 1.

Design Instructions:

The circuit of Figure 9 can be tailored for any FSK decoding application by the choice of five key circuit components: R_0, R_1, C_0, C_1 and C_F. For a given set of FSK mark and space frequencies, f_1 and f_2, these parameters can be calculated as follows:

a) Calculate PLL center frequency, f_0:

$$f_0 = \frac{f_1 + f_2}{2}$$

b) Choose value of timing resistor R_0, to be in the range of 10 KΩ to 100 KΩ. This choice is arbitrary. The recommended value is $R_0 \equiv 20$ KΩ. The final value of R_0 is normally fine-tuned with the series potentiometer, R_X.

c) Calculate value of C_0 from design equation (1) or from Figure 6:

$C_0 = 1/R_0 f_0$

d) Calculate R_1 to give a Δf equal to the mark space deviation:

$R_1 = R_0 [f_0/(f_1 - f_2)]$

e) Calculate C_1 to set loop damping. (See design equation no. 4.):

Normally, $\zeta \approx 1/2$ is recommended.

Then: $C_1 = C_0/4$ for $\zeta = 1/2$

f) Calculate Data Filter Capacitance, C_F:

For $R_F = 100$ KΩ, $R_B = 510$ KΩ, the recommended value of C_F is:

$C_F \approx 3/$(Baud Rate) μF

Note: All calculated component values except R_0 can be rounded to the nearest standard value, and R_0 can be varied to fine-tune center frequency, through a series potentiometer, R_X. (See Figure 9.)

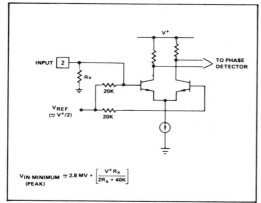

Figure 3:   Desensitizing Input Stage

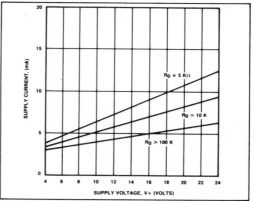

Figure 4:   Typical Supply Current vs V^+ (Logic Outputs Open Circuited).

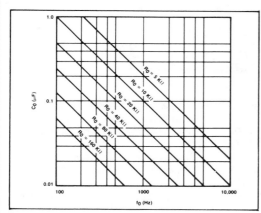

Figure 5:   VCO Frequency vs Timing Resistor

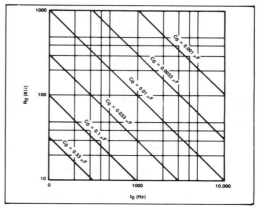

Figure 6:   VCO Frequency vs Timing Capacitor

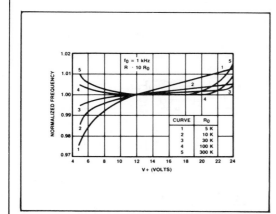

Figure 7:   Typical f_0 vs Power Supply Characteristics

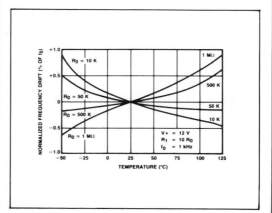

Figure 8:   Typical Center Frequency Drift vs Temperature

XR-2211

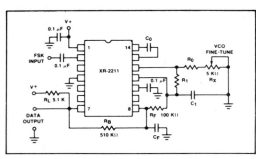

Figure 9:   Circuit Connection for FSK Decoding

Design Example:

75 Baud FSK demodulator with mark space frequencies of 1110/1170 Hz:

Step 1:   Calculate f_0: f_0 = (1110 + 1170) (1/2) = 1140 Hz
Step 2:   Choose R_0 = 20 KΩ (18 KΩ fixed resistor in series with 5 KΩ potentiometer)
Step 3:   Calculate C_0 from Figure 6: C_0 = 0.044 μF
Step 4:   Calculate R_1: R_1 = R_0 (2240/60) = 380 KΩ
Step 5:   Calculate C_1: C_1 = C_0/4 = 0.011 μF

Note: All values except R_0 can be rounded to *nearest* standard value.

Table 1.   Recommended Component Values for Commonly Used FSK Bands.
(See Circuit of Figure 9.)

FSK BAND	COMPONENT VALUES	
300 Baud f_1 = 1070 Hz f_2 = 1270 Hz	C_0 = 0.039 μF C_1 = 0.01 μF R_1 = 100 KΩ	C_F = 0.005 μF R_0 = 18 KΩ
300 Baud f_1 = 2025 Hz f_2 = 2225 Hz	C_0 = 0.022 μF C_1 = 0.0047 μF R_1 = 200 KΩ	C_F = 0.005 μF R_0 = 18 KΩ
1200 Baud f_1 = 1200 Hz f_2 = 2200 Hz	C_0 = 0.027 μF C_1 = 0.01 μF R_1 = 30 KΩ	C_F = 0.0022 μF R_0 = 18 KΩ

FSK DECODING WITH CARRIER DETECT:

The lock detect section of XR-2211 can be used as a carrier detect option, for FSK decoding. The recommended circuit connection for this application is shown in Figure 10. The open collector lock detect output, Pin 6, is shorted to data output (Pin 7). Thus, data output will be disabled at "low" state, until there is a carrier within the detection band of the PPL, and the Pin 6 output goes "high," to enable the data output.

The minimum value of the lock detect filter capacitance C_D is inversely proportional to the capture range, $\pm\Delta f_C$. This is the range of incoming frequencies over which the loop can acquire lock and is always less than the tracking range. It is further limited by C_1. For most applications, $\Delta f_C > \Delta f/2$. For R_D = 470 KΩ, the approximate minimum value of C_D can be determined by:

$$C_D (\mu F) \geq 16/\text{capture range in Hz.}$$

With values of C_D that are too small, chatter can be observed on the lock detect output as an incoming signal frequency approaches the capture bandwidth. Excessively large values of C_D will slow the response time of the lock detect output.

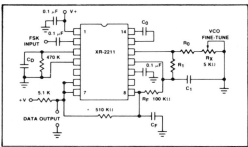

Figure 10: External Connectors for FSK Demodulation with Carrier Detect Capability

Note: Data Output is "Low" When No Carrier is Present.

TONE DETECTION:

Figure 11 shows the generalized circuit connection for tone detection. The logic outputs, Q and $\overline{Q}$ at Pins 5 and 6 are normally at "high" and "low" logic states, respectively. When a tone is present within the detection band of the PLL, the logic state at these outputs become reversed for the duration of the input tone. Each logic output can sink 5 mA of load current.

Both logic outputs at Pins 5 and 6 are open collector type stages, and require external pull-up resistors R_{L1} and R_{L2}, as shown in Figure 11.

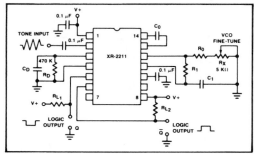

Figure 11:   Circuit Connection for Tone Detection.

With reference to Figures 2 and 11, the functions of the external circuit components can be explained as follows: R_0 and C_0 set VCO center frequency; R_1 sets the detection bandwidth; C_1 sets the low pass-loop filter time constant and the loop damping factor. R_{L1} and R_{L2} are the respective pull-up resistors for the Q and $\overline{Q}$ logic outputs.

Design Instructions:

The circuit of Figure 11 can be optimized for any tone detection application by the choice of the 5 key circuit components: R_0, R_1, C_0, C_1 and C_D. For a given input, the tone frequency, f_S, these parameters are calculated as follows:

a) Choose R_0 to be in the range of 15 KΩ to 100 KΩ. This choice is arbitrary.

b) Calculate C_0 to set center frequency, f_0 equal to f_s (see Figure 6): $C_0 = 1/R_0 f_S$

c) Calculate R_1 to set bandwidth $\pm \Delta f$ (see design equation no. 5):

$$R_1 = R_0 (f_0/\Delta f)$$

Note: The total detection bandwidth covers the frequency range of $f_0 \pm \Delta f$.

d) Calculate value of C_1 for a given loop damping factor;

$$C_1 = C_0/16\zeta 2$$

Normally $\zeta \approx 1/2$ is optimum for most tone detector applications, giving $C_1 = 0.25\ C_0$.

Increasing C_1 improves the out-of-band signal rejection, but increases the PLL capture time.

e) Calculate value of filter capacitor C_D. To avoid chatter at the logic output, with $R_D = 470$ KΩ, C_D must be:

$$C_D(\mu F) \geqslant (16/\text{capture range in Hz})$$

Increasing C_D slows down the logic output response time.

Design Examples:

Tone detector with a detection band of 1 kHz ± 20 Hz:

a) Choose $R_0 = 20$ KΩ (18 KΩ in series with 5 KΩ potentiometer).

b) Choose C_0 for $f_0 = 1$ kHz (from Figure 6): $C_0 = 0.05\ \mu F$.

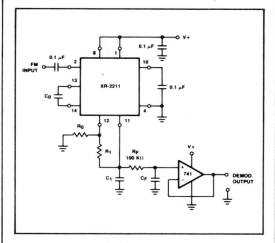

Figure 12: Linear FM Detector Using XR-2211 and an External Op Amp. (See section on Design Equation for Component Values.)

c) Calculate R_1: $R_1 = (R_0)\ (1000/20) = 1$ MΩ.

d) Calculate C_1: for $\zeta = 1/2$, $C_1 = 0.25$, $C_0 = 0.013\ \mu F$.

e) Calculate C_D: $C_D = 16/38 = 0.42\ \mu F$.

f) Fine-tune center frequency with 5 KΩ potentiometer, R_X.

LINEAR FM DETECTION:

XR-2211 can be used as a linear FM detector for a wide range of analog communications and telemetry applications. The recommended circuit connection for this application is shown in Figure 12. The demodulated output is taken from the loop phase detector output (Pin 11), through a post-detection filter made up of R_F and C_F, and an external buffer amplifier. This buffer amplifier is necessary because of the high impedance output at Pin 11. Normally, a non-inverting unity gain op amp can be used as a buffer amplifier, as shown in Figure 12.

The FM detector gain, i.e., the output voltage change per unit of FM deviation can be given as:

$$V_{out} = R_1\ V_R/100\ R_0\ \text{Volts/\%deviation}$$

where V_R is the internal reference voltage ($V_R = V+/2 - 650$ mV). For the choice of external components R_1, R_0, C_D, C_1 and C_F, see section on design equations.

XR-2211

PRINCIPLES OF OPERATION

Signal Input (Pin 2): Signal is ac coupled to this terminal. The internal impedance at Pin 2 is 20 KΩ. Recommended input signal level is in the range of 10 mV rms to 3 V rms.

Quadrature Phase Detector Output (Pin 3): This is the high impedance output of quadrature phase detector and is internally connected to the input of lock detect voltage comparator. In tone detection applications, Pin 3 is connected to ground through a parallel combination of R_D and C_D (see Figure 2) to eliminate the chatter at lock detect outputs. If the tone detect section is not used, Pin 3 can be left open circuited.

Lock Detect Output, Q (Pin 5): The output at Pin 5 is at "high" state when the PLL is out of lock and goes to "low" or conducting state when the PLL is locked. It is an open collector type output and requires a pull-up resistor, R_L, to V+ for proper operation. At "low" state, it can sink up to 5 mA of load current.

Lock Detect Complement, $\overline{Q}$ (Pin 6): The output at Pin 6 is the logic complement of the lock detect output at Pin 5. This output is also an open collector type stage which can sink 5 mA of load current at low or "on" state.

FSK Data Output (Pin 7): This output is an open collector logic stage which requires a pull-up resistor, R_L, to V+ for proper operation. It can sink 5 mA of load current. When decoding FSK signals, FSK data output is at "high" or "off" state for low input frequency, and at "low" or "on" state for high input frequency. If no input signal is present, the logic state at Pin 7 is indeterminate.

FSK Comparitor Input (Pin 8): This is the high impedance input to the FSK voltage comparator. Normally, an FSK post-detection or data filter is connected between this terminal and the PLL phase detector output (Pin 11). This data filter is formed by R_F and C_F of Figure 2. The threshold voltage of the comparator is set by the internal reference voltage, V_R, available at Pin 10.

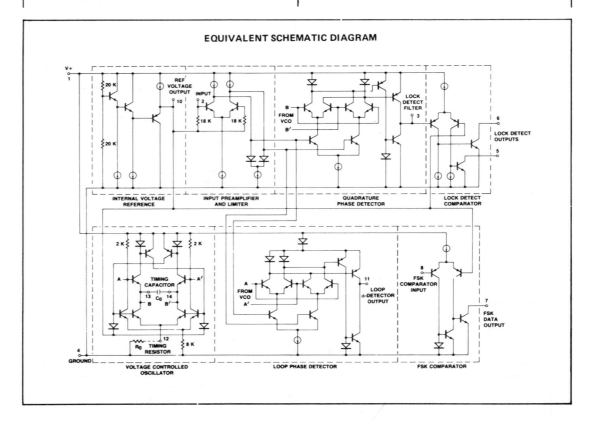

EQUIVALENT SCHEMATIC DIAGRAM

EXAR

XR-567

Monolithic Tone Decoder

GENERAL DESCRIPTION

The XR-567 is a monolithic phase-locked loop system designed for general purpose tone and frequency decoding. The circuit operates over a wide frequency band of 0.01 Hz to 500 kHz and contains a logic compatible coutput which can sink up to 100 milliamps of load current. The bandwidth, center frequency, and output delay are independently determined by the selection of four external components.

Figure 1 contains a functional block diagram of the complete monolithic system. The circuit consists of a phase detector, low-pass filter, and current-controlled oscillator which comprise the basic phase-locked loop; plus an additional low-pass filter and quadrature detector that enable the system to distinguish between the presence or absence of an input signal at the center frequency.

FEATURES

Bandwidth adjustable from 0 to 14%.
Logic compatible output with 100mA current sinking capability.
Highly stable center frequency.
Center frequency adjustable from 0.01 Hz to 500 kHz.
Inherent immunity to false signals.
High rejection of out-of-band signals and noise.
Frequency range adjustable over 20:1 range by external resistor.

APPLICATIONS

Touch-Tone® Decoding
Sequential Tone Decoding
Communications Paging
Ultrasonic Remote-Control
Telemetry Decoding

ABSOLUTE MAXIMUM RATINGS

Power Supply	10 volts
Power Dissipation (package limitation)	
Ceramic package	385 mW
Plastic Package	300 mW
Derate above +25°C	2.5 mW/°C
Temperature	
Operating	
XR-567M	−55°C to +125°C
XR-567CN/567CP	0°C to +70°C
Storage	−65°C to +150°C

ORDER INFORMATION

Part Number	Package	Operating Temperature
XR-567M	Ceramic	−55°C to +125°C
XR-567CN	Ceramic	0°C to +75°C
XR-567CP	Plastic	0°C to +75°C

EQUIVALENT SCHEMATIC DIAGRAM

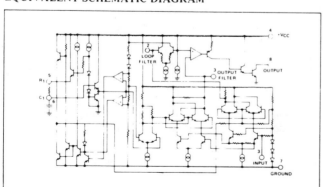

FUNCTIONAL BLOCK DIAGRAM

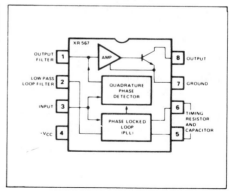

10-79 REV 3

 **EXAR** Integrated Systems, Inc., 750 Palomar Avenue, Sunnyvale, CA 94086 * (408) 732-7970 * TWX 910-339-9233

ELECTRICAL SPECIFICATIONS

Test Conditions: V_{CC} = +5V. T_A = 25°C, unless otherwise specified. Test circuit of Figure 2.

CHARACTERISTICS	LIMITS			UNITS	CONDITIONS
	MIN	TYP	MAX		
GENERAL					
Supply Voltage Range	4.75		9.0	V dc	
Supply Current					
Quiescent XR-567M		6	8	mA	R_L = 20 kΩ
XR-567C		7	10	mA	R_L = 20 kΩ
Activated XR-567M		11	13	mA	R_L = 20 kΩ
XR-567C		12	15	mA	R_L = 20 kΩ
Output Voltage			15	V	
Negative Voltage at Input			−10	V	
Positive Voltage at Input			V_{CC} + 0.5	V	
CENTER FREQUENCY					
Highest Center Frequency	100	500		kHz	
Center Frequency Stability					
Temperature T_A = 25°C		35		ppm/$^\circ$C	See Figure 9
0 < T_A < 70°C		±60		ppm/$^\circ$C	See Figure 9
−55 < T_A < +125°C		±140		ppm/$^\circ$C	See Figure 9
Supply Voltage					
XR-567M		0.5	1.0	%/V	f_o = 100 kHz
XR-567C		0.7	2.0	%/V	f_o = 100 kHz
DETECTION BANDWIDTH					
Largest Detection Bandwidth					
XR-567M	12	14	16	% of f_o	f_o = 100 kHz
XR-567C	10	14	18	% of f_o	f_o = 100 kHz
Largest Detection Bandwidth Skew					
XR-567M		1	2	% of f_o	
XR-567C		2	3	% of f_o	
Largest Detection Bandwidth Variation					
Temperature		±0.1		%/$^\circ$C	V_{in} = 300 mV rms
Supply Voltage		±2		%/V	V_{in} = 300 mV rms
INPUT					
Input Resistance		20		kΩ	
Smallest Detectable Input Voltage		20	25	mV rms	I_L = 100 mA, f_i = f_o
Largest No-Output Input Voltage	10	15		mV rms	I_L = 100 mA, f_i = f_o
Greatest Simultaneous Outband Signal to Inband Signal Ratio		+6		dB	
Minimum Input Signal to Wideband Noise Ratio		−6		dB	B_n = 140 kHz
OUTPUT					
Output Saturation Voltage		0.2	0.4	V	I_L = 30 mA, V_{in} = 25 mV rms
		0.6	1.0	V	I_L = 100 mA, V_{in} = 25 mV rms
Output Leakage Current		0.01	25	μA	
Fastest ON-OFF Cycling Rate		f_o/20			
Output Rise Time		150		ns	R_L = 50Ω
Output Fall Time		30		ns	R_L = 50Ω

DEFINITION OF XR-567 PARAMETERS

CENTER FREQUENCY f_o

f_o is the free-running frequency of the current-controlled oscillator with no input signal. It is determined by resistor R_1 between pins 5 and 6, and capacitor C_1 from pin 6 to ground. f_o can be approximated by

$$f_o \approx \frac{1}{R_1 C_1}$$

where R_1 is in ohms and C_1 is in farads.

DETECTION BANDWIDTH (BW)

The *detection bandwidth* is the frequency range centered about f_o, within which an input signal larger than the threshold voltage (typically 20 mV rms) will cause a logic zero state at the output. The detection bandwidth corresponds to the capture range of the PLL and is determined by the low-pass bandwidth filter. The bandwidth of the filter, as a percent of f_o, can be determined by the approximation

$$BW = 1070 \sqrt{\frac{V_i}{f_o C_2}}$$

where V_i is the input signal in volts, rms, and C_2 is the capacitance at pin 2 in μF.

LARGEST DETECTION BANDWIDTH

The *largest detection bandwidth* is the largest frequency range within which an input signal above the threshold voltage will cause a logical zero state at the output. The maximum detection bandwidth corresponds to the lock range of the PLL.

DETECTION BAND SKEW

The *detection band skew* is a measure of how accurately the largest detection band is centered about the center frequency, f_o. It is defined as $(f_{max} + f_{min} - 2 f_o)/f_o$, where f_{max} and f_{min} are the frequencies corresponding to the edges of the detection band. If necessary, the detection band skew can be reduced to zero by an optional centering adjustment. (See Optional Controls).

DESCRIPTION OF CIRCUIT CONTROLS

OUTPUT FILTER — C_3 (Pin 1)

Capacitor C_3 connected from pin 1 to ground forms a simple low-pass *post detection* filter to eliminate spurious outputs due to out-of-band signals. The time constant of the filter can be expressed as $T_3 = R_3 C_3$, where R_3 (4.7 kΩ) is the internal impedance at pin 1.

The precise value of C_3 is not critical for most applications. To eliminate the possibility of false triggering by spurious signals, it is recommended that C_3 be $\geq 2 C_2$, where C_2 is the loop filter capacitance at pin 2.

If the value of C_3 becomes too large, the *turn-on* or *turn-off* time of the output stage will be delayed until the voltage change across C_3 reaches the threshold voltage. In certain applications, the delay may be desirable as a means of suppressing spurious outputs. Conversely, if the value of C_3 is too small, the beat rate at the output of the quadrature detector (see Figure 1) may cause a false logic level change at the output. (Pin 8)

The average voltage (during lock) at pin 1 is a function of the inband input amplitude in accordance with the given transfer characteristic.

LOOP FILTER — C_2 (Pin 2)

Capacitor C_2 connected from pin 2 to ground serves as a single pole, low-pass filter for the PLL portion of the XR-567. The

filter time constant is given by $T_2 = R_2 C_2$, where R_2 (10 kΩ) is the impedance at pin 2.

The selection of C_2 is determined by the detection bandwidth requirements, as shown in Figure 6. For additional information see section on "Definition of XR-567 Parameters".

The voltage at pin 2, the phase detector output, is a linear function of frequency over the range of 0.95 to 1.05 f_o, with a slope of approximately 20 mV/% frequency deviation.

INPUT (Pin 3)

The input signal is applied to pin 3 through a coupling capacitor. This terminal is internally biased at a dc level 2 volts above ground, and has an input impedance level of approximately 20 kΩ.

TIMING RESISTOR R_1 AND CAPACITOR C_1 (Pins 5 and 6)

The center frequency of the decoder is set by resistor R_1 between pins 5 and 6, and capacitor C_1 from pin 6 to ground, as shown in Figure 3.

Pin 5 is the oscillator squareware output which has a magnitude of approximately $V_{CC} - 1.4$V and an average dc level of $V_{CC}/2$. A 1 kΩ load may be driven from this point. The voltage at pin 6 is an exponential triangle waveform with a peak-to-peak amplitude of 1 volt and an average dc level of $V_{CC}/2$. Only high impedance loads should be connected to pin 6 to avoid disturbing the temperature stability or duty cycle of the oscillator.

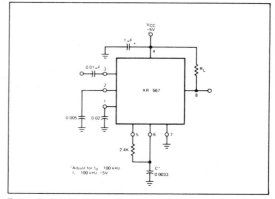

Figure 2. XR-567 Test Circuit

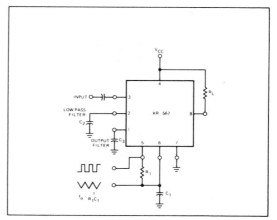

Figure 3. XR-567 Connection Diagram

TYPICAL CHARACTERISTIC CURVES

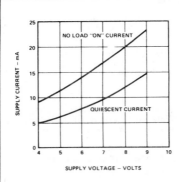

Figure 4. Supply Current Versus Supply Voltage

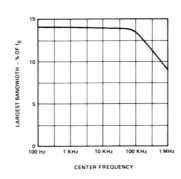

Figure 5. Largest Detection Bandwidth Versus Operating Frequency

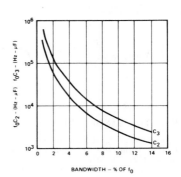

Figure 6. Detection Bandwidth as a Function of C_2 and C_3

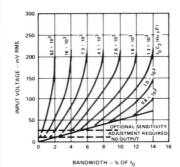

Figure 7. Bandwidth Versus Input Signal Amplitude (C_2 in μF)

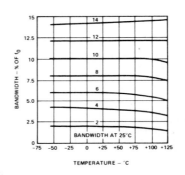

Figure 8. Bandwidth Variation with Temperature

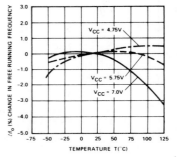

Figure 9. Frequency Drift with Temperature

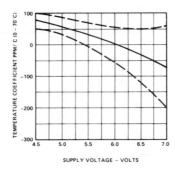

Figure 10. Temperature Coefficient of Center Frequency (Mean and S.D.)

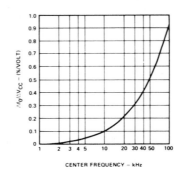

Figure 11. Power Supply Dependence of Center Frequency

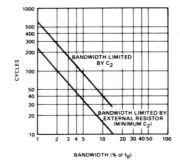

Figure 12. Greatest Number of Cycles Before Output

LOGIC OUTPUT (Pin 8)

Terminal 8 provides a binary logic output when an input signal is present within the pass-band of the decoder. The logic output is an uncommitted, "bare-collector" power transistor capable of switching high current loads. The current level at the output is determined by an external load resistor, R_L, connected from pin 8 to the positive supply.

When an in-band signal is present, the output transistor at pin 8 saturates with a collector voltage less than 1 volt (typically 0.6V) at full rated current of 100 mA. If large output voltage swings are needed, R_L can be connected to a supply voltage, V+, higher than the V_{CC} supply. For safe operation, V+ $\leq$ 20 volts.

INPUT

OUTPUT

Response to 100 mV rms tone burst.
R_L = 100 ohms.

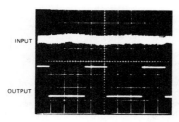

INPUT

OUTPUT

Response to same input tone burst with wideband noise.
$\frac{S}{R}$ = -6 dB R_L = 100 ohms
Noise Bandwidth = 140 Hz

Figure 13. Typical Response

OPERATING INSTRUCTIONS

SELECTION OF EXTERNAL COMPONENTS

A typical connection diagram for the XR-567 is shown in Figure 3. For most applications, the following procedure will be sufficient for determination of the external components R_1, C_1, C_2, and C_3.

1. R_1 and C_1 should be selected for the desired center frequency by the expression $f_0 \approx 1/R_1 C_1$. For optimum temperature stability, R_1 should be selected such that $2k\Omega \leq R_1 \leq 20k\Omega$, and the $R_1 C_1$ product should have sufficient stability over the projected operating temperature range.

2. Low-pass capacitor, C_2, can be determined from the Bandwidth versus Input Signal Amplitude graph of Figure 7. One approach is to select an area of operation from the graph, and then adjust the input level and value of C_2 accordingly. Or, if the input amplitude variation is known, the required $f_0 C_2$ product can be found to give the desired bandwidth. Constant bandwidth operation requires $V_i > 200$ mV rms. Then, as noted on the graph, bandwidth will be controlled solely by the $f_0 C_2$ product.

3. Capacitor C_3 sets the band edge of the low-pass filter which attenuates frequencies outside of the detection band and

thereby eliminates spurious outputs. If C_3 is too small, frequencies adjacent to the detection band may switch the output stage off and on at the beat frequency, or the output may pulse off and on during the turn-on transient. A typical minimum value for C_3 is 2 C_2.

Conversely, if C_3 is too large, turn-on and turn-off of the output stage will be delayed until the voltage across C_3 passes the threshold value.

PRINCIPLE OF OPERATION

The XR-567 is a frequency selective tone decoder system based on the phase-locked loop (PLL) principle. The system is comprised of a phase-locked loop, a quadrature AM detector, a voltage comparator, and an output logic driver. The four sections are internally interconnected as shown in Figure 1.

When an input tone is present within the pass-band of the circuit, the PLL synchronizes or "locks" on the input signal. The quadrature detector serves as a lock indicator: when the PLL is locked on an input signal, the dc voltage at the output of the detector is shifted. This dc level shift is then converted to an output logic pulse by the amplifier and logic driver. The logic driver is a "bare collector" transistor stage capable of switching 100 mA loads.

The logic output at pin 8 is normally in a "high" state, until a tone that is within the capture range of the decoder is present at the input. When the decoder is locked on an input signal, the logic output at pin 8 goes to a "low" state.

The center frequency of the detector is set by the free-running frequency of the current-controlled oscillator in the PLL. This free-running frequency, f_0, is determined by the selection of R_1 and C_1 connected to pins 5 and 6, as shown in Figure 3. The detection bandwidth is determined by the size of the PLL filter capacitor, C_2; and the output response speed is controlled by the output filter capacitor, C_3.

OPTIONAL CONTROLS

PROGRAMMING

Varying the value of resistor R_1 and/or capacitor C_1 will change the center frequency. The value of R_1 can be changed either mechanically or by solid state switches. Additional C_1 capacitors can be added by grounding them through saturated npn transistors.

SPEED OF RESPONSE

The minimum lock-up time is inversely related to the loop frequency. As the natural loop frequency is lowered, the turn-on transient becomes greater. Thus maximum operating speed is obtained when the value of capacitor C_2 is minimum. At the instant an input signal is applied its phase may drive the oscillator away from the incoming frequency rather than toward it. Under this condition, the lock-up transient is in a worst case situation, and the minimum theoretical lock-up time will not be achievable.

The following expressions yield the values of C_2 and C_3, in microfarads, which allow the maximum operating speeds for various center frequencies. The minimum rate that digital information may be detected without losing information due to turn-on transient or output chatter is about 10 cycles/bit, which corresponds to an information transfer rate of $f_0/10$ baud.

$$C_2 = \frac{130}{f_0}, \ C_3 = \frac{260}{f_0} \ \mu F$$

In situations where minimum turn-off time is of less importance than fast turn-on, the optional sensitivity adjustment circuit of Figure 14 can be used to bring the quiescent C_3 voltage closer to the threshold voltage. Sensitivity to beat frequencies, noise, and extraneous signals, however, will be increased.

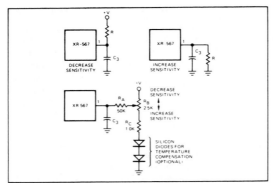

Figure 14. Optional Sensitivity Connections

CHATTER

When the value of C_3 is small, the lock transient and ac components at the lock detector output may cause the output stage to move through its threshold more than once, resulting in output chatter.

Although some loads, such as lamps and relays will not respond to chatter, logic may interpret chatter as a series of output signals. Chatter can be eliminated by feeding a portion of the output back to the input (pin 1) or, by increasing the size of capacitor C_3. Generally, the feedback method is preferred since keeping C_3 small will enable faster operation. Three alternate schemes for chatter prevention are shown in Figure 15. Generally, it is only necessary to assure that the feedback time constant does not get so large that it prevents operation at the highest anticipated speed.

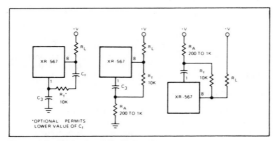

Figure 15. Methods of Reducing Chatter

SKEW ADJUSTMENT

The circuits shown in Figure 16 can be used to change the position of the detection band (capture range) within the largest detection band (or lock range). By moving the detection band to either edge of the lock range, input signal variations will expand the detection band in one direction only. Since R_3 also has a slight effect on the duty cycle, this approach may be useful to obtain a precise duty cycle when the circuit is used as an oscillator.

OUTPUT LATCHING

In order to latch the output of the XR-567 "on" after a signal is received, it is necessary to include a feedback resistor around the output stage, between pin 8 and pin 1, as shown in Figure 17. Pin 1 is pulled up to unlatch the output stage.

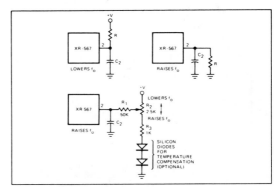

Figure 16. Connections to Reposition Detection Band

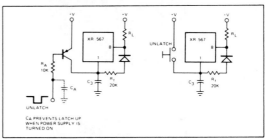

Figure 17. Output Latching

BANDWIDTH REDUCTION

The bandwidth of the XR-567 can be reduced by either increasing capacitor C_2 or reducing the loop gain. Increasing C_2 may be an undesirable solution since this will also reduce the damping of the loop and thus slow the circuit response time.

Figure 18 shows the proper method of reducing the loop gain for reduced bandwidth. This technique will improve damping and permit faster performance under narrow band operation. The reduced impedance level at pin 2 will require a larger value of C_2 for a given cutoff frequency.

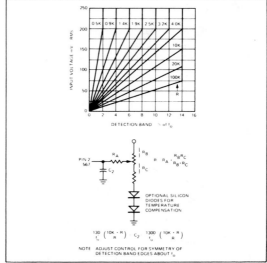

Figure 18. Bandwidth Reduction

PRECAUTIONS

1. The XR-567 will lock on signals near $(2n + 1)$ f_o and produce an output for signals near $(4n + 1)$ f_o, for $n = 0,1,2$ — etc. Signals at $5 f_o$ and $9 f_o$ can cause an unwanted output and should, therefore, be attenuated before reaching the input of the circuit.

2. Operating the XR-567 in a reduced bandwidth mode of operation at input levels less than 200 mV rms results in maximum immunity to noise and out-band signals. Decreased loop damping, however, causes the worst-case lock-up time to increase, as shown by the graph of Figure 12.

3. Bandwidth variations due to changes in the in-band signal amplitude can be eliminated by operating the XR-567 in the high input level mode, above 200 mV. The input stage is then limiting, however, so that out-band signals or high noise levels can cause an apparent bandwidth reduction as the in-band signal is suppressed. In addition, the limited input stage will create inband components from sub-harmonic signals so that the circuit becomes sensitive to signals at $f_o/3$, $f_o/5$ etc.

4. Care should be exercised in lead routing and lead lengths should be kept as short as possible. Power supply leads should be properly bypassed close to the integrated circuit and grounding paths should be carefully determined to avoid ground loops and undesirable voltage variations. In addition, circuits requiring heavy load currents should be provided by a separate power supply, or filter capacitors increased to minimize supply voltage variations.

ADDITIONAL APPLICATIONS

DUAL TIME CONSTANT TONE DECODER

For some applications it is important to have a tone decoder with narrow bandwidth and fast response time. This can be accomplished by the dual time constant tone decoder circuit shown in Figure 19. The circuit has two low-pass loop filter capacitors, C_2 and C'_2. With no input signal present, the output at pin 8 is high, transistor Q_1 is off, and C'_2 is switched out of the circuit. Thus the loop low-pass filter is comprised of C_2, which can be kept as small as possible for minimum response time.

When an in-band signal is detected, the output at pin 8 will go low, Q_1 will turn on, and capacitor C'_2 will be switched in parallel with capacitor C_2. The low-pass filter capacitance will then be $C_2 + C'_2$. The value of C'_2 can be quite large in order to achieve narrow bandwidth. Notice that during the time that no input signal is being received, the bandwidth is determined by capacitor C_2.

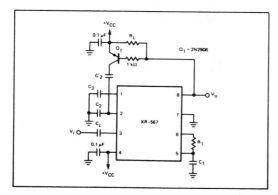

Figure 19. Dual Time Constant Tone Decoder

NARROW BAND FM DEMODULATOR WITH CARRIER DETECT

For FM demodulation applications where the bandwidth is less than 10% of the carrier frequency, an XR-567 can be used to detect the presence of the carrier signal. The output of the XR-567 is used to turn off the FM demodulator when no carrier is present, thus acting as a squelch. In the circuit shown, an XR-215 FM demodulator is used because of its wide dynamic range, high signal/noise ratio and low distortion. The XR-567 will detect the presence of a carrier at frequencies up to 500 kHz.

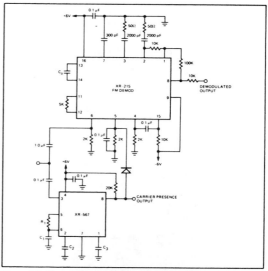

Figure 20. Narrow Band FM Demodulator with Carrier Detect

DUAL TONE DECODER

In dual tone communication systems, information is transmitted by the simultaneous presence of two separate tones at the input. In such applications two XR-567 units can be connected in parallel, as shown in Figure 21, to form a dual tone decoder. The resistor and capacitor values of each decoder are selected to provide the desired center frequencies and bandwidth requirements.

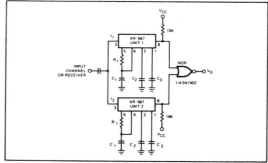

Figure 21. Dual Tone Decoder

PRECISION OSCILLATOR

The current-controlled oscillator (CCO) section of the XR-567 provides two basic output waveforms as shown in Figure 22. The squarewave is obtained from pin 5, and the exponential ramp from pin 6. The relative phase relationships of the wave-

XR-567

forms are also provided in the figure. In addition to being used as a general purpose oscillator or clock generator, the CCO can also be used for any of the following special purpose oscillator applications:

1. **High-Current Oscillator**

    The oscillator output of the XR-567 can be amplified using the output amplifier and high-current logic output available at pin 8. In this manner, the circuit can switch 100 mA load currents without sacrificing oscillator stability. A recommended circuit connection for this application is shown in Figure 23. The oscillator frequency can be modulated over ±6% in frequency by applying a control voltage to pin 2.

2. **Oscillator with Quadrature Outputs**

    Using the circuit connection of Figure 24 the XR-567 can function as a precision oscillator with two separate square-wave outputs (at pins 5 and 8, respectively) that are at nearly quadrature phase with each other. Due to the internal biasing arrangement the actual phase shift between the two outputs is typically 80°

3. **Oscillator with Frequency Doubled Output**

    The CCO frequency can be doubled by applying a portion of the squarewave output at pin 5 back to the input at pin 3, as shown in Figure 25. In this manner, the quadrature detector functions as a frequency doubler and produces an output of $2 f_O$ at pin 8.

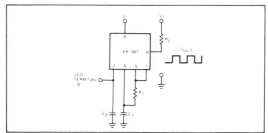

Figure 22.   Oscillator Output Waveform Available From CCO Section.
Top: Square Wave Output at Pin 5:
Amplitude = $(V^+ -1.4V)$,pp., Avg. Value = $V^+/2$
Bottom: Exponential Triangle Wave at Pin 6:
Amplitude = 1 V pp., Avg. Value = $V^+/2$

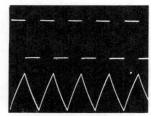

Figure 23.   Precision Oscillator to Switch 100 mA Loads

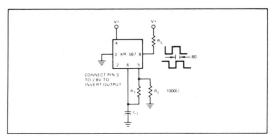

Figure 24.   Oscillator with Quadrature Output

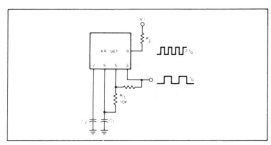

Figure 25.   Oscillator with Double Frequency Output

FSK DECODING

XR-567 can be used as a low speed FSK demodulator. In this application the center frequency is set to one of the input frequencies, and the bandwidth is adjusted to leave the second frequency outside the detection band. When the input signal is frequency keyed between the *in-band* signal and the *out-band* signal, the logic state of the output at pin 8 is reversed. Figure 26 shows the FSK input ($f_2 = 3 f_1$) and the demodulated output signals, with $f_O = f_2 = 1$ kHz. The circuit can handle data rates up to $f_O/10$ baud.

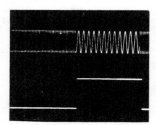

Figure 26.   Input and Output Waveforms for FSK Decoding
Top: Input FSK Signal ($f_2 = 3f_1$)
Bottom: Demodulated Output

APPENDIX B
Parameter Glossary

DIODE PARAMETERS

I_F = forward current

$I_{FSM} = I_{FM(surge)}$ = maximum nonrepetitive forward surge current

I_0 = average forward current

I_R = reverse current = leakage current

I_{RM} = maximum reverse current rating

I_Z = zener current = reverse current in the zener breakdown region for zener diodes

I_{ZM} = maximum zener current

I_{ZT} = zener test current

R_B = bulk resistance of a semiconductor material

T_J = junction temperature

T_{stg} = junction storage temperature

V_B = barrier potential = 0.2 V to 0.3 V for germanium and 0.6 V to 0.75 V for silicon

V_F = forward-bias *pn* junction voltage

V_R = reverse-bias junction voltage that produces leakage current = DC blocking voltage

$V_r = V_{R(RMS)}$ = the RMS value of the reverse voltage

$V_{RM} = V_{RM(rep)} = V_{RRM} = PIV$ = maximum repetitive reverse voltage rating = peak inverse voltage rating

V_Z = nominal zener voltage

TRANSISTOR PARAMETERS

DC PARAMETERS

$\alpha = h_{FB} = I_C/I_E = \beta_{DC}/(1 + \beta_{DC})$ = collector/emitter current transfer ratio = current efficiency factor always less than one (1)

$B_{DC} = \beta_{DC} = h_{FE} = I_C/I_B = \alpha/(1 - \alpha) =$ DC beta = base-to-collector current gain

$I_B =$ base current $= I_E - I_C$

$I_C =$ collector current $= I_E - I_B$

$I_{CBO} =$ collector-to-base leakage current with emitter open

$I_{CEO} =$ collector-to-emitter leakage current with base open

$I_{C(cutoff)} \cong 0$ A $=$ collector current with transistor cut off

$I_{C(sat)} = V_{CC}/(R_C + R_E) =$ DC saturation current for DC load line

$I_{C(Q)} = (V_{CC} - V_{CE})/(R_C + R_E) =$ the DC quiescent collector current

$I_E =$ emitter current $= I_C + I_B$

$P_D =$ transistor power dissipation $= V_{CE} \cdot I_C$

$R_B =$ base biasing resistor

$R_C =$ collector resistor

$R_E =$ emitter resistor

$R_L =$ load resistor

$V_B =$ voltage from base to ground

$V_{BE} =$ forward voltage from base to emitter

$V_{BR(CBO)} =$ collector-to-base breakdown voltage, maximum rating

$V_{BR(CEO)} =$ collector-to-emitter breakdown voltage, maximum rating

$V_{BR(EBO)} =$ emitter-to-base breakdown voltage, maximum rating

$V_C =$ voltage from collector to ground

$V_{CC} =$ the collector supply voltage

$V_{CE} =$ collector-to-emitter voltage

$V_{CEO} =$ collector-to-emitter voltage with the base open

$V_{CE(cutoff)} = V_{CC} =$ collector-to-emitter voltage with the transistor off

$V_{CE(sat)} =$ collector-to-emitter saturation voltage with the transistor biased full on

$V_{CE(Q)} =$ the quiescent collector-to-emitter voltage

$V_E =$ voltage from emitter to ground

$V_{EBO} =$ maximum reverse bias voltage rating across the base-emitter junction

AC PARAMETERS

$\alpha' = h_{FB} = i_c/i_e =$ AC emitter-to-collector current transfer

$A_i = i_{out}/i_{in} = (v_{out}/Z_{out})/(v_{in}/Z_{in}) =$ AC current gain less than β and includes total input and output impedance values

$A_P = A_i A_V = P_{out}/P_{in} = (v_{out}^2/Z_{out})/(v_{in}^2/Z_{in}) =$ CE stage power gain

$A_V = v_{out}/v_{in} = r_C/(r'_e + r'_e) =$ CE stage voltage gain

$\beta = h_{FE} = i_c/i_b = \Delta I_C/\Delta I_B =$ AC current gain

$C_{ibo} = C_{BE}$ = input capacitance = internal base-to-emitter capacitance with collector open

$C_{obo} = C_{cb}$ = output capacitance = internal collector-to-base capacitance with base grounded and emitter open

$C_{oeo} = C_{ce}$ = output capacitance at the collector with the emitter grounded and the base open

$f_T = A_V \cdot BW$ = the gain-bandwidth product (GBP) or unity-gain frequency

$h_{ie} = v_b/i_b$ = the base input impedance with the output shorted representing a full-load condition

$h_{fe} = i_c/i_b$ = the base-to-collector current gain with output shorted representing a full-load condition

$h_{oe} = i_c/v_{ce}$ = the maximum output admittance, the reciprocal of the output impedance from collector-to-emitter with the base open

$h_{re} = v_{be}/v_{ce}$ = the reverse voltage feedback ratio with a signal applied between the collector and emitter while the base is open and v_{be} is measured

i_b = AC base current = a change in $I_B = \Delta I_B$

i_e = AC emitter current = a change in $I_E = \Delta I_E$

i_c = AC collector current = a change in $I_C = \Delta I_C$

$i_{c(sat)} = I_{C(Q)} + (V_{CE(Q)}/(r_C + r_E))$ = saturation voltage for AC load line

r_c = a very large internal AC collector resistance

r_b = a very small internal AC base resistance

$r'_e = h_{re}/h_{oe} \cong 25 \text{ mV}/I_E$ = a small but significant internal AC emitter resistance

r_C = the total external AC collector resistance which includes $R_C \| R_L$ where R_L is a load resistance

r_E = an external emitter resistor that opposes AC and DC (unbypassed)

$v_b = v_{in}$ = AC base voltage = a change in $V_B = \Delta V_B$

v_{be} = AC base-emitter voltage = a change in $V_{BE} = \Delta V_{BE}$

$v_c = v_{out}$ = AC collector voltage = a change in $V_C = \Delta V_C$

v_{ce} = AC collector-emitter voltage = a change in $V_{CE} = \Delta V_{CE}$

$v_{ce(cutoff)} = V_{CE(Q)} + (I_{C(Q)} \cdot (r_C + r_E))$ = collector-to-emitter cutoff voltage for the AC load line

v_e = AC emitter voltage = a change in $V_E = \Delta V_E$

$Z_b = \beta r'_e \cong h_{ie} = h_{fe} r'_e$ = base-to-emitter impedance

$Z_b = \beta \cdot (r'_e + r_E)$ = base terminal impedance to ground for CE configuration

$Z_e = r'_e = h_{ie}/h_{fe}$ = emitter-to-base impedance with base grounded

$Z_e = r'_e + ((R_g \| R_1 \| R_2)/\beta)$ = emitter impedance for CE amplifiers

$Z_{in} = R_1 \| R_2 \| Z_b$ = total input impedance from base to ground including voltage-divider resistors

$Z_{out} \cong R_C$ = the AC output impedance of a CE or CB amplifier stage

FET PARAMETERS

DC PARAMETERS

I_D = drain current

I_{DSS} = drain-to-source saturation current when $V_{GS} = 0$ V

$I_{D(Q)}$ = the quiescent drain current

$I_{D(sat)}$ = maximum drain current at a specific value of V_{GS}

I_{GSS} = source-to-gate leakage current at a specific temperature and bias voltage

R_D = an external drain resistor

$r_{DS} = V_{DS}/I_{DS}$ = an internal static drain-to-source resistance

$r_{DS(on)}$ = lowest value of r_{DS} with the FET saturated

$R_{in} = V_{GS}/I_{GSS}$ = gate-to-source resistance and input resistance for CS amplifiers

R_G = an external gate resistor

R_L = an external load resistor

R_S = an external source resistor

$V_{BR(DSS)}$ = the value of V_{DS} at which the channel-to-gate junction breaks down

$V_{BR(GSS)}$ = the value of V_{GS} at which the gate-to-source junction breaks down

V_D = drain to ground voltage

V_{DD} = drain supply voltage

V_{DS} = drain-to-source voltage

$V_{DS(sat)} = V_{pinch\text{-}off}$ = the drain-to-source voltage when the FET is saturated where I_D is maximum

$V_{DS(Q)}$ = the quiescent drain-to-source voltage

V_{GS} = the gate-to-source bias voltage

$V_{GS(off)}$ = the value of gate-to-source bias voltage needed to cut the FET off where $I_D \cong 0$ A

$V_{GS(Q)}$ = the quiescent gate-to-source bias voltage

AC PARAMETERS

$A_V = v_{out}/v_{in} = g_m(R_D \| R_L)$ = voltage gain for CS and CG amplifiers

$C_{gs} = C_{iss} - C_{rss}$ = the internal gate to source capacitance

$C_{iss} = C_{dg} + C_{gs}$ = the sum of the drain to gate and gate to source internal capacitances

$C_{oss} = C_{dg} + C_{ds}$ = the sum of the drain to gate and drain to source internal capacitances

$C_{rss} = C_{dg}$ = the internal drain to gate capacitance

$g_m = \Delta I_D/\Delta V_{GS}$ = forward transconductance measured in Seimens

g_{m0} = forward transconductance at I_{DSS} and $V_{GS} = 0$ V

$g_{os} = \Delta I_D / \Delta V_{DS}$ = output conductance

$r_{ds} = 1/g_{os} = \Delta V_{DS}/\Delta I_D$ = the dynamic drain-to-source resistance

$v_g = v_{in}$ = AC gate voltage = a change in $V_G = \Delta V_G$

v_{gs} = AC gate-to-source voltage = a change in $V_{GS} = \Delta V_{GS}$

$v_d = v_{out}$ = AC drain voltage = a change in $V_D = \Delta V_D$

v_{ds} = AC drain-to-source voltage = a change in $V_{DS} = \Delta V_{DS}$

$v_{ds(cutoff)} = V_{DS(Q)} + (I_{D(Q)} \cdot (R_D \| R_L))$ = drain-to-source cutoff voltage for the AC load line

v_s = AC source voltage = a change in $V_S = \Delta V_S$

y_{fs} = forward transfer admittance equal to g_{m0}

y_{os} = output admittance equal to g_{os}

$Z_{in} \cong R_G$ = input impedance for CS and CD amplifiers

$Z_{in} = (1/g_m \| R_S)$ = input impedance for CG amplifiers

$Z_{out} \cong R_D$ = output impedance for CS and CG amplifiers

$Z_{out} = (1/g_m \| R_S)$ = output impedance for CD amplifiers

$Z_S = 1/g_m$ = source impedance

OP-AMP PARAMETERS

DC PARAMETERS

$I_{IB} = I_B$ = input bias current, the very small amount of current needed to bias the differential transistor on

$I_{IO} = |I_{B1} - I_{B2}|$ = input offset current

R_F = external feedback resistor from output to inverting input

R_I = external input resistor from inverting input to ground or to a voltage source

V_{IO} = input offset voltage, differential input voltage needed to zero or null the output voltage

$V_{OO} = A_{OL}V_{IO}$ = output offset voltage

AC PARAMETERS

A_{OL} = open-loop gain

$A_V = 1/B$ = closed-loop gain

$A_{V(com)}$ = common-mode voltage gain

$B = 1/A_V = R_I/(R_I + R_F)$ = voltage feedback ratio for noninverting amplifiers

$CMRR = A_{OL}/A_{V(com)}$ = common-mode rejection ratio

$r_{in} = \Delta V_{in}/\Delta I_{in}$ = impedance between the inverting and noninverting input terminals

r_{out} = the small-signal impedance seen at the output of the op-amp without feedback

$SR = \Delta V/\Delta t$ = slew rate

$v_{diff} = v_{in} - v_f$ = differential voltage between the inverting and noninverting inputs

$v_f = Bv_{out}$ = feedback voltage at the inverting input (noninverting configuration)

v_{in} = voltage at the noninverting input (noninverting configuration)

$v_{out} = v_{diff}A_{OL}$ = AC output voltage

V_0 = maximum output voltage swing

$Z_{in} = r_{in}(1 + BA_{OL})$ = input impedance for noninverting configuration

$Z_{in} = R_F/A_{OL}$ = input impedance at the inverting input for the inverting configuration

$Z_{in} \cong R_I$ = the input impedance for the inverting configuration

$Z_{out} = r_{out}/(1 + BA_{OL})$ = output impedance with negative feedback

THYRISTOR PARAMETERS

SUS, SCR, DIAC, SBS, AND TRIAC PARAMETERS

dv/dt − the critical rise of off-state voltage

I_{DRM} − maximum peak repetitive blocking current corresponding with V_{DRM}

I_{GM} − forward peak gate current

I_{GT} − maximum value of gate trigger current

I_H − the holding current

$I_{T(RMS)}$ − maximum continuous RMS current

I_{TSM} − maximum non-repetitive surge current

$V_{AK(on)}$ − forward anode-to-cathode voltage with device conducting V_{BO} − breakover voltage

V_{DRM} − maximum peak repetitive forward-blocking voltage without the device triggering on

V_{GT} − gate voltage needed to produce the specified value of I_{GT}

UJT/PUT PARAMETERS

I_{EB2} = off-state leakage current

I_{EB1} = on-state forward current

I_P = peak-point current, trigger current

I_V = valley-point current

$n = r_{B1}/(r_{B1} + r_{B2}) = r_{B1}/r_{BB}$ = intrinsic standoff ratio for UJT

V_P − peak-point voltage, trigger voltage

V_V − valley-point voltage, on voltage

OPTOELECTRONIC-DEVICE PARAMETERS

$\beta_{CTR} = I_C/I_F$ = current transfer ratio from the forward diode current to the output collector current for a transistor-output optoisolator

I_C = collector current for transistor-output optoisolators

I_F = forward current for diodes and LEDs

I_L = light current, current that corresponds to a given light intensity in photodiodes

I_R = reverse current for photodiodes

λ = lambda = symbol for wavelength = $(300 \cdot 10^6)/f$

VACUUM-TUBE PARAMETERS

DC PARAMETERS

E_f = filament voltage

E_g = gate bias voltage

$E_{g(Q)}$ = quiescent gate bias voltage

E_P = plate voltage

$E_{p(Q)}$ = quiescent plate voltage

I_f = filament current

I_g = control-grid current

I_p = plate current

$I_{p(Q)}$ = quiescent plate current

I_s = screen current

$R_g = Z_{in}$ = resistor from control grid to ground or control grid to the negative bias supply, also called grid-leak resistor

$R_k = |E_g|/I_{p(Q)}$ = cathode self-bias resistor

$R_L = R_p$ = load or plate resistor; R_L may be separate from and not equal to R_p where $Z_L = R_p \| R_L$

AC PARAMETERS

$A_V = \Delta E_p/\Delta E_g = g_m \cdot Z_L$ = actual voltage gain

$g_m = \Delta I_p/\Delta E_g$ = forward transconductance

$i_{p(\text{sat})} = I_{p(Q)} + E_{p(Q)}/Z_L = $ AC plate saturation current for AC load line

$r_p = \Delta E_p/\Delta I_p = $ dynamic or AC plate resistance

$\mu = g_m \cdot r_p = $ ideal voltage amplification factor

$v_{p(\text{cutoff})} = E_{p(Q)} + (I_{p(Q)} \cdot Z_L) = $ AC plate cutoff voltage for AC load line

$Z_L = R_p \| R_L = $ total AC plate impedance used in calculating voltage gain

APPENDIX C
Formula Derivations

DERIVATION OF FORMULA 2–8:
$C = 0.289/(f \cdot (R_S + R_L) \cdot r)$

Ripple occurs as the capacitor discharges during the time between applied voltage peaks. The ripple is a change in voltage ΔV resulting from a change in quantity of charge ΔQ where $\Delta V = \Delta Q/C$.

$\Delta V = V_{r(P-P)} = \Delta Q/C$

$V_{r(P-P)}/T = \Delta Q/CT$

where T is the discharge time between the maximum and minimum capacitor voltage that makes up the ripple voltage.

$\Delta Q/T = I =$ discharge current, therefore $V_{r(P-P)}/T = I/C$

$V_{r(P-P)} = TI/C$

$V_{r(P)} = TI/2C$

Since $f = 1/T$,

$V_{r(P)} = I/2Cf$

$V_r = V_{r(P)}/\sqrt{3} = 0.5774\ V_{r(P)}$

$V_{r(P)} = V_r/0.5774$

By substitution,

$V_r/0.5774 = I/2Cf$ and $V_r = 0.5774 \cdot I/2Cf$

$V_r = 0.5774 \cdot I/2Cf = 0.289 \cdot I/Cf$

Because the capacitor is discharging through the load resistance,

$I = V_{DC}/R_L$

By substitution,

$V_r = 0.289 \cdot V_{DC}/CfR_L$

Rearranging to solve for C we get

$C = 0.289 \cdot V_{DC}/V_r f R_L$

r = ripple factor = V_r/V_{DC}, therefore $V_{DC}/V_r = 1/r$.

By substitution,

$$C = 0.289/rfR_L = \frac{0.289}{f \cdot R_L \cdot r}$$

$$C = \frac{0.289}{f \cdot (R_S + R_L) \cdot r} \quad \text{if a series-dropping resistor } R_S \text{ is used.}$$

DERIVATION OF FORMULA 6–2: $r'_e \cong 25$ mV/I_E

We must start with Schockley's equation for the total forward current through a *pn* junction.

$I_F = I_R(e^{Vq/kT} - 1)$

where

I_R is the reverse leakage current through the *pn* junction

e is the natural log base = 2.718

V is the *pn* depletion-region voltage

q is the charge on one electron equal to $1.6 \cdot 10^{-19}$ V

k is Boltzmann's constant equal to $1.38 \cdot 10^{-23}$ J/°K

T is the junction temperature in degrees kelvin (°K = °C + 273°)

At room temperature (294°K) the value of $q/kT = 40$, therefore

$I_F = I_R(e^{40\ V} - 1)$

We must now differentiate this formula to get

$\Delta I_F/\Delta V = 40 I_R e^{40\ V}$

Expanding and rearranging $I_F = I_R(e^{40\ V} - 1)$ we get

$I_R e^{40\ V} = I_F + I_R$

Since I_R is very small compared to I_F

$I_R e^{40\ V} \cong I_F$

By substitution

$\Delta I_F/\Delta V \cong 40 I_F$

By inversion

$\Delta V/\Delta I \cong 1\ \text{V}/40 I_F = 25\ \text{mV}/I_F$

$\Delta V/\Delta I$ is the AC emitter resistance r'_e and I_F is the emitter current I_E. Therefore,

$r'_e \cong 25$ mV/I_E

DERIVATION OF FORMULA 9–16: $UF_{co} = 0.35/t_r$

The derivation begins with the formula used to determine a capacitor's charge voltage after time t, in this case t_r, the rise time.

$v = V_F + (V_I - V_F)e^{-t/RC}$

In this case, $V_F = 1$, $V_I = 0.1$ and $v = 0.9$ since the rise time is the time between 10% rise and 90% rise where V_F is at 100% rise.

$0.9 = 1 + (0.1 - 1)e^{-t/RC}$

$0.9 - 1 = -0.9e^{-t/RC}$

$-0.1 = -0.9e^{-t/RC}$

$-0.1/-0.9 = e^{-t/RC}$

$0.111 = e^{-t/RC}$

$\ln(0.111) = -t/RC$

$-2.2 = -t/RC$

$t = 2.2RC = t_r$

$RC = t_r/2.2$

For RC filters, $f_{co} = 0.159/RC$.

By substitution,

$f_{co} = 0.159/(t_r/2.2) = 2.2 \cdot 0.159/t_r = 0.35/t_r$

Thus, $Uf_{co} = 0.35/t_r$

DERIVATION OF FORMULA 10–20: $Z_{out} = r_{out}/(1 + BA_{OL})$

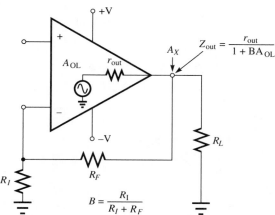

Because r_{out} and R_L form a voltage divider, the open-loop gain is reduced according to the voltage-divider ratio as follows.

$A_X = A_{OL} \cdot R_L/(r_{out} + R_L)$

Thus, A_X takes the place of A_{OL} in Formula 10–16.

$A_V = A_{OL}/(1 + A_{OL}B)$ (Formula 10–16)

$A_V = A_X/(1 + A_XB)$

Now substitute $A_{OL} \cdot R_L/(r_{out} + R_L)$ for A_X and expand the expression.

$$A_V = \frac{A_{OL} \cdot R_L/(r_{out} + R_L)}{1 + [BA_{OL} \cdot R_L/(r_{out} + R_L)]}$$

Next, reduce the expression by dividing both numerator and denominator by $R_L/(r_{out} + R_L)$.

$$A_V = \frac{A_{OL}}{A_{OL}B + 1/[R_L/(r_{out} + R_L)]} = \frac{A_{OL}}{A_{OL}B + [(r_{out} + R_L)/R_L]}$$

$$A_V = \frac{A_{OL}}{A_{OL}B + 1 + r_{out}/R_L}$$

Now, if $R_L = Z_{out}$, the output voltage will be cut in half, which is to say the amplification factor A_V is cut in half. In the formula above, this actually takes place when $(r_{out}/R_L) = (A_{OL}B + 1)$. In other words, when R_L is very small and is equal to the amplifier's output impedance, Z_{out}, (r_{out}/R_L) becomes equal to $(A_{OL}B + 1)$. This doubles the value of the denominator causing A_V to be cut in half. Therefore, when $R_L = Z_{out}$,

$r_{out}/R_L = r_{out}/Z_{out}$

and

$r_{out}/Z_{out} = A_{OL}B + 1$

By inversion

$Z_{out}/r_{out} = 1/(A_{OL}B + 1)$

and

$Z_{out} = r_{out}/(1 + BA_{OL})$

Answers
to Odd-Numbered
Problems

CHAPTER 2

1. $V_{DC} = +7.63$ V
3. $V_P = 25.2\ V_P$
5. $V_{avg} = 4.77$ V, $I_{avg} = 145$ mA
7. $V_{avg} = 7$ V, $I_{avg} = 149$ mA
9. $V_P = 35.6\ V_P$
   PIV $\cong$ total secondary voltage minus one diode drop
   $= 35.6\ V_P - 0.7$ V $= 34.9$ V
11. $V_{P(out)} = 8.21\ V_P$, $V_{avg} = 5.23$ V, $I_{avg} = 194$ mA (total)
    Average current for each diode is 194 mA/2 = 97 mA.
13. PIV $\cong 35.6\ V_P$ (Use at least 50-V diodes).
    $V_{P(load)} = 34.2\ V_P$, $V_{avg} = 21.8$ V, $I_{avg} = 2.18$ A (total)
    Average current for each diode is 2.18 A/2 = 1.09 A.
    Use diodes with at least a 1-A rating, preferably a 2-A rating.
15. $V_{P(load)} = 70\ V_P$, $V_{avg} = 44.6$ V
    For the 220-Ω resistor, $I_{avg} = 44.6$ V/220 Ω = 203 mA.
    For the 330-Ω resistor, $I_{avg} = 44.6$ V/330 Ω = 135 mA.
    The average ground current at the center tap is 68 mA.
17. 17 VDC maximum
19. $V_{DC} = 10.3$ V, $V_r = 0.405$ V, $r = 0.039$, 3.9% ripple
21. $V_r = 0.737$ V, $r = 0.024$, 2.4% ripple
23. (a) $I_{sec} = 400$ mA
    The secondary must be rated for at least 400 mA. A 500-mA to 1-A secondary is best.

(b) PIV $\cong 8.91\ V_P$, $I_{avg} = 400$ mA (total)
    Average current for each diode is 400 mA/2 = 200 mA.
    Use standard 50-V, 1-A diodes.
(c) $R_S = 3.78$ Ω   Use a 3.74 Ω, 1% resistor.
    $P_{RS} = 0.604$ W   Use a 1-W resistor.
(d) $C = 2,580\ \mu F$ Use a 2,500- or 3,000-μF capacitor.
(e) $I_{pri} = 22$ mA
    Since the primary current is so low, it is best to use a 1/2 A fuse on the secondary side.
25. (a) $I_{sec} = 225$ mA
    The secondary must be rated for at least 225 mA. A 300-mA to 1-A secondary is best.
(b) PIV $\cong 17.8\ V_P$, $I_{avg} = 225$ mA (total)
    Average current for each diode is 225 mA/2 = 113 mA.
    Use standard 50-V, 1-A diodes.
(c) $R_S = 33$ Ω   Use a 33 Ω, 5% resistor.
    $P_{RS} = 1.67$ W   Use a 5-W resistor.
(d) $C = 330\ \mu F$ Use a 500-μF capacitor.
(e) $I_{pri} = 12.3$ mA
    Since the primary current is so low, it is best to use a 1/4 A fuse on the secondary side.
27. (a) $V_{P(load)} = 17.1\ V_P$ b. $V_{avg} = 5.44$ V
    c. $I_{avg} = 181$ mA
(d) 181 mA e. PIV = 17.8 V_P
29. (a) $V_{P(load)} = 33.2$ V b. $V_{avg} = 21.1$ V
    c. $I_{load} = 1.06$ A
(d) Each diode conducts an average of 503 mA. e. PIV $\cong 67.9\ V_P$

31. (a) $V_{C(peak)} = 8.21$ V, $V_{P(load)} = 5.47$ V
    (b) $r = 0.0064$, 0.64% ripple
    (c) $V_{DC} \cong 8.21$ V and $r = V_r/V_{DC}$, so
        $V_r = r \cdot V_{DC} = 0.0064 \cdot 8.21$ V =
        52.5 mV
    (d) $V_r = 0.289 \cdot V_{r(P-P)}$, so
        $V_{r(P-P)} = V_r/0.289 = 52.5$ mV/0.289 =
        182 mV$_{P-P}$
    (e) $V_C = V_{C(peak)} - (V_{r(P-P)}/2) = 8.21$ V −
        (182 mV$_{P-P}$/2) = 8.12 V
    (f) $V_L = V_C \cdot R_L/(R_L + R_S) = 8.12$ V ·
        50 Ω/75 Ω = 5.41 V
    (g) $I_L = V_L/R_L = 5.41$ V/50 Ω = 108 mA
        The average current for each half of
        the secondary is 54 mA.

33. (a) $V_{C(peak)} = (V_{sec} \cdot 1.414) - 1.4$ V = (24
        V · 1.414) − 1.4 V = 32.5 V
    (b) $r = 0.289/[f \cdot (R_S + R_L) \cdot C] =$
        0.0015, 0.15% ripple
    (c) $V_r = r \cdot V_{DC} = 0.0015 \cdot 32.5$ V =
        48.8 mV
    (d) $V_{r(P-P)} = V_r/0.289 = 48.8$ mV/0.289 =
        169 mV$_{P-P}$
    (e) $V_C = V_{C(peak)} - (V_{r(P-P)}/2) = 32.5$ V −
        (169 mV$_{P-P}$/2) = 32.42 V
    (f) $V_L = V_C \cdot R_L/(R_L + R_S) = 32.42$ V ·
        100 Ω/156 Ω = 20.8 V
    (g) $I_L = V_L/R_L = 20.8$ V/100 Ω = 208
        mA, therefore, the average diode
        current is 104 mA

35. (a) The minimum current rating for the
        secondary must be 3A.
    (b) PIV $\cong 35.6$ V
        The maximum average current
        through each diode is 1.5 A. Use
        50-V, 2-A diodes.
    (c) $R_S = 3.4$ Ω   Use a 3.4 Ω, 1%
        resistor.
        $P_{RS} = 30.6$ W   Use a 50-W resistor
        or greater.
    (d) $C = 2,113$ μF   Use a 50-V, 2,500-μF
        capacitor.
    (e) $I_{pri} = 0.657$ A   Use a 5/8 or 3/4 A
        fuse.

CHAPTER 3

1. $I_T = I_{RS} = 12$ mA, $I_L = 3$ mA, $I_Z = 9$ mA,
   $P_Z = 270$ mW, $P_{RS} = 144$ mW, $P_L =$
   90 mW

3. $I_T = I_{RS} = 236$ mA, $I_L = 174$ mA, $I_Z =$
   62 mA, $P_Z = 378$ mW, $P_{RS} = 1.39$ W,
   $P_L = 1.06$ W
5. $I_{Z(max)} = I_T = 236$ mA, $P_{Z(max)} = 1.44$ W
7. $I_L = 109$ mA, $I_{RS} = 120$ mA, $I_Z = 11$ mA,
   $R_S = 91$ Ω
   $P_{RS} = 1.31$ W, $P_{RS(rating)} \geq 2$ W, $P_{Z(max)} =$
   0.612 W, $P_{Z(rating)} \geq 1$ W
9. $I_L = 156$ mA, $I_{RS} = 172$ mA, $I_Z = 16$ mA
   $R_S = 23.3$ Ω   Use a 22-Ω series resistor.
   $I_{RS} = 182$ mA, $I_Z = 26$ mA, $P_{RS} = 728$
   mW, $P_{RS(rating)} \geq 2$ W, $P_{Z(max)} = 2.55$ W,
   $P_{Z(rating)} \geq 5$ W
11. (a) 325 V (b) 650 V (c) 650 V
    (d) 1300 V
13. (a) 424 V (b) 848 V (c) 848 V
    (d) 1700 V
15. $V_L = 1132$ V, PIV = 1132 V
17. Positive limiter—only the positive peak is
    limited to +6.7 V.
19. Positive clamper—the capacitor charges
    to +24.3 V. Thus, the 50-V_{P-P} signal is
    riding on a +24.3-V reference.
21. $R_S = 4,600$ Ω   Use 4.7 kΩ.
23. $C_{T(min)} = 310$ pF, $C_{T(max)} = 380$ pF
    $f_{o(low)} = 2.72$ MHz, $f_{o(high)} = 3.01$ MHz
25. $I_T = I_{RS} = 27.9$ mA, $I_L = 24$ mA, $I_Z =$
    3.9 mA
    $P_Z = 140$ mW, $P_{RS} = 335$ mW, $P_L =$
    864 mW
27. $I_{Z(max)} = I_T = 27.9$ mA, $P_{Z(max)} = 1$ W
29. $I_L = 826$ mA, $I_{RS} = 909$ mA, $I_Z = 83$ mA
    $R_S = 5.5$ Ω   Use a 5.6-Ω series resistor.
    $I_{RS} = 893$ mA, $I_Z = 67$ mA, $P_{RS} = 4.5$ W,
    $P_{RS(rating)} \geq 10$ W, $P_{Z(max)} = 17$ W, $P_{Z(rating)}$
    ≥ 25 W
31. $I_{Z(max)} = I_T = I_{RS} = 80.6$ mA, $R_S =$
    34.7 Ω   Use 36 Ω.
33. $R_S = 220$ Ω

CHAPTER 4

1. 27 dB gain
3. $V_{out} = 90$ mV, 25.1 dB gain
5. #dB = 10 log (P_{out}/P_{in})
   20 dB = 10 log(P_{out}/50 mW)
   2 = log(P_{out}/50 mw)
   invlog 2 = P_{out}/50 mW
   100 = P_{out}/50 mW

$P_{out} = 100 \cdot 50$ mW $= 5$ W

7. $I_B = 200$ μA

9. $I_E = 82.435$ mA

11. $P_D = 7.5$ W

13. $I_C = 4.92$ mA, $\beta_{DC} = 61.5$

15. $\beta_{DC} = h_{FE} = \alpha/(1 - \alpha) = 262$

17. $\alpha = \beta_{DC}/(1 + \beta_{DC}) = 0.99237$

19. $I_{C(sat)} = 5.88$ mA

The DC load line is drawn from $V_{CE} = 0$ V and $I_C = 5.88$ mA to $V_{CE} = 20$ V and $I_C = 0$ A.

21. $P_{D(max)} \cong 0.25\, I_{C(sat)} V_{CC} = 29.4$ mW

23. $V_{out}/V_{in} = 24.55$
$V_{in} = 545$ mV$/24.55 = 22.2$ mV

25. Stage 1: 5.41 dB gain, Stage 2: 6.65 dB gain, Stage 3: 6.87 dB gain

27. $\beta_{DC} = h_{FE} = \alpha/(1 - \alpha) = 92$

29. $\alpha = h_{FB} = I_C/I_E = 0.85562 =$
$(I_E - 11$ mA$)/I_E$
$0.85562 = 1 - (11$ mA$/I_E)$
11 mA$/I_E + 1 - 0.85562 = 0.14438$
$I_E = 11$ mA$/0.14438 = 76.2$ mA
$I_C = I_E - I_B = 76.2$ mA $- 11$ mA $= 65.2$ mA

31. $P_{D(max)} = I_{C(Q)} \cdot V_{CE(Q)} = 54$ mW

CHAPTER 5

1. $I_{B(Q)} = 24.04$ μA, $I_{C(Q)} = 4.09$ mA, $V_{CE(Q)} = 5.86$ V
DC load line from $I_C = 8$ mA and $V_{CE} = 0$ V to $I_C = 0$ A and $V_{CE} = 12$ V.

3. $R_C = 240$ Ω, $I_{C(Q)} = 20.8$ mA, $I_{B(Q)} = 130$ μA, $R_B = 86.9$ kΩ
Use an 86.6-kΩ, 2% resistor for R_B.

5. $I_{C(Q)} = 24$ mA, $V_{CE(Q)} = 10.1$ V, $I_{B(Q)} = 185$ μA
Load line from $I_C = 54.5$ mA and $V_{CE} = 0$ V to $I_C = 0$ A and $V_{CE} = 18$ V.

7. $R_C = 150$ Ω, $I_{C(Q)} = 46.7$ mA, $I_{B(Q)} = 425$ μA, $R_B = 17.2$ kΩ
Use a 17.4-kΩ, 1% resistor for R_B.

9. $P_D = 374$ mW

11. $V_B \cong V_{CC} \cdot R_2/(R_2 + R_3) = 1.85$ V
$V_E \cong V_B - 0.7$ V $= 1.15$ V, $I_{C(Q)} \cong I_{E(Q)} = 9.58$ mA
$V_{CE(Q)} = V_{CC} - V_{RE} - V_{RC} = 11.4$ V

Load line from $I_C = 18.2$ mA and $V_{CE} = 0$ V to $I_C = 0$ A and $V_{CE} = 24$ V.

13. $R_C + R_E = V_{CC}/I_{C(sat)} = 12$ V$/25$ mA $= 480$ Ω
$R_E = (R_C + R_E)/16 = 480$ $\Omega/16 = 30$ Ω
$R_C = 480$ $\Omega - R_E = 480$ $\Omega - 30$ $\Omega = 450$ Ω
$I_{C(Q)} = (V_{CC} - V_{CE})/(R_E + R_C) = (12$ V $- 6$ V$)/480$ $\Omega = 12.5$ mA
$I_{B(Q)} = I_{C(Q)}/\beta_{DC} = 12.5$ mA$/190 = 65.8$ μA
$I_{R2} = 10 \cdot I_{B(Q)} = 10 \cdot 65.8$ μA $= 658$ μA
$V_{R2} = 0.7$ V $+ V_E = 0.7$ V $+ (I_{C(Q)} \cdot R_E)$
$= 0.7$ V $+ (12.5$ mA $\cdot 30$ $\Omega) = 1.08$ V
$R_2 = V_{R2}/I_{R2} = 1.08$ V$/658$ μA $= 1,641$ Ω
(Use 1.6 kΩ)
$I_{R2} = 1.08$ V$/1.6$ k$\Omega = 675$ μA
$I_{R1} = I_{R2} + I_{B(Q)} = 675$ μA $+ 65.8$ μA $= 741$ μA
$R_1 = (V_{CC} - V_B)/I_{R1} = (12$ V $- 1.08$ V$)/741$ μA $= 14.74$ kΩ
Use a 14.7-kΩ, 2% resistor for R_1.

15. $P_D = 75$ mW

17. $I_{C(Q)} \cong I_{E(Q)} = 9.46$ mA, $V_{CE(Q)} = 8.63$ V

19. (a) h_{FE} increases, I_C increases, and V_{CE} decreases
    (b) R_B increases in resistance, I_C decreases, and V_{CE} increases
    (c) R_B becomes shorted, I_C increases, and V_{CE} decreases to $\cong 0.7$ V

21. (a) h_{FE} increases, I_C increases slightly, and V_{CE} decreases slightly
    (b) R_2 increases in resistance, I_C increases, and V_{CE} decreases
    (c) R_C decreases in resistance, I_C remains unchanged, and V_{CE} increases
    (d) R_1 increases in resistance, I_C decreases, and V_{CE} increases
    (e) The ambient temperature increases, I_C increases slightly, and V_{CE} decreases slightly

23. $I_{B(Q)} = 368$ μA, $I_{C(Q)} = 31.3$ mA, $V_{CE(Q)} = 8.61$ V
DC load line from $I_C = 60$ mA and $V_{CE} = 0$ V to $I_C = 0$ A and $V_{CE} = -18$ V.

25. $I_{C(Q)} = (V_{CC} - V_{BE})/(R_C + (R_B/\beta_{DC}))$
$= (13.6$ V $- 0.7$ V$)/(1.2$ kΩ $+ (130$ k$\Omega/130))$

$= 12.9 \text{ V}/2200 \ \Omega = 5.86 \text{ mA}$

$I_{C(Q)} = (V_{CC} - V_{CE(Q)})/R_C = (13.6 \text{ V} - 6.6 \text{ V})/1.2 \text{ k}\Omega = 5.83 \text{ mA}$

$I_{B(Q)} = I_{C(Q)}/\beta_{DC} = 5.83 \text{ mA}/130 = 44.8 \ \mu\text{A}$

Load line from $I_C = 11.3$ mA and $V_{CE} = 0$ V to $I_C = 0$ A and $V_{CE} = 13.6$ V

27. $R_C = 300 \ \Omega$, $I_{C(Q)} = 40$ mA, $I_{B(Q)} = 571 \ \mu\text{A}$, $R_B = 19.8 \text{ k}\Omega$
Use a 20-kΩ, 5% resistor for R_B.

29. $V_B \cong V_{CC} \cdot R_2/(R_2 + R_3) = -24 \text{ V} \cdot 4.7 \text{ k}\Omega/(4.7 \text{ k}\Omega + 68 \text{ k}\Omega) = -1.55$ V

$V_E \cong V_B - 0.7 \text{ V} = -1.55 \text{ V} - (-0.7 \text{ V})$
$= -0.85$ V

$I_{C(Q)} \cong I_{E(Q)} = V_E/R_E = -0.85 \text{ V}/120 \ \Omega = -7.08$ mA

$V_{CE(Q)} = V_{CC} - V_{RE} - V_{RC} = -24 \text{ V} - (-0.85 \text{ V}) - (-I_{C(Q)} \cdot R_C)$
$\quad = -24 \text{ V} - (-0.85 \text{ V}) - (-7.08 \text{ mA} \cdot 1.8 \text{ k}\Omega) = -10.4$ V

Load line from $I_C = 12.5$ mA and $V_{CE} = 0$ V to $I_C = 0$ A and $V_{CE} = -24$ V.

31. $I_{C(Q)} \cong I_{E(Q)} = 10.1$ mA, $V_{CE(Q)} = -5.76$ V, $P_{D(Q)} = 58.2$ mW

CHAPTER 6

1. $I_{C(sat)} = 988 \ \mu\text{A}$, $V_{CE(cutoff)} = 24$ V
3. $V_E \cong V_B - 0.7 \text{ V} = 1.85 \text{ V} - 0.7 \text{ V} = 1.15$ V
5. $V_{CE(Q)} = 11.85$ V
7. $A_V = (R_C\|R_L)/((r_E + r'_e)) = 14.3$
9. $v_{out(max)} = 2 \cdot (19.85 \text{ V} - 11.85 \text{ V}) = 16 \ V_{P\text{-}P}$
11. $Z_{in} = R_1\|R_2\|(\beta \cdot (r'_e + r_E)) = 3.24 \text{ k}\Omega$
13. $A_i = A_V \cdot Z_{in}/Z_{out} = 2.11$
15. $r_C = R_C\|R_L = 11.6 \text{ k}\Omega$
17. $I_E \cong I_{C(Q)} = 303 \ \mu\text{A}$, $r'_e = 82.5 \ \Omega$
19. $I_{R1} = I_{R2} + I_B = 22.22 \ \mu\text{A}$, $R_1 = 484 \text{ k}\Omega$
Use a 487-kΩ, 2% resistor for R_1.
21. $R_E = R_{EDC} - r_E = 1.3 \text{ k}\Omega$
23. $C_1 = 0.157 \ \mu\text{F}$ Use a 0.2-μF capacitor for C_1.
25. $C_3 = 91 \ \mu\text{F}$ Use a 100-μF capacitor for C_3.
27. $r'_e \cong 7.27 \ \Omega$, $Z_{out} = r'_e + [1/(\beta \cdot ((1/R_1) + (1/R_2)))] = 20.6 \ \Omega$
29. $A_P = Z_{in}/R_E = 0.491$
31. $I_B \cong I_E/\beta = 50 \ \mu\text{A}$, $V_B = 5.7$ V, $R_2 = 11.4 \text{ k}\Omega$ (Use 11 kΩ)

33. $Z_{in} \cong 1/[(1/R_1) + (1/R_2) + (1/\beta R_E)] = 3.64 \text{ k}\Omega$
35. $V_E \cong 6.23$ V
37. $\beta_{(total)} = 50 \cdot 100 = 5{,}000$
39. $Z_{in} \cong R_1\|R_2 = 248 \ \Omega$
41. $A_i = Z_{in}/R_E = 24.8$
43. $r'_e \cong 25 \text{ mV}/I_E = 48.6 \ \Omega$
45. $C_2 \geq 0.16 \ \mu\text{F}$
47. Source to input loss factor = 0.393 (-8.11 dB)
49. Overall system amplification = 62.1 = 35.9 dB gain
Total dB gain = 46.3 dB $-$ 8.11 dB $-$ 2.3 dB = 35.9 dB
51. $I_{C(sat)} = 1.1$ mA, $V_{CE(cutoff)} = 12$ V
53. $V_E \cong 0.6$ V
55. $V_{CE(Q)} = 5.08$ V
57. $A_V = (R_C\|R_L)/(r'_e + r_E) = 24.8$
59. $v_{out(max)} = 2 \cdot (10.1 \text{ V} - 5.08 \text{ V}) = 10 \ V_{P\text{-}P}$

CHAPTER 7

1. $I_{C(Q)} \cong I_{E(Q)} = 5.6$ mA, $V_{CE(Q)} = V_{CC} - V_{RE} - V_{RC} = 9.04$ V
$P_D = I_{C(Q)} \cdot V_{CE(Q)} = 50.6$ mW
3. $P_{DC} = I_{C(Q)} \cdot V_{CC} = 101$ mW
5. $I_{C(Q)} \cong I_{E(Q)} = 1.77$ mA, $V_{CE(Q)} = V_{CC} - V_{RE} - V_{RC} = 11.1$ V
$P_D = I_{C(Q)} \cdot V_{CE(Q)} = 19.6$ mW
7. $P_{DC} = I_{C(Q)} \cdot V_{CC} = 42.5$ mW
9. $P_{D(max)} = (V_{CE(Q)})^2/10R_L = 22.5$ W
11. $P_{DC(max)} = i_{c(max \ ave)} \cdot V_{CC} = 143.1$ W
13. $P_{D(max)} = (V_{CE(Q)})^2/10R_L = 7.2$ W
15. $P_{DC(max)} = i_{c(max \ ave)} \cdot V_{CC} = 45.8$ W
17. $f_r = 1/(2\pi\sqrt{LC}) \cong 0.159/\sqrt{LC} = 3.39$ MHz
19. $i_{c(sat)} = V_{CC}/(Z_{tank}\|R_L) = 368 \ \mu\text{A}$, $T = 1/f_r = 295$ ns
$P_D = i_{c(sat)} \cdot v_{ce(sat)} \cdot t/T = 9.98 \ \mu\text{W}$
21. $P_{tank} = 0.5 \cdot V_{CC}^2/Z_{tank} = 27.8 \ \mu\text{W}$
$P_{DC} = P_L + P_D + P_{tank} = 2.218$ mW
23. $f_r = 1/(2\pi\sqrt{LC}) \cong 0.159/\sqrt{LC} = 503$ kHz
25. $i_{c(sat)} = V_{CC}/(Z_{tank}\|R_L) = 2.07$ mA, $T = 1/f_r = 1.99 \ \mu\text{s}$
$P_D = i_{c(sat)} \cdot v_{ce(sat)} \cdot t/T = 20.8 \ \mu\text{W}$
27. $P_{tank} = 0.5 \cdot V_{CC}^2/Z_{tank} = 2.43$ mW
$P_{DC} = P_L + P_D + P_{tank} = 18.65$ mW
29. $P_{D(max \ at \ operating \ temp)}$
$= P_{D(max \ at \ 25°C)} - [(T_C - 25°C) \cdot D]$

$= 80 \text{ W} - [(75° - 25°) \cdot 0.38 \text{ W/°C}]$
$= 80 \text{ W} - 19 \text{ W} = 61 \text{ W}$

31. $T_C = (P_D \cdot R_\theta) + T_A = (10 \text{ W} \cdot 3.5°\text{C/W})$
$+ 60°\text{C} = 95°\text{C}$

$P_{D(\text{max at operating temp})} = P_{D(\text{max at 25°C})} - [(T_C$
$- 25°\text{C}) \cdot \text{D}]$
$= 90 \text{ W} - [(95° - 25°)$
$\cdot 0.55 \text{ W/°C}]$
$= 90 \text{ W} - 38.5 \text{ W} =$
51.5 W

33. Using Figure 7–25, the case temperature must not be greater than approximately 140°C if the power dissipation is 40 W.
$R_\theta = (T_C - T_A)/P_D = (140° - 40°)/40 \text{ W} = 2.5°\text{C/W}$
$R_{\theta \text{SA}} = R_\theta - R_{\theta \text{CS}} = 2.5°\text{C/W} - 0.6°\text{C/W} = 1.9°\text{C/W}$
The heat sink must have a thermal resistance less than 1.9°C/W.

35. $I_{C(Q)} \cong I_{E(Q)} = 15.2 \text{ mA}, V_{CE(Q)} = V_{CC} - V_{RE} - V_{RC} = 7.63 \text{ V}$
$P_D = I_{C(Q)} \cdot V_{CE(Q)} = 15.2 \text{ mA} \cdot 7.63 \text{ V} = 116 \text{ mW}$

37. $P_{DC} = I_{C(Q)} \cdot V_{CC} = 274 \text{ mW}$

39. $P_{D(\text{max})} = (V_{CE(Q)})^2/10R_L = 81 \text{ mW}$

41. $P_{DC(\text{max})} = i_{c(\text{max ave})} \cdot V_{CC} = 515 \text{ mW}$

43. $f_r = 1/(2\pi\sqrt{LC}) \cong 0.159/\sqrt{LC} = 1.03 \text{ MHz}$

45. $i_{c(\text{sat})} = V_{CC}/(Z_{\text{tank}}\|R_L) = 3.61 \text{ mA}, T = 1/f_r = 971 \text{ ns}$
$P_D = i_{c(\text{sat})} \cdot v_{ce(\text{sat})} \cdot t/T = 149 \text{ } \mu\text{W}$

47. $P_{\text{tank}} = 0.5 \text{ } V_{CC}^2/Z_{\text{tank}} = 54.4 \text{ } \mu\text{W}$
$P_{DC} = P_L + P_D + P_{\text{tank}} = 16.4 \text{ mW}$

CHAPTER 8

1. $I_D = 442 \text{ } \mu\text{A}$
3. $g_m = 2,200 \text{ } \mu\text{S}$
5. $g_{m\text{-VGS}} = 2,250 \text{ } \mu\text{S}$
7. $R_{\text{in}} = 25 \text{ G}\Omega$
9. $r_{ds} = 120 \text{ k}\Omega$
11. $I_{D(Q)} = 600 \text{ } \mu\text{A}, V_{RD(Q)} = 2.82 \text{ V}, V_{DS(Q)} = 5.58 \text{ V}$
13. $I_{D(Q)} = 3.39 \text{ mA}, R_S = 295 \text{ }\Omega$ (Use 300 Ω)
$R_D = 1,843 \text{ }\Omega$ (Use 1.8 kΩ), $C_B \geq 1.59/(R_S f_{\text{low}}) = 177 \text{ } \mu\text{F}$ (Use 200 μF)
15. $g_{m\text{-VGS}} = 3,500 \text{ } \mu\text{S}, A_V = 6.3$ (no load)
#dB = 20 log(6.3) = 16 dB gain

17. $Z_{\text{in}} \cong R_G = 5.6 \text{ M}\Omega, Z_{\text{out}} \cong R_D = 4.7 \text{ k}\Omega$
19. $Z_{\text{in}} \cong R_G = 270 \text{ k}\Omega, Z_{\text{out}} = ((1/g_m)\|R_S) = 178 \text{ }\Omega$
$v_{\text{out}} = 2.28 \text{ V}, A_V = 0.76, \text{#dB} = 20 \log(0.76) = -2.38 \text{ dB (a loss)}$
21. $Z_{\text{in}} = 276 \text{ }\Omega, Z_{\text{out}} \cong R_D = 10 \text{ k}\Omega$
$A_V = 18.4, v_{\text{out}} = 552 \text{ mV}$
23. $R_D = 909 \text{ }\Omega$ (Use 910 Ω)
25. $R_1 = 6.37 \text{ M}\Omega, I_{D(Q)} = 10.5 \text{ mA}, R_D = 1143 \text{ }\Omega$ (Use 1,150 Ω, 2%)
$g_{m\text{-VGS}} = 9,516 \text{ } \mu\text{S}, A_V = 10.9, v_{\text{out}} = 927 \text{ mV}$
27. $K = I_D/(V_{GS} - V_{GS(\text{th})})^2 = 100 \text{ mA}/(5 \text{ V} - 2.8 \text{ V})^2 = 0.02066 \text{ A/V}^2$
$I_D = K(V_{GS} - V_{GS(\text{th})})^2 = 0.02066 \text{ A/V}^2 \cdot (3.3 \text{ V} - 2.8 \text{ V})^2 = 5.17 \text{ mA}$
29. Stage 1 amplifies the input signal as it should, having an amplification factor of $g_m R_2 \cong 12$. This indicates stage 2 has failed in some way. Check for $V_D = +6 \text{ V}$ at the drain of Q_2. Make sure +4.6 V is present at the gate of Q_2. If +4.6 V is present at the gate and something very different than +6 V is present at the drain, the MOSFET is probably bad. Other possibilities are: open connection, cracked foil, cold solder joint, R_4 open (doubtful), or C_3 open (doubtful).
31. This indicates the amplification factor of stage 1 is less than it should be. It is possible that C_2 have become disconnected or the gm of Q_1 is lower than expected.
33. Stage 1: $AV = 2,500 \text{ } \mu\text{S} \cdot 4.7 \text{ k}\Omega = 11.75$
Stage 2: $AV = 6,000 \text{ } \mu\text{S} \cdot 688 \text{ }\Omega = 4.13$
Total amplification factor is $11.75 \cdot 4.13 = 48.5$
$v_{\text{out}} = 25 \text{ mV} \cdot 48.5 = 1.21 \text{ V}$
35. (b)
37. (b)
39. $I_{D(Q)} = 6.93 \text{ mA}, R_S = 86.6 \text{ }\Omega$ (Use 86.6 Ω, 2%)
$R_D = 663 \text{ }\Omega$ (Use 680 Ω)
$C_B \geq 1.59/(R_S f_{\text{low}}) = 459 \text{ } \mu\text{F}$
A more accurate value for C_B can be found once g_m is known.
$g_{m\text{-VGS}} = g_{m0} \cdot [1 - (V_{GS}/V_{GS(\text{off})}]$
$= 6,000 \text{ } \mu\text{S} \cdot [1 - (-0.6 \text{ V}/-2.5 \text{ V})] = 4560 \text{ } \mu\text{S}$
$C_B \geq 1.59 \text{ } gm/f_{\text{low}} = 1.59 \cdot 4,560 \text{ } \mu\text{S}/40 \text{ Hz}$

$= 181 \ \mu\text{F}$ (Use $200 \ \mu\text{F}$)

41. $A_V = 2.9$, #dB $= 20 \log(2.9) = 9.25$ dB
43. $R_D = V_{DD}/2I_{DSS} = 200 \ \Omega$

CHAPTER 9

1. $f_{co} = 74.7$ kHz
3. $f_{co} = 72.3$ Hz
5. $f_{co} = 87.5$ kHz
7. $f_{co} = 12.9$ kHz
9. $Z_{\text{in}} = 556 \ \Omega$, $f_{co} = 0.159/C(R_g + Z_{\text{in}}) = 27.5$ Hz
11. $Z_e = R_E \| [r_E + r'_e + ((R_g \| R_1 \| R_2)/\beta)] = 26.9 \ \Omega$
     $f_{co} = 0.159/(C_B Z_e) = 59.1$ Hz
13. $f_{co} = 48$ Hz
15. $Z_S = 1/g_m \| R_S = 121 \ \Omega$, $f_{co} = 0.159/(C_B Z_S) = 13.1$ Hz
17. $X_C = 662.5$ kΩ, $\angle \theta = \arctan (X_C/(R_g + Z_{\text{in}})) = 63.5°$
19. $C_{\text{out(total)}} \cong 4.5$ pF, $f_{co} = 0.159/((R_C \| R_L) \cdot C_{\text{out(total)}}) = 428.5$ kHz
21. $A_V = g_m(R_D \| R_L) = 7.1$, $C_{\text{in(Miller)}} = 12.2$ pF, $C_{\text{in(total)}} = 18.2$ pF
     $R_{\text{Th}} \cong R_g = 600 \ \Omega$, $f_{co} = 0.159/(R_{\text{Th}} C_{\text{in(total)}}) = 14.6$ MHz
23. The 14.6 MHz cutoff frequency of the input network is dominant.
25. $A_V = g_m \cdot 1/g_m = 1$, $C_{\text{in(Miller)}} = 2$ pF
     $C_{\text{in(total)}} = 6.5$ pF, $R_{\text{Th}} \cong R_g = 600 \ \Omega$
     $f_{co} = 0.159/(R_{\text{Th}} C_{\text{in(total)}}) = 40.8$ MHz
27. The 16.2 MHz upper cutoff frequency of the output network is dominant.
29. $BW = Uf_{CO} - Lf_{CO} = 50$ kHz $- 0.5$ KHz $= 49.5$ kHz
31. $BW = f_T/A_V = 100$ MHz$/50 = 2$ MHz
33. $T = 6.8$ div. $\cdot 0.5$ ms/div. $= 3.4$ ms, $f = 1/T = 1/3.4$ ms $= 294$ Hz
35. #dB $= 20 \ (\log(2.6 \ \text{V}_{\text{P-P}}/0.033 \ \text{V}_{\text{P-P}}) = 37.9$ dB, slope $= 37.9$ dB/dec
37. $Lf_{co} = 0.35/t_f = 0.35/0.23$ ms $= 1522$ Hz
39. $f_{co} = 0.159/C(R_C + R_L) = 3.86$ Hz
41. The 4.09-Hz cutoff frequency of the bypass network is dominant.
43. $C_{\text{out(Miller)}} = 2.07$ pF, $C_{\text{out(total)}} \cong 3.07$ pF
     $f_{co} = 0.159/((R_D \| R_L) \cdot C_{\text{out(total)}}) \cong 7.77$ MHz
45. $X_C = 0.159/(2f_{co} C_{\text{in(total)}}) = 501 \ \Omega$
     $\angle \theta = \arctan (X_C/R) = \arctan (501 \ \Omega/1$

kΩ$) = 26.6° =$ the phase angle between the applied voltage and the voltage across R_g. However, the phase angle of the voltage across the shunting input capacitance is $90° - 26.6° = 63.4°$. The voltage across the shunting input capacitance lags the applied signal voltage by 63.4° at a frequency of 4.74 MHz. This is because at the lowpass cutoff frequency of 2.37 MHz the phase angle of the voltage at the gate must be $-45°$ because $X_C = R_g$ and $\angle \theta = \arctan (1/1) = 45°$. At any frequency above the 2.37 MHz cutoff the phase angle must increase (lag by more than 45°).

47. $A_V = g_m(R_D \| R_L) = 25$, $C_{\text{out(Miller)}} = 2.08$ pF, $C_{\text{out(total)}} = 3.58$ pF
     $f_{co} = 0.159/((R_D \| R_L) \cdot C_{\text{out(total)}}) = 7.48$ MHz

CHAPTER 10

1. $r'_e = 97.3 \ \Omega$, $A_V = R_C/2r'_e = 113$
    $v_{\text{out}} = v_{\text{in}} \cdot A_V = 113$ mV for single-ended output, 226 mV for a differential output
3. $A_{V(\text{diff})} = R_C/2r'_e = 113$
    $v_{\text{out}} = v_{\text{in}} \cdot A_V = 565$ mV for single-ended output, 1.13 V for a differential output
5. CMRR $= A_{V(\text{diff})}/A_{V(\text{com})} = 3125$, #dB $= 20 \log (3{,}125) = 70$ dB
7. $I_{IB} = (I_{B1} + I_{B2})/2 = 95$ nA, $I_{IO} = |I_{B1} - I_{B2}| = 10$ nA
9. $V_{IO} = (I_{B1} \cdot R_{B1}) - (I_{B2} \cdot R_{B2}) = -47 \ \mu\text{V}$
11. #dB $= 20 \log (175{,}000) = 105$ dB
13. $A_{V(OL)} = \text{invlog}(110 \text{ dB}/20) = 316{,}228$
     CMRR $= A_{OL}/A_{V(\text{com})} = 48{,}650 = 93.7$ dB
15. $A_{V(OL)} = \text{invlog}(106 \text{ dB}/20) = 200{,}000$
     $v_{\text{diff}} = v_{\text{out}}/A_{OL} = 13 \ \mu\text{V}$
17. $B = R_I/(R_I + R_F) = 0.0414$, $A_V = 1/B = 24.2$
     $v_{\text{diff}} = v_{\text{out}}/A_{OL} = 22.5 \ \mu\text{V}$, $v_{\text{in}} \cong v_f = v_{\text{out}} \cdot B = 186$ mV
     loop gain $= A_{OL}B = 8{,}280 = 78.4$ dB
     $Z_{\text{in}} = 24.8$ GΩ, $Z_{\text{out}} = 9.66$ mΩ
19. $R_F = v_{\text{in}}/i_{\text{out}} = 30 \ \Omega$, $g_m = 1/R_F = 33.3$ mS
21. $R_F = V_{\text{out}}/I_{\text{in}} = 20 \ \Omega$, $Z_{\text{in}} = V_{\text{out}}/A_{OL}I_{\text{in}} = 154 \ \mu\Omega$

23. $A_V = R_F/R_I = 46.8$, $v_{out} = v_{in} \cdot A_V = 2.34$ V
    $A_{OL} = \text{invlog}(100 \text{ dB}/20) = 100,000$
    $v_{diff} = v_{out}/A_{OL} = 23.4 \ \mu V$. $Z_{in} = R_I = 4.7 \text{ k}\Omega$
25. $I_{out} = I_{meter} = 250 \ \mu A$, $R_1 = 3,280 \ \Omega$
27. $CMRR = A_{OL}/A_{V(com)} = 17,500 = 84.9$ dB
29. $A_V = 1/B = (R_F + R_I)/R_I = 17.5$, $v_{out} = v_{in} \cdot A_V = 263$ mV, $v_{diff} = v_{out}/A_{OL} = 2.63 \ \mu V$
31. $B = R_I/(R_I + R_F) = 0.0656$, loop gain $= BA_{OL} = 9,512$, $Z_{in} = 19 \text{ G}\Omega$, $Z_{out} = 6.31 \text{ m}\Omega$
33. $Z_{in} = R_F/A_{OL} = 31.9 \text{ m}\Omega$
35. $Z_{in} = R_I = 18 \text{ k}\Omega$, $B = R_I/(R_I + R_F) = 0.0369$, loop gain $= BA_{OL} = 3690$, $Z_{out} = 20.3 \text{ m}\Omega$, $i_{in} = v_{in}/Z_{in} = v_{in}/R_I = 3.78 \ \mu A$, $A_V = 1/B = 27.1$, $v_{out} = v_{in} \cdot A_V = 1.84$ V, $v_{diff} = v_{out}/A_{OL} = 18.4 \ \mu V$

CHAPTER 11

1. $BW_P = 29.8$ kHz
3. $V_{P(max)} = 10.6 \ V_P$
5. $f_{co(open)} = 16.7$ Hz
7. $f_T = 1.44$ MHz, $f_{co(closed)} = 4,800$ Hz
9. $A_V = 7.5$
11. $A_{OL(max)} = 72,700$
13. $\Phi_{t(500 \text{ kHz})} = -73.9°$, $\Phi_{t(5 \text{ MHz})} = -146.3°$
15. >60 MHz
17. 1 MHz
19. $\Phi_{PM} = 32°$
21. $BW_P = 26$ kHz
23. $f_{co(open)} = 10.9$ Hz
25. $A_V = 17.3$
27. $\Phi_{t(200 \text{ kHz})} = -70.3°$, $\Phi_{t(2 \text{ MHz})} = -163.5°$
29. $\Phi_{PM} = 17°$

CHAPTER 12

1. $R_F = 140 \text{ k}\Omega$ Use a 140-kΩ, 2% resistor for R_F.
   $R_D = 2Z_{in} = 80 \text{ k}\Omega$ Use two 82-kΩ resistors.
   $C_C \geq 0.08 \ \mu F$, $C_B \geq 3.16 \ \mu F$, VDC $\geq V_{P-P} + 2$ V $= 8$ V
3. $R_{I1} = R_{I2} = R_{I3} = 10 \text{ k}\Omega$, 20 dB is an $A_V = 10$.
   $R_F = R_I A_V = 10 \text{ k}\Omega \cdot 10 = 100 \text{ k}\Omega$

5. (a) Input #1: $V_{out(1)} = -1 \cdot (A_V \cdot V_{in}) = -1 \cdot (1 \cdot +1) = -1$ V
   Input #2: $V_{out(2)} = -1 \cdot (A_V \cdot V_{in}) = -1 \cdot (0.5 \cdot -1) = +0.5$ V
   Input #3: $V_{out(3)} = -1 \cdot (A_V \cdot V_{in}) = -1 \cdot (2 \cdot -1) = +2$ V
   $V_{out(total)} = V_{out(1)} + V_{out(2)} + V_{out(3)}$
   $= -1$ V $+ 0.5$ V $+ 2$ V $= +1.5$ V

   (b) Input #1: $V_{out(1)} = -1 \cdot (A_V \cdot V_{in}) = -1 \cdot (1 \cdot +4) = -4$ V
   Input #2: $V_{out(2)} = -1 \cdot (A_V \cdot V_{in}) = -1 \cdot (0.5 \cdot -3) = +1.5$ V
   Input #3: $V_{out(3)} = -1 \cdot (A_V \cdot V_{in}) = -1 \cdot (2 \cdot +2) = -4$ V
   $V_{out(total)} = V_{out(1)} + V_{out(2)} + V_{out(3)}$
   $= -4$ V $+ 1.5$ V $- 4$ V $= -6.5$ V

7. $V_{out(total)} = V_{out(2k)} + V_{out(16k)} + V_{out(32k)} + V_{out(128k)}$
   $V_{out(2k)} = +5 \text{ V} \cdot 1 \text{ k}\Omega/2 \text{ k}\Omega = +2.500$ V
   $V_{out(16k)} = +5 \text{ V} \cdot 1 \text{ k}\Omega/16 \text{ k}\Omega = +0.313$ V
   $V_{out(32k)} = +5 \text{ V} \cdot 1 \text{ k}\Omega/32 \text{ k}\Omega = +0.156$ V
   $V_{out(128k)} = +5 \text{ V} \cdot 1 \text{ k}\Omega/128 \text{ k}\Omega = \underline{+0.039 \text{ V}}$
   $+3.008$ V

9. $A_V = 11$, $v_{in(threshold)} = 227 \text{ mV}_P$, $v_{in(maximum)} = 21.6 \ V_P$
   Dynamic range (dB) $= 39.6$ dB
11. $I_{C(max)} = I_{B(max)} \cdot \beta_{DC} = 30 \text{ mA} \cdot 70 = 2.1$ A
13. $V_{RE} = 12 \text{ V} - 10 \text{ V} = 2$ V therefore, $I_L \cong I_{RE} = 2 \text{ V}/10 \ \Omega = 200$ mA
15. $R_I = 300 \ \Omega$, $R_F = 300 \ \Omega$, $R_1 = 150 \ \Omega$ $R_2 = 150 \ \Omega$
    $Z_{in} = R_I + R_1 + R_2 = 300 \ \Omega + 150 \ \Omega + 150 \ \Omega = 600 \ \Omega$
17. $V_{trip \ on} = 0.378$ V, $V_H = 0.16$ V, $V_{trip \ off} = 0.218$ V
19. $A_V + 0.7 \text{ V}/100 \text{ mV} = 7$
21. $Q = 2.13 \ \mu C$, $V = Q/C = 2.13 \ \mu C/0.5 \ \mu F = 4.26$ V
23. $RC = 4.7 \text{ k}\Omega \cdot 0.1 \text{ F} = 470$ s, T $= 50$ ms, V $= 200$ mV
    $V_{out} = 200,000 \cdot [V - (V \cdot e^{-T/RC})]$
    $= 200,000 \cdot [200 \text{ mV} - (200 \text{ mV} \cdot e^{-(50ms/470s)})]$
    $= 200,000 \cdot [200 \text{ mV} - (200 \text{ mV} \cdot e^{-(106E-6)})]$

= 200,000 · [200 mV − (200 mV · 0.999894)]

= 200,000 · [200 mV − 199.9788 mV]

= 200,000 · 21.2 μV = 4.24 V (slight difference due to rounding)

25. $V_{in(average)}$ = 100 mV, A_V = 30, R_F = 300 kΩ

27. I = 100 μA, V_{out} = ±1 V

29. A_V = 213, $v_{out(peak)}$ = ±10.7 V_P

31. R_F = 1.4 MΩ Use a 1.4-MΩ, 2% resistor for R_F.

R_D = 2Z_{in} = 200 kΩ Use two 200-kΩ resistors.

$C_{C(in)}$ ≥ 0.064 μF, $C_{C(out)}$ ≥ 2.12 μF, C_B ≥ 0.64 μF

VDC ≥ V_{P-P} + 2 V = 15 V_{P-P} + 2 V = 17 V

33. R_F = R_I/N = 4.7 kΩ/5 = 940 Ω

35. I_L ≅ I_{RE} = V_{RE}/R_E = 3.3 V/0.5 Ω = 6.6 A

37. $V_{trip\ on}$ = 0.495 V, V_H = 0.378 V, $V_{trip\ off}$ = 0.117

39. Q = 2.21 μC, V = 1.105 V

C_{Miller} = A_{OL} · C = 200,000 · 2 μF = 0.4 F

CHAPTER 13

1. K = 1.68, DF = 1.32

3. R = 1060 V

Two stages: First stage is single-pole highpass of any value $A_V(K)$. Second stage is two-pole highpass where K = 2, making R_I = R_F.

5. f_{co} ≅ 294 Hz, 80 dB/dec

7. f_o = 563 Hz, K = A_V = 3.7, Q = 4.71, BW = 120 Hz

9. f_o = 22.1 kHz, Q = 21.9, BW = 1009 Hz, A_o = 100

11. Q = 17.5, R_2 = 318 kΩ (Use 316 kΩ, 2%)

R_1 = 3,160 Ω (2%), R_3 = 281 Ω (Use 280 Ω, 1%)

13. f_o = 2,944 Hz, Q = 12.6, BW = 234 Hz

15. R = 13,250 Ω (Use 13.3 kΩ, 2%)

Q = 12, R_A = 350 kΩ (Use 348 kΩ, 2%)

17. f_c = 398 Hz, K = 1.715, Q = 1.75, band-stop BW = 227 Hz

19. For both the highpass and the lowpass

filters R_I = 10 kΩ and R_F = 5.6 kΩ, so K is close to the desired 1.586 value. Let C = 0.01 μF.

Highpass (2.75 kHz): R = 5.78 k   (Use 4.9 kΩ, 2%)

Lowpass (4.5 kHz): R = 3.53 kΩ (Use 3.48 kΩ, 2%)

21. This is a two-pole (second-order) highpass filter. Therefore, K must equal 1.586, or be close to it. Let R_I = 10 kΩ and R_F = 5.9 kΩ. R = 1272 Ω (Use 1.27 kΩ, 2%)

23. f_{co} = 318 Hz, 80 dB/dec

25. R = 7.5 kΩ, Q = 3.75, K = 3.62

27. Q = 19, R_2 = 14.5 kΩ (Use 14.7 kΩ, 2%)

R_1 = 147 Ω (Use 147 Ω, 2%), R_3 = 11 Ω

29. R = 26.5 kΩ (Use 27 kΩ), Q = 12, R_A = 350 kΩ (Use 360 kΩ)

CHAPTER 14

1. $K_{(+8V)}$ = 0.307, $K_{(+2V)}$ = 0.521

V_{out} = (+8 V · 0.307) + (+2 V · 0.521) = 3.5 V

3. $v_{in(1)}$ = +0.055 V, $v_{in(2)}$ = +3.56 V, $K_{(1)}$ = 2.13, $K_{(2)}$ = 1

V_{out} = −1 · [(+0.055 V · 2.13) + (+3.56 V · 1)] = −3.68 V

The factor −1 represents the 180° phase inversion. As an alternative, the K factors can be represented as negative values to indicate the 180° phase inversion.

5. Sum = 3.515 MHz, Difference = 455 kHz

7. USF = 861.5 kHz, LSF = 858.5 kHz

9. USB = 910.1 kHz to 913.5 kHz, LSB = 909.9 kHz to 906.5 kHz

11. $K_{(+3V)}$ = 0.266, $K_{(−1V)}$ = 0.292, $K_{(+6V)}$ = 0.177

V_{out} = (+3 V · 0.266) + (−1 V · 0.292) + (+6 · 0.177) = 1.57 V

13. $v_{in(1)}$ = +7.68 mV, $v_{in(2)}$ = +749 mV

$K_{(1)}$ = 2.13, $K_{(2)}$ = 1

V_{out} = −1 · [(+7.68 mV · 2.13) + (+749 mV · 1)] = −765 mV

15. Sum = 2.875 MHz, difference = 455 kHz

17. USF = 922 kHz, LSF = 918 kHz

19. USB = 14.25008 MHz to 14.2528 MHz
LSB = 14.24992 MHz to 14.2472 MHz

CHAPTER 15

1. A_V must be 6.7 so the product of A_V and B will equal 1.
3. Wien-bridge oscillator $- f_o = 15.9$ kHz
5. $C = 0.04 \, \mu$F
7. $R = 1{,}693 \, \Omega$ (Use 1.69 kΩ, 2%)
   The resistor to ground in the highpass T is $1{,}693 \, \Omega/2 = 847 \, \Omega$ (Use 845 Ω, 1%)
9. $R \cong 650 \, \Omega$
11. $L = 12.2 \, \mu$H
13. Clapp oscillator
    Low end:
    $C_t = 1/((1/0.002 \, \mu\text{F}) + (1/200 \text{ pF}) + (1/140 \text{ pF})) = 79.1 \text{ pF}$
    $f_{\text{low}} = 1/(2\pi\sqrt{LC}) = 1/(2\pi \cdot \sqrt{20 \, \mu\text{H} \cdot 79.1 \text{ pF}}) = 4 \text{ MHz}$
    High end:
    $C_t = 1/((1/0.002 \, \mu\text{F}) + (1/200 \text{ pF}) + (1/120 \text{ pF})) = 72.3 \text{ pF}$
    $f_{\text{high}} = 1/(2\pi\sqrt{LC}) = 1/(2\pi \cdot \sqrt{20 \, \mu\text{H} \cdot 72.3 \text{ pF}}) = 4.185 \text{ MHz}$
15. $f_{\text{series}} = 1/(2\pi\sqrt{LC}) = 1/(2\pi \cdot \sqrt{1 \text{ H} \cdot 0.02 \text{ pF}}) = 1.125 \text{ MHz}$
    $C_{\text{loop}} = (C_M \cdot C_S)/(C_M + C_S)$
    $= (5 \text{ pF} \cdot 0.02 \text{ pF})/(5 \text{ pF} + 0.02 \text{ pF})$
    $= 0.01992 \text{ pF}$
    $f_{\text{parallel}} = 1/(2\pi\sqrt{LC}) = 1/(2\pi \cdot \sqrt{1 \text{ H} \cdot 0.01992 \text{ pF}}) =$
    1.128 MHz
17. The peak-to-peak triangle-wave voltage at the output of the LF356 will be approximately $2 \cdot (3 \text{ V} + 1.4 \text{ V}) = 8.8 \, V_{\text{P-P}}$. $f_o = 568$ Hz
19. $f_{\text{low}} = 6.6$ kHz, $f_{\text{high}} = 666.7$ kHz
21. Astable multivibrator—square-wave oscillator
    $t_1 = t_{\text{on}} = 0.693 \cdot (R_1 + R_2) \cdot C = 0.693 \cdot 69 \text{ k}\Omega \cdot 0.022 \, \mu\text{F} = 1.05 \text{ ms}$
    $t_2 = t_{\text{off}} = 0.693 \cdot R_2 \cdot C = 0.693 \cdot 47 \text{ k}\Omega \cdot 0.022 \, \mu\text{F} = 0.717 \text{ ms}$
    $T = t_1 + t_2 = 1.05 \text{ ms} + 0.717 \text{ ms} = 1.767 \text{ ms}$
    % duty cycle $= 100\% \cdot t_{\text{on}}/T = 100\% \cdot 1.05 \text{ ms}/1.767 \text{ ms} = 59.4\%$
23. Control voltage is from $+3$ V to $+6$ V. According to the graph, the capacitance of the varactor varies from 80 pF to 30 pF as the voltage is varied from 3 to 6 volts.

Low end:
$C_t = 1/((1/0.001 \, \mu\text{F}) + (1/100 \text{ pF}) + (1/130 \text{ pF})) = 53.5 \text{ pF}$
$f_{\text{low}} = 1/(2\pi\sqrt{LC}) = 1/(2\pi \cdot \sqrt{20 \, \mu\text{H} \cdot 53.5 \text{ pF}}) = 4.866 \text{ MHz}$
High end:
$C_t = 1/((1/0.001 \, \mu\text{F}) + (1/100 \text{ pF}) + (1/80 \text{ pF})) = 42.6 \text{ pF}$
$f_{\text{high}} = 1/(2\pi\sqrt{LC}) = 1/(2\pi \cdot \sqrt{20 \, \mu\text{H} \cdot 42.6 \text{ pF}}) = 5.453 \text{ MHz}$
25. $f_o = 22.7$ kHz, loop filter $f_{co} = 5.3$ kHz
    $f_{\text{upper capture}} \cong 28$ kHz, $f_{\text{lower capture}} \cong 17.4$ kHz
27. 0.001% is equal to 10 Hz change for every 1 MHz. $0.001\% = 0.00001$ and $0.00001 \cdot 1$ MHz $= 10$ Hz. Therefore, the maximum change in frequency is 10 Hz $\cdot 6.25 = 62.5$ Hz.
29. $R = 6{,}366 \, \Omega$ (Use 6.34 kΩ, 1%). See Figures 15–4 and 15–5.
31. $R \cong 2{,}955 \, \Omega$ (Use 2.94 kΩ, 1%). See Figure 15–8.
33. Low end: $C_t = 75.8$ pF, $f_{\text{low}} = 3.66$ MHz
    High end: $C_t = 68.5$ pF, $f_{\text{high}} = 3.85$ MHz
35. $C = 1/Rf_o = 0.25 \, \mu$F Note: The ratio of $R_2/(R_2 + R_1)$ must be close to 0.245 for this formula to be accurate.
37. $R = T/(1.1 \, C)$: If $C = 0.1 \, \mu$F, then R must be 9.09 MΩ. If $C = 1 \, \mu$F, then R must be 909 kΩ. If $C = 10 \, \mu$F, then R must be 90.9 kΩ. If $C = 50 \, \mu$F, then R must be 18.2 kΩ.

CHAPTER 16

1. $I_E = 39.2 \, \mu$A, $f_o = 560$ Hz
3. No. The 39.2 μA supplied by the transistor will hold the SUS on. It will be latched. However, the bias setting of Problem 2 will allow it to oscillate since $I_E < I_H$.
5. $V_P \cong 14.2$ V
7. $V_P \cong 9.7$ V, $R < 2.65$ MΩ, $R > 6650 \, \Omega$
9. $V_P \cong 8.7$ V
11. $I_E = 141 \, \mu$A, $f_o = 88.1$ Hz
13. $I_E = 254 \, \mu$A. The circuit will not oscillate because $I_E > I_H$.
15. $V_P \cong 7.27$ V

17. $V_P \cong 11.1$ V, $R < 2.72$ MΩ, $R > 4176$ Ω
19. $V_P \cong 12.3$ V

CHAPTER 17

1. $V_{RL} = 8.4$ V, $I_L = 840$ mA, $I_B = 21$ mA, $V_{RS} = 4.5$ V, $I_{RS} = 22.5$ mA, $I_Z = 1.5$ mA, $P_Z = 13.7$ mW, $P_{RS} = 101$ mW, $P_L = 7.06$ W, $P_{Q1} = 4.37$ W, % Eff = 61.8%

3. $I_{B(Q1,max)} = 167$ mA, $I_{B(Q2,max)} = 2.78$ mA, $V_Z \cong 14$ V, $I_{Z(min)} = 278$ μA, $I_{Z(max)} = 3.06$ mA, $P_{Z(Rating)} > 42.8$ mW   (Use a 250-mW, 14-V zener diode). $R_S = 980$ Ω, $P_{RS} = 9.18$ mW   (Use 1/8 W). $P_{Q1(Rating)} > 22$ W   (Use 40 W or greater, depends on thermal resistance of heat sink and ambient temperature), $P_{Q2(Rating)} > 0.62$ W (Use at least 1 W)

5. $I_{Limit} \cong 3$ A, $V_Z \cong 6.8$ V

7. $V_Z = 18$ V, $I_{Limit} \cong 0.7$ V/0.2 $\Omega = 3.5$ A
   The fuse should be equal to or greater than 4-A rating.
   $I_{Limit} < I_{fuse} < I_{SCR(surge)}$

9. $K = 0.406$, $V_L = V_{out} \cong 8.87$ V

11. $K = 0.353$, $V_{out} = V_{RL} \cong 11$ V, $I_{RL} = 138$ mA, $P_L = 1.52$ W, $V_{RS} = 5$ V, $I_{RS} = 250$ mA, $P_{RS} = 1.25$ W, $I_{C(Q1)} = 112$ mA, $P_{Q1} = 1.23$ W, % Eff = 38%

13. $V_{out} = 18.5$ V

15. At approximately 700 mA of load current (0.7 V/1 $\Omega = 700$ mA).

17. $R_2 = 2,045$ Ω

19. $V_{out} = 5.98$ V, $I_{Limit} \cong 50$ mA

21. $R_1 = 3116$ Ω

23. $\Delta I_L = 1$ A, $L > 80.4$ μH, $C > 62.5$ μF

25. $\Delta I_L = 0.3$ A, $L > 20.6$ μH, $C > 66.7$ μF

27. $\Delta I_L = 0.8$ A, $L > 54.3$ μH, $C > 337$ μF

29. $I_{B(Q1,max)} = 120$ mA, $I_{B(Q2,max)} = 2$ mA, $V_Z \cong 12.1$ V   (Use a 12-V zener), $I_{Z(min)} = 200$ μA, $I_{Z(max)} = 2.2$ mA, $P_{Z(Rating)} > 26.4$ mW   Use a 250-mW, 12-V zener diode.
   $R_S = 3,636$ Ω Use 3.6 kΩ for R_S. $P_{RS} = 17.6$ mW (Use 1/8 W)
   $P_{Q1(Rating)} > 27.9$ W   (Use 50 W or greater, depends on thermal resistance of heat sink and ambient temperature).
   $P_{Q2(Rating)} > 1.03$ W   (Use at least 2 W).

31. $I_{Limit} \cong 2.33$ A, $V_Z \cong 12.7$ V   (Use a 13-V zener).

33. $K \cong 0.17$, $R_2 = 16.1$ kΩ
    Use a 16-kΩ, 5% resistor for R_2 or an adjustable resistor.

35. $V_{out} = 25.8$ V

37. $\Delta I_L = 1.2$ A, $L > 81$ μH, $C > 33.3$ μF

CHAPTER 18

1. $\lambda = 2.04$ m
3. $\lambda = 315.8$ nm
5. $f = 600$ THz
7. $f = 714.3$ THz
9. 0.079 mW/m^2
11. 12.664 μW/cm^2
13. 1470.6 mW = 1.4706 W
15. $I = 1.2$ mA
17. 12 V
19. The relay will securely energize as long as the impinging irradiance is greater than 3.3 mW/cm^2.
21. If we assume the LED forward voltage to be 2 V, the series resistor must be no greater than (5 V − 2 V)/9.53 mA = 315 Ω. Use a 270-Ω or 300-Ω series resistor.
23. $V_{out} = 3.3$ kΩ · 5.58 mA = 18.4 V
25. 4 V
27. To set the output voltage (V_C) to +6 V, the collector current of the output transistor must be (12 V − 6 V)/2.2 kΩ = 2.73 mA. That means V_E must be 2.73 mA · 360 Ω = 0.98 V. Therefore, the base voltage of the output transistor must be approximately 0.7 V + 0.98 V = 1.68 V. Thus, the current through the phototransistor must be great enough to produce a 1.68-V drop across the 330-Ω resistor. The light current must be 1.68 V/330 Ω = 5.09 mA. According to the graph for the MRD300, the irradiance must be approximately 4 mW/cm^2 for a light current of 5 mA.
29. With an irradiance of 2 mW/cm^2, the light current is approximately 2.3 mA. Thus, $V_{R(330\,\Omega)} = 2.3$ mA · 330 $\Omega = 0.76$ V. $V_E = V_{R(360\,\Omega)} \cong 0.76$ V − 0.7 V = 0.06 V. $I_C \cong I_E = 0.06$ V/360 $\Omega = 167$ μA. Therefore,

$V_{R(2.2\ k\Omega)} = 167\ \mu A \cdot 2.2\ k\Omega = 0.367\ V.$
$V_C = 12\ V - 0.367\ V = 11.63\ V.$

31. The relay coil current must be 12 V/150 Ω = 80 mA. The base current of the relay driver must be 80 mA/80 = 1 mA. With a β_{CTR} of 0.8, the LED current must be 1 mA/0.8 = 1.25 mA. Assuming a LED forward voltage of 2 V, the series resistor must be no greater than (5 V − 2 V)/1.25 mA = 2400 Ω. Use a 2-kΩ resistor.

CHAPTER 19

1. $\Delta E_g = 200\ V,\ \Delta I_p = 7\ A,\ g_m = 35\ mS = 35{,}000\ \mu S$
3. $\mu = 5.75$
5. $r_p = 1000\ \Omega$
7. Saturation = $I_{p(sat)} = 400\ V/4\ k\Omega = 100$ mA while $E_p = 0\ V$
   Cutoff = $E_{p(cutoff)} = 400\ V$ while $I_p = 0\ A$
   $I_{p(Q)} \cong 62\ mA$ and $E_{p(Q)} \cong 155\ V$
9. $g_m = 1{,}200\ \mu S$
11. $i_{p(sat)} = I_{p(Q)} + (E_{p(Q)}/Z_L) = 62\ mA +$
    $(155\ V/2857\ \Omega)$

$= 62\ mA + 54\ mA = 116\ mA$
$e_{p(cutoff)} = E_{p(Q)} + (I_{p(Q)} \cdot Z_L) = 155\ V +$
$(62\ mA \cdot 2857\ \Omega)$
$= 155\ V + 177\ V = 332\ V$

13. Saturation = $I_{p(sat)} = 300\ V/(3.6\ k\Omega + 470\ \Omega) = 73.7\ mA$ while $E_p = 0\ V$
    Cutoff = $E_{p(cutoff)} = 300\ V$ while $I_p = 0\ A$
    $I_{p(Q)} \cong 40\ mA$ and $E_{p(Q)} \cong 137\ V$
15. $g_m = 1{,}400\ \mu S$
17. $A_V = 4.15$
19. Saturation = $I_{p(sat)} = 500\ V/(2.5\ k\Omega + 150\ \Omega) = 189\ mA$ while $E_p = 0\ V$
    Cutoff = $E_{p(cutoff)} = 500\ V$ while $I_p = 0\ A$
21. $i_{p(sat)} = 244\ mA,\ e_{p(cutoff)} = 407\ V$
23. $A_V = g_m \cdot Z_L = 11.7$
25. $P_p = I_{p(Q)} \cdot E_{p(Q)} = 24\ W$
27. $P_{in(total)} = I_{p(Q)} \cdot E_{supply} = 100\ mA \cdot 500\ V = 50\ W$
    %Eff = $100\% \cdot P_{out}/P_{in(total)} = 100\% \cdot 0.34$ W/50 W = 0.68%
    This is the efficiency with a 10-V_{P-P} sine wave signal applied to the control grid.

Glossary

AC load line a line drawn diagonally on a family of characteristic curves for a BJT or FET to show the limits of the current and voltage operating range for the device in circuit

acceptor atoms trivalent atoms in a p-material lattice structure that have a hole (lack one electron) that can accept a free electron

active filter a filter that includes an active device in the design

active region the region of normal operation for a device—the region between saturation and cutoff

alpha (α) the ratio of collector current to emitter current—a current transfer efficiency factor—a factor less than one (1)

amplification the process of increasing the voltage amplitude and/or power level of a signal

amplification factor, current (A_i) the ratio of output current over input current for an amplifier

amplification factor, power (A_P) the ratio of output power over input power for an amplifier

amplification factor, voltage (A_V) the ratio of output voltage over input voltage for an amplifier

amplitude the size of a signal—measured in volts, amperes, or watts

amplitude modulation (AM) the process in which audio frequencies are mixed nonlinearly with a radio frequency with the purpose of converting the audio information to a much higher frequency range for transmission

analog-to-digital converter (ADC) a circuit that is used to convert analog voltages to digital binary numbers for storage in computer memory

angstrom (Å) a unit of measurement—1 Å = 1 · 10^{-10} meters

anode the positive terminal of a device—the plate of a vacuum tube—the most positive electrode in a vacuum tube

aquadag the inside surface of the surrounding glass envelope in a CRT—a conductive coating of colloidal graphite

Armstrong oscillator an oscillator that uses a transformer secondary winding (tickler coil) to provide the needed positive feedback to start and sustain oscillation

astable multivibrator (meaning "not stable") a switching circuit that acts as a square-wave oscillator

asymmetrical limiting AC voltage limiting in which the alternations are limited to different voltage levels

atom the smallest part of an element that still retains the characteristics of that element—has a nucleus containing neutrons and protons—has surrounding energy shells containing electrons

atomic number the number of protons in the nucleus of an atom

attack time the time it takes for an automatic gain control system to respond to a large input signal

attenuate to reduce in amplitude

attenuation bands stopbands—frequency bands other than the passband in which frequencies are reduced in amplitude where amplitude is a function of frequency

audion first vacuum-tube amplifier—developed by American inventory Lee de Forest

automatic gain control (AGC) or **automatic level control (ALC)** a means by which the amplitude of a signal is automatically maintained at a specific level

avalanche breakdown takes place as valence electrons leave their shells and collide with other valence electrons, knocking them from their valence shell

average value the average voltage or current contained in pulsating DC—for full wave it equals 0.637 × peak value—for half wave it equals 0 .318 × peak value

averaging amplifier (averager)   an amplifier acting as an analog computer that produces the arithmetic average of all input voltages

balanced inputs   inputs to a transformer or a differential amplifier—both input have the same inductance, capacitance to ground, and resistance to ground—can be floating or referenced to ground

bandpass filter   a filter that passes a band of frequencies and attenuates all others

bandstop filter   also called *bandreject, notch,* and *trap filter*—a filter that rejects a band of frequencies and passes all others above and below that band

Bardeen, John   coinventer of the first transistor in 1947 at Bell Labs

barrier potential   the difference of potential that exists across the depletion region due to positive and negative ions—a potential that forms a barrier to further diffusion

base   the center layer of a bipolar transistor—the terminal used to control the amount of current flowing through the transistor

base bias   a DC source and a series resistor are used to establish the quiescent base current and collector current

beam power tube   a vacuum pentode in which the suppressor grid is formed into plates that are used to deflect and concentrate the electron beam between the cathode and plate—a high-gain power tube

Bessel response   a filter response that is sloped downward in the passband and is caused by overdamping

beta (β, h_{FE})   the ratio of collector current to base current

bias   to offset or to establish preset conditions

bipolar junction transistor (BJT)   a transistor in which p and n materials are layered together and majority current is conduction-band electron flow in the n material and valence-band drift current in the p material—a transistor having a base, an emitter, and a collector

Bode plot   a frequency-response graph plotted on a semilog graph system that utilizes decibels for the vertical scale and frequency for the horizontal scale

Bohr, Niels   in 1913 introduced the initial concept of atomic structure

Boot, Henry   codesigner of the magnetron microwave transmitting tube in 1939

Brattain, Walter   coinventer of the first transistor in 1947 at Bell Labs

breakdown region   that portion of a characteristic curve in which the forward or reverse voltage has exceeded the capability of the device and current increases rapidly with possible destruction to the device

break frequencies   frequencies at which the slope of rolloff changes abruptly

bridge rectifier   a full-wave rectifier that uses four diodes and a transformer secondary that is not tapped

buffer stage   an amplifier stage that acts as an impedance matcher and an isolator between a load and a source

bulk resistance (R_B)   the opposition the semiconductor material offers to majority carrier current

Butterworth response   often called a *maximally-flat* response—filter response in which the passband is flat having no ripple and results from moderate damping

bypass capacitor   a capacitor used to route an AC signal around a resistor or other circuit element—used to place the emitter or source of an amplifier at AC ground—a filter capacitor from a DC line to ground

capture range   in reference to phase-locked loops, the range of frequencies above and below the free-running frequency of a VCO that a PLL will respond to and lock on to

cascade   to connect together consecutively in a one-after-the-other fashion as in cascaded amplifiers

cascode   to connect in series—two devices sharing the same quiescent current

cascode amplifier   a CE, or CS, amplifier in series with a CB, or CG, amplifier sharing the same collector or drain current—a low-input-capacitance, high-frequency amplifier

cathode   the negative terminal of a device—the source of electrons in a vacuum tube

cathode-ray tube (CRT)   a vacuum tube used as a display screen for oscilloscopes, monitors, and TVs—has an electron-gun assembly that generates and controls the electron beam as it is directed at a phosphorus-coated screen

charge carriers   the means of charge flow, or current

Chebyshev response   (also spelled Tschebyscheff and Tchebysheff) filter response in which ripple is in the passband and is caused by underdamping

clamper   a waveform shifter, shifting the waveform up or down, positive or negative—a circuit that is able to create a DC reference for an AC signal

Clapp oscillator   a variation of the Colpitts oscillator in which a trimmer capacitor is placed in series with the inductor

class A amplifier   an amplifier that is biased in such a way that it amplifies the entire input waveform without clipping—100% duty cycle, power efficiency less than 25%

class B amplifier   an amplifier that is biased in such a way that it amplifies only one alternation of the input waveform—50% duty cycle, power efficiency approximately 75% for class B push-pull

class C amplifier   an amplifier that is biased in such a way that it amplifies only a small portion of one alternation of the input waveform—less than 50% duty cycle, power efficiency greater than 80%

class D amplifier   an amplifier that is not biased—an amplifier that is either fully saturated or fully cut-off—acts as a switch—has the highest power efficiency, approaching 100%

closed-loop voltage gain (A_V)   the overall voltage gain of an op-amp with negative feedback

CMOS   complementary metal-oxide semiconductor—a cascade arrangement of two E-type MOS-FETs, one n channel and the other p channel, gates tied together—a CMOS inverter

coherent   in phase, as in *coherent* light rays from a laser

collector   the region of a bipolar transistor that receives or collects majority charge carriers that cross the forward-biased base—emitter junction

collector-feedback bias   the collector voltage is used as a bias voltage along with a series feedback resistor to establish the quiescent operating point—slightly more temperature stable than base bias

collimated   made in parallel, as in the *collimated rays* emitted from a laser

Colpitts oscillator   perhaps the most common *LC* oscillator—has two capacitors that appear to be in series but have their center common connection tied to ground

common-anode display   a numeric or alphanumeric display unit in which the anodes of all display elements are tied together to a common terminal

common-base (CB) amplifier   a BJT amplifier in which the emitter is the input and the collector is the output—often called a grounded—base amplifier

common-cathode display   a numeric or alphanumeric display unit in which the cathodes of all display elements are tied together to a common terminal

common-collector (CC) amplifier   a BJT amplifier in which the base is the input and the emitter is the output—also known as an *emitter-follower* amplifier

common-drain (CD) amplifier   an FET amplifier in which the gate is the input and the source is the output

common-emitter (CE) amplifier   a BJT amplifier in which the base is the input and the collector is the output

common-gate (CG) amplifier   an FET amplifier in which the source is the input and the drain is the output

common mode   exists when both inputs of a differential amplifier receive the same signal (same in amplitude and phase)

common-mode gain ($A_{V(com)}$)   the amount a differential amplifier amplifies a common-mode signal

common-mode rejection   the rejection or cancellation of common-mode signals applied to a differential amplifier

common-mode rejection ratio (CMRR)   for a differential amplifier it is the ratio of differential voltage gain ($A_{V(diff)}$) to common-mode voltage gain ($A_{V(com)}$), for an op-amp it is the ratio of open-loop gain to common-mode gain

common-source amplifier (CS)   an FET amplifier in which the gate is the input and the drain is the output

comparator   a high-gain amplifier that has a differential input and uses no negative feedback—op-amps can be used as comparators—the slightest difference voltage between the two inputs will saturate the output either plus or minus—used to detect voltage levels

compensation, frequency   a means by which an amplifier is externally stabilized from oscillation—to make unconditionally stable—to make stable over a wide range of closed-loop gain and frequency

complementary pair   a pair of transistors that are opposites yet have similar characteristics, which enable the devices to work together—an NPN and a PNP transistor pair

complementary push-pull amplifier   a push-pull amplifier having a cascoded arrangement of an NPN and a PNP transistor where each transistor is responsible for amplifying one alternation of the AC signal

complementary symmetry   the symmetrical arrangement that results from using complementary transistors in a push-pull amplifier

compliance, range of   the range within the limits of normal operation for an active device—the maximum output voltage swing for an amplifier

conditionally stable   amplifier stability from oscillation that depends on amplifier closed-loop gain

conduction angle   the portion of the input signal over which the transistor conducts—the portion of the DC pulse, in degrees, during which the SCR is on and the load is receiving current and voltage (power)—the portion of the AC alternations, in degrees, during which the TRIAC is on and the load is receiving current and voltage (power)

conduction band   the energy level at which free electrons exist

conduction-band current   electron flow—flow of free electrons

conductivity modulation   the process that takes place between the emitter and base 1 of a UJT in which the bulk resistance decreases as forward current increases which decreases the bulk resistance further in a chain-reaction fashion

conductor   a material that has many free electrons—valence is less than four (4)

constant-current source   a BJT or FET circuit that delivers a constant amount of current to a load device regardless of the resistance of the load device

constant-K active filter   (also referred to as a voltage-controlled voltage source (VCVS) filter and Sallen and Key active filter) recognized as noninverting amplifiers having an RC filter network at the noninverting input

control grid   a screen or wire mesh type structure placed close to the cathode in a vacuum-tube amplifier—used to control the flow of electrons from cathode to anode in the vacuum tube

conventional current   hole flow—majority carriers are holes—flow is from a positive potential to a negative potential

converter   a circuit that changes an AC voltage to a DC voltage—a circuit that changes a DC voltage to a higher DC voltage—a circuit that changes one polarity of DC to the opposite polarity

coupling capacitor   a capacitor used to provide an AC connection between cascaded amplifier stages

covalent bonding   formed when valence electrons are shared between atoms of an element or between two or more different elements

critical frequency   the frequency at which the total phase shift created within an amplifier is 180°—the frequency at which an amplifier will turn into an oscillator if the loop gain is one (1) or greater

Crookes, Sir William   a British scientist who, in 1878, discovered that electric current consisted of particles—developed an early forerunner of the cathode ray tube

Crookes tube   the early forerunner of the cathode ray tube and picture tube

crossover distortion   distortion near zero-crossing caused by insufficient bias for transistors of a push-pull amplifier

crowbar   related to overvoltage protection—a circuit that triggers full on when a predetermined voltage threshold is reached, the purpose for which is to deliberately short the DC supply and prevent the load device from being damaged due to excessive voltage—usually an SCR placed from DC line to ground

crystal laser   a solid laser such as a ruby laser

current mirror   a transistor that is biased using the barrier voltage of a forward-biased diode—diode current nearly matches the collector current

curve tracer   an electronic instrument used to generate a single, or family, of characteristic curves on a CRT display—it may be an instrument that is used in conjunction with an oscilloscope or it may be built in with a CRT screen

current transfer ratio (β_{CTR})   applies to optoisolators having transistor outputs and is equal to I_C/I_F where I_C is the output collector current and I_F is the input forward diode current

cutoff frequency (f_{co})   the frequency whose voltage is -3dB in amplitude at the filter output compared to the highest-amplitude passband frequency—also known as the half-power frequency

damping factor (DF)   a factor that determines the overall frequency response characteristics of an active filter

dark resistance   the resistance of a photoresistor in total darkness

Darlington pair   one transistor piggybacked on a second for the purpose of greatly increasing current gain—collector current of one transistor is the base current of the other—collectors tied together, emitter of first transistor tied to the base of the second, base of the first transistor serves as the base for both transistors

dBm   decibel values referenced to the milliwatt—dB values using the milliwatt as the standard—all values compared to 1 mW

DC load line   a line drawn on a family of characteristic curves for a BJT or FET that shows the DC operating range of current and voltage for the device within its circuit

decade   related to frequency response, a decade is 10 times or 1/10 a specified frequency, i.e., 100 Hz is one decade below 1 kHz

decibel (dB)   one tenth of a Bel—used to express the relationship between two voltage levels or between two power levels—scale marked on a VU meter—one Bel is a ten times increase in power, corresponding to a 3.16 times increase in voltage across a given load

de Forest, Lee   the American inventor who, in 1907, patented the first amplifying device, the audion, a vacuum triode

delay angle   the portion of applied pulses or AC alternations during which a thyristor is cut off and the load receives no current

depletion region (depletion layer)   the ionized region on both sides of a junction—charges have been depleted due to diffusion and recombination

depletion-type (D-type) MOSFET   a MOSFET that

normally conducts (saturates) without a bias voltage applied—a MOSFET that requires a bias voltage to increase the size of the depletion region in the channel in order to control majority carriers—a normally on MOSFET

derating factor (D) a factor used to reduce the power rating of a device to match a specific operating temperature—expressed as a certain number of mW per degree centigrade

DIAC a dual-electrode AC trigger device—can be triggered on the positive or negative alternation of an AC signal—a bidirectional latch

differential amplifier (diff-amp) an amplifier that amplifies the difference between two voltages, has a balanced input and a balanced output

differentiator a circuit that is used to compute the rate of change of a waveform, the waveform must be changing in amplitude over time ($\Delta V/\Delta t$), otherwise the output of the differentiator is zero

diffusion the process of recombination in which electrons move through a p material and fall into holes—the formation of a pn junction

digital-to-analog converter (DAC) a circuit able to convert digital binary numbers into analog voltages

diode an electronic device that passes current in only one direction—semiconductor diodes and vacuum-tube diodes

DIP dual in-line package

directly heated cathode a heater filament made of thoriated tungsten that serves as a cathode in a vacuum tube

discontinuity applies to the inductor's action in the filter network of a switching regulator—means the inductor voltage and current drops to zero, leaving just the capacitor to supply load current during the remaining portion of the off time

distortion undesirable changes in the output voltage waveform caused by the amplifier

dominant cutoff frequency the cutoff frequency at which attenuation greater than -3 dB first begins

donor atom a pentavalent atom used as an impurity to create n-type semiconductor material—donates a free electron to the structure

doping atoms of another element are added to the silicon structure to modify its structure and electrical characteristics

dropout voltage applies to voltage regulators—the minimum input–output voltage differential needed for the regulator to continue to regulate

DUT device under test—any device can be a DUT when placed in a test circuit

duty cycle the ratio of ON time to total cycle time for a multivibrator or switching device—usually expressed as a percentage

dynamic headroom the maximum undistorted peak-to-peak voltage swing at the output of an amplifier

Edison effect in an evacuated glass bulb, electrons flow from a heated filament to a metal plate when a positive potential is applied to the metal plate

Edison, Thomas discovered that, in an evacuated glass bulb, electrons flow from a heated filament to a metal plate when a positive potential is applied to the metal plate

electroluminescent panels thin panels that radiate light evenly from their entire surface—used as backlighting on control panels and as backlighting for liquid-crystal displays

electron a negatively charged particle that exists at specific energy levels surrounding the nucleus of an atom

electron-hole pair an electron in the conduction band and a corresponding hole in the valence shell

electron-hole-pair generation the process of creating holes by electrons becoming free due to the influence of some source of energy

elements the simplest and most basic substances in the universe

emitter the semiconductor layer of a bipolar transistor that supplies majority charge carriers that cross the forward-biased base–emitter junction into the collector region

emitter bias a method of biasing a bipolar transistor in which a DC source supplies current to the emitter via a series emitter resistor—the base is at near ground potential—this method of biasing is more temperature stable than voltage-divider biasing

enhancement-type (E-type) MOSFET a MOSFET that does not conduct unless a bias voltage is applied to enhance the channel—a normally off MOSFET—*see* **inversion layer**

ENIAC *E*lectronic *N*umerical *I*ntegrator *A*nd *C*alculator—contained some 18,000 vacuum tubes, weighed 30 tons, and used over 130,000 watts of power

envelope (as in *AM envelope*) the composite signal resulting from amplitude modulation as can be observed using an oscilloscope

epitaxy the controlled growth of a layer of semiconductor material on the surface of an existing semiconductor substrate

extrinsic (meaning *impure*) semiconductor material containing impurities

Fabry-Perot resonator the area between reflective surfaces inside a laser where stimulated emissions takes place

fall time (t_f)   the time it takes for a pulse to fall from 90% to 10% of maximum amplitude

field-effect transistor (FET)   a transistor made of one type semiconductor material (*n* or *p*) forming a channel from source to drain—majority current is controlled by the presence of an electric field between the gate and channel, which forms a depletion region that controls the effective channel width and conductivity—a unipolar transistor

flag   an electronic indicator used to inform a human operator of a fault that has occurred in a system—an LED or a lamp

Fleming, John   a British scientist who, in 1904, designed and constructed a vacuum-tube diode

Fleming valve   first vacuum diode—developed by John Fleming in 1904

fluorescence   luminescence in the presence of an excitation voltage or applied source of energy

flyback   refers to the collapsing magnetic field surrounding an energized coil when the current source is removed

flyback converter   a type of DC to DC converter in which a transformer is used in an intermediate inverter section and the collapsing magnetic field in the transformer produces one half of the AC cycle that is then rectified and filtered for the DC output

foot candle (ft-cd or fc)   one lumen of light falling on a surface area of one square foot (1 fc = 1 lm/ft^2)

forbidden bands   zones between energy levels of atoms in which electrons cannot exist

forced commutation   a voltage of reverse polarity is momentarily applied across a unilateral latch device as a CEMF to oppose the anode current, thereby reducing it below the holding value and turning the device off

forward bias   a potential applied to a junction that causes majority current to flow across the junction

forward current transfer ratio (β_{DC}, h_{FE})   the ratio of collector current to base current for a bipolar transistor

free electrons   electrons that normally exist in the valence shell of an atom but are able to break free under the influence of an external source of energy

frequency   the repetition rate for a waveform—measured in cycles per second or hertz (Hz)

frequency converter   an electronic circuit composed of a mixer and oscillator, the purpose for which is to convert one frequency to another frequency

full-power bandwidth (BW_P)   the bandwidth in which all signals are amplified to maximum possible voltage swing without distortion—limited by the slew rate of the amplifier

full-wave rectifier   converts both alternations of an AC signal to either positive or negative pulsating DC

functional block   a circuit that performs a specific task, service, or function for an overall system

function generator   an oscillator circuit that is able to produce a variety of waveforms such as square waves, triangle waves, and sine waves

gain   the ratio of output over input for an amplifier or attenuator—often expressed in decibels

gain-bandwidth product (GBP)   the product of amplifier gain and amplifier bandwidth—always equal to the unity-gain frequency (f_T)

gas laser   gas-filled lasers such as HeNe lasers and CO_2 lasers

gate-controlled switches (GCSs)   SCR-type devices that can be controlled completely by the gate—also called *gate turn-off* devices (GTOs)

germanium   a semiconductor material that has a higher conductivity than silicon at any given temperature

grid-leak bias   also known as signal bias—a form of self bias in which the input signal causes grid current to flow during positive alternations, which charges a coupling capacitor whose charge leaks off slightly during negative alternations through the grid-leak resistor (R_g), thereby creating a negative potential at the top of the grid-leak resistor, which clamps the input signal to a negative reference

half-wave rectification   converts AC to DC by blocking the unwanted alternation of the applied AC

harmonic   a multiple of a fundamental frequency—a member of a harmonic series in which the fundamental frequency is the first harmonic

Hartley oscillator   an oscillator that is recognized by its use of a tapped inductor in the tuned circuit having the tap connected to ground

headroom   the maximum undistorted peak-to-peak voltage swing at the output of an amplifier

hermetically sealed   airtight—totally encapsulated so there is no contamination from the outside

heterodyne receiver   also called *superheterodyne receiver*—a receiver in which the incoming station is mixed with an oscillator frequency to yield a difference frequency known as the *intermediate frequency*

highpass filter   a filter that passes all frequencies above a specific cutoff frequency with less than 3 dB of attenuation

hole   the absence of an electron in an atomic structure—cause for the existence of a positive ion

hybrid   a combination of technologies or types—a mixture

hysteresis   to lag behind

hysteresis voltage   the difference in voltage between the two trip points of a Schmitt trigger—the OFF trip point lags behind the ON trip point

illuminance (illumination)   the amount of light that actually falls on the surface of an object or device—measured in foot-candles or lumens per square meter

impurities   atoms that are added to a semiconductor material to change its electrical characteristics—atoms used to make n or p semiconductor material

indirectly heated cathode   usually a nickel cylinder coated with barium or strontium oxide that is heated by a separate filament

injection laser   diode laser

input bias current (I_{IB})   the very small amount of current that is needed to bias a differential transistor ON in a diff-amp or op-amp

input offset current (I_{IO})   the difference between the two input bias currents of a diff-amp or op-amp

input offset voltage (V_{IO})   the differential voltage at the two inputs that is required to zero, or null, the output of the op-amp

input-output voltage differential   applies to voltage regulators—the difference between the voltage applied to the regulator and the regulator's output voltage

integrated circuits   many transistors and other devices formed on a single semiconductor chip or substrate

integrator   a circuit that acts as an analog computer, calculating the area under the curve of an applied pulse—the output voltage is determined by input amplitude and duration—used to create a DC level that represents the average voltage of applied input pulses

interelectrode capacitance   capacitances that exist between the terminals of a device (internally)

intermediate-frequency section (IF section)   the section in a radio receiver in which most selectivity and amplification takes place—at a radio frequency that is usually somewhere between the received radio frequency and the audio-frequency range

intermodulation distortion (IMD)   a very undesirable distortion created by the nonlinearity of amplifiers—unwanted mixing products in linear amplifiers

intrinsic   pure, as in pure silicon—not doped with impurities—neither n nor p material

intrinsic standoff ratio (η)   the voltage divider ratio that exists inside a UJT due to its two regions of bulk resistance—from base 2 to emitter and emitter to base 1, $r_{B1}/(r_{B1} + r_{B2})$—symbolized with the lowercase Greek letter eta (η)

inversion layer   a thin layer in an E-type MOSFET that is formed when bias is applied—if the channel is p material, the application of a positive gate voltage attracts electrons to the area of the channel near the insulated gate, which causes the holes of the p material to be filled in and enhances the channel in that area to enable conduction-band electron flow—in effect, a thin layer of the p channel is converted to n material as long as the positive bias is applied

inverter   a circuit that changes DC to AC

inverting amplifier   an amplifier whose output is 180° out of phase with its input

irradiance   a radiometric term equivalent to illuminance—the amount of electromagnetic energy falling on a surface

junction capacitance (C_J)   the capacitance of a reverse-biased pn junction—usually insignificant when junction is forward biased

junction field-effect transistor (JFET)   a unipolar transistor—a transistor made of one type semiconductor material (n or p) forming a channel from source to drain—majority current is controlled by the presence of an electric field between the gate and channel, which forms a depletion region that controls the effective channel width and conductivity—the depletion region is the reverse-biased pn junction between the gate and channel

kernel   the core of an atom—composed of the nucleus and all shells except the outer shell

Kilby, Jack   of Texas Instruments, in 1958 opened a whole new frontier of technology by designing the first monolithic chip that contained more than one transistor

lag network   lowpass filter—a reactive network whose output voltage lags behind the input voltage

large-scale integration (LSI)   thousands of transistors on a single chip

LASCR   *Light-Activated Silicon-Controlled Rectifier*

laser   a device that produces *light amplification* by *stimulated emission* of *radiation*

laser head   a laser tube enclosed in a protective aluminum cylinder with insulated electrode caps and high-voltage leads

latch   a device or circuit that is activated by some means and must be deactivated by another means

LATRIAC   light-activated TRIAC

lead inductance   small inductance contributed to a circuit by the leads of components and devices—significant at very high frequencies

lead network   a highpass filter—a reactive network whose output voltage leads the input voltage

leakage current   reverse current—minority current through a pn junction

lifetime   the length of time the electron remains in the conduction band until recombination takes place

light current (I_L)   the amount of reverse current flowing in a photodiode in the presence of light

light-emitting diode (LED)   a diode that is operated with forward bias and emits light as electrons cross the junction and recombine

linear mixer   an adder circuit—a circuit in which voltages, both AC and DC, are added together in much the same way positive and negative numbers are added—*see* **summing amplifier**

linear power supply   uses a linear voltage regulator to drop a DC source down to a desired level and regulate it at that level—uses power devices that are operated in the region between saturation and cutoff, along the linear region

line regulation   applies to voltage regulators—expressed as a change in output voltage of so many millivolts over a certain range of change in input voltage

liquid crystal display (LCD)   display technology that uses the light-blocking characteristics or light-rotating characteristics of liquid crystal in response to the application of a difference of potential

loading effect   the effect an impedance has when connected to the output of a circuit

load regulation   applies to voltage regulators—expressed as a change in output voltage of so many millivolts over a certain range of change in load (current)

lock range (tracking range)   in reference to phase-locked loops, the range of lock which is equal to the range of the VCO

loop gain ($A_{OL}B$)   the product of the voltage-feedback ratio and the open-loop gain

lowpass filter   a filter that passes all frequencies below a specific cutoff frequency with less than 3 dB of attenuation

lumen (lm)   the unit of luminous flux—one candle of light intensity produces one lumen of flux per steradian

luminescent   emit light

luminous intensity   the amount of light produced by a light source measured in candelas or candles (cd)

luminous flux   lines of light energy measured in lumens (lm)

lux   a unit of illuminance equal to 1 lm/m^2

majority carriers   the charge carriers that represent the majority current—electrons in n material—holes in p material

metal oxide semiconductor field-effect transistor (MOSFET)   an FET that has an insulated gate—an IGFET (insulated-gate FET)—an FET having no pn junction between gate and channel

midpoint bias   a bias point established near the center of a load line—provides nearly equal voltage swing for both alternations of the amplified signal—point of maximum power dissipation for the active device

minority carriers   the charge carriers that represent the minority current in a semiconductor material—leakage current carriers—electrons in p material, holes in n material

molecules   formed when valence electrons are shared between atoms of an element or between two or more different elements

monochromatic   light that is all of the same color and wavelength

monostable multivibrator   a switching circuit that has one normal output condition, high or low, and is normally at rest—a timer circuit

multiplex   to combine many into one—many signals on one line

multiplier, frequency   a circuit used to amplify the harmonic content of an applied signal—the output circuit of the amplifier is tuned to the desired harmonic, usually only up to the fourth harmonic

negative feedback   signal feedback that is out of phase with the input signal—a means to reduce overall amplifier gain and reduce distortion

netting   using a small trimmer capacitor to adjust the frequency of a crystal

neutralization   the technique of adding external capacitance to a vacuum-tube amplifier circuit so as to cancel the effects of the plate, to control grid interelectrode capacitance

neutron   a neutrally charged nuclear particle having a mass slightly greater than the proton

n material   semiconductor material that has been doped with pentavalent atoms in order to create a surplus of electrons in the structure—semiconductor material having many free electrons

noninverting amplifier   an amplifier whose output is in phase with its input

nonlinear mixer   circuit that uses a device that has nonlinear output vs input characteristics, diodes, BJTs, and FETs—a mixer that creates sum and difference frequencies two or more applied frequencies

nonlinear power supplies   operate power devices in saturation or cutoff, alternating rapidly between the two—the device is either fully ON or OFF—very little power is dissipated by the device or devices—also called *switching supplies, switching regulators, switchers,* or *choppers*

NPN transistor   a bipolar transistor in which the emitter is n material, the base is p material and the collector is n material

nucleus   the central part of an atom—contains neutrons and protons—positively charged

octave twice or half a specified frequency—i.e., 100 Hz is one octave below 200 Hz and one octave above 50 Hz

ohmic region the portion of an FET's drain curve in which drain current increases linearly with drain voltage—the region in which the channel acts as a fixed resistor—the linear region—the constant-resistance region

one-shot a monostable multivibrator

open-loop voltage gain (A_{OL}) sometimes called the *large-signal voltage gain*—the maximum possible voltage gain of the op-amp with no negative feedback

operational amplifier (op-amp) an amplifier that acts as an analog computer—an amplifier that can be configured to perform many different operations such as integration, differentiation, addition, etc.

optical pumping using light pulses to stimulate lasing action in a crystal laser

optocoupler optical coupling device—*see* **optoisolator**

optointerrupter special kind of optocoupler designed to permit mechanical interference between the LED and the optodetector

optoisolator a hybrid integrated circuit that includes an LED on one side and a photodetector on the other—used to electrically isolate a low-voltage circuit from a high-voltage circuit—used as a computer interface device

oscillator an electronic circuit that is designed to continuously create, or generate, a periodic waveform at a particular frequency—a circuit that is able to convert DC into some form of pulsating DC or AC

overtone crystal a radio-frequency crystal cut to resonate at an odd multiple of its fundamental frequency, usually 3×, 5×, or 7×

parameter a rating, value, or characteristic of a device, component, circuit, or system

passband the band of frequencies that passes through a filter with no attenuation or through an amplifier with maximum amplification

peak inverse voltage (PIV) the peak reverse voltage applied across a device such as a diode—can be a rating of the maximum reverse voltage permitted across a device

pentavalent having five valence electrons—atoms of elements such as antimony, arsenic, and phosphorus

persistence the length of time the coating on a CRT screen phosphoresces (glows after the beam has passed)

phase-locked loop (PLL) a circuit, or small system, composed of a voltage-controlled oscillator, a low-pass filter, and a phase comparator—a voltage-to-frequency and frequency-to-voltage converter

phase margin (Φ_{PM}) the difference in phase angle between 180° and the phase angle of the frequency at unity loop gain

phase response for a filter or amplifier, the change in output-voltage phase angle as related to a change in frequency

phosphorescence luminescence that continues after excitation is removed

photodiode a diode that is used to detect light intensity—operated with reverse bias

photometric unit a unit that is used to quantify visible light

photoresistor also known as a *photoconductive cell*—a simple flat-surface device whose between-terminal resistance varies with impinging light intensity

photothyristor a light-activated thyristor such as a LASCR or LATRIAC

phototransistor a transistor that has its collector–base junction exposed to light through a glass window or lens, collector current increases with increasing impinging light intensity

Pierce oscillator a crystal-controlled oscillator

piezoelectric effect stress on a crystal produces a difference of potential and a difference of potential applied to a crystal produces stress or warping of the crystal

pinchoff voltage the value of V_{DS} across an FET above which there is no further increase in drain current

PIN diode constructed as a three-layer "sandwich" of heavily doped p material, intrinsic material, and heavily doped n material—when forward biased, it acts as a variable resistance, with the resistance of the intrinsic material decreasing as forward current increases—used as a high-frequency modulator and as an electronically controlled attenuator (variable resistance)

planar transistor fabricated so all pn junctions terminate in the same geometric plane at the surface of the semiconductor chip

plate resistance (r_p) the equivalent AC resistance of the tube—the ratio of a change in plate voltage (ΔE_p) resulting from a change in plate current (ΔI_p)

p material semiconductor material that has been doped with trivalent atoms to create a deficiency of electrons in the structure—a semiconductor material having many holes

PNP transistor a bipolar transistor in which the emitter is p material, the base is n material, and the collector is p material

poles   (as in active filters) same as order—the number of reactive components in the filter network(s)

power dissipation (P_D)   current times voltage of a device—power transfer—power expelled in the form of heat and transferred by conduction through air or some other material and by radiation in the form of infrared

power efficiency factor (n)   the ratio of output power (load power) to total DC input power (does not include power supplied to bias network)

power supplies   electronic circuits, or minor systems, that are designed to produce a specified AC or DC voltage at a specified maximum current from an existing AC or DC source

precision rectifier   an op-amp circuit configured to rectify an applied AC signal without the usual 0.7-V diode drop—capable of rectifying AC signals in the millivolts

programmable unijunction transistor (PUT)   not a unijunction transistor at all—a thyristor, a four-layer device much like an SUS—an SUS that can be programmed (biased) to trigger over a wide range of voltage—acts like a UJT

propagation delay   same as rise time—output rise time resulting from an instantaneous input pulse

proton   a positively charged particle existing in the nucleus of an atom—has a mass 1836 times that of an electron

pulse duration   the length of time a pulse exists—time between the 50% points on the rise and fall side of a pulse

pulse duration modulation (PDM)   a modulation technique in which the duty cycle of a square wave is change or varied

Q point   the quiescent operating point—the initial bias point for an amplifier

quasi-complementary power amplifier   both push-pull output transistors are of the same type—one output transistor is driven by the same type and the other output transistor is driven by a complementary transistor

quiescent values   values of current and voltage established at a specific bias point—the DC bias values

radio-frequency crystal   usually a thin slice of quartz crystal between two metal plates in a holder and case—used as the frequency-determining element in an oscillator—operates in series- and parallel-resonant modes

radiometric unit   unit used to quantify the entire frequency spectrum including visible and invisible light—uses the watt as its basic unit

Randall, John   codesigner of the magnetron microwave transmitting tube in 1939

receptor (acceptor)   an atom containing a hole in a semiconductor structure—can potentially receive an electron—a positively charged ion

recirculation diode   part of the output filter network of a switching regulator—conducts when the inductor's magnetic field is collapsing

recombination   occurs when an electron falls back into a hole

recovery time   the time it takes for an automatic gain control system to return to a high-gain condition after a large input signal is removed

rectifier   a device used to convert AC to pulsating DC

regulation   the means by which the DC output voltage from a supply is held at a constant, or near-constant, level regardless of variations in load, line voltage, or temperature

relaxation oscillator   uses a switching device or latch to automatically discharge a capacitor every time it charges to a threshold voltage or breakover voltage—produces a sawtooth waveform

resolution   (as in digital-to-analog converters) the weight of the least significant bit which determines the smallest increment of output voltage

reverse bias   a potential applied across a *pn* junction or device that causes only minority leakage current to flow

ripple factor (r)   the ratio of the RMS ripple voltage to the average DC level

ripple rejection   the ability of a voltage regulator to reject DC ripple voltage that is applied to the regulator

ripple voltage (DC ripple)   repetitive variations in DC voltage due to incomplete filtering—ripple frequency is equal to twice the applied AC frequency when using a full-wave rectifier

rise time (t_r or t_{TLH})   the time it takes for a pulse to rise from 10% to 90% of maximum amplitude

rolloff   the rate of change in amplitude related to a change in frequency, usually expressed in dB/octave or dB/decade

root mean square (RMS) value   the DC equivalent of an AC voltage or current—equal to 0.707 × peak value

saturation region   that portion of a characteristic curve in which there is no significant increase in forward current as forward voltage increases—for a bipolar transistor, it is in this region that the collector-base junction becomes forward biased and normal transistor action ceases—for an FET it is the area of the drain curve where drain current increases very little with a large increase in drain voltage

Schmitt trigger a comparator with hysteresis (different ON and OFF threshold voltages)—used to convert noisy signals to clean ON/OFF pulses

Schottky diode (hot-carrier diode) used for high-speed switching in computer circuits and very-high-frequency rectification in radio circuits—junction is formed between lightly doped silicon (usually *n*-type) and metal (gold, silver, platinum)

screen grid acts as a shield between the plate and the control grid of a vacuum tetrode or pentode—used to reduce interelectrode capacitance between the control grid and the plate

secondary emissions electron emissions that take place because of bombardment from other electrons

self bias a method of biasing an FET or vacuum tube in which a source or cathode resistor is used to drop a voltage that serves as the bias voltage

semiconductor a material that conducts electrical current poorly—silicon (Si), germanium (Ge), gallium arsenida (GaAs)—used in diodes, transistors, and integrated circuits—usually has 4 valence electrons

semiconductor optical amplifier (SOA) an in-line laser used to reamplify light signals in a long fiber-optic system

series-pass voltage regulator a regulator circuit that uses a power device in series with the load for the purpose of dropping voltage as needed to insure the load voltage remains constant

shell an energy level that exists surrounding the nucleus of an atom—electrons are found to exist in these distinct energy levels

Shockley, William coinventer of the first transistor in 1947 at Bell Labs

shunt regulator a voltage regulator in which the regulating device is placed in parallel with the load device—total current is shared by the regulator and the load

silicon bilateral switch (SBS) similar to the DIAC, however, the SBS is faster, made for low breakover voltages, has a gate that may or may not be used, and is an integrated circuit (IC) instead of a single four-layer device

silicon-controlled rectifier (SCR) a unilateral four-layer device that has a control terminal called the *gate*—a diode that has a breakover voltage that must be reached before any significant forward conduction begins—the breakover voltage can be lowered by applying a voltage and current to the gate

silicon unilateral switch (SUS) (also known as the *Shockley diode*) a four-layer diode that has forward-current blocking characteristics up to a certain voltage threshold, after which the SUS quickly switches

ON and conducts forward current in one direction only

slew rate (*SR*) the highest rate at which the output voltage of an op-amp is able to increase when an input pulse is applied

slew rate distortion a deformation of a signal at the amplifier's output because the amplifier is unable to keep up with the rate of change in voltage of the signal, caused by internal capacitances that must charge and discharge

snubber a circuit consisting of a capacitor in series with a resistor that is placed in parallel with a thyristor such as an SCR or TRIAC in order to prevent false triggering sue to a high rate of change in terminal voltage—the snubber reduces dV/dt

solid-state formed of a single solid block—refers to semiconductor devices

space charge a cloud of electrons that forms around an electrode

spectral response a device's response to a range of frequencies

spontaneous emission the normal type of light emission that takes place in neon, fluorescent, and incandescent lamps—characterized as being, random, scattered, incoherent, and polychromatic covering a wide portion of the light spectrum—light emitted as electrons fall to a lower energy level

static amplification factor (μ) for a vacuum-tube amplifier, the ratio of the change in plate voltage (ΔE_p) to a change in control-grid voltage (ΔE_g) while the plate current is held constant

step-recovery diode used in very-high-frequency and switching applications—has fast OFF time due to very low junction charge storage

steradian (sr) a conically shaped angle that encloses a spherical surface area equal to the square of the radius of the sphere

stimulated emission the emission of light that takes place when a photon collides with an excited electron as in lasers

stray capacitance exists between wire leads and ground—can affect the frequency response and performance of an amplifier

summing amplifier (adder or linear mixer) an amplifier such as an op-amp that has many input resistors (inverting configuration)—applied frequencies remain distinct while instantaneous voltages add—no new frequencies are created in the mixing process (linear mixing)

suppressor grid a metal mesh or bar arrangement that is placed between the screen grid and the plate in a vacuum pentode—used to suppress secondary emissions from the plate

swamping resistor   an emitter resistor used to nullify the effects of r'_e in the emitter of a bipolar transistor—stabilizes the bias point and voltage gain

switching regulators   nonlinear power supplies that operate power devices in saturation or cutoff, alternating rapidly between the two—the device is either fully ON or OFF—very little power is dissipated by the device or devices—also called **switching supplies, switchers,** or **choppers**

symmetrical limiting   AC voltage limiting in which both alternations are limited to the same voltage level

system concept   all electronic systems, regardless of how complex, are made up of interconnected functional blocks that are an aid in design and troubleshooting

tetravalent   having four valence electrons

thermal resistance (R_θ)   the total resistance to heat transfer that exists between the device's case and the air—exists between the device's case and a heat sink ($R_{\theta CS}$) and between the heat sink and the air ($R_{\theta SA}$)—expressed in units of °C/W

thermal runaway   a snowball effect that takes place as temperature and current increase in a transistor—both temperature and current act as cause and effect

thermionic effect   electrons escaping the surface of a conductor and returning when heated to high temperatures

thermistor   a semiconductor resistor whose bulk resistance changes dramatically with changes in temperature

thyratron   a gas-filled, or mercury-vapor, vacuum tube equivalent in operation to the SCR—a rectifier tube that has a control grid used to control the firing point (firing voltage) for each pulsating alternation

tickler coil   a secondary winding of a transformer used to stimulate an amplifier into oscillation by providing positive feedback—used in Armstrong oscillators and power inverters

TMOS   a type of fabrication of E-type power MOSFETs in which a T-shaped channel is formed

transconductance (g_m)   a change in current that results from a change in voltage ($\Delta I / \Delta V$)—for an FET, $g_m = \Delta I_D / \Delta V_G$—for a vacuum-tube amplifier, $g_m = \Delta I_p / \Delta V_g$—measured in siemens (S)

transconductance amplifier   the output current is a function of input voltage, $g_m = i_{out} / v_{in}$

transconductance curve   the transfer curve for an FET

transfer curve   a characteristic curve, or graph, showing the relationship between a device's input and output—for a BJT the transfer curve shows the relationship between I_C and V_B, or I_C and I_B—for an FET the transfer curve shows the relationship between I_D and V_G

transresistance amplifier   output voltage is a function of input current ($V_{out}/I_{in} = R$, the transresistance)

TRIAC   a three-terminal AC switch (latch), one of the terminals being a gate that is used to determine the main-terminal breakover voltage—similar to two SCRs paralleled in opposite polarity

triode   a three-electrode device—vacuum-tube amplifier—first developed by American inventor Lee de Forest—has cathode (−), anode (+plate), and a control grid

trivalent   having three valence electrons—atoms of elements such as boron, gallium, and indium

tunnel diode   a special diode that is operated with forward bias and exhibits negative resistance characteristics when the forward-bias voltage exceeds a certain voltage (V_P, peak voltage)—past the peak voltage, diode resistance increases and current decreases as bias voltage increases

unconditionally stable   an amplifier is stable from oscillations regardless of the amount of closed loop gain

unijunction transistor (UJT)   a single-junction transistor that operates as a latch and is used in relaxation oscillators

unity-gain frequency (f_T)   the frequency at which the open-loop gain of an amplifier is unity (1)

vacuum diode   a vacuum tube that has only two electrodes: a cathode and an anode (plate)—used as a rectifier

vacuum pentode   a vacuum-tube amplifier that has five electrodes: the cathode, the control grid, the screen grid, the suppressor grid, and the plate, in that order—has characteristics similar to an n-channel JFET

vacuum tetrode   a vacuum tube that has four main electrodes: the cathode, the plate, the control grid, and a screen grid positioned between the control grid and the plate

vacuum triode   a vacuum tube that has three electrodes: a cathode, an anode, and a control grid between the two—has a control grid used to control the amount of electron flow from cathode to plate—a vacuum amplifier

vacuum tube   an electronic device having electrodes in an evacuated chamber, electrons travel internally in one direction from a heated cathode to a collector known as the plate or anode

valence   the number of electrons in the outer shell of an atom

valence-band current often called *drift current* or *hole flow*

valence shell the outermost shell of an atom

vapor-phase cooling system a cooling system used to cool high-power vacuum tubes—a cooling system in which water is converted to steam in order to remove a greater quantity of heat

varactor diode a diode that is used as a variable capacitance device—operated with reverse bias—increasing reverse bias voltage decreases junction capacitance

variable-frequency oscillator (VFO) an oscillator that is variable—its frequency can be varied with a control

Varian, Russell and Sigurd American scientists who invented the klystron microwave power tube in 1939

very-large-scale integration hundreds of thousands of transistors on a single chip

virtual ground a point in a circuit that acts like ground because it has a very low voltage—the inverting input of an inverting op-amp amplifier

VMOS deep V-groove fabrication of a MOSFET—a type of E-type power MOSFET

voltage-controlled crystal oscillator (VCXO) a crystal oscillator whose frequency can be varied by varying a control voltage which is usually applied to a varactor diode

voltage-controlled oscillator (VCO) an oscillator circuit whose frequency can be varied with an applied DC or low-frequency AC voltage

voltage-divider bias a method of biasing in which a resistive voltage divider is used to establish the quiescent base voltage and current of a bipolar transistor—more temperature stable than collector-feedback bias or base bias

voltage-feedback ratio (B) the ratio of feedback voltage to output voltage—a ratio less than one (1)—the voltage-divider ratio used to provide the feedback voltage

voltage limiter circuit designed to limit the amplitude of voltage that is passed on to a load—also called a *clipper*

voltage multiplier a rectifier circuit used to convert an AC source to a higher DC level using diodes and capacitors

wavelength (λ) the physical distance between wavefronts or pulse peaks of wave as the energy travels through free space—$\lambda = c/f$, where c is the speed of electromagnetic energy is free space equal to $300 \cdot 10^6$ meters per second and f is the frequency in cycle per second

weighted input an input to a summing amplifier (op-amp) that has a specific gain as established by the feedback resistor and input resistance that differs from that of other inputs

window comparator a comparator used to determine if a voltage is either within or outside a specific range

zener breakdown takes place when the reverse voltage is high enough to tear large numbers of electrons from the atoms in the depletion region of a *pn* diode structure

zener diode a semiconductor diode that is operated in reverse bias and is used as a constant-voltage source—a shunt voltage regulator

zero-crossing the points in an AC waveform where the amplitude is 0 V or 0 A

Zworykin, Vladimir the American scientist who developed the iconoscope television camera and the kinescope picture tube

Index